C000007880

Writers' & Artists' Yearbook 1999

Writers' & Artists' Yearbook 1999

Ninety-second Year of Issue

A directory for writers,
artists, playwrights, writers
for film, radio and television,
designers, illustrators and
photographers

A & C Black · London

© 1999 A & C Black (Publishers) Limited
35 Bedford Row, London WC1R 4JH
Reprinted 1999

A CIP record for this book is available
from the British Library.

ISBN 0–7136–4931–3

Printed and bound in Great Britain
by Biddles Ltd, Guildford and King's Lynn

Foreword

It was always such a romantic title: *Writers' & Artists' Yearbook*. When I was a child it sat so importantly on the parental bookshelf. This I assumed to be the book of arcane knowledge, the book which magically contained all other books, entrance ticket to the world you longed for. Just by looking inside you were as good as published! And what's more if you were a Writer you came first, before Artists. Children notice these things.

My mother, now 91, would point out to me that she was born the same year as the *Yearbook*: 1907. The very notion, she claims, had made a writer of her. She published good novels (*Via Panama*) and short stories, and romances in instalments that the world queued at news-stands to buy and which thrilled me to the core. (*Velvet and Steel*; *The Cups of Alexander* – such wonderful titles!)

As of right, a copy of the *Writers' & Artists' Yearbook 1930* travelled with her from England to New Zealand, where we lived through my childhood. My mother's father, Edgar Jepson, whose novels best-sold in the 'twenties and 'thirties (*Lady Noggs Assists*; *An Accidental Don Juan*), always had a copy of the *Yearbook* on his bookshelves, she told me, though he was always faithful to his publisher, Herbert Jenkins. (Herbert Jenkins' books, if you disobediently read them in the bath, would leach red dye onto your childish hand which would run all the way down your arm, and adults would shriek if they came into the bathroom, thinking you were wounded. Serve them right.) Consulting this year's edition, I find, alas, that Herbert Jenkins are no more. But yes, there's Curtis Brown, under *Literary agencies*, the firm that handled my Uncle Selwyn Jepson's thrillers (*Stagefright*,

which was turned into a Hitchcock film; *A Noise in the Night*). I'm a Curtis Brown client now as well: I still feel the romance of it. This grown-up world of artists and writers is as exciting and mysterious as I had always believed.

And every decade the *Yearbook* gets better, more informative, more helpful. Flick through it. Specimen scripts ... using the Internet, and Good Lord! How to control yourself on the word processor: how not to let it run away with you. All the contacts and addresses you could possibly need the better to get what's in your head out of it and into the outside world.

The problem for new writers becomes not how to say it, but what it is you have to say, and why it should be said, and exactly what it is you have to offer others. What do you know that they don't? – these days people know so much! This alone the *Yearbook* can't tell you. So far and no further. I know that now.

I get asked from time to time if I have any advice to offer new writers and all I can say is well, first of all I admire you very much: you have such fortitude, such resolution, such faith. Secondly, if you get to three chapters and are then stuck, you're not stuck, you're finished: you haven't bitten off enough to chew, that's all. And thirdly, all rules are made to be broken. What others say are your weak points may, if you drive into the skid, be your strongest. I used to frown on the over-generous use of adjectives until one day a student showed me an Iris Murdoch sentence which contained 18 adjectives in a row for one single noun, and a brilliant sentence it was. That's when I gave up offering advice.

Fay Weldon, June 1998

Contents

Classified index to listings for quick reference

Newspapers and magazines

Submitting material

Over a thousand titles are included in the newspapers and magazines section of the Yearbook, almost all of them offering opportunities to the writer. Many publications do not appear in our lists because the market they offer for the freelance writer is either too small or too specialised, or both. We give here some guidelines to bear in mind when submitting material to a newspaper or magazine.

Before submitting a manuscript to any newspaper or magazine it is advisable to first contact the relevant editor. The listings on page 3 give the names of editors for each section of the national newspapers and a quick telephone call to a magazine will establish the name of the relevant commissioning editor.

Magazine editors frequently complain to us about the unsuitability of many manuscripts submitted to them, as well as the omission of return postage. In their own interests, writers and others are advised to enclose postage for the return of unsuitable material.

Study the market

Before submitting manuscripts, always study carefully the editorial requirements of a magazine, not only for the subjects dealt with but for the approach, treatment, style and length. These comments will be obvious to the practised writer but the beginner can be spared much disappointment by buying copies of magazines and studying the market in depth.

The importance of studying the market cannot be overemphasised. It is an editor's job to know what readers want, and to see that they get it. Thus, freelance contributions must be tailored to fit a specific market; subject, theme, treatment, length, etc, must meet the editor's requirements. This is looked at further in *Writing for newspapers* on page 137 and *Writing magazine articles* on page 141.

Editors expect material to be well presented: neatly typed, double-spaced, with good margins, on A4 paper is the standard to aim at. An increasing number of editors are asking writers to submit their articles on disk. Always verify with the editor that your system and theirs are compatible before submission. Most editors also require a hard copy (printout) in addition to the disk. See *Preparing and submitting a manuscript* on page 551 and *Word processing* on page 555.

Illustrations

It is not advisable to send illustrations 'on spec'; check with the editor first. See page 144 for further information; listings of *Picture agencies and libraries* start on page 412.

For a list of magazines and newspapers willing to pay for cartoons, see *Newspapers and magazines which accept cartoons* on page 405, and *A serious look at marketing cartoons* (page 402) offers guidance for success.

Payment

It has always been our aim to obtain and publish the rates of payment offered for contributions by newspapers and magazines. Many publications, however, are reluctant to state a standard rate, since the value of a contribution may be dependent not upon length but upon the standing of the writer or of the information given. Many other periodicals, in spite of efforts to extract more precise information from them, prefer to state 'by negotiation' or 'by arrangement'. See *Getting paid for writing* on page 146.

A number of magazines will accept and pay for letters to the editor, brief fillers and gossip paragraphs, as well as puzzles and quizzes. *Magazines by subject area* on page 126 provides a rough guide to these markets.

Overseas contributions

The lists of overseas newspapers and magazines in the *Yearbook* contain only a selection of those journals which offer a market for the freelance writer. For fuller listings, refer to *Willings Press Guide Volume 2 Overseas*. The overseas market for stories and articles is small and editors often prefer their fiction to have a local setting.

Some overseas magazine titles have little space for freelance contributions but many of them will consider outstanding work. Potential contributors sending material overseas should always enclose return postage in the form of International Reply Coupons (IRCs) when submitting queries or manuscripts. IRCs can be exchanged in any foreign country for stamps representing the minimum postage payable on a letter sent from one country to another.

Using an agent to syndicate material written from overseas is worth considering. Most agents operate on an international basis and are more aware of current market requirements. Again, return postage should always be included.

Newspapers and syndicates

The larger newspapers and magazines buy many of their stories, and the smaller papers buy general articles, through one or other of the well-known syndicates. Another avenue for writers is to send printed copies of stories he or she has had published at home to an agent for syndication overseas. Listings for *Syndicates, news and press agencies* start on page 149. Listings of *National newspapers UK and Ireland* start on page 3, and the names of editors are included in each.

Most of the larger UK and overseas newspapers depend for news on their own staffs and press agencies. The most important overseas newspapers have permanent representatives in Britain who keep them supplied, not only with news of especial interest to the country concerned, but also with regular summaries of British news and with articles on events of particular importance. While many overseas newspapers and magazines have a London office, it is usual for manuscripts from freelance contributors to be submitted to the headquarters' editorial office overseas.

See also ...

- *Regional newspapers UK and Ireland*, page 11
- Newspapers are listed together with magazines for *Australia* (page 110), *Canada* (page 116), *New Zealand* (page 120) and *South Africa* (page 122)
- *USA*, page 124
- *Recent changes to newspapers and magazines*, page 136
- *Tape-recording interviews*, page 147

National newspapers UK and Ireland

Daily Mail
Northcliffe House, 2 Derry Street, London W8 5TT
tel 0171-938 6000 *fax* 0171-937 3251
Editor Paul Dacre
Daily Mon-Fri 35p Sat 45p
Supplement **Weekend**
Highest payment for good, exclusive news. Ideas welcomed for leader page articles (500-800 words). Exclusive news photos always wanted. Founded 1896.
> *City Editor* Andrew Alexander
> *Diary Editor* Nigel Dempster
> *Education Editor* Tony Halpin
> *Features Editor* Veronica Wadley
> *Deputy Foreign Editor* Gerry Hunt
> *Health Editor* Rory Clements
> *Industrial Editor* David Norris
> *Literary Editor* Jane Mays
> *Media Editor* Sean Poulter
> *Money Editor* Margaret Stone
> *News Editor* Ian MacGregor
> *Picture Editor* Geoff Webster
> *Political Editor* David Hughes
> *Showbiz Editor* Rebecca Hardy
> *Sports Editor* Bryan Cooney
> *Travel Editor* Cathy Wood
> *Weekend Editor* Aileen Doherty

Daily Record
Anderston Quay, Glasgow G3 8DA
tel 0141-248 7000 *fax* 0141-204 0770
web site http://www.record-mail.co.uk/rm
London office 1 Canada Square, Canary Wharf, London E14 5AP
tel 0171-293 3000
Editor-in-Chief Martin Clarke
Daily Mon-Sat 30p
Topical articles, from 300-700 words; exclusive stories of Scottish interest and exclusive colour photos.
> *Features Editor* Allan Rennie
> *Health and Science Correspondent* Jim McLean
> *News Editor* Murray Morse
> *Picture Editor* Stuart Nicol
> *Scottish Political Editor* Chris Decrin
> *Sports Editor* Andy Swinburne
> *Women's Page Editor* Lorna Frame

Daily Sport
19 Great Ancoats Street, Manchester M60 4BT
tel 0161-236 4466 *fax* 0161-236 4535

Editor-in-chief Tony Livesey
Editor Jeff McGowan
Daily Mon-Fri 32p
Factual stories and series. Length: up to 1000 words. Illustrations: b&w and colour photos, cartoons. Payment: £30-£5000. Founded 1988.
> *Features and News Editor* Tony Hore
> *Letters Editor* Belinda Charlton
> *Sports Editor* Mark Smith

Daily Star
Ludgate House, 245 Blackfriars Road, London SE1 9UX
tel 0171-928 8000 *fax* 0171-922 7960
Editor Phil Walker
Daily Mon-Sat 28p
Hard news exclusives, commanding substantial payment. Major interviews with big-star personalities; short features; series based on people rather than things; picture features. Payment: short features £75-£100; full page £250-£300; double page £400-£600, otherwise by negotiation. Illustrations: line, half-tone. Founded 1978.
> *Associate Editor* Kay Goddard
> *Entertainment Editor* Sandro Monetti
> *Features Editor* Linda Duff
> *News Editor* Hugh Whittow
> *Political Editor* Henry Macrory
> *Sports Editor* Jim Mansell
> *Women's Editor* Dawn Neesom

The Daily Telegraph
1 Canada Square, Canary Wharf, London E14 5DT
tel 0171-538 5000 *fax* 0171-538 6242
Editor Charles Moore
Daily Mon-Fri 40p Sat 75p
Supplements **Appointments, Arts & Books, Business News, Connected, Motoring, Telegraph Magazine, Television & Radio, Young Telegraph, Weekend**
Articles on a wide range of subjects of topical interest considered. Preliminary letter and synopsis required. Length: 700-1000 words. Payment: by arrangement. Founded 1855.

Arts Editor Sarah Crompton
City Editor Neil Collins
Education Editor John Clare
Environment Editor Charles Clover
Fashion Editor Hilary Alexandra
Features Editor Corrina Honan
Foreign Editor Stephen Robinson
Health Editor Christine Doyle
Literary Editor John Coldstream
Media Editor Alison Boshoff
News Editor Martin Newland
Picture Editor Bob Bodman
Political Editor George Jones
Sports Editor David Welch

Telegraph Magazine
Editor Emma Soames
Free with Sat paper

Short profiles (about 1600 words); articles of topical interest. Preliminary study of the magazine essential. Illustrations: all types. Payment: by arrangement. Founded 1964.

Electronic Telegraph
e-mail et@telegraph.co.uk
web site http://www.telegraph.co.uk/
Editor Derek Bishton
Daily Free to Internet subscribers

Based on *The Daily Telegraph*, contains news, sport, City, features, Internet News, Hyperlinks to Archive. Founded 1994.

Juiced
web site http://www.juiced.com
Weekly Free to Internet subscribers

Student magazine.

Planet
web site http://www.the-planet.co.uk
Free to Internet subscribers

Travel writing from the *Daily Telegraph* and the *Sunday Telegraph*.

The Express
Ludgate House, 245 Blackfriars Road,
London SE1 9UX
tel 0171-928 8000 *fax* 0171-260 1654
Great Ancoats Street, Manchester M60 4HB
tel 0161-236 2112
Editor Richard Addis
Daily Mon-Fri 35p Sat 40p
Supplements **Saturday**, **The Sport**, **Weekend**

Exclusive news; striking photos. Leader page articles (600 words); facts preferred to opinions. Payment: according to value.

Arts Editor Mal Peachey
Business Editor John Murray
Diary Editor John McEntee
Environment Editor John Ingham
Features Editor Jack Wright
Foreign Editor Mike Graham
Health Editor Liz Wilson

Literary Editor Maggie Pringle
Media Editor David Wigg
News Editor Ian Walker
Political Editor Nicholas Wood
Sports Editor Alex Butler
Women's Editor Rachel Simone

Express on Sunday
Ludgate House, 245 Blackfriars Road,
London SE1 9UX
tel 0171-928 8000 *fax* 0171-620 1656
Editor Richard Addis
Sun 70p

Exclusive news stories, photos, personality profiles and features of controversial or lively interest. Length: 800-1000 words. Payment: top rates. Founded 1918.

City Editor Kirsty Hamilton
Features Editor Jack Wright
Finance Editor John Murray
Literary Editor Maggie Pringle
News Editor Shan Lancaster
Political Editor Peter Obourne
Sports Editor Alex Butler

Express on Sunday Magazine
fax 0171-928 7262
Editor Tessa Hilton
Free with paper

Homes, gardens, cookery, general interest features. Length: 1000 words. Payment: from £250 per 1000 words. Illustrations: colour, half-tone, artwork.

Financial Times
1 Southwark Bridge, London SE1 9HL
tel 0171-873 3000 *fax* 0171-873 3076
web site http://www.ft.com
Editor Richard Lambert
Daily Mon-Sat 80p
Supplements **Business Books**, **Companies & Markets**, **FT-IT**, **How To Spend It**, **Reporting Britain**, **Surveys**, **Weekend FT**, **Weekend Money**

Articles of financial, commercial, industrial and economic interest. Length: 800-1000 words. Payment: by arrangement. Founded 1888.

Arts Editor Annalena McAfee
Banking Editor George Graham
Head of Consumer Industries John Willman
Economics Editor Robert Chote
Features Editor John Parker
Financial Editor Martin Dickson
Foreign Editor Quentin Peel
International Editor Peter Martin
Markets Editor Philip Coggan
News Editor Julia Cuthbertson
Head of Observer Michael Cassell
Political Editor Robert Peston
Small Businesses Editor Kathrine Campbell
Surverys Editor Rhys David

Travel Editor Robert Thompson
Weekend FT Editor Robert Thomson

The Guardian

119 Farringdon Road, London EC1R 3ER
tel 0171-278 2332 *fax* 0171-837 2114
164 Deansgate, Manchester M60 2RR
tel 0161-832 7200 *fax* 0161-832 5351
Editor Alan Rusbridger
Daily Mon-Fri 45p Sat 60p
Supplements **Education, Friday Review, The Guardian 2, Online, Society, The Week, Weekend**

Few articles are taken from outside contributors except on its specialist pages. Length: not exceeding 1200 words. Illustrations: news and features photos. Payment: from £170.83 per 1000 words; from £50.94 for illustrations. Founded 1821.

Arts Editor Claire Armitstead
Business Editor Patrick Donovan
Community Affairs Editor James Meikie
Economics Editor Larry Elliot
Education Editor John Carvel
Fashion Editor Susannah Frankel
Features Editor Roger Alton
Foreign Editor Rosemary Collins
Health Editor Dr Luisa Dillner
Literary Editor Stephen Moss
Media Editor John Mulholland
News Editor Harriet Sherwood
Political Editor Michael White
Religious Editor Madeleine Bunting
Science Editor Tim Radford
Sports Editor Mike Averis
Technology Editor Nicholas Bannister
Women's Editor Sally Weale

Weekend

Editor Deborah Orr
Free with Sat paper

Features on world affairs, major profiles, food and drink, home life, the arts, travel, leisure, etc. Also good reportage on social and political subjects. Illustrations: b&w photos and line, cartoons. Payment: apply for rates.

Guardian Online

web site http://www.guardian.co.uk

The Herald

Scottish Media Newspapers Ltd, 195 Albion Street, Glasgow G1 1QP
tel 0141-552 6255 *fax* 0141-552 2288
web site http://www.cims.co.uk/herald
London office Gray's Inn House,
127 Clerkenwell Road, London EC1R 5DB
tel 0171-405 2121
Editor Harry Reid
Daily Mon-Sat 48p

Articles up to 1000 words. Founded 1783.

Arts Editor Keith Bruce

Associate Editor John Ryan
Business Editor Robert Powell
Chief Financial Editor Ronnie Dundas
Deputy Editor Alf Young
Diary Editor Tom Shields
European Correspondent Rory Watson
Executive Editor Ron Anderson
Associate Features Editor Drew Allan
Managing Editor Bob Jeffrey
News Editor Bill McDowall
Sports Editor Iain Scott

The Independent

1 Canada Square, Canary Wharf, London E14 5AP
tel 0171-293 2000 *fax* 0171-293 2435
Editor Simon Kelner
Daily Mon-Fri 40p Sat 50p
Supplements **City+, The Eye, The Independent Magazine, The Independent Tabloid, The Long Weekend, Weekend**

Occasional freelance contributions; preliminary letter advisable. Payment: by arrangement. Founded 1986.

Arts Editor Mark Pappenheim
Business Editor Jeremy Warner
City Editor Tom Stevenson
Education Editor Judith Judd
Environment Editor Nicholas Schoon
Features Editor David Robson
Foreign Editor Andrew Marshall
Health Editor Jeremy Laurancet
Labour Editor Barrie Clement
Literary Editor Boyd Tonkin
Media Editor Rob Brown
News Editor David Felton
Picture Editor David Swanborough
Political Editor Tony Bevins
Sports Editor Paul Newman

The Independent Magazine

Editor Michael Watts
Free with Sat paper

Profiles and illustrated articles of topical interest; all material commissioned. Preliminary study of the magazine essential. Length: 500-3000 words. Illustrations: cartoons; commissioned colour and b&w photos. Payment: by arrangement. Founded 1988.

Independent on Sunday

1 Canada Square, Canary Wharf, London E14 5DL
tel 0171-293 2000 *fax* 0171-293 2043
Editor Kim Fletcher, *Deputy Editor* Stephen Fay
Sun £1.00
Supplements **Business, Real Life, Smart Moves, The Sunday Review, Travel & Money**

News, features and articles. Illustrated, including cartoons. Payment: by negotiation. Founded 1990.

Arts Editor Rosanna de Lisle

Environment Editor Geoffrey Lean
Features Editor Laura Tennant
Foreign Editor Ray Whitaker
News Editor Michael Streeter
Picture Editor David Sandison
Political Editor Stephen Castle
Sports Editor Neil Morton

The Sunday Review
tel 0171-293 2000 *fax* 0171-293 2027
Editor Laurence Earle
Free with paper

Original features of general interest with potential for photographic illustration. Material mostly commissioned. Length: 1000-5000 words. Illustrations: colour transparencies. Payment: £150 per 1000 words.

Irish Independent
Independent House, 90 Middle Abbey Street, Dublin 1, Republic of Ireland
tel (01) 7055333 *fax* (01) 8720304/8731787
Editor Vincent Doyle
Daily Mon-Sat 85p

Special articles on topical or general subjects. Length: 700-1000 words. Payment: editor's estimate of value.
Arts Editor Bruce Arnold
Business Editor Frank Mulrennan
Diary Editor Angela Phelan
Features Editor John Spain
News Editor Philip Molloy
Picture Editor Tom Brady
Political Editor Chris Glennon
Sports Editor Patrick J. Cunningham

Irish Times
11-15 D'Olier Street, Dublin 2, Republic of Ireland
tel (01) 6792022 *fax* (01) 6719407
Editor Conor Brady
Daily Mon-Sat 85p

Mainly staff-written. Specialist contributions (800-2000 words) by commission on basis of ideas submitted. Payment: at editor's valuation. Illustrations: photos and line drawings.
Arts Editor Victoria White
Business Editor Bill Murdoch
Features Editor Caroline Walsh
Finance Editor Cliff Taylor
Foreign Editor Paul Gillespie
Literary Editor John Banville
News Editor Niall Kiely
Picture Editor Dermot O'Shea
Political Editor Dick Walsh
Special Reports Editor Ray Comiskey
Sports Editor Malachy Logan
Supplements Editor Karl Jones

The Irish Times on the Web
web site http://www.irish-times.co.

Mail on Sunday
Northcliffe House, 2 Derry Street, London W8 5TS
tel 0171-938 6000 *fax* 0171-937 3829
Editor Jonathan Holborow
Sun 85p
Supplements **Financial Mail on Sunday, Night & Day, Programme, You**

Articles. Payment: by arrangement. Illustrations: line, half-tone; cartoons. Founded 1982.
City Editor William Kay
Diary Editor Nigel Dempster
Features Editor Sian James
Literary Editor Paula Johnson
News Editor Paul Henderson
Picture Editor Andy Kyle
Political Editor Joe Murphy
Sports Editor Dan Evans

Financial Mail on Sunday
tel 0171-938 6984
e-mail fmos@mailonsunday.co.uk
web site http://www.financialmail.co.uk
Free with paper
City Editor William Kay
Executive Editor David Sinclair
Personal Finance Editor Jeff Prestridge

City, industry, business, and personal finance. News stories up to 1500 words. Payment by arrangement. Full colour illustrations and photography commissioned.

Night & Day
tel 0171-938 7051 *fax* 0171-937 7488
Acting Editor Kate Carr
Free with paper

Investigative journalism, profiles, personal columns and book reviews – mostly commissioned. Length: 3000 words for main feature; 1000 words for personal column. Illustrations: colour photos. Founded 1993.

You
Editor Dee Nolan
Features Editor Jane Phillimore
Free with paper

Women's interest features. Length: 500-2500 words. Payment: by arrangement. Illustrations: full colour and b&w drawings commissioned; also colour photos.

The Mirror
1 Canada Square, Canary Wharf, London E14 5AP
tel 0171-293 3000 *fax* 0171-293 3409
Editor Piers Morgan
Daily Mon-Sat 28p
Supplements **Mirror Football Mania, Mirror TVplus**

Top payment for exclusive news and news pictures. Freelance articles used, and ideas bought: send synopsis only. 'Unusual' pictures and those giving a new angle on the news are welcomed; also cartoons. Founded 1903.

Business Editor Clinton Manning
Environment Editor Jeremy Armstrong
Features Editor Tina Weaver
Health Editor Jill Palmer
Letters Editor Jo Dipple
News Editor Eugene Duffy
Picture Editor Ron Morgans
Political Editor Kevin Maguire
Sports Editor David Balmforth

Morning Star

(formerly Daily Worker)
The Morning Star Co-operative Society Ltd,
1-3 Ardleigh Road, London N1 4HS
tel 0171-254 0033 *fax* 0171-254 5950
e-mail morsta@geo2.poptel.org.uk
Editor John Haylett
Daily Mon-Sat 50p

Newspaper for the labour movement. Articles of general interest. Illustrations: photos, cartoons and drawings. Founded 1930.

Arts & Media Editor Jeff Sawtell
Diary Editor Mike Ambrose
Features Editor Paul Corry
Financial Editor Ian Morrison
Foreign Editor Brian Denny
Health Editor Mike Parker
Industrial Editor Chris Kasrils
News Editor Paul Corry
Political Editor Mike Ambrose
Sports Editor Amanda Kendal

News of the World

1 Virginia Street, London E1 9XR
tel 0171-782 1000 *fax* 0171-583 9504
Editor Phil Hall
Deputy Editor Bob Bird
Sun 60p

Uses freelance material. Payment: by negotiation. Founded 1843.

Assistant Editor (Features) Gary Thompson
Assistant Editor (News) Greg Miskiw
Money Editor Peter Prendergast
Political Editor Eben Black
Royal Editor Clive Goodman
Sports Editor Mike Dunn
Travel Editor David Gordois

Sunday Magazine

Phase 2, 5th Floor, 1 Virginia Street,
London E1 9BD
tel 0171-782 7900 *fax* 0171-782 7474
Editor Judy McGuire
Free with paper

Ideas and material from freelance writers welcomed. Payment: by arrangement. Founded 1981.

The Observer

119 Farringdon Road, London EC1R 3ER
tel 0171-278 2332 *fax* 0171-713 4250
Editor Will Hutton
Sun £1.00
Supplements **Business**, **Life**, **The Observer Review**, **Sport**

Some articles and illustrations commissioned. Payment: by arrangement. Founded 1791.

Arts Editor Jane Ferguson
Business Editor Ben Laurance
City Editor Heather Connon
Economics Editor William Keegan
Education Editor Martin Bright
Fashion Editor Jo Adams
Features Editor Lisa O'Kelly
Foreign Editor Leonard Doyle
Literary Editor Robert McCrum
Media Editor Richard Brooks
News Editor Paul Dunn
Picture Editor Greg Whitmore
Political Editor Patrick Wintour
Sports Editor Alan Hubbard
Travel Editor Desmond Balmer

Life

tel 0171-713 4175 *fax* 0171-713 4217
Editor Justine Picardy
Free with paper

Commissioned features. Length: 2000-3000 words. Illustrations: first-class colour and b&w photos. Payment: NUJ rates; £150 per illustration.

The Observer Online

web site http://www.observer.co.uk

The People

1 Canada Square, Canary Wharf, London E14 5AP
tel 0171-293 3000 *fax* 0171-293 3810
Editor Neil Wallis
Sun 55p
Supplements **TV First!**, **Yes!**

Investigative features, single articles and series considered; pictures should be supplied with contributions if possible. Features should be of deep human interest, whether the subject is serious or light-hearted. Very strong sports following. Exclusive news and news-feature stories also considered. Payment: rates high, even for tips that lead to published news stories.

Features Editor Tom Petrie
Finance Editor Cathy Gunn
News Editor Danny Buckland
Picture Editor Martin Spaven
Political Editor Nigel Nelson
Sports Editor Ed Barry

Yes!

Editor Tom Petrie

Free with paper
Feature articles. Illustrations: colour.
Payment: by arrangement.

Scotland on Sunday

20 North Bridge, Edinburgh EH1 1YT
tel 0131-225 2468 *fax* 0131-220 2443
Glasgow office
tel 0141-332 6163
Editor John C. McGurk
Sun 50p

Features on all subjects, not necessarily
Scottish. Payment: £88 per 1000 words.
Founded 1988.
News Editor William Paul
Political Editor Iain Martin

Scotland on Sunday Magazine

Editor Margot Wilson
Free with paper

The Scotsman

20 North Bridge, Edinburgh EH1 1YT
tel 0131-225 2468 *fax* 0131-226 7420
Editor Alan Ruddock
Daily Mon-Fri 42p Sat 50p
Supplements **Business Daily**, **Property Weekly**,
Recruitment, **The Scotsman Weekend**, **Sports
Weekly**

Considers articles on political, economic
and general themes which add substan-
tially to current information. Prepared to
commission topical and controversial
series from proved authorities. Length:
800-1000 words. Illustrations: outstand-
ing news pictures, cartoons. Payment: by
arrangement. Founded 1817.
Arts Editor Robert Dawson-Scott
Business Editor Mark McSherry
Education Editor Tom Little
Environment Editor Christopher Cairns
Features Editor Jane Johnstone
Foreign Editor Andrew McCleod
Internet Editor Nick Clayton
Literary Editor Catherine Lockerbie
News Editor Richard Neville
Political Editor John Penman
Sports Editors Kevin McKenna/Donald Walker
Women's Editor Gillian Glover

The Scotsman Weekend

Editor Alastair McKay
Free with Sat paper

Features, reviews. Illustrated.

The Star

Independent Star Ltd, Star House,
62A Terenure Road North, Dublin 6w,
Republic of Ireland
tel (01) 4901228 *fax* (01) 4902193/4902188
Editor Gerard O'Regan
Daily Mon-Sat 60p

General articles relating to news and
sport, and features. Length: 1000 words.
Illustrations: colour photos. Payment: by
negotiation. Founded 1989.
Deputy Editor Danny Smyth
News Editors Dave O'Connell, Bernard Phelan
Picture Editor James Dunne
Political Editor John Donlon
Sports Editor Connie Clinton

The Sun

News Group Newspapers Ltd, Virginia Street,
London E1 9XP
tel 0171-782 4000 *fax* 0171-488 3253
Editor David Yelland
Daily Mon-Fri 28p, Sat 30p
Supplement **Super Goals, Sportsweek**

Takes freelance material, including car-
toons. Payment: by negotiation. Founded
1969.
Business Editor Isabelle Murray
Education Editor David Wooding
Features Editor John Worsnop
Health Editor Dr Rosemary Leonard
Letters Editor Sue Cook
News Editor Glenn Goodey
Picture Editor Ken Lennox
Political Editor Trevor Kavanagh
Showbiz Editor Dominic Mohan
Sports Editor Steve McKenlay
Television Editor Charles Yates
Travel Editor Katie Wood
Women's Editor Sam Carlisle

Sunday Business

200 Gray's Inn Road, London WC1X 8XR
tel 0171-418 9600 *fax* 0171-418 9605
Editor Jeff Randall
Sun 50p

Standalone Sunday newspaper for the
business and financial community.
Covers all aspects of business news with
in-depth features ranging from captains
of industry to the entrepreneurial and
small business sector. Wide economic
coverage, IT news, and personal finance
features. Length: from 200-word news
stories to 2500-word features. Payment:
by arrangement.
City Editor Nils Pratley
Deputy Editor Richard Northedge
Diary Editor Damien McCrystal
Economics Editor Martin Essex
Features Editor Vivien Goldsmith
News Editor Frank Kane
Stock Markets Editor Paul Murphy

The Sunday Business Post

Merchants House, 27-30 Merchants Quay,
Dublin 8, Republic of Ireland

tel (01) 6026000 *fax* (01) 6796496/6796498
Editor Damien Kiberd
Sun £1.00

Features on financial, economic and political topics; also lifestyle, media and science articles. Illustrations: colour and b&w photos, graphics, cartoons. Payment: by negotiation. Founded 1989.

> *Arts Editor* Marion McKeon
> *Business Editor* Ted Harding
> *Features Editor* Aileen O'Toole
> *Financial Editor* Gail Seekamp
> *IT Editor* Carissa Casey
> *Media Editor* Christine Doherty
> *News Editor* Aileen O'Toole
> *Political Editor* Emily O'Reilly
> *Sports Editor* Eoghan Corry

Sunday Independent

Independent House, 90 Middle Abbey Street, Dublin 1, Republic of Ireland
tel (01) 7055333 *fax* (01) 7055779
Editor Aengus Fanning
Sun £1.00

Special articles. Length: according to subject. Illustrations: topical or general interest, cartoons. Payment: at editor's valuation.

> *Arts Editor* Ronan Farren
> *Business Editor* Shane Ross
> *Diary Editor* Terry Keane
> *Features Editor* Anne Harris
> *News Editor* Willie Kealy
> *Political Editor* Joe O'Malley
> *Sports Editor* Adhamhnan O'Sullivan

Sunday Life

124 Royal Avenue, Belfast BT1 1EB
tel (01232) 264300 *fax* (01232) 554507
e-mail barnold@belfasttelegraph.co.uk
Editor Martin Lindsay
Sun 60p

Items of interest to Northern Ireland Sunday tabloid readers. Payment: by arrangement. Illustrations: colour and b&w pictures and graphics. Founded 1988.

> *Features Editor* Sue Corbett
> *Photographic Editor* Fred Hoare
> *Sports Editor* Jim Gracey
> *Women's Page Editor* Sue Corbett

Sunday Mail

Anderston Quay, Glasgow G3 8DA
tel 0141-248 7000 *fax* 0141-242 3587
web site http://www.record-mail.co.uk/rm
London office 1 Canada Square, Canary Wharf, London E14 5AP
Editor Jim Cassidy
Sun 55p
Supplements **XS**

Exclusive stories and pictures (in colour if possible) of national and Scottish interest; also cartoons. Payment: above average.

> *Assistant Editor* Andrew Sannholm
> *Features Editor* Rob Bruce
> *Financial Editor* Jim Fyfe
> *Health Editor* Dr Tom Smith
> *News Editor* Brian Steel
> *Picture Editor* David NcNeil
> *Political Editor* Angus Macleod
> *Showbiz Editor* Scott Robinson
> *Sports Editor* George Cheyne
> *Women's Page Editor* Melanie Reid
> *XS Editor* Janette Harkess

Sunday Mirror

1 Canada Square, Canary Wharf, London E14 5AP
tel 0171-293 3000 *fax* 0171-293 3939
Editor Colin Myler
Sun 60p
Supplements **Personal**, **TV Week**

Concentrates on human interest news features, social documentaries, dramatic news and feature photos. Ideas, as well as articles, bought. Payment: high, especially for exclusives. Founded 1963.

> *City Editor* Diane Boliver
> *Assistant Editor (Features)* Fiona Wyton
> *Assistant Editor (News)* John McShane
> *Executive Editor (Pictures)* Paul Bennett
> *Editor (Sport)* Alan McKenlay

Personal

tel 0171-293 3826 *fax* 0171-293 3835
Contact Fiona Wingett, Paul Bennett
Free with paper

Human interest, celebrity articles, and original amusing ideas. Length: 1000 words. Illustrations: colour photos. Payment: articles and photographs high, especially for exclusives. Founded 1988.

Sunday Post

D.C. Thomson & Co. Ltd, 144 Port Dundas Road, Glasgow G4 0HZ
tel 0141-332 9933 *fax* 0141-331 1595
Albert Square, Dundee DD1 9QJ
tel (01382) 223131 *fax* (01382) 201064
185 Fleet Street, London EC4A 2HS
tel 0171-404 0199 *fax* 0171-404 5694
Editor Russell Reid
Sun 55p

Human interest, topical, domestic and humorous articles, and exclusive news. Payment: on acceptance.

The Sunday Post Magazine

tel (01382) 223131 *ext* 5820 *fax* (01382) 201064
Editor Maggie Dun

Monthly Free with paper

General interest articles. Length: 1000-2000 words. Illustrations: colour transparencies. Payment: varies. Founded 1988.

Sunday Sport

19 Great Ancoats Street, Manchester M60 4BT
tel 0161-236 4466 *fax* 0161-236 4535
Executive Editor Tony Livesey
Editor Jon Wise
Deputy Editor Mark Harris
Sun 55p

Founded 1986.

Features Editor Phil Johnson
News Editor Paul Carter
Picture Editor Paul Currie
Sports Editor Marc Smith

Sunday Telegraph

1 Canada Square, Canary Wharf,
London E14 5DT
tel 0171-538 5000 *fax* 0171-513 2504
Editor Dominic Lawson
Sun 90p
Supplements **Appointments**, **Review**, **Sunday Telegraph Magazine**

Occasional freelance material accepted.

Arts Editor John Preston
City Editor Neil Bennett
Comment Editor Stuart Reid
Deputy Editor Kim Fletcher
Deputy Editor (Comment) Matthew d'Ancona
Diary Editor Mark Inglefield
Features Editor Rebecca Nicolson
Literary Editor Miriam Gross
News Editor Chris Anderson
Picture Editor Nigel Skelsey
Sports Editor Colin Gibson
Women's Editor Kim Fletcher

Sunday Telegraph Magazine

tel 0171-538 7590 *fax* 0171-538 7074
e-mail sunmag@telegraph.co.uk
Editor Joanna Prior
Free with paper

All material is commissioned. Founded 1995.

The Sunday Times

1 Pennington Street, London E1 9XW
tel 0171-782 5000 *fax* 0171-782 5658
web site http://www.sunday-times.co.uk
Editor John Witherow
Sun £1.00
Supplements **Appointments, Books, Business, Culture, Money, Sport, Style, The Sunday Times Magazine**

Special articles by authoritative writers on politics, literature, art, drama, music, finance and science, and topical matters. Payment: top rate for exclusive features.

Illustrations: first class photos of topical interest and pictorial merit welcome; also topical drawings and cartoons. Founded 1822.

Arts Editor Helen Hawkins
Economics Editor David Smith
Education Editor Judith O'Reilly
Literary Editor Geordie Greig
News Editor Charles Hymas
News Review Sarah Baxter
Political Editor Andy Grice
Sports Editor Alex Butler
Travel Editor Christine Walker

Culture

Articles and reviews of current performing arts.

Style

Lifestyle articles.

The Sunday Times Magazine

tel 0171-782 7000
Editor Robin Morgan
Free with paper

Articles and pictures. Illustrations: colour and b&w photos. Payment: by negotiation.

The Sunday Times Scotland

Times Newspapers Ltd, 124 Portman Street, Kinning Park, Glasgow G41 1EJ
tel 0141-420 5100 *fax* 0141-420 5262
Editor Will Peakin
Free with *The Sunday Times*

News, features and sport. Illustrations: colour photos, cartoons and graphics. Payment: £100 per feature; £50 for illustrations. Founded 1988.

The Sunday Tribune

Tribune Publications plc, 15 Lower Baggot Street, Dublin 2, Republic of Ireland
tel (01) 661 5555 *fax* (01) 661 5302
e-mail stribune@indigo.ie
Editor Matt Cooper
Sun £1.00
Supplement **Sunday Tribune Magazine**

Newspaper containing news (inc. foreign), articles, features and photo features. Length: 600-2800 words. Illustrations: colour and b&w photos and cartoons. Payment: £100 per 1000 words; £100 for illustrations. Founded 1980.

Arts Editor Ciaran Carty
Assistant Editors Richard Curran/Ger Siggins
Business Editor Shane Coleman
News Editor Miriam Donohoe
Photo Desk Sarah Gillespie
Sports Editor Brian Carey
Sunday Tribune Magazine Editor Ros Dee

The Times

1 Pennington Street, London E1 9XN
tel 0171-782 5000 *fax* 0171-488 3242
web site http://www.the-times.co.uk
Editor Peter Stothard
Daily Mon-Fri 35p Sat 45p
Supplements **The Directory, Interface, Meg@,
The Times 2, The Times 3, The Times Magazine,
Times Sport, Weekend**

Outside contributions considered from: experts in subjects of current interest and writers who can make first-hand experience or reflection come readably alive. Phone appropriate section editor. Length: up to 1200 words. Founded 1785.

   Arts Editor Richard Morrison
   Business Editor Patience Wheatcroft
   Economics Editor Janet Bush
   Education Editor John O'Leary
   Environment Correspondent Nick Nuttall
   Features Editor Sandra Parsons
   Foreign Editor Graham Patterson
   Health Correspondent Ian Murray
   Industrial Correspondent Christine Buckley
   Literary Editor Erica Wagner
   Media Editor Ray Snoddy
   News Editor Graham Duffil
   Political Editor Philip Webster
   Science Editor Nigel Hawkes
   Sports Editor David Chappell
   Weekend Times Editor Andrew Yates

The Times Magazine

Editor Gill Morgan
Free with Sat paper
Features. Illustrated.

Wales on Sunday

Thomson House, Havelock Street,
Cardiff CF1 1XR
tel (01222) 583583 *fax* (01222) 583725
Editor Alan Edmunds
Sun 55p

National Sunday newspaper of Wales offering comprehensive news, features and entertainments coverage at the weekend, with a particular focus on events in Wales. Accepts general interest articles, preferably with a Welsh connection. Founded 1989.

   News Editor Alastair Milburn
   Senior Assistant Editor Mike Smith
   Sports Editor Richard Morgans

Regional newspapers UK and Ireland

Regional newspapers are listed in alphabetical order under region. Some will accept and pay for letters to the editor, brief fillers, and gossip paragraphs, as well as puzzles and quizzes. See also Writing for newspapers on page 137.

Belfast

Belfast Telegraph

124-144 Royal Avenue, Belfast BT1 1EB
tel (01232) 321242 *fax* (01232) 554506 (also photographic), 554540 (news only), 554517 (features), 554508 (sport)
Editor Edmund Curran
Daily Mon-Sat 26p

   Features Editor John Caruth
   News Editor Janet Devlin
   Picture Editor Gerry Fitzgerald
   Sports Editor John Laverty

Any material relating to Northern Ireland. Payment: by negotiation. Founded 1870.

Irish News

113-117 Donegall Street, Belfast BT1 2GE
tel (01232) 322226 *fax* (01232) 337505
Editor Tom Collins
Daily Mon-Sat 35p

   Business Editor Jim Fitzpatrick
   Features Editor Ann-Marie McFarl
   News Editor Dan Stanton
   Picture Editor Brendan Murphy
   Sports Editor John Haughey

Articles of historical and topical interest. Payment: by arrangement. Founded 1855.

News Letter

46-56 Boucher Crescent, Boucher Road,
Belfast BT12 6QY
tel (01232) 680000 *fax* (01232) 664412
Editor Geoff Martin
Daily Mon-Sat 35p

   Features Editor Geoff Hill
   Picture Editor John Rush
   Sports Editor Brian Millar

Pro-Union. Founded 1737.

Channel Islands

Guernsey Evening Press and Star
Braye Road, Vale, Guernsey GY1 3BW
tel (01481) 45866 *fax* (01481) 48972
Editor Nick Machon
Daily Mon-Sat 32p
 Features Editor Anthony Warlow
 News Editor Dave Edmonds
 Sports Editor Rob Batiste

News and feature articles. Length: 500-
700 words. Illustrations: colour and b&w
photos. Payment: by negotiation.
Founded 1897.

Jersey Evening Post
PO Box 582, Five Oaks, St Saviour, Jersey JE4 8XQ
tel (01534) 611611 *fax* (01534) 611622
e-mail jepdaily@itl.net
Editor Chris Bright
Daily Mon-Sat 36p
 Features Editor Richard Pedley
 News Editor Sue le Ruez
 Picture Editor Peter Mourant
 Sports Editor Ron Felton

News and features with a Channel Islands
angle. Length: 1000 words (articles/fea-
tures), 300 words (news). Illustrations:
colour and b&w. Payment: £80 (articles/
features), £25 (news); £30. Founded 1890.

Cork

Evening Echo (Cork)
Cork Examiner Publications Ltd,
1-6 Academy Street, Cork, Republic of Ireland
tel (021) 272722 *fax* (021) 275477
Editor Brian Feeney
Daily Mon-Sat 50p
 Features Editor Maurice Gubbins
 News Editor Vincent Kelly
 Picture Editor Norma Cuddihy
 Sports Editor Mark Woods

Articles, features and news for the area.
Illustrations: colour prints.

The Examiner
1-6 Academy Street, Cork, Republic of Ireland
tel (021) 272722 *fax* (021) 275477
Editor Brian Looney
Daily Mon-Sat 85p
 Features Editor Dan Buckley
 News Editor Ann Cahill
 Picture Editor Norma Cuddihy
 Sports Editor Tony Leen

Features. Material mostly commissioned.
Length: 1000 words. Payment: by
arrangement. Founded 1841.

Dublin

Evening Herald
90 Middle Abbey Street, Dublin 1,
Republic of Ireland
tel (01) 8731333
Editor Paul Drury
Daily Mon-Sat 65p
 Features Editor David Robbins
 News Editor Martin Brennan
 Picture Editor Liam Mulcahy
 Sports Editor David Courtney

Articles. Payment: by arrangement.
Illustrations: line, half-tone, cartoons.

East Anglia

Cambridge Evening News
Winship Road, Milton, Cambs. CB4 6PP
tel (01223) 434438 *fax* (01223) 434415
e-mail edit.camnews@dial.pipex.com
Editor Robert Satchwell
Daily Mon-Sat 31p
 Features Editor Angela Singer
 News Editor Peter Wells
 Picture Editor Keith Heppell
 Sports Editor Alex Martin

The voice of Mid-Anglia – news, views
and sport. Illustrations: colour prints,
b&w and colour graphics. Payment: by
negotiation. Founded 1888.

East Anglian Daily Times
30 Lower Brook Street, Ipswich, Suffolk IP4 1AN
tel (01473) 230023 *fax* (01473) 233228
Editor Terry Hunt
Daily Mon-Sat 38p
 Features Editor Steve Hughes
 News Editor Mark Hindle
 Picture Editor Paul Nixon
 Sports Editor Nick Garnham

Features of East Anglian interest, preferably with pictures. Length: 500 words.
Illustrations: colour, b&w. Payment: £50
per feature; illustrations NUJ rates.
Founded 1874.

Eastern Daily Press
Prospect House, Rouen Road, Norwich NR1 1RE
tel (01603) 628311 *fax* (01603) 612930
Editor Peter Franzen
London office House of Commons Press Gallery,
House of Commons, London SW1A 0AA
tel 0171-219 3384 *fax* 0171-222 3830
Daily Mon-Sat 40p

Limited market for articles of East
Anglian interest not exceeding 900
words. Founded 1870.

Evening News

Prospect House, Rouen Road, Norwich NR1 1RE
tel (01603) 628311 *fax* (01603) 612930
Editor Bob Crawley
Daily Mon-Sat 30p
  Features Editor Derek James
  News Editor Mark Langlands
  Picture Editor Nolan Lincoln
  Sports Editor David Cuffley
Interested in local news-based features.
Length: up to 500 words. Payment: NUJ
or agreed rates. Founded 1882.

East Midlands

Burton Mail

Burton Daily Mail Ltd, 65-68 High Street,
Burton on Trent DE14 1LE
tel (01283) 512345 *fax* (01283) 515351
Editor Brian J. Vertigen
Daily Mon-Sat 29p
  Features Editor Bill Pritchard
  News and Picture Editor Andy Parker
  Sports Editor Rex Page
Features, news and articles of interest to
Burton and south Derbyshire readers.
Length: 400-500 words. Illustrations:
colour and b&w. Payment: by
negotiation. Founded 1898.

Chronicle & Echo, Northampton

Northamptonshire Newspapers Ltd, Upper
Mounts, Northampton NN1 3HR
tel (01604) 231122 *fax* (01604) 233000
Editor Mark Edwards
Daily Mon-Sat 28p
Articles, features and news – mostly commissioned – of interest to the Northampton
area. Length/illustrations: varies. Payment:
by negotiation. Founded 1931.

Derby Evening Telegraph

Northcliffe House, Meadow Road,
Derby DE1 2DW
tel (01332) 291111 *fax* (01322) 253027
Editor Keith Perch
Daily Mon-Sat 29p
  Features Editor Nigel Powlson
  News Editor Robert Irvine
  Picture Editor Stuart Wilde
  Sports Editor Steve Nicholson
Articles and news of local interest.
Payment: by negotiation.

The Leicester Mercury

St George Street, Leicester LE1 9FQ
tel 0116-251 2512 *fax* 0116-253 0645
Editor Nick Carter
Daily Mon-Sat 27p

Occasional articles, features and news;
submit ideas to editor first. Length/pay-
ment: by negotiation. Founded 1874.

Nottingham Evening Post

Forman Street, Nottingham NG1 4AB
tel 0115-948 2000 *fax* 0115-964 4027
Daily Mon-Sat 27p
Material on local issues considered.
Founded 1878.

London

Evening Standard

Northcliffe House, 2 Derry Street,
London W8 5EE
tel 0171-938 6000
Editor Max Hastings
Daily Mon-Fri 30p
  Features Editor Bernice Davison
  News Editor Stephen Clackson
  Picture Editor David Ofield
  Sports Editor Simon Greenberg
Articles of general interest considered,
1500 words or shorter; also news, pic-
tures and ideas. Founded 1827.

ES Magazine

Editor Adam Edwards
Weekly Free with paper
Feature ideas, exclusively about London.
Payment: by negotiation. Illustrations: all
types.

North

Evening Chronicle

Newcastle Chronicle and Journal Ltd,
Thomson House, Groat Market,
Newcastle upon Tyne NE1 1ED
tel 0191-232 7500 *fax* 0191-232 2256
Editor Alison Hastings
Daily Mon-Sat 26p
  Features Editor Richard Ord
  News Editor Mick Smith
  Picture Editor Rod Wilson
  Sports Editor Paul New
News, photos and features covering
almost every subject of interest to readers
in Tyne and Wear, Northumberland and
Durham. Payment: according to value.

Evening Gazette

North Eastern Evening Gazette Ltd,
Borough Road, Middlesbrough TS1 3AZ
tel (01642) 245401 *fax* (01642) 232014
Editor Ranald Allan
Daily Mon-Sat 25p

News, and topical and lifestyle features.
Length: 600-800 words. Illustrations:
line, half-tone, colour, graphics, cartoons.
Payment: £50 per 1000 words; scale rate
or by agreement for illustrations.
Founded 1869.

Hartlepool Mail
Northeast Press Ltd, New Clarence House,
Wesley Square, Hartlepool, Cleveland TS24 8BX
tel (01429) 274441 *fax* (01429) 869024
e-mail post@hartmail.demon.co.uk
Editor Peter Barron
Daily Mon-Sat 29p
　Features Editor Bernice Saltzer
　News Editor Neil Hunter
　Picture Editor Dirk van der Werff
　Sports Editor Roy Kelly
Features of local interest. Length: 500
words. Illustrations: colour, b&w photos,
line, cartoons. Payment: by negotiation.
Founded 1877.

The Journal
Thomson House, Groat Market,
Newcastle upon Tyne NE1 1ED
tel 0191-232 7500 *fax* 0191-261 8869
e-mail journal@ncjlib.demon.co.uk
Editor Mark Dickinson
Daily Mon-Sat 32p
　News and Features Editor Paul Dutton
　Picture Editor Nigel Roddis
　Sports Editor Nick Crockford
News, sport items and features of topical
interest considered. Payment: by arrange-
ment.

The Northern Echo
Priestgate, Darlington, Co. Durham DL1 1NF
tel (01325) 381313 *fax* (01325) 380539
Editor Andrew Smith
Daily Mon-Sat 30p
　Features Editor Chris Lloyd
　News Editor Sarah Andrews
　Picture Editor Mike Gibb
　Sports Editor Kevin Dinsdale
Articles of interest to North-East and
North Yorkshire; all material commis-
sioned. Preliminary study of newspaper
advisable. Length: 800-1000 words.
Illustrations: line, half-tone, colour –
mostly commissioned. Payment: by nego-
tiation. Founded 1870.

North-West Evening Mail
Newspaper House, Abbey Road,
Barrow-in-Furness, Cumbria LA14 5QS
tel (01229) 821835 *fax* (01229) 840164/832141
Editor Sara Hadwin
Daily Mon-Sat 28p

　News Editor Mike Rushton
　Sports Editor Leo Clarke
'The Voice of Furness and West
Cumbria.' Articles, features and news.
Length: 500 words. Illustrations: b&w
photos and occasional artwork. Payment:
£30 (minimum); £10 for illustrations.
Founded 1898.

The Sunday Sun
Thomson House, Groat Market,
Newcastle upon Tyne NE1 1ED
tel 0191-201 6330 *fax* 0191-230 0238
Editor Peter Montellier
Sun 60p
Key requirements: immediate topicality
and human sidelights on current prob-
lems. Particularly welcomed are special
features of family appeal and news stories
of special interest to the North of England.
Length: 200-700 words. Payment: normal
lineage rates, or by arrangement.
Illustrations: photos. Founded 1919.

Sunderland Echo
Echo House, Pennywell, Sunderland,
Tyne & Wear SR4 9ER
tel 0191-534 3011 *fax* 0191-534 5975
ad-doc DX60743
web site http://www.sunderland.com/echo
Editor I. Holland
Daily Mon-Sat 29p
Local news, features and articles. Length:
500 words. Illustrations: colour and b&w
photos, line, cartoons. Payment: negotiable. Founded 1875.

North West

Bolton Evening News
Newspaper House, Churchgate, Bolton,
Lancs. BL1 1DE
tel (01204) 522345 *fax* (01204) 365068
Daily Mon-Sat 27p
Articles, particularly those with South
Lancashire appeal. Length: up to 500
words. Illustrations: photos; considered
at usual rates. Payment: by arrangement.
Founded 1867.

Daily Post
PO Box 48, Old Hall Street, Liverpool L69 3EB
tel 0151-227 2000 *fax* 0151-236 4682
Editor Alastair Machray
Daily Mon-Sat 32p
　Features Editor Claire Stocks
　News Editor Mark Davies
　Picture Editor Steve Shakeshaft

Sports Editor Len Capeling

Articles of general interest and topical features of special interest to North West England and North Wales. No verse or fiction. Payment: according to value. News and feature illustrations. Founded 1855.

The Gazette, Blackpool

Blackpool Gazette & Herald Ltd,
Avroe House, Avroe Crescent,
Blackpool Business Park,
Squires Gate, Blackpool FY4 2DP
tel (01253) 400888 *fax* (01253) 361870
e-mail bpl_editorial@upn.co.uk
web site http://www.blackpool.com
Director and General Manager Philip Welsh
Daily Mon-Sat 27p

Local news and articles of general interest, with photos if appropriate. Length: varies. Payment: on merit. Founded 1929.

Lancashire Evening Post

Oliver's Place, Fulwood, Preston PR2 9ZA
tel (01772) 254841 *fax* (01772) 880173
Editor Neil Hodgkinson
Daily Mon-Sat 27p

Topical articles on all subjects. Area of interest Wigan to Lake District, Lancs, and coast. Length: 600-900 words. Illustrations: colour and b&w photos, cartoons. Payment: by arrangement.

Lancashire Evening Telegraph

Newspaper House, High Street, Blackburn,
Lancs. BB1 1HT
tel (01254) 678678
web site http://www.newsquest.co.uk
Editor Peter Butterfield
Daily Mon-Sat 26p
   News Editor Nick Nunn
   Picture Editor John Napier
   Sports Editor Neil Brahwell

Will consider general interest articles, such as holidays, property, motoring, finance, etc. Payment: by arrangement. Founded 1886.

Liverpool Echo

PO Box 48, Old Hall Street, Liverpool L69 3EB
tel 0151-227 2000 *fax* 0151-236 4682
Editor John Griffith
Daily Mon-Sat 28p
   News Editor John Thompson
   Picture Editor Stephen Shakeshaft
   Sports Editor Ken Rogers

Articles of up to 600-800 words of local or topical interest; also cartoons. Payment: according to merit; special rates for exceptional material. This newspaper is connected with, but independent of, the *Liverpool Daily Post*. Articles not interchangeable.

Manchester Evening News

164 Deansgate, Manchester M60 2RD
tel 0161-832 7200 editorial *fax* 0161-834 3814
features fax 0161-839 0968
Editor Paul Horrocks
Daily Mon-Sat 30p
   Features Editor Maggie Henfield
   News Editor Lisa Roland
   Picture Editor Dave Thomas
   Sports Editor Peter Spencer

Feature articles of up to 1000 words, topical or general interest and illustrated where appropriate, should be addressed to the Features Editor. Payment: on acceptance.

Oldham Evening Chronicle

PO Box 47, Union Street, Oldham,
Lancs. OL1 1EQ
tel 0161-633 2121 *fax* 0161-627 0905
Editor Philip Hirst
Daily Mon-Fri 30p

News and features on current topics and local history. Length: 1000 words. Illustrations: colour and b&w photos and line. Payment: £20-£25 per 1000 words; £16.32-£21.90 for illustrations. Founded 1854.

Northern Ireland – see Belfast

Scotland

Aberdeen Evening Express

Aberdeen Journals Ltd, PO Box 43, Lang Stracht,
Mastrick, Aberdeen AB15 6DF
tel (01224) 690222 *fax* (01224) 699575
Editor Donald Martin
Daily Mon-Sat 27p
   Features Editor Ron Ferrier
   News Editor Yvonne Flynn
   Picture Editor Kenny Allan
   Sports Editor Darren Thwaites

Lively evening paper reading. Illustrations: colour and b&w, cartoons. Payment: by arrangement.

The Courier and Advertiser

D.C. Thomson & Co. Ltd, 80 Kingsway East,
Dundee DD4 8SL
tel (01382) 223131 *fax* (01382) 454590
185 Fleet Street, London EC4A 2HS
tel 0171-242 5086
Daily Mon-Sat 30p

Founded 1816 and 1801.

Dundee Evening Telegraph and Post
D.C. Thomson & Co. Ltd, 80 Kingsway East,
Dundee DD4 8SL
tel (01382) 223131 *fax* (01382) 454590
London office 185 Fleet Street, London EC4A 2HS
tel 0171-242 5086 *fax* 0171-404 5694
Daily Mon-Sat 25p

Edinburgh Evening News
20 North Bridge, Edinburgh EH1 1YT
tel 0131-225 2468 *fax* 0131-225 7302
Editor John McLellan
Daily Mon-Sat 25p
   Features Editor Helen Martin
   News Editor David Lee
   Picture Editor Tony Marsh
   Sports Editor Paul Greaves
Features on current affairs, preferably in
relation to our circulation area. Women's
talking points, local historical articles;
subjects of general interest.

Glasgow Evening Times
195 Albion Street, Glasgow G1 1QP
tel 0141-552 6255 *fax* 0141-553 1355
web site http://www.cims.co.uk/eveningtimes
London office 127 Clerkenwell Road,
London EC1R 5DB
tel 0171-405 2121 *fax* 0171-405 1888
Editor John Scott
Daily Mon-Sat 30p
Founded 1876.

Inverness Courier
PO Box 13, 9-11 Bank Lane, Inverness IV1 1QW
tel (01463) 233059 *fax* (01463) 243439
e-mail courier@zetnet.co.uk
Editor John Macdonald
2 p.w. Tue 39p Fri 42p
   News Editor Ron Lyon
   Sports Editor David Beck
Articles of Highland interest only.
Unsolicited material accepted.
Illustrations: colour and b&w photos.
Payment: by arrangement. Founded 1817.

The Press and Journal
Lang Stracht, Aberdeen AB9 8AF
tel (01224) 690222
e-mail editor@pj.ajl.co.uk
web site http://www.pressandjournal.co.uk
Editor Derek Tucker
Daily Mon-Sat 35p
   Features Editor Kay Drummond
   News Editor David Knight
   Picture Editor John Lindsay
   Sports Editor Jim Dolan
Contributions of Scottish interest.
Payment: by arrangement. Illustrations:
half-tone. Founded 1748.

The Sun
News International Newspapers, Scotland,
124 Portman Street, Kinning Park,
Glasgow G41 1EJ
tel 0141-420 5200 *fax* 0141-420 5248
Editor Bruce Waddell
Daily Mon-Sat 25p
   News Editor Derek Stewart Brown
   Picture Editor Mark Sweeney
   Sports Editor Steve Wolstencroft
Scottish edition of *The Sun*. Illustrations:
transparencies, colour and b&w prints,
colour cartoons. Payment: by arrange-
ment. Founded 1985.

South East

Evening Echo
Newspaper House, Chester Hall Lane, Basildon,
Essex SS9 1RE
tel (01268) 522792 *fax* (01268) 282884
Editor Martin McNeill
Daily Mon-Fri 30p
   Features Editor Pamela Horne
   News Editor Claire Ogley
   Picture Editor Nick Ansell
   Sports Editor Andy Stephens
Mostly staff-written. Only interested in
local material. Payment: by arrangement.
Founded 1969.

Kent Today
395 High Street, Chatham, Kent ME4 4PQ
tel (01634) 830999 *fax* (01634) 829484
Daily Mon-Fri 25p
   Features Editor Helen Daly
   News Editor Kathy Moran
   Picture Editor Barry Hollis
   Sports Editor Mike Rees
Paper with emphasis on local news and
sport, plus regular feature pages.
National news; with editions covering
the Medway Towns, Gravesend and
Dartford, Swale, Maidstone. Illustrations:
line, half-tone.

The News, Portsmouth
The News Centre, Hilsea, Portsmouth PO2 9SX
tel (01705) 664488 *fax* (01705) 673363
e-mail feedback@thenews.co.uk
web site http://www.thenews.co.uk
Editor Geoffrey Elliott
Daily Mon-Sat 29p
   Features Editor Rachel Hughes
   News Editor Mark Acheson
   Picture Editor Kevin Clifford
   Sports Editor Dave King
Articles of relevance to southeast Hamp-

shire and West Sussex. Payment by
arrangement. Founded 1877.

Reading Evening Post

8 Tessa Road, Reading, Berks. RG1 8NS
tel 0118-9575833 *fax* 0118-9599363
Editor Kim Chapman
Daily Mon-Fri 25p
   Features Editor Kate Magee
   News Editor Phil Pledger
   Picture Editor Steve Templeman
   Sports Editor Dave Wright

Topical articles based on current local
news. Length: 800-1200 words. Payment:
based on lineage rates. Illustrations: half-
tone. Founded 1965.

The Southern Daily Echo

Newspaper House, Test Lane, Redbridge,
Southampton SO16 9JX
tel (01703) 424777 *fax* (01703) 424770
Editor Mike Woods
Daily Mon-Sat 30p
   Features Editor Annie Bullen
   News Editor Gordon Sutter
   Picture Editor John Gilbride
   Sports Editor David Briers

News, articles, features, sport. Length:
varies. Illustrations: line, half-tone, colour.
Payment: NUJ rates. Founded 1888.

South West

The Bath Chronicle

Bath Newspapers, Windsor House,
Windsor Bridge, Bath BA2 3AU
tel (01225) 322322 *fax* (01225) 322291
Editor David Gledhill
Daily Mon-Sat 30p
   Features Editor Andrew Knight
   News Editor Paul Wiltshire
   Picture Editor Kevin Bates
   Sports Editor Neville Smith

Welcomes local news and features.
Length: 200-500 words. Illustrations:
colour photos. Payment: 8p-15.7p per
printed line; £5 per photo where commissioned. Founded 1760.

Bristol Evening Post

Temple Way, Bristol BS99 7HD
tel 0117-934 3000
Editor Mike Lowe
Daily Mon-Sat 28p
   Features Editor Matthew Shelley
   News Editor Kevan Blackadder
   Picture Editor Peter Watson
   Sports Editor Chris Bartlett

Takes freelance news and articles. Payment: by arrangement. Founded 1932.

The Citizen

Gloucestershire Newspapers Ltd, St John's Lane,
Gloucester GL1 2AY
tel (01452) 424442 *fax* (01452) 420664
Editor Spencer Feeney
Daily Mon-Sat 30p

Local news and features for Gloucester
and its districts. Length: 1000 words
(articles/features), 300 words (news).
Illustrations: colour. Payment: negotiable.

Dorset Evening Echo

Southern Newspapers, 57 St Thomas Street,
Weymouth, Dorset DT4 8EU
tel (01305) 784804 *fax* (01305) 760387
e-mail echo@wdi.co.uk
Editor David Lee
Daily Mon-Sat 27p
   Features Editor Mike Clarke
   News Editor Paul Thomas
   Picture Editor Jim Tampin
   Sports Editor Jack Wyllie

News and occasional features (1000-2000
words). Illustrations: b&w photos.
Payment: by negotiation. Founded 1921.

Express & Echo

Express & Echo Publications Ltd, Heron Road,
Sowton, Exeter, Devon EX2 7NF
tel (01392) 442211 *fax* (01392) 442294/442287
Editor Steve Hall
Daily Mon-Sat 27p
   Features Editor Sue Kemp
   News Editor Chris Styles
   Picture Editor John Ffoulkes
   Sports Editor Jerry Charge

Features and news of local interest.
Length: features 500-800 words, news up
to 400 words. Illustrations: colour.
Payment: lineage rates; illustrations
negotiable. Founded 1904.

Gloucestershire Echo

Cheltenham Newspaper Co. Ltd, 1 Clarence
Parade, Cheltenham, Glos. GL50 3NZ
tel (01242) 271900 *fax* (01242) 217803
Editor Anita Syvret
Daily Mon-Sat 30p

Specialist articles with Gloucestershire
connections; no fiction. Material mostly
commissioned. Length: 350 words.
Payment: £30 per article, negotiable.
Founded 1873.

Sunday Independent (West of England)

Southern Newspapers plc, Burrington Way,
Plymouth PL5 3LN
tel (01752) 206600 *fax* (01752) 206164
Editor Anna Jenkins

Sun 55p

News features on West Country topics; features/articles with a nostalgic theme; short quirky news briefs (must be original). Length: 600 words (articles/features), 300 words (news). Illustrations: colour and b&w. Payment: by arrangement. Founded 1808.

Western Daily Press

Bristol Evening Post and Press Ltd, Temple Way, Bristol BS99 7HD
tel 0117-934 3000 *fax* 0117-934 3574
web site http://www.westpress.co.uk
Editor Ian Beales
Daily Mon-Sat 34p

National, international or West Country topics for features or news items, from established journalists, with or without illustrations. Payment: by negotiation. Founded 1858.

The Western Morning News

Brest Road, Derriford, Plymouth PL6 5AA
tel (01752) 765500 *fax* (01752) 765535
Editor Barrie Williams
Daily Mon-Sat 32p
   News Editor Jason Clark
   Picture Editor Michael Cranmer
   Sports Editor Rick Cowdery

Articles of 600-800 words, plus illustrations, considered on West Country subjects. Founded 1860.

Wales

South Wales Argus

South Wales Argus Ltd, Cardiff Road, Maesglas, Newport, Gwent NP9 1QW
tel (01633) 777219 *fax* (01633) 777202
Editor Gerry Keighley
Daily Mon-Sat 32p

News and features of relevance to Gwent. Length: 500-600 words (features); 350 words (news). Illustrations: colour prints and transparencies. Payment: £30 (features), £20 (news) per item; £20-25 (photos). Founded 1892.

South Wales Echo

Thomson House, Havelock Street, Cardiff CF1 1XR
tel (01222) 583583/223333 *fax* (01222) 583624
Editor Robin Fletcher
Daily Mon-Sat 28p

Evening paper: features, showbiz, news features, personality interviews. Length: up to 700 words. Illustrations: photos,

cartoons. Payment: by negotiation. Founded 1884.

The Western Mail

Thomson House, Havelock Street, Cardiff CF1 1XR
tel (01222) 223333 *fax* (01222) 583652
Editor Neil Fowler
Daily Mon-Sat 35p

Articles of political, industrial, literary or general and Welsh interest are considered. Illustrations: topical general news and feature pictures, cartoons. Payment: according to value; special fees for exclusive news. Founded 1869.

West Midlands

Birmingham Evening Mail

28 Colmore Circus, Queensway,
Birmingham B4 6AX
tel 0121-236 3366 *fax* 0121-625 1105
London office 1 Canada Square, Canary Wharf,
London E14 5AP
tel 0171-293 3000 *fax* 0171-293 3793
Editor I. Dowell
Daily Mon-Sat 30p

Features of topical Midland interest considered. Length: 400-800 words. Payment: by arrangement. Founded 1870.

The Birmingham Post

PO Box 18, 28 Colmore Circus,
Birmingham B4 6AX
tel 0121-236 3366 *fax* 0121-625 1105
London office 22nd Floor, 1 Canada Square,
Canary Wharf, London E14 5AP
tel 0171-293 3455 *fax* 0171-293 3400
Editor N. Hastilow
Daily Mon-Sat 37p
   Features Editor Peter Bacon
   News Editor Chris Russon
   Picture Editor Paul Vokes
   Sports Editor Mark Woodward

Authoritative and well-written articles of industrial, political or general interest are considered, especially if they have relevance to the Midlands. Length: up to 1000 words. Payment: by arrangement.

Coventry Evening Telegraph

Corporation Street, Coventry CV1 1FP
tel (01203) 633633 *fax* (01203) 550869
Editor Dan Mason
Daily Mon-Sat 30p

Topical, illustrated articles, those with a Warwickshire interest particularly acceptable. Length: up to 600 words. Payment: by arrangement.

Express and Star

Queen Street, Wolverhampton WV1 1ES
tel (01902) 313131 *fax* (01902) 319721
Editor Warren Wilson
London office Room 110, Temple Chambers,
Temple Avenue, London EC4Y 0DT
Daily Mon-Sat 30p
  Features Editor Gary Copeland
  News Editor John Bray
  Picture Editor Geoff Wright
  Sports Editor Steve Gordos
Founded 1874.

The Sentinel

Staffordshire Sentinel Newspapers Ltd,
Sentinel House, Etruria, Stoke-on-Trent ST1 5SS
tel (01782) 602525 *fax* (01782) 602616
e-mail editor@thesentinel.co.uk
web site http://www.thisisstaffordshire.co.uk
Editor Sean Dooley
Daily Mon-Sat 27p

Articles and features of topical interest to
the north Staffordshire/south Cheshire
area. Illustrations: colour and b&w.
Payment: by arrangement. Founded
1873.
  Arts and Features Editor Roy Coates
  Business Editor Peter Brown
  News Editor Michael Wood
  Picture Editor Trevor Slater
  Sports Editor Nigel Wiskar

Shropshire Star

Ketley, Telford TF1 4HU
tel (01952) 242424 *fax* (01952) 254605
Editor Andy Wright
Daily Mon-Sat 28p
  Features Editor Alun Owen
  News Editor Sarah Jane Smith
  Picture Editor Ken Done
  Sports Editor Peter Byram

Evening paper: news and features. No
unsolicited material; write to features
editor with outline of ideas. Payment: by
arrangement. Founded 1964.

Sunday Mercury

Colmore Circus, Birmingham B4 6AZ
tel 0121-236 3366 *fax* 0121-233 0271
Editor Fiona Alexander
Sun 55p
  Features Editor Alf Bennett
  News Editor James Windle
  Picture Editor Ed Maynard
  Sports Editor Lee Gibson

News specials or features of Midland
interest. Illustrations: colour, b&w, cartoons. Special rates for special matter.

Yorkshire/Humberside

Evening Courier

PO Box 19, King Cross Street, Halifax HX1 2SF
tel (01422) 365711 *fax* (01422) 260200
Editor Edward Riley
2 per day Mon-Sat 30p
  Features Editor William Marshall
  News Editor John Kenealy
  Sports Editor Ian Rushworth

Articles of local interest and background
to news events. Length: up to 500 words.
Illustrations: b&w photos. Payment: £25-
£40 per article; photos per quality/size
used. Founded 1832.

The Evening Press

York and County Press, PO Box 29,
76-86 Walmgate, York YO1 1YN
tel (01904) 653051 *fax* (01904) 612853
Editor Elizabeth Page
Daily Mon-Sat 30p
  Features Editor Chris Buxton
  News Editor Francine Clee
  Picture Editor Martin Oates
  Sports Editor Martin Jarred

Articles of North and East Yorkshire
interest, humour, personal experience of
current affairs. Length: 500-1000 words.
Payment: by arrangement. Illustrations:
line, half-tone, cartoons. Founded 1882.

Grimsby Evening Telegraph

80 Cleethorpe Road, Grimsby,
North East Lincolnshire DN31 3EH
tel (01472) 360360 *fax* (01472) 372257
e-mail grimsbytelegraph@dial.pipex.com
web site http://www.grimsbytelegraph.co.uk
Editor Peter Moore
Daily Mon-Sat 27p
  Features Editor Barrie Farnsworth
  News Editor Steven Richards
  Picture Editor David Moss
  Sports Editor Geoff Ford

Considers general interest articles. Illustrations: line, half-tone, colour, cartoons.
Payment: by arrangement. Founded 1897.

The Star

York Street, Sheffield S1 1PU
tel 0114-276 7676 *fax* 0114-272 5978
web site http://www.sheffweb.co.uk
Editor Peter Charlton
Daily Mon-Sat 27p
  Features Editor Jim Collins
  News Editor Bob Westerdale
  Picture Editor Dennis Lound
  Sports Editor Martin Smith

Well-written articles of local character.
Length: about 500 words. Payment: by

negotiation. Illustrations: topical photos, line drawings, graphics, cartoons. Founded 1887.

Telegraph & Argus

Hall Ings, Bradford, West Yorkshire BD1 1JR
tel (01274) 729511 *fax* (01274) 723634
e-mail bradford.editorial@telegraph-and-argus.co.uk
web site http://www.telegraph-and-argus.co.uk
Editor Perry Austin-Clarke
Daily Mon-Sat 28p
> *Features Editor* Lynn Ashwell
> *News Editor* Jan Brierley
> *Picture Editor* Mike Sharp
> *Sports Editor* Alan Birkinshaw

Evening paper: news, articles and features relevant to or about the people of West Yorkshire. Length: up to 1000 words. Illustrations: line, half-tone, colour. Payment: features from £15; line from £5, b&w photos from £14.40, colour photos from £19.50. Founded 1868.

Yorkshire Evening Post

PO Box 168, Wellington Street, Leeds LS1 1RF
tel 0113-2432701 *fax* 0113-2388535
Editor C.H. Bye
Daily Mon-Sat 28p

> *Features Editor* Anne Pickles
> *News Editor* David Helliwell
> *Picture Editor* Andy Manning
> *Sports Editor* Steve White

News stories and feature articles. Illustrations: colour and b&w, cartoons. Payment: by negotiation. Founded 1890.

Yorkshire Post

Wellington Street, Leeds LS1 1RF
tel 0113-243 2701 *fax* 0113-238 8537
Editor Tony Watson
London office Ludgate House,
245 Blackfriars Road, London SE1 9UY
tel 0171-921 5000
Daily Mon-Sat 38p
> *Features Editor* Michael Hickling
> *News Editor* John Furbisher
> *Picture Editor* Ian Day
> *Sports Editor* Bill Bridge

Authoritative and well-written articles on new topics or on topical subjects of general, literary or industrial interests. Length: 1200-1500 words. Illustrations: photos and frequent pocket cartoons (single column width), topical wherever possible. Payment: by arrangement. Founded 1754.

Magazines UK and Ireland

Listings for regional newspapers start on page 11 and listings for national newspapers start on page 3. For quick reference, magazines are listed by subject area on page 126. See page 136 for recent changes to newspapers and magazines.

AA Magazine
Redwood Publishing Ltd, 12-26 Lexington Street, London W1R 4HQ
tel 0171-312 2600 *fax* 0171-312 2679
Editor Andrew Duffy
Quarterly Free to members
Articles on motoring, travel and lifestyle. Length: 500-1500 words. Illustrations: colour. Payment: negotiable. Founded 1992.

Accountancy
40 Bernard Street, London WC1N 1LD
tel 0171-833 3291 *fax* 0171-833 2085
e-mail postmaster@theabg@.demon.co.uk
web site http://www.accountancymag.co.uk
Editor Brian Singleton-Green
Monthly £3.90
Articles on accounting, taxation, financial, legal and other subjects likely to be of professional interest to accountants in practice or industry, and to top management generally; cartoons. Payment: £120 per page. Founded 1889.

Accountancy Age
VNU Business Publications, VNU House, 32-34 Broadwick Street, London W1A 2HG
tel 0171-316 9000 *fax* 0171-316 9008
web site http://www.accountancyage.vnu.co.uk
Editor Douglas Broom
Weekly £2.00 (£100 p.a.)
Articles of accounting, financial and business interest. Illustrations: colour photos; freelance assignments commissioned. Payment: by arrangement. Founded 1969.

ace
Lawn Tennis Association, Queen's Club, London W14 9EG
tel 0171-381 7000 *fax* 0171-381 6656
e-mail postmaster@acemag.demon.co.uk
Editor Dominic Bliss
11 p.a. £2.50

International high profile tennis, including interviews with top players, coaching articles, big tournament reports, health and fitness. Submit synopsis in first instance. Payment: 15p per word. Founded 1996.

Achievement
Response Publishing Group plc, 41-45 Goswell Road, London EC1V 7EH
tel 0171-490 0550 *fax* 0171-490 0375
e-mail response@compulink.co.uk
Quarterly £15.00 p.a.
In-depth articles, news and updates on major international projects. Illustrations: first-class photos. Payment: by arrangement.

Active Life
Aspen Publishing, Christ Church, Cosway Street, London NW1 5NJ
tel 0171-262 2622
Editor Helene Hodge
Bi-monthly £2.30
Lifestyle advice for the over 50s, including holidays and health, fashion and food, finance and fiction, hobbies and home, personality profiles. Submit ideas in writing. Length: 600-1200 words. Illustrations: colour. Payment: £100 per 1000 words; photos by negotiation. Founded 1989.

Acumen
6 The Mount, Higher Furzeham, Brixham, South Devon TQ5 8QY
tel (01803) 851098
Editor Patricia Oxley
Tri-annual (Jan/May/Sept) £10.00 p.a.
Poetry, literary and critical articles, reviews, literary memoirs, etc, 100pp or more. Send sae with submissions. Payment: by negotiation. Founded 1985.

Aeromodeller

Nexus Special Interests Ltd, Nexus House,
Swanley, Kent BR8 8HU
tel (01322) 660070 *fax* (01322) 667633
Editor Ken Shepherd
13 p.a. £2.35

Articles and news concerning model aircraft. Suitable articles and first-class photos by outside contributors are always considered. Length: 750-2000 words, or by arrangement. Illustrations: photos and line drawings to scale. Payment: by negotiation. Founded 1935.

Aeroplane Monthly

IPC Magazines Ltd, King's Reach Tower,
Stamford Street, London SE1 9LS
tel 0171-261 5849 *fax* 0171-261 5269
Acting Editor Michael Oakey
Monthly £2.80

Articles and photos relating to historical aviation. Length: up to 3000 words. Illustrations: line, half-tone, colour, cartoons. Payment: £50 per 1000 words, payable on publication; photos £10; colour £80 per page. Founded 1973.

Africa Confidential

Blackwell Publishing Ltd, 73 Farringdon Road,
London EC1M 3JB
tel 0171-831 3511 *fax* 0171-831 6778
web site http://africa-confidential.com.uk
Editor Patrick Smith
Fortnightly £222.00 p.a.

News and analysis of political and economic developments in Africa. Unsolicited contributions welcomed, but must be exclusive and not published elsewhere. Length: 1200-word features, 200-word pointers. Payment: £200 per 1000 words. No illustrations. Founded 1960.

Africa: St Patrick's Missions

St Patrick's, Kiltegan, Co. Wicklow,
Republic of Ireland
tel (0508) 73233 *fax* (0508) 73281
Editor Rev. Gary Howley
9 p.a. £5.00 p.a. (IR£6.00)

Articles of missionary and topical religious interest. Length: up to 1000 words. Illustrations: line, half-tone, colour.

African Business

IC Publications Ltd, 7 Coldbath Square,
London EC1R 4LQ
tel 0171-713 7711 *fax* 0171-713 7970
Editor Anver Versi
Monthly £2.00

Articles on business, economic and financial topics of interest to businessmen, ministers, officials concerned with African affairs. Length: 400-750 words; shorter coverage 100-400 words. Illustrations: line, half-tone. Payment: £70 per 1000 words; £1 per column cm for illustrations. Founded 1978.

Agenda

5 Cranbourne Court, Albert Bridge Road,
London SW11 4PE
tel/fax 0171-228 0700
Editor William Cookson, *Assistant Editor* Anita Money
Quarterly £24.00 p.a. (libraries, institutions and overseas: rates on application); £18.00 students

Poetry and criticism. Contributors should study the journal before submitting MSS with an sae. Illustrations: half-tone. Payment: variable – depends on finances.

Air International

Key Publishing Ltd, PO Box 100, Stamford,
Lincs. PE9 1XQ
tel (01780) 755131 *fax* (01780) 757261
Editor Malcolm English
Monthly £2.65

Technical articles on aircraft; features on topical aviation subjects – civil and military; historical aviation subjects. Length: up to 5000 words. Illustrations: colour transparencies/prints, b&w prints/line drawings, cartoons. Payment: £50 per 1000 words or by negotiation; £25 colour, £10 b&w. Founded 1971.

Air Pictorial International

HPC Publishing, Drury Lane, St Leonards-on-Sea,
East Sussex TN38 9BJ
tel (01424) 720477 *fax* (01424) 443693/434086
Editor Barry C. Wheeler
Monthly £2.55

Covers all aspects of aviation. Many articles commissioned, and the editor is glad to consider competent articles exploring fresh ground or presenting an individual point of view on technical matters. All articles are illustrated, mainly with photos. Payment: by arrangement.

Amateur Gardening

IPC Magazines Ltd, Westover House,
West Quay Road, Poole, Dorset BH15 1JG
tel (01202) 680586 *fax* (01202) 674335
e-mail amateurgardening@ipc.co.uk
Editor Adrian Bishop
Weekly 95p

Articles up to 1500 words of interest to experienced gardeners. Payment: by arrangement. Illustrations: colour. Founded 1884.

Amateur Photographer

IPC Magazines Ltd, King's Reach Tower, Stamford Street, London SE1 9LS
tel 0171-261 5100 *fax* 0171-261 5404
e-mail amateurphotographer@ipc.co.uk
Editor Keith Wilson
Weekly £1.65

Original articles of pictorial or technical interest, preferably illustrated with either photos or diagrams. Good instructional features especially sought. Length preferred: (unillustrated) 400-800 words; articles up to 1500 words; (illustrated) 2-4 pages. Payment: weekly, rates according to usage. Illustrations unaccompanied by text considered – indicate if material can be held on file. Founded 1884.

Amateur Stage

Platform Publications Ltd, Hampden House, 2 Weymouth Street, London W1N 3FD
tel 0171-636 4343 *fax* 0171-636 2323
e-mail cvtheatre@aol.com
web site http://www.amdram.org.uk/amstagel.htm
Editor Charles Vance
Monthly £2.00

Articles on all aspects of the amateur theatre, preferably practical and factual. Length: 600-2000 words. Illustrations: photos, line drawings. Payment: none. Founded 1946.

Ambit

17 Priory Gardens, London N6 5QY
tel 0181-340 3566
Poetry Editors Martin Bax, Henry Graham, Carol-Ann Duffy, *Prose Editor* J.G. Ballard, *Art Editor* Mike Foreman, *Assistant Editor* Richard Dyer
Quarterly £6.00 inc. p&p (£22.00 p.a. UK, £24/$48 p.a. overseas; £33.00 p.a., £35.00/$70.00 p.a. institutions)

Poetry, short fiction, art, reviews. New and established writers and artists. Payment: by arrangement. Illustrations: line, half-tone, colour. Founded 1959.

American Markets Newsletter

175 Westland Drive, Glasgow G14 9JQ
e-mail sheila.oconnor@juno.com
Editor Sheila O'Connor
10 p.a. £29.00 p.a. (£53 for 2 years)

Editorial guidelines for US, Canadian and other overseas markets, plus information on press trips, non-fiction/fiction markets and writers' tips. Sample issue £2.95 (payable to S. O'Connor).

Amiga Format

Future Publishing Ltd, 30 Monmouth Street, Bath BA1 6PS
tel (01225) 442244 *fax* (01225) 732341
e-mail amformat@futurenet.co.uk
web site http://www.amiganet.co.uk
Editor Nick Veitch
13 p.a. £4.50 (disk) £5.99 (CD)

Features, news, interviews, reviews covering the whole of the Amiga market. Length: 100-150 words (news). Payment: £100 per 1000 words. Colour transparencies and digital images. Founded 1989.

AN Magazine

(formerly Artists Newsletter)
AN Publications, PO Box 23, Sunderland SR4 6DG
tel 0191-567 3589 *fax* 0191-564 1600
e-mail edit@anpubs.demon.co.uk
Contact Julie Crawshaw
Monthly £2.95 (£24.50 p.a.)

Articles, news and features for practising artists and makers. Illustrations: transparencies, colour and b&w photos. Payment: £100 per 1000 words. Founded 1980.

Angler's Mail

IPC Magazines Ltd, King's Reach Tower, Stamford Street, London SE1 9LS
tel 0171-261 5778 *fax* 0171-261 6016
Editor Roy Westwood
Weekly £1.00

News items about coarse and sea fishing. Payment: by agreement.

Angling Times

EMAP Pursuit Publishing Ltd, PO Box 231, Bretton Court, Bretton, Peterborough PE3 8EN
tel (01733) 266222/264666 *fax* (01733) 465257
e-mail john.kelly@ecm.emap.com
Editor John Kelly
Weekly 83p

Articles, pictures, news stories, on all forms of angling. Illustrations: line, half-tone, colour. Payment: by arrangement. Founded 1953.

Animals and You

D.C. Thomson & Co Ltd, Albert Square, Dundee DD1 9QJ
tel (01382) 223131 *fax* (01382) 225511
185 Fleet Street, London EC4A 2HS
tel 0171-242 5086 *fax* 0171-404 5694
Fortnightly (Fri) 99p

Features, stories and pin-ups for girls who love animals. Founded 1998.

The Antique Dealer & Collectors Guide

PO Box 805, London SE10 8TD
tel 0181-691 4820
Editor Philip Bartlam
Monthly £2.75

Articles on antique collecting and art. Length: 1500-2000 words. Payment: £76 per 1000 words. Illustrations: half-tone, colour.

Apollo

1-2 Castle Lane, London SW1E 6DR
tel 0171-233 6640 *fax* 0171-630 7791
Editor David Ekserdjian
Monthly £7.80

Scholarly articles of about 2500 words on art, architecture, ceramics, furniture, armour, glass, sculpture, and any subject connected with art and collecting. Payment: by arrangement. Illustrations: half-tone, colour. Founded 1925.

The Aquarist and Pondkeeper

MJ Publications Ltd, 20 High Street, Charing, Kent TN27 0XH
tel (01233) 713188 *fax* (01233) 714188
Editor Dick Mills
Monthly £2.25

Illustrated authoritative articles by professional and amateur biologists, naturalists and aquarium hobbyists on all matters concerning life in and near water, conservation and herpetology. Length: about 1500 words. Illustrations: line, half-tone, colour, cartoons. Payment: by arrangement. Founded 1924.

Aquila

New Leaf Publishing Ltd, PO Box 2518, Eastbourne, East Sussex BN21 2BB
tel (01323) 431313 *fax* (01323) 731136
e-mail aquila@pavilion.co.uk
web site http://www.aquila.co.uk/aquila
Editor Jacqueline Berry
Monthly £31.50 p.a. (£18.50 6 months)

Dedicated to encouraging children aged 8-13 to reason and create, and to develop a caring nature. Short stories and serials of up to 4 parts. Occasional features commissioned from writers with specialist knowledge of interest to the age group. Approach in writing with ideas and sample of writing style, with sae. Length: 700-800 words (features), 1000-1100 words (stories or per episode of a serial). Illustrations: colour and b&w, cartoons.

Payment: £75 (features); £90 (stories), £80 (per episode). Founded 1992.

The Architects' Journal

EMAP Business Communications, 151 Rosebery Avenue, London EC1R 4QX
tel 0171-505 6700 *fax* 0171-505 6701
Editor Paul Finch
Weekly £1.80 (£75 p.a.)

Articles (mainly technical) on architecture, planning and building accepted only with prior agreement of synopsis. Illustrations: photos and drawings. Payment: by arrangement. Founded 1895.

Architectural Design

Academy Group Ltd, 42 Leinster Gardens, London W2 3AN
tel 0171-262 5097 *fax* 0171-262 5093
Editor Maggie Toy
6 double issues p.a. £74.00 p.a. (£53.00 p.a. students)

International magazine comprising an extensively illustrated thematic profile presenting architecture and critical interpretations of architectural history, theory and practice. Uncommissioned articles not accepted. Illustrations: drawings and photos, line (colour preferred). Payment: by arrangement. Founded 1930.

The Architectural Review

EMAP Construct, 151 Rosebery Avenue, London EC1R 4QX
tel 0171-505 6725 *fax* 0171-505 6701
e-mail peterd@construct.emap.co.uk
web site http://www.arplus.com/
Editor Peter Davey
Monthly £5.95

Articles on architecture and the allied arts. Writers must be thoroughly qualified. Length: up to 3000 words. Payment: by arrangement. Illustrations: photos, drawings, etc. Founded 1896.

Architecture Today

161 Rosebery Avenue, London EC1R 4QX
tel 0171-837 0143 *fax* 0171-837 0155
Editors Ian Latham, Mark Swenarton
10 p.a. £3.00 Free to architects

Mostly commissioned articles and features on today's European architecture. Length: 200-800 words. Illustrations: colour. Payment: by negotiation. Founded 1989.

Arena

3rd Floor Block A, Exmouth House, Pine Street, London EC1R 0JL

tel 0171-689 2266 *fax* 0171-689 0900
Editor Ekow Eshun
Monthly £2.70

Profiles, articles on a wide range of subjects intelligently treated; art, architecture, politics, sport, business, music, film, design, media, fashion. Length: up to 3000 words. Illustrations: b&w and colour photos. Payment: £200 per 1000 words; varies for illustrations. Founded 1986.

Army Quarterly & Defence Journal
1 West Street, Tavistock, Devon PL19 8DS
tel (01822) 613577/612785 *fax* (01822) 612785
Editor T.D. Bridge
Quarterly £52.00 p.a. (£138.00 3-yr saver contract)

Articles on a wide range of British, UN, Commonwealth and worldwide defence issues, historical and current; also Quarterly Diary, Defence Contracts, International Defence Reports, book and video reviews. Preliminary letter with synopsis preferred. Length: 1000-4800 words. Illustrations: b&w photos, line drawings, maps. Payment: by arrangement. Founded 1829.

Art & Craft
Scholastic Ltd, Villiers House,
Clarendon Avenue, Leamington Spa,
Warks. CV32 5PR
tel (01926) 887799 *fax* (01926) 883331
Editor Siân Morgan
Monthly £2.25

Articles offering fresh, creative ideas of a practical nature, based on teaching art, design and technology in the National Curriculum, for the infant/junior school teacher. Articles by teachers and other experts for teachers. Illustrations: colour. Payment: by arrangement. Founded 1936.

Art Business Today
The Fine Art Trade Guild, 16-18 Empress Place, London SW6 1TT
tel 0171-381 6616 *fax* 0171-381 2596
Editor Anne Beaton
Quarterly £15.00 p.a.

Distributed to the fine art and framing industry. Covers essential information on new products and technology, market trends and business analysis. Length: 800-1600 words. Illustrations: colour photos, cartoons. Payment: by arrangement. Founded 1991.

Art Monthly
Britannia Art Publications Ltd, Suite 17,
26 Charing Cross Road, London WC2H 0DG
tel 0171-240 0389 *fax* 0171-497 0726
e-mail artmonthly@compuserve.com
Editor Patricia Bickers
10 p.a. £2.95

Features on modern and contemporary visual artists and art history, art theory and art-related issues; exhibition and book reviews. All material commissioned. Length: 750-1500 words. Illustrations: b&w photos. Payment: features £100-£150; none for photos. Founded 1976.

The Art Newspaper
27-29 Vauxhall Grove, London SW8 1SY
tel 0171-735 3331 *fax* 0171-735 3332
Editor Anna Somers Cocks
11 p.a. £4.50 (£45.00 p.a.)

International coverage of the art market, news, commentary. Length: 200-1000 words. Illustrations: b&w photos. Payment: £120 per 1000 words. Founded 1990.

Art Review
Art Review Ltd, Hereford House,
23-24 Smithfield Street, London EC1A 9LB
tel 0171-236 4880 *fax* 0171-236 4881
Editor David Lee
Monthly £3.80

Art news and features. Commissioned work only. Payment: from £200 per 1000 words. Illustrations: line, half-tone, colour. Founded 1949.

The Artist
The Artists' Publishing Co. Ltd, Caxton House,
63-65 High Street, Tenterden, Kent TN30 6BD
tel (01580) 763673
Editor Sally Bulgin
Monthly £2.10

Practical, instructional articles on painting for all amateur and professional artists. Payment: by arrangement. Illustrations: line, half-tone, colour. Founded 1931.

Artists and Illustrators
The Fitzpatrick Building, 188-194 York Way,
London N7 9QR
tel 0171-700 8500 *fax* 0171-700 4985
Editor Laura Gascoigne
Monthly £2.40

Practical and business articles for amateur and professional artists. Length: 1000-1500 words. Illustrations: colour

transparencies. Payment: variable.
Founded 1986.

The Asian Age

Media Asia Europe Ltd, Dolphin Media House,
Spring Villa Park, Spring Villa Road, Edgware,
Middlesex HA8 7EB
tel 0181-951 4401 *fax* 0181-951 4839
Editor M.J. Akbar
Daily 50p
Articles and features of interest to the
Asian community; material mostly com-
missioned. Length: 200-1500 words. Illus-
trations: b&w photos. Payment: £50 per
1000 words; £40 per photo. Founded 1994.

Asian Times

Ethnic Media Group, 1st Floor, 148 Cambridge
Heath Road, London E1 5QJ
tel 0171-702 8012 *fax* 0171-702 7937
Editor Sanjay Gohil
Weekly 50p
News stories, articles and features of
interest to Britain's Asian community.
Founded 1983.

Astronomy Now

Pole Star Publications, PO Box 175, Tonbridge,
Kent TN10 4ZY
tel (01732) 367542 *fax* (01732) 356230
e-mail editorial@astronow.demon.co.uk
Editor Pam Spence
Monthly £2.40
Aimed at amateur and professional
astronomers. Interested in news items
and longer features on astronomy and
some space-related activities. Writers'
guidelines available (send sae). Length:
1500-3000 words. Illustrations: line, half-
tone, colour. Payment: 5p per word; from
£10 per photo. Founded 1987.

Athletics Weekly

EMAP Pursuit Publishing Ltd, Bretton Court,
Bretton, Peterborough PE3 8DZ
tel (01733) 261144 *fax* (01733) 465206
e-mail nigel.walsh@ecm.emap.com
Editor Nigel Walsh
Weekly £1.50
News and features on track and field athletics, road running, cross country, fell
and race walking. Material mostly commissioned. Length: 1000-3000 words.
Illustrations: colour and b&w action and
head/shoulder photos, line. Payment:
varies. Founded 1946.

Attitude

Northern & Shell plc, Northern & Shell Tower,
City Harbour, London E14 9GL
tel 0171-308 5090 *fax* 0171-308 5075
e-mail phunwick@norshell.co.uk
Editor Paul Hunwick
Monthly £2.20
Men's style magazine aimed primarily but
not exclusively at gay men. Covers style/
fashion, interviews, reviews. Illustrations:
colour transparencies, b&w prints.
Payment: £150 per 1000 words; £100 per
full page illustration. Founded 1994.

The Author

84 Drayton Gardens, London SW10 9SB
tel 0171-373 6642
Editor Derek Parker
Quarterly £7.00
Organ of The Society of Authors.
Commissioned articles from 1000-2000
words on any subject connected with the
legal, commercial or technical side of
authorship. Little scope for the freelance
writer: preliminary letter advisable.
Illustrations: line, occasional cartoons.
Payment: by arrangement. Founded 1890.

Auto Express

Dennis Publishing Ltd, 19 Bolsover Street,
London W1P 7HJ
tel 0171-631 1433 *fax* 0171-917 5556
Editor David Johns
Weekly £1.30
News stories, and general interest fea-
tures about drivers as well as cars.
Illustrations: colour photos. Payment:
features £250 per 1000 words; photos,
varies. Founded 1988.

Autocar

Haymarket Publishing Ltd, 60 Waldegrave Road,
Teddington, Middlesex TW11 8LG
tel 0181-943 5630 *fax* 0181-943 5759
e-mail autocar@compuserve.com
Editor Patrick Fuller
Weekly £1.80
Articles on all aspects of cars, motoring
and the motor industry: general, practical, competition and technical.
Illustrations: line (litho), colour and electronic (Illustrator). Press day news:
Thursday. Payment: varies; mid-month
following publication. Founded 1895.

Babycare and Pregnancy

(formerly First Steps)
D.C. Thomson & Co. Ltd, 80 Kingsway East,
Dundee DD4 8SL
tel (01382) 223131 *fax* (01382) 452491
Editor Irene K. Duncan
Monthly £1.70

Cares about the mother and her needs as well as the baby. Interested in articles on pregnancy, birth and childcare, and fillers. Illustrations: colour transparencies and colour artwork. Length/payment: negotiable. Founded 1994.

Back Street Heroes
PO Box 28, Altrincham, Cheshire WA14 2FG
tel 0161-928 3480 *fax* 0161-941 6897
Editor Stu Garland
Monthly £2.70
Custom motorcycle features plus informed lifestyle pieces. Illustrations: colour, cartoons. Payment: by arrangement. Founded 1983.

Balance
British Diabetic Association, 10 Queen Anne Street, London W1M 0BD
tel 0171-323 1531 *fax* 0171-637 3644
e-mail balance@diabetes.org.uk
web site http://www.diabetes.org.uk
Editor John Isitt
Bi-monthly £2.00
Articles on diabetes or related topics. Length: 1000-2000 words. Payment: by arrangement. Illustrations: colour. Founded 1935.

Ballroom Dancing Times
The Dancing Times Ltd, Clerkenwell House, 45-47 Clerkenwell Green, London EC1R 0EB
tel 0171-250 3006 *fax* 0171-253 6679
e-mail dancing-times@compuserve.com
Editor Mary Clarke, *Executive Editor* Bronya Seifert
Monthly £1.10
Ballroom and social dancing from every aspect, but chiefly from the serious competitive, teaching and medal test angles. Well-informed freelance articles are occasionally used, but only after preliminary arrangements. Payment: by arrangement. Illustrations: action photos preferred, b&w or colour. Founded 1956.

The Banker
Maple House, Tottenham Court Road, London W1P 9LL
tel 0171-896 2525 *fax* 0171-896 2586
e-mail 100617,1135.compuserve.com
Editor Stephen Timewell
Monthly £7.50
Articles on capital markets, trade finance, bank analysis and top 1000 listings. Illustrations: half-tones and full colour of people, charts, tables, maps etc. Payment: by negotiation. Founded 1926.

Baptist Times
PO Box 54, 129 Broadway, Didcot, Oxon OX11 8XB
tel (01235) 512012 *fax* (01235) 512013
Editor John Capon
Weekly 50p
Religious or social affairs material, up to 1000 words. Payment: by arrangement. Illustrations: half-tone. Founded 1855.

BBC Family Life
BBC Worldwide, Room A1136, Woodlands, 80 Wood Lane, London W12 0TT
tel 0181-576 3635 *fax* 0181-576 2608
Editor Anita Bevan
Monthly £1.95
Topical articles of interest to families with children aged 4-14, in particular health, nutrition and education issues; also features on fashion and beauty. No unsolicited material. Contact by telephone in first instance with ideas. Illustrations: transparencies. Payment: by arrangement. Founded 1997.

BBC Gardeners' World Magazine
BBC Worldwide, Woodlands, 80 Wood Lane, London W12 0TT
tel 0181-576 3959 *fax* 0181-576 3986
Editor Adam Pasco
Monthly £2.20
Features and ideas on plants, garden design and garden visits. All material commissioned. Study of magazine essential before submitting ideas. Length: varies, mainly 800-1000 words. Illustrations: colour transparencies; all artwork commissioned. Payment: by negotiation. Founded 1991.

BBC Good Homes
BBC Worldwide, Woodlands, 80 Wood Lane, London W12 0TT
tel 0181-576 2000 *fax* 0181-576 2691
Editor Julie Savill
Monthly £2.00
Articles in a lively and contemporary format of interest to homeowners aged 25-45. Includes features on real-life homes, makeovers, etc. Contact by letter in first instance. Illustrations: transparencies. Payment: by arrangement. Founded 1998.

BBC GoodFood
BBC Worldwide, Woodlands, 80 Wood Lane, London W12 0TT
tel 0181-576 2000 *fax* 0181-576 3825
Editor Orlando Murrin
Monthly £1.75

Recipes from TV and radio, cookery features, food and wine news. No unsolicited material. Length: 700-1400 words. Illustrations: colour photos and line. Payment: by arrangement. Founded 1989.

BBC Homes & Antiques
BBC Worldwide, Woodlands, 80 Wood Lane, London W12 0TT
tel 0181-576 3490 *fax* 0181-576 3867
Editor Judith Hall
Monthly £2.20

Upmarket home interest magazine with an antiques and heritage slant. Commissioned features only except for Home Thoughts (800 words of childhood memories). Payment: by arrangement. Founded 1993.

BBC Match of the Day
BBC Worldwide Publishing, Room A1064, Woodlands, 80 Wood Lane, London W12 0TT
tel 0181-576 3170 *fax* 0181-576 2898
e-mail tim.glynne-jones@bbc.co.uk
Editor Tim Glynne-Jones
Monthly £2.50

Highly illustrated features, interviews and reviews of football events and personalities. Seeks features of a quirky nature. Length: 1000-2000 words. Illustrations: colour artwork. Payment: £150 per 1000 words; £170 per piece. Founded 1996.

BBC Music Magazine
BBC Worldwide, Room A1004, Woodlands, 80 Wood Lane, London W12 0TT
tel 0181-576 3283 *fax* 0181-576 3292
Editor Graeme Kay
Monthly £3.75

Articles, features, news and reviews on classical music. All material commissioned. Length: up to 2000 words. Illustrations: line, half-tone, colour. Payment: £180 per 1000 words; varies for illustrations. Founded 1992.

BBC Top Gear Magazine
BBC Worldwide, Woodlands, 80 Wood Lane, London W12 0TT
tel 0181-576 2000 *fax* 0181-576 3754
web site http://www.topgear.com
Editor Kevin Blick
Monthly £3.00

Features on any aspect of cars and motoring; car tests. Material mostly commissioned. Length: 1500-3000 words. Illustrations: colour photos and line

drawings. Payment: £200 per 1000 words; by agreement for illustrations. Founded 1993.

BBC Vegetarian GoodFood
BBC Worldwide, Woodlands, 80 Wood Lane, London W12 0TT
tel 0181-576 3767 *fax* 0181-576 3825
Editor Gilly Cubitt
Monthly £1.85

Cooking, nutrition, environmental issues. Accepts feature ideas; no unsolicited material. Illustrated, including cartoons. Payment: by arrangement. Founded 1992.

BBC Wildlife Magazine
Broadcasting House, Whiteladies Road, Bristol BS8 2LR
tel 0117-973 8402 *fax* 0117-946 7075
e-mail wildlifemag@gn.apc.org
Editor Rosamund Kidman Cox
Monthly £2.50

Popular but scientifically accurate articles about wildlife and conservation (national and international), some linked by subject to TV and radio programmes. Two news sections for short, topical biological and environmental stories. Length of articles: 3000 words. Illustrations: top-quality colour photos. Payment: £200-£350 per article; photos according to reproduction size, £45-£150.

The Beano
D.C. Thomson & Co. Ltd, Albert Square, Dundee DD1 9QJ
tel (01382) 223131 *fax* (01382) 322214
185 Fleet Street, London EC4A 2HS
tel 0171-242 5086 *fax* 0171-404 5694
Weekly 45p

Comic strips for children. Series, 11-22 pictures. Payment: on acceptance.

Beano Comic Library
D.C. Thomson & Co. Ltd, Albert Square, Dundee DD1 9QJ
tel (01382) 223131 *fax* (01382) 322214
185 Fleet Street, London EC4A 2HS
tel 0171-242 5086 *fax* 0171-404 5694
2 p.m. 55p

Extra-long comic adventure stories featuring well-known characters from the weekly *Beano* publication.

Bella
Shirley House, 25-27 Camden Road, London NW1 9LL
tel 0171-241 8000 *fax* 0171-485 3774
Editor Jackie Highe
Weekly 60p

General interest magazine for women: practical articles on fashion and beauty, health, cooking, home, travel; real life stories, plus fiction up to 2000 words. Payment: by arrangement. Illustrations: line including cartoons, half-tone, colour. Founded 1987.

Best

197 Marsh Wall, London E14 9SG
tel 0171-519 5500 *fax* 0171-519 5521
Editor Louise Court
Weekly 60p

Short stories. No other uncommissioned work accepted, but always willing to look at ideas/outlines. Length: 1300 words for short stories, variable for other work. Illustrations: line, half-tone, colour, cartoons. Payment: by agreement. Founded 1987.

Best of British

CMS Publishing, Rock House, Scotgate, Stamford, Lincs. PE9 2YQ
tel/fax (01780) 763063 *fax* (01780) 765788
Editor Peter Kelly
Monthly £2.40

Nostalgic features about life in the 1930s, 1940s and 1950s and personal memories. Length: 1000 words. Illustrations: colour and b&w. Payment: £40 (words); £20 (pictures). Founded 1994.

Big!

EMAP Metro, Mappin House, 4 Winsley Street, London W1N 7AR
tel 0171-436 1515 *fax* 0171-631 0781
Editor Richard Galpin, *Features Editor* Frances Sheen
Fortnightly 95p

Teenage entertainment, aimed at 11-17-year-olds, covering pop, video, and film and soap stars. Approach features editor by phone with ideas for celebrity interviews, and gossip. All material commissioned. Length: features, 800 words. Illustrations: colour and b&w photos, cartoons. Payment: features £80-£250, illustrations £80-£250. Founded 1989.

The Big Issue

57-61 Clerkenwell Road, London EC1M 5NP
tel 0171-418 0418
Editor Becky Gardiner
Weekly £1.00

Features, news, reviews, interviews – of general interest and on social issues. Length: features 500-2000 words. Illus-

trations: colour and b&w photos and line. Payment: £150 per 1000 words. Founded 1991.

The Big Issue in the North

The Big Issue in the North Ltd,
135-141 Oldham Street, Manchester M4 1LL
tel 0161-834 6300 *fax* 0161-819 5000
Editor Karen Lang
Weekly £1.00

Articles of general interest and on social issues; arts features and news covering the north of England. No fiction or poetry, except by the homeless. Contact the news, arts or features editors to discuss ideas. Length: 1500 words (features/articles), 300-500 (news), 700 (arts features), 350 words (comment). Payment: £90 per 1000 words. Colour transparencies, puzzles and quizzes. Founded 1992.

The Big Issue in Scotland

The Big Issue in Scotland Ltd, 29 College Street, Glasgow G1 1QH
tel 0141-559 5555 *fax* 0141-552 3200
e-mail edit.scot@bigissue.com
Editor Ken Laird
Weekly 80p

Features on human rights, animal issues, injustices, Scotland, medical, scientific, the paranormal, health and crime, plus news and reviews. Length: 1000-2000 words (articles); 500-800 words (news). Illustrations: colour and b&w. Payment: £95 per 1000 words; £30 per photo/illustration. Founded 1993.

The Big Issues

Niall Skelly, 110 Amien Street, Dublin 3, Republic of Ireland
tel (01) 8553969
Fortnightly £1.50

Articles, features and news on the homeless, unemployed and social issues, plus general articles and celebrity interviews. Length: 800-3000 words. Payment: negotiable. Founded 1994.

Bike

EMAP Nationals, Bushfield House, Orton Centre, Peterborough PE2 5UW
tel (01733) 237111 *fax* (01733) 370283
e-mail richard.fincher@ecm.emap.com
Editor Richard Fincher
Monthly £2.90

'Britain's biggest motorcycle magazine.' Interested in articles, features, news. Length: articles/features 1000-3000 words. Illustrations: colour and b&w photos, line, cartoons. Payment: £120 per 1000 words; illustrations per size/position. Founded 1971.

Bird Keeper

IPC Magazines Ltd, King's Reach Tower, Stamford Street, London SE1 9LS
tel 0171-261 6201 *fax* 0171-261 6095
Editor Peter Moss
Monthly £2.30

Articles on the care, health and breeding of birds, beginner bird keepers and how-to. Send synopsis of ideas. Length: up to 1200 words. Illustrations: colour photos and transparencies of birds in collections, or how-to. Payment: £45-£85 per 1000 words; £20-£45 per illustration. Founded 1988.

Bird Watching

EMAP Pursuit Publishing Ltd, Bretton Court, Bretton, Peterborough PE3 8DZ
tel (01733) 264666 *fax* (01733) 465939
e-mail dave.cromack@ecm.emap.com
Editor David Cromack
Monthly £2.50

Broad range of bird-related features, particularly looking at bird behaviour and birdwatching sites. Emphasis on providing accurate information in entertaining ways. Send synopsis first. Length: 1200 words. Illustrations: colour photos, cartoons. Payment: by negotiation. Founded 1986.

Birding World

Sea Lawn, Coast Road, Cley next the Sea, Holt, Norfolk NR25 7RZ
tel (01263) 740913 *fax* (01263) 741014
e-mail steve@birdingw.demon.co.uk
Editor Steve Gantlett
Monthly £36.00 p.a. (£43.00 p.a. Europe; £49.00 p.a. rest of the world, airmail)

Magazine for keen birdwatchers. Articles and news stories about mainly European ornithology, with the emphasis on ground-breaking new material. Length: up to 3000 words (articles); up to 1500 words (news). Illustrations: good quality colour photos of birds. Payment: up to £25 per 500 words; £10-£40 (illustrations). Founded 1987.

Birdwatch

Solo Publishing Ltd, 310 Bow House, 153-159 Bow Road, London E3 2SE
tel 0181-983 1855 *fax* 0181-983 0246
Editor Dominic Mitchell
Monthly £2.45

Topical articles on all aspects of birds and birding, including conservation, identification, sites and habitats, equipment, overseas expeditions. Length: 700-1500 words. Illustrations: colour slides, b&w photos, colour and b&w line. Payment: from £40 per 1000 words; colour: photos £15-£40, cover £70, line by negotiation; b&w: photos £10, line £10-£40. Founded 1991.

Black Beauty & Hair

Hawker Publications, 13 Park House, 140 Battersea Park Road, London SW11 4NB
tel 0171-720 2108 *fax* 0171-498 3023
Editor Irene Shelley
Bi-monthly £2.00

Beauty and style articles relating specifically to the black woman; celebrity features. No short stories. Length: approx. 1000 words. Illustrations: colour and b&w photos. Payment: £95 per 1000 words; photos £25-£75. Founded 1982.

Bliss

Emap Elan Ltd, Endeavour House, 189 Shaftesbury Avenue, London WC2H 8JG
tel 0171-437 9011 *fax* 0171-208 3591
Editor Kerry Parnell
Monthly £1.70

Glamorous young women's glossy magazine. Bright intimate American-style format, with readers' true-life stories (length 1000 words, payment from £50); beauty, fashion, gossip, advice, quizzes (payment by arrangement). Founded 1995.

Blueprint

Christ Church, 35 Cosway Street, London NW1 5NJ
tel 0171-262 2622 *fax* 0171-706 4811
Editor Marcus Field
11 p.a. £3.50

The magazine of modern architecture and design. Interested in articles, features and reviews. Length: up to 2500 words. Illustrations: colour and b&w photos and line. Payment: negotiable. Founded 1983.

BMA News Review

British Medical Association, BMA House, Tavistock Square, London WC1H 9JP
tel 0171-383 6122 *fax* 0171-383 6566
Editor Julie Coulson

GP edition

20 p.a. £52 p.a.

News and features.

Hospital doctors edition
12 p.a. £52 p.a.
News and features. Length: 700-1200 words (features), 100-400 words (news). Illustrations: colour transparencies, colour and b&w artwork and cartoons. Payment: by negotiation. Founded 1966.

BMW Magazine
River Publishing, Victory House, Leicester Square, London WC2H 7QH
tel 0171-306 0304 *fax* 0171-306 0303
e-mail rwilsher@aol.com
Editor Roger Wilsher
Quarterly £3.50
Lifestyle magazine for BMW car and bike owners. Discuss ideas for features and articles with the editor before submitting material. Length: 800-2500 (articles/features); 50-400 (news). Illustrations: colour. Payment £250 per 1000 words; £100 per quarter-page illustration. Founded 1996.

Boards
Yachting Press Ltd, 196 Eastern Esplanade, Southend-on-Sea, Essex SS1 3AB
tel (01702) 582245 *fax* (01702) 588434
e-mail 106003.3405@compuserve.com
web site http://www.boards.co.uk
Editor Bill Dawes
Monthly during summer, Bi-monthly during winter £2.50 (10 p.a.)
Articles, photos and reports on all aspects of windsurfing and boardsailing. Payment: by arrangement. Illustrations: line, half-tone, colour, cartoons. Founded 1982.

The Book Collector
(incorporating Bibliographical Notes and Queries)
The Collector Ltd, PO Box 12426, London W11 3GW
tel/fax 0171-792 3492
Editorial Board Nicolas Barker (Editor), A. Bell, J. Fergusson, T. Hofmann, D. McKitterick, Joan Winterkorn
Quarterly £38.00 p.a. (£40.00/$64.00 overseas)
Articles, biographical and bibliographical, on the collection and study of printed books and MSS. Payment: for reviews only. Founded 1952.

Book and Magazine Collector
Diamond Publishing Group Ltd, 43-45 St Mary's Road, London W5 5RQ
tel 0181-579 1082 *fax* 0181-566 2024
Editor Crispin Jackson
Monthly £2.70

Articles about collectable authors/publications/subjects. Articles must be bibliographical and include a full bibliography and price guide (no purely biographical features). Approach in writing with ideas. Length: 2000-4000 words. Illustrations: colour and b&w artwork. Payment: £30 per 1000 words. Founded 1984.

Books in Wales – see Llais Llyfrau

Books Ireland
11 Newgrove Avenue, Dublin 4, Republic of Ireland
tel (01) 2692185 *fax* (01) 260 4927
Editor Jeremy Addis, *Features Editor* Shirley Kelly
Monthly (exc. Jan, Jul, Aug) £2.00 (£20.00 p.a.)
Reviews of Irish-interest and Irish-author books, articles of interest to librarians, booksellers and readers. Length: 800-1400 words. Payment: £35 per 1000 words. Founded 1976.

Books Magazine
43 Museum Street, London WC1A 1LY
tel 0171-404 0304 *fax* 0171-242 0762
Editor Liz Thomson
Quarterly £1.50
Reviews, features, interviews with authors. No unsolicited MSS. Payment: negotiable but little bought in. Founded 1987.

The Bookseller
J. Whitaker and Sons Ltd, 12 Dyott Street, London WC1A 1DF
tel 0171-420 6000 *fax* 0171-420 6103
e-mail letters.to.editor@bookseller.co.uk
web site http://www.the.Bookseller.com
Editor Louis Baum
Weekly £135.00 p.a.
Journal of the publishing and bookselling trades. While outside contributions are welcomed, most of the journal's contents are commissioned. Length: about 1000-1500 words. Payment: by arrangement. Founded 1858.

Bowls International
Key Publishing Ltd, PO Box 100, Stamford, Lincs. PE9 1XQ
tel (01780) 755131 *fax* (01780) 757261
Editor Melvyn Beck
Monthly £2.20
Sport and news items and features; occasional, bowls-oriented short stories. Illustrations: colour transparencies, b&w photos, occasional line, cartoons.

Payment: sport/news approx. 25p per line, features approx. £50 per page; colour £25, b&w £10. Founded 1981.

Brewing & Distilling International

52 Glenhouse Road, London SE9 1JQ
tel 0181-859 4300 *fax* 0181-859 5813
Editor Bruce Stevens
Monthly £48.00 p.a. (£82.00/$115.00 p.a. airmail)
Journal for brewers, maltsters, hop merchants, distillers, soft drinks manufacturers, bottlers and allied traders, circulating in over 80 countries. Technical and marketing articles (average 1000 words) accepted, by prior arrangement, from authors with specialist knowledge. Illustrations: line drawings, photos. Payment: by agreement with editor. Founded 1865.

Bridge Magazine

Chess & Bridge Ltd, 369 Euston Road, London NW1 3AR
tel 0171-388 2404 *fax* 0171-388 2407
e-mail chesscentre@easynet.co.uk
web site http://www.bridgemagazine.co.uk
Editor Mark Horton
Monthly £2.95
Articles on bidding and play; instruction, competitions, tournament reports and humour. Payment: by arrangement. Illustrations: line, half-tone. Founded 1926.

British Birds

Fountains, Park Lane, Blunham, Bedford MK44 3NJ
tel/fax (01767) 640025
Managing Editor Dr J.T.R. Sharrock
Monthly £61.00 p.a.
Original observations relating to birds of Britain, Europe and North Africa. Illustrations: line, half-tone, colour. Payment: none for articles, nominal for illustrations. Founded 1907.

British Chess Magazine

BCM Chess Shop, 69 Masbro Road, London W14 0LS
Editor M. Chandler
Monthly £2.70 (£28.00 p.a.)
Commissioned articles, 800-2500 words, on historical and cultural aspects of chess. Illustrations: colour, b&w, line, cartoons. Payment: by arrangement. Founded 1881.

The British Deaf News

PO Box 12, Carlisle CA1 1HU
tel (01228) 599994 (voice and text)
fax (01228) 541420
Editor Irene Hall
Monthly £1.25, £15.00 p.a. non-members (£1.00/£12.00 p.a. members)
Official journal of the British Deaf Association. Articles, news items, letters dealing with deafness. Payment: by arrangement. Illustrations: line, half-tone. Founded 1955.

British Journal of General Practice

(formerly Journal of the Royal College of General Practitioners)
14 Princes Gate, Hyde Park, London SW7 1PU
tel 0171-581 3232 *fax* 0171-584 6716
e-mail info@rcgp.org.uk
web site http://www.rcgp.org.uk
Editor Dr A.F. Wright MBE, MD, FRCGP
Monthly £130.00 p.a. (£147.00 overseas, £166.50 airmail)
Articles relevant to general medical practice. Illustrations: half-tone, colour. Payment: none.

The British Journal of Photography

Timothy Benn Publishing, 39 Earlham Street, London WC2H 9LD
tel 0171-306 7000 *fax* 0171-306 7017
e-mail bjp@benn.co.uk
web site http://www.bjphoto.co.uk
Editor Reuel Golden
Weekly £1.50
Articles on professional, commercial and press photography, and on the more advanced aspects of amateur, technical, industrial, medical, scientific and colour photography. Illustrations: line, half-tone, colour. Payment: by arrangement. Founded 1854.

British Journal of Special Education

The University of Birmingham, School of Education, Edgbaston, Birmingham B15 2TT
tel 0121-414 4805 *fax* 0121-414 4865
Editor Christina Tilstone
Quarterly (non-member institutions/individuals Europe £52.50 p.a., rest of the world £74.00 p.a.)
Official Journal of the National Association for Special Educational Needs. Articles by specialists on the education of children and young people with a range of special educational needs; plus research findings, and examples of good practice in education and associated areas: medical, psychological, therapeutic and sociological. Length: about 3000 words. Payment: none. Illustrations: line, half-tone.

British Journalism Review

BJR Publishing Ltd, c/o John Libbey Media,
Faculty of Humanities, University of Luton,
75 Castle Street, Luton, Beds. LU1 3AJ
tel (01582) 743297 *fax* (01582) 743298
e-mail ulp@luton.ac.uk
Editor Geoffrey Goodman
Quarterly £25.00 p.a. (overseas rates on
application)
Comment/criticism/review of matters
published by, or of interest to, the media.
Length: 1000-3000 words. Illustrations:
b&w photos. Payment: by arrangement.
Founded 1989.

British Medical Journal

BMA House, Tavistock Square,
London WC1H 9JR
tel 0171-387 4499 *fax* 0171-383 6418
e-mail editor@bmj.com
web site http://www.bmj.com
Editor Richard Smith BSc, MB, ChBEd, MFPHM, FRCPE
Weekly £6.70
Medical and related articles. Payment: by
arrangement. Founded 1840.

British Philatelic Bulletin

Royal Mail, 22 Finsbury Square, London EC2A 1NL
fax 0171-614 7209
Editor J.R. Holman
Monthly 85p
Articles on any aspect of British philately – stamps, postmarks, postal history;
also stamp collecting in general. Length:
up to 1500 words (articles); 250 words
(news). Payment: £45 per 1000 words.
Illustrations: colour. Founded 1963.

British Postmark Bulletin

Fortnightly £10 p.a. (£21.75 p.a. overseas)
Articles on British postmarks – past and
present. Founded 1971.

British Printer

Miller Freeman Plc, Sovereign Way, Tonbridge,
Kent TN9 1RW
tel (01732) 364422 *fax* (01732) 377362
web site http://www.dotprint.com
Editor Jane Ellis
Monthly £72.00 p.a.
Articles on technical and aesthetic
aspects of printing processes and graphic
reproduction. Payment: by arrangement.
Illustrations: offset litho from photos,
line drawings and diagrams, cartoons.
Founded 1888.

Broadcast

EMAP Media, 33-39 Bowling Green Lane,
London EC1R 0DA
tel 0171-505 8014 *fax* 0171-505 8050
Editor Matt Baker
Weekly £2.00
News and authoritative articles designed
for all concerned with the UK and international television and radio industry,
and with programmes and advertising on
television, radio, video, cable, satellite,
business. Illustrations: colour, b&w, line,
cartoons. Payment: by arrangement.

Brownie

The Guide Association, 17-19 Buckingham Palace
Road, London SW1W 0PT
tel 0171-834 6242
Editor Marion Thompson
Monthly £1.20
Official Magazine of The Guide
Association. Short articles for Brownies
(girls 7-10 years); fiction with Brownie
background (500-600 words); puzzles;
'things to make', etc. Illustrations: colour.
Payment: £50 per 1000 words; varies for
illustrations.

Budgerigar World

The County Press, Bala, Gwynedd LL23 7PG
tel (01678) 520262 *fax* (01678) 521262
Editor Terry A. Tuxford, 145 Western Way,
Basingstoke, Hants RG22 6EX
tel (01256) 328898 *fax* (01256) 329462
e-mail 101610.1547@compuserve.com
Monthly £30.00 p.a.
Articles about exhibition budgerigars.
Payment: by arrangement. Illustrations:
half-tone, colour. Founded 1982.

Building

The Builder Group, Exchange Tower,
2 Harbour Exchange Square, London E14 9GE
tel 0171-560 4141 *fax* 0171-560 4004
e-mail 106173.632@compuserve.com
Editor Adrian Barrick
Weekly £2.20
Covers the entire professional, industrial
and manufacturing aspects of the building industry. Articles on architecture and
techniques at home and abroad considered, also news and photos. Payment: by
arrangement. Founded 1842.

Building Design

30 Calderwood Street, London SE18 6QH
tel 0181-855 7777 *fax* 0181-854 8058
Editor Louise Rogers
Weekly Controlled circulation (£65.00 p.a.)
News and features on all aspects of
building design. All material commissioned. Length: up to 1500 words.

Illustrations: colour and b&w photos, line, cartoons. Payment: £120 per 1000 words; illustrations by negotiation. Founded 1970.

Built Environment

Alexandrine Press, PO Box 15, 51 Cornmarket Street, Oxford OX1 3EB
tel (01865) 724627 *fax* (01865) 792309
Editors Prof Peter Hall, Prof David Banister
Quarterly £70.00 p.a.

Articles about architecture, planning and the environment. Preliminary letter advisable. Length: 1000-5000 words. Payment: by arrangement. Illustrations: photos and line.

Bunty

D.C. Thomson & Co. Ltd, Albert Square, Dundee DD1 9QJ
tel (01382) 223131 *fax* (01382) 322214
185 Fleet Street, London EC4A 2HS
tel 0171-242 5086 *fax* 0171-404 5694
Weekly 65p

Vividly told picture-story serials for young girls of school age: 16-18 frames in each 2-page instalment; 23-24 frames in each 3-page instalment. Comic strips and features. Payment: on acceptance.

Bunty Library

D.C. Thomson & Co. Ltd, Albert Square, Dundee DD1 9QJ
tel (01382) 223131 *fax* (01382) 322214
185 Fleet Street, London EC4A 2HS
tel 0171-242 5086 *fax* 0171-404 5694
Fortnightly 60p

Picture-stories for schoolgirls, 64 pages (about 140 line drawings): ballet, school, adventure, theatre, sport. Scripts considered; promising artists and scriptwriters encouraged. Payment: on acceptance.

Burlington Magazine

14-16 Duke's Road, London WC1H 9AD
tel 0171-388 1228 *fax* 0171-388 1230
e-mail editorial@burlington.org.uk
Editor Caroline Elam
Monthly £11.00

Deals with the history and criticism of art; book and exhibition reviews; illustrated monthly Calendar section. Potential contributors must have special knowledge of the subjects treated; MSS compiled from works of reference are unacceptable. Length: 500-5000 words. Payment: up to £100. Illustrations: b&w and colour photos. Founded 1903.

Buses

Riverdene, Molesey Road, Hersham, Surrey KT12 4RG
tel (01932) 266600 *fax* (01932) 266601
Editor Stephen Morris
Monthly £2.60

Articles of interest to both road passenger transport operators and bus enthusiasts. Preliminary enquiry essential. Illustrations: colour transparencies, halftone, line maps. Payment: on application. Founded 1949.

Business Life

Premier Magazines, Haymarket House, 1 Oxenden Street, London SW1Y 4EE
tel 0171-925 2544 *fax* 0171-839 4508
Editor Sandra Harris
Monthly Free

Inflight magazine for British Airways. Articles and features of interest to the European business traveller. All material commissioned; approach in writing with ideas. Length: 850-1500 words. Illustrations: colour photos and line. Payment: £300 per 1000 words; £100-£400 for illustrations. Founded 1985.

Business Scotland

Peebles Publishing Group, Bergius House, Clifton Street, Glasgow G3 7LA
tel 0141-567 6000 *fax* 0141-331 1395
Editor Graham Lironi
Monthly Controlled circulation

Features, profiles and news items of interest to business and finance in Scotland. Payment: by arrangement. Founded 1947.

BusinessMatters

GMC Publications, Castle Place, 166 High Street, Lewes, East Sussex BN7 1XU
tel (01273) 477374 *fax* (01273) 486300
Editor Neil Bell
Bi-monthly £2.95

How to run and market small- to medium-sized businesses. Articles based on case studies; relevant news. Length: 400-2400 words. Illustrations: colour and b&w photos, cartoons. Payment: £50 per 500 words; £50 per illustration. Founded 1992.

Buster

Egmont Fleetway Ltd, Egmont House, 25-31 Tavistock Place, London WC1H 9SU
tel 0171-344 6400 *fax* 0171-388 4020
Fortnightly £1.00

Juvenile comic. Comedy characters in picture strips, for children aged 6-12. Full colour. Payment: by arrangement. Founded 1960.

Cage and Aviary Birds
IPC Magazines Ltd, King's Reach Tower, Stamford Street, London SE1 9LS
tel 0171-261 6116 *fax* 0171-261 6095
Editor-in-Chief Peter Moss
Weekly 98p
Practical articles on bird-keeping. First-hand knowledge only. Illustrations: line, half-tone, colour, cartoons. Payment: by arrangement. Founded 1902.

Camcorder User
(incorporating Video Editing and Desktop Video)
WV Publications, 57-59 Rochester Place, London NW1 9JU
tel 0171-331 1000 *fax* 0171-331 1242
e-mail wvmags@compuserve.com
Editor Christine Morgan
Monthly £2.60
Features on film/video-making techniques, specifically tailored to the amateur enthusiast. Material mostly commissioned. Length: 1000-2500 words. Illustrations: colour and b&w; contact editor for details. Payment: by arrangement. Founded 1988.

Campaign
Haymarket Business Publications Ltd, 174 Hammersmith Road, London W6 7JP
tel 0171-413 4036 *fax* 0171-413 4507
e-mail 100560.1626@compurserve.com
Editor Stefano Hatfield
Weekly £2.00
News and articles covering the whole of the mass communications field, particularly advertising in all its forms, marketing and the media. Features should not exceed 2000 words. News items also welcome. Press day, Wednesday. Payment: by arrangement.

Camping Magazine
Garnett Dickinson Publishing, Fitzwilliam Road, Rotherham S65 1JU
tel/fax (editorial) (01273) 477421
Editor John Lloyd
Monthly £2.30
Covers the spectrum of camping and related activities in all shapes and forms – camping is more than a tent on a site! Lively, anecdotal articles and photos are welcome, but call to discuss your ideas with the editor first. Length: 500-1500

words on average. Illustrations: colour. Payment: by arrangement. Founded 1961.

Car
EMAP National Publications Ltd, Abbots Court, 34 Farringdon Lane, London EC1R 3AV
tel 0171-216 6200 *fax* 0171-216 6259
e-mail 101740.3504@compuserve.com
web site http://www.erack.com/car
Editor Rob Munro-Hall
Monthly £3.00
Top-grade journalistic features on car driving, car people and cars. Length: 1000-2500 words. Payment: minimum £260 per 1000 words. Illustrations: b&w and colour photos to professional standards. Founded 1962.

Car Mechanics
Cudham Tithe Barn, Berrys Hill, Cudham, Kent TW16 3AG
tel (01959) 541444 or (01733) 203749
fax (01959) 541400
e-mail info@kelsey.co.uk
Editor Peter Simpson
Monthly £2.50
Practical articles on maintaining, repairing and uprating modern cars for DIY plus the motor trade. Always interested in finding new talent for our rather specialised market but please study the magazine before submitting ideas or features. Preliminary letter or phone call outlining feature recommended. Payment: by arrangement. Illustrations: line drawings, colour prints or transparencies. Rarely use words only; please supply text and pictures.

Caravan Magazine
Link House, Dingwall Avenue, Croydon CR9 2TA
tel 0181-686 2599 *fax* 0181-781 6044/760 0973
web site http://www.linkhouse.co.uk/
Editor Paul Carter
Monthly £2.50
Lively articles based on real experience of touring caravanning, especially if well illustrated by photos. General countryside or motoring material not wanted. Payment: by arrangement. Founded 1933.

Caribbean Times
(incorporating African Times)
Ethnic Media Group, 1st Floor, 148 Cambridge Heath Road, London E1 5QJ
tel 0171-702 8012 *fax* 0171-702 7937
e-mail ct@eeye.demon.co.uk
Editor Clive Morgan
Weekly 50p

News stories, articles and features of interest to Britain's African-Caribbean community. Founded 1981.

Carousel – The Guide to Children's Books

7 Carrs Lane, Birmingham B4 7TG
tel 0121-643 6411 *fax* 0121-643 3152
Editor Jenny Blanch
3 p.a. £9.00 p.a. (£12.00 p.a. Europe; £15.00 p.a. overseas)

Reviews of fiction, non-fiction and poetry books for children, plus in-depth articles; profiles of authors and illustrators. Length: 1200 words (articles); 150 words (reviews). Illustrations: colour and b&w. Payment: by arrangement. Founded 1995.

Cat World

Ashdown Publishing, Avalon Court, Star Road, Partridge Green, West Sussex RH13 8RY
tel (01403) 711511 *fax* (01403) 711521
e-mail joanmoore@ashdown.co.uk
web site http://www.catworld.co.uk
Editor Joan Moore
Monthly £1.95

Bright, lively articles on any aspect of cat ownership. Articles on breeds of cats and veterinary articles by acknowledged experts only. No unsolicited fiction. Illustrations: colour prints or transparencies. Payment: by arrangement; £7.50 per illustration. Founded 1981.

Caterer & Hotelkeeper

Reed Business Information Ltd, Quadrant House, The Quadrant, Sutton, Surrey SM2 5AS
tel 0181-652 8680 *fax* 0181-652 8973/8947
Editor Forbes Mutch
Weekly £1.65

Articles on all aspects of the hotel and catering industries. Length: up to 1500 words. Illustrations: line, half-tone, colour. Payment: by arrangement. Founded 1893.

Catholic Gazette

The Chase Centre, 114 West Heath Road, London NW3 7TX
tel 0181-458 3316 *fax* 0181-905 5780
e-mail cms@csm.org.uk
web site http://www.cms.org.uk/cms-home
Editor Fr. Paul Daly
Monthly £1.20

Articles on evangelisation and the Christian life. Length: up to 2000 words. Illustrations: b&w photos, line, cartoons. Payment: by arrangement. Founded 1910.

The Catholic Herald

Herald House, Lambs Passage, Bunhill Row, London EC1Y 8TQ
tel 0171-588 3101 *fax* 0171-256 9728
e-mail catholic@atlas.co.uk
Editor Deborah Jones
Weekly 50p

Independent newspaper covering national and international affairs from a Catholic/Christian viewpoint as well as church news. Length: articles 600-1100 words. Illustrations: photos of Catholic and Christian interest. Payment: by arrangement.

Catholic Pictorial

Media House, Mann Island, Pier Head, Liverpool L3 1DQ
tel 0151-236 2191 *fax* 0151-236 2216
Editor David Mahon
Weekly 50p

News and photo features (maximum 800 words plus illustration) of Merseyside, regional and national Catholic interest only; also cartoons. Has a strongly social editorial and is a trenchant tabloid. Payment: by arrangement. Founded 1961.

Catholic Times

1st Floor, St James's Buildings, Oxford Street, Manchester M1 6FP
tel 0161-236 8856 *fax* 0161-237 5590
Editor Gregory Murphy
Weekly 50p

News (400 words) and news features (800 words) of Catholic interest. Illustrations: colour and b&w photos. Payment: £30-£80; photos £50. Relaunched 1993.

Cencrastus: Scottish & International Literature, Arts and Affairs

Unit One, Abbeymount Techbase, 2 Easter Road, Edinburgh EH8 8EJ
tel/fax 0131-661 5687
e-mail RichardMoore4@compuserve.com
Editor Raymond Ross, *Managing Editor* Richard Moore
Quarterly £2.25 (back copies £2.50); £12.00 p.a.

Articles, short stories, poetry, reviews. Payment: by arrangement. Illustrations: line, half-tone. Founded 1979.

Chapman

4 Broughton Place, Edinburgh EH1 3RX
tel 0131-557 2207 *fax* 0131-556 9565
Editor Joy Hendry
Quarterly £3.70 (£15.00 p.a.)

'Scotland's Quality Literary Magazine.' Poetry, short stories, reviews, criticism, articles on Scottish culture. Illustrations: line, half-tone, cartoons. Payment: £8.00 per page; illustrations by negotiation. Founded 1969.

Chartered Secretary

(formerly Administrator)
16 Park Crescent, London W1N 4AH
tel 0171-580 4741 *fax* 0171-323 1132
e-mail chartsec@dial.pipex.com
web site http://www.icsa.org.uk/icsa/
Monthly £4.00 (£37.00 p.a. post free UK)

Official Journal of The Institute of Chartered Secretaries and Administrators. Practical and topical articles (750-1600 words) on law, finance and management affecting company secretaries and other senior administrators in business, nationalised industries, local and central government and other institutions in Britain and overseas. Payment: by arrangement.

Chat

IPC Magazines Ltd, King's Reach Tower, Stamford Street, London SE1 9LS
tel 0171-261 6565 *fax* 0171-261 6534
Editor Keith Kendrick
Weekly 60p

Tabloid weekly for women; fiction. Length: up to 1000 words. Illustrations: half-tone, colour. Payment: by arrangement. Founded 1986.

Chemist & Druggist

Miller Freeman plc, Miller Freeman House, Sovereign Way, Tonbridge, Kent TN9 1RW
tel (01732) 364422 *fax* (01732) 361534
e-mail chemdrug@dotpharmacy.com
web site http://www.@dotpharmacy.com
Editor Patrick Grice
Weekly £127.00 p.a.

'The newsweekly for pharmacy.' News stories and feature items relating to any aspect of community pharmacy or small independent retailing. Length: 1000 or 1500 words (features), up to 300 words (news). Illustrations: colour. Payment: £110 per 1000 words. Founded 1859.

Chess Monthly

Chess & Bridge Ltd, 369 Euston Road, London NW1 3AR
tel 0171-388 2404 *fax* 0171-388 2407
e-mail chesscentre@easynet.co.uk
web site http://www.chesscenter.com
Executive Editor Malcolm Pein

Technical Editor Jimmy Adams
Monthly £2.95

Tournament reports, news and technical articles. Length: 1-4 pages. Illustrations: colour and b&w. Payment: £15.20. Founded 1935.

Chic

Northern & Shell plc, Northern & Shell Tower, City Harbour, London E14 9GL
tel 0171-308 5090 *fax* 0171-308 5075
Editor Ruth Corbett
Monthly £2.25

In depth human interest articles aimed at women aged over 35. Show business interviews, 'at home' with personalities and stories about ordinary women. Submit written synopsis. Length: 2000-3000 words. Illustrations: all commissioned. Payment: by arrangement. Founded 1995.

Child Education

Scholastic Publications Ltd, Villiers House, Clarendon Avenue, Leamington Spa, Warks. CV32 5PR
tel (01926) 887799 *fax* (01926) 883331
Editor Gill Moore
Monthly £2.60

For teachers and preschool staff concerned with children aged 3-8. Articles by specialists on practical teaching ideas and methods. Length: 600-1200 words. Payment: by arrangement. Profusely illustrated with photos, line drawings and cartoons; also large full colour pictures. Founded 1924.

The China Quarterly

School of Oriental and African Studies, Thornhaugh Street, Russell Square, London WC1H 0XG
tel 0171-323 6129 *fax* 0171-580 6836
e-mail chinaq@soas.ac.uk
Editor Dr Richard Louis Edmonds
Quarterly £29/$56 p.a. (£36/$70 institutions, £15/$28 students)

Articles on contemporary China. Length: 8000 words approx.

Choice

Apex House, Oundle Road, Peterborough PE2 9NP
tel (01733) 555123 *fax* (01733) 898487
Editor-in-Chief Sue Dobson
Monthly £2.10

Pre- and retirement magazine for 50+ readership. Positive attitude to life – experiences, hobbies, holidays, finance, relationships. About half the magazine commissioned. Unsolicited material accompanied by an sae will be read. If suggesting feature material, include selection of cuttings of previously published work. Payment: by agreement, on publication. Founded 1974.

Church of England Newspaper

10 Little College Street, London SW1P 3SH
tel 0171-878 1545 *fax* 0171-976 0783
Weekly 50p

Anglican news and articles relating the Christian faith to everyday life. Evangelical basis; almost exclusively commissioned articles. Study of paper desirable. Length: up to 1000 words. Illustrations: photos, line drawings, cartoons. Payment: c. £40 per 1000 words; photos £22, line by arrangement. Founded 1828.

Church of Ireland Gazette

36 Bachelor's Walk, Lisburn,
Co. Antrim BT28 1XN
tel (01846) 675743 *fax* (01846) 675743
Editor Rev. Canon C.W.M. Cooper
Weekly 30p

Church news, articles of religious and general interest. Length: 600-1000 words. Payment: according to length and interest. New Series 1963. Founded 1885.

Church Times

33 Upper Street, London N1 0PN
tel 0171-359 4570 *fax* 0171-226 3073
Editor Paul Handley
Weekly 50p

Articles on religious topics are considered. No verse or fiction. Length: up to 1000 words. Illustrations: news photos, sent promptly. Payment: £100 per 1000 words; Periodical Publishers' Association negotiated rates for illustrations. Founded 1863.

City Life – What's on in Manchester

Diverse Media Ltd, 164 Deansgate,
Manchester M60 2RD
tel 0161-839 1416 *fax* 0161-839 1488
e-mail citylife@mcr-evening-news.co.uk
web site http://www.poptel.org.uk/citylife/
Editor Chris Sharratt
Fortnightly £1.60

Listings magazine for Greater Manchester with features, reviews and previews. Length: 200-1500 words. Illustrations: colour and b&w. Payment: by negotiation. Founded 1983.

Classic & Sports Car

Haymarket Specialist Motoring Publications Ltd,
38-42 Hampton Road, Teddington,
Middlesex TW11 0JE
tel 0181-943 5995 *fax* 0181-943 5844
Managing Editor James Elliott
Monthly £3.00

Features on classic cars and sportscars; shows, news and reviews, features and stories. Length: varies. Illustrations: half-tone, colour. Payment: £150 per 1000 words; varies for illustrations. Founded 1982.

Classic Boat

Boating Publications Ltd, Link House,
Dingwall Avenue, Croydon CR9 2TA
tel 0181-686 2599 *fax* 0181-781 6535
e-mail cb@lhm.co.uk
web site http://www.mazinedata.co.uk/classic
Editor Nic Compton
Monthly £3.20

Cruising and technical features, restorations, events, new boat reviews, practical, maritime history; news. Study of magazine essential: read 3-4 back issues and send for contributors' guidelines. Length: 500-2000 words. Illustrations: colour and b&w photos; line drawings of hulls. Payment: £75-£100 per published page. Founded 1987.

Classic Cars

EMAP National Publications Ltd, Bushfield House, Orton Centre, Peterborough PE2 5UW
tel (01733) 237111 *fax* (01733) 465857
e-mail classic.cars@ecm.emap.com
Editor John Westlake
Monthly £3.10

Specialist articles on older cars. Length: from 500-4000 words (subject to prior contract). Illustrations: half-tone, colour, cartoons. Payment: by negotiation.

Classic CD

Future Publishing, 30 Monmouth Street,
Beauford Court, Bath BA1 2BW
tel (01225) 442244 *fax* (01225) 462986
e-mail nevans@futurenet.co.uk
Editor Neil Evans
Monthly £3.95

Covers classical music on CD. Aims to inform, educate and entertain, with features on composers and performers, reviews and news. Commissioned material only. Length: up to 2000 words. Illustrations: colour and b&w photos, b&w line, including collage and cartoons.

Payment: £125 per 1000 words; colour up to £300, b&w £35 ⅛ page. Founded 1990.

Classic Stitches

D.C. Thomson & Co. Ltd, 80 Kingsway East, Dundee DD4 8SL
tel (01382) 462276 *fax* (01382) 452491
Editor Mrs Bea Neilson
Bi-monthly £3.00

Creative needlework ideas and projects; needlework-based features on designers, collections, work-in-progress and exhibitions. Length: 1000-2000 words. Illustrations: colour photos, preferably not 35 mm. Payment: negotiable. Founded 1994.

Classical Music

Rhinegold Publishing Ltd, 241 Shaftesbury Avenue, London WC2H 8EH
tel 0171-333 1742 *fax* 0171-333 1769
e-mail classical.music@rhinegold.co.uk
Editor Keith Clarke
Fortnightly £2.95

News, opinion, features on the classical music business. All material commissioned. Illustrations: b&w photos and line; colour covers. Payment: minimum £100 per 1000 words; from £50 for illustrations. Founded 1976.

Classics

Security Publications Ltd, Berwick House, 8-10 Knoll Rise, Orpington, Kent BR6 0PS
tel (01689) 887200 *fax* (01689) 838844
e-mail classics@splgroup.demon.co.uk
Editor Andrew Noakes
Monthly £2.80

News photos and stories of classic car interest and illustrated features on classic car repairs, maintenance and restoration. Study writing and photography style of magazine before submitting material. Length: up to 2000 words (features); 200 words (news). Illustrations: colour and b&w. Payment: £120 per 1000 words; typically £90 per set of photos supporting feature article. Founded 1997.

Climber

Myatt McFarlane plc, Trident House, Heath Road, Hale, Altrincham, Cheshire WA14 2UJ
tel 0161-928 3480 *fax* 0161-941 6897
Editor Bernard Newman
Monthly £2.60

Articles on all aspects of mountaineering in Great Britain and abroad, and on related subjects. Study of magazine essential. Length: 1500-2000 words, illustrated

(colour transparencies). Payment: according to merit. Founded 1962.

Coin News

Token Publishing Ltd, PO Box 14, Honiton, Devon EX14 9YP
tel (01404) 46972 *fax* (01404) 831 895
Editor John W. Mussell
Monthly £2.25

Articles of high standard on coins, tokens, paper money. Length: up to 2000 words. Payment: by arrangement. Founded 1964.

Commando

D.C. Thomson & Co. Ltd, Albert Square, Dundee DD1 9QJ
tel (01382) 223131 *fax* (01382) 322214
185 Fleet Street, London EC4A 2HS
tel 0171-242 5086 *fax* 0171-404 5694
8 p.m. 60p

Fictional war stories told in pictures. Scripts should be of about 135 pictures. Synopsis required as an opener. New writers encouraged; send for details. Payment: on acceptance.

Commercial Motor

Reed Business Information Ltd, Quadrant House, The Quadrant, Sutton, Surrey SM2 5AS
tel 0181-652 3302/3303 *fax* 0181-652 8969
Editor Brian Weatherley
Weekly £1.30

Technical and road transport articles only. Length: up to 1500 words. Payment: varies. Illustrations: drawings and photos. Founded 1905.

Communicate

DMG Business Media Ltd, Queensway House, 2 Queensway, Redhill, Surrey RH1 1QS
tel (01737) 768611 *fax* (01737) 855470
Editor Simon Dux
Monthly Controlled circulation

Covers all aspects of telecommunications management: analysis pieces (200-700 words), features (800-1800 words), case studies (1000 words). All material commissioned. Illustrations: colour and b&w photos, line, diagrams. Payment: £180 per 1000 words; illustrations by negotiation. Founded 1980.

Community Care

Reed Business Information Ltd, Quadrant House, The Quadrant, Sutton, Surrey SM2 5AS
tel 0181-652 4861 *fax* 0181-652 4739
Editor Terry Philpot
Weekly £1.45

Articles of professional interest to local authority and voluntary body social workers, managers, teachers and students. Preliminary letter advisable. Length: 900-1500 words. Payment: at current rates. Founded 1974.

Company

National Magazine House, 72 Broadwick Street, London W1V 2BP
tel 0171-439 5000
Editor Fiona McIntosh
Monthly £2.00

Articles on a wide variety of subjects, relevant to young, independent women. Most articles are commissioned. Payment: usual magazine rate. Illustrated. Founded 1978.

Computer Weekly

Reed Business Information Ltd, Quadrant House, The Quadrant, Sutton, Surrey SM2 5AS
tel 0181-652 3122 *fax* 0181-652 3038
web site http://www.computerweekly.co.uk
Editor Helena Sturridge, *News Editor* Karl Schneider, Features *Editor* David Evans
Weekly £1.70

Feature articles on computer-related topics for business/industry users. Length: 1200 words. Illustrations: b&w photos, line, cartoons. Payment: £150 per feature; negotiable for illustrations. Founded 1966.

Computing

VNU Business Publications, VNU House, 32-34 Broadwick Street, London W1A 2HG
tel 0171-316 9601 *fax* 0171-316 9160
web site http://www.computingnet.co.uk
Editor Peter Kirwan
Weekly £100.00 p.a.

Features and news items on corporate procurement and deployment of IT infrastructure, and on applications and implications of computers and telecommunications. Particular sections address the IT professional career development, and the desktop computing environment. Length: 1600-2200 words. Payment: by negotiation. Illustrations: colour photos, line drawings, cartoons. Founded 1973.

Condé Nast Traveller

Vogue House, Hanover Square, London W1R 0AD
tel 0171-499 9080 *fax* 0171-493 3758
e-mail traveller@msmail.condenast.co.uk
web site http://www.cntraveller.co.uk
Editor Sarah Miller
Monthly £2.70

Highly illustrated features on travel, style, food and wine, beauty and health. Illustrations: colour. Payment: by arrangement. Founded 1997.

Contemporary Review

(incorporating the Fortnightly)
Contemporary Review Co. Ltd, Cheam Business Centre, 14 Upper Mulgrave Road, Cheam, Surrey SM2 7AZ
tel 0181-643 4846 *fax* 0181-241 7507
Editor Dr Richard Mullen
Monthly £2.95

Independent review dealing with questions of the day, chiefly politics, international affairs, theology, literature, the arts. Mostly commissioned, but with limited scope for freelance authors with authoritative knowledge. TS returned only if sae enclosed. Intending contributors should study journal first. Length: 2000-3000 words. No illustrations. Payment: £5 per page (500 words), 2 complimentary copies. Founded 1866.

contemporary visual arts

197 Knightsbridge, 8th Floor North, London SW7 1RB
tel 0171-823 8373 *fax* 0171-823 7969
e-mail cva@gbhap.com
web site http://www.gbhap.com/cont.visarts
Editor Keith Patrick
Quarterly £4.95

Articles and reviews on all aspects of contemporary art; book reviews. Length: articles 1000-2000 words, reviews 1000 words. Illustrations: colour photos. Payment: £100 per 1000 words; none for photos. Founded 1992.

Control & Instrumentation

Miller Freeman plc, 1st Floor, City Reach, 5 Greenwich View Place, Millharbour, London E14 9NN
tel 0171-861 6159 *fax* 0171-861 6231
e-mail mpeach@unmf.com
Editor Matthew Peach
Monthly £82.00 p.a.

Authoritative main feature articles on measurement, automation, control systems, instrumentation and data processing; also export, business and engineering news. Regular supplement entitled *Sys.Build* details all aspects of system building and system integration – news, projects, feedback, comment and features. Length of articles: 750 words for highly technical pieces, 1000-2500 words main features. Payment: according to value. Illustrations: photos and drawings of equipment using automatic techniques, control engineering personalities, cartoons. Founded 1958.

Convenience Store

William Reed Publishing Ltd, Broadfield Park, Crawley, West Sussex RH11 9RT
tel (01293) 613400 *fax* (01293) 610330
e-mail editorial@c-store.co.uk
Editor Sonia Young
Fortnightly Controlled circulation

News, reports and retailer profiles of interest to convenience store owners, management and suppliers. Length: 800 words (articles/features), 200 words (news). Illustrations: colour. Payment: £125 per 1000 words. Founded 1985.

Cosmetic World News

130 Wigmore Street, London W1H 0AT
tel 0171-486 6757/8 *fax* 0171-487 5436
Editors M.A. Murray-Pearce, Caroline Marcuse, Norman Clare
Bi-monthly £96.00 p.a.

International news magazine of perfumery, cosmetics and toiletries industry. Worldwide reports, photo-news stories, articles (500-1000 words) on essential oils and new cosmetic raw materials, and exclusive information on industry's companies and personalities welcomed. Payment: by arrangement, minimum 10p per word. Illustrations: b&w and colour photos or colour separations. Founded 1949.

Cosmopolitan

National Magazine House, 72 Broadwick Street, London W1V 2BP
tel 0171-439 5000 *fax* 0171-439 5016
Editor Mandi Norwood
Monthly £2.40

Articles. Commissioned material only. Payment: by arrangement. Illustrated. Founded 1972.

Country

Country Gentlemen's Association, Shuttleworth, Old Warden Park, Biggleswade, Beds. SG18 9EA
tel (01767) 626242 *fax* (01767) 627158
Editor Tim New
Monthly £2.50

The Magazine of the Country Gentlemen's Association. News and features covering rural events, countryside, leisure, heritage, homes and gardens.

Some outside contributors used; approach in writing in first instance. Payment: by arrangement. Founded 1893.

Country Garden & Smallholding

Broad Leys Publishing Company, Buriton House, Station Road, Newport, Saffron Walden, Essex CB11 3PL
tel (01799) 540922 *fax* (01799) 541367
Editor Helen Sears
Monthly £2.10

The magazine for smallholders. Practical, how-to articles, and seasonal features, on organic gardening, small-scale poultry and livestock keeping, country crafts, cookery and smallholdings. Approach editor in writing with ideas. Length: up to 2000 words. Illustrations: colour and b&w photos, line for instructive articles. Payment: £30 per 1000 words; photos £10, £40 cover. Founded 1975 as *Home Farm*.

Country Homes and Interiors

IPC Magazines Ltd, King's Reach Tower, Stamford Street, London SE1 9LS
tel 0171-261 6451 *fax* 0171-261 6895
Editor Katherine Hadley
Monthly £2.30

Articles on property, country homes, interior designs. Illustrations: colour. Payment: from £250 per 1000 words. Founded 1986.

Country Life

IPC Magazines Ltd, King's Reach Tower, Stamford Street, London SE1 9LS
tel 0171-261 7058 *fax* 0171-261 5139
Editor Clive Aslet
Weekly £2.25

Illustrated journal chiefly concerned with British country life, social history, architecture and the fine arts, natural history, agriculture, gardening and sport. Length: about 1000 or 1300 words (articles). Illustrations: mainly colour photos. Payment: according to merit. Founded 1897.

Country Living

National Magazine House, 72 Broadwick Street, London W1V 2BP
tel 0171-439 5000 *fax* 0171-439 5093
Editor Susy Smith
Monthly £2.70

Up-market magazine for country dwellers and townies who have the country at heart. No unsolicited material and do not send valuable transparencies;

magazine cannot accept responsibility for loss of unsolicited material. Illustrations: line, half-tone, colour. Payment: by arrangement. Founded 1985.

Country Quest
7 Aberystwyth Science Park, Aberystwyth, Dyfed SY23 3TN
tel (01970) 611611 *fax* (01970) 612505
Editor Beverly Davies
Monthly £1.80

Illustrated articles on matters relating to countryside, history and personalities of Wales and border counties. No fiction. Illustrated work preferred. Length: 700-1500 words. Payment: by arrangement.

Country Walking
EMAP Pursuit Publishing, Bretton Court, Bretton, Peterborough PE3 8DZ
tel (01733) 264666 *fax* (01733) 465939
Editor Lynne Maxwell
Monthly £2.40

Features and readers' stories. Length: 1000 words on average (features), 800 words (stories), more if commissioned. Illustrations: colour transparencies. Payment: £60 per 1000 words, £35 fee for readers' stories; £15 (1/4 page), £50 (full page). Founded 1987.

The Countryman
Sheep Street, Burford, Oxon OX18 4LH
tel (01993) 822258
Editor Tom Quinn
Bi-monthly £2.40

Every department of rural life except field sports. Copy must be trustworthy, well-written, brisk, cogent and light in hand. Articles up to 1200 words. Skilful sketches of life and character from personal knowledge and experience. Dependable natural history based on writer's own observation. Really good matter from old unpublished letters and MSS. Illustrations: b&w and colour photos and drawings, but all must be exclusive and out of the ordinary. Payment: £70 per 1000 words minimum, usually in excess of this figure, according to merit. Founded 1927.

Country-Side
PO Box 87, Cambridge CB1 3UP
tel/fax (01933) 314672
Editor Dr David Applin
Bi-annual £15.00 p.a.

Official journal of the British Naturalists' Association (BNA), the national body for naturalists. Original observations on wildlife and its protection, and on natural history generally, but not on killing for sport. Preliminary letter or study of magazine advisable. Payment: 1200 words plus pictures £50, shorter articles pro-rata. Illustrations: photos, drawings, cartoons. Founded 1905.

Creative Camera
CC Publishing, 5 Hoxton Square, London N1 6NU
tel 0171-729 6993
e-mail info@ccamera.demon.co.uk
web site http://www.ccamera.demon.co.uk
Editor David Brittain
Bi-monthly £3.95

Illustrated articles and pictures dealing with serious photography, sociology of, history of and criticism of photos; book and exhibition reviews. Arts Council supported. Payment: by arrangement. Illustrations: b&w, colour. Founded 1968.

The Cricketer International
Third Street, Langton Green, Tunbridge Wells, Kent TN3 0EN
tel (01892) 862551 *fax* (01892) 863755
e-mail editorial@cricketer.co.uk
Editor Peter Perchard
Monthly £2.45

Articles on cricket at any level. Illustrations: line, half-tone, colour, cartoons. Payment: £50 per 1000 words; illustrations minimum £17.50. Founded 1921.

The Criminologist
Tolley House, 2 Addiscombe Road, Croydon, Surrey CR9 5AF
tel 0181-686 9141 *fax* 0181-287 3337
e-mail jpn@tolley.co.uk
Editor R.W. Stone
Quarterly £40.80 p.a.

Specialised material designed for an expert and professional readership on national and international criminology, the police, forensic science, the law, penology, sociology and law enforcement. Articles welcomed, up to 4000 words, from those familiar with the journal's style and requirements. A preliminary letter with a brief résumé is requested. Payment: according to merit. Founded 1966.

Critical Quarterly

Address for contributions Kate Mellor,
The London Consortium, PO Box 13843,
London EC1V 0LB
web site http://www.blackwellpublishers.co.uk
Editor Colin MacCabe
Quarterly £31.00 p.a. (£62.00 p.a. institutions)

Fiction, poems, literary criticism. Length:
2000-5000 words. Interested contributors
should study magazine before submitting
MSS. Payment: by arrangement. Founded
1959.

CTN (Confectioner, Tobacconist, Newsagent)

Quantum House, 19 Scarbrook Road,
Croydon CR9 1LX
tel 0181-565 4241 *fax* 0181-565 4245
Editor Anne Bingham
Weekly 95p. (£48.00 p.a.)

Trade news and brief articles illustrated
when possible with photos or line drawings; also cartoons. Must be of current
interest to retail confectioner-tobac-
conists and newsagents. Length: articles
600-800 words. Payment: by negotiation.

Cumbria and Lake District Magazine

(formerly Cumbria)
Dalesman Publishing Company Ltd,
Stable Courtyard, Broughton Hall, Skipton,
North Yorkshire BD23 3AE
tel (01756) 701381 *fax* (01756) 701326
e-mail www.yorkshirenet.co.uk/dalesman
Editor Terry Fletcher
Monthly £1.00

Articles of genuine rural interest concerning Lakeland and Cumbria. Short
length preferred. Illustrations: line drawings and first-class photos. Payment:
according to merit. Founded 1951.

Custom Car

Kelsey Publishing Ltd, Kelsey House,
77 High Street, Beckenham, Kent BR3 1AN
tel 0181-658 3531 *fax* 0181-650 8035
Editor Tim Baggaley
Monthly £2.60

Customising, drag racing and hot rods.
Length: by arrangement. Payment: by
arrangement. Founded 1970.

CWU Voice

150 The Broadway, London SW19 1RX
tel 0181-971 7200 *fax* 0181-971 7497
web site http://www.101354.1117@compuserve.com
Editor Linda Quinn
Monthly Free to members

Main journal of CWU members. Articles

on postal and telecommunications workers in the UK and abroad and on other
questions of interest to a trade union
readership. Payment: NUJ rates. Illustrations: line and colour. Founded 1920.

Cycling & Mountain Biking Today

Yachting Press Ltd, 196 Eastern Esplanade,
Southend-on-Sea, Essex SS1 3AS
tel (01702) 582245 *fax* (01702) 588434
Editor Roger St Pierre
Monthly £2.60

Material mostly commissioned. Accepts
unsolicited travel/expedition features (UK
and abroad), written to style (emphasis on
anecdotes and on characters met, rather
than bland travelogue) with professional-
quality colour transparencies, including
cycle action shots; and general cycling
news. Interested to hear from health and
fitness writers with some knowledge of
cycling. Length: features 1500-2000
words, news 150-200 words. Payment:
£150 per feature inc. pix; news £20 per
item. Founded 1993 as *New Cyclist*.

Cycling Weekly

IPC Magazines Ltd, King's Reach Tower,
Stamford Street, London SE1 9LS
tel 0171-261 5588 *fax* 0171-261 5758
Editor Andrew Sutcliffe
Weekly £1.30

Racing and technical articles; topical
photos with a cycling interest also considered; cartoons. Length: not exceeding
1500 words. Payment: by arrangement.
Founded 1891.

Cyphers

3 Selskar Terrace, Dublin 6, Republic of Ireland
fax (01) 4978866
£6.00 for 3 issues
Editors Leland Bardwell, Pearse Hutchinson,
Eiléan Ní Chuilleanáin, Macdara Woods

Poems, fiction, articles on literary subjects, translations. Payment: £10 per
page. Founded 1975.

Dairy Farmer and Dairy Beef Producer

Wharfedale Road, Ipswich IP1 4LG
tel (01473) 241122 *fax* (01473) 240501
e-mail dairyfarmer@dotfarming.com
Editor Graeme Kirk
Monthly Controlled circulation

Authoritative articles dealing in practical, lively style with dairy farming.
Topical controversial articles invited.

Well-written, illustrated accounts of new ideas being tried on dairy farms are especially wanted. Length: normally 800-1400 words with colour photos. Payment: by arrangement.

Dalesman
Dalesman Publishing Company Ltd, Stable Courtyard, Broughton Hall, Skipton, North Yorkshire BD23 3AE
tel (01756) 701381 *fax* (01756) 701326
e-mail www.yorkshirenet.co.uk/dalesman
Editor Terry Fletcher
Monthly £1.25

Articles and stories of genuine rural interest concerning Yorkshire (1000-1500 words). Payment: according to merit. Illustrations: line drawings and first-class photos preferably featuring people. Founded 1939.

Dance & Dancers
214 Panther House, 38 Mount Pleasant, London WC1X 0AP
tel/fax 0171-837 2711
Editor John Percival
Monthly £1.75

Specialist features, reviews on modern/classical dance, dancers. Length: by prior arrangement. Payment: by arrangement. Illustrations: line, half-tone; colour covers. Founded 1950.

Dancing Times
The Dancing Times Ltd, Clerkenwell House, 45-47 Clerkenwell Green, London EC1R 0EB
tel 0171-250 3006 *fax* 0171-253 6679
e-mail dancing_times@compuserve.com
Editor Mary Clarke
Editorial Adviser Ivor Guest
Executive Editor Frances Palmer
Monthly £2.00

Ballet, contemporary dance and all forms of stage dancing, both from general, historical, critical and technical angles. Well-informed freelance articles are occasionally used, but only after preliminary arrangements. Payment: by arrangement. Illustrations: occasional line, action photos always preferred; colour invited. Founded 1910.

The Dandy
D.C. Thomson & Co. Ltd, Albert Square, Dundee DD1 9QJ
tel (01382) 223131 *fax* (01382) 322214
185 Fleet Street, London EC4A 2HS
tel 0171-242 5086 *fax* 0171-404 5694
Weekly 45p

Comic strips for children. 10-12 pictures per single page story, 18-20 pictures per 2-page story. Promising artists are encouraged. Payment: on acceptance.

Dandy Comic Library
D.C. Thomson & Co. Ltd, Albert Square, Dundee DD1 9QJ
tel (01382) 223131 *fax* (01382) 322214
185 Fleet Street, London EC4A 2HS
tel 0171-242 5086 *fax* 0171-404 5694
2 p.m. 55p

Extra-long comic adventure stories featuring the well-known characters from the weekly Dandy publication.

Darts World
World Magazines Ltd, 28 Arrol Road, Beckenham, Kent BR3 4PA
tel 0181-650 6580 *fax* 0181-654 4343
Editor Tony Wood
Monthly £1.95

Articles and stories with darts theme. Illustrations: half-tone, cartoons. Payment: £40-£50 per 1000 words; illustrations by arrangement. Founded 1972.

Day by Day
Woolacombe House, 141 Woolacombe Road, London SE3 8QP
tel 0181-856 6249
Editor Patrick Richards
Monthly 80p

Articles and news on non-violence and social justice. Reviews of art, books, films, plays, musicals and opera. Cricket reports. Short poems and very occasional short stories in keeping with editorial viewpoint. Payment: £2 per 1000 words. No illustrations required. Founded 1963.

Dental Update
George Warman Publications (UK) Ltd, Unit 2, Riverview Business Park, Walnut Tree Close, Guildford, Surrey GU1 4UX
tel (01483) 304944 *fax* (01483) 303191
Editor Angela Stroud
10 p.a. £55.00 p.a. (£25.00 p.a. students; £39.00 p.a. vocational trainees)

Clinical articles, clinical quizzes. Illustrations: line, colour. Payment: £100-£150 per 1000 words; £75 cover photos only. Founded 1973.

Derbyshire Life and Countryside
Heritage House, Lodge Lane, Derby DE1 3HE
tel (01332) 347087/8/9 *fax* (01332) 290688
Monthly £1.20

Articles, preferably illustrated, about

Derbyshire life, people and history. Length: up to 800 words. Some short stories set in Derbyshire accepted; no verse. Payment: according to nature and quality of contribution. Illustrations: photos of Derbyshire subjects. Founded 1931.

The Dickensian
Dickens House, 48 Doughty Street, London WC1N 2LF
Editor Dr Malcolm Andrews, School of English, Rutherford College, University of Kent, Canterbury, Kent CT2 7NX
fax (01227) 827001
e-mail M.Y.Andrews@ukc.ac.uk
Published by The Dickens Fellowship
3 p.a. £9.50 p.a. (£12.00 p.a. institutions; overseas rates on application)

Welcomes articles on all aspects of Dickens' life, works and character. Payment: none. Send contributions (enclose sae if return required) and editorial correspondence to the editor.

Director
116 Pall Mall, London SW1Y 5ED
tel 0171-766 8950 *fax* 0171-766 8840
Editor Tom Nash
Monthly £3.00

Authoritative business-related articles. Send synopsis of proposed article and examples of printed work. Length: 500-3000 words. Payment: by arrangement. Illustrated mainly in colour. Founded 1947.

Dirt Bike Rider
Key Publishing Ltd, PO Box 100, Stamford, Lincs. PE9 1XQ
tel (01780) 755131 *fax* (01780) 757261
e-mail dbr@keymags.demon.co.uk
Editor Roddy Brooks
Monthly £2.50

Features, track tests, coverage on all aspects of off-road motor-cycling. Length: up to 1000 words. Illustrations: half-tone, colour, cartoons. Founded 1981.

Disability Now
(published by Scope)
6 Market Road, London N7 9PW
tel 0171-619 7323 *fax* 0171-619 7331
Minicom 0171-619 7332
e-mail editor@disabilitynow.org.uk
web site http://www.@disabilitynow.org.uk
Editor Mary Wilkinson
Monthly £16.00 p.a., free to people on income support; tape version free to people with visual impairment or severe disability

Newspaper for people with different types of disability, carers and professionals, and anyone interested in disability. News and comment on anything of interest in the disability field: benefits, services, equipment, jobs, politics, motoring, holidays, sport, relationships, the arts. All regular contributors have a disability (unless they are a parent of someone with a disability). Preliminary letter desirable. Founded 1957.

Diva
Millivres Ltd, Worldwide House, 116-134 Bayham Street, London NW1 0BA
tel 0171-482 2576 *fax* 0171-284 0329
e-mail diva@gaytimes.co.uk
web site http://www.gaytimes.co.uk
Editor Gillian Rodgerson
Monthly £2.00

Lesbian life and culture: articles, features, news, short fiction. Length: 1000-2000 words (articles/features); 300-500 words (news); 1000-2000 words (short stories). Illustrations: colour and b&w. Payment: £10 per 100 words; £30-£50 per photo; £25-£80 per drawing. Founded 1994.

Diver
55 High Street, Teddington, Middlesex TW11 8HA
tel 0181-943 4288 *fax* 0181-943 4312
e-mail 100737.2226@compuserve.com
Editor Nigel Eaton
Monthly £2.75

Articles on sub aqua diving and underwater developments. Length: 1500-4000 words. Illustrations: line, half-tone and colour. Payment: by arrangement. Founded 1953.

Dogs Today
Pet Subjects Ltd, Pankhurst Farm, Bagshot Road, West End, Nr Woking, Surrey GU24 9QR
tel (01276) 858880 *fax* (01276) 858860
e-mail dogstoday@dial.pipex.com
Editor Claire Horton-Bussey
Monthly £2.80

Study of magazine essential before submitting ideas. Interested in human interest dog stories, celebrity interviews, holiday features and anything unusual – all must be entertaining and informative and accompanied by illustrations. Length: 800-1200 words. Illustrations: colour, preferably transparencies, colour cartoons. Payment: negotiable. Founded 1990.

Dorset Life – The Dorset Magazine

95 North Street, Wareham, Dorset BH20 4AE
tel (01929) 551264
Editor John Newth
Monthly £1.70

Articles (500-1200 words), photos (colour or b&w) and line drawings with a specifically Dorset theme. Payment: by arrangement. Founded 1967.

The Downside Review

Downside Abbey, Stratton-on-the-Fosse, Nr Bath, Somerset BA3 4RH
tel (01761) 235136
Editor Dom Dunstan O'Keeffe
Quarterly £6.00 (£22.00 p.a.)

Articles and book reviews on theology, metaphysics, mysticism and modernism, and monastic and church history. Payment: not usual.

Drapers Record

EMAP Business Communications, Angel House, 338-346 Goswell Road, London EC1V 7QP
tel 0171-520 1509 *fax* 0171-837 4699
Editor Jo Jeffery
Weekly £2.00

Editorial aimed at fashion retailers, large and small. No unsolicited material. Payment: by negotiation. Illustrations: colour and b&w: photos, drawings and cartoons. Founded 1887.

Early Music

Oxford University Press, 70 Baker Street, London W1M 1DJ
tel 0171-616 5902 *fax* 0171-616 5901
e-mail jnl.early-music@oup.co.uk
web site http://www.oup.co.uk/earlyj
Editor Tess Knighton
Quarterly £10.00 (£40.00 p.a., institutions £65.00 p.a.)

Lively, informative and scholarly articles on aspects of medieval, renaissance, baroque and classical music. Payment: £20 per 1000 words. Illustrations: line, half-tone, colour. Founded 1973.

East Lothian Life

2 Beveridge Row, Belhaven, Dunbar, East Lothian EH42 1TP
tel/fax (01368) 863593
web site http://www.east-lothian.co.uk/life/index.htm
Editor Pauline Jaffray
Quarterly £2.00

Articles and features with an East Lothian slant. Length: up to 1000 words. Illustrations: b&w photos, line, cartoons. Payment: negotiable. Founded 1989.

Eastern Art Report

Eastern Art Publishing Group, PO Box 13666, 27 Wallorton Gardens, London SW14 8WF
tel 0181-392 1122 *fax* 0181-392 1422
e-mail easternart@compuserve.com
Managing Sajid Rizvi, *Executive Editor* Shirley Rizvi
Bi-monthly £10.95 (individual £25.00 p.a., institutions £40.00 p.a.)

Original, well-researched articles on all aspects of the visual arts – Islamic, Indian, Chinese and Japanese; reviews. Length of articles: min. 1500 words. Illustrations: colour transparencies, b&w photos; no responsibility accepted for unsolicited material. Payment: by arrangement. Founded 1989.

Eastern Eye

Ethnic Media Group, 1st Floor, 148 Cambridge Heath Road, London E1 5QJ
tel 0171-702 8012 *fax* 0171-702 7937
Editor Sanjay Gohil
Weekly 70p

Articles, features and news of interest to British Asians. Magazine covers music, fashion, film gossip. Freelance material considered. Illustrations: colour. Founded 1989.

The Ecologist

Agriculture House, Bath Road, Sturminster Newton, Dorset DT10 1DU
tel/fax (01258) 473476
Editors Edward Goldsmith, Zac Goldsmith
6 p.a. £4.00

Fully-referenced articles on economic, social and environmental affairs from an ecological standpoint. Study magazine first for level and approach. Length: 1000-5000 words. Illustrations: line, half-tone. Payment: by arrangement.

Economica

STICERD, London School of Economics, Houghton Street, London WC2A 2AE
tel 0171-955 7855 *fax* 0171-242 2357
Editors Prof F.A. Cowell, David Webb
Quarterly £21.00 (apply for subscription rates)

Learned journal covering the fields of economics, economic history and statistics. Payment: none. Founded 1921; New Series 1934.

The Economist

25 St James's Street, London SW1A 1HG
tel 0171-830 7000
web site http://www.economist.com
Editor Bill Emmott

Weekly £2.40

Articles staff-written. Founded 1843.

The Edge

111 Guinness Buildings, Fulham Palace Road,
London W6 8BQ
tel 0181-741 7757
e-mail houghtong@globalnet.co.uk
web site http://www.users.globalnet.co.uk/
~houghtong/edge1.htm
Editor Graham Evans
Bi-monthly £2.50

Modern imaginative urban stories for
today and tomorrow; modern/borderline
horror, fantasy, science fiction, crime fiction. Interviews and articles on films,
books, modern popular culture. Return
postage essential with submisisons.
Illustrations: b&w prints, artwork, cartoons – send samples. Payment: £20-
£300 negotiable (articles), £20 per 1000
words (stories), £40 per 1000 words
(reviews); illustrations/cartoons £20-
£50.Founded 1996.

Edinburgh Review

22A Buccleugh Place, Edinburgh EH8 9LN
tel/fax 0131-650 1415
Editor tba
Bi-annual £34.00 p.a.

Fiction, poetry, clearly written articles on
Scottish and international cultural and
philosophical ideas. Payment: by
arrangement. Founded 1969.

Education

17 Park Road, Hampton Hill, Middlesex TW12 1HE
tel/fax 0181-979 9473
Editor George Low
Monthly £32.00 p.a.

Specialist articles on educational administration, all branches of education; technical education; universities; school
building; playing fields; environmental
studies; physical education; school
equipment; school meals and health;
teaching aids. Length: 1000 words.
Illustrations: photos, cartoons. Payment:
by arrangement. Founded 1903;
relaunched 1996.

Electrical Review

Reed Business Information Ltd, Quadrant House,
The Quadrant, Sutton, Surrey SM2 5AS
tel 0181-652 3113 *fax* 0181-652 8951
Editor T. Tunbridge
Fortnightly £2.95

Technical and business articles on electrical and control engineering; outside

contributions considered. Electrical news
welcomed. Illustrations: photos and
drawings, cartoons. Payment: according
to merit. Founded 1872.

Electrical Times

Reed Business Information Ltd, Quadrant House,
The Quadrant, Sutton, Surrey SM2 5AS
tel 0181-652 3115 *fax* 0181-652 8972
Editor Steve Hobson
Monthly £2.75

Business and technical articles of interest
to contractors and installers in the electrical industries, with illustrations as necessary. Length: 750-1000 words. Payment:
£150 per article. Illustrations: line, half-
tone, colour, cartoons. Founded 1891.

Electronics Times

Miller Freeman plc, City Reach, 5 Greenwich
View Place, Millharbour, London E14 9NN
tel 0181-876 6417 *fax* 0181-861 6253
e-mail luke.collins@unmf.com
Editor Luke Collins
Weekly £3.25 (£85 p.a.)

News, reviews and features on the electronics industry. Length: 2000 words
(features), 200 words (news).
Illustrations: colour transparencies,
colour and b&w artwork and cartoons.
Payment: variable. Founded 1978.

Elle (UK)

EMAP Women's Group, Endeavour House,
189 Shaftesbury Avenue, London WC2H 8JG
tel 0171-437 9011 *fax* 0171-208 3599
Editor Marie O'Riordan
Monthly £2.30

Commissioned material only. Payment:
by arrangement. Illustrations: colour.
Founded 1985.

Empire

Mappin House, 4 Winsley Street,
London W1N 7AR
tel 0171-436 1515/1601 *fax* 0171-312 8249
Editor Ian Nathan
Monthly £2.70

Guide to film and video: articles, features, news. Length: various.
Illustrations: colour and b&w photos.
Payment: approx. £125 per 1000 words;
varies for illustrations. Founded 1989.

The Engineer

Miller Freeman plc, City Reach, 5 Greenwich
View Place, Millharbour, London E14 9NN
tel 0171-861 6117 *fax* 0171-861 6229
Editor Paul Carslake
34 p.a. Controlled circulation (£115.00 p.a.)

Articles, features and news on the business and technology of the engineering industry, including profiles, analysis and new products. Length: news up to 200 words, features average 1000 words. Illustrations: colour transparencies or prints, line diagrams, graphs. Payment: £150 per page; £50 per illustration. Founded 1856.

Engineering

Gillard Welch Ltd, Chester Court, High Street, Knowle, Solihull, West Midlands B93 0LL
tel (01564) 771772 *fax* (01564) 774776
Editor Mike Farish
11 p.a. £5.50

'For innovators in technology, manufacturing and management': features and news. Contributions considered on all aspects of engineering, particularly design. Illustrations: colour. Founded 1866.

English Historical Review

Addison Wesley Longman Higher Education, Edinburgh Gate, Harlow, Essex CM20 2JE
tel (01279) 623623
Editors Dr J.R. Maddicott, Dr J. Stevenson
5 p.a. £89.00 p.a.

High-class scholarly articles, documents, and reviews or short notices of books. Contributions are not accepted unless they supply original information and should be sent direct to Dr J.R. Maddicott, Editor, EHR, Exeter College, Oxford OX1 3DP. Books for review should be sent to Dr J. Stevenson, Editor, EHR, Worcester College, Oxford OX1 2HB. Payment: none. Founded 1886.

Enterprise

Martin Leach Publishing, 3rd Floor, 2-6 Northburgh Street, London EC1V 0AY
tel 0171-608 8000 *fax* 0171-608 8001
e-mail enterprise@martin-leach-group.co.uk
Editor Liz Jones
Bi-monthly £2.25

'The magazine for today's growing businesses': news, features and profiles of companies and people. Length: 1500 words (features). Illustrations: colour transparencies and artwork. Payment: £225 per 1000 words; £300 per illustration. Founded 1991.

Envoi

44 Rudyard Road, Biddulph Moor, Stoke-on-Trent, Staffs. ST8 7JN
tel (01782) 517892
Editor Roger Elkin
3 p.a. £12.00 p.a.

New poetry, including sequences, collaborative works and translations, reviews, articles on modern poets and poetic style; poetry competitions; editorial criticism of subscribers' poems (with sae) at no charge. Sample copy: £3.00. Payment: 2 complimentary copies. Founded 1957.

ES Magazine – see Evening Standard in Regional newspapers UK and Ireland, page 11

Esquire

National Magazine House, 33 Broadwick Street, London W1V 1FR
tel 0171-439 5000 *fax* 0171-312 3920
Editor Peter Howarth
Monthly £2.80

Quality men's general interest magazine – articles, features. No unsolicited material or short stories. Length: various. Illustrations: colour and b&w photos, line. Payment: by arrangement. Founded 1991.

Essentials

IPC Magazines Ltd, King's Reach Tower, Stamford Street, London SE1 9LS
tel 0171-261 6970
Editor Karen Livermore
Monthly £1.80

Features, plus fashion, health and beauty, cookery. Illustrations: colour. Payment: by negotiation. Founded 1988.

Essex Countryside

MLP plc, PO Box 78, Saffron Walden, Essex CB11 4YR
tel (01799) 544272 *fax* (01799) 544205
Editor Sue Corner
Monthly £1.70

Features, profiles and occasional short stories, all with Essex emphasis. Length: up to 1200 words. Illustrations: colour and b&w photos. Payment: negotiable. Founded 1953.

Estates Gazette

151 Wardour Street, London W1V 4BN
tel 0171-437 0141 *fax* 0171-437 0294
Editor Helen Pearce
Weekly £2.10

Property, legislation, planning, architecture – articles, features and business news. Length: 1500 words. Illustrations: colour, line, cartoons. Payment: none. Founded 1858.

The European

200 Gray's Inn Road, London WC1X 8NE
tel 0171-418 7777 *fax* 0171-713 1840
web site http://www.the-european.com
Editor-in-Chief Andrew Neil, *Assistant Editor (Features)* Nicola Davidson, *News Editor* David Meilton, *Picture Editor* Jeannette Downing, *Sports Editor* Dominic O'Reilly
Weekly Mon 75p

Business magazine: news, financial reports, business features about Europe as a whole.

European Chemical News

Reed Business Information, Quadrant House, The Quadrant, Sutton, Surrey SM2 5AS
tel 0181-652 3187 *fax* 0181-652 3375
e-mail ecne@rbi.co.uk
Editor John Baker
Weekly £257 p.a. Europe (£295 p.a. overseas)

Articles and features concerning business, markets and investments in the chemical industry. Length: 1000-2000 words; news items up to 400 words. Payment: £120-£150 per 1000 words.

European Drinks Buyer

Crier Publications, Arctic House, Rye Lane, Dunton Green, Sevenoaks, Kent TN14 5HB
tel (01732) 451515 *fax* (01732) 451383
web site http://www.crier.co.uk/crier/general@crier.demon.co.uk
Editor Edward Hart
Bi-monthly Controlled free circulation

Articles of European interest on business, marketing, branding, catering, retail, duty free, EU legislation, packaging, labelling, product surveys, consumption trends. No unsolicited material but enquiries for editorial guidelines welcome (enclose sae/samples of published work). Overseas correspondents wanted. Length: features, profiles, interviews, opinion pieces 1000-2000 words, news 150-500 words. Illustrations: half-tone, colour. Payment: from £80 per 1000 words; none for illustrations. Founded 1991.

European Frozen Food Buyer

Crier Publications, Arctic House, Rye Lane, Dunton Green, Sevenoaks, Kent TN14 5HB
tel (01732) 451515 *fax* (01732) 451383
Editor Alwyn Brice
Bi-monthly Controlled free circulation

Articles of European interest on business, marketing, branding, catering, retail, EU legislation, packaging, labelling, product surveys, food hygiene, consumption trends. No unsolicited material but enquiries for editorial guidelines welcome (enclose sae/samples of published work). Overseas correspondents wanted. Length: features, profiles, interviews 1000-2000 words, news 150-500 words. Illustrations: half-tone, colour. Payment: £100 per 1000 words; none for illustrations. Founded 1989.

Eva

IPC Magazines, King's Reach Tower, Stamford Street, London SE1 9LS
tel 0171-261 5857 *fax* 0171-261 6442
web site http://www.ipc.co.uk
Editor Terry Tavener
Weekly 60p

For women in the 18-24 age group. Readers' real-life stories. Length: from 400 words. Payment: from £150. Human interest features and celebrity gossip. Payment: by arrangement. Founded 1994.

Eventing

IPC Magazines Ltd, Room 2105, King's Reach Tower, Stamford Street, London SE1 9LS
tel 0171-261 5388 *fax* 0171-261 5429
Editor Kate Green
Monthly £2.60

News, articles, features, event reports and opinion pieces – all with bias towards the sport of horse trials. Mostly commissioned, but all ideas welcome. Length: up to 1500 words. Illustrations: colour and b&w, mostly commissioned. Payment: by arrangement; illustrations £30-£45. Founded 1984.

Everyday Practical Electronics

Wimborne Publishing Ltd, Allen House, East Borough, Wimborne, Dorset BH21 1PF
tel (01202) 881749 *fax* (01202) 841692
e-mail editorial@epemag.wimborne.co.uk
web site http://www.epemag.wimborne.co.uk
Editor Mike Kenward
Monthly £2.65

Constructional and theoretical articles aimed at the student and hobbyist. Length: 1000-5500 words. Payment: £55-£90 per 1000 words. Illustrations: line, half-tone, cartoons. Founded 1971.

Executive PA

Hobsons Publishing plc, Bateman Street, Cambridge CB2 1LZ
tel (01223) 354551 *fax* (01223) 322850
e-mail executive.pa@hobsons.co.uk
Editor Penny Cottee
Quarterly Complimentary

Business to business for working senior secretaries. Length: 700-1400 words. Illustrations: colour. Payment: £120 per 1000 words. Founded 1991.

Executive Woman

Saleworld Ltd, 2 Chantry Place, Harrow, Middlesex HA3 6NY
tel 0181-420 1210 *fax* 0181-420 1691/3
Editor Angela Giveon
Bi-monthly £2.50

News and features with a holistic approach to the world of successful working women. Strong business features; articles on management, personnel, networking and mentoring. Length: 500-1000 words. Illustrations: colour and b&w, line drawings. Payment: £150 per 1000 words; £50-£100. Founded 1987.

Express on Sunday Magazine – see Express on Sunday in National newspapers UK and Ireland, page 3

The Face

Exmouth House, Pine Street, London EC1R 0JL
tel 0171-689 9999 *fax* 0171-689 0300
Editor Adam Higginbotham
Monthly £2.40

Articles on music, fashion, films, popular youth culture. Contributors must be familiar with the magazine, its audience and culture. Illustrations: half-tone, colour. Payment: £250 per 1000 words; illustrations approx. £150 per page. Founded 1980.

Family Circle

IPC Magazines Ltd, King's Reach Tower, Stamford Street, London SE1 9LS
tel 0171-261 5000 *fax* 0171-261 5929
Editor Sue James
13 p.a. £1.20

Practical, medical human interest material – mostly commissioned. Payment: NUJ rates.

Family Law

21 St Thomas Street, Bristol BS1 6JS
tel 0117-923 0600 *fax* 0117-925 0486
e-mail familylaw@jordanpublishing.co.uk
web site http://www.familylaw.co.uk
Editors Elizabeth Walsh, Miles McColl
Monthly £100.00 p.a.

Articles dealing with all aspects of the law as it affects the family, written from a legal or socio-legal point of view. Length: from 1000 words. Payment: by arrangement. No illustrations. Founded 1971.

Family Tree Magazine

61 Great Whyte, Ramsey, Huntingdon, Cambs. PE17 1HL
tel (01487) 814050
Editor Eric Probert
Monthly £2.00 (£22.00 p.a.)

Articles on any genealogically related topics. Illustrations: half-tone, line, cartoons. Payment: £25 per 1000 words; by arrangement for illustrations. Founded 1984.

Farmers Weekly

(incorporating Power Farming)
Reed Business Information, Quadrant House, The Quadrant, Sutton, Surrey SM2 5AS
tel 0181-652 4911 *fax* 0181-652 4005
e-mail farmers.weekly@rbi.co.uk
web site http://www.fwi.co.uk
Editor Stephen Howe
Weekly £1.35

Articles on agriculture from freelance contributors will be accepted subject to negotiation. Founded 1934.

Farming News

Miller Freeman plc, Miller Freeman House, Sovereign Way, Tonbridge, Kent TN9 1RW
tel (01732) 377209 *fax* (01732) 377675
e-mail farmingnews@dotfarming.co.uk
web site http://www.dotfarming.com
Editor Donald Taylor
Weekly £1.40 (£66.00 p.a.)

News, business, technical features and articles. Payment: by arrangement. Founded 1983.

Fashion Forecast International

23 Bloomsbury Square, London WC1A 2PJ
tel 0171-637 2211 *fax* 0171-637 2248
e-mail itbd@itbdhquk.demon.co.uk
Managing Editor Stephen Higginson
2 p.a. (Feb, Aug) £30.00 p.a. UK/Europe, £40.00 p.a. outside Europe

Hosiery Forecast and Lingerie Forecast are included in each issue. Factual articles on fashions and accessories with forecast trends. Length: 800-1000 words. Illustrations: line, half-tone. Payment: by arrangement. Founded 1946.

Fasttrack

Angela Mortimer plc, 1-3 Frederick's Place, London EC2R 8AB
tel 0171-494 1448 *fax* 0171-606 2010
e-mail editors@fasttrack.u-net.com
web site http://www.business.u-net.com/~fast-track
Editor Laura Pank
Quarterly £2.50

'The magazine for professional and executive personnel.' Work-related features and articles for people in business, including technology and training. Length: 750-1500 (features/articles); 300-750 words (news). Illustrations: colour and b&w. Payment: £350 for 1500 words (features), £200 for 750 words (news). Founded 1995.

FHM (For Him Magazine)
EMAP Metro, Mappin House, 4 Winsley Street, London W1N 7AR
tel 0171-436 1515 *fax* 0171-312 8191
e-mail fhm@ecm.emap.com
web site http://www.erack.com/fhm
Editor Ed Needham
Monthly £2.70

Features, fashion, grooming, travel (adventure) and men's interests. Length: 1200-2000 words. Illustrations: colour and b&w photos, line and colour artwork. Payment: by negotiation. Founded 1987.

The Field
IPC Magazines Ltd, King's Reach Tower, Stamford Street, London SE1 9LS
tel 0171-261 5198 *fax* 0171-261 5358
Monthly £2.80

Specific, topical and informed features on the British countryside and country pursuits, including natural history, field sports, gardening and farming. Overseas subjects considered but opportunities for such articles are limited. No fiction or children's material. Articles, length 800-2000 words, by outside contributors considered; also topical 'shorts' of 200-300 words on all countryside matters. Illustrations: colour photos of a high standard. Payment: on merit. Founded 1853.

Film Review
Visual Imagination Ltd, 9 Blades Court, Deodar Road, London SW15 2NU
tel 0181-875 1520 *fax* 0181-875 1588
e-mail star@cix.compulink.co.uk
Editor Neil Corry
Monthly £2.75

Features and interviews on mainstream cinema; film and video reviews. Length: 1000-3000 words (features), 350 words (reviews). Illustrations: colour and b&w. Payment: £80 per 1000 words; £20 for first image, £10 per additional image. Founded 1951.

Financial Accountant
PO Box 752, Dartford, Kent DA2 7UD
tel (01322) 664096 *fax* (01322) 614941
Editor Leon Hopkins
Bi-monthly £12.00 p.a.

Journal of The Institute of Financial Accountants. Articles on accounting, management, company law, data processing, information technology, pensions, factoring, investment, insurance, fraud prevention and general business administration. Length: 1000-2000 words. Illustrations: offset litho (mono or colour). Payment: by arrangement. Founded 1920.

Financial Adviser
FT Finance Ltd, Maple House, 149 Tottenham Court Road, London W1P 9LL
tel 0171-896 2525 *fax* 0171-896 2699/2588
Editor Kevin O'Donnell
Weekly (£90.00 p.a.) Free to financial intermediaries working in financial services

Topical personal finance news and features. Length: variable. Payment: by arrangement. Founded 1987.

Financial Director
VNU Business Publications, VNU House, 32-34 Broadwick Street, London W1A 2HG
tel 0171-316 9000 *fax* 0171-316 9250
web site http://www.financialdirector.co.uk
Monthly £2.50 (£35.00 p.a.) Free to finance directors

Features on financial and strategic management issues. Length: 750-2000 words. Illustrations: colour and b&w photos, line drawings. Payment: £200 per 1000 words; photos, variable; line, £250-£300. Founded 1984.

Financial Mail on Sunday – see Mail on Sunday in National newspapers UK and Ireland, page 3

Fire
Queensway House, 2 Queensway, Redhill, Surrey RH1 1QS
tel (01737) 768611 *fax* (01737) 855470
Managing Editor Simon Hoffman
Monthly £6.95 (£56.07 p.a.)

Articles on firefighting and fire prevention from acknowledged experts only. Length: 850 words. Illustrations: dramatic firefighting or fire brigade rescue colour photos sometimes bought. Also *Fire Europe* (quarterly). Payment: by arrangement. Founded 1908.

Fishing News

Emap Business International, Meed House,
21 John Street, London WC1N 2BP
tel 0171-470 6209 *fax* 0171-831 9362
e-mail timo@meed.emap.co.uk
Editor Tim Oliver
Weekly 80p

News and features on all aspects of the
commercial fishing industry. Length: up
to 1000 words (features), up to 500
words (news). Illustrations: colour and
b&w photos. Payment: £100 per 1000
words; £25 per photo. Founded 1913

Flicks

Flicks Publications Ltd, First floor,
25 The Coda Centre, 189 Munster Road,
London SW6 6AW
tel 0171-381 8811 *fax* 0171-381 1811
e-mail flicks@flicks.co.uk
Editor Nick Thomas
Monthly Free in cinemas (£25.00 p.a.)

Articles, features and reviews on new
mainstream film releases; reviews of
videos and film tie-ins. Length: 100-1200
words. Illustrations: colour. Payment: by
negotiation. Founded 1985.

Flight International

Reed Business Information Ltd,
Quadrant House, The Quadrant, Sutton,
Surrey SM2 5AS
tel 0181-652 3882 *fax* 0181-652 3840
e-mail flight.international@rbi.co.uk
Editor C. Reed
Weekly £2.00

Deals with all branches of aerospace:
operational and technical articles, illustrated by photos, engineering cutaway
drawings; also news, paragraphs, reports
of lectures, etc. News press days: Thu,
Fri. Illustrations: tone, line, colour.
Payment: by agreement. Founded 1909.

Fly-Fishing & Fly-Tying

Rolling River Publications,
Aberfeldy Road, Kenmore,
Perthshire PH15 2HF
tel/fax (01887) 830526
e-mail markb.ffft@btinternet.com
web site http://www.pixnet.co.uk/flyfishing-and-
flytying
Editor Mark Bowler
8 p.a. £2.30

Fly-fishing and fly-tying articles, fishery
features, limited short stories, some fishing travel. Length: 800-1500 words.
Illustrations: colour photos. Payment: by
arrangement. Founded 1990.

FlyPast

Key Publishing Ltd, PO Box 100, Stamford,
Lincs. PE9 1XQ
tel (01780) 55131 *fax* (01780) 57261
Editor Ken Delve
Monthly £2.80

Articles and features on historic aviation.
Particularly interested in personal recol-
lections of flying or visits to interesting
aeroplane collections anywhere in the
world. Length: up to 3000 words.
Illustrations: colour and b&w photos.
Payment: £50 per 1000 words; £25
colour; £10 b&w. Founded 1981.

Football Picture Story Library

D.C. Thomson & Co. Ltd, Albert Square,
Dundee DD1 9QJ
tel (01382) 223131 *fax* (01382) 322214
185 Fleet Street, London EC4A 2HS
tel 0171-242 5086 *fax* 0171-404 5694
2 p.m. 60p

Football stories for boys told in pictures.

For Women

Fantasy Publications, 4 Selsdon Way,
London E14 9GL
tel 0171-308 5327 *fax* 0171-308 5075
Editor Zak Jane Keir, *Fiction Editor* Elizabeth
Coldwell
Monthly £2.95

Women's magazine with erotic emphasis.
Features on sex and health; celebrity
interviews; erotic fiction and photos.
Submit written synopsis for features;
erotic fiction welcomed on spec. Fiction
guidelines on receipt of sae. Length:
1500-2000 words. Illustrations: colour
and b&w photos. Payment: £150 per
story (fiction), features by arrangement;
£150 per illustration. Founded 1991.

Fore!

EMAP Pursuit Publishing Ltd, Bretton Court,
Bretton, Peterborough PE3 8DZ
tel (01733) 264666 *fax* (01733) 465221
Editor Paul Hamblin
Monthly £2.25

Interested in off-beat features on golf –
thought provoking, fun and occasionally
irreverent. Length: up to 1000 words.
Illustrations: colour, line, cartoons.
Payment: £100 per 1000 words; illustrations per quality/size used. Founded
1993.

Fortean Times

Box 2409, London NW5 4NP
tel/fax 0171-485 5002

e-mail rickard@forteantimes.com
web site http://www.forteantimes.com/
Editors Bob Rickard, Paul Sieveking
Monthly £2.50

The journal of strange phenomena, experiences, related subjects and philosophies. Articles, features, news, reviews. Length: 500-3000 words; longer by arrangement. Illustrations: colour photos, line and tone art, cartoons. Payment: by negotiation. Founded 1973.

Fortnight – An Independent Review of Politics and the Arts

7 Lower Crescent, Belfast BT7 1NR
tel (01232) 232353/311337/324141
fax (01232) 232650
e-mail mairtin@fortnite.dnet.co.uk
Editors John O'Farrell, Mairtin Crawford
Monthly £1.80

Current affairs analysis, reportage, opinion pieces, cultural criticism, book reviews, poems. Illustrations: line, half-tone, cartoons. Payment: by arrangement. Founded 1970.

FourFourTwo

Haymarket Trade and Leisure Publications Ltd, 60 Waldegrave Road, Teddington TW11 8LG
tel 0181-943 5603 *fax* 0181-943 5668
Editor Karen Buchanan
Monthly £2.40

Football magazine with 'adult' approach: interviews, in-depth features, issues pieces, odd and witty material. Length: 2000-3000 (features), 100-500 words (news/latest score). Illustrations: colour transparencies and artwork, b&w prints. Payment: £150 per 1000 words. Founded 1994.

FRANCE Magazine

The Square, Stow-on-the-Wold, Glos. GL54 1BN
tel (01451) 831398 *fax* (01451) 830869
e-mail francemag@btinernet.com
Editor Philip Faiers
Quarterly £4.25

An armchair journey to the real France – features and articles ranging from cuisine to customs to architecture to exploring the hidden France. Informed speculative submissions welcome. Length: 800-2500 words. Illustrations: colour transparencies (mounted and captioned). Payment: £100 per 1000 words; £50 per page/pro rata for illustrations. Founded 1989.

Freelance Market News

Sevendale House, 7 Dale Street,
Manchester M1 1JB

tel 0161-237 1827 *fax* 0161-228 3533
Editor Angela Cox
11 p.a. £29.00 p.a.; £17.00 6 issues

Information on UK and overseas publications with editorial content, submission requirements and contact details. News of editorial requirements for writers paid for. Features on the craft of writing, competitions, letters page. Founded 1968.

Fresh Produce Journal

Lockwood Press Ltd, 430-438 Market Towers, 1 Nine Elms Lane, London SW8 5NN
tel 0171-622 6677 *fax* 0171-720 2047
e-mail fpj.edit@fpj.fruitnet.com
Editor Kathy Miller
Weekly £1.60

Articles dealing with fruit, vegetable and flower trades on the marketing aspects of production but particularly importing, distribution and post-harvest handling; articles should average 500-700 words. Payment: by arrangement. Illustrations: half-tone. Founded 1895.

The Friend

Drayton House, 30 Gordon Street,
London WC1H 0BQ
tel 0171-387 7549
Editor Harry Albright
Weekly 75p

Material of interest to the Religious Society of Friends and like-minded people; political, social, economic or devotional, considered from outside contributors. Length: up to 1000 words. Illustrations: b&w or colour prints, b&w line drawings. Payment: none. Founded 1843.

The Furrow

St Patrick's College, Maynooth, Co. Kildare, Republic of Ireland
tel (01) 6286215 *fax* (01) 7083908
Editor Rev. Ronan Drury
Monthly £1.60

Religious, pastoral, theological, social articles. Length: 3000 words. Payment: average £15 per page (450 words). Illustrations: line, half-tone. Founded 1950.

FW

(formerly Fashion Weekly)
EMAP Fashion, Angel House,
338-346 Goswell Road, London EC1V 7QP
tel 0171-520 1648 *fax* 0171-520 1646
Editor William Drew
8 p.a. £66.00 p.a.

Fashion business magazine primarily for retailers. Payment: by arrangement. Illustrations: line, half-tone, colour. Founded 1959.

The Garden
Apex House, Oundle Road,
Peterborough PE2 9NP
tel (01733) 898100 *fax* (01733) 341895
Editor Ian Hodgson
Monthly £2.75
Journal of The Royal Horticultural Society. Features of horticultural or botanical interest on a wide range of subjects. Commissioned material only. Length: 1200-2500 words. Illustrations: 35mm or medium format colour transparencies, occasional b&w prints, botanical line drawings. Payment: £150 per 1000 words; varies for illustrations. Founded 1866.

Garden Answers
(incorporating Practical Gardening)
EMAP Apex Publications Ltd, Apex House,
Oundle Road, Peterborough PE2 9NP
tel (01733) 898100 *fax* (01733) 898433
Editor Jim Ward
Monthly £2.10
Commissioned features and articles on all aspects of gardening. Study of magazine essential. Approach by letter with examples of published work. Length: 750 words. Illustrations: colour transparencies and artwork. Payment: by negotiation. Founded 1982.

Garden News
EMAP Apex Publications Ltd, Apex House,
Oundle Road, Peterborough PE2 9NP
tel (01733) 898100 *fax* (01733) 898433
e-mail geoff.hodge@ecm.emap.com
Editor Geoff Hodge
Weekly 75p
Up-to-date information on everything to do with plants, growing and gardening. Illustrations: line, colour, cartoons. Payment: by negotiation. Founded 1958.

Gardens Illustrated
John Brown Publishing, 136-142 Bramley Road,
London W10 6SR
tel 0171-565 3000 *fax* 0171-565 3056
Editor Rosie Atkins
10 p.a. £3.50
Upmarket, inspirational glossy for those interested in garden history, plants and gardening merchandise. Material mostly

commissioned; send synopsis, samples of past work and sae to the editor. Length: 1000 words. Illustrations: colour. Payment: by negotiation. Founded 1993.

Gay Times
Ground Floor, Worldwide House,
116-134 Bayham Street, London NW1 0BA
tel 0171-482 2576 *fax* 0171-284 0329
Deputy Editor Colin Richardson, *Arts Editor* James Cary-Parkes
Monthly £2.50
Feature articles, full news and review coverage of all aspects of gay and lesbian life. Length: up to 2000 words. Illustrations: colour, line and half-tone, cartoons. Payment: by arrangement. Founded 1982.

Geographical Journal
Royal Geographical Society (with the Institute of British Geographers), Kensington Gore,
London SW7 2AR
tel 0171-591 3025 *fax* 0171-591 3021
e-mail g.lowman@rgs.org
Editor Prof V. Gardiner
3 p.a. £25.00 (post free), (£60.00 p.a.)
Papers on all aspects of geography, including some read before the Royal Geographical Society. Length: up to 4500 words. Payment: for reviews. Illustrations: photos, maps, diagrams. Founded 1893.

Geographical Magazine
(under licence from the Royal Geographical Society)
Campion Interactive Publishing Ltd,
47c Kensington Court, London W8 5DA
tel 0171-938 4011 *fax* 0171-938 4022
e-mail geogmag@gn.apc.org
Editor-in-Chief Alan Armsden
Monthly £2.75
Topical geography in a broad sense and travel . Illustrations: colour slides, b&w prints or vintage material; maps and graphs always needed. Payment: by negotiation. Founded 1935.

Geological Magazine
Cambridge University Press, The Edinburgh Building, Shaftesbury Road, Cambridge CB2 2RU
tel (01223) 312393
Editors Prof I.N. McCave, Dr N.H. Woodcock, Dr M.J. Bickle, Dr T.J. Palmer
Bi-monthly (£188.00 p.a. institutions, £40.00 p.a. students, US$324 USA/Canada/Mexico)
Original articles on all earth science topics containing the results of independent research by experts. Also reviews and

notices of current geological literature, correspondence on geological subjects – illustrated. Length: variable. Payment: none. Founded 1864.

Gibbons Stamp Monthly

Stanley Gibbons Ltd, 5 Parkside, Ringwood, Hants BH24 3SH
tel (01425) 472363 *fax* (01425) 470247
Editor Hugh Jefferies
Monthly £1.95 (£23.40 p.a.)

Articles on philatelic topics. Contact the editor first. Length: 500-2500 words. Payment: by arrangement, £30 or more per 1000 words. Illustrations: photos, line, stamps or covers.

Gifts International

Nexus Media, Nexus House, Swanley, Kent BR8 8HU
tel (01322) 660070 *fax* (01322) 667633
Editor Elinore Mackay
Monthly £39.00 p.a. (£46-52 p.a. overseas)

News of gift industry – products, trends, shops; articles on retailing, exporting, importing, manufacturing, crafts (UK and abroad). Illustrations: products, news, personal photos.

Girl About Town Magazine

7-9 Rathbone Street, London W1P 1AF
tel 0171-636 6651 *fax* 0171-255 2352
Editor Bill Williamson
Weekly Free

Articles of general interest to women. Length: about 1100-1500 words. Payment: negotiable. Founded 1973.

Girl Talk

BBC Worldwide Ltd, Room A1136, Woodlands, 80 Wood Lane, London W12 0TT
tel 0181-576 3543 *fax* 0181-576 3267
e-mail gill.smith@bbc.co.uk
Editor Gill Smith
Fortnightly 90p

Highly illustrated magazine for 6-12 year-old girls. No unsolicited articles or features; stories only considered (500 words). Illustrations: colour artwork. Payment: on application. Founded 1995.

Glaucus

Glaucus House, 14 Corbyn Crescent, Shoreham-by-Sea, West Sussex BN43 6PQ
tel (01273) 465433 *fax* (01273) 465433
e-mail 106127.206@compuserve.com
web sites http://ourworld.compuserve.com/homepages/bmlss/homepage.htm (England)
http://www.ed.ac.uk/~evah01/bmlss.htm (Scotland)

Editor Andy Horton
Quarterly £20.00 p.a.

Official journal of the British Marine Life Study Society, aimed at the popular market. Observations and scientific research on the natural history, and related subjects, of the marine environment surrounding the British Isles. Send sae for Guide to Submissions. Length: up to 2500 words. Illustrations: b&w line, occasional b&w photos. Payment: expenses only. Founded 1990.

Goldlife 50-Forward

2nd Floor, 1-5 Clerkenwell Road, London EC1M 5PA
tel 0171-251 5489 *fax* 0171-251 5490
Editor Miss N. Parmer
Bi-monthly £19.95 p.a.

Celebrity profiles and articles, health, travel and gardening features and news of interest to the over 50s age group. Length: approx. 700 words. Illustrated. Payment: £150 per 1000 words; £20 per illustration. Founded 1989.

Golf Monthly

IPC Magazines Ltd, King's Reach Tower, Stamford Street, London SE1 9LS
tel 0171-261 7237 *fax* 0171-261 7240
e-mail golfmonthly@ipc.co.uk
Editor Colin Callander
Monthly £2.80

Original articles on golf considered (not reports), golf clinics, handy hints. Illustrations: half-tone, colour, cartoons. Payment: by arrangement. Founded 1911.

Golf Weekly

EMAP Pursuit Publishing Ltd, Bretton Court, Bretton, Peterborough PE3 8DZ
tel (01733) 465223 *fax* (01733) 465221
Editor Bob Warters
Weekly £1.70

News, tournament reports and articles on golf of interest to golfers. Payment: 15p per word published. Illustrations: photos of golf news and new courses.

Golf World

Emap Pursuit Publishing Ltd, Angel House, 338-346 Goswell Road, London EC1V 7QP
tel (01733) 264666 *fax* 0171-477 7275
Editor David Clarke
Monthly £2.90

Expert golf instructional articles, 500-3000 words; general interest articles, personality features 500-3000 words. Little fiction. Payment: by negotiation. Illustrations: line, half-tone, colour, cartoons. Founded 1962.

Good Health

Pantile Publications Ltd, Shadwell House, 65 Lower Green Road, Rusthall, Tunbridge Wells, Kent TN4 8TW
tel (01892) 535300 *fax* (01892) 535311
e-mail editorial@good-health.co.uk
web site http://www.healthandherbal.com/good-health
Editor Sandra White
Monthly £2.00

Covers all aspects of family health and wellbeing with emphasis given to real-life experiences. No unsolicited articles; submit synopsis first. Length: up to 1000 words. Illustrations: colour transparencies. Payment: £120 per 1000 words. Founded 1997.

Good Housekeeping

National Magazine House, 72 Broadwick Street, London W1V 2BP
tel 0171-439 5000 *fax* 0171-439 5591
Editor-in-Chief Pat Roberts Cairns
Monthly £2.00

Articles of 1000-2500 words on topics of interest to intelligent women. No unsolicited features or stories accepted; approach by letter only. Domestic subjects covered by staff writers. Personal experiences and humorous articles occasionally used. Payment: magazine standards. Illustrations: mainly commissioned. Founded 1922.

GQ

Vogue House, Hanover Square, London W1R 0AD
tel 0171-499 9080 *fax* 0171-495 1679
web site http://www.gq/magazine.co.uk
Editor James Brown
Monthly £2.70

Style, fashion and general interest magazine for men. Illustrations: b&w and colour photos, line drawings, cartoons. Payment: by arrangement. Founded 1988.

Gramophone

135 Greenford Road, Harrow, Middlesex HA1 3YD
tel 0181-422 4562 *fax* 0181-869 8403
e-mail editor@gramophone.co.uk
web site http://www.gramophone.co.uk
Editor James Jolly
Monthly £3.95

Features on classical recording artists and hi-fi, with main focus on record reviews. Outside contributions are rarely used.

Granta

2-3 Hanover Yard, Noel Road, London N1 8BE
tel 0171-704 9776 *fax* 0171-704 0474
Editor Ian Jack
Quarterly £7.99 (£24.95 p.a.)

Original literary fiction, non-fiction and journalism. Length: determined by content. Illustrations: photos. Payment: by arrangement. Founded 1889; new series 1979.

Greetings Magazine

Lema Publishing, Unit No. 1, Queen Mary's Avenue, Watford, Herts. WD1 7JR
tel (01923) 250909 *fax* (01923) 250995
Publisher Malcolm Naish, *Editor* Nicholas Eyriey
10 p.a. £30.00 p.a. (other rates on application)

Official journal of the Greeting Card Association. Articles, features and news related to the greetings card and giftwrap industry. Mainly written in-house; some material taken from outside. Length: varies. Illustrations: line, colour and b&w photos. Payment: by arrangement. Founded 1992.

The Grocer

William Reed Publishing Ltd, Broadfield Park, Crawley, West Sussex RH11 9RT
tel (01293) 613400 *fax* (01293) 610333
e-mail editorial@the-grocer.co.uk
Editor C. Beddall
Weekly 95p

Trade journal: articles or news or illustrations of general interest to the grocery and provision trades. Payment: by arrangement. Founded 1861.

The Grower

Nexus Media Ltd, Nexus House, Azalea Drive, Swanley, Kent BR8 8HU
tel (01322) 660070 *fax* (01322) 667633
e-mail grower@nexusmedia.co.uk
Editor Peter Rogers
Weekly £1.30

News and practical articles on commercial horticulture, covering all sectors including fruit, vegetable, salad crop and ornamentals. Founded 1923.

Guiding

17-19 Buckingham Palace Road, London SW1W 0PT
tel 0171-834 6242 *fax* 0171-828 8317

Editor Nora Warner
Monthly £1.25
Official magazine of The Guide Association. Articles of interest to women of all ages, with special emphasis on youth work and the Guide Movement. Articles on simple crafts, games and the outdoors also welcome. Length: 500-1200 words. Illustrations: line, half-tone, colour, cartoons. Payment: £70 per 1000 words; £100 full colour page, £60 b&w (negotiable).

Hairflair
James Kimber Publishing Ltd, 49 King Street, London W6 9HW
tel 0181-563 2266 *fax* 0181-563 2299
Editor Rebecca Barnes
Bi-monthly £2.00
Hair, beauty, fashion – and related features – for the 16-35 age group. Preliminary letter essential. Length: 800-1000 words. Illustrations: colour and b&w photos, occasional line drawings. Payment: £100-£120 per 1000 words. Founded 1985.

Hampshire – The County Magazine
74 Bedford Place, Southampton SO15 2DF
tel (01703) 223591/333457
Monthly £1.60
Factual articles concerning all aspects of Hampshire and Hampshire life, past and present. Length: 400-1000 words. Payment: by arrangement. Illustrations: photos and line drawings.

Harpers & Queen
National Magazine House, 72 Broadwick Street, London W1V 2BP
tel 0171-439 5000 *fax* 0171-439 5506
Editor Fiona Macpherson
Monthly £2.90
Features, fashion, beauty, art, theatre, films, travel, interior decoration – all commissioned. Illustrations: line, wash, full colour and 2- and 3-colour, and photos. Founded 1929.

Health Club Management
Leisure Media Company Ltd, Portmill House, Portmill Lane, Hitchin, Herts. SG5 1DJ
tel (01462) 431385 *fax* (01462) 433909
e-mail catherine@leisuremedia.com
web site http://www.leisuremedia.co.uk
Editor Catherine Larner
Monthly £48 p.a. with *Leisure Management* magazine

Official publication of the Fitness Industry Association. Articles on the operation of health clubs, day spas, fitness and sports centres, items on consumer issues and lifestyle trends as they affect club management are all welcomed. Length: up to 1500 words. Illustrations: colour and b&w photos. Payment: by arrangement. Founded 1995.

Health & Efficiency International
Bow House Business Centre, 153-159 Bow Road, London E3 2ST
tel 0181-983 3011 *fax* 0181-983 6322
Editor Helen Ludbrook

H&E Monthly
Monthly £2.60
Articles on naturist travel, clubs and beaches. Also well-researched articles on health, piercing and tattooing.

H&E Lifestyle
Bi-monthly £2.95
Articles on the above plus humour and naked lifestyle and relationships. Length: 750-1500 words. Illustrations: line, half-tone, colour transparencies, colour prints, cartoons. Payment: by negotiation. Founded 1900.

Health & Fitness
Nexus Media, Nexus House, Azalea Drive, Swanley, Kent BR8 8HU
tel (01322) 660070 *fax* (01322) 615636
Editor Sharon Walker
Monthly £2.20
Articles on all aspects of health and fitness. Illustrations: line, half-tone, colour. Payment: by arrangement. Founded 1984.

Healthy Eating
Spendlove Centre, Charlbury, Oxon OX7 3PQ
tel (01608) 811266 *fax* (01608) 811380
Editor Sandy Bisp
Bi-monthly £2.50
Articles on health and nutrition, how food affects the body, celebrity food and health stories. Length: 1000-1200 words. Illustrations: colour food photography and illustrations. Payment: £150-£250 per article; £30-£50 for illustrations; £25-£80 for transparencies. Founded 1990.

Helicon Poetry Magazine
Cherrybite Publications, Linden Cottage, 45 Burton Road, Little Neston, South Wirral L64 4AE
tel 0151-353 0967
Editor Shelagh Nugent

Quarterly £2.50 (£9.00 p.a.)
Poems in any style or length. Illustrations: b&w to illustrate poems. Payment: £2 per poem plus free copy. Founded 1995.

Hello!
Wellington House, 69-71 Upper Ground, London SE1 9PQ
tel 0171-667 8721 *fax* 0171-667 8716
Editor Maggie Koumi
Weekly £1.35
News-based features – showbusiness, celebrity, royalty; exclusive interviews. Payment: by arrangement. Illustrated. Founded 1988.

Here's Health
EMAP Élan, Endeavour House,
189 Shaftesbury Avenue, London WC2H 8JG
tel 0171-957 8383 *fax* 0171-957 8857
Editor Elaine Griffiths
Monthly £2.30
Articles on nutrition, alternative medicine, environment and health, natural treatment success stories. Preliminary letter and clippings essential. Length: 750-1800 words. Payment: on publication. Illustrated, including cartoons.

Heritage
Bulldog Magazines Ltd, 4 The Courtyard, Denmark Street, Wokingham, Berks. RG40 2AZ
tel (01189) 771677 *fax* (01189) 772903
Editor Siân Ellis
Bi-monthly £2.95
Features on British topics only: towns and villages to visit, tours/off the beaten track, customs, craftsmen, people, all historic/ heritage subjects. Length: 1200 words. Illustrations: high quality colour transparencies. Payment: £100 per 1000 words; illustrations by negotiation. Founded 1984.

Hertfordshire Countryside
Beaumonde Publications Ltd, 4 Mill Bridge, Hertford, Herts. SG14 1PY
tel (01992) 553571 *fax* (01992) 587713
Editor Sandra Small
Monthly £1.25
Articles of county interest. No poetry. Length: 1000 words. Payment: £25 per 1000 words. Illustrations: line, half-tone. Founded 1946.

Hi-Fi News & Record Review
Link House, Dingwall Avenue, Croydon CR9 2TA
tel 0181-686 2599 *fax* 0181-781 6046
e-mail 101574.223@compuserve.com
Editor Steve Harris

Monthly £2.75
Articles on all aspects of high quality sound recording and reproduction; also extensive record review section and supporting musical feature articles. Audio matter is essentially technical, but should be presented in a manner suitable for music lovers interested in the nature of sound. Length: 2000-3000 words. Illustrations: line, half-tone. Payment: by arrangement. Founded 1956.

History
Editorial office History Department, University of Edinburgh, Edinburgh EH8 9JY
tel 0131-650 3785
Published by Blackwell (Oxford) for the Historical Association, 59a Kennington Park Road, London SE11 4JH
tel 0171-735 3901
Editor H.T. Dickinson BA, DipEd, MA, PhD, DLitt
Quarterly £38.00 p.a. (£16.00 p.a. members)
Historical articles and reviews by experts. Length: usually up to 8000 words. Illustrations: only exceptionally. Payment: none. Founded 1916.

History Today
20 Old Compton Street, London W1V 5PE
tel 0171-534 8000
e-mail admin@historytoday.com
web site http://admin@historytoday.com
Editor Peter Furtado
Monthly £3.25
History in the widest sense – political, economic, social, biography, relating past to present; world history as well as British. Length: articles 3500 words; shorter news/views pieces 600-1200 words. Illustrations: from prints and original photos. Please do not send original material until publication is agreed. Payment: by arrangement. Founded 1951.

Home and Country
104 New King's Road, London SW6 4LY
tel 0171-731 5777 *fax* 0171-736 4061
Editor Amber Tokeley
Monthly £1.45
Official Journal of the National Federation of Women's Institutes for England and Wales. Publishes material related to the Federation's and members' activities; also considers articles of general interest to women, particularly country women, e.g. craft, environment, humour, health, rural life stories, of 800-1200 words. Illustrations: colour and

b&w photos and drawings, cartoons. Payment: by arrangement. Founded 1919.

Home and Family

The Mothers' Union, Mary Sumner House, 24 Tufton Street, London SW1P 3RB
tel 0171-222 5533 *fax* 0171-222 1591
Editor Jill Worth
Quarterly £1.25

Short articles related to Christian family life. Payment: approx. £70 per 1000 words. Illustrations: colour photos. Founded 1954.

Home Words

Chansitor Publications Ltd, St Mary's Works, St Mary's Plain, Norwich, Norfolk NR3 3BH
tel (01603) 615995 *fax* (01603) 624483
Publisher G.A. Knights
Monthly

Illustrated C of E magazine insert. Articles of popular Christian interest with an Anglican slant (400-800 words) with relevant photos; also cartoons. Payment: by arrangement. Founded 1870.

HomeFlair Magazine

Hamerville Magazines Ltd, Regal House, Regal Way, Watford, Herts. WD2 4YJ
tel (01923) 237799 *fax* (01923) 246901
Editor Nicola Shannon
Monthly £1.70

Homes' conversions, inspirational looks, what's new in products and design. Approach in writing, with samples of previously published work. Length: up to 1500 words. Payment: £120 per 1000 words. Illustrated. Founded 1990.

Homes and Gardens

IPC Magazines Ltd, King's Reach Tower, Stamford Street, London SE1 9LS
tel 0171-261 5000 *fax* 0171-261 6247
Editor Matthew Line
Monthly £2.40

Articles on home interest or design. Length: articles, 900-1000 words. Illustrations: all types. Payment: generous, but exceptional work required; varies. Founded 1919.

Homes & Ideas

IPC Magazines Ltd, King's Reach Tower, Stamford Street, London SE1 9LS
tel 0171-261 7325 *fax* 0171-261 7495
Editor Debbie Djordjevic´
Monthly £1.60

Features on any aspect of style for the home. Send cuttings to the editor. Length: by arrangement. Illustrations: colour photos and drawings. Payment: NUJ rates plus; illustrations by arrangement. Founded 1993.

Homestyle

RAP Publishing, Friars House, 157-168 Blackfriars Road, London SE1 8EZ
tel 0171-928 5869 *fax* 0171-928 6199
Editor Linda Clark
Monthly £1.70

Ideas and practical features on home and garden improvements. Merchandise reviews. Length: 2 or 4-page spreads. Illustrations: colour transparencies. Payment: by negotiation. Founded 1992.

Horse & Hound

IPC Magazines Ltd, King's Reach Tower, Stamford Street, London SE1 9LS
tel 0171-261 6315 *fax* 0171-261 5429
e-mail jenny_sims@ipc.co.uk
web site http://www.ipc.co.uk
Editor Arnold Garvey
Weekly £1.55

Special articles, news items, photos, on all matters appertaining to equestrian sports. Payment: by negotiation.

Horse & Pony

EMAP Pursuit Publishing Ltd, Bretton Court, Bretton, Peterborough PE3 8DZ
tel (01733) 264666 *fax* (01733) 465939
Editor Andrea Oakes
Fortnightly £1.20

All material relevant to young people with equestrian interests. Payment: on value to publication rather than length. Illustrations: colour, with a strong story line, cartoons. Founded 1970.

Horse and Rider

Haslemere House, Lower Street, Haslemere, Surrey GU27 2PE
tel (01428) 651551 *fax* (01428) 653888
e-mail djm@djmurphy.co.uk
web site http://www.equestrian.co.uk
Editor Alison Bridge, *Assistant Editor* Sarah Muir
Monthly £2.30

Sophisticated magazine covering all forms of equestrian activity at home and abroad. Good writing and technical accuracy essential. Length: 1500-2000 words. Illustrations: photos and drawings, the latter usually commissioned. Payment: by arrangement. Founded 1959.

Horticulture Week

Haymarket Magazines Ltd, 174 Hammersmith
Road, London W6 7JP
tel 0171-413 4595
Editor Vicky Browning
Weekly £1.50 (£63.50 p.a.)

News, technical and business journal for
the nursery and garden centre trade,
landscape industry and public parks and
sports ground staff. Outside contributions considered. No fiction. Length: 500-
1500 words. Illustrations: line, half-tone,
colour. Payment: by arrangement.

Hortus

Bryan's Ground, Stapleton, Nr Presteigne,
Herefordshire LD8 2LP
tel (01544) 260001 *fax* (01544) 260015
e-mail all@hortus.co.uk
web site http://www.hortusco.uk
Editor David Wheeler
Quarterly £30.00 p.a. (UK)

Articles on decorative horticulture:
plants, gardens, history, design, literature, people; book reviews. Length: 1500-
5000 words, longer by arrangement.
Illustrations: line, half-tone and wood-
engravings. Payment: by arrangement.
Founded 1987.

Hospital Doctor

Reed Healthcare Publishing,
Quadrant House, The Quadrant, Sutton,
Surrey SM2 5AS
tel 0181-652 8745 *fax* 0181-652 8701
Editor Phil Johnson
Weekly Free to 45,000 doctors. (£70.00 p.a.)

Commissioned features of interest to all
grades and specialities of hospital doctors; demand for news tip-offs. Length:
features 800-1000 words. Illustrations:
colour photos, transparencies, cartoons
and commissioned artwork. Payment:
£120 per 1000 words features, £10 per
100 words news. Founded c.1980.

Hospitality

Pavillon (Publishing) Ltd, Rose Cottage,
Lidwells Lane, Goudhurst, Cranbrook,
Kent TN17 1EJ
tel (01580) 211580 *fax* (01580) 211118
Editor Janet Simpson
10 p.a. £2.60 (£26.00 p.a. UK, £41.00 overseas)

Official magazine of the Hotel Catering &
Institutional Management Association.
Articles for a management readership on
food, accommodation services and related topics in hotels, restaurants, tourism,
educational establishments, the health
service, industrial situations, educational
and other institutions. Illustrations: photos, line, cartoons. Payment: by arrangement. Founded 1980.

Hot Air

John Brown Contract Publishing Ltd,
The New Boathouse, 136-142 Bramley Road,
London W10 6SR
tel 0171-565 3000 *fax* 0171-565 3202
Editor Alex Finer
Quarterly Free

Inflight magazine for Virgin Atlantic
Airways. Sport, trends/lifestyle, celebrities. Length: 1500-3000 words. Illustrations: high quality colour transparencies. Payment: by negotiation. Founded
1984.

Hot Press

Niall Stokes, 13 Trinity Street, Dublin 2,
Republic of Ireland
tel (01) 6795077/67955091 *fax* (01) 6795097
Editor Mairin Sheehy
Fortnightly £1.25

High-quality, investigative stories, or
punchily written offbeat pieces, of interest to 16-39-year-olds, including politics,
music, sport, sex, religion – whatever's
happening on the street. Length: varies.
Illustrations: b&w photos, colour sometimes used. Payment: by negotiation.
Founded 1977.

Hotel and Catering Review

Jemma Publications Ltd, Marino House,
52 Glasthule Road, Sandycove, Co. Dublin,
Republic of Ireland
tel (01) 2800000 *fax* (01) 2801818
e-mail fcorr@homenet.ie
Editor Frank Corr
Monthly £22.00 p.a.

Short news and trade news pieces.
Length: approx. 200 words. Features.
Payment: £80 per 1000 words.
Illustrations: half-tone, cartoons.

House & Garden

Vogue House, Hanover Square,
London W1R 0AD
tel 0171-499 9080 *fax* 0171-629 2907
Editor Susan Crewe
Monthly £2.70

Articles (always commissioned), on subjects relating to domestic architecture,
interior decorating, furnishing, gardening, household equipment, food and
wine.

House Beautiful
National Magazine House, 72 Broadwick Street, London W1V 2BP
tel 0171-439 5500 *fax* 0171-439 5595
Editor Caroline Atkins
Monthly £1.70
Specialist 'home' features for the homes of today. Preliminary study of magazine advisable. Payment: according to merit. Illustrated. Founded 1989.

HouseBuilder
56-64 Leonard Street, London EC2A 4JX
tel 0171-608 5132
Editor Ben Roskrow
11 p.a. £6.00
Official Journal of the House-Builders Federation and National House-Building Council. Technical articles on design, construction and equipment of dwellings, estate planning and development, and technical aspects of house-building, aimed at those engaged in house and flat construction and the development of housing estates. Preliminary letter advisable. Length: articles from 500 words, preferably with illustrations. Payment: by arrangement. Illustrations: photos, plans, construction details, cartoons.

HQ Poetry Magazine
(The Haiku Quarterly)
39 Exmouth Street, Swindon SN1 3PU
tel (01793) 523927
Editor Kevin Bailey
3-4 p.a. £2.60 (4 issues £9.00 p.a. UK, £12.00 p.a. non-UK)
A range of experimental and traditional poetry from all over the world. About one third of the content is devoted to haiku, haikuesque, and imagistic poetry. Review section and articles. Payment: small. Founded 1990.

HU (The Honest Ulsterman)
49 Main Street, Greyabbey, Co. Down BT22 2NF
Editor Tom Clyde
3 p.a. £2.50
Poetry, short stories, reviews, critical articles, poetry pamphlets. Payment: notional. Founded 1968.

i-D Magazine
Universal House, 251-255 Tottenham Court Road, London W1P 0AB
tel 0171-813 6170 *fax* 0171-813 6179£2.20
Editor Avril Mair
Monthly £2.20

Youth and general interest magazine: i-Deas, fashion, clubs, music, people. Will consider unsolicited material. Illustrations: colour and b&w photos. Payment: £100 per 1000 words; photos £50 per page. Founded 1980.

Ideal Home
IPC Magazines Ltd, King's Reach Tower, Stamford Street, London SE1 9LS
tel 0171-261 5000
Editor Sally O'Sullivan
Monthly £2.00
Lifestyle magazine, articles usually commissioned. Contributors advised to study editorial content before submitting material. Payment: according to material. Illustrations: usually commissioned. Founded 1920.

The Illustrated London News
20 Upper Ground, London SE1 9PF
tel 0171-805 5555 *fax* 0171-805 5911
Editor Alison Booth
2-3 p.a. £2.50
Two special issues published annually: Summer and Christmas, plus occasional additional issues to tie in with major events. Focuses on London and the UK: culture, the arts, people, dining, fashion, entertainment. All material commissioned but ideas welcome. Founded 1842.

IMAGE
22 Crofton Road, Dún Laoghaire, Co. Dublin, Republic of Ireland
tel (01) 2808415 *fax* (01) 2808309
Editor Jane McDonnell
Monthly £2.20
Short stories of a high literary standard and of interest to women. Length: up to 3000 words. Interviews with actors, writers, etc; human interest stories. Payment: by arrangement. Founded 1975.

In Britain
Premier Magazines, Haymarket House, 1 Oxendon Street, London SW1Y 4EE
tel 0171-925 2544 *fax* 0171-976 1088
Editor Andrea Spain
Monthly £2.75 (£23.95 p.a. UK/Europe; $39.95 p.a. US)
Upmarket features magazine about places and people in Britain. Limited freelance material is accepted. Illustrated. Payment: by arrangement. Founded 1930.

In Dublin
6-7 Camden Place, Dublin 2,
Republic of Ireland
tel (01) 4784322 *fax* (01) 4781055
Editor Declan Buche
Fortnightly £1.95

Dublin-related news features, oddball items, humour and interviews. Length: 500-1000 words. Payment: £80 per 1000 words. Illustrated. Founded 1976.

The Independent Magazine – see The Independent in National newspapers UK and Ireland, page 3

Index on Censorship
Lancaster House, 33 Islington High Street, London N1 9LH
tel 0171-278 2313 *fax* 0171-278 1878
e-mail judith@indexoncensorship.org
Editor Ursula Owen
Bi-monthly £7.99 (£36.00 p.a.)

Articles up to 3000 words dealing with all aspects of free speech and political censorship. Illustrations: b&w, cartoons. Payment: £75 per 1000 words. Founded 1972.

The Indexer
Society of Indexers, Mermaid House, 1 Mermaid Court, London SE1 1HR
tel 0171-403 4947
e-mail shuter@cix.compulink.co.uk
Editor Janet Shuter
2 p.a. (£40.00 p.a.) Free to members

Journal of the Society of Indexers, American Society of Indexers, Australian Society of Indexers, and Indexing & Abstracting Society of Canada. Articles of interest to professional indexers and providers and users of information in any form. Payment: none. Founded 1958.

Infant Projects
Scholastic Ltd, Villiers House, Clarendon Avenue, Leamington Spa, Warks. CV32 5PR
tel (01926) 887799 *fax* (01926) 337322
e-mail scholastic@compuserve.com
Editor Jane Morgan
Bi-monthly £2.60

Practical articles suggesting project activities for teachers of children aged 4-8; material mostly commissioned. Length: 500-1000 words. Illustrations: b&w photos and line illustrations, colour posters. Payment: by arrangement. Founded 1978.

InformationWeek
CMP Media (UK) Ltd, Greater London House, Hampstead Road, London NW1 7QZ
tel 0171-388 2430 *fax* 0171-388 2574
web site http://www.iweek.co.uk
Editor-in-Chief John Lamb
Fortnightly Controlled circulation

Broad-based multi-platform magazine with product reviews, technology news and strategy for IT professionals. No unsolicited articles. Illustrations: colour photos and artwork. Payment: by arrangement. Founded 1997.

The Inquirer
1-6 Essex Street, London WC2R 2HY
tel 0171-240 2384
Editor Keith Gilley
Fortnightly 40p

Journal of news and comment for Unitarians and religious liberals. Articles, liberal and progressive in tone, of general religious, social, cultural and international interest. Length: up to 750 words. Payment: none. Founded 1842.

Inspirations
GE Publishing Ltd, 133 Long Acre, London WC2E 9AD
tel 0171-836 0519 *fax* 0171-836 0280
Editor Deborah Barker
Monthly £2.30

Practical features on all aspects of home interest – home design, cookery, crafts, gadgets. Length: 800-2000 words. Payment: by arrangement. Illustrated. Founded 1993.

Insurance Age
EMAP Business Communications, 33-39 Bowling Green Lane, London EC1R 0DA
tel 0171-505 8181 *fax* 0171-505 8186
e-mail johnj@finance.emap.co.uk
web site http://www.insuranceage.com
Publisher and Editor John Jackson
Monthly

News and features on general insurance, personal, commercial, private medical, health and Lloyd's of London. Length: 650 words. Illustrations: transparencies. Payment: by negotiation. Founded 1979.

Insurance Brokers' Monthly
7 Stourbridge Road, Lye, Stourbridge, West Midlands DY9 7DG
tel (01384) 895228 *fax* (01384) 893666
e-mail sadler@dircon.co.uk
web site http://www.sadler.co.uk/brokers-monthly
Editor Brian Susman
Monthly £3.00

Articles of technical and non-technical interest to insurance brokers and others engaged in the insurance industry. Occasional articles of general interest to the City, on finance, etc. Length: 1000-1500 words. Payment: from £30 per 1000 words on last day of month following publication. Authoritative material written under true name and qualification receives highest payment. Illustrations: line and half-tone, 100-120 screen. Founded 1950.

InterMedia

International Institute of Communications, Tavistock House South, Tavistock Square, London WC1H 9LF
tel 0171-388 0671 *fax* 0171-380 0623
Editor Daniella Goldman
Bi-monthly £70.00 p.a.

International journal concerned with policies, events, trends and research in the field of communications, broadcasting, telecommunications and associated issues, particularly cultural and social. Preliminary letter essential. Illustrations: b&w line. Payment: by arrangement. Founded 1970.

International Affairs

Royal Institute of International Affairs, Chatham House, 10 St James's Square, London SW1Y 4LE
tel 0171-957 5700 *fax* 0171-957 5710
e-mail IA-CH@riia.org
web site http://www.riia.org
Quarterly £12.00 (£40.00 p.a.individuals, £65.00 p.a. institutions)

Serious long-term articles on international affairs; more than 100 books reviewed each quarter. Preliminary letter advisable. Article length: average 7000 words. Illustrations: none. Payment: by arrangement. Founded 1922.

International Construction

Ground Floor, Montrose House, 412-6 Eastern Avenue, Gants Hill, Ilford, Essex IG2 6NQ
tel 0181-518 2525 *fax* 0181-518 1020
Editor Tom Whitley
Monthly Controlled circulation

Articles dealing with new techniques of construction, applications of construction equipment and use of construction materials in any part of the world. Length: maximum 1500 words plus illustrations. Illustrations: line, half-tone, colour; some 2-colour line illustrations

used, cartoons. Payment: from £150 per 1000 words, plus illustrations.

International Stamp & Exhibition News

Stanley Gibbons Ltd, Unit 5, Parkside, Christchurch Road, Ringwood, Hants. BH24 3SH
tel (01425) 472363 *fax* (01425) 470247
e-mail info@stangib.demon.co.uk
Editor John Moody
Quarterly Free

Articles and news stories on philately from around the world. Length: 1000-2000 words. Illustrations: colour and b&w. Payment: £120 per article. Founded 1996.

Internet

EMAP Apex, Priory Court, 30-32 Farringdon Lane, London EC1R 3AU
tel 0171-309 2700
web site http://www.emap.com/internet
Editor Gail Robinson
Monthly £2.99

Magazine for consumer users, people who use the net at work and business users. Articles, news and features and guide to web sites on the Internet. Length: 800-1000 words. Illustrations: colour photos, cartoons. Payment: £150 per 1000 words. Founded 1994.

Interzone

217 Preston Drove, Brighton, East Sussex BN1 6FL
tel (01273) 504710
Editor David Pringle
Monthly £3.00 (£32.00 p.a.)

Science fiction and fantasy short stories, articles, interviews and reviews. Please read magazine before submitting. Length: 2000-6000 words. Illustrations: line, half-tone, colour. Payment: by arrangement. Founded 1982.

Investors Chronicle

Greystoke Place, Fetter Lane, London EC4A 1ND
tel 0171-463 3000 *fax* 0171-463 3153
Editor Ceri Jones
Weekly £2.20

Journal covering investment and personal finance. Occasional outside contributions for surveys are accepted. Payment: by negotiation.

IPA Magazine

(formerly Involvement)
42 Colebrooke Row, London N1 8AF
tel 0171-354 8040 *fax* 0171-354 8041
Editor Jonathan Hewett
Quarterly £45.00 p.a. (£60.00 p.a. overseas)

Magazine of the Involvement & Participation Association, which promotes social partnership and employee involvement. Articles, mostly commissioned, on participation and involvement in all sections of business and industry, employee shareholding, joint consultation, the sharing of information, labour-management relations, employee representation, etc with emphasis on practical experiences and new developments in particular enterprises, including the views of managers, employees and their representatives, and with a strong factual background. Length: up to 2000 words. Payment: by negotiation. Founded 1884.

Ireland of the Welcomes

Irish Tourist Board, Baggot Street Bridge, Dublin 2, Republic of Ireland
tel (01) 6024000 *fax* (01) 6024335
e-mail iow@irishtouristboard.ie
Editor Letitia Pollard
Bi-monthly £2.00

Irish items with cultural, sporting or topographical background designed to arouse interest in Irish holidays. Mostly commissioned – preliminary letter preferred. Length: 1200-1800 words. Payment: by arrangement. Illustrations: scenic and topical transparencies, cartoons.

Ireland's Own

North Main Street, Wexford
tel (053) 22155 *fax* (053) 23801
Editors Gerry Breen, Margaret Galvin
Weekly 50p

Short stories: non-experimental, traditional with an Irish orientation (2000-2500 words); articles of interest to Irish readers at home and abroad (750-1000 words); general and literary articles (750-1000 words). Monthly special bumper editions, each devoted to a particular seasonal topic. Jokes and funny stories always welcome; suggestions for new features considered. Payment: varies according to quality and length. Illustrations: photos, cartoons. Founded 1902.

Irish Farmers Journal

Irish Farm Centre, Bluebell, Dublin 12, Republic of Ireland
tel (01) 4501166 *fax* (01) 4520876
e-mail editdept@ifj.ie
web site http://www.farmersjournal.ie
Editor Matthew Dempsey
Weekly Ir£1.10 (90p)

Readable, technical articles on any aspect of farming. Length: 700-1000 words. Payment: £100-£150 per article. Illustrated. Founded 1948.

Irish Journal of Medical Science

Royal Academy of Medicine, 6 Kildare Street, Dublin 2, Republic of Ireland
tel (01) 6767650 *fax* (01) 6611684
e-mail journal@rami.ie
web site http://www.iol.ie/~rami/
Quarterly Ir.£15.00 (Ir.£70.00 EU, Ir.£110.00 outside EU)

Official Organ of the Royal Academy of Medicine in Ireland. Original contributions in medicine, surgery, midwifery, public health, etc; reviews of professional books, reports of medical societies, etc. Illustrations: line, half-tone, colour.1st series 1832, 6th series January 1926, Volume 167, 1998.

Irish Medical Times

15 Harcourt Street, Dublin 2, Republic of Ireland
tel (01) 4757461 *fax* (01) 4757468
Editor Dr John O'Connell
Weekly £2.50 (£104.00 p.a.)

Medical articles, also humorous articles with medical slant. Length: 850-1000 words. Payment: £60 per 1000 words. Illustrations: line, half-tone, colour, cartoons.

Irish Printer

Jemma Publications Ltd, 52 Glasthule Road, Sandycove, Co. Dublin, Republic of Ireland
tel (01) 2800000 *fax* (01) 2801818
e-mail fcorr@homenet.ie
Editor Frank Corr
Monthly £22.00 p.a.

Technical articles and news of interest to the printing industry. Length: 800-1000 words. Illustrations: colour and b&w photos. Payment: £80 per 1000 words; photos £30. Founded 1974.

IT (Irish Tatler)

Smurfit Publications Ltd, 2 Clanwilliam Court, Lower Mount Street, Dublin 2, Republic of Ireland
tel (01) 6623158 *fax* (01) 6619757
Editor Morag Prunty
Monthly £1.95

General interest women's magazine: beauty, interiors, fashion, cookery, current affairs, fiction, reportage and celebrity interviews. Length: 2000-4000 words. Payment: by arrangement.

J17
EMAP Élan, Endeavour House,
189 Shaftesbury Avenue, London WC2H 8JG
tel 0171-437 9011 *fax* 0171-434 0656
Editor Ally Oliver
Monthly £1.60

Articles of interest to girls aged 14-16: fashion, beauty, pop, and various features; real life stories up to 1500 words; quizzes. Payment: by arrangement. Illustrations: colour. Founded 1983.

Jane's Defence Weekly
Sentinel House, 163 Brighton Road, Coulsdon, Surrey CR5 2NH
tel 0181-700 3700 *fax* 0181-763 1007
web site http://www.jdw.janes.com
Editor Clifford Beal
Weekly £170.00 p.a. (5-year archive on CD-Rom)

International defence news; military equipment; budget analysis, industry, military technology, business, political, defence market intelligence. Payment: minimum £150 per 1000 words used. Illustrations: line, half-tone, colour. Founded 1984.

Jazz Journal International
Jazz Journal Ltd, 1-5 Clerkenwell Road, London EC1M 5PA
tel 0171-608 1348/1362 *fax* 0171-608 1292
Publisher and Editor-in-Chief Eddie Cook
Monthly £3.00

Articles on jazz, record reviews. Prospective contributors should telephone or write before submitting material. Payment: by arrangement. Illustrations: photos. Founded 1948.

Jewish Chronicle
25 Furnival Street, London EC4A 1JT
tel 0171-405 9252
Editor Edward J. Temko
Weekly 50p

Authentic and exclusive news stories and articles of Jewish interest from 500-1500 words are considered. There is a lively arts and leisure section, as well as regular travel pages. Payment: by arrangement. Illustrations: of Jewish interest, either topical or feature. Founded 1841.

The Jewish Quarterly
PO Box 2078, London W1A 1JR
tel/fax 0181-830 5367 (editorial)
Editor Matthew Reisz
Quarterly £3.95 (£15.00 p.a., £17.50 p.a. Europe, £25.00 p.a. overseas)

Articles of Jewish interest, literature, history, music, politics, poetry, book reviews, fiction. Illustrations: half-tone. Founded 1953.

Jewish Telegraph
Telegraph House, 11 Park Hill,
Bury Old Road, Prestwich,
Manchester M25 0HH
tel 0161-740 9321 *fax* 0161-740 9325
1 Shaftesbury Avenue, Leeds LS8 1DR
tel 0113-295 6000 *fax* 0113-295 6006
Harold House, Dunbabin Road,
Liverpool L15 6XL
tel 0151-475 6666/2222 *fax* 0151-475 2222
43 Queen Square, Glasgow G41 2BD
tel 0141-423 9200/1/2 *fax* 0141-423 9200
Editor Paul Harris
Weekly Man. 35p, Leeds 25p, Liverpool 25p, Glasgow 40p

Non-fiction articles of Jewish interest, especially humour. Exclusive Jewish news stories and pictures, international, national and local. Length: 1000-1500 words. Payment: by arrangement. Illustrations: line, half-tone, cartoons. Founded 1950.

Journal of Alternative and Complementary Medicine
9 Rickett Street, London SW6 1RU
tel 0171-385 0012 *fax* 0171-385 4566
Editor Graeme Miller
Monthly £2.95 (£33.50 p.a.)

Feature articles (length: up to 2000 words) and news stories (length: up to 250 words). Unsolicited material welcome but not eligible for payment unless commissioned. Illustrations: line, half-tone, colour. Payment: by negotiation. Founded 1983.

Journalist
NUJ, Acorn House, 314 Gray's Inn Road, London WC1X 8DP
tel 0171-278 7916 *fax* 0171-837 8143
e-mail the.journalist @mcr1.poptel.org.uk
Editor Tim Gopsill
Bi-monthly £2.50 (£12.00 p.a., £20.00 p.a. overseas)

Magazine of the National Union of Journalists (mailed to all members). Accepts material relating to journalism, trade unionism and general conditions in the media – newspapers, magazines, books, broadcasting and electronic. Mainly contributed by members, and outside written contributions not paid.

Junior Education

Scholastic Ltd, Villiers House,
Clarendon Avenue, Leamington Spa,
Warks. CV32 5PR
tel (01926) 887799 fax (01926) 883331
Editor Mrs Terry Saunders
Monthly £2.60

For teachers, educationalists and students concerned with children aged 7-12. Articles by specialists on practical teaching ideas and methods, plus in-depth coverage and debate on news issues in education. Length: 800-1000 words. Payment: by arrangement. Illustrated with photos and drawings; includes colour poster. Founded 1977.

Junior Focus

Scholastic Ltd, Villiers House, Clarendon
Avenue, Leamington Spa, Warks. CV32 5PR
tel (01926) 887799 fax (01926) 883331
Editor Maggie Heeley
Monthly £2.50

Aimed at teachers of 7-12 year olds, each issue is based on a theme, closely linked with the National Curriculum. Includes A1 and A3 full-colour posters, 16 pages of photocopiable material and 12 pages of project notes. All material commissioned. Length: 1-4 pages. Illustrations: commissioned b&w line; welcomes samples of work from new illustrators. Payment: £100 per double-page spread; varies for illustrations. Founded 1982.

Justice of the Peace

Tolley House, 2 Addiscombe Road, Croydon,
Surrey CR9 5AF
tel 0181-686 9141 fax 0171-287 3337
e-mail jpn@tolleys.co.uk
Editors Adrian Turner
Weekly £165.50 p.a.

Professional journal. Articles on magisterial and local government law and associated subjects including family law, criminology, medico-legal matters, penology, police, probation (length preferred, under 1400 words). Information on articles and contributions sent on request. Payment: £200 per feature article. Founded 1837.

Kerrang!

EMAP Metro Ltd, Mappin House,
4 Winsley Street, London W1N 7AR
tel 0171-436 1515 fax 0171-312 8910
Editor Phil Alexander
Weekly £1.50

News, views and reviews; the noise of the new generation. All material commissioned. Illustrations: colour. Payment: by arrangement. Founded 1981.

Kids Alive! (The Young Soldier)

101 Queen Victoria Street, London EC4P 4EP
tel 0171-332 0022 ext 2345 fax 0171-236 3491
e-mail wcry@globalnet.co.uk
Editor Ken Nesbitt
Weekly 20p (£26.00 p.a.)

The Salvation Army's children's weekly. Stories, pictures, cartoon strips, puzzles etc, Christian-based with emphasis on education re addictive substances. Payment: by arrangement. Illustrations: half-tone, line and 4-colour line, cartoons. Founded 1881.

Kids Out

Time Out Guides Ltd, Universal House,
251 Tottenham Court Road, London W1P 0AB
tel 0171-813 6018 fax 0171-813 6153
e-mail editor@kidsout.co.uk
Editor Dorothy Garrett Boswell
Monthly £1.75

Contains a comprehensive calendar of London events in London for families, plus travel, education and parenting articles of interest to parents of under 12 year-olds in the London area. For picture requirements call Kerri Miles 0171-813 6089. Length: 200-8000 words. Payment: £100 per 1000 words. Founded 1995.

Ladies First

Hils Publications Ltd, 33 Wellfield Road,
Cardiff CF2 3PA
tel (01222) 461007 fax (01222) 493605
Editor Hilary Hughes
Quarterly Free

Articles on fashion, beauty, children's interests, homes and interiors, entertaining. Length: 1800 words. Payment: £50-£75 (negotiable). Founded 1986.

The Lady

39-40 Bedford Street, Strand, London WC2E 9ER
tel 0171-379 4717 fax 0171-836 4620
Editor Arline Usden
Weekly 70p

British and foreign travel, countryside, human-interest, celebrity interviews, animals, cookery, art and antiques, historic-interest and commemorative articles (preliminary letter advisable for articles dealing with anniversaries). Length: 900-1200 words; Viewpoint: 600 words.

Annual Short Story Competition with prize of £1000 plus. Winning entries printed in magazine. Illustrations: colour transparencies, b&w photos and drawings. Payment: by arrangement. Founded 1885.

Lancashire Magazine

33 Beverley Road, Driffield, Yorkshire YO25 6SD
tel/fax (01377) 253232
Editor Winston Halstead
Bi-monthly £1.40

Articles about people, life and character of all parts of Lancashire. Length: 1500 words. Payment: £30-£35 approx. per published page. Illustrations: line, half-tone, colour. Founded 1977.

Lancet

42 Bedford Square, London WC1B 3SL
tel 0171-436 4981 *fax* 0171-323 6441
web site http://www.thelancet.com
Editor Dr Richard Horton
Weekly £3.95

Research papers, review articles, editorials, correspondence and commentaries on the international medicosocial scene. Regular contributors are paid by arrangement; others should consult the editor before submitting. Founded 1823.

Land & Liberty

177 Vauxhall Bridge Road, London SW1V 1EU
tel 0171-834 4266 *fax* 0171-834 4979
e-mail HGF_IGU@compurserve.com
Editor Fred Harrison
Quarterly £3.00 (£12.00 p.a.)

Articles on land economics, land taxation, land prices, land speculation as they relate to housing, the economy, production, politics. Study of journal essential. Length: up to 3000 words. Payment: by arrangement. Illustrations: half-tone. Founded 1894.

The Latest

Canon Publishing, Suite 3, The Octagon, Village Square, Brighton Marina, Brighton BN2 5WB
tel (01273) 818150 *fax* (01273) 818152
e-mail canon@pavilion.co.uk
web site http://www.thelatest.co.uk
Editor Bill Smith
Monthly 30p

Lively local newspaper (covering Sussex, Surrey, South London, Hampshire and Dorset) for young professionals. Contains news and arts features, listings. Payment: £100 per 1000 words. Founded 1996.

The Lawyer

Centaur Communications Group, 50 Poland Street, London W1V 4AX
tel 0171-970 4346 *fax* 0171-970 4395
Editor Mary Heaney
Weekly £1.75 (£60.00 p.a.)

News, articles, features and views relevant to the legal profession. Length: 600-900 words. Illustrations: as agreed. Payment: £125-£150 per 1000 words. Founded 1987.

Learned Publishing

17 Orchard Close, Shillingford, Oxon OX10 7HQ
tel/fax (01865) 858799
e-mail alpsp@storrie.demon.co.uk
Editor Eileen Storrie
Quarterly £150.00 p.a. Free to members

Journal of the Association of the Learned and Professional Society Publishers. Articles, reviews and reports on topics and events of interest to academic, medical, scientific and learned society publishers. Editorial, production, copyright, electronic publishing, distribution and marketing issues are all addressed. Length: 1000-5000 words. Illustrations: half-tone, line. Payment: none. Founded 1988; successor to *ALPSP Bulletin*.

The Leisure Manager

The Institute of Leisure and Amenity Management, ILAM House, Lower Basildon, Reading, Berks. RG8 9NE
tel (01491) 874800 *fax* (01491) 874801
Editor Jonathan Ives
Monthly £40.00 p.a. (£50.00 p.a. overseas)

Official Journal of The Institute of Leisure and Amenity Management. Articles on amenity, children's play, tourism, leisure, parks, entertainment, recreation and sports management, cultural services. Payment: by arrangement. Illustrations: line, half-tone. Founded 1985.

Leisure Painter

63-65 High Street, Tenterden, Kent TN30 6BD
tel (01580) 763315 *fax* (01580) 765411
Editor Irene Briers
Monthly £2.10

Instructional articles on painting and fine arts. Payment: £65 per 1000 words. Illustrations: line, half-tone, colour, original artwork. Founded 1966.

Leisureweek

Centaur Publishing Ltd, St Giles House, 50 Poland Street, London W1V 4AX
tel 0171-970 4000 *fax* 0171-970 4891
e-mail leisure-week@centaur.co.uk

Editor Michael Nutley
Weekly £2.00

News and features relating to the leisure industry. All material commissioned. Length: features from 800 words, news from 200 words. Illustrations: line, half-tone. Payment: by agreement. Founded 1989.

The Library

(published by Oxford University Press for the Bibliographical Society)
The Brotherton Library, University of Leeds, Leeds LS2 9JT
Editor Dr O.S. Pickering
Quarterly £65.00 p.a. (£32.00 p.a. to members)

Articles up to 15,000 words as well as shorter Notes, embodying original research on subjects connected with bibliography; reviews. Illustrations: line, half-tone. Payment: none. Founded 1889.

Life – see The Observer in National newspapers UK and Ireland, page 3

Life & Work: Record of the Church of Scotland

121 George Street, Edinburgh EH2 4YN
tel 0131-225 5722 *fax* 0131-220 3113
e-mail lifework@dial.pipex.com
Editor Dr Robin Hill
Monthly 80p

Articles not exceeding 1000 words and news; poems and occasional stories. Study the magazine first. Payment: up to £50 per 1000 words, or by arrangement. Illustrations: photos and line, cartoons.

Lincolnshire Life

PO Box 81, Lincoln LN1 1HD
tel (01522) 527127 *fax* (01522) 560035
e-mail jezashberry@lincolnshirelife.co.uk
web site http://www.lincolnshirelife.co.uk
Editor Jez Ashberry
Monthly £1.45

Articles and news of county interest. Length: up to 1200 words. Illustrations: b&w and colour photos and line drawings. Payment: varies. Founded 1961.

The Linguist

The Institute of Linguists, Saxon House, 48 Southwark Street, London SE1 1UN
tel 0171-690 9665 *fax* 0171-607 6824
e-mail 100442.2203@compuserve.com
Editor Pat Treasure
Bi-monthly £5.00 (£25.00 p.a.)

Articles of interest to professional linguists in translating, interpreting and teaching fields. Articles usually contributed, but payment by arrangement. All contributors have special knowledge of the subjects with which they deal. Length: 1500-2000 words. Illustrations: line, half-tone.

The Literary Review

44 Lexington Street, London W1R 3LH
tel 0171-437 9392 *fax* 0171-734 1844
Editor Auberon Waugh
Monthly £2.40 (£26.00 p.a.)

Reviews, articles of cultural interest, interviews, profiles, monthly poetry competitions. Material mostly commissioned. Length: articles and reviews 800-1500 words. Illustrations: line and b&w photos. Payment: £25 per article; none for illustrations. Founded 1979.

Live & Kicking Magazine

BBC Worldwide, Woodlands, Wood Lane, London W12 0TT
tel 0181-576 3254 *fax* 0181-576 3267
Editor Jeremy Mark
Monthly £1.40

Features and news stories on current pop, TV, film and sports stars with teenage appeal. Length: features 1000-1500 words. Illustrations: occasionally commission cartoons and caricatures. Payment: varies. Founded 1993.

Llais Llyfrau/Books in Wales

Welsh Books Council, Castell Brychan, Aberystwyth, Ceredigion SY23 2JB
tel (01970) 624151 *fax* (01970) 625385
e-mail wbc.marketing@cllc.org.uk
Editors Katie Gramich, Hedd ap Emlyn, Lorna Herbert Egan
Quarterly £6.00 p.a.

Articles in Welsh and English on authors and their books, Welsh publishing; reviews and book lists. Mainly commissioned. Payment: by arrangement. Founded 1964.

Loaded

IPC Magazines, King's Reach Tower, Stamford Street, London SE1 9LS
tel 0171-261 5000 *fax* 0171-261 5640
e-mail (features) david-bennun@ipc.co.uk
web site http://www.uploaded.com
(handbook) danny-plunkett@ipc.co.uk
Editor Derek Harbinson
Monthly £2.60

Magazine for men in their twenties. Music, sport, sex, humour, travel, fashion, hard news and popular culture.

Address longer features (2000 words) to Features Editor, and shorter items to Handbook Editor. Payment: by arrangement. Founded 1994.

Local Government Chronicle
EMAP Business Publishing, 33-39 Bowling Green Lane, London EC1R 0DA
tel 0171-833 7311 *fax* 0171-837 2725
Editor Jake Arnold-Forster
Weekly £2.95

Articles relating to financial, political, legal and administrative work of the local government manager. Payment: by arrangement. Illustrations: half-tone, cartoons. Founded 1855.

The Local Historian
(formerly The Amateur Historian)
British Association for Local History, 25 Lower Street, Harnham, Salisbury, Wilts. SP2 8EY
tel (01722) 332158 *fax* (01722) 413242
web site http://www./e.ac.uk/hi/LOCAL_HISTORY/index.html
Editor Dr Margaret Bonney, 7 Carisbrooke Park, Knighton, Leicester LE2 3PQ
tel 0116-270 5028
Reviews Editor Peter Christie, 30 Lime Grove, Bideford, North Devon EX39 3JL
Quarterly £6.00

Articles, popular in style but based on original historical research, covering methods of research, sources and background material helpful to regional, local and family historians – histories of particular places, people or incidents not wanted. Reviews of recently published books on local history (send to Reviews Editor). Length: maximum 7000 words. Illustrations: line and photos. Payment: none. Founded 1952.

LOGOS
5 Beechwood Drive, Marlow, Bucks. SL7 2DH
tel/fax (01628) 477577
Editor Gordon Graham
Quarterly £36.00 p.a. (£72.00 p.a. institutions)

In-depth articles on publishing, librarianship and bookselling with international or interdisciplinary appeal. Length: 3500-7000 words. Payment: 25 offprints/copy of issue. Founded 1990.

London Magazine: A Review of the Arts
30 Thurloe Place, London SW7 2HQ
tel 0171-589 0618
Editor Alan Ross, Deputy *Editor* Jane Rye
Bi-monthly £5.99 (£28.50 p.a.)

Poems, stories (2000-5000 words), literary memoirs, critical articles, features on art, photography, sport, theatre, cinema, music, architecture, events, reports from abroad, drawings. Sae necessary. Payment: by arrangement. Founded 1954.

London Review of Books
28-30 Little Russell Street, London WC1A 2HN
tel 0171-209 1101 *fax* 0171-209 1102
e-mail editorial@lrb.co.uk
Editor Mary-Kay Wilmers
Bi-monthly £2.50

Features, essays, poems. Payment: by arrangement. Founded 1979.

Looks
EMAP Élan, Endeavour House,
189 Shaftesbury Avenue, London WC2H 8JG
tel 0171-437 9011 *fax* 0171-208 3586
Editor Eleni Kyriacou
Monthly £1.80

Fashion, beauty and hair for 15-24 age range; features, especially with a celebrity bias. No unsolicited material, but ideas welcome. Length: up to 2000 words. Illustrations: colour, b&w. Payment: by arrangement.

Make: the magazine of women's art
(formerly Women's Art Magazine)
Women's Art Library, Fulham Palace,
Bishops Avenue, London SW6 6EA
tel 0171-731 7618 *fax* 0171-384 1110
e-mail womensart.lib@ukonline.co.uk
Editor Series of guest editors, *Assistant Editor* Nicky Hodge
Bi-monthly £3.00

Interviews, book reviews and exhibition reviews on the work of contemporary and historical women artists. Material mostly commissioned. Length: up to 3000 words. Illustrations: b&w photos, line drawings. Payment: by negotiation; none for illustrations.

Making Music
Nexus Media Ltd, Nexus House, Swanley,
Kent BR8 8HU
tel (01322) 660070 *fax* (01322) 615636
e-mail makingmusic@cerbernet.co.uk
web site http://cerbernet.co.uk/makingmusic/
Editor Paul Quinn
Monthly £18.00 p.a.

Technical, musicianly and instrumental features on rock, pop, blues, dance, world, jazz, soul; little classical. Length: 500-2500 words. Payment: £95 per 1000 words. Illustrations: colour, including cartoons and photos. Founded 1986.

Management Today
174 Hammersmith Road, London W6 7JP
tel 0171-413 4566 *fax* 0171-413 4138
Editor Rufus Olins
Monthly £40.00 p.a.

Company profiles and analysis – columns from 1000 words, features up to 3000 words. Payment: £300 per 1000 words. Illustrations: colour transparencies, usually commissioned. Founded 1966.

Mandy Library
D.C. Thomson & Co. Ltd, Albert Square, Dundee DD1 9QJ
tel (01382) 223131 *fax* (01382) 322214
185 Fleet Street, London EC4A 2HS
tel 0171-242 5086 *fax* 0171-404 5694
Fortnightly 60p

Picture-stories for schoolgirls (about 140 line drawings): adventure, animal, mystery, school, sport. Scripts considered; promising scriptwriters and artists encouraged. Payment: on acceptance.

Marie Claire
European Magazines Ltd, 2 Hatfields, London SE1 9PG
tel 0171-261 5240 *fax* 0171-261 5277
Editor Juliet Warkentin
Monthly £2.30

Feature articles of interest to today's woman; plus fashion, beauty, health, food, drink and travel. Commissioned material only. Payment: by negotiation. Illustrated in colour. Founded 1988.

Market Newsletter
Focus House, 497 Green Lanes, London N13 4BP
tel 0181-882 3315/6 *fax* 0181-886 5174
Editor John Tracy
Published by Bureau of Freelance Photographers
Monthly Private circulation

Current information on markets and editorial requirements of interest to writers and photographers. Founded 1965.

Marketing Week
St Giles House, 50 Poland Street, London W1V 4AX
tel 0171-439 4222 *fax* 0171-439 9669
web site http://www.marketing-week.co.uk/mw001
Editor Stuart Smith
Weekly £2.10

Aimed at marketing management. Accepts occasional features and analysis.

Length: 1000-2000 words. Payment: £150 per 1000 words. Founded 1978.

Mayfair
2 Archer Street, London W1V 8JJ
tel 0171-292 8000 *fax* 0171-734 5030
Editor Steve Shields
Monthly £2.60

Short humorous articles, sport, music, motoring. Payment: by arrangement. Illustrations: colour transparencies to illustrate highly visual feature ideas. Founded 1966.

Medal News
Token Publishing Ltd, PO Box 14, Honiton, Devon EX14 9YP
tel (01404) 46972 *fax* (01404) 831895
Editor Diana Birch
10 p.a. £2.50

Well-researched articles on military history with a bias towards medals. Length: up to 2000 words. Illustrations: b&w preferred. Payment: £20 per 1000 words; none for illustrations. Founded 1989.

Media Week
Quantum Publishing Ltd, Quantum House, 19 Scarbrook Road, Croydon CR9 1LX
tel 0181-565 4317 *fax* 0181-565 4394
e-mail mweeked@media.emap.co.uk
Editor Conor Dignam
Weekly £1.85

News and analysis of UK advertising media industry. Illustrations: full colour and b&w. Founded 1985.

Melody Maker
IPC Magazines Ltd, King's Reach Tower, Stamford Street, London SE1 9LS
tel 0171-261 6229 *fax* 0171-261 6706
Editor Mark Sutherland
Weekly 90p

Technical, entertaining and informative articles on rock and pop music. Payment: by arrangement. Illustrations: line, half-tone, colour.

Men Only
2 Archer Street, London W1V 8JJ
tel 0171-292 8000 *fax* 0171-734 5030
Publisher Paul Raymond, *Editor* Mike Collier
Monthly £2.60

High quality glamour photography; explicit sex stories (no erotic fiction); male interest features – sport, humour, entertainment, hedonism! Proposals welcome. Payment: by arrangement. Founded 1971.

Men's Health

Rodale Press Ltd, 7-10 Chandos Street,
London W1M 0AD
tel 0171-291 6000 *fax* 0171-291 6060
Editor Phil Hilton
10 p.a. £2.90

Active pursuits, grooming, fitness, fashion, sex, career and general men's interest issues. Length 1000-4000 words. Ideas on any subject welcome. No unsolicited MSS. Payment: by arrangement. Founded 1994.

Methodist Recorder

122 Golden Lane, London EC1Y 0TL
tel 0171-251 8414
e-mail editorial@methodistrecorder.co.uk
web site http://www.methodistrecorder.co.uk/index.htm
Editor Moira Sleight
Weekly 48p

Methodist newspaper; ecumenically involved. Limited opportunities for freelance contributors. Preliminary letter advised. Founded 1861.

Military Modelling

Nexus Special Interests Ltd, Nexus House,
Swanley, Kent BR8 8HU
tel (01322) 660070 *fax* (01322) 667633
Editor Ken Jones
Monthly £2.30

Articles on military modelling. Length: up to 2000 words. Payment: by arrangement. Illustrations: line, half-tone, colour.

Mind

Oxford University Press, Great Clarendon Street,
Oxford OX2 6DP
tel (01865) 56767 *fax* (01865) 267773
Editor Prof Mark Sainsbury
Quarterly £8.00 (£28.00 p.a. UK/Europe, $52.00 p.a. rest of world; institution/student rates on application)

Review of philosophy intended for those who have studied and thought on this subject. Articles from about 5000 words; shorter discussion notes; critical notices and reviews. Payment: none. Founded 1876.

Mizz

IPC Magazines Ltd, King's Reach Tower,
Stamford Street, London SE1 9LS
tel 0171-261 6319 *fax* 0171-261 6032
e-mail mizz@ipc.co.uk
web site http://www.ipc.co.uk
Editor Lucie Tobin

Fortnightly £1.25

Articles on any subject of interest to teenage girls. Approach in writing. Payment: by arrangement. Illustrated. Founded 1985.

Mobile and Cellular Magazine

Nexus Media, Nexus House, Azalea Drive,
Swanley, Kent BR8 8HU
tel (01322) 660070 *fax* (01322) 661257
Editor Peter Sayer
Monthly £38.00 p.a.

Aimed at radio communications professionals – technical features, company profiles and news analysis; cartoons. Length: features up to 1500 words, analysis up to 800 words. Payment: £150 per 1000 words. Founded 1989.

Model Boats

Nexus Special Interests Ltd, Nexus House,
Swanley, Kent BR8 8HU
tel (01322) 660070 *fax* (01322) 667633
Editor John L. Cundell
13 p.a. £2.30

Articles, drawings, plans, sketches of model boats. Payment: £25 per page; plans £100. Illustrations: line, half-tone. Founded 1964.

Model Engineer

Nexus Special Interests Ltd, Nexus House,
Swanley, Kent BR8 8HU
tel (01322) 660070 *fax* (01322) 667633
Editor Ted Jolliffe
2 p.m. £1.85

Detailed description of the construction of models, small workshop equipment, machine tools and small electrical and mechanical devices; articles on small power engineering, mechanics, electricity, workshop methods, clocks and experiments. Payment: up to £35 per page. Illustrations: line, half-tone, colour. Founded 1898.

Modern Believing

(formerly Modern Churchman)
The Lincoln Theological Institute for the Study of Religion in Society, University of Sheffield,
36 Wilkinson Street, Sheffield SI0 2GB
Editor The Revd Dr Martyn Percy
Quarterly £4.00

Covers 'liberal theology in the contemporary world'. Length: up to 3500 words. Intending contributors advised to write to the editor for a copy of instructions to authors. Founded 1911.

Modern Language Review

Modern Humanities Research Association,
King's College, Strand, London WC2R 2LS
Quarterly £75.00 p.a. (£90.00 overseas, $180.00 USA)

Articles and reviews of a scholarly or specialist character on English, Romance, Germanic and Slavonic languages and literatures. Payment: none, but offprints are given. Founded 1905.

Modern Painters

Fine Art Journals Ltd, Universal House,
251-255 Tottenham Court Road,
London W1P 9AD
tel 0171-636 6305 *fax* 0171-580 5615
Editor Karen Wright
Quarterly £4.95

Journal of modern fine arts and architecture – commissioned articles and features; also interviews. Length: 1000-2500 words. Payment: £120 per 1000 words. Illustrated. Founded 1986.

Modern Woman

Meath Chronicle Ltd, Market Square, Navan,
Co. Meath, Republic of Ireland
tel (046) 21442 *fax* (046) 23565
Editor Margot Davis
Monthly 50p

Articles and features on a wide range of subjects of interest to women over the age of 18 (e.g. politics, religion, health and sex). Length: 200-1000 words. Illustrations: colour and b&w photos, line drawings and cartoons. Payment: NUJ rates. Founded 1984.

Modus

Hamilton House, Mabledon Place,
London WC1H 9BJ
tel 0171-387 1441 *fax* 0171-383 7230
Editor Geoffrey Thompson
8 p.a. £3.50 (£28.00 p.a.)

Official Journal of the National Association of Teachers of Home Economics and Technology: aimed at teachers and educationists. Articles on the teaching of home economics and technology, including textiles, nutrition, and social and technical background information for teachers. Length: up to 1500 words. Payment: by arrangement. Illustrations: line, half-tone, cartoons.

Mojo

EMAP Metro, Mappin House, 4 Winsley Street,
London W1N 7AR
tel 0171-436 1515 *fax* 0171-312 8296
e-mail mojo@ecm.emap.com
Editor Mat Snow
Monthly £3.10

Serious rock music magazine: interviews, news and reviews of books, live shows and albums. Length: up to 10,000 words. Illustrations: colour and b&w photos, colour caricatures. Payment: £180 per 1000 words; £150-£350 illustrations. Founded 1993.

MoneyMarketing

Centaur Communications Ltd, St Giles House,
50 Poland Street, London W1V 4AX
tel 0171-970 4000 *fax* 0171-970 4397
Editor Grant Ringshaw
Weekly £1.50

News, features, surveys and viewpoints; cartoons. Length: features from 900 words. Illustrations: b&w photos, colour and b&w line. Payment: £150 per 1000 words; colour line £200, b&w line £150. Founded 1985.

Moneywise

RD Publications Ltd, 11 Westferry Circus,
Canary Wharf, London E14 4HE
tel 0171-715 8069 *fax* 0171-715 8725
web site http://www.moneywise.co.uk
Editor Matthew Vincent
Monthly £2.70

Financial and consumer interest features, articles and news stories. Length: 1500-2000 words. Illustrations: willing to see designers, illustrators and photographers for fresh new ideas. Payment: by arrangement. Founded 1990.

The Month

114 Mount Street, London W1Y 6AH
tel 0171-491 7596 *fax* 0171-629 6936
e-mail tim.noble@dial.pipex.com
Editor Tim Noble SJ
Monthly £1.50

Review of Christian thought, and world affairs, with arts and literary sections, edited by the Jesuit Fathers. Preliminary letter desirable. Length: up to 2500 words. Payment: by arrangement. Illustrations: b&w photos. Founded 1864.

More!

EMAP Élan, Endeavour House, 189 Shaftesbury Avenue, London WC2H 8JG
tel 0171-437 9011 *fax* 0171-434 0656
Editor Tammy Butt
Fortnightly £1.25

Celebrities, fun and sexy features, 'how to' articles aimed at young women. Short erotic fiction. Study of magazine essential. Length: 1800 words. Payment: £150 per 1000 words. Illustrated. Founded 1988.

Mother & Baby

EMAP Élan, Endeavour House,
189 Shaftesbury Avenue, London WC2H 8JE
tel 0171-437 9011 *fax* 0171-208 3584
Editor Melanie Deeprose
Monthly £1.80

Features and practical articles. Length: 1200-1800 words. Payment: by negotiation. Illustrated. Founded 1956.

Motor Boat and Yachting

IPC Magazines Ltd, King's Reach Tower,
Stamford Street, London SE1 9LS
tel 0171-261 5333
e-mail mby@ipc.co.uk
web site http://www.ybw.com
Editor Alan Harper
Monthly £2.85

General interest as well as specialist motor boating material welcomed. Features up to 2000 words considered on all aspects, sea-going and on inland waterways. Payment: varies. Illustrations: photos (mostly colour and transparencies preferred) and line, cartoons. Founded 1904.

Motor Boats Monthly

Boating Publications Ltd, Link House,
Dingwall Avenue, Croydon CR9 2TA
tel 0181-686 2599 *fax* 0181-781 6065
e-mail mbm@lhm.co.uk
web site http://www.marinedata.co.uk/mbm
Editor Kim Hollamby
Monthly £2.80

News on motorboating in the UK and Europe, cruising features and anecdotal stories. Mostly commissioned – send synopsis to editor. Length: news up to 200 words, features up to 4000 words. Illustrations: colour transparencies. Payment: by arrangement. Founded 1987.

Motor Caravan Magazine

Link House Magazines Ltd, Link House,
Dingwall Avenue, Croydon CR9 2TA
tel 0181-686 2599 *fax* 0181-781 6044
e-mail motorcaravan@lhm.co.uk
web site http://www.linkhouse.co.uk/motorcaravan
Editor Gary Martin
Monthly £2.50

Practical features, touring features (home and abroad). Length: up to 1500 words. Payment: £50 per page. Illustrations: line, half-tone, colour, cartoons. Founded 1985.

Motor Cycle News

EMAP National Publications Ltd,
20-22 Station Road, Kettering NN15 7HH
tel (01536) 411111 *fax* (01536) 411750
e-mail mcn@mcnl.demon.co.uk
web site http://www.erack.com/mcw
Editor Adam Duckworth
Weekly £1.15

Features (up to 1000 words), photos and news stories of interest to motorcyclists. Founded 1955.

Motorcaravan and Motorhome Monthly (MMM)

14 Eastfield Close, Andover, Hants SP10 2QP
fax (01264) 324794
Editor Mike Jago
Monthly £2.50

Articles including motorcaravan travel, owner reports and DIY. Length: up to 2500 words. Payment: by arrangement. Illustrations: line, half-tone, colour prints and transparencies. Founded 1966 as Motor Caravan and Camping.

Ms London

The Commuter Publishing Partnership,
7-9 Rathbone Street, London W1P 1AF
tel 0171-636 6651
Editor Bill Williamson
Weekly Free

Features and lifestyle pieces of interest to young professional working women. All material commissioned; contributors must live in the capital. Length: 1000-2000 words. Illustrations: no unsolicited illustrations; enquire first. Payment: by negotiation. Founded 1968.

Music and Letters

Editorial Dr Nigel Fortune, Prof Tim Carter, Dr Katharine Ellis, Music Department, Royal Holloway, University of London, Egham, Surrey TW20 0EX
tel (01784) 443532
Other matters Oxford University Press (Journals Production), Great Clarendon Street, Oxford OX2 6DP
Quarterly £39.00 p.a. (personal rate)

Scholarly articles, up to 10,000 words, on musical subjects, neither merely topical nor purely descriptive. Technical, historical and research matter preferred. Illustrations: music quotations and plates. Payment: none. Founded 1920.

Music Teacher

Rhinegold Publishing Ltd, 241 Shaftesbury Avenue, London WC2H 8EH

tel 0171-333 1747 *fax* 0171-333 1769
e-mail music.teacher@rhinegold.co.uk
Editor Lucien Jenkins
Monthly £2.95

Provides information and articles for both school and private music teachers. Articles and illustrations must both have a teacher, as well as a musical, interest. Length: articles 1000-3000 words. Payment: by arrangement. Founded 1908.

Music Week
Miller Freeman Entertainment Ltd,
8 Montague Close, London SE1 9UR
tel 0171-620 3636 *fax* 0171-401 8035
Editor Selina Webb
Weekly £3.35 (£130.00 p.a.)

News and features on all aspects of producing, manufacturing, marketing and retailing music. Payment: by negotiation. Founded 1959.

Musical Opinion
2 Princes Road, St Leonards-on-Sea,
East Sussex TN37 6EL
tel (01424) 715167 *fax* (01424) 712214
Editor Denby Richards
Quarterly (plus 8 supplements) £3.50 (£24 p.a.)

Suggestions for contributions of musical interest, scholastic, educational, anniversaries, ethnic, and also relating to the organ world. Record, video, CD-Rom, opera, festival, book, music reviews. All editorial matter must be commissioned. Payment: on publication. Illustrations: b&w photos, cartoons. Founded 1877.

Musical Times
63B Jamestown Road, London NW1 7DB
tel/fax 0171-482 5697
Editor Antony Bye
Quarterly £8.00

Musical articles, reviews, 500-6000 words. All material commissioned; no unsolicited material. Illustrations: music. Founded 1844.

My Weekly
D.C. Thomson & Co. Ltd, 80 Kingsway East,
Dundee DD4 8SL
tel (01382) 223131 *fax* (01382) 452491
185 Fleet Street, London EC4A 2HS
tel 0171-242 5086 *fax* 0171-404 5694
Weekly 50p

Serials, from 30,000-80,000 words, suitable for family reading. Short complete stories of 1000-3500 words with humorous, romantic or strong emotional themes. Articles on television stars and

on all subjects of women's interest. Contributions should appeal to women everywhere. Payment: on acceptance. Illustrations: colour and b&w. Founded 1910.

My Weekly Puzzle Time
D.C. Thomson & Co. Ltd, Albert Square,
Dundee DD1 9QJ
tel (01382) 223131 *fax* (01382) 322214
Monthly £1.50

Broad range of puzzles appealing mainly to women. Entertainment value more important than intellectual. Payment: by arrangement. No illustrations. Founded 1993.

My Weekly Story Library
D.C. Thomson & Co. Ltd, Albert Square,
Dundee DD1 9QJ
tel (01382) 223131 *fax* (01382) 322214
185 Fleet Street, London EC4A 2HS
tel 0171-242 5086 *fax* 0171-404 5694
4 p.m. 60p

35,000-37,500-word romantic stories aimed at the post-teenage market. Payment: by arrangement; competitive for the market. No illustrations.

The National Trust Magazine
The National Trust, 36 Queen Anne's Gate,
London SW1H 9AS
tel 0171-222 9251 *fax* 0171-222 5097
web site http://www.ukindex.co.uk/nationaltrust
Editor Gina Guarnieri
3 p.a. Free to members

News and features on the conservation of historic houses, coasts and countryside in the UK. Length: 1000 words (features), 200 words (news). Illustrations: colour transparencies and artwork. Payment: by arrangement; picture library rates. Founded 1969.

Nationwide Magazine
BLA Group Ltd, Vinery Court, 50 Banner Street,
London EC1Y 8QE
tel 0171-577 9300 *fax* 0171-577 9344
Group Editor Andrew Erskine
2 p.a. Free to customers

Home interest and financial articles for Nationwide customers. Founded 1994.

Natural World
River Publishing, Victory House,
14 Leicester Place, London WC2H 7QH
tel 0171-306 0304 *fax* 0171-306 0303
Editor Sarah-Jane Forder
3 p.a. Free to members

National magazine of The Wildlife Trusts. Short articles on UK nature conservation, particularly the work of The Wildlife Trusts; contributors normally have special knowledge of subjects on which they write. Length: up to 1200 words. Payment: by arrangement. Illustrations: line, colour. Founded 1981.

Naturalist

The University, Bradford BD7 1DP
tel (01274) 234212 fax (01274) 234231
e-mail m.r.d.seaward@bradford.ac.uk
Editor Prof M.R.D. Seaward MSc, PhD, DSc
Quarterly £20.00 p.a.

Original papers on all kinds of British natural history subjects, including various aspects of geology, archaeology and environmental science. Length: immaterial. Illustrations: photos and line drawings. Payment: none. Founded 1875.

Nature

Macmillan Magazines Ltd, Porters South, 4-6 Crinan Street, London N1 9XW
tel 0171-833 4000 fax 0171-843 4596
web site http://www.nature.com
Editor Philip Campbell
Weekly £4.95

Devoted to scientific matters and to their bearing upon public affairs. All contributors of articles have specialised knowledge of the subjects with which they deal. Illustrations: line, half-tone. Founded 1869.

Nautical Magazine

Brown, Son & Ferguson Ltd, 4-10 Darnley Street, Glasgow G41 2SD
tel 0141-429 1234 fax 0141-420 1694
e-mail info@skipper.co.uk
web site http://www.skipper.co.uk
Editor L. Ingram-Brown MIMgt, MBIM, MRIN
Monthly £27.60 p.a. (£31.80 p.a. overseas)

Articles relating to nautical and shipping profession, from 1500-2000 words; also translations. Payment: by arrangement. No illustrations. Founded 1832.

Needlecraft

Future Publishing Ltd, 30 Monmouth Street, Bath BA1 2BW
tel (01225) 442244 fax (01225) 732398
e-mail sgrant@futurenet.co.uk
Editor Sue Grant
4-weekly £2.99

Mainly project-based stitching designs with step-by-step instructions. Features with tight stitching focus (e.g. technique,

personality). Length: 1000 words. Illustrated. Payment: £150-£200. Founded 1991.

.net The Internet Magazine

Future Publishing Ltd, 30 Monmouth Street, Bath BA1 2BW
tel (01225) 442244 fax (01225) 732291
e-mail netmag@futurenet.co.uk
web site http://www.netmag.co.uk
Editor Richard Longhurst
Monthly CD edition £3.99 (non-CD edition £2.99)

Articles, features and news on the Internet. Length: 1000-3000 words. Payment: negotiable. Illustrations: colour. Founded 1994.

New Beacon

RNIB, 224 Great Portland Street, London W1N 6AA
tel 0171-388 1266
Editor Ann Lee
Monthly £1.70

Articles on all aspects of living with a visual impairment (blindness or partial sight). Published in clear print, braille, disk and tape editions. Length: from 500 words. Payment: by arrangement. Illustrations: half-tone. Founded 1930; as Beacon 1917.

New Blackfriars

(incorporating Life of the Spirit)
Blackfriars, 25 George Square, Edinburgh EH8 9LD
tel 0131-650 0901 fax 0131-650 0902
Editor Rev. Fergus Kerr OP
Monthly £2.20 (£17.00 p.a.)

Critical review, surveying the field of theology, philosophy, sociology and the arts, from the standpoint of Christian principles and their application to the problems of the modern world. Length: 2500-6000 words. Payment: none. Founded 1920.

New Buckinghamshire Countryside

4 Mill Bridge, Hertford SG14 1PY
tel (01992) 553571 fax (01992) 587713
Editor Sandra Small
Bi-monthly £1.25

Articles relating to Buckinghamshire. No poetry. Length: 1000 words. Illustrations: colour transparencies and b&w prints, artwork. Payment: £25 (articles); £20. Founded 1995.

New Christian Herald

Christian Media, 96 Dominion Road, Worthing, West Sussex BN14 8JP

tel (01903) 821082 *fax* (01903) 821081
e-mail editorial@newchristianherald.co.uk
web site http://www.newchristianherald.org
Weekly 55p

Evangelical Christian paper with strong emphasis on news and current affairs. Features up to 700 words – profiles, the changing church, Christians, and contemporary culture (e.g. media, TV, music); cartoons. No short stories. Payment: £20-£50, depending on length/pictures used.

New Electronics

Findlay Publications Ltd, Franks Hall, Franks Lane, Horton Kirby, Dartford, Kent DA4 9LL
tel (01322) 222222 *fax* (01322) 289577
e-mail ne@findlay.co.uk
web site http://www.neon.co.uk
Editor Graham Pitcher
Fortnightly (£88 p.a. UK, £165 p.a. airmail)

Technical/technology news articles, case studies, and career and skills development articles. Length: 1500 words (features), 800 words (news). Illustrations: colour photos, artwork and cartoons. Payment: £120 per 1000 words. Founded 1968.

New Humanist

Rationalist Press Association, Bradlaugh House, 47 Theobald's Road, London WC1X 8SP
tel 0171-430 1371 *fax* 0171-430 1271
e-mail jim.rpa@humanism.org.uk
Editor Jim Herrick
Quarterly £2.50

Articles on current affairs, philosophy, science, literature and humanism. Length: 1000-3000 words. Illustrations: b&w photos. Payment: nominal; none for photos. Founded 1885.

New Impact

Anser House, Courtyard Offices, 3 High Street, Marlow, Bucks. SL7 1AX
tel (01628) 481581 *fax* (01628) 475570
Managing Editor Elaine Sihera
Bi-monthly £35.00 p.a. (business), £25.00 p.a. (individual), £12.00 p.a. (students)

'Promoting enterprise, training and diversity.' Articles, features and news on any aspect of training, business and women's issues to suit a multicultural audience; also profiles of personalities, short stories. Length: 900-1000 words. Illustrations: b&w photos if related to profiles. Payment: £40 (depending on merit); none for photos. Founded 1993.

New Internationalist

55 Rectory Road, Oxford OX4 1BW
tel (01865) 728181 *fax* (01865) 793152
e-mail ni@newint.org
web site http://www.newint.org
Editors Vanessa Baird, Chris Brazier, David Ransom, Nikki van der Gaag
Monthly £2.50 (£24.85 p.a.)

World issues, ranging from food to feminism to peace – examines one subject each month. Length: up to 2000 words. Illustrations: line, half-tone, colour, cartoons. Payment: £150 per 1000 words. Founded 1973.

New Law Journal

Butterworth & Co. (Publishers) Ltd, Halsbury House, 35 Chancery Lane, London WC2A 1EL
tel 0171-400 2500 *fax* 0171-400 2583
Editor James Morton
48 p.a. £4.00

Articles and news on all aspects of the legal profession. Length: up to 1800 words. Payment: by arrangement. Founded 1975.

New Library World

MCB University Press, 60-62 Toller Lane, Bradford, West Yorkshire BD8 9BY
tel (01274) 777700 *fax* (01274) 785200
web site http://www.mcb.co.uk
7 p.a. £1249.00 p.a.

Professional and bibliographical articles. Includes Librarians' World (6 p.a.), 16pp newsletter 'for librarians by librarians'. Payment: none. Founded 1898.

New Media Age

Centaur Newsletters, St Giles House, 50 Poland Street, London W1V 4AX
tel 0171-970 4000 *fax* 0171-970 4899
e-mail mikeb@centaur.co.uk
Editor Mike Butcher
Weekly £164.00 p.a.

News and articles on all areas of the communications revolution for multimedia companies. Phone first with ideas; no uncommissioned material. Length: 1000-3000 (articles), 250-500 words (news). Illustrations: none. Payment: £150-£170 per 1000 words. Founded 1995.

New Musical Express

IPC Magazines Ltd, 25th Floor, King's Reach Tower, Stamford Street, London SE1 9LS
tel 0171-261 5000 *fax* 0171-261 5185
Editor Steve Sutherland
Weekly £1.05

Authoritative articles and news stories on the world's rock and movie personalities. Length: by arrangement. Preliminary letter or phone call desirable. Payment: by arrangement. Illustrations: action photos with strong news angle of recording personalities, cartoons.

New Scientist

RBI Ltd, 151 Wardour Street, London W1V 4BN
tel 0171-331 2701 *fax* 0171-331 2772
e-mail news@newscientist.com
web site http://www.newscientist.com
Editor Alun Anderson
Weekly £1.80

Authoritative articles of topical importance on all aspects of science and technology (length: 1000-3000 words); preliminary letter or telephone call desirable. Short items from specialists also considered for Science, This Week, Forum and Technology. Intending contributors should study recent copies of the magazine. Payment: varies but average £300 per 1000 words. Illustrations: line, half-tone, colour, cartoons.

New Statesman

(formerly New Statesman & Society)
Victoria Station House, 191 Victoria Street, London SW1E 5NE
tel 0171-828 1232 *fax* 0171-828 1881
e-mail info@newstatesman.co.uk
Editor Peter Wilby
Weekly £2.00

Interested in news, reportage and analysis of current political and social issues at home and overseas, plus book reviews, poetry, general articles and coverage of the arts, environment and science seen from the perspective of the British Left but written in a stylish, witty and unpredictable way. Length: strictly according to the value of the piece. Illustrations: commissioned for specific articles, though artists' samples considered for future reference; occasional cartoons. Payment: by agreement. Founded 1913.

New Theatre Quarterly

Great Robhurst, Woodchurch, Ashford, Kent TN26 3TB
Editors Clive Barker, Simon Trussler
Quarterly £13.00 (£28.00 p.a.)

Articles, interviews, documentation, reference material covering all aspects of live theatre. An informed, factual and serious approach essential. Preliminary discussion and synopsis desirable. Payment: by arrangement. Illustrations: line, half-tone. Founded 1985; as *Theatre Quarterly* 1971.

The New Welsh Review

Chapter Arts Centre, Market Road, Cardiff CF5 1QE
tel/fax (01222) 665529/515014
Editor Robin Reeves
Quarterly £5.50 (£16.00 p.a., £30.00 2 yrs)

Literary – critical articles, short stories, poems, book reviews, interviews and profiles. Especially, but not exclusively, concerned with Welsh writing in English. Theatre in Wales section. Length: (articles) up to 4000 words. Illustrations: line, half-tone, cartoons; colour cover. Payment: £15-£20 per 1000 words (articles); £10-£25 per poem, £40-£70 per short story, £15-£25 per review, £10-£20 per illustration. Founded 1988.

New Woman

EMAP Élan, Endeavour House,
189 Shaftesbury Avenue, London WC2H 8JG
tel 0171-437 9011 *fax* 0171-208 3585
Editor Dawn Bebe
Monthly £2.00

Features up to 2000 words. Occasionally accepts unsolicited articles; enclose sae for return. No fiction. Payment: at or above NUJ rates. Illustrated. Founded 1988.

New World

United Nations Association, 3 Whitehall Court, London SW1A 2EL
tel 0171-930 2931 *fax* 0171-930 5893
e-mail UNA_UK@compuserve.com
4 p.a. £1.00

Review of UN activities, of UNA campaigns and of different viewpoints on major international issues confronting the United Nations. Occasionally takes cartoons. No payment.

The New Writer

(incorporating Acclaim and Quartos)
PO Box 60, Cranbrook, Kent TN17 2ZR
tel (01580) 212626 *fax* (01580) 212041
Editor Suzanne Ruthven
Publisher Merric Davidson
10 p.a. £2.95

Features, short stories from the annual Ian St James Awards shortlist and from subscribers, poems, news and reviews. Seeks forward-looking articles on all aspects of the written word that demonstrate the writer's grasp of contemporary writing and current editorial/publishing policies. Length: approx. 1000 words (articles), longer pieces considered; 1000-2000 words (features). Payment: £20 per 1000 words (articles), £10 (stories), £3 (poems). Founded 1996.

Night & Day – see Mail on Sunday in National newspapers UK and Ireland, page 3

19

IPC Magazines Ltd, King's Reach Tower, Stamford Street, London SE1 9LS
tel 0171-261 6410
Editor Lee Kynaston
Monthly £1.80

Glossy fashion and general interest magazine for young women aged 17-22, including beauty, music and social features of strong contemporary interest. All illustrations commissioned. Payment: by arrangement. Founded 1968.

Numismatic Chronicle

Department of Coins and Medals, Fitzwilliam Museum, Cambridge CB2 1RB
tel (01223) 332917 *fax* (01223) 332923
Editor Dr Mark Blackburn
£24.00 per annual volume

Journal of the Royal Numismatic Society. Articles on coins and medals. Articles relating to coins and medals are unpaid, and contributions should reach a high academic standard. Founded 1839.

Nursery Projects

Scholastic Ltd, Villiers House, Clarendon Avenue, Leamington Spa, Warks. CV32 5PR
tel (01926) 887799 *fax* (01926) 337322
e-mail scholastic@compuserve.com
web site http://www.scholastic.co.uk
Editor Jane Morgan
Bi-monthly £2.75

Practical theme-based activities for educators working with 3-5 year-olds. All ideas based on the Desirable Outcomes. Material mostly commissioned. Length: 500-1000 words. Illustrations: b&w and line; colour posters. Payment: by arrangement. Founded 1997.

Nursery World

Admiral House, 66-68 East Smithfield, London E1 9XY
tel 0171-782 3000
Editor Liz Roberts
Weekly £1.10

For all grades of primary school, nursery and child care staff, nannies, foster parents and all concerned with the care of expectant mothers, babies and young children. Authoritative and informative articles, 800 or 1600 words, and photos, on all aspects of child welfare and early education, from 0-8 years, in the UK. Practical ideas and leisure crafts. No short stories. Payment: by arrangement. Illustrations: line, half-tone, colour.

Nursing Times and Nursing Mirror

Macmillan Magazines Ltd, Porters South, 4-6 Crinan Street, London N1 9XW
tel 0171-843 4600 *fax* 0171-843 4633
Editor Tricia Reid
Weekly £1.00

Articles of clinical interest, nursing education and nursing policy. Illustrated articles not longer than 2000 words. Contributions from other than health professionals sometimes accepted. Press day, Monday. Illustrations: photos, line, cartoons. Payment: NUJ rates; by arrangement for illustrations. Founded 1905.

Occupational Health

Reed Business Information, Quadrant House, The Quadrant, Sutton, Surrey SM2 5AS
tel 0181-652 4669 *fax* 0181-652 8805
e-mail catrionamarchant@@rbi.co.uk
Editor Catriona Marchant
12 p.a. Subscription rates on application

News and features on occupational health-related subjects for the OH profession. Length: 1500-2400 words. Illustrations: colour transparencies. Payment: by arrangement; none. Founded 1947.

Off Licence News

William Reed Publishing Ltd, Broadfield Park, Crawley, West Sussex RH11 9RT
tel (01293) 613400 *fax* (01293) 610320
e-mail editorial@off-licence-news.co.uk
web site http://www.foodanddrink.co.uk
Weekly £55 p.a.

News and features for the off licence trade. Length: 1000-2000 words (features); news: flexible. Payment: £130 per 1000 words (features). Founded 1970.

Office Secretary

Peebles Publishing, Brookmead House, 8 Thorney Leys Business Park, Witney, Oxon OX8 7GE
tel (01993) 775545 *fax* (01993) 778884
Editor Elizabeth Toppin
Quarterly £10.00 p.a.

Serious features on anything of interest to senior secretaries and executive PAs. No unsolicited MSS; ideas only. Illustrations: colour transparencies, cartoons. Payment: by negotiation. Founded 1986.

OK! Magazine

Northern & Shell plc, Northern & Shell Tower, City Harbour, London E14 9GL
tel 0171-308 5091 *fax* 0171-308 5082
Editor Sharon Ring
Weekly £1.20

Exclusive celebrity interviews and photographs. Submit ideas in writing. Length: 1000 words. Illustrations: colour. Payment: £150-£250,000 per feature. Founded 1993.

The Oldie

45-46 Poland Street, London W1V 4AU
tel 0171-734 2225 *fax* 0171-734 2226
Editor Richard Ingrams
Monthly £2.20

General interest magazine reflecting attitudes of older people but aimed at a wider audience. Welcomes features (800-2000 words) on all subjects. Enclose sae for reply/return of MSS. Illustrations: welcomes b&w and colour cartoons. Payment: approx. £80-£100 per 1000 words; minimum £40 for cartoons. Founded 1992.

ONtheBALL

Moondance Publications Ltd, Design Works, William Street, Gateshead, Tyne & Wear NE10 0JP
tel 0191-420 8383 *fax* 0191-420 4950
e-mail ONtheBALL@cableinet.co.uk
Editor Jennifer O'Neill
Bi-monthly £1.50

News, features and reviews of women's football in the UK and abroad. Aimed at the player rather than the spectator, it includes training tips and articles on tactics in the game, etc and addresses a wide range of both serious and humorous issues relating to the women's game. Length: 1000 words (features/articles), 100 words (news), 500 words (stories). Illustrations: colour. Founded 1996.

Opera

1A Mountgrove Road, London N5 2LU
tel 0171-359 1037 *fax* 0171-354 2700
Editor Rodney Milnes
13 p.a. £2.70

Articles on general subjects appertaining to opera; reviews; criticisms. Length: up to 2000 words. Payment: by arrangement. Illustrations: photos.

Opera Now

241 Shaftesbury Avenue, London WC2H 8EH
tel 0171-333 1740 *fax* 0171-333 1769
web site http://www.operadata.co.uk
Editor Ashutosh Khandekar
Bi-monthly £4.95

Articles, news, reviews on opera. All material commissioned only. Length: 150-1500 words. Illustrations: colour and b&w photos, line, cartoons. Payment: £120 per 1000 words. Founded 1989.

Options

IPC Magazines Ltd, King's Reach Tower, Stamford Street, London SE1 9LS
tel 0171-261 5000 *fax* 0171-261 7344
Editor Maureen Rice
Monthly £2.00

Aimed at women aged 25-35. Careers, emotional and sexual matters, health and well-being, women's issues, first-class celebrity interviews and profiles. Mostly commissioned. Length: 1000-3000 words. Payment: by arrangement. Founded 1982.

Orbis

27 Valley View, Primrose, Jarrow, Tyne & Wear NE32 5QT
tel 0191-489 7055 *fax/modem* 0191-430 1297
e-mail mikeshields@compuserve.com
Editor Mike Shields
Quarterly £15.00 p.a.

Poetry, prose pieces (up to 1000 words), reviews, letters. Submit material by post. Annual competition for rhymed poetry. Do not submit material by fax or e-mail. Payment: by arrangement. Illustrations: line. Founded 1968.

The Organ

5 Aldborough Road, St Leonards-on-Sea, East Sussex TN37 6SE
tel (01424) 422225 *fax* (01424) 712214
Editor Dr Brian Hick
Quarterly £17.00 p.a. (£23.00 p.a. overseas)

Articles, 1000-5000 words, relating to any type of organ, organist or composer: historical, technical and artistic; reviews of music, recordings, performances. Payment: nominal. Illustrations: line, half-tone, colour. Founded 1921.

Organic Gardening

Wardnest Ltd, PO Box 4, Wiveliscombe, Taunton, Somerset TA4 2QY

tel (01984) 623998 *fax* (01984) 623998
Editor Basil Caplan
Monthly £2.15

Articles and features on all aspects of organic gardening. All material commissioned. Length: 600-2000 words. Illustrations: colour and b&w photos, line drawings, cartoons. Payment: by arrangement. Founded 1988.

Our Baby

IPC Magazines Ltd, King's Reach Tower, Stamford Street, London SE1 9LS
tel 0171-261 7986 *fax* 0171-261 6542
web site http://www.ipc.co.uk
Editor-in-Chief Jayne Marsden
Monthly £1.80

Aimed at first-time mums and dads, including product information as well as health news and features on pregnancy and baby care; also readers' birth stories (£25 for 500 words). Material mostly commissioned. Length: varies. Illustrations: brilliant, colour photos of mums- and dads-to-be and newborn babies. Payment: negotiable. Founded 1994.

Our Dogs

Oxford Road Station Approach, Manchester M60 1SX
tel 0161-236 2660 *fax* 0161-236 5534/0892
Editor William Moores
Weekly £1.35

Articles and news on the breeding and showing of pedigree dogs. Illustrations: b&w photos. Payment: NUJ rates; £7.50 per photo. Founded 1895.

Outposts Poetry Quarterly

22 Whitewell Road, Frome, Somerset BA11 4EL
tel/fax (01373) 466653
Editor Roland John
Founder Howard Sergeant MBE
Quarterly £4.00 (£14.00 p.a.)

Poems, essays and critical articles on poets and their work; poetry competitions. Payment: by arrangement. Founded 1943.

Oxford Poetry

Magdalen College, Oxford OX1 4AU
Editors Graham Nelson, Robert Macfarlane
3 p.a. £3.00 (£9.00 p.a.)

Previously unpublished poems, both unsolicited and commissioned. Payment: none. Founded 1983.

Parents

EMAP Élan, Endeavour House, 189 Shaftesbury Avenue, London WC2H 8JG
tel 0171-437 9011 *fax* 0171-208 3584
Associate Editor Ruth Beattie
Monthly £1.80

The magazine with smart solutions for today's mums. Articles on pregnancy, childbirth, general family health, food, fashion, child upbringing, development and early education up to age 4, and marital relations. No unsolicited MSS. Illustrations: b&w or colour. Payment: in accordance with national magazine standards; by arrangement for illustrations. Founded 1976.

Park Home & Holiday Caravan

(formerly Mobile & Holiday Homes)
Link House, Dingwall Avenue, Croydon CR9 2TA
tel 0181-686 2599 *fax* 0181-781 6044
Editor Anne Webb
Monthly £2.00

Informative articles on residential mobile homes (park homes) and holiday static caravans – personal experience articles, site features, news items. No preliminary letter. Payment: by arrangement. Illustrations: line, half-tone, colour transparencies, cartoons. Founded 1960.

PC Direct

Ziff-Davis UK Ltd, International House, 1 St Katharine's Way, London E1 9UN
tel 0171-903 6800 *fax* 0171-903 6006
web site http://www.pcdirect.co.uk
Editor-in-Chief Karen Packham
Monthly £1.99

News, features, reviews and technical information for the direct computer buyer. All material commissioned. Length: 500-6000 words. Illustrations: colour photos and illustrations, including computer generated. Payment: £200 per 1000 words; varies for illustrations according to subject/media. Founded 1991.

PC Review

Future Publishing, 30 Monmouth Street, Bath BA1 2BW
tel (01225) 442244 *fax* (01225) 732361
e-mail pcreview@futurenet.co.uk
web site http://www.futurenet.co.uk
Editor Garrick Webster
Monthly £4.99

Features, previews, reviews of PC entertainment – commissioned only, by

arrangement. Illustrations: colour transparencies; ideas for line art, diagrams,
charts, etc. Payment: by negotiation.

PCS, The Magazine
(formerly Red Tape)
Public and Commercial Services Union,
160 Falcon Road, London SW11 2LN
tel 0171-924 2727 *fax* 0171-924 1847
Editor Val Stansfield
10 p.a. Free to members
Well-written articles on Civil Service,
trade union and general subjects considered. Length: 750-1400 words. Also photos and humorous drawings of interest to
Civil Servants. Illustrations: line, half-
tone. Payment: NUJ rates.

Peace News
5 Caledonian Road, London N1 9DX
tel 0171-278 3344 *fax* 0171-278 0444
e-mail peacenews@gn.apc.org
web site http://www.gn.apc.org/peacenews
Monthly £1.00
Political articles based on nonviolence in
every aspect of human life. Illustrations:
line, half-tone. No payment. Founded
1936.

Peninsular Magazine
Cherrybite Publications, Linden Cottage,
45 Burton Road, Little Neston,
South Wirral L64 4AE
tel 0151-353 0967
Editor Shelagh Nugent
Quarterly £3.00 (£10.50 p.a.)
Literary magazine. Entertaining and
unusual stories and interesting, amusing
or informative articles. Length: 1000-
3000 words. Payment: £5 per 1000 words
plus free copy. Founded 1996.

Pensions World
Tolley Publishing Co. Ltd, Tolley House,
2 Addiscombe Road, Croydon,
Surrey CR9 5AF
tel 0181-686 9141 *fax* 0181-760 0588
e-mail stephanie_hawthorne@tolley.co.uk
web site http://www.pensionsworld.co.uk
Editor Stephanie Hawthorne
Monthly £60.00 p.a.
Specialist articles on pensions, investment and law. No unsolicited articles; all
material is commissioned. Length: 1500
words. Payment: by negotiation.
Founded 1972.

People Management
Personnel Publications Ltd, 17 Britton Street,
London EC1M 5NQ

tel 0171-880 6200 *fax* 0171-336 7635
Editor Rob MacLachlan
Fortnightly £5.00 (£75.00 p.a.)
Journal of the Institute of Personnel and
Development. News items and feature
articles on recruitment and selection,
training and development; pay and performance management; industrial psychology; employee relations; employment law; working practices and new
practical ideas in personnel management
in industry and commerce. Length: up to
2500 words. Payment: by arrangement.
Illustrations: contact art editor.

People's Friend
D.C. Thomson & Co. Ltd, 80 Kingsway East,
Dundee DD4 8SL
tel (01382) 223131 *fax* (01382) 452491
185 Fleet Street, London EC4A 2HS
tel 0171-242 5086 *fax* 0171-404 5694
Weekly 50p
Illustrated weekly appealing to women of
all ages and devoted to their personal
and home interests, especially knitting,
fashion and cookery. Serials (60,000-
70,000 words) and complete stories
(1500-3000 words) of strong romantic
and emotional appeal. Stories for children are considered. No preliminary letter required. Illustrations: colour and
b&w. Payment: on acceptance. Founded
1869.

People's Friend Library
D.C. Thomson & Co. Ltd, 2 Albert Square,
Dundee DD1 9QJ
tel (01382) 223131*fax* (01382) 322214
185 Fleet Street, London EC4A 2HS
tel 0171-242 5086 *fax* 0171-404 5694
2 p.m. 90p
50,000-55,000-word family and romantic
stories aimed at 30+ age group. Payment:
by arrangement. No illustrations.

Perfect Home
DMG Home Interest Magazines Ltd,
Equitable House, Lyon Road, Harrow,
Middlesex HA1 2EW
tel 0181-515 2000 *fax* 0181-515 2080
e-mail perfect-home@dmgexhib.co.uk
Editor Julia Smith
Monthly £1.60
Home-related features: readers' homes,
craft, finance, DIY, show houses, product
testing/reviews, gardening. Length: 800-
1000 words. Payment: by merit.
Illustrated. Founded 1992.

82   Newspapers and magazines

Period Living & Traditional Homes
EMAP Élan, Endeavour House,
189 Shaftesbury Avenue, London WC2H 8JG
tel 0171-437 9011 *fax* 0171-434 0656
Editor Sue Garland
Monthly £2.70
Articles and features on decoration, furnishings, renovation of period homes; traditional cookery; gardens, crafts, decorating in a period style. Illustrated. Payment: varies, according to work required. Founded 1990.

Personal – see Sunday Mirror in National newspapers UK and Ireland, page 3

Personal Computer World
VNU House, 32-34 Broadwick Street,
London W1A 2HG
tel 0171-316 9000 *fax* 0171-316 9313
e-mail pcw@vnu.co.uk
web site http://www.pcw.co.uk
Editor Gordon Laing
Monthly £2.95
Articles about computers; reviews. Length: 800-5000 words. Payment: from £150 per 1000 words. Illustrations: line, half-tone, colour. Founded 1978.

Personal Finance
Charterhouse Communications Group plc,
4 Tabernacle Street, London EC2A 4LU
tel 0171-638 1916 *fax* 0171-638 3128
e-mail chartcom@dircon.co.uk
Editor Juliet Oxborrow
Monthly £2.60
Articles and features on savings and investment, general family finance, of interest both to new investors and financially aware readers. All material commissioned: submit ideas in writing to the editor. Length: 1500-3000 words. Illustrations: colour and b&w photos, colour line drawings. Payment: £150-£175 per 1000 words; £50-£150 for illustrations. Founded 1994.

Petroleum Economist
(incorporating Gas World International)
Petroleum Economist Ltd, Baird House,
15-17 St Cross Street, London EC1N 8UN
tel 0171-831 5588 *fax* 0171-831 4567
Editor Derek Bamber
Monthly £12.00 (£95.00 p.a., £120/$195 p.a. USA/Europe)
Full news coverage and technical articles on all aspects of engineering and man-

agement in the gas industry. Length: up to 2500 words. Pictures and news items of topical interest accepted. Payment: by arrangement. Founded 1884.

The Pharmaceutical Journal
1 Lambeth High Street, London SE1 7JN
tel 0171-735 9141 *fax* 0171-582 7327
e-mail editor@pharmj.org.uk
Editor D. Simpson FRPharmS
Weekly £3.00
Official Journal of the Royal Pharmaceutical Society of Great Britain. Articles on any aspect of pharmacy may be submitted. Payment: by arrangement. Illustrations: half-tone, colour. Founded 1841.

Photo Answers
EMAP Apex Publications, Apex House,
Oundle Road, Peterborough PE2 9NP
tel (01733) 898100 *fax* (01733) 894472
e-mail photo-answers@ecm.emap.com
Editor Roger Payne
Monthly £2.30
Aimed at photographic beginners. Little opportunity for freelance writers, but plenty of scope for quality photos. Payment: £25 upwards, depending on size used; colour or mono.

Photo Technique
IPC Magazines, Kings Reach Tower,
Stamford Street, London SE1 9LS
tel 0171-261 5100 *fax* 0171-261 5404
Editor Liz Walker
Monthly £2.60
For all photographers seeking to improve their camera, studio and darkroom skills. Aims to inspire the reader with great photography and an editorial tone which doesn't baffle or patronise. Please read magazine before submitting illustrated ideas for step-by-step features and general photo features. Some scope for field testing new equipment. Illustrations: max. 20 prints or transparencies; no prints over 10 x 8in. Payment: £100 per 1000 words; £90 per full page. Founded 1993.

Photon
(formerly photo pro)
Icon Publications Ltd, Maxwell Place,
Maxwell Lane, Kelso, Roxburghshire TD5 7BB
tel (01573) 226032 *fax* (01573) 226000
e-mail david@maxwellplace.demon.co.uk
web site http://www.photonpub.co.uk/photon/
Editor David Kilpatrick
Monthly £2.95

Illustrated features on professional and craft photography. All material commissioned. Length: 750-2500 words. Illustrations: b&w and colour photos. Payment: £50-£300 per feature, including photos. Founded 1989.

Picture Postcard Monthly
15 Debdale Lane, Keyworth,
Nottingham NG12 5HT
tel 0115-937 4079 *fax* 0115-937 6197
Editor Brian Lund
Monthly £1.95 (£22.00 p.a.)
Articles, news and features for collectors of old or modern picture postcards. Length: 500-2000 words. Illustrations: colour and b&w. Payment: £25 per 1000 words; 50p per print. Founded 1978.

Pig Farming
Wharfedale Road, Ipswich IP1 4LG
tel (01473) 241122 *fax* (01473) 240501
Editor Roger Abbott
Monthly £26.00 p.a.
Practical, well-illustrated articles on all aspects of pigmeat production required, particularly those dealing with new ideas in pig management, feeding, housing, health and hygiene, product innovation and marketing. Length: 800-1200 words. Payment: by arrangement. Illustrations: line, half-tone, colour, cartoons.

Pilot
The Clock House, 28 Old Town, London SW4 0LB
tel 0171-498 2506 *fax* 0171-498 6920
e-mail pilotmagazine@compuserve.com
Editor James Gilbert
Monthly £2.75
Feature articles on general aviation, private and business flying. Illustrations: line, half-tone, colour, cartoons. Payment: £100-£1000 per article on acceptance; £26 for each photo used. Founded 1968.

The Pink Paper
72 Holloway Road, London N7 8NZ
tel 0171-296 6000 *fax* 0171-957 0046
e-mail editorial @pinkpaper.co.uk
Editor Tim Teeman
Weekly Free
National newspaper for lesbians and gay men. Features (500-1500 words) and news (100-500 words) plus lifestyle section (features 350-1300 words) on any gay-related subject. Illustrations: b&w photos and line plus colour 'scene' pho-

tos. Payment: £40-£100 for words; £30-£60 for illustrations. Founded 1987.

Planet
PO Box 44, Aberystwyth, Ceredigion SY23 5BS
tel (01970) 611255 *fax* (01970) 611197
Editor John Barnie
6 p.a. £2.75 (£13.00 p.a.)
Short stories, poems, topical articles on Welsh current affairs, politics, the environment and society. New literature in English. Length of articles: 1000-3500 words. Payment: £40 per 1000 words for prose; £25 minimum per poem. Illustrations: line, half-tone, cartoons. Founded 1970-9; relaunched 1985.

Playdays
BBC Worldwide Ltd, Room A1130, Woodlands, 80 Wood Lane, London W12 0TT
tel 0181-576 2164 *fax* 0181-576 2941
Editor Andrea Wickstead
Fortnightly 95p
Highly illustrated magazine of short stories, poems and activities for children aged 2-6 years old. No written material considered. Illustrations: colour and b&w artwork. Payment: £100 per page. Founded 1994.

Plays & Players Applause
Northway House, 1379 High Road,
London N20 9LP
tel 0181-343 9977 *fax* 0181-492 0439
Editor Sandra Rennie
Monthly £2.95
Articles, reviews and photos on world theatre. Payment: by arrangement. Illustrations: line, photos.

PN Review
(formerly Poetry Nation)
Carcanet Press Ltd, 4th Floor, Conavon Court, 12 Blackfriars Street, Manchester M3 5BQ
tel 0161-834 8730 *fax* 0161-832 0084
e-mail pnr@carcanet.u-net.com
Editor Robert Minhinnick
6 p.a. £4.50 (£29.50 p.a.)
Poems, essays, reviews, translations. Submissions by post only. Payment: by arrangement. Founded 1973.

Poetry Ireland Review/Éigse Éireann
Bermingham Tower, Upper Yard, Dublin Castle, Dublin 2, Republic of Ireland
tel (01) 671 4632 *fax* (01) 671 4634
e-mail poetry@iol.ie
Editor Catherine Phil MacCarthy
Managing Editor Niamh Morris
Quarterly £5.99 (£24.00/$52.00 p.a.)

Poetry. Features and articles by arrangement. Payment: £10 per contribution. Founded 1981.

Poetry London Newsletter

26 Clacton Road, London E17 8AR
tel 0181-520 6693 fax 0171-404 3598
e-mail pdaniels@easynet.co.uk
Editors Pascale Petit, Katherine Gallagher, Peter Daniels, Greta Stoddart, Kevan Johnson
3 p.a. £9.00 p.a.

Poems of the highest standard, articles/reviews on any aspect of modern poetry. Contributors must be knowledgeable about contemporary poetry. Payment: £20 minimum or 4 copies of magazine. Founded 1988.

Poetry Nottingham International

71 Saxton Avenue, Heanor,
Derbyshire DE75 7PZ
Editor Cathy Grindrod
Quarterly £2.25 (£9.00 p.a. UK, 15.00 p.a. overseas)

Poems; letters; articles up to 500 words on current issues in the poetry world. Payment: complimentary copy. Founded 1946.

Poetry Review

22 Betterton Street, London WC2H 9BU
tel 0171-420 9880 fax 0171-240 4818
e-mail poetrysoc@dial.pipex.com
web site http://www.poetrysoc.com/
Editor Peter Forbes
Quarterly £23.00 p.a. (£30.00 p.a. institutions, schools and libraries)

Poems, features and reviews; also cartoons. Send no more than 6 poems with sae. Preliminary study of magazine essential. Payment: £40 per poem.

Poetry Wales

First Floor, 2 Wyndham Street,
Bridgend CF31 1EF
Editor Robert Minhinnick
Books for review Amy Wack,
20 Denton Road, Canton,
Cardiff CF5 1PE
Quarterly £3.00 (£12.00 p.a. inc. postage)

Poems mainly in English and mainly by Welsh people or resident: other contributors (and Welsh language poetry) also published. Articles on Welsh literature in English and in Welsh, as well as on poetry from other countries. Special features; reviews on poetry and wider matters. Payment: by arrangement. Founded 1965.

Police Journal

Tolley House, 2 Addiscombe Road, Croydon,
Surrey CR9 5AF
tel 0181-686 9141 fax 0181-287 3337
e-mail jpn@tolleys.co.uk
Editor Peter Hermitage QPM
Quarterly £62.00 p.a.

Articles of technical or professional interest to the Police Service throughout the world. Payment: by negotiation. Illustrations: half-tone. Founded 1928.

Police Review

Celcon House, 5th Floor, 289-293 High Holborn,
London WC1V 7HU
tel 0171-440 4700 fax 0171-405 7163
Editor Gary Mason
Weekly £1.25

News and features of interest to the police and legal professions. Length: 200-2000 words. Illustrations: colour and b&w photos, line, cartoons. Payment: NUJ rates. Founded 1893.

The Political Quarterly

Basil Blackwell Ltd, 108 Cowley Road,
Oxford OX4 1JF
tel (01865) 791100
Editors Tony Wright MP, House of Commons, Westminster, London SW1A 0AA; and Andrew Gamble, Professor of Politics, University of Sheffield S10 2TU
Literary Editor Bernard Crick, 8A Bellevue Terrace, Edinburgh EH7 4DT
Assistant Editor Gillian Bromley, PO Box 26, Wheatley, Oxon OX33 1FR
5 p.a.

Journal devoted to topical aspects of national and international politics and public administration; takes a progressive, but not a party, point of view. Send articles to Assistant Editor; send books for review to the Literary Editor. Length: average 5000 words. Payment: about £100 per article. Founded 1930.

Pony

Haslemere House, Lower Street, Haslemere,
Surrey GU27 2PE
tel (01428) 651551 fax (01428) 653888
Editor Janet Rising
Monthly £1.65

Lively articles and short stories with a horsy theme aimed at young readers, 8 to 14 years old. Technical accuracy and young, fresh writing essential. Length: up to 800 words. Payment: by arrangement. Illustrations: drawings (commissioned), photos, cartoons. Founded 1949.

Popular Crafts

Nexus Special Interests Ltd, Nexus House,
Swanley, Kent BR8 8HU
tel (01322) 660070 *fax* (01322) 667633
Editor Carolyn Schulz
Monthly £2.25

Covers all kinds of crafts. Projects with
full instructions, profiles and successes
of craftspeople, news on craft group
activities, readers' homes, celebrity interviews, general craft-related articles.
Welcomes written outlines of ideas.
Payment: by arrangement. Illustrated.

Post Magazine & Insurance Week

Timothy Benn Publishing Ltd, 39 Earlham Street,
London WC2H 9LD
tel 0171-306 7000 *fax* 0171-306 7101
e-mail postmag@benn.co.uk
Editor-in-Chief David Worsfold
Weekly £2.00 (£99.00 p.a.)

Commissioned specialist articles on topics of interest to insurance professionals;
news, especially from overseas stringers.
Length: 1700-2000 words. Illustrations:
colour photos, colour and b&w cartoons
and line drawings. Payment: £150-£200
per 1000 words; photos £30-£60, car-
toons/line by negotiation. Founded 1840.

Poultry World

Quadrant House, The Quadrant, Sutton,
Surrey SM2 5AS
tel 0181-652 4021 *fax* 0181-652 4042
e-mail poultry.world@rbi.co.uk
Editor John Farrant
Monthly £2.00

Articles on poultry breeding, production,
marketing and packaging. News of international poultry interest. Payment: by
arrangement. Illustrations: photos, line.

PR Week

Haymarket Marketing Publications,
174 Hammersmith Road, London W6 7JP
tel 0171-413 4520 *fax* 0171-413 4509
Editor Stephen Farish
Weekly Controlled circulation (£60.00 p.a.)

News and features on public relations.
Length: approx. 800-3000 words.
Payment: £185 per 1000 words. Illustra-
tions: colour and b&w. Founded 1984.

Practical Boat Owner

Westover House, West Quay Road, Poole,
Dorset BH15 1JG
tel (01202) 680593
e-mail pbo@ipc.co.uk
web site http://www.ybw.com

Editor Rodger Witt
Monthly £2.70

Hints, tips and practical articles for
cruising skippers – power and sail. Send
synopsis first. Payment: by negotiation.
Illustrations: photos or drawings.
Founded 1967.

Practical Caravan

Haymarket Magazines Ltd, 60 Waldegrave Road,
Teddington, Middlesex TW11 8LG
tel 0181-943 5664 *fax* 0181-943 5777
e-mail practicalcaravan@dial.pipex.com
Editor Rob McCabe
Monthly £2.50

Caravan-related travelogues, human
interest features, technical and DIY matters. Length: 1500-2500. Illustrations:
Colour. Payment: £120 per 1000 words;
negotiable. Founded 1967.

Practical Fishkeeping

(incorporating Fishkeeping Answers)
EMAP Apex, Apex House, Oundle Road,
Peterborough PE2 9NP
tel (01733) 898100
Editor Steve Windsor
Monthly £2.25

Practical fishkeeping in tropical and
coldwater aquaria and ponds. Heavy
emphasis on inspiration and involvement. Good colour photography always
needed, and used. No verse or humour,
no personal biographical accounts of
fishkeeping unless practical. Payment: by
worth. Founded 1966.

Practical Householder

Nexus Media Ltd, Nexus House, Azalea Drive,
Swanley, Kent BR8 8HU
tel (01322) 660070 *fax* (01322) 667633
Editor John McGowan
Monthly £2.15

Articles about 1500 words in length,
about practical matters concerning home
improvement. Payment: according to
subject. Illustrations: line, half-tone.
Founded 1955.

Practical Parenting

IPC Magazines Ltd, King's Reach Tower,
Stamford Street, London SE1 9LS
tel 0171-261 5058 *fax* 0171-261 5366
Editor-in-Chief Jayne Marsden
Monthly £1.85

Articles on parenting, baby and childcare, health, psychology, education, children's activities, personal birth/parenting
experiences. Send synopsis, with sae.

Illustrations: commissioned only; colour: photos, line, cartoons. Payment: £100-£150 per 1000 words; illustrations by agreement. Founded 1987.

Practical Photography

Apex House, Oundle Road, Peterborough PE2 9NP
tel (01733) 898100 *fax* (01733) 894472
Editor William Cheung
Monthly £2.70

Features on any aspect of photography with practical bias. Mostly written by staff journalists, but freelance ideas welcome. Send brief synopsis only in first instance. Illustrations: line, half-tone, colour, cartoons. Payment: from £50 per 1000 words; from £10 b&w or colour. Founded 1959.

Practical Wireless

PW Publishing Ltd, Arrowsmith Court, Station Approach, Broadstone, Dorset BH18 8PW
tel (01202) 659910 *fax* (01202) 659950
e-mail robepwpub.demon.co.uk
Editor Rob Mannion G3XFD
Monthly £2.20

Articles on the practical and theoretical aspects of amateur radio and communications. Constructional projects. Illustrations: in b&w and colour; photos, line drawings and wash half-tone for offset litho. Payment: by arrangement. Founded 1932.

Practical Woodworking

Nexus Special Interests Ltd, Nexus House, Azalea Drive, Swanley, Kent BR8 8HU
tel (01322) 660070 *fax* (01322) 667633
Editor Mark Chisholm
Monthly £2.45

Articles of a practical nature covering any aspect of woodworking, including woodworking projects, tools, joints or timber technology. Payment: £70 per published page. Illustrated.

The Practising Midwife

(formerly Modern Midwife)
Hochland & Hochland Ltd, 174A Ashley Road, Hale, Cheshire WA15 9SF
tel 0161-929 0190/0929 *fax* 0161-929 1818
e-mail practimid@hochland.demon.co.uk
Editor Jilly Rosser
Monthly £30 p.a.

Disseminates research-based material to a wide professional audience. Research and review papers, viewpoints and news items pertaining to midwifery, maternity

care, women's health and neonatal health with both a national and an international perspective. All articles submitted are anonymously reviewed by at least 2 external acknowledged experts. Length: 1000-2000 words (articles); 150-400 words (news); up to 1000 words (viewpoints). Illustrations: colour transparencies and artwork. Payment: by arrangement. Founded 1991.

The Practitioner

Miller Freeman plc, City Reach, 5 Greenwich View Place, Millharbour, London E14 9NN
tel 0171-861 6472 *fax* 0171-861 6259
e-mail gmathin@unmf.com
Editor Harvey Jones
Monthly £11.00 (£69.00 p.a. UK, $163.00 p.a. overseas)

Articles of interest to GPs and vocational trainees, and others in the medical profession. Payment: approx. £200 per 1500 words. Founded 1868.

Prediction

Link House, Dingwall Avenue, Croydon CR9 2TA
tel 0181-686 2599 *fax* 0181-781 1159
Editor Jo Logan
Monthly £2.00

Articles on astrology and all occult subjects. Length: up to 2000 words. Payment: by arrangement. Illustrations: for cover use only: large colour transparencies (i.e. not 35mm). Founded 1936.

Prep School

Abbey Cottage, Blythburgh, Suffolk IP19 9LQ
Editor David Tytler
3 p.a. £9.00 p.a.

Journal of the Preparatory School world: the magazine of IAPS and SATIPS. Articles of educational interest covering ages 4-13. Length: about 1000 words. Illustrations: line, half-tone.

Press Gazette

Quantum Publishing Ltd, Quantum House, 19 Scarbrook Road, Croydon, Surrey CR9 1LX
tel 0181-565 4200 *fax* 0181-565 4295
Editor Adam Leyland
Weekly £1.90

News and features of interest to journalists and others working in the media. Length: 1200 words (features), 300 words (news). Payment: approx. £200 (features), news stories negotiable. Founded 1965.

Pride

Hamilton House, 55 Battersea Bridge Road,
London SW11 3AX
tel 0171-228 3110 *fax* 0171-228 3130
Publishing Editor Clare Gorham
Monthly £2.20

Lifestyle magazine incorporating fashion
and beauty, travel, food and entertaining
articles for the young woman of colour.
Length: 1000-3000 words. Illustrations:
colour photos and drawings. Payment:
£100 per 1000 words. Founded 1993;
relaunched 1997, 1998.

Priests & People

Blackfriars, Buckingham Road,
Cambridge CB3 0DD
tel (01223) 359376
Editor Rev. D.C. Sanders OP
Monthly £2.25

Journal of pastoral theology especially
for parish ministry and for Christians of
English-speaking countries. Illustrations:
occasional b&w photos, cartoons. Length
and payment by arrangement.

Prima

197 Marsh Wall, London E14 9SG
tel 0171-519 5500 *fax* 0171-519 5514
Editor Lindsay Nicholson
Monthly £1.70

Articles on fashion, crafts, health and
beauty, cookery; features. Illustrations:
half-tone, colour. Founded 1986.

Printing World

Miller Freeman Publishers Ltd, Miller Freeman
House, Sovereign Way, Tonbridge,
Kent TN9 1RW
tel (01732) 364422 *fax* (01732) 377552
Editor Gareth Ward
Weekly £2.70 (£78.00 p.a., overseas £112.00 p.a.)

Commercial, technical, financial and
labour news covering all aspects of the
printing industry in the UK and abroad.
Outside contributions. Payment: by
arrangement. Illustrations: line, half-tone,
colour, cartoons. Founded 1878.

Private Eye

6 Carlisle Street, London W1V 5RG
tel 0171-437 4017 *fax* 0171-437 0705
e-mail strobes @cix.compulink.co.uk
web site http://www.compulink.co.uk/~private-eye/
Editor Ian Hislop
Fortnightly £1.00

Satire. Payment: by arrangement.
Illustrations: b&w, line, cartoons.
Founded 1961.

Professional Nurse

Macmillan Magazines Ltd, Porters South,
4-6 Crinan Street, London N1 9SQ
tel 0171-843 4684 *fax* 0171-843 4699
e-mail pn@healthcare.emap.co.uk
Editor Rosemary Rogers
Monthly £35.00 p.a.

Articles of interest to the professional
nurse. Length: articles: 2000-4000 words;
letters: 250-500 words. Payment: by
arrangement. Illustrations: line, half-tone,
colour. Founded 1985.

Professional Photographer

Market Link Publishing Ltd, The Mill,
Bearwalden Business Park, Royston Road,
Wendens Ambo, Saffron Walden, Essex CB11 4JX
tel (01799) 544200 *fax* (01799) 544201
Editor Steve Hynes
Monthly £2.50

Articles on professional photography,
including technical articles, photographer profiles and coverage of issues affecting the industry. Length: 1000-2000
words. Illustrations: colour and b&w
prints and transparencies, diagrams if
appropriate. Payment: from £90 per page
for articles and pro rata for illustrations.
Founded 1961.

Prospect

Prospect Publishing Ltd, 4 Bedford Square,
London WC1B 3RA
tel 0171-255 1281 *fax* 0171-255 1279
e-mail prospect_magazine@compuserve.com
web site http://www.prospect-magazine.co.uk
Editor David Goodhart
Monthly £2.95

Politics and current affairs. Essays, features, special reports, reviews, short stories, opinions/analysis. Length: 3000-
6000 words (essays, special reports, short
stories), 1000 words (opinions). Illustrations: colour and b&w. Payment: by
negotiation. Founded 1995.

Publishing News

43 Museum Street, London WC1A 1LY
tel 0171-404 0304
Editor Rodney Burbeck
Weekly £1.80

Articles and news items on books and
publishers. Payment: £80-£100 per 1000
words. Illustrations: half-tone, cartoons.
Founded 1979.

Pulse

Miller Freeman plc, City Reach, 5 Greenwich
View Place, Millharbour, London E14 9NN

tel 0171-861 6481 fax 0171-861 6257
Editor Howard Griffiths
Weekly £150.00 p.a.

Articles and photos of direct interest to GPs. Purely clinical material can only be accepted from medically qualified authors. Length: up to 750 words. Payment: £150 average. Illustrations: b&w and colour photos.

Punch

Liberty Publishing, 100 Brompton Road, London SW3 1ER
tel 0171-225 6716 fax 0171-225 6766
e-mail edit@punch.co.uk
Editor James Steen
Fortnightly £1.00

A satirical and investigative magazine with cartoons. Illustrations: colour and b&w. Payment: by arrangement. Founded 1841; relaunched 1996.

Q Magazine

EMAP Metro, Mappin House, 4 Winsley Street, London W1N 7AR
tel 0171-436 1515 fax 0171-312 8247
e-mail q_magazine@dial.pipex.com
web site http://www.qonline.co.uk
Editor David Davies
Monthly £2.70

Glossy modern guide to more than just rock music. All material commissioned. Length: 1200-2500 words. Illustrations: colour and b&w photos. Payment: £180 per 1000 words; illustrations by arrangement. Founded 1986.

Quaker Monthly

Quaker Home Service, Friends House, Euston Road, London NW1 2BJ
tel 0171-663 1018 fax 0171-663 1001
Editor Elizabeth Cave
Monthly 80p (£12.50 p.a.)

Articles, poems, reviews, expanding the Quaker approach to the spiritual life. Writers should be members or attenders of a Quaker meeting. Illustrations: line, half-tone. Payment: none. Founded 1921.

QWF

80 Main Street, Linton, Nr Swadlincote, Derbyshire DE12 6QA
tel (01283) 761042
Editor Jo Good
Bi-monthly £3.75 (£20.00 p.a.)

'Extending the boundaries of women's fiction.' Short stories to appeal to a predominantly female readership and occasional articles on writing. Length: up to

4000 words. Illustrations: b&w cover design only. Payment: £5 (articles/features), £10 or free subscription (short stories); £10 (cover). Founded 1994.

RA Magazine

Royal Academy of Arts, Burlington House, Piccadilly, London W1V 0DS
tel 0171-300 5820 fax 0171-287 9023
Editor Nick Tite
Quarterly £4.00

Topical articles relating to the Royal Academy, its history and its exhibitions. Length: 500-1500 words. Illustrations: consult editor. Payment: £100 per 1000 words; illustrations by negotiation. Founded 1983.

Radio Control Models and Electronics

Nexus Special Interests Ltd, Nexus House, Swanley, Kent BR8 8HU
tel (01322) 660070 fax (01322) 667633
Editor Kevin Crozier
Monthly £2.25

Well-illustrated articles on topics related to radio control. Payment: £35 per published page. Illustrations: line, half-tone. Founded 1960.

Radio Times

BBC Worldwide Ltd, 80 Wood Lane, London W12 0TT
tel 0181-576 3999 fax 0181-576 3160
web site http://www.rtguide.beeb.com
Editor Sue Robinson
Weekly 79p

Articles that preview the week's programmes on British television and radio. All articles are specially commissioned – ideas and synopses are welcomed but not unsolicited MSS. Length: 600-2500 words. Payment: by arrangement. Illustrations: in colour and b&w; photos, graphic designs or drawings.

Rail

Emap Apex Publications, Apex House, Oundle Road, Peterborough PE2 9NP
tel (01733) 898100 fax (01733) 894472
e-mail rail@ecm.emap.com
Managing Editor Nigel Harris
Fortnightly £2.00

News and in-depth features on current UK railway operations. Length: 2000-3000 words (features), 250-400 words (news). Illustrations: colour and b&w photos and artwork. Payment: £75 per

1000 words; £20 per photo except cover (£70) and Comment (£50). Founded 1981.

Railway Gazette International

Reed Business Information, Quadrant House, The Quadrant, Sutton, Surrey SM2 5AS
tel 0181-652 3739 *fax* 0181-652 3738
web site http://railgaz.co.uk
Editor Murray Hughes
Monthly £55.00 p.a.

Deals with management, engineering, operation and finance of railways worldwide. Articles of practical interest on these subjects are considered and paid for if accepted. Illustrated articles, of 1000-3000 words, are preferred. A preliminary letter is required.

Railway Magazine

IPC Magazines Ltd, King's Reach Tower, Stamford Street, London SE1 9LS
tel 0171-261 5821 *fax* 0171-261 5269
Editor Nick Pigott
Monthly £2.50

Illustrated magazine dealing with all railway subjects; no fiction or verse. Articles from 1500-2000 words accompanied by photos. Preliminary letter desirable. Payment: by arrangement. Illustrations: colour transparencies, half-tone and line. Founded 1897.

Rambling Today

1-5 Wandsworth Road, London SW8 2XX
tel 0171-339 8500 *fax* 0171-339 8501
e-mail ramblers@ramblers.org.uk
Editor Annabelle Birchall
Quarterly Free to members

Official magazine of The Ramblers' Association. Articles on walking, access to countryside and related issues. Material mostly commissioned. Length: about 1000 words. Illustrations: colour slides. Payment: by agreement. Founded 1935.

Reader's Digest

The Reader's Digest Association Ltd, 11 Westferry Circus, Canary Wharf, London E14 4HE
tel 0171-715 8000
e-mail excerpts@readersdigest.co.uk
web site http://www.readersdigest.co.uk
Editor Russell Twisk
Monthly £1.90

Original anecdotes – £200 for up to 150 words – are required for humorous features. Booklet 'Writing for Reader's Digest' available £5.00 post free.

Reality

Redemptorist Publications, Orwell Road, Rathgar, Dublin 6, Republic of Ireland
tel (01) 4922488 *fax* (01) 4922654
Editor Rev. Gerry Moloney CSSR
Monthly 80p

Illustrated magazine for Christian living. Articles on all aspects of modern life, including family, youth, religion, leisure. Illustrated articles, b&w photos only. Short stories. Length: 1000-1500 words. Payment: by arrangement; average £25 per 1000 words. Founded 1936.

Red

EMAP Élan, Endeavour House, 189 Shaftesbury Avenue, London WC2H 8JG
tel 0171-437 9011 *fax* 0171-208 3218
Editor Kathryn Brown
Monthly £2.50

High-quality articles on topics of interest to women aged 25-40: humour, memoirs, interviews and well-researched investigative features. Approach with ideas in first instance. Length: 2000-3000 words. Illustrations: transparencies. Payment: NUJ rates. Founded 1998.

Red Pepper

Socialist Newspaper (Publications) Ltd, 1A Waterlow Road, London N19 5NJ
e-mail redpepper@online.rednet.co.uk
web site http://www.redpepper.org.uk
Editor Hilary Wainwright
Monthly £1.95

Independent radical magazine: news and features on politics, culture and everyday life of interest to the left and greens. Material mostly commissioned. Length: news/news features 200-800 words, other features 800-2000 words. Illustrations: b&w photos, cartoons, graphics. Payment: by arrangement. Founded 1994.

Reform

86 Tavistock Place, London WC1H 9RT
tel 0171-916 8630 *fax* 0171-916 2021 (fao 'Reform')
e-mail reform@urc.cix.co.uk
Editor David Lawrence
Monthly £1.25 (£9.75 p.a.)

Published by United Reformed Church. Articles of religious or social comment. Length: 600-1000 words. Illustrations: line, half-tone, colour, cartoons. Payment: by arrangement. Founded 1972.

Report

ATL, 7 Northumberland Street,
London WC2N 5DA
tel 0171-782 1517 *fax* 0171-925 0529
e-mail newsdesk@atl.org.uk
web site http://www.atl.org.uk
Editor Nick Tester
8 p.a. £2.50 (£10.00 p.a. UK; £12.00 p.a. overseas)
The magazine from the Association of Teachers and Lecturers (ATL). Features, articles, comment, news about nursery, primary, secondary and further education. Payment: minimum £120 per 1000 words.

Retail Week

EMAP Maclaren, Leon House, 233 High Street, Croydon, Surrey CR0 9XT
tel 0181-277 5331 *fax* 0181-277 5344
Editor Kate Oppenheim
Weekly Controlled circulation (£95.00 p.a.)
Features and news stories on all aspects of retail management. Length: up to 1000 words. Illustrations: colour photos. Payment: by arrangement. Founded 1988.

The Rialto

PO Box 309, Aylsham, Norwich NR11 6LN
Editor Michael Mackmin
3 p.a. £3.90 (£10.00 p.a., £8.00 p.a. low income)
Poetry and criticism. Sae essential. Payment: by arrangement. Founded 1984.

Ride

Emap National Publications Ltd,
Bushfield House, Orton Centre,
Peterborough PE2 5UW
tel (01733) 237111 *fax* (01733) 465804
Editor Tim Thompson
Monthly £2.40
Review features on tests of used motorbikes, services and related products. Length: 2000 words (features), 200 words (news). Illustrations: colour. Payment: £120 per 1000 words (features), £200 per 1000 words (news); £220 per day (photos). Founded 1995.

Right Start

Needmarsh Publishing Ltd, 71 Newcomen Street, London SE1 1YT
tel 0171-403 0840 *fax* 0171-378 6883
Editor Lynette Lowthian
Bi-monthly £1.60
Features on all aspects of pre-school and infant education, child health and behaviour. No unsolicited MSS. Length: 1200-1500 words. Illustrations: colour photos, line. Payment: varies. Founded 1989.

Rugby World

IPC Magazines Ltd, Kings Reach Tower, Stamford Street, London SE1 9LS
tel 0171-261 6830 *fax* 0171-261 5419
Editor Paul Morgan
Monthly £2.40
Features and exclusive news stories on rugby. Length: approx. 1200 words. Illustrations: colour photos, cartoons. Payment: £120. Founded 1960.

Runner's World

Rodale Press Ltd, 7-10 Chandos Street, London W1M 0AD
tel 0171-291 6000 *fax* 0171-291 6080
Editor Steven Seaton
Monthly £2.60
Articles on jogging, running and fitness. Payment: by arrangement. Illustrations: line, half-tone, colour, cartoons. Founded 1979.

RUSI Journal

Whitehall, London SW1A 2ET
tel 0171-930 5854 *fax* 0171-321 0943
e-mail journal@editrusi.demon.co.uk
web site http://www.rusi.org/rusi/
Editorial Manager Alexandra Citron
Bi-monthly £7.50
Journal of the Royal United Services Institute for Defence Studies. Articles on international security, the military sciences, defence technology and procurement, and military history; also book reviews and correspondence. Length: 3000-4000 words. Illustrations: b&w photos, maps and diagrams. Payment: £12.50 per printed page upon publication.

Safety Education

Royal Society for the Prevention of Accidents, Edgbaston Park, 353 Bristol Road, Birmingham B5 7ST
tel 0121-248 2000 *fax* 0121-248 2001
web site http://www.rospa.org.uk
Editor Carole Wale
3 p.a. £8.00 p.a. for members of Safety Education Department (£9.41 p.a. non-members)
Articles on every aspect of good practice in safety education including safety of teachers and pupils in school, and the teaching of road, home, water, leisure and personal safety by means of established subjects on the school curriculum. All ages. Commissioned material only. Illustrations: line, half-tone, colour. Payment: by negotiation. Founded as *Child Safety* 1937; became *Safety Training* 1940; 1966.

Saga Magazine

The Saga Building, Middelburg Square,
Folkestone, Kent CT20 1AZ
tel (01303) 711523 *fax* (01303) 712699
Editor Paul Bach
Monthly £12.95 p.a.

Articles relevant to interests of 50-plus age group, and profiles of celebrities in same age group. Mostly commissioned or written in-house, but genuine exclusives always welcome. Length: 1200-1600 words. Illustrations: colour transparencies, commissioned colour artwork. Payment: competitive rate. Founded 1984.

Sainsbury's: The Magazine

New Crane Publishing, 20 Upper Ground,
London SE1 9PD
tel 0171-633 0266 *fax* 0171-401 9423
Editor Michael Wynn Jones
Monthly £1.00

Features: general, food and drink, health and humour; all material commissioned. Length: from 1500 words. Illustrations: colour and b&w photos and line illustrations. Payment: varies; £300 per full page for illustrations. Founded 1993.

Satellite Times

Everpage Ltd, The Stables, West Hill Grange,
North Road, Horsforth, Leeds LS18 5HG
tel (01273) 204259 *fax* (01273) 321605
Editor Eric Woods
Monthly £2.20

Television and film personality articles and interviews, sports articles, music, competitions. Payment: from £120 per 1000 words. Founded 1988.

Scale Models International

Nexus Special Interests Ltd, Nexus House,
Swanley, Kent BR8 8HU
tel (01322) 660070 *fax* (01322) 667633
Editor Kelvin Barber
Monthly £2.10

Articles on scale models. Length: up to 2500 words. Payment: £25-£30 per page. Illustrations: line, half-tone, colour.

School Librarian

The School Library Association,
Liden Library, Barrington Close, Liden,
Swindon, Wilts. SN3 6HF
tel (01793) 617838
Editor Raymond Astbury *tel* (01745) 730203
e-mail 101704.2701@compuserve.com
Review Editor Keith Barker
SL2001 Editor Mary Mabey

Quarterly Free to members (£45.00 p.a.)

The official journal of the School Library Association. Reviews of books, CD-Roms and other library resources from pre-school to young adult. Articles on school library organisation, use and skills, and on authors and illustrators. Length: 1800-3000 words. Payment: by arrangement. Founded 1937.

Science Progress

Science Reviews, 41-43 Green Lane, Northwood,
Middlesex HA6 3AE
tel (01923) 823586 *fax* (01923) 825066
e-mail scilet@scilet.com
Editors Prof David Phillips, Prof Robin Rowbury
Quarterly £105.00 p.a. (£120.00 p.a. overseas)

Articles of 6000 words on new scientific developments, written so as to be intelligible to workers in other disciplines. Imperative to submit synopsis before full-length article. Payment: by arrangement. Illustrations: line, half-tone.

Scientific Computing World

IOP Publishing Ltd, Dirac House, Temple Back,
Bristol BS1 6BE
tel 0117-929 7481 *fax* 0117-930 1178
e-mail scicomp@ioppublishing.co.uk
web site http://www.iop.org/mags/scw
Editor Vanessa Spedding
10 p.a. Free to qualifying subscribers

Features on hardware and software developments for the scientific community, plus news articles and reviews. Length: 800-2000 words. Illustrations: colour transparencies, photos, electronic graphics. Payment: by negotiation. Founded 1994.

Scotland on Sunday Magazine – see Scotland on Sunday in National newspapers UK and Ireland, page 3

The Scots Magazine

D.C. Thomson & Co. Ltd, 2 Albert Square,
Dundee DD1 9QJ
tel (01382) 223131 *fax* (01382) 322214
Monthly £1.20

Articles on all subjects of Scottish interest. Short stories, poetry, but must be Scottish. Illustrations: colour and b&w photos, drawings, cartoons. Payment: £22 per 1000 words; from £12. Founded 1739.

The Scotsman Weekend – see The Scotsman in National newspapers UK and Ireland, page 3

Scottish Book Collector

c/o 36 Lauriston Place, Edinburgh EH3 9EZ
tel 0131-228 4837 *fax* 0131-228 3904
Editor Jennie Renton
Quarterly £2.50

Articles on collecting Scottish books; literary/bibliographical articles on books published in Scotland or by Scottish writers. Length: 1500-2500 words. Payment: £25 per article. Founded 1987.

Scottish Educational Journal

Educational Institute of Scotland,
46 Moray Place, Edinburgh EH3 6BH
tel 0131-225 6244 *fax* 0131-220 3151
Editor Simon Macaulay
6 p.a. plus Specials £9.00 p.a.

The Scottish Farmer

6th Floor, 195 Albion Street, Glasgow G1 1QP
tel 0141-302 7700 *fax* 0141-302 7799
Editor Alasdair Fletcher
Weekly £1.35

Articles on agricultural subjects. Length: 1000-1500 words. Payment: £80 per 1000 words. Illustrations: line, half-tone, colour. Founded 1893.

Scottish Field

Special Publications, Royston House,
Caroline Park, Edinburgh EH5 1QJ
tel 0131-551 2942 *fax* 0131-551 2938
e-mail editor@scottishfield.co.uk
Editor Archie Mackenzie
Monthly £2.50

Will consider all material with a Scottish link and good photos. Payment: by negotiation. Founded 1903.

Scottish Home and Country

42A Heriot Row, Edinburgh EH3 6ES
tel 0131-225 1934 *fax* 0131-225 8129
Editor Stella Roberts
Monthly 75p

Articles on crafts, cookery, travel, personal experience, DIY; humorous rural stories; fashion, health, books. Length: up to 1000 words, preferably illustrated. Illustrations: colour prints/transparencies, b&w, cartoons. Payment: by arrangement. Founded 1924.

Scouting

The Scout Association, Baden-Powell House,
Queens Gate, London SW7 5JS
tel 0171-584 7030 *fax* 0171-590 5124
Editor David Easton
Monthly £1.25

National magazine of the Scout Association. Ideas, news, views, features and programme resources for Leaders and Supporters. Training material, accounts of Scouting events and articles of general interest with Scouting connections. Illustrations: photos – action shots preferred rather than static posed shots for use with articles or as fillers or cover potential, cartoons. Payment: on publication by arrangement.

Screen International

EMAP Business Publishing,
33-39 Bowling Green Lane, London EC1R 0DA
tel 0171-505 8080 *fax* 0171-505 8117
e-mail boydf@media.emap.co.uk,
100064.2744@compuserve.com
Editor Boyd Farrow
Weekly £1.90

International news and features on every aspect of films, television and associated media. Length: variable. Payment: by arrangement.

Scuba World

Freestyle Publications Ltd, Alexander House,
Ling Road, Tower Park, Poole, Hants BH12 4NZ
tel (01202) 735090 *fax* (01202) 733969
web site http://www.freepubs.co.uk
Editor Richard Chumbley
Monthly £2.75

The official magazine of the Sub-Aqua Association. Articles, features, news and short stories related to diving. Unsolicited material welcome. Length: 1500-2000 words (articles/features); 200-1000 words (news); 800 words (short stories); 2000 words (interviews). Payment: negotiable. Founded 1990.

Sea Angler

EMAP Pursuit Publishing Ltd, Bretton Court,
Bretton, Peterborough PE3 8DZ
tel (01733) 465307 *fax* (01733) 465436
Editor Mel Russ
Monthly £2.30

Topical articles on all aspects of sea-fishing around the British Isles. Payment: by arrangement. Illustrations: colour. Founded 1973.

Sea Breezes

Units 28-30, Spring Valley Industrial Estate,
Braddan, Isle of Man IM2 2QS
tel (01624) 626018 *fax* (01624) 661655
Editor A.C. Douglas
Monthly £1.95

Factual articles on ships and the sea past and present, preferably illustrated. Length: up to 4000 words. Illustrations:

line, half-tone, colour. Payment: by arrangement. Founded 1919.

Select Magazine

EMAP Metro, Mappin House, 4 Winsley Street, London W1N 5AR
tel 0171-436 1515 *fax* 0171-637 0456
Editor Andrew Harrison
Monthly £2.20

Off-the-wall youth/music feature ideas for hip 18-25-year-olds. Length: decided on commissioning. Illustrations: colour and b&w rock/pop photography with an arty/provocative bent. Payment: £120 per 1000 words; illustrations £110 per page. Founded 1990.

She

National Magazine House, 72 Broadwick Street, London W1V 2BP
tel 0171-439 5000 *fax* 0171-439 5350
Editor Alison Pylkkanen
Monthly £2.10

No unsolicited MSS. Ideas with synopses welcome on subjects ranging from health and relationships to child care. Payment: NUJ freelance rates. Illustrations: photos, cartoons. Founded 1955.

Ship & Boat International

Royal Institution of Naval Architects, 10 Upper Belgrave Street, London SW1X 8BQ
tel 0171-235 4622 *fax* 0171-245 6959
Editor Richard White
Monthly £50.00 p.a.

Technical articles on the design, construction and operation of all types of specialised small ships and workboats. Length: 500-1500 words. Payment: by arrangement. Illustrations: line and half-tone, photos and diagrams.

Ships Monthly

Link House Magazines Ltd, 222 Branston Road, Burton-on-Trent DE14 3BT
tel (01283) 542721 *fax* (01283) 546436
Editor Robert Shopland
Monthly £2.10

Illustrated articles of shipping interest – both mercantile and naval, preferably of 20th century ships. Well-researched, factual material only. No short stories or poetry. 'Notes for Contributors' available. Mainly commissioned material; preliminary letter essential, with sae. Payment: by arrangement. Illustrations: half-tone and line, colour transparencies and prints. Founded 1966.

Shoot

(incorporating 90 Minutes)
IPC Magazines Ltd, King's Reach Tower, Stamford Street, London SE1 9LS
tel 0171-261 6287 *fax* 0171-261 6019
Editor David C. Smith
Weekly 85p

Football magazine for young males. News, features, profiles of big names in football, posters. Length: 300-400 words (features), 100 words (news). Illustrations: colour transparencies, artwork and cartoons. Payment: negotiable. Founded 1969.

Shooting Times and Country Magazine

IPC Magazines Ltd, King's Reach Tower, Stamford Street, London SE1 9LS
tel 0171-261 6180 *fax* 0171-261 7179
Editor John Gregson
Weekly £1.50

Articles on fieldsports, especially shooting, and on related natural history and countryside topics. Unsolicited MSS not encouraged. Length: up to 2000 words. Payment: by arrangement. Illustrations: photos, drawings, colour transparencies. Founded 1882.

The Short Wave Magazine

Arrowsmith Court, Station Approach, Broadstone, Dorset BH18 8PW
tel (01202) 659910 *fax* (01202) 659950
e-mail kevin@pwpublishing.ltd.uk
web site http://www.pwpublishingltd.uk
Editor Kevin Nice
Monthly £2.75 (£30.00 p.a.)

Technical and semi-technical articles, 500-5000 words, on design, construction and operation of radio receiving equipment. Radio-related photo features welcome. Payment: £55 per page. Illustrations: line, half-tone, colour. Founded 1937.

Shout

D.C. Thomson & Co. Ltd, Albert Square, Dundee DD1 9QJ
tel (01382) 223131 *fax* (01382) 200880
185 Fleet Street, London EC4A 2HS
tel 0171-242 5086 *fax* 0171-404 5694
Fortnightly £1.00

Colour gravure magazine for 12-16 year-old girls. Pop, film and 'soap' features and pin-ups; general features of teen interest; emotional features, fashion and beauty advice. Illustrations: colour transparencies. Payment: on acceptance. Founded 1993.

The Shropshire Magazine

The Leopard Press Ltd, 77 Wyle Cop,
Shrewsbury, Shropshire SY1 1UT
tel (01743) 362175
Editor Keith Parker
Monthly £1.00

Articles on topics related to Shropshire, including countryside, history, characters, legends, education, food; also home and garden features. Length: up to 1500 words. Illustrations: colour. Founded 1950.

Sight and Sound

21 Stephen Street, London W1P 1PL
tel 0171-255 1444 *fax* 0171-436 2327
Editor Nick James
Published by British Film Institute
Monthly £2.90

Topical and critical articles on the cinema of any country; book reviews; reviews of every film theatrically released in London; reviews of every video released; regular columns from the USA and Europe. Length: 1000-5000 words. Payment: by arrangement. Illustrations: relevant photos, cartoons. Founded 1932.

The Sign

Chansitor Publications Ltd, St Mary's Works, St Mary's Plain, Norwich, Norfolk NR3 3BH
tel (01603) 615995 *fax* (01603) 624483
Publisher G.A. Knights
Monthly 5p

Leading national insert for C of E parish magazines. Articles of interest to parishes. Items should bear the author's name and address; return postage essential. Length: up to 400 words. Illustrations: unusual b&w photos, drawings considered. Payment: by arrangement. Founded 1905.

Signal, Approaches to Children's Books

Lockwood, Station Road, South Woodchester, Stroud, Glos. GL5 5EQ
tel (01453 87) 3716/2208 *fax* (01453 87) 8599
Editor Nancy Chambers
3 p.a. £4.25 (£12.75 p.a.)

Articles on any aspect of children's books or the children's book world. Length: no limit but average 2500-3000 words. Payment: £3 per printed page. Illustrations: line occasionally. Founded 1970.

The Skier and The Snowboarder Magazine

48 London Road, Sevenoaks, Kent TN13 1AS
tel (01732) 743644 *fax* (01732) 743647
Editor Frank Baldwin
5 p.a. (July-May) £2.50

Ski features, based around a good story. Length: 800-1000 words. Illustrations: colour action ski photos. Payment: by negotiation. Founded 1984.

Sky Magazine

Hachette Emap, Mappin House, 4 Winsley Street, London W1N 7AR
tel 0171-436 1515 *fax* 0171-312 8248
Editor Christopher Hemblade
Monthly £2.30

People, movies, music and style. Length: varies. Illustrations: colour and b&w photos. Payment: by arrangement.

Slimmer Magazine

Turret Rai plc, Armstrong House, 38 Market Square, Uxbridge, Middlesex UB8 1TG
tel (01895) 454545 *fax* (01895) 454647
Editor Sarah Stowe
Bi-monthly £1.95

Features on health, nutrition, slimming. Personal weight loss stories. Sae essential. Length: 600 or 1200 words. Payment: £30 per 100 words. Founded 1972.

Slimming Magazine

Endeavour House, 189 Shaftesbury Avenue, London WC2H 8JG
tel 0171-208 3213 *fax* 0171-208 3302
Acting Editor Juliette Kellow
11 p.a. £1.85

Articles on psychology, lifestyle and health related to diet and nutrition. Approach editor in writing with ideas. Length: 1000-1500 words. Payment: by negotiation. Founded 1969.

Smallholder

Hook House, Hook Road, Wimblington, March, Cambs. PE15 0QL
tel/fax (01354) 741182
e-mail baileygroup.co.uk
web site http://www.smallholder.co.uk
Editor Liz Wright
Monthly £1.90

Articles of relevance to small farmers about livestock and crops; items relating to the countryside considered. Send for copy. Payment: £20 per 1000 words or by arrangement. Illustrations: line, half-tone, cartoons. Founded 1985.

Smash Hits

Mappin House, 4 Winsley Street,
London W1N 7AR
tel 0171-436 1515 *fax* 0171-636 5792
Editor Gavin Reeve
Fortnightly 90p

News interviews and posters of pop, TV and film stars. Illustrations: colour photos. Payment: £100 per page and per photo.

Snooker Scene

Cavalier House, 202 Hagley Road, Edgbaston,
Birmingham B16 9PQ
tel 0121-454 2931 *fax* 0121-452 1822
Editor Clive Everton
Monthly £1.80 (£15.00 p.a.)

News and articles about snooker and billiards. Payment: by arrangement. Illustrations: photos. Founded 1971.

Solicitors Journal

Sweet & Maxwell, 21-27 Lamb's Conduit Street,
London WC1N 3NJ
tel 0171-420 7500 *fax* 0171-420 7595
Weekly £2.40

Articles, by practising lawyers or specialist journalists, on subjects of practical interest to solicitors. Articles sent on spec should be on computer disk. Length: up to 1800 words. Payment: by negotiation. Founded 1856.

Somerset Magazine

Smart Print Publications Ltd, 23 Market Street,
Crewkerne, Somerset TA18 7JU
tel (01460) 78000 *fax* (01460) 76718
Editor Roy Smart
Monthly £1.90

Articles, features with particular reference to Somerset locations, facilities and other interests. Length: 1000-1500 words. Illustrations: half-tone, colour. Payment: by arrangement. Founded 1977 as Somerset & West.

The Songwriter

International Songwriters Association,
PO Box 46, Limerick City, Republic of Ireland
tel (061) 228837
Editor James D. Liddane
Monthly Available to members only as part of membership fee

Articles on songwriting and interviews with music publishers and recording company executives. Length: 400-5000 words. Payment: from £100 per page and by arrangement. Illustrations: photos. Founded 1967.

Songwriting and Composing

Sovereign House, 12 Trewartha Road,
Praa Sands, Penzance, Cornwall TR20 9ST
tel (01736) 762826 *fax* (01736) 763328
e-mail songmag@aol.com
web site http://www.icn.co.uk/gisc.html
General Secretary Carole Jones
Quarterly Free to members

Magazine of the Guild of International Songwriters and Composers. Short stories, articles, letters relating to songwriting, publishing, recording and the music industry. Payment: negotiable upon content £25-£60. Illustrations: line, halftone. Founded 1986.

The Spectator

56 Doughty Street, London WC1N 2LL
tel 0171-405 1706 *fax* 0171-242-0603
Editor Frank Johnson
Weekly £2.20

Articles on current affairs, politics, the arts; book reviews. Illustrations: b&w, cartoons. Payment: on merit. Founded 1828.

Speech and Drama

4 Fane Road, Old Marston, Oxford OX3 0SA
tel (01865) 728304
web site http://www.stsd.org.uk
Editor Dr Paul Ranger
2 p.a. £6.50 p.a.

Published by the Society of Teachers of Speech and Drama, the journal covers theatre, drama and all levels of education relating to speech and drama; specialist articles only; preliminary abstract of 300 words; photos welcome. Length: 1500-2000 words. Payment: none, complimentary copy. Founded 1951.

Spoken English

English Speaking Board (International),
26A Princes Street, Southport, Merseyside PR8 1EQ
tel (01704) 501730 *fax* (01704) 539637
e-mail admin@esbuk.demon.co.uk
web site http://www.esbuk.demon.co.uk
Editor Malcolm Dale
£20.00 p.a. (ESB membership inc. 2 issues)

Serious articles (1000-plus words) on spoken English, communication ventures and training, poetry, drama, and English-teaching from primary to university levels, in Britain and overseas. Payment: by arrangement. Founded 1968.

Springboard

30 Orange Hill Road, Prestwich,
Manchester M25 1LS
tel 0161-7735911

e-mail leobrooks@compuserve.com
Editor Leo Brooks
Quarterly £8.00 p.a.

Articles on writing, competition news, markets. Winning articles, stories and poems from internal competitions – £45 prize money each quarter. Includes copy of *The Curate's Egg*, poetry submissions for which contributors receive free copy. Founded 1990.

The Squash Player

460 Bath Road, Longford, Middlesex UB7 0EB
tel (01753) 775511 *fax* (01753) 775512
e-mail editor@squashplayer.co.uk
Editor Ian McKenzie
10 p.a. £39.95 p.a.

Covers all aspects of playing squash. All features are commissioned – discuss ideas with editor. Length: 1000-1500 words. Illustrations: unusual photos (e.g. celebrities), cartoons. Payment: £75 per 1000 words; £25-£40 for illustrations. Founded 1971.

The Stage

(incorporating Television Today)
Stage House, 47 Bermondsey Street,
London SE1 3XT
tel 0171-403 1818 *fax* 0171-357 9287
Editor Brian Attwood
Weekly 80p

Original and interesting articles on professional stage and broadcasting topics may be sent for the editor's consideration. Length: 500-800 words. Payment: £100 per 1000 words. Founded 1880.

Stamp Lover

National Philatelic Society,
British Philatelic Centre, 107 Charterhouse Street,
London EC1M 6PT
tel 0171-336 0882
Editor Michael Furnell
6 p.a. £1.50

Original articles on stamps and postal history. Illustrations: line, half-tone. Payment: by arrangement. Founded 1908.

Stamp Magazine

Link House Magazines Ltd, Link House,
Dingwall Avenue, Croydon CR9 2TA
tel 0181-686 2599 *fax* 0181-781 6044
Editor Richard West
Monthly £2.10

Informative articles and exclusive news items on stamp collecting and postal history. No preliminary letter. Payment: by arrangement. Illustrations: line, half-tone, colour. Founded 1934.

Stand Magazine

179 Wingrove Road,
Newcastle upon Tyne NE4 9DA
tel/fax 0191-273 3280
Editors Lorna Tracy, Rodney Pybus, Peter Bennet
Quarterly £3.95 inc. p&p (£11.95 p.a.)

Poetry, short stories, translations, literary criticism. Send sae for return. Biennial Short Story Competition for unpublished original short story in English (see page 534) and alternates with biennial Poetry Competition. Payment: £25 per 1000 words of prose; £25 per poem. Founded 1952.

Staple New Writing

Gilderoy East, Upperwood Road, Matlock Bath,
Derbyshire DE4 3PD
tel (01629) 583867/582764
Editors Bob Windsor, Donald Measham
4 p.a. £12.00 p.a. (£14.00 Europe and overseas surface mail/£17.50 air overseas)

Mainstream poems and short stories. Payment: £5-£10. Founded 1982.

Starburst

Visual Imagination Ltd, 9 Blades Court,
Deodar Road, London SW15 2NU
tel 0181-875 1520 *fax* 0181-875 1588
e-mail starburst@vismag.com
web site http://www.wisimag.com
Editor Stephen Payne
Monthly plus 4 specials p.a. £2.99

Features and interviews on all aspects of science fiction. Length: 2000 words. Illustrations: colour and b&w photos. Payment: £80 per 1000 words; £10-20 per image. Founded 1977.

Steam Classic

Ebony Media Ltd, Trevithick House, Moorswater,
Liskeard, Cornwall PL14 4LH
tel (01579) 340100 *fax* (01579) 340200
Editor John Huxley
Bi-monthly £2.60

Features on the history, design and performance of British-built and overseas steam locomotives; news stories and features on present-day steam locomotive preservation. Length: 2000-3000 words. Illustrations: archive and contemporary colour transparencies and b&w photos; apply for list of specific required material (topical material always welcome). Payment: approx. £50 per 1000 words; £20 colour, £10 b&w. Founded 1990.

Studies, An Irish quarterly review

35 Lower Leeson Street, Dublin 2,
Republic of Ireland
tel (01) 6766785 *fax* (01) 6762984
e-mail studies@tinet.ie
Editor Rev. Noel Barber SJ
Quarterly £4.00
General review of social comment, literature, history, the arts. Articles written by specialists for the general reader. Critical book reviews. Preliminary letter. Length: 3500 words. Founded 1912.

Studio Sound

Miller Freeman Entertainment Ltd,
8 Montague Close, London SE1 9UR
tel 0171-620 3636 *fax* 0171-401 8036
Editor Tim Goodyer
Monthly £3.00
Articles on all aspects of professional sound recording. Technical and operational features on the functional aspects of studio equipment; general features on studio affairs. Length: widely variable. Payment: by arrangement. Illustrations: line, half-tone, colour. Founded 1959.

Success Now

(formerly Personal Success)
Sphinx Inc. Ltd, Compass House,
30-36 East Street, Bromley, Kent BR1 1QU
tel 0181-402 5252 *fax* 0181-402 5353
e-mail successnow@dial.pipex.com
Editor Colin C. Edwards
Quarterly £3.50
Positive and inspirational articles on business and human development; features on success stories of entrepreneurs, famous people, business trailblazers and motivated individuals. Length: 1200 words (features), 300 words (news). Illustrations: colour photos, artwork. Payment: rates on application. Founded 1993.

Sugar

Attic Futura (UK) Ltd, 17-18 Berners Street,
London W1P 3DD
tel 0171-664 6400 *fax* 0171-636 5055
Editor Marina Gask
Monthly £1.60
Magazine for young women aged 13-17. Fashion, beauty, entertainment, features. Interested in real-life stories (1200 words), quizzes. Payment: by arrangement. Opportunities for freelance writers, illustrators and designers. Founded 1994.

Sunday Magazine – see News of the World in National newspapers UK and Ireland, page 3

The Sunday Post Magazine – see Sunday Post in National newspapers UK and Ireland, page 3

The Sunday Review – see Independent on Sunday in National newspapers UK and Ireland, page 3

Sunday Telegraph Magazine – see Sunday Telegraph in National newspapers UK and Ireland, page 3

The Sunday Times Magazine – see Sunday Times in National newspapers UK and Ireland, page 3

The Sunday Times Scotland – see Sunday Times in National newspapers UK and Ireland, page 3

Swimming Times

Swimming Times Ltd, 18 Derby Square,
Loughborough LE11 5AL
tel (01509) 618743 *fax* (01509) 618746
Editor Peter Hassall
Monthly £1.70
Official journal of the Amateur Swimming Association and the Institute of Swimming Teachers and Coaches. Reports of major events and championships; news and features on all aspects of swimming including synchronised swimming, diving and water polo, etc; accompanying photos where appropriate; short fiction with a swimming theme. Unsolicited material welcome. Length: 800-1500 words. Payment: by arrangement. Founded 1923.

The Tablet

1 King Street Cloisters, Clifton Walk,
London W6 0QZ
tel 0181-748 8484 *fax* 0181-748 1550
Editor John Wilkins
Weekly £1.40
The senior Catholic weekly. Religion, philosophy, politics, society, books and arts. International coverage. Freelance work welcomed. Length: 1500 words. Illustrations: cartoons. Payment: by arrangement. Founded 1840.

Take a Break

25-27 Camden Road, London NW1 9LL
tel 0171-284 0909 *fax* 0171-284 3778
Editor John Dale
Weekly 60p

Lively, tabloid women's weekly. True life features, celebrities, health and beauty, family, travel; short stories (up to 1500 words); lots of puzzles. Payment: by arrangement. Illustrated. Founded 1990.

Take a Break's Take a Puzzle

H. Bauer Publishing, 25-27 Camden Road, London NW1 9LL
tel 0171-284 0909 *fax* 0171-284 255
e-mail puzzles@bauer.demon.co.uk
Editor Douglas Carter
Monthly £1.40

Puzzles. Fresh ideas always welcome. Illustrations: colour transparencies and b&w prints and artwork. Work supplied on Mac-compatible disk preferred. Payment: from £25 per puzzle, £30-£90 for picture puzzles and for illustrations not an integral part of a puzzle. Founded 1991.

tate: The Art Magazine

Blueprint Media Ltd, Christ Church, Cosway Street, London NW1 5NJ
tel 0171-706 4596 *fax* 0171-479 8515
e-mail charlotte.mullins@aspenmags.co.uk
Editor Tim Marlow
3 p.a. £3.50

Independent visual arts magazine: features, news, interviews, reviews, previews and opinion pieces. Length: up to 5000 words but usually commissioned. Illustrations: colour and b&w photos. Payment: negotiable. Founded 1993.

The Tatler

Vogue House, Hanover Square, London W1R 0AD
tel 0171-499 9080 *fax* 0171-409 0451
web site http://www.tatler.co.uk
Editor Jane Procter
Monthly £2.60

Smart society magazine favouring sharp articles, profiles, fashion and the arts. Illustrations: colour, b&w, but all commissioned. Founded 1709.

The Teacher

National Union of Teachers, Hamilton House, Mabledon Place, London WC1H 9BD
tel 0171-380 4708 *fax* 0171-387 8458
Editor Mitch Howard
8 p.a. Free to NUT members

Articles, features and news of interest to all those involved in the teaching profession. Length: 750 words. Payment: NUJ rates to NUJ members. Founded 1872.

Technology Ireland

Forbairt (Irish Science and Technology Agency), Glasnevin, Dublin 9, Republic of Ireland
tel (01) 8082282 *fax* (01) 8082227
Editors Mary Mulvihill, Tom Kennedy
Monthly £33.00 p.a. (£38.00 p.a. overseas)

Articles, features, reviews and news on current science and technology. Length: 1500-2000 words. Illustrations: line, half-tone, colour. Payment: varies. Founded 1969.

Telegraph Magazine – see Daily Telegraph in National newspapers UK and Ireland, page 3

Television

Reed Business Information Ltd, Quadrant House, The Quadrant, Sutton, Surrey SM2 5AS
tel 0181-652 8120 *fax* 0181-652 8956
Monthly £2.50

Articles on the technical aspects of domestic TV and video equipment, especially servicing, long-distance television, constructional projects, satellite TV, video recording, teletext and viewdata, test equipment, monitors. Payment: by arrangement. Illustrations: photos and line drawings for litho. Founded 1950.

Tempo

Boosey & Hawkes, Music Publishers, Ltd, 295 Regent Street, London W1R 8JH
tel 0171-580 2060 *fax* 0171-436 5675
Editor Calum MacDonald
Quarterly £3.50 (£17.50 p.a.)

Authoritative articles about 2000-4000 words on contemporary music. Payment: by arrangement. Illustrations: music type, occasional photographic or musical supplements.

Tennis World

Presswatch Ltd, The Spendlove Centre, Enstone Road, Charlbury, Oxford OX7 3PQ
tel (01608) 811446 *fax* (01608) 811380
Editor Alastair McIver
Monthly £2.50

Tournament reports, topical features, personality profiles, instructional articles. Length: 600-1500 words. Payment: by arrangement. Illustrations: line, half-tone, colour.

TGO (The Great Outdoors) Magazine

Caledonian Magazines Ltd, 6th Floor,
195 Albion Street, Glasgow G1 1QQ
tel 0141-302 7700 *fax* 0171-302 7799
e-mail info@calmags.co.uk
Editor Cameron McNeish
Monthly £2.25 (£26.00 p.a.)

Articles on walking or lightweight camping in specific areas, preferably illustrated. Length: 1200-1800 words. Payment: by arrangement. Illustrations: colour. Founded 1978.

that's life!

H. Bauer Publishing, 2nd Floor, 1-5 Maple Place, London W1P 5FX
tel 0171-462 4700 *Mercury* 19059412
fax 0171-636 1824
Editor Janice Turner
Weekly 49p

Dramatic true life stories about women. Length: average 1000 words. Illustrations: colour photos and cartoons. Payment: £650. Founded 1995.

Theology

SPCK, Holy Trinity Church, Marylebone Road, London NW1 4DU
tel 0171-387 5282 *fax* 0171-388 2352
e-mail theology@spck
Editor William Jacob
Bi-monthly £3.25

Articles and reviews on theology, ethics, Church and Society. Length: up to 3500 words. Payment: none. Founded 1920.

Therapy Weekly

Emap Healthcare Ltd, Porters South,
4-6 Crinan Street, London N1 9SQ
tel 0171-843 4730 *fax* 0171-843 4744
Acting Editor Melissa Oliveck
Weekly Free to NHS and local authority therapists (£47.50 p.a.)

Articles of interest to chartered physiotherapists, occupational therapists and speech and language therapists. Guidelines to contributors available. Send proposals only initially. Length: up to 1000 words. Illustrations: colour and b&w photos, line, cartoons. Payment: by arrangement. Founded 1974 as *Therapy*.

Third Way

St Peter's, Sumner Road, Harrow,
Middlesex HA1 4BX
tel 0181-423 8494 *fax* 0181-423 5367
e-mail editor@thirdway.org.uk
10 p.a. £2.90

Aims to present biblical perspectives on the political, social and cultural issues of the day. Payment: by arrangement on publication. Founded 1977.

This Caring Business

1 St Thomas' Road, Hastings,
East Sussex TN34 3LG
tel (01424) 718406 *fax* (01424) 718460
Editor Michael J. Monk
Monthly £50.00 p.a.

Specialist contributions relating to the commercial aspects of nursing and residential care, including hospitals. Payment: £75 per 1000 words. Illustrations: line, half-tone. Founded 1985.

This England

PO Box 52, Cheltenham, Glos. GL50 1YQ
tel (01242) 577775
Editor Roy Faiers
Quarterly £3.50

Articles on towns, villages, traditions, customs, legends, crafts of England; stories of people. Length: 250-2000 words. Payment: £25 per page and pro rata. Illustrations: line, half-tone, colour. Founded 1968.

The Times Magazine – see The Times in National newspapers UK and Ireland, page 3

The Times Educational Supplement

Admiral House, 66-68 East Smithfield,
London E1 9XY
tel 0171-782 3000 *fax* 0171-782 3200
e-mail copy@tesl.demon.co.uk
web site http://www.tes.co.uk
Editor Caroline St John-Brooks
Weekly £1.00

Articles on education written with special knowledge or experience; news items; books, arts and equipment reviews. Advisable to check with news or picture editor before submitting. Outlines of feature ideas should be faxed. Illustrations: suitable photos and drawings of educational interest, cartoons. Payment: standard rates, or by arrangement.

Times Educational Supplement Scotland

37 George Street, Edinburgh EH2 2HN
tel 0131-220 1100 *fax* 0131-220 1616
Editor Willis Pickard
Weekly £1.00

Articles on education, preferably 800-1200 words, written with special knowledge or experience. News items about Scottish educational affairs. Illustrations: line, half-tone. Payment: by arrangement. Founded 1965.

Times Higher Education Supplement
Admiral House, 66-68 East Smithfield,
London E1 9XY
tel 0171-782 3000 *fax* 0171-782 3300
Editor Auriol Stevens
Weekly £1.10

Articles on higher education written with special knowledge or experience, or articles dealing with academic topics. Also news items. Illustrations: suitable photos and drawings of educational interest. Payment: by arrangement. Founded 1971.

The Times Literary Supplement
Admiral House, 66-68 East Smithfield,
London E1 9XY
tel 0171-782 3000 *fax* 0171-782 3100
Editor Ferdinand Mount
Weekly £2.20

Will consider poems for publication, literary discoveries and articles, particularly of an opinionated kind, on literary and cultural affairs. Payment: by arrangement.

Today's Golfer
EMAP Pursuit Publishing Ltd, Bretton Court,
Bretton, Peterborough PE3 8DZ
tel (01733) 264666 *fax* (01733) 465221
Editor Neil Pope
Monthly £2.70

Specialist features and articles on golf instruction and equipment. Founded 1988.

Today's Runner
EMAP Pursuit Publishing, Bretton Court, Bretton,
Peterborough PE3 8DZ
tel (01733) 264666 *fax* (01733) 267198
Editor Paul Larkins
Monthly £2.50

Practical articles on all aspects of running lifestyle, especially road running training and events, and advice on health, fitness and injury. Illustrations: colour photos, cartoons. Payment: by negotiation. Founded 1985.

Together with Children
The National Society, Church House,
Great Smith Street, London SW1P 3NZ
tel 0171-222 1672 *fax* 0171-233 2592
Editor Pam Macnaughton
Monthly £1.80 (£15.00 p.a.)

Short, practical or topical articles and resources dealing with all forms of children's Christian education and all-age learning and worship. Length: up to 1200 words. Payment: by arrangement. Founded 1956.

Top of the Pops Magazine
BBC Worldwide, 80 Wood Lane,
London W12 0TT
tel 0181-576 2964 *fax* 0181-576 2694
Editor Ian McLeish
Monthly £1.35

Fun, lively and humorous articles on pop music aimed at fans of the TV show aged 12-17 – mostly commissioned. Length: 700-1000 words (features). Payment: £200 per 1000 words. Founded 1995.

Top Santé Health & Beauty
Emap Elán, Endeavour House,
189 Shaftesbury Avenue, London WC2H 8JG
tel 0171-938 3033 *fax* 0171-938 5464
Editor Annabel Goldstaub
Monthly £1.95

Articles, features and news on all aspects of health and beauty. Ideas welcome. Length: 1-2 pages. Illustrations: colour photos and drawings. Payment: £200 per 1000 words; illustrations by arrangement. Founded 1993.

Total Film
Future Publishing Ltd, 30 Monmouth Street,
Bath BA1 2BW
tel (01225) 442244 *fax* (01225) 732252
e-mail totalfilm@futurenet.co.uk
Editor Emma Cochrane
Monthly £2.50

Movie magazine with strong emphasis on major mainstream feature action and adventure films. Phone to discuss ideas before submitting material. Length: 400 words (news items); 1000 words (funny features); 400/800/1500 words (interviews). Payment: £150 per 1000 words; free-£1500 per picture. Founded 1996.

Total Football
Future Publishing Ltd, 30 Monmouth Street,
Bath BA1 2BW
tel (01225) 442244 *fax* (01225) 732248
e-mail rjones@futurenet.co.uk
Editor Richard Jones
Monthly £2.60

News, features and reviews of domestic and international football events and related stories. Illustrations: colour and b&w. Payment: 12-15p a word/variable page rate. Founded 1995.

Total Sport

Emap Metro, Mappin House, 4 Winsley Street, London W1N 7AR
tel 0171-312 8933 *fax* 0171-312 8936
Editor Keith Nelson
Monthly £2.50

For people who enjoy watching and talking about sport, in particular football, cricket, rugby, athletics and car racing. Features, photofeatures, profiles and news: the angle is entertainment and popular culture, rather than traditional. Founded 1995.

Toy Trader

Peebles Publishing Group, Brookmead House, Thorney Leys Business Park, Witney, Oxon OX8 7GE
tel (01993) 775545 *fax* (01993) 778884
e-mail trdmedia@aol.com
web site http://www.toy.co.uk/toytrader
Editor Sarah Sheppard
Monthly £60.00 p.a.

Trade journal specialising in anything to do with games and toys, circulated to manufacturers and retailers. Length: by negotiation. Illustrations: colour photos and diagrams. Payment: by negotiation. Founded 1908.

Traveller

Wexas Ltd, 45 Brompton Road, London SW3 1DE
tel 0171-581 4130 *fax* 0171-581 1357
e-mail miranda@wexas.com
Editor Miranda Haines
Quarterly £39.58 p.a.

Features usually based on long-haul and offbeat destinations, with a particular emphasis on cultural or anthropological angles. Recent features include: Maskmaking in Mali; The Skeleton Coast of Namibia; New Year in Laos. Length: 1000-2000 words. Illustrations: first-class transparencies. Payment: £125 per 1000 words; colour £25 (£50 cover). Founded 1970.

The Trefoil

C.H.Q., The Guide Association, 17-19 Buckingham Palace Road, London SW1W 0PT
tel 0171-834 6242 *fax* 0171-828 8317
Editor Gillian Ellis
Quarterly

Official Journal of The Trefoil Guild. Articles on the activities of the Guild in the UK and overseas and on the work of voluntary organisations. Length: not more than 500 words. No fiction. Illustrations: photos. No payment.

Tribune

308 Gray's Inn Road, London WC1X 8DY
tel 0171-278 0911
Editor Mark Seddon, *Reviews Editor* Caroline Rees
Weekly £1.00

Political, literary, with Socialist outlook. Informative articles (about 700 words), news stories (250-300 words). No unsolicited reviews or fiction. Payment: by arrangement. Illustrations: cartoons and photos.

Trout and Salmon

EMAP Pursuit Publishing Ltd, Bretton Court, Bretton Centre, Peterborough PE3 8DZ
tel (01733) 264666 *fax* (01733) 465436
Editor Sandy Leventon
Monthly £2.40

Articles of good quality with strong trout or salmon angling interest. Length: 400-2000 words, accompanied if possible by colour transparencies or good-quality colour prints. Payment: by arrangement. Illustrations: line, colour transparencies and prints, cartoons. Founded 1955.

Truck & Driver

Reed Business Information, Quadrant House, The Quadrant, Sutton, Surrey SM2 5AS
tel 0171-652 3682 *fax* 0171-652 8988
Editor Dave Young
Monthly £1.85

News, articles on trucks, personalities and features of interest to truck drivers. Words (on disk) and picture packages preferred. Length: approx. 2000 words. Illustrations: colour transparencies and artwork, cartoons. Payment: negotiable. Founded 1984.

Trucking International

A & S Publishing, Messenger House, 35 St Michael's Square, Gloucester GL1 1HX
tel (01452) 307181 *fax* (01452) 307170
Editor Richard Simpson
Monthly £1.95

For truck drivers, owner-drivers and small fleet operators: news, articles, features and technical advice. Length: 750-2500 words. Illustrations: mostly 35 mm colour transparencies. Payment: by negotiation. Founded 1983.

TV Quick

25-27 Camden Road, London NW1 9LL
tel 0171-284 0909 *fax* 0171-284 0593
Editor Lori Miles
Weekly 60p

Real life features, readers' tips and letters. No fiction. Illustrations: colour. Payment: £250 (real life stories). Founded 1991.

TV Times

IPC Magazines Ltd, 10th Floor, King's Reach Tower, Stamford Street, London SE1 9LS
tel 0171-261 7000 *fax* 0171-261 7777
Editor Liz Murphy
Weekly 62p

Features with an affinity to ITV, BBC1, BBC2, Channel 4, satellite and radio personalities and television generally. Length: by arrangement. Photographs: commissioned only. Payment: by arrangement.

Twinkle

D.C. Thomson & Co. Ltd, Albert Square, Dundee DD1 9QJ
tel (01382) 223131 *fax* (01382) 322214
185 Fleet Street, London EC4A 2HS
tel 0171-242 5086 *fax* 0171-404 5694
Weekly 60p

Picture stories, features and comic strips. Drawings in colour for gravure. Special encouragement to promising writers and artists. Payment: on acceptance.

U magazine

Smurfit Publications Ltd, 2 Clanwilliam Court, Lower Mount Street, Dublin 2,
Republic of Ireland
tel (01) 6623158 *fax* (01) 6619757
Editor Annette O'Meara, *Deputy Editor* Lucy Taylor
Monthly Ir.£2.00

Fashion and beauty magazine for 18-25 year-old Irish women, with celebrity interviews, talent profiles, sex and relationship features, plus regular pages on the arts, the club scene, music and film. Also travel, interiors, health, food, horoscopes. Material mostly commissioned. Payment: varies. Founded 1978.

Ulster Grocer

Greer Publications, 5B Edgewater Business Park, Belfast Harbour Estate, Belfast BT3 9JQ
tel (01232) 783200 *fax* (01232) 783210
Editor Brian McCalden
Monthly Controlled circulation

Topical features (500-1000 words) on agribusiness – retail and manufacturing – and exhibitions; news (200 words) with a Northern Ireland bias. All features commissioned; no speculative articles accepted. Illustrations: colour and b&w photos. Payment: features £75, news £30; photos £40. Founded 1972.

Under Five Contact

Pre-school Learning Alliance,
69 Kings Cross Road, London WC1X 9LL
tel 0171-833 0991 *fax* 0171-837 4942
Editor Ann Henderson
10 p.a. £25.00 p.a.

Articles on the role of adults – especially parents/preschool workers – in young children's learning and development, including children from all cultures and those with special needs. Length: 1000 words. Payment: £50 per article. Founded 1962.

The Universe

1st Floor, St James's Buildings, Oxford Street, Manchester M1 6FP
tel 0161-236 8856 *fax* 0161-236 8530
Editor Joe Kelly
Weekly 50p

Catholic Sunday newspaper. News stories, features and photos on all aspects of Catholic life required; also cartoons. MSS should not be submitted without sae. Payment: by arrangement. Founded 1860.

Vanity Fair

The Condé Nast Publications Ltd, Vogue House, Hanover Square, London W1R 0AD
tel 0171-499 9080 *fax* 0171-499 4415
web site http://www.vanityfair.co.uk
International Editor Henry Porter
tel 0171-221 6228 *fax* 0171-221 6269
Monthly £2.00

Media, glamour and politics for grown-up readers. No unsolicited material. Payment: by arrangement. Illustrated.

The Vegan

The Vegan Society, Donald Watson House,
7 Battle Road, St Leonards-on-Sea,
East Sussex TN37 7AA
tel (01424) 427393 *fax* (01424) 717064
Editor Richard Farhall
Quarterly £1.75

Articles on animal rights, nutrition, cookery, agriculture, Third World, health. Length: approx. 1500 words. Payment: by arrangement. Illustrations: photos, cartoons, line drawings – foods, animals, livestock systems, crops, people, events; colour for cover. Founded 1944.

Venue

Greetlake Services Ltd, 64-65 North Road,
Bristol BS6 5AQ
tel 0117-942 8491 *fax* 0117-942 0369
e-mail editor@venue.co.uk
web site http://www.venue.co.uk
Editor Dave Higgitt
Fortnightly £1.80

Listings magazine for Bristol and Bath combining comprehensive entertainment information with local features, profiles and interviews. Length: by agreement. Illustrations: colour and b&w. Payment: £7.00-£7.50 per 100 words. Founded 1982.

The Veterinary Review

John C. Alborough Ltd, Battisford Road,
Ringshall, Suffolk IP14 2JA
tel (01473) 658006 *fax* (01473) 658922
e-mail 100762.1214@compuserve.com
Editor Tim Wesley
Bi-monthly £40 p.a.

News, articles – both topical and general – and product listings for veterinarians. Articles and illustrations are both negotiable.

Farm & Country Retailer

News, articles and product listings for the agricultural supply trade.

Video Camera

WV Publications & Exhibitions,
57-59 Rochester Place, London NW1 9JU
tel 0171-331 1000 *fax* 0171-331 1242
e-mail wvmags@compuserve.com
Editor Tracey Smith
Monthly £2.60

Technique articles on how to use camcorders and equipment tests of camcorders and digital cameras. Material mostly commissioned. Length: 1000-1500 words. Illustrations: colour photos, diagrams. Payment: £90 per 1000 words; £90 per page for illustrations. Founded 1989.

Viz

House of Viz, PO Box 1PT,
Newcastle upon Tyne NE99 1PT
fax 0191-2819048
e-mail web@johnbrown.co.uk
web site http://www.viz.co.uk
Editor Chris Donald
6 p.a. £1.60

Cartoons, spoof tabloid articles, spoof advertisements. Illustrations: half-tone, line, cartoons. Payment: £300 per page (cartoons). Founded 1979.

Vogue

Vogue House, Hanover Square, London W1R 0AD
tel 0171-499 9080 *fax* 0171-408 0559
web site http://www.vogue.co.uk
Editor Alexandra Shulman
Monthly £2.80

Fashion, beauty, health, decorating, art, theatre, films, literature, music, travel, food and wine. Length: articles from 1000 words. Illustrated.

The Voice

370 Coldharbour Lane, London SW9 8PL
tel 0171-737 7377 *fax* 0171-274 8994
e-mail veeteeay@gn.apc.org
Editor Annie Stewart
Weekly 65p

News, general and arts features of interest to black readers. Illustrations: colour and b&w photos, cartoons. Payment: £100 per 1000 words; £20-£35 for illustrations. Founded 1982.

Voice Intelligence Report

15A Lowndes Street, London SW1X 9EY
tel 0171-235 5966 *fax* 0171-259 6694
Editor Ann Morris
Quarterly £18.00 (£60.00 p.a.)

Background intelligence reports on the Press, media, Parliament, European Parliament, banking, diplomats, Saudi Arabia and the Arab Gulf countries, with specific reference to Middle East. All material commissioned. Write for specimen copy. Illustrations: none. Founded 1972.

Vox

IPC Magazines Ltd, 25th Floor, King's Reach Tower, Stamford Street, London SE1 9LS
tel 0171-261 6312 *fax* 0171-261 5627
Editor Steve Sutherland
Monthly £2.40

Music and movies, aimed at 18-35 market – interviews, non-interview features, reviews. Illustrations: colour and b&w photos; commissioned illustrations and cartoons. Payment: by negotiation. Founded 1990.

Wanderlust

PO Box 1832, Windsor SL4 6YP
tel (01753) 620426
Editor Lyn Hughes
Bi-monthly £2.80

Features on independent and special-interest travel. Send sae for 'Guidelines for contributors'. Length: up to 2500 words. Illustrations: colour (send stock-list first). Payment: by arrangement. Founded 1993.

War Cry

101 Queen Victoria Street, London EC4P 4EP
tel 0171-332 0022 *fax* 0171-236 3491
e-mail wcry@globalnet.co.uk
Editor Captain Charles King
Weekly 20p (£26.00 p.a.)

Voluntary contributions; puzzles. Illustrations: line and photos, cartoons. Published by The Salvation Army. Founded 1879.

Wasafiri

Queen Mary & Westfield College, English Department, Mile End Road, London E1 4NS
tel 0171-775 3120
e-mail wasafiri@qmw.ac.uk
web site http://www.qmw.ac.uk/~english/wasafiri.html
Editor Susheila Nasta
Managing Editor Anthony Ilona
Bi-annual £12.00 p.a. (£16.00 p.a. institutions)

Published at University of London. Short stories, poetry, reviews, essays on literature and film. Submit MSS in duplicate, with an sae. Illustrations: b&w photos. Payment: negotiable. Founded 1984.

Waterways World

Waterways World Ltd, The Well House, High Street, Burton-on-Trent, Staffs. DE14 1JQ
tel (01283) 742951
Editor Hugh Potter
Monthly £2.20

Feature articles on all aspects of inland waterways in Britain and abroad, including historical material; factual and technical articles preferred. No short stories or poetry. Send sae for 'Notes for WW Contributors'. Payment: £37 per 1000 words. Illustrations: colour transparencies or prints, line. Founded 1972.

Wedding and Home

IPC Magazines Ltd, King's Reach Tower, Stamford Street, London SE1 9LS
tel 0171-261 7471 *fax* 0171-261 7459
e-mail weddingandhome@ipc.co.uk
Editor Christine Prunty
Deputy Editor Helen Salmon
Bi-monthly £3.25

Ideas and inspiration for modern brides. Fashion and beauty, information for grooms, real life weddings, planning advice, gift list ideas and honeymoon features. Approach Deputy Editor in

writing or by e-mail. Most features are commissioned to regular freelancers; ideas will receive consideration if presented clearly and briefly. Payment: by negotiation. Founded 1985.

Weekend – see The Guardian in National newspapers UK and Ireland, page 3

The Weekly Journal

Positive Time & Space Ltd, 36 Skylines, London E14 9TS
tel 0171-537 3222 *fax* 0171-537 2288
Editor Barbara Campbell
Weekly 60p

Features, news, interviews, arts, society, business from an African Caribbean, multicultural perspective. Length: 300-3000 words. Illustrations: half-tone, cartoons. Payment: negotiable. Founded 1992.

The Weekly News

D.C. Thomson & Co. Ltd, Albert Square, Dundee DD1 9QJ
tel (01382) 223131
137 Chapel Street, Manchester M3 6AA
tel 0161-834 5122
144 Port Dundas Road, Glasgow G4 0HZ
tel 0141-332 9933
185 Fleet Street, London EC4A 2HS
tel 0171-242 5086
Weekly 45p

Real-life dramas of around 2000 words told in the first person. Non-fiction series with lively themes or about interesting people. Keynote throughout is strong human interest. Joke sketches. Illustrations: cartoons. Payment: on acceptance.

Weight Watchers Magazine

Bloomsbury House Ltd, 1 Cecil Court, 49-55 London Road, Enfield, Middlesex EN2 6DN
tel 0181-342 2222 *fax* 0181-342 2223
8 p.a. £1.70

Features page – health, beauty, news, astrology; food-orientated articles; success stories. All material commissioned. Length: 1/2-3 pages. Illustrations: colour photos and cartoons. Payment: by arrangement.

West Africa

43-45 Coldharbour Lane, London SE5 9NR
tel 0171-737 2946 *fax* 0171-978 8334
Editor Maxwell Nwagboso
Weekly £1.95

Weekly summary of West African news, with articles on political, economic and commercial matters, and on all matters of general interest affecting Africa; also book reviews. Length: articles about 1200 words. Payment: as arranged. Illustrations: half-tone.

West Lothian Life

Ballencrieff Cottage, Ballencrieff Toll, Bathgate, West Lothian EH48 4LD
tel (01506) 632728 *fax* (01506) 635444
e-mail wll@pages.clara.net
web site http://home.clara.net/pages
Editor Susan Coon
Quarterly £2.00

Articles, profiles etc with a West Lothian angle. Length: 800-3000 words. Illustrations: colour and b&w photos, b&w artwork and cartoons. Payment: £10 per 1000 words. Founded 1995.

What Car?

Haymarket Motoring Magazines Ltd, 60 Waldegrave Road, Teddington, Middlesex TW11 8LG
tel 0181-943 5688 *fax* 0181-943 5750
Editor Mark Payton
Monthly £3.00

Road tests, buying guide, consumer stories and used car features. No unsolicited material. Illustrations: colour and b&w photos, line drawings. Payment: by negotiation. Founded 1973.

What's on TV

IPC Magazines Ltd, 10th Floor, King's Reach Tower, Stamford Street, London SE1 9LS
tel 0171-261 7769 *fax* 0171-261 7739
Editor Mike Hollingsworth
Weekly 49p

Features on TV programmes and personalities. All material commissioned. Length: up to 500 words. Illustrations: colour and b&w photos, cartoons. Payment: by agreement. Founded 1991.

When Saturday Comes

When Saturday Comes Ltd, 4th Floor, 2 Pear Tree Court, London EC1R 0DS
tel 0171-251 8595 *fax* 0171-490 1598
e-mail editorial@wsc.co.uk
web site http://www.wsc.cp/uk/wsc/
Editor Andy Lyons
Monthly £1.40

Features on football from the fans' perspective. Read the magazine for style first. Length: 500-2000 words. Illustrations: colour and b&w photos,

occasional illustrations. Payment: £50-£100 for words; £50-£75 for illustrations. Founded 1986.

Wine

Quest Magazines Ltd, Publishing House, 652 Victoria Road, South Ruislip, Middlesex HA4 0SX
tel 0181-842 1010 *fax* 0181-841 2557
Editor Susan Vumback Low
11 p.a. £2.95

Articles, features and news on new developments in wine; travelogues, tastings and profiles. Illustrations: colour. Payment: £125 per 1000 words. Founded 1983.

Wisden Cricket Monthly

The New Boathouse, 136-142 Bramley Road, London W10 6SR
tel 0171-565 3000 *fax* 0171-565 3054
e-mail wisden@johnbrown.co.uk
web site http://www.wisden.com
Editor Tim de Lisle
Monthly £2.60

Cricket articles of exceptional interest (unsolicited pieces seldom used). Length: up to 3000 words. Payment: by arrangement. Illustrations: half-tone, colour. Founded 1979.

Woman

IPC Magazines Ltd, King's Reach Tower, Stamford Street, London SE1 9LS
tel 0171-261 5000 *fax* 0171-261 5997
Editor Carole Russell
Weekly 60p

Practical articles of varying length on all subjects of interest to women. No unsolicited fiction. Payment: by arrangement. Illustrations: colour transparencies, photos, sketches, cartoons. Founded 1937.

Woman Alive

(formerly Christian Woman)
Christian Media Centre, 96 Dominion Road, Worthing, West Sussex BN14 8JP
tel (01903) 821082 *fax* (01903) 821081
Editor Elizabeth Proctor
Monthly £1.80

Aimed at women aged 25 upwards. Celebrity interviews, topical features, Christian issues, 'Day in the life of' profiles of women in interesting occupations, Christian testimonies, fashion, beauty, health, crafts. Unsolicited material should include colour slides or b&w photos. Length: 'Day in the life of'/testimonies 750 words, interviews/features

1300 words. Payment: £50 per 1000 words published. Founded 1982.

Woman and Home
(incorporating Living)
IPC Magazines Ltd, King's Reach Tower, Stamford Street, London SE1 9LS
tel 0171-261 5000 *fax* 0171-261 7346
Editor Jan Henderson
Monthly £1.80

Centres on the personal and home interests of the lively-minded woman with or without career and family. Articles dealing with fashion, beauty, leisure pursuits, gardening; things to buy and make for the home; features on people and places. Fiction: complete stories from 1000-5000 words in length. Illustrations: commissioned colour photos and sketches. Please note: non-commissioned work is rarely accepted and regrettably cannot be returned. Founded 1926.

The Woman Journalist
59 Grace Avenue, Maidstone, Kent ME16 0BS
Editor Barbara Haynes
3 p.a. Free to members

Periodical of the Society of Women Writers and Journalists. See under Societies section for further information. Founded 1894.

Woman's Journal
IPC Magazines Ltd, King's Reach Tower, Stamford Street, London SE1 9LS
tel 0171-261 6622 *fax* 0171-261 7061
Editor Marcelle d'Argy Smith
Monthly £2.20

Magazine devoted to the looks and lives of intelligent women aged 30 plus: interviews and articles (1000-2000 words) dealing with topical subjects and personalities; fashion, beauty and health, food and houses. No fiction accepted. Illustrations: full colour, line and wash, first-rate photos. Payment: by arrangement. Founded 1927.

Woman's Own
IPC Magazines Ltd, King's Reach Tower, Stamford Street, London SE1 9LS
tel 0171-261 5474
Editor Keith McNeill
Weekly 57p

Modern women's magazine aimed at the 20-35 age group. No unsolicited features or fiction. Illustrations: colour and b&w: interior decorating and furnishing, fash-

ion. Address work to relevant department editor. Payment: by arrangement.

Woman's Realm
IPC Magazines Ltd, King's Reach Tower, Stamford Street, London SE1 9LS
tel 0171-261 5000
Weekly 60p

Lively general interest weekly magazine. Articles on celebrities, topical subjects, health, cookery, fashion, beauty, home. Human interest features; dramatic emotional stories. (Regretfully, no unsolicited features or fiction accepted.) Payment: by arrangement. Illustrated. Founded 1958.

Woman's Way
Smurfit Publications Ltd, 2 Clanwilliam Court, Lower Mount Street, Dublin 2, Republic of Ireland
tel (01) 6623158 *fax* (01) 6619757
Editor Celine Naughton
Weekly 80p

Short stories, personality interviews, general features. Length: 1000-1500 words. Payment: £25-£100 approx. Illustrations: line, half-tone, colour. Founded 1963.

Woman's Weekly
IPC Magazines Ltd, King's Reach Tower, Stamford Street, London SE1 9LS
tel 0171-261 5000 *fax* 0171-261 6322
Editor Olwen Rice
Weekly 52p

Lively, family-interest magazine. One serial, averaging 4000 words, each instalment of strong romantic interest, and several short stories of 1000- 2500 words of general emotional interest. Celebrity and strong human interest features; also inspirational and entertaining personal stories. Payment: by arrangement. Illustrations: full colour fiction illustrations, small sketches and photos. Founded 1911.

The Woodworker
Nexus Special Interests Ltd, Nexus House, Azalea Drive, Swanley, Kent BR8 8HU
tel (01322) 660070
Editor Mark Ramuz
Monthly £2.40

For the craft and professional woodworker. Practical illustrated articles on cabinet work, carpentry, wood polishing, wood turning, wood carving, rural crafts, craft history, antique and period furniture;

also wooden toys and models, musical instruments; timber procurement, conditioning, seasoning; tool, machinery and equipment reviews. Payment: by arrangement. Illustrations: line drawings and photos.

The Word

Divine Word Missionaries, Donamon, Roscommon, Republic of Ireland
tel/fax (0903) 62608
e-mail wordeditor@tinet.ie
Editor Fr Tom Cahill SVD
Monthly 50p

General interest magazine with religious emphasis. Illustrated articles up to 2000 words and good picture features. Payment: by arrangement. Illustrations: photos and large colour transparencies, cartoons. Founded 1936.

Workbox

Ebony Media Ltd, Cave Canem, King Street, Gunnislake, Cornwall PL18 9JS
tel/fax (01822) 833946
Editor Victor Briggs
Bi-monthly £1.95

Features, of any length, on all aspects of needlecrafts. No 'how-to' articles. Send sae with enquiries and submissions. Illustrations: good colour transparencies. Payment: by agreement. Founded 1984.

The World of Embroidery

The Embroiderers' Guild, PO Box 42B, East Molesey, Surrey KT8 9BB
tel 0181-943 1229
6 p.a. £3.75 (£22.50 p.a.)

Articles on historical and contemporary embroidery by curators, artists and craftsmen; exhibition and book reviews; saleroom report; diary of events. Illustrations: line, half-tone, colour. Payment: by arrangement.

The World of Interiors

The Condé Nast Publications Ltd, Vogue House, Hanover Square, London W1R 0AD
tel 0171-499 9080 *fax* 0171-493 4013
web site http://www.worldofinteriors.co.uk
Editor Min Hogg
Monthly £3.20

All material commissioned: send synopsis/visual reference for article ideas. Length: 1000-1500 words. Illustrations: colour photos. Payment: £500 per 1000 words; photos from £100. Founded 1981.

World Fishing

Nexus Media Ltd, Nexus House, Azalea Drive, Swanley, Kent BR8 8HU
tel (01322) 660070 *fax* (01322) 667633
e-mail Mark.Say@nexusmedia.co.uk
Editor Mark Say
Monthly £49.00 p.a.

International journal of commercial fishing. Technical and management emphasis on catching, processing and marketing of fish and related products; fishery operations and vessels covered worldwide. Length: 500-1500 words. Payment: by arrangement. Illustrations: photos and diagrams for litho reproduction. Founded 1952.

World Soccer

IPC Magazines Ltd, King's Reach Tower, Stamford Street, London SE1 9LS
tel 0171-261 5737 *fax* 0171-261 7474
Editor Gavin Hamilton
Monthly £2.30

Articles, features, news concerning football, its personalities and worldwide development. Length: 600-2000 words. Illustrations: colour and b&w photos, cartoons. Payment: by arrangement. Founded 1960.

The World Today

The Royal Institute of International Affairs, Chatham House, 10 St James's Square, London SW1Y 4LE
tel 0171-957 5700 *fax* 0171-957 5710
e-mail wt-ch@riia.org
web site http://www.riia.org
Editor Graham Walker
Monthly £2.50

Analysis of international issues and current events by journalists, diplomats, politicians and academics. Length: 1700-3000 words. Payment: nominal. Founded 1945.

World's Children

Save the Children, 17 Grove Lane, London SE5 8RD
tel 0171-703 5400 *fax* 0171-708 2508
e-mail publications@scfuk.org.uk
web site http://www.scfuk.org.uk
Editor Lotte Hughes
Quarterly Sent free to regular donors

The magazine of Save the Children. Articles on child welfare and rights, related to Save the Children's work overseas and in the UK. No unsolicited features. Illustrations: colour and b&w photos. Founded 1920.

Writers' Forum

21 Belle Vue Street, Filey,
North Yorkshire YO14 9HU
Editor Morgan Kenney
Quarterly £3.75 (£14.50 p.a.)

Welcomes articles on any aspect of the craft and business of writing. Length: 300-1500 words. Payment: by arrangement. Administers 2 annual prizes: the Petra Kenney Memorial Poetry Prize (total £1750) and a Short Story Competition (total £300), plus poetry and short story competitions for subscribers in each issue. Founded 1993.

Writers News

PO Box 4, Nairn IV12 4HU
tel (01667) 454441 *fax* (01667) 454401
Editor Richard Bell
Monthly £43.90 p.a. (£38.90 p.a. CC/DD)

News, competitions and articles on all aspects of writing. Length: 800-1500 words. Illustrations: line, half-tone. Payment: by arrangement. Founded 1989.

Writing Magazine

PO Box 4, Nairn IV12 4HU
tel (01667) 454441 *fax* (01667) 454401
Editor Richard Bell
Bi-monthly £2.50 (free to *Writers News* subscribers)

Articles on all aspects of writing. Length: 800-1500 words. Illustrations: line, half-tone. Payment: by arrangement. Founded 1992.

Yachting Monthly

IPC Magazines Ltd, King's Reach Tower,
Stamford Street, London SE1 9LS
tel 0171-261 6040 *fax* 0171-261 7555
Editor James Jermain
Monthly £2.75

Technical articles, up to 2250 words, on all aspects of seamanship, navigation, the handling of sailing craft, and their design, construction and equipment. Well-written narrative accounts, up to 2500 words, of cruises in yachts. Payment: quoted on acceptance. Illustrations: b&w, colour transparencies, line or wash drawings, cartoons. Founded 1906.

Yachting World

IPC Magazines Ltd, King's Reach Tower,
Stamford Street, London SE1 9LS
tel 0171-261 6800 *fax* 0171-261 6818
e-mail yachting_world@ipc.co.uk
Editor Andrew Bray
Monthly £2.85

Practical articles of an original nature, dealing with sailing and boats. Length: 1500-2000 words. Payment: varies. Illustrations: colour transparencies, drawings, cartoons. Founded 1894.

Yachts and Yachting

196 Eastern Esplanade, Southend-on-Sea,
Essex SS1 3AB
tel (01702) 582245 *fax* (01702) 588434
Editor Frazer Clark
Fortnightly £2.35

Short articles which should be technically correct. Payment: by arrangement. Illustrations: line, half-tone, colour. Founded 1947.

Yes! – see The People in National newspapers UK and Ireland, page 3

Yorkshire Ridings Magazine

33 Beverley Road, Driffield, Yorkshire YO25 6SD
tel/fax (01377) 253232
Editor Winston Halstead
Bi-monthly £1.00

Articles exclusively about people, life and character of the 3 Ridings of Yorkshire. Length: up to 1500 words. Payment: approx. £30-£35 per published page. Illustrations: line, half-tone, colour. Founded 1964.

You – see Mail on Sunday in National newspapers UK and Ireland, page 3

You & Your Wedding

You & Your Wedding Publications Ltd,
Silver House, 31-35 Beak Street,
London W1R 3LD
tel 0171-437 2998 *fax* 0171-287 8655
Editor Carole Hamilton
Bi-monthly £3.25

Articles, features and news covering all aspects of planning a wedding. Illustrations: colour. Payment: £200 per 1000 words. Founded 1985.

Young People Now

National Youth Agency, 17-23 Albion Street,
Leicester LE1 6GD
tel 0116-285 6789 *fax* 0116-247 1043
Editor Sharon Hurley
Monthly £2.00 (£22.80 p.a.)

Informative articles, highlighting issues of concern to all those who work with young people – including youth workers, probation and social services, teachers and volunteers. Guidelines for contributors available on request. Founded 1989.

Young Writer

Glebe House, Weobley, Herefordshire HR4 8SD
tel (01544) 318901 *fax* (01544) 318901
e-mail youngwriter@enterprise.net
web site http://www.mystworld.com/youngwriter
Editor Kate Jones
3 p.a. £2.50 (£6.50 for 3 issues)

Specialist magazine for young writers aged about 7-15 years: ideas for them and writing by them. Includes interviews of famous writers by children, fiction and non-fiction pieces, poetry; also explores words and grammar, issues related to writing (e.g. dyslexia), plus competitions with prizes. Length: 750 or 1500 words (features), up to 400 words (news), 750 words (short stories – unless specified otherwise in a competition), poetry of any length. Illustrations: colour – drawings by children, snapshots to accompany features. Payment: most children's material is published without payment; £25-£100 (features); £25 (cover cartoon). Founded 1995.

Your Dog

EMAP Apex Publications, Oundle Road,
Peterborough PE2 9NP
tel (01733) 898100 *fax* (01733) 898487
Editor Sarah Wright
Monthly £2.35

Articles and information of interest to dog lovers; features on all aspects of pet dogs. Length: approx. 1500 words. Illustrations: colour transparencies, prints and line drawings. Payment: £70 per 1000 words. Founded 1994.

Your Garden

IPC Magazines Ltd, Westover House,
West Quay Road, Poole, Dorset BH15 1JG
tel (01202) 680603 *fax* (01202) 674335
Editor Michael Pilcher
Monthly £2.10

Anything on gardening for the enthusiastic beginner. Commissioned material only; send brief synopsis of ideas. Length: 800-2000 words. Illustrations: colour photos and line. Payment: £100 per published 1000 words. Founded 1993.

Yours

Apex House, Oundle Road,
Peterborough PE2 9NP
tel (01733) 555123 *fax* (01733) 312025
Editor Neil Patrick
Monthly 80p

Features and news about and /or of interest to the over-60s age group, including nostalgia and short stories. Study of magazine essential; approach in writing in first instance. Length: articles up to 1000 words, short stories up to 1800 words. Illustrations: preferably colour transparencies/prints but will consider good b&w prints/line drawings, cartoons. Payment: at editor's discretion or by agreement. Founded 1973.

Zest

National Magazine House, 72 Broadwick Street,
London W1V 2BP
tel 0171-439 5000 *fax* 0171-439 5632
e-mail zest.mail@natmags.co.uk
Editor Eve Cameron
Monthly £2.20

Health and beauty magazine. Commissioned material only: health, fitness and beauty, features, news and shorts. Length: 50-2000 words. Illustrations: colour and b&w photos and line. Payment: £250 per 1000 words. Founded 1994.

Newspapers and magazines overseas

Listings are given for newspapers and magazines in Australia (below), Canada (page 116), New Zealand (page 120) and South Africa (page 122). For information on submitting material to the USA, see page 124. Newspapers are listed under the towns in which they are published.

Australia

(Adelaide) Advertiser
121 King William Street, Adelaide, SA 5000
tel (08) 8206 2000 *fax* (08) 8206 3669
London office PO Box 481, 1 Virginia Street,
London E1 9BD
tel 0171-702 1355 *fax* 0171-702 1384
Editor Steve Howard
Daily Mon-Fri 70c, Sat$1.00
Descriptive and news background material, 400-800 words, preferably with pictures; also cartoons. Founded 1858.

(Adelaide) Sunday Mail
121 King William Street, Adelaide, SA 5000
postal address GPO Box 339, Adelaide, SA 5001
tel (08) 206 2796 *fax* (08) 206 3646
web site http://www.news.com.au
Editor K. Sullivan
Weekly $1.30
Founded 1912.

Art and Australia
Fine Arts Press Pty Ltd, Tower A,
112 Talavera Road, North Ryde, NSW 2113
tel (02) 9878 8222 *fax* (02) 9878 8122
e-mail info@gbpub.com.au
web site http://www.artaustralia.com
Editor Laura Murray Cree
Quarterly $14.50 (plus $6.00 postage)
Articles with a contemporary perspective on Australia's traditional and current art, and on international art of Australian relevance, plus exhibition and book reviews. Length: 2000-4000 words (articles), 600-1500 words (reviews). Payment: $200 per 1000 words. Colour transparencies. Founded 1916 as *Art in Australia*.

Australasian Post
32 Walsh Street, Melbourne, Victoria 3003
tel (03) 320 7000 *fax* (03) 9320 7410

Editor Sharon McCrohan
Weekly $3.50
Feature stories about Australia and Australians, both urban and rural; characters and achievers, known and unknown; short stories and poems. Material mostly commissioned. Length: 750-1000 words. Illustrations: colour transparencies. Payment: $300-500 per feature/illustration. Founded 1864.

Australian Bookseller & Publisher
D.W. Thorpe, 18 Salmon Street, Port Melbourne,
Victoria 3207
tel (03) 9245 7370 *fax* (03) 9245 7395
Editor Caroline Birrell
Monthly $62.00 p.a. ($96.00 p.a. NZ/Asia; $107.00 p.a. USA/Canada; $114.00 p.a. UK/Europe)
Founded 1921.

The Australian Financial Review
IBM Building, Level 25, 201 Sussex Street,
Sydney 2001
tel (02) 282 2512 *fax* (02) 282 3137
London office 95 Fetter Lane, London EC4A 1HE
tel 0171-242 0044 *fax* 0171-242 0066
New York office Suite 1720, 317 Madison
Avenue, New York, NY 10017
tel 212-398-9494
Editor Deborah Light
Daily Mon-Fri $1.60
Investment business and economic news and reviews; government and politics, production, banking, commercial, and Stock Exchange statistics; company analysis. General features in Friday *Weekend Review* supplement.

Australian Flying
Yaffa Publishing Group, 17-21 Bellevue Street,
Surry Hills, NSW 2010
tel (02) 281 2333 *fax* (02) 281 2750
e-mail yaffa@flex.com.au

Editor Doug Nancarron
London office 64 The Mall, London W5 5LS
tel 0181-579 4836
Editor Robert Logan
6 p.a. $5.25
Covers the Australian aviation industry, from light aircraft to airliners. Payment: by arrangement.

Australian Geographic
PO Box 321, Terrey Hills, NSW 2084
tel (02) 9450 2344 *fax* (02) 9450 2990
e-mail www.ausgeo.com.au
Editor Howard Whelan
Quarterly $39.60 p.a.
Short articles and features about Australia, particularly life, technology and natural history in remote parts of the country. Material mostly commissioned. Length: articles, 300-800 words, features, 2000-3000 words. Illustrations: all commissioned. Payment: $500 per 1000 words; illustrations by negotiation. Founded 1986.

Australian Home Beautiful
32 Walsh Street, West Melbourne, Victoria 3003
tel (03) 9320 7000 *fax* (03) 9320 7410
Editor W. Buttner
Monthly $4.40
Deals with home building, interior decoration, furnishing, gardening, cookery, etc. Short articles with accompanying photos with Australian slant accepted. Preliminary letter advisable. Payment: Australian average. Founded 1913.

Australian House and Garden
54 Park Street, Sydney, NSW 2000
tel (02) 9282 8456 *fax* (02) 9267 4912
e-mail h&g@publishing.acp.com.au
Editor Anny Friis
Monthly $4.95
Factual articles dealing with interior decorating, home design, gardening, wine, food. Preliminary letter essential. Payment: by arrangement. Illustrations: line, half-tone, colour. Founded 1948.

Australian Journal of International Affairs
Department of International Relations, RSPAS, Australian National University, Canberra, ACT 0200
tel (06) 249 2169 *fax* (06) 279 8010
Editor Dr Ramesh Thakur, Vice-Rector (Peace & Governance), United Nations University, 53-70 Jingumae 5-chome, Shibuya-ku, Tokyo 150-8925, Japan

3 p.a. Personal rate A$64.00 p.a., institutions A$132.00 p.a. (Australia); other rates on application
Scholarly articles on international affairs. Length: 3000-7000 words. Payment: none.

Australian Journal of Politics and History
Department of Government, University of Queensland, St Lucia, Queensland 4067
tel (07) 3365 3163 *fax* (07) 3365 1388
e-mail g.stokes@mailbox.uq.edu.au
Editors Geoffrey Stokes and Ross Johnston
4 p.a. $50.00 (US $50.00, UK £30.00) individuals; $100.00 (US$125.00, UK £75.00) institutions
Australian, European, Asian, Pacific and international articles. Special feature: regular surveys of Australian Foreign Policy and State and Commonwealth politics. Length: 8000 words max. Illustrations: line, only when necessary. Payment: none.

Australian Photography
Yaffa Publishing Group, 17-21 Bellevue Street, Surry Hills, NSW 2010
tel (02) 9281 2333 *fax* (02) 9281 2750
Editor Robin Nichols
Monthly $4.95
Illustrated articles – picture-taking techniques, technical. Length/illustrations: 1000 words/colour and b&w prints or slides. Payment: $80 per page. Founded 1950.

Australian Powerboat
Yaffa Publishing Group, GPO Box 606, Sydney, NSW 1041
tel (02) 9213 8257 *fax* (02) 9281 2750
Editor Graham Lloyd
Bi-monthly $5.20
Articles and news on boats and boating, racing, water skiing and products. Length: 1500 words (articles), 200 words (news). Illustrations: colour (transparencies preferred). Payment: $100 per 1000 words; from $30. Founded 1976.

The Australian Quarterly
Australian Institute of Political Science, PO Box 145, Balmain, NSW 2041
tel (02) 810 5642 *fax* (02) 810 2406
Editors Damian Grace and Ian Marsh
Quarterly $55.00 p.a. individuals, $95.00 p.a. institutions ($65/$105 overseas)
Peer-reviewed articles for the informed non-specialist on politics, law, economics, social issues, etc. Length: 3500 words preferred. Payment: none. Founded 1929.

Australian Short Stories

Pascoe Publishing Pty Ltd, PO Box 42,
Apollo Bay, Victoria 3233
tel (03) 523 76311 *fax* (03) 523 76559
Editors Bruce Pascoe and Lyn Harwood
Quarterly $9.95

Contemporary short stories from around
the world. Length: 500-5000 words.
Illustrations: b&w artwork. Payment $90
per 1000 words; $70 illustrations.
Founded 1983.

The Australian Way

BRW Media, Level 2, 469 Latrobe Street,
Melbourne, Victoria 3000
postal address GPO Box 55A, Melbourne,
Victoria 3001
tel (03) 9603 3888 *fax* (03) 9642 0852
Editor Tom Brentnall
Monthly Free

Inflight magazine for Qantas Airways.
Articles of international interest; profiles,
third-person stories that use locations as a
backdrop, pictorial essays and features on
prominent Australians. Length: 800-1500
words. Illustrations: colour transparencies.
Payment: by negotiation. Founded 1986.

The Australian Women's Weekly

Australian Consolidated Press Ltd,
54 Park Street, Sydney, NSW 2000
postal address GPO Box 4178, Sydney, NSW 1028
tel (02) 9282 8000 *fax* (02) 9267 4459
Editorial Director Nene King
Monthly $3.80

Fiction and features. Length: fiction 1000-
5000 words; features 750-1500 words plus
colour or b&w photos. Payment: according
to length and merit. Fiction illustrations:
sketches by own artists and freelances.

(Brisbane) The Courier-Mail

Queensland Newspapers Pty Ltd, Campbell
Street, Bowen Hills, Brisbane, Queensland 4006
tel (07) 3252 6011 *fax* (07) 3252 6696
e-mail cmletters@qup.newsltd.com.au
web site http://www.news.com.au
Editor-in-Chief C. Mitchell
Daily 70c

Occasional topical special articles
required. Length: 1000 words.

(Brisbane) Sunday Mail

Queensland Newspapers Pty Ltd, PO Box 130,
Campbell Street, Bowen Hills, Brisbane,
Queensland 4006
tel (07) 3252 6011 *fax* (07) 3252 6687
Editor Michael Prain
Weekly $1.30

Anything of general interest. Length: up
to 1500 words. Illustrations: line, photos,
b&w and colour, cartoons. Rejected MSS
returned if postage enclosed.

The Bulletin with Newsweek

54 Park Street, Sydney, NSW 2000
tel (02) 282 8200 *fax* (02) 267 4359
Editor Lyndall Crisp
Weekly $3.30

General interest articles, features;
humour. Length: 750 words per page,
max. 2100 words. Illustrations: colour
photos and cartoons. Payment: $450 per
1000 words published; $100 colour car-
toons and photos, according to size used.

Cleo

Level 4, 54 Park Street, Sydney, NSW 1028
tel (02) 9282 8617 *fax* (02) 9267 4368
Editor Deborah Thomas
Monthly $4.90

Articles (relationship, emotional, self-
help) up to 3000 words, short quizzes.
Payment: by negotiation. Founded 1972.

Countryman

50 Hasler Road, Osborne Park,
Western Australia 6017
tel (08) 9482 3322 *fax* (08) 9482 3324
e-mail countryman@wanews.com.au
Editor Gary McGay
Weekly $1.00

Agriculture, farming or country interest
features and service columns. Payment:
standard rates. Illustrations: line, half-
tone, colour, cartoons.

Current Affairs Bulletin

CAB, PO Box 81, Ainslie Act, 2602 Australia
tel/fax (06) 230 1734
e-mail cabedit@ozemail.com.au
web site http://www.cabpub.com.au
Editors Dr R. Catley, Dr Lenore Coltheart
6 p.a. $6.50 ($40.00 p.a., $57.00 p.a. overseas)

Authoritative well-documented articles
on all national and international affairs:
politics, economics, science, the arts,
business and social questions. Length:
3000-5000 words. Illustrations: line, half-
tone. Payment: none. Founded 1947.

Dance Australia

Yaffa Publishing Group, Box 606, GPO Sydney,
NSW 2001
tel (02) 281 2333 *fax* (02) 281 2750
e-mail yaffa@yaffa.com.au
Editor Karen van Ulzen
Bi-monthly $5.50

Articles and features on all aspects of dance in Australia. Material mostly commissioned, but will consider unsolicited contributions. Length: as appropriate. Illustrations: b&w photos, line drawings, cartoons. Payment: $200 per 1000 words; illustrations by negotiation. Founded 1980.

Dolly
54 Park Street, Sydney, NSW 1028
tel (02) 9282 8437 *fax* (02) 9267 4911
web site http://dolly.ninemsn.com.au
Editor Susie Pitts
Monthly $3.60

Features on fashion, health and beauty, personalities, music, social issues and how to cope with growing up, etc. Length: not less than 1000 words. Illustrations: colour, b&w, line, cartoons. Payment: by arrangement. Founded 1970.

Electronics Australia with ETI
PO Box 199, Alexandria, NSW 2015
tel (02) 9353 0620 *fax* (02) 9353 0613
e-mail electaus@magna.com.au
web site http://electronicsaustralia.com.au
Editor Jamieson Rowe
Monthly $5.95

Articles on technical television and radio, hi-fi, popular electronics, microcomputers and avionics. Length: up to 2000 words. Payment: by arrangement. Illustrations: line, half-tone, cartoons.

Elle (Australia)
Level 4, 80 Clarence Street, Sydney, NSW 2000
tel (02) 9249 3553 *fax* (02) 9249 3555
Editor Marina Go
Monthly $5.20

Profiles, news reports, cultural essays, fashion stories. Length: 300-3000 words. Payment: varies. Founded 1990.

Fishing World Magazine
Yaffa Publishing Group, 17-21 Bellevue Street, Surry Hills, NSW 2010
tel (02) 9281 2333 *fax* (02) 9281 2750
telex AA 121887
web site http://www.yaffa.com.au/fw
Editor Jim Harnwell
Monthly $4.95

Rock, surf, stream, deep sea and game fishing, with comprehensive sections on gear, equipment and boats. Payment: by arrangement.

Geo Australasia
Hallmark Editions, PO Box 84, Hampton, Victoria 3188

tel (03) 9555 7377 *fax* (03) 9555 7599
e-mail hallmark@halledit.com.au
Editor Peter Stirling
Bi-monthly $7.95 ($55.00 p.a. surface mail, $85.00 p.a. airmail)

Non-fiction articles on wildlife, adventure, culture and lifestyles, natural history and the environment in Australia, New Zealand, the Pacific and SE Asia. Length: 1500-3000 words. Payment: $600-$1500 by arrangement. Illustrations: photos, colour transparencies. Founded 1978.

Guns Australia
Yaffa Publishing Group Pty Ltd, 17-21 Bellevue Street, Surry Hills, NSW 2010
tel (02) 9281 2333 *fax* (02) 9281 2750
Editor Daniel Cotterill
Quarterly $4.50

Articles, features, technical pieces, news. All material commissioned. Length: 2000 words. Illustrations: colour slides, b&w photos. Payment: $50 per page.

Harper's Bazaar & Mode
ACP Publishing Pty Ltd, 54 Park Street, Sydney, NSW 2001
tel (02) 282 8703 *fax* (02) 267 4456
e-mail bazaar@publishing.qcp.com.au
Editor Karin Upton Baker
10 p.a. $6.50

Fashion, health and beauty, celebrity news, plus features. Length: 3000 words. Illustrations: colour and b&w photos. Payment: $500 per 1000 words; $150. Founded 1998.

Herald of the South
PO Box 285, Mona Vale, NSW 2103
tel (02) 9913 2771 *fax* (02) 9970 7275
e-mail herald@bahai.org.au
Quarterly $28.00 p.a.

The Baha'i magazine for world citizens focusing on new and challenging perpsectives to global issues. Features, fiction and non-fiction. Length: up to 3500 words. Illustrations: colour and b&w photos. Payment: by negotiation. Founded 1925.

Hobo
PO Box 166, Hazelbrook, NSW 2779
Editor Dane Thwaites
Quarterly £20.00 p.a.

Poetry, Haiku, book reviews, articles about poetry and Haiku. Payment: approx. $12 per page. No illustrations. Founded 1993.

HQ Magazine
54 Park Street, Sydney, NSW 2000
tel (02) 9282 8260 *fax* (02) 9267 3616
e-mail hq@publishing.acp.com.au
web site http://hq.ninemsn.com.au
Editor Kathy Bail
Bi-monthly $5.95
General interest features and profiles for a literate readership. Length: 1500-5000 words. Illustrations: colour and b&w photos. Payment: by negotiation. Founded 1989.

Hobo
PO Box 166, Hazelbrook, NSW 2779
Editor Dane Thwaites
Quarterly $20.00 p.a. ($30.00 p.a. overseas)
Poetry, Haiku, book reviews, articles about poetry and Haiku. Payment: approx. $12 per page. No illustrations. Founded 1993.

Imago: new writing
School of Media & Journalism, QUT,
GPO Box 2434, Brisbane, Queensland 4001
tel (07) 3864 2976 *fax* (07) 3864 1810
Editor Philip Neilsen
3 p.a. $30 p.a. airmail
New writing: short stories, poems, essays and articles on writers and writing or on some aspect of Australian culture. Length: 2000-3000 words (articles), 1500-3000 words (stories), 14-40 lines (poems). Payment: $90 (articles and stories), $40 (poems). No illustrations. Founded 1989.

(Launceston) Examiner
Box 99A, PO Launceston, Tasmania 7250
tel (03) 633 15111 *fax* (03) 633 47328
Editor Rod Scott
Daily 75c
Accepts freelance material. Payment: by arrangement.

(Melbourne) Age
David Syme & Co. Ltd, 250 Spencer Street,
Melbourne, Victoria 3000
tel (03) 9600 4211 *fax* (03) 9670 7514
Editor Michael Gawenda
London office 95 Fetter Lane, London EC4A 1HE
Daily Mon-Fri 90c Sat, Sun $1.50
Independent liberal morning daily; room occasionally for outside matter. An illustrated weekend magazine and literary review is published on Saturday; accepts occasional freelance material.

(Melbourne) Aussie Post
Pacific Publications Pty Ltd, 32 Walsh Street,
GPO Box 4529RR, Melbourne, Victoria 3003
tel (03) 9320 7000

Deputy Editor Peter Mayer
Weekly $3.50
Opening for casual contributions of topical factual illustrated articles of Australian interest. General appeal. Payment: by arrangement.

(Melbourne) Herald Sun
HWT Tower, 40 City Road, Southbank,
Victoria 3006
tel (03) 9292 1816 *fax* (03) 9292 1776
Editor Peter Blunden
Daily Mon-Fri 70c Sat 90c Sun $1.20
Accepts freelance articles, preferably with illustrations. Length: up to 750 words. Illustrations: half-tone, line, cartoons. Payment: on merit.

(Melbourne) Sunday Herald Sun
HWT Tower, 40 City Road, Southbank,
Victoria 3006
tel (03) 9292 2000 *fax* (03) 9292 2080
Editor Alan Howe
Weekly $1.30
Accepts freelance articles, preferably with illustrations. Length: up to 2000 words. Illustrations: colour. Payment: on merit.

New Idea
32 Walsh Street, PO Box 1743Q, Melbourne,
Victoria 3001
tel (03) 9320 7000 *fax* (03) 9320 7439
Editor A. Johnston
Weekly $2.70
General interest women's magazine; news stories, features, fashion, services, short stories of general interest to women of all ages. Length: stories, 500-4000 words: articles, 500-2000 words. Payment: on acceptance. Founded 1902.

New Weekly
54 Park Street, Sydney, NSW 2000
tel (02) 9282 8285 *fax* (02) 9264 6005
Editor-in-Chief Juliet Ashworth
Weekly $2.90
News and features on celebrities, food, new products, fashion and astrology. Illustrated. Payment: by negotiation. Founded 1993.

New Woman
Level 4, 45 Jones Street, Sydney, NSW 2007
tel (02) 9692 2000 *fax* (02) 9692 2488
Editor-in-Chief Cyndi Tebbel
Monthly $4.90
Self-development for the thirty-something woman: articles, features, fashion, beauty, health, reviews and

book excerpts. Material mostly commissioned. Length: average 1200 words. Payment: 55c a word. Illustrated. Founded 1989.

Overland

PO Box 14146 MCMC, Melbourne, Victoria 8001
tel (03) 9687 9785 *fax* (03) 9687 5918
Editor Ian Syson
Quarterly $32.00 p.a.

Literary and cultural. Australian material preferred. Payment: by arrangement. Illustrations: line, half-tone, cartoons.

People Magazine

54 Park Street, Sydney, NSW 2000
tel (02) 282 8743 *fax* (02) 267 4365
Editor Simon Butler-White
Weekly $2.90

National weekly news-pictorial. Mainly people stories. Photos depicting exciting happenings, glamour, show business, unusual occupations, rites, customs. Payment: $300 per page, text and photos.

(Perth) Sunday Times

34-40 Stirling Street, Perth,
Western Australia 6000
tel (09) 326 8326 *fax* (09) 221 1121
Managing Editor Don Smith
Weekly $1.30

Topical articles to 800 words. Payment: on acceptance. Founded 1897.

(Perth) The West Australian

55 Hasler Road, Osborne Park,
Western Australia 6017
tel (09) 9482 3111 *fax* (09) 9482 3452
Editor Paul Murray
Daily Mon-Fri 70c Sat $1.20

Articles and sketches about people and events in Australia and abroad. Length: 300-700 words. Payment: Award rates or better. Illustrations: line, half-tone. Founded 1833.

Quadrant

46 George Street, Fitzroy, Victoria 3065
postal address PO Box 1495, Collingwood, Victoria 3066
tel (03) 9417 6855 *fax* (03) 9416 2980
e-mail quadrnt@ozemail.com.au
Editor P.P. McGuinness
Monthly $6.00

Articles, short stories, verse, etc. Prose length: 2000-5000 words. Payment: minimum $90 articles/stories, $60 reviews, $40 poems; illustrations by arrangement.

Reader's Digest (Australia)

PO Box 4353, Sydney, NSW 2001
tel (02) 690 6111 *fax* (02) 699 8165
Editor-in-Chief Bruce Heilbuth
Monthly $3.95

Articles on Australian subjects by commission only. No unsolicited MSS accepted. Length: 2500-5000 words. Payment: up to $6000 per article; brief filler paragraphs, $50-$250. Illustrations: half-tone, colour.

Redoubt

Faculty of Communication, University of Canberra, PO Box 1, Belconnen, ACT 2616
tel (06) 201 2945 *fax* (06) 201 5300
e-mail redoubt@comserver.canberra.edu.au
web site http://services.canberra.edu.au/uc/comm/schiflgcs/profwr/redoubt/redoubt.html
Managing Editor Gillian Ferguson
Bi-annual $10.50 inc. postage

Literary magazine: mainly short stories, poetry, reviews, articles and profiles of writers. Length: short poetry; prose up to 3000 words; reviews up to 600 words. Illustrations: b&w photos and line drawings. Payment: copy of magazine. Founded 1988.

Scuba Diver

Yaffa Publishing Group, 17-21 Bellevue Street, Surry Hills, NSW 2010
tel (02) 9281 2333 *fax* (02) 9281 2750
e-mail yaffa@flex.com.au
Editor Sue Crowe
Bi-monthly $5.75

News, features, articles and short stories on scuba diving. Length: 1500 words (articles/features), 300-800 words (news), 800-1000 (short stories). Illustrations: colour. Payment: $70 per page, negotiable (words and pictures).

She

ACP Publishing Pty Ltd, 54 Park Street, Sydney, NSW 2000
tel (02) 9282 8585 *fax* (02) 9267 4457
Editorial Director Pat Ingram
Monthly $4.80

Lifestyle magazine for young women. Length: 2000 words, variable (articles/features). Illustrations: colour and b&w. Founded 1993.

The Sun-Herald

GPO Box 506, Sydney, NSW 2001
tel (02) 9282 2822 *fax* (02) 9282 2151
Publisher and Editor Alan Revell
London office John Fairfax (UK) Ltd, 93 Fetter Lane, London EC4A 1HE

tel 0171-242 0044
Weekly $1.00
Topical articles to 1000 words; sections on politics, social issues, show business, finance and fashion. Payment: by arrangement.

(Sydney) The Daily Telegraph

News Ltd, 2 Holt Street, Surry Hills, NSW 2010
tel (02) 9288 3000 *fax* (02) 9288 3481
Editor-in-Chief John Hartigan
Daily Mon-Fri 80c Sat $1.00
Modern feature articles and series of Australian or world interest. Length: 1000-2000 words. Payment: according to merit/length.

The Sydney Morning Herald

PO Box 506, Sydney, NSW 2001
tel (02) 9282 2858
Publisher and Editor-in-Chief John Alexander
London office 95 Fetter Lane, London EC4A 1HE
tel 0171-242 0044 *fax* 0171-242 0066
Daily 90c
Saturday edition has pages of literary criticism and also magazine articles, plus glossy colour magazine. Topical articles 600-4000 words. Payment: varies, but minimum $100 per 1000 words. Illustrations: all types. Founded 1831.

(Sydney) The Sunday Telegraph

News Ltd, 2 Holt Street, Surry Hills, Sydney, NSW 2010
tel (02) 9288 3305 *fax* (02) 9288 2300
Editor Roy Miller
Weekly $1.00
News and features. Illustrations: colour transparencies. Payment: varies. Founded 1935.

Wild

Wild Publications Pty Ltd, PO Box 415, Prahran, Victoria 3181
tel (03) 9826 8482 *fax* (03) 9826 3787
e-mail wild@wild.com.au
web site http://www.wild.com.au
Editor Naomi Peters
4 p.a. $7.50
'Australia's wilderness and adventure magazine.' Illustrated articles of first-hand experiences of the Australian wilderness, plus book and track reviews, product tests. Send sae for guidelines for contributors. Length: 2500 words (articles), 200 words (news). Colour transparencies. Payment: $125 per published page. Founded 1981.

Woman's Day

54-58 Park Street, Sydney, NSW 2000
tel (02) 9282 8000 *fax* (02) 9267 4360
Editor-in-Chief Juliet Ashworth
Weekly $2.70
National women's magazine; news, show business, fiction, fashion, general articles, cookery, home economy.

World Art

G&B Arts International, 1st Floor, 478 Chapel Street, South Yarra, Victoria 3141
Postal address PO Box 95, Prahran 3181
tel (03) 9827 5499 *fax* (03) 9827 5281
e-mail ed21c@peg.apc.org
web site http://www.worldartmag.com
Editors Ashley Crawford, Sarah Bayliss, Ray Edgar
Quarterly £5.95
Features, reviews and profiles on contemporary painting, photography, performance and installation art worldwide. Welcomes material from freelances. Length: 2000-3000 words (features), 800-1500 words (profiles), 800 words (reviews). Payment: 10p per word. Founded 1993.

Canada

ArtsAtlantic

Confederation Centre of the Arts, 145 Richmond Street, Charlottetown, Prince Edward Island C1A 1J1
tel 902-628-6138 *fax* 902-566-4648
e-mail artsatlantic@isn.net
web site http://www.isn.net/artsatlantic
Editor Joseph Sherman
3 p.a. $29.95 for 4 issues ($45.95 for 8 issues)
Features and reviews on the art history of Atlantic Canada, the work of contemporary artists and the ideas and issues affecting Canadian culture. No fiction or poetry. All material commissioned; send enquiries (plus CV and samples of published work). Length: reviews, 300-900 words, features, 1000-3000 words. Illustrations: colour and b&w. Payment: $75 per review, features 15c per word to $250 maximum; illustrations by negotiation. Founded 1977.

The Beaver: Exploring Canada's History

Canada's National History Society, Suite 478, 167 Lombard Avenue, Winnipeg, Manitoba R3B 0T6

tel 204-988-9300 *fax* 204-988-9309
Editor Annalee Greenberg
Bi-monthly $27.50 p.a. ($38.50 USA, $40.50 p.a. elsewhere)

Articles, historical and modern, on Canadian history. Length: 1500-4000 words, with illustrations. Payment: on acceptance, approx. 15c per word. Illustrations: b&w and colour photos or drawings.

Books in Canada
50 St Clair Avenue East, 3rd Floor, Toronto, Ontario M4T 1M9
tel 416-924-2777 *fax* 416-924-8682
e-mail binc@istar.ca
Editor Gerald Owen
9 p.a. $4.50

Commissioned reviews, informed criticism and articles on Canadian literary, intellectual and political books. Query first – do not send unsolicited material. Payment: 10c per word. Founded 1971.

C Magazine
PO Box 5, Station B, Toronto, Ontario M5T 2T2
tel 416-539-9495 *fax* 416-539-9903
e-mail cmag@istar.ca
Editor Joyce Mason
Quarterly US$8.25

Arts and artists' projects, features, reviews. Accept submissions. Length: features, varies; reviews, 500 words. Illustrations: b&w photos. Payment: $250-$500 features, $100 reviews. Founded 1972.

Canadian Author
PO Box 419, Campbellford, Ontario K0L 1L0
tel 705-653-0323 *fax* 705-653-0593
Editor Doug Bale
Quarterly $20.00 p.a. individual, $30.00 p.a. corporate (add $5.00 p.a. outside Canada)

Published by Canadian Authors Association. Interested in an international view on writing techniques, profiles, interviews, freelance opportunities for Canadian writers. Query only. Payment: $30 per printed page.

The Canadian Forum
251 Laurier Avenue W, Suite 804, Ottawa, Ontario K1P 5J6
tel 613-230-3078 *fax* 613-233-1458
Editor Duncan Cameron
10 p.a. $3.50 ($29.96 p.a.)

Articles on public affairs and the arts; book reviews. Length: up to 2500 words. Payment: varies. Illustrations: line and photos.

Canadian Interiors
Crailer Communications, 360 Dupont Street, Toronto, Ontario M5R 1V9
tel 416-966-9944 *fax* 416-966-9946
Editor Sheri Craig
8 p.a. $34.24 p.a. (US$75.00 p.a. elsewhere)

Articles on all aspects of the interior design industry. Illustrations: half-tone, colour.

Canadian Literature
167-1855 West Mall, University of British Columbia, Vancouver, BC V6T 1Z2
tel 604-882-2780 *fax* 604-822-5504
Editor E.M. Kröller
4 p.a. $40.00 p.a. individual; $55.00 p.a. institutions

Articles on Canadian writers and writing in English and French. Length: up to 5000 words. Founded 1959.

Canadian Theatre Review (CTR)
Dept of Drama, University of Guelph, Guelph, Ontario N1G 2W1
Contact Editorial Committee
Quarterly $9.50 ($32.00 p.a.)

Feature and review articles on Canadian theatre aimed at theatre professionals; book and play reviews. Send MSS accompanied by PC compatible disk. Length: 2000-3000 words. Illustrations: b&w. Payment: $200-275 (features/articles), $50 (book/play reviews). Founded 1974.

Canadian Yachting
Kerrwil Publications Ltd, 395 Matheson Boulevard East, Mississauga, Ontario L4Z 2H2
tel 905-890-1846 *fax* 905-890-5769
e-mail canyacht@kerrwil.com
web site http://www.canyacht.com
Editor Heather Ormerod
6 p.a. $3.95

Features, news and views. Query letters preferred. Length: regulars, 1000-2000 words; features, 1800-2700 words. Illustrations: line, half-tone, colour, cartoons. Payment: up to $350 regulars, up to $350 features; $50-$250 line, $30-$100 photos, $200 cover shots. Founded 1974.

Chatelaine
777 Bay Street, Toronto, Ontario M5W 1A7
tel 416-596-5425
Editor Rona Maynard
Monthly $2.99

Women's interest articles; Canadian angle preferred. Payment: on acceptance; from $1000.

Chickadee

The Owl Group, Bayard Press Canada,
179 John Street, Suite 500, Toronto,
Ontario M5T 3G5
tel (416) 340 2700 *fax* (416) 340 9769
e-mail kat@owl.on.ca
web site http://www.owl.on.ca
Editor Kat Mototsune
9 p.a. $2.95 ($24.00 p.a. Canada, US$14.95 USA,
$34.00 rest of world)

Highly illustrated mix of stories and
activities on the theme of the world
around kids; aimed at children aged 6-9.
Length: 10-100 words (articles), 800-900
words (fiction). Illustrations: colour.
Payment: $250 (fiction). Founded 1979.

The Dalhousie Review

Dalhousie University, Halifax,
Nova Scotia B3H 3J5
tel 902-494-2541 *fax* 902-494-3561
e-mail Dalhousie.Review@dal.ca
Editor Ronald Huebert
Associate Editor Stephen Brooke
3 p.a. ($32.10 p.a., $85.60 for 3 years;
($40.00/$100.00 outside Canada)

Articles on history, literature, political
science, philosophy, sociology, popular
culture, fine arts; short fiction; verse;
book reviews. Usually not more than 3
stories and 10-12 poems in any one
issue. Length: prose, up to 5000 words;
verse, less than 40 words. Contributors
receive 2 copies of issue and 10 offprints
of their work.

Equinox

11450 Albert-Hudon Blvd, Montreal,
Montreal, QC H1G 3J9
tel 514-327-4464 *fax* 514-327-0514
e-mail equinox@kos.net
Editor Alan Morantz
Bi-monthly ($22.95 p.a. Canada; Can.$29.00 p.a.
USA; Can.$35.00 elsewhere)

Magazine of discovery in science, human
cultures, technology and geography.
Accepts articles on hard science topics
(length: 250-350 words); welcomes
queries (2-3-page outline) for specific
assignments. No phone queries please.
Illustrations: colour transparencies.
Payment: by arrangement. Founded 1982.

The Fiddlehead

Campus House, University of New Brunswick,
PO Box 4400, Fredericton, NB E3B 5A3
tel 506-453-3501
Editor Ross Leckie
Quarterly $9.00 ($26.00 p.a.)

Reviews, poetry, short stories. Payment:
approx. $10-$12 per printed page.
Founded 1945.

(Hamilton) The Spectator

44 Frid Street, Hamilton, Ontario L8N 3G3
tel 905-526-3333
Publisher Patrick J. Collins
Daily Mon-Fri 75c Sat $1.75

Articles of general interest, political
analysis and background; interviews, stories of Canadians abroad. Length: 800
words maximum. Payment: rate varies.
Founded 1846.

Inuit Art Quarterly

2081 Merivale Road, Nepean, Ontario K2G 1G9
tel 613-224-8189 *fax* 613-224-2907
e-mail iaf@inuitart.org
web site http://www.inuitart.org
Editor Marybelle Mitchell
Quarterly $6.25

Features, original research, artists' perspectives, news. Freelance contributors
are expected to have a thorough knowledge of the arts. Length: varies.
Illustrations: colour and b&w photos and
line. Payment: by arrangement. Founded
1985.

Journal of Canadian Studies

Trent University, Peterborough, Ontario K9J 7B8
tel 705-748-1279 *fax* 705-748-1564
e-mail jcs_rec@trentu.ca
Editors Robert M. Campbell, Kerry Cannon
Quarterly US$35.00 p.a. (US$55.00 p.a.
institutions)

Major academic review of Canadian studies. Articles of general as well as scholarly interest on history, politics, literature,
society, arts. Length: 7000-10,000 words.

The Malahat Review

University of Victoria, PO Box 1700, Victoria,
BC V8W 2Y2
tel 604-721-8524
Editor Derk Wynand
Quarterly $25.00 p.a. ($35.00 p.a. overseas)

Short stories, poetry, short plays,
reviews, some graphics. Payment: $25
per magazine page. Illustrations: half-
tone. Founded 1967.

Performing Arts & Entertainment in Canada (PA&E)

104 Glenrose Avenue, Toronto, Ontario M4T 1K8
tel 416-484-4534 *fax* 416-484-6214
Editor Karen Bell
Quarterly $8.00 p.a. ($14.00 p.a. elsewhere)

Feature articles on Canadian theatre, music, dance and film artists and organisations; technical articles on scenery, lighting, make-up, costumes, etc. Length: 600-1200 words. Payment: $150-$175, one month after publication. Illustrations: b&w photos, colour slides. Founded 1961.

Photo Life
1 Dundas Street West, Suite 2500, PO Box 84, Toronto, Ontario M5G 1Z3
tel 800-905-7468 *fax* 800-664-2739
e-mail apex@photolife.com
web site http://www.photolife.com
Editor Suzie Ketene
8 p.a. $3.95
Covers all aspects of photography of interest to amateur and professional photographers. Length: 1500-2500 words. Illustrations: colour and b&w photos. Payment: by arrangement. Founded 1976.

Queen's Quarterly
184 Union Street, Kingston, Ontario K7L 3N6
tel 613-545-2667 *fax* 613-545-6822
e-mail qquartly@post.queensu.ca
web site http://info.queensu.ca/quarterly
Editor Dr Boris Castel
Quarterly $6.50 ($20 p.a.; $40 p.a. institutions)
A multidisciplinary scholarly journal aimed at the general educated reader – articles, short stories and poems. Length: 2500-3500 words (articles), 2000 (stories). Payment: by negotiation. Founded 1893.

Quebec Chronicle Telegraph
Quebec Chronicle-Telegraph Inc., 3484 chemin Ste-Foy, Quebec City, Quebec G1X 1S8
tel 418-650-1764
Editor Karen Macdonald
Weekly 40c
Covers local events within English community in Quebec City. Some feature articles. Founded 1764.

Quill & Quire
70 The Esplanade, Suite 210, Toronto, Ontario M5E 1R2
tel 416-360-0044 *fax* 416-955-0794
e-mail quill@idirect.com
Editor Scott Anderson
12 p.a. $59.95 p.a. (outside Canada $85p.a.)
Articles of interest about the Canadian book trade. Payment: from $100. Illustrations: line, half-tone. Subscription includes Canadian Publishers Directory (2 p.a.). Founded 1935.

Reader's Digest (Canada)
215 Redfern Avenue, Montreal, Quebec H3Z 2V9
tel 514-934-0751
Editor Alexander Farrell
Monthly $2.49
Original articles on all subjects of broad general appeal, thoroughly researched and professionally written. Outline or query only. Length: 3000 words approx. Payment: from $2700. Also previously published material. Illustrations: line, half-tone, colour.

Saturday Night
184 Front Street East, Suite 400, Toronto, Ontario M5A 4N3
tel 416-368-7237 *fax* 416-368-5112
Editor Kenneth Whyte
10p.a. $3.95
Magazine of Canada's people, politics, business, entertainment and life. For non-fiction send a query letter, including details of preliminary research and writing experience. For fiction, send MSS with sae or IRCs for its return. No poetry. Length: 1500-4000 words. Payment: $1 per word. Founded 1887.

(Toronto) The Globe and Mail
444 Front Street West, Toronto, Ontario M5V 2S9
Publisher Roger Parkinson, *Editor-in-Chief* William Thorsell
Daily 60c
Unsolicited material considered. Payment: by arrangement. Founded 1844.

Toronto Life
59 Front Street East, Toronto, Ontario M5E 1B3
tel 416-364-3333 *fax* 416-861-1169
Editor John Macfarlane
Monthly $3.95
Articles, profiles on Toronto and Torontonians. Illustrations: line, half-tone, colour. Founded 1966.

Toronto Star
One Yonge Street, Toronto, Ontario M5E 1E6
tel 416-367-2000
London office Level 4A, PO Box 495, Virginia Street, London E1 9XY *tel* 0171-833 0791
Daily Mon-Fri 30c Sat$1.00 Sun 75c
Features, life, world/national politics. Payment: by arrangement. Founded 1892.

(Vancouver) Province
2250 Granville Street, Vancouver, BC V6H 3G2
tel 604-732-2007 *fax* 604-732-2378
Editor-in-Chief Michael Cooke
Daily Mon-Fri 60c Sun $1.00
Founded 1898.

Vancouver Sun
200 Granville Street, Vancouver, BC V6C 3N3
tel 604-605-2318 *fax* 604-605-2323
e-mail jcruickshank@pacpress.southam.ca
web site http://www.vancouversun.com
Editor-in-Chief John Cruickshank
London office Southam News, 4th Floor,
8 Bouverie Street, London EC4Y 8AX
tel 0171-583 7322
Daily Mon-Thu 60c Fri, Sat $1.25
Saturday Review, arts magazine, accepts contributions. Travel, Op-Ed pieces considered. Payment: by arrangement.

Wascana Review of Contemporary Poetry & Short Fiction
c/o English Department, University of Regina,
Regina, Sask. S4S 0A2
tel 306-585-4302 *fax* 306-585-4827
Editor Kathleen Wall
Bi-annual $10.00 p.a. ($12.00 p.a. outside Canada)
Criticism, short stories, poetry, reviews. Manuscripts from freelance writers welcome. Length: prose, not more than 6000 words; verse, up to 100 lines. Payment: $3 per page for prose; $10 per printed page for verse; $3 per page for reviews. Contributors also receive 2 free copies and a year's subscription. Founded 1966.

Windspeaker
15001-112 Ave NW, Edmonton, Alberta T5M 2V6
tel 403-455-2700 *fax* 403-455-7639
Editor Debora Lockyer
Monthly ($36.00 p.a.)
National newspaper by and about Aboriginal people: articles, features, news, guest editorials. Write for 'Freelancer's guidelines'. Length: 300-800 words. Illustrations: prefer colour prints. Payment: $3.00 per published column inch; $15-$50 per photo. Founded 1983.

Winnipeg Free Press
PO Box 9500, Winnipeg, Manitoba R2X 3A2
tel 204-694-2022
Editor John Dafoe
Daily Mon-Fri 25c Sat $1.25 Sun 35c
Some freelance articles. Payment: $100. Founded 1872.

New Zealand

(Auckland) New Zealand Herald
PO Box 32, Auckland
tel (09) 379-5050 *fax* (09) 373-6421
Editor Gavin Ellis
Daily 90c

Topical and informative articles 800-1100 words. Payment: minimum $150-$300. Illustrations: colour negatives or prints. Founded 1863.

(Auckland) Sunday News
155 New North Road, Auckland
tel (09) 302-1300 *fax* (09) 358-3003
e-mail editor@sunday-news.co.nz
Editor Suzanne Chetwin
Weekly $1.00
Will consider anything. Length: varies. Illustrations: colour and b&w photos and line. Payment: depends on quality. Founded 1963.

(Auckland) Sunday Star-Times
News Media Auckland Ltd, PO Box 1327,
Auckland 1
tel (09) 302-1300 *fax* (09) 309-0258
e-mail feedback@star-times.co.nz
Editor Michael Forbes
Sun $1.30

(Christchurch) The Press
Private Bag 4722, Christchurch
tel (03) 379-0940 *fax* (03) 364-8238
Editor Tim Pankhurst
Daily 70c
Articles of general interest not more than 800 words. Illustrations: photos and line drawings, cartoons. Payment: by arrangement.

Christchurch Star
PO Box 1467, Christchurch
tel (03) 379-7100 *fax* (03) 366-0180
Editor Mike Fletcher
Bi-weekly Free
Will consider freelance material, excluding travel; also cartoons. Founded 1868.

(Dunedin) Otago Daily Times
PO Box 181, Dunedin
tel (03) 477-4760 *fax* (03) 474-7422
Editor R.L. Charteris
Daily 60c
Any articles of general interest up to 1000 words, but preference is given to NZ writers. Topical illustrations and personalities. Payment: current NZ rates. Founded 1861.

Hawke's Bay Herald Tribune
PO Box 180, Karamu Road North, Hastings
tel (06) 878-5155 *fax* (06) 876-0655
e-mail hbherald@xtra.co.nz
Editor J.E. Morgan
Daily 70c
Limited requirements. Payment: $40

upwards for articles, $10 upwards for photos. Illustrations: web offset.

(Invercargill) The Southland Times
PO Box 805, Invercargill
tel (03) 218-1909 *fax* (03) 214-9905
e-mail editor@stl.co.nz
web site http://www.press.co.nz
Editor C.A. Lind
Daily 70c

Articles of up to 800 words on topics of Southland interest. Payment: by arrangement. Illustrations: line, half-tone, colour, cartoons. Founded 1862.

Management
Profile Publishing, PO Box 5544, Auckland
tel (09) 630-8940 *fax* (09) 630-1046
e-mail sprofile@iconz.co.nz
Editor Sherrill Tapsell
Monthly $5.95

Articles on the practice of management skills and techniques, individual and company profiles, coverage of business trends and topics. A NZ/Australian angle or application preferred. Length: 2000 words. Payment: by arrangement; minimum 23c per word. Illustrations: photos, line drawings.

(Napier) The Daily Telegraph
PO Box 343, Napier
tel (06) 835-4488 *fax* (06) 835-1129
e-mail editor@telegraph.co.nz
Editor L.H. Pierard
Daily 70c

Limited market for features. Illustrations: line, half-tone, colour. Payment: $50 upwards per 1000 words; $20 a picture. Founded 1871.

The Nelson Mail
PO Box 244, 15 Bridge Street, Nelson
tel (03) 548-7079 *fax* (03) 546-2802
e-mail editor@nelsonmail.co.nz
Editor David Mitchell
Daily 70c

Features, articles on NZ subjects. Length: 500-1000 words. Payment: up to $100 per 1000 words. Illustrations: half-tone, colour.

(New Plymouth) The Daily News
PO Box 444, Currie Street, New Plymouth
tel (06) 758-0559 *fax* (06) 758-6849
e-mail editor@tnl.co.nz
Editor Murray Goston
Daily 70c

Articles preferably with a Taranaki connection. Payment: by negotiation. Illustrations: half-tone, cartoons. Founded 1857.

New Truth and TV Extra
News Media Auckland Ltd, 155 New North Road, Auckland, PO Box 1074
tel (09) 302-1300 *fax* (09) 309-2279
Editor Mike Smith
Weekly $1.50

Bold investigative reporting, exposés. Length: 500-1000 words, preferably accompanied by photos. Payment: about $150 per 500 words, extra for photos.

New Zealand Farmer
NZ Rural Press Ltd, PO Box 4233, 300 Great South Road, Greenlane, Auckland 5
tel (09) 520-9451 *fax* (09) 520-9459
e-mail ruralprs@iconz.co.nz
Editor Sean Stephens
Weekly

Authoritative, simply written articles on new developments in livestock husbandry, grassland farming, cropping, farm machinery, marketing. Length: 500 words. Payment: $200 per 1000 words.

New Zealand Woman's Day
Private Bag 92512, Wellesley Street, Auckland
tel (09) 308-2718 *fax* (09) 357-0978
Editor Wendy Nissen
Weekly $3.10

Celebrity interviews, exclusive news stories, short stories, gossip. Length: 1000 words. Illustrations: colour transparencies; payment according to use. Payment: £400. Founded 1989.

She & More
Private Bag 92512, Wellesley Street, Auckland 1036
tel (09) 308-2735 *fax* (09) 357-0097
Editor Jane Binsley
Monthly $5.95

Lifestyle magazine for young women. Length: 1000-2000 words (features), 300 words (profiles). Illustrations: colour. Payment: negotiable. Founded 1996.

Straight Furrow
PO Box 715, Wellington
tel (04) 473-7269 *fax* (04) 473-3324
Editor Susan Grant
Fortnightly $2.50

News and features of interest to the farming/rural sector with emphasis on agri-political issues. Length: 500 words news, 1000 words features. Illustrations: colour and b&w photos. Payment: 25c per published word; $20 per published photo. Founded 1933.

Takahe
Takahe Collective Trust, PO Box 13335,
Christchurch 8001
tel (03) 359-8133
3-4 p.a. $24 p.a. ($32 p.a. international)
Quality short fiction and poetry by both
new and established writers. Payment:
approx. $30 per issue. Founded 1989.

The Timaru Herald
PO Box 46, Bank Street, Timaru
tel (03) 684-4129 *fax* (03) 688-1042
e-mail editor@hcl.co.nz
Editor D.H. Wood
Daily 60c
Topical articles. Payment: by arrangement. Illustrations: colour or b&w prints,
cartoons.

(Wellington) The Evening Post
PO Box 3740, 40 Boulcott Street, Wellington
tel (04) 474-0444 *fax* (04) 474-0237
Editor's fax (04) 474-0536
Editor S.L. Carty
Daily Mon-Fri 70c, Sat 80c
General topical articles, 600 words.
Payment: NZ current rates or by arrange-
ment. News illustrations, cartoons.
Founded 1865.

Your Home and Garden
Australian Consolidated Press (New Zealand) Ltd,
Private Bag 92512, Wellesley Street, Auckland
tel (09) 308-2700 *fax* (09) 377 6725
Editor Sharon Newey
Monthly $5.95
Advice, ideas and projects for homeown-
ers – interiors and gardens. Length: 1000
words. Illustrations: good quality colour
transparencies. Payment: 30c per word/
$75 per transparency. Founded 1991.

South Africa

(Cape Town) Cape Times
Newspaper House, 122 St George's Street,
Cape Town 8001
tel (021) 488-4911
postal address PO Box 11, Cape Town 8000
Editor J.C. Viviers
London office 1st Floor, 32-33 Hatton Garden,
London EC1N 8DL
tel 0171-405 3742
Daily R1.20
Contributions must be suitable for a daily
newspaper and must not exceed 800
words. Illustrations: photos of outstanding
South African interest. Founded 1876.

Car
PO Box 180, Howard Place 7450
tel (021) 531-1391 *fax* (021) 531-3333
e-mail car@rsp.co.za
web site http://www.cartoday.com
Editor John Wright
Monthly R7.95
New car announcements with pictures
and full colour features of motoring
interest. Payment: by arrangement. Illustrations: colour, cartoons. Founded 1957.

Daily Dispatch
Dispatch Media (Pty) Ltd, 33 Caxton Street,
East London 5201
tel (0431) 430-010 *fax* (0431) 435-155
e-mail eledit@iafrica.com
web site http://www.dispatch.co.za
Editor Gavin Stewart
Daily Mon-Sat R1.20
Newspaper for the Eastern Cape region.
Features of general interest, especially
successful development projects in
developing countries. Colour and b&w
photographs, artwork, cartoons.
Contributions welcome. Length: approx.
1000 words (features). Payment: R250;
R50 photographs. Founded 1872.

(Durban) The Mercury
Independent Newspapers KwaZulu-Natal Ltd,
Editorial PO Box 950, Durban 4000
tel (031) 308-2300 *fax* (031) 308-2333
Editor D.C. Wightman
Daily Mon-Fri R2.40
Serious background news and inside
details of world events. Length: 700-900
words. Illustrations: photos of general
interest. Founded 1852.

Fair Lady
National Magazines, PO Box 1802,
Cape Town 8000
tel (021) 406-2204
Editor Roz Wrottesley
London office tel 0171-404 3216
Fortnightly R6.95
Fashion, beauty, articles and stories for
women including showbiz, travel,
humour. Length: articles up to 2000
words, short stories approx. 3000 words;
short novels and serialisation of book
material. Illustrations: cartoons. Payment: on quality rather than length – by
arrangement.

Femina Magazine
Associated Magazines, Box 3647, Cape Town 8000
tel (021) 462-3070

Editor Jane Raphaely
Monthly R9.80

For busy young professionals, often with families. Humour, personalities, real-life drama, medical breakthroughs, popular science, news-breaking stories and human interest. Payment: by arrangement. No illustrations.

Independent Newspapers Holdings Ltd

Cape Town **Argus**, Daily R1.70
Weekend Argus Sat R3.90
Cape Times R2.00
Durban **Daily News** R1.60
The Saturday Paper R2.20
Ilanga, R1.20
Post (Natal) R2.50
Natal Mercury R2.20
Sunday Tribune R4.00
Johannesburg **The Star** R2.00
Saturday Star R2.50
Sunday Star R2.50
Sunday Independent R5.50
Sowetan, R1.30
Pretoria **Pretoria News** R1.70
web site http://www.star.co.za

Accepts articles of general and South African interest; also cartoons. Payment: in accordance with an editor's assessment. Contributions should be addressed to PO Box 1014, Johannesburg 2000.

The Star & SA Times online
web site http://www.satimes.press.net/

(Johannesburg) Sunday Times

PO Box 1742, Saxonwold 2132
tel (011) 280-5102 *fax* (011) 280-5111
e-mail suntimes@tml.co.za
Editor M.W. Robertson
Sun R4.50

Illustrated articles of political or human interest, from a South African angle if possible. Maximum 1000 words long and 2 or 3 photos. Shorter essays, stories and articles of a light nature from 500-750 words. Payment: average rate £100 a column. Illustrations: photos (colour or b&w) and line.

Natal Witness

244 Longmarket Street, Pietermaritzburg, KwaZulu-Natal 3201
tel (0331) 551-111 *fax* (0331) 551-122
e-mail nw.subs@alpha.futurenet.co.za
Editor J.H. Conyngham
Daily R1.80

Accepts topical articles. All material should be submitted direct to the editor in Pietermaritzburg. Length: 500-1000 words. Payment: average of R250 per 1000 words. Founded 1846.

Republican Press

PO Box 32083, Mobeni 4060, Natal
tel (031) 422-041
UK office Suite 15-17, The Outer Temple, 222-225 Strand, London WC2R 1BA
tel 0171-353 2580 *fax* 0171-353 2578

Bona
Monthly R4.95

Articles on fashion, cookery, sport, music of interest to black people. Length: up to 3000 words. Payment: by arrangement. Illustrations: line, half-tone, colour, cartoons.

Farmer's Weekly
Editor C. Venter
Weekly R6.50

Articles, generally illustrated, up to 1000 words, on all aspects of practical farming and research with particular reference to conditions in Southern Africa. Includes women's section which accepts suitable, illustrated articles. Illustrations: line, half-tone, colour, cartoons. Payment: according to merit. Founded 1911.

Garden and Home
Editor Margaret Wasserfall
Monthly R12.95

Well-illustrated articles on gardening, suitable for southern hemisphere. Articles for home section on furnishings, flower arrangement, food. Payment: by arrangement. Illustrations: half-tone, colour, cartoons.

Living and Loving
Editor Fiona Wayman
Monthly R7.50

Romantic fiction, 1500-4000 words. Articles dealing with first-person experiences; baby, family and marriage, medical articles up to 3000 words. Payment: by merit. Illustrations: line, half-tone, colour, cartoons. Founded 1970.

Personality
Editor D. Mullany
Weekly R6.00

Illustrated. Primarily an entertainment-oriented magazine but also a market for articles about people and places, preferably with South African angle. Strong news features and/or photojournalism, 1000-4000 words, with b&w and colour photos. Short stories 1500-5000 words; also cartoons. Payment: by arrangement. Illustrations: usually commissioned.

Your Family
Editor Debbie-Lee Kelly
Monthly R7.70

Cookery, knitting, crochet and homecrafts. Family drama, happy ending. Payment: by arrangement. Illustrations: continuous tone, colour and line, cartoons.

South African Yachting
Neil Rusch, PO Box 3473, Cape Town 8000
tel (021) 461-7472 *fax* (021) 461-3758
e-mail 10077,260
Monthly R6.70

Articles on yachting, boating or allied subjects. Payment: R24 per 100 words. Illustrations: line, half-tone, cartoons; colour covers. Founded 1957.

Southern Cross
PO Box 2372, Cape Town 8000
tel (021) 465-5007 *fax* (021) 465-3850
e-mail scross@global.co.za
Editor Michael Shackleton
Weekly R2.00

National English-language Catholic weekly. Catholic news reports, world and South African. Length: 700-word articles. Illustrations: cartoons of Catholic interest acceptable from freelance contributors. Payment: 10c per word; illustrations R23.10.

Woman's Value
Nasionale Media, PO Box 1802, Cape Town 8000
tel (021) 406-2205 *fax* (021) 406-2929
e-mail abell@naspers.com
web site http://www.womansvalue.com
Editor Alice Bell
Monthly R8.70

Features on beauty, food, finance, knitting, needlecraft, crafts, home and garden, health and parenting; short stories. 1000-word accounts of experiences published on the 'My own story' page. Length: up to 1200 words (features/stories). Payment: by negotiation. Colour transparencies. Founded 1980.

World Airnews
PO Box 35082, Northway, Durban 4065
tel (031) 84-1319 *fax* (031) 83-7115
Editor Tom Chalmers
Monthly £36.00 p.a.

Aviation news and features with an African angle. Payment: by negotiation.

USA

The Yearbook does not contain a detailed list of US magazines and journals. The Overseas volume of Willings Press Guide is the most useful general reference guide to US publications, available in most reference libraries. For readers with a particular interest in the US market, the publications listed here will be helpful (please make payments to the US in US funds).

American Markets Newsletter
175 Westland Drive,
Glasgow G14 9JQ
e-mail sheila.oconnor@juno.com
Editor Sheila O'Connor
10 p.a. £29.00 p.a. (£53 for 2 years)

Editorial guidelines for US, Canadian and other overseas markets, plus information on press trips, non-fiction/fiction markets and writers' tips. Sample issue £2.95 (payable to S. O'Connor).

Willings Press Guide
Hollis Directories Ltd, 7 High Street, Teddington, Middlesex TW11 8EL
tel 0181-977 7711 *fax* 0181-977 1133
e-mail willings@hollis-pr.co.uk
web site http://www.hollis-pr.co.uk
£189 2-volume set; or £145 UK volume, £145 international volume

Two volumes contain details on 30,000 newspapers, periodicals and special interest titles in the UK and internationally. Usually available at local reference libraries or direct from the publisher.

The Writer
The Writer Inc., 120 Boylston Street, Boston, MA 02116
Monthly $28.00 p.a. ($38.00 p.a. surface mail, $58.00 p.a. airmail)

Contains articles of instruction on all writing fields, lists of markets for MSS and special features of interest to freelance writers everywhere.

The Writer Inc. also publishes books on writing fiction, non-fiction, poetry, articles, plays, etc.

Writer's Digest
Writer's Digest Books (address below)
($27.00 plus $10 surface post, $56.00 airmail p.a.)

Monthly handbook for writers who want to write better and sell more; aims to inform, instruct and inspire the freelance.

Writer's Digest Books

Writer's Digest Books, 1507 Dana Avenue, Cincinnati, OH 45207

Also publishes annually *Novel and Short Story Writer's Market, Children's Writer's and Illustrator's Market, Poet's Market, Photographer's Market, Artist's & Graphic Designer's Market, Guide to Literary Agents* and many other books on creating and selling writing and illustrations.

The Writer's Handbook

The Writer Inc. (address above)
$29.95 ($34.45 p.a. surface mail, $54.95 p.a. airmail)

A substantial volume containing 110 chapters, each written by an authority, giving practical instruction on a wide variety of aspects of freelance writing and includes details of 3200 markets, payment rates and addresses.

Writer's Market

Writer's Digest Books (address above)
($27.99 plus $4.00 p&p)

An annual guidebook giving editorial requirements and other details of over 4000 US markets for freelance writing. Aslo available on CD-Rom.

Submitting manuscripts

When submitting material to US journals, include a covering letter, together with return postage in the form of International Reply Coupons (IRC). IRCs can be exchanged in any foreign country for stamps representing the minimum postage payable on a letter sent from one country to another. Make it clear what rights are being offered for sale as some editors like to purchase MSS outright, thus securing world copyright, i.e. the traditional British market as well as the US market. Send the MSS direct to the US office of the journal and not to any London office.

In many cases it is best to send a preliminary letter giving a rough outline of your article or story (enclose IRCs for a reply). Most magazines will send a leaflet giving guidance to authors.

Magazines by subject area

These lists can be only a broad classification. They should be regarded as a pointer to possible markets and should be used with discrimination. Addresses for magazines start on page 21.

Fiction (see also Literary)

The following take short stories, unless otherwise stated. 'Long' refers to long complete stories, from 35,000 words upwards.

Active Life
Acumen
Ambit
Aquila
Australian Short Stories (Aus.)
The Australian Women's Weekly
Bella
Best
Brownie
Canadian Author (Can.)
Cencrastus
Chat
Chickadee (Can.)
The Dalhousie Review (Can.)
The Edge
Fair Lady (SA) (also serials)
Femina (SA)
The Fiddlehead (Can.)
Fly-Fishing & Fly-Tying
Girl Talk
HU (The Honest Ulsterman) (Ire.)
Imago (Aus.)
Infant Projects
Interzone
Ireland's Own
IT (Ire.)
The Lady
Living and Loving (SA)
London Magazine
The Malahat Review (Can.)
More!
My Weekly (also serials)
My Weekly Story Library (long only)
New Idea (Aus.)
New Impact
New Zealand Woman's Day (NZ)
Overland (Aus.)
Peninsular Magazine
People's Friend (also serials)
People's Friend Library (long only)

Personality (SA)
Planet
Pride
Prospect
Quadrant (Aus.)
QWF
Redoubt (Aus.)
Reality (Ire.)
Saturday Night
Scots Magazine
Scuba Diver* (Aus.)
Songwriting and Composing
Springboard
Stand Magazine
Staple New Writing
Starburst
Takahe (NZ)
Take a Break
Wascana Review (Can.)
Woman and Home (also serials)
Woman's Day (Aus.)
Woman's Own
Woman's Way (Ire.)
Woman's Weekly (also serials)
Young Writer
Yours

Letters to the Editor

The Australian Woman's Weekly
BBC Gardeners' World Magazine
Bella
Best
The Big Issue
The Big Issue in Scotland
Caravan Magazine
Chat
Child Education
Control & Instrumentation
Dolly (Aus.)
Electrical Times
Fair Lady (SA)
Family Circle
Femina (SA)
Freelance Market News
The Furrow (Ire.)
Goldlife 50-Forward
Ideal Home
Junior Education

Mobile & Holiday Homes
Modern Painters
Moneywise
Mother & Baby
Motor Caravan Magazine
My Weekly
New Scientist
New Weekly (Aus.)
New Zealand Woman's Day (NZ)
Our Baby
Park Home & Holiday Caravan
Penthouse
Police Journal
Practical Householder
Practical Parenting
Practical Photography
Practical Woodworking
Prima
Right Start
Saga Magazine
She
Shout
Slimmer Magazine
Slimming Magazine
Take a Break
Television
that's life!
True Story
TV Quick
The Weekly News
What's on TV
Woman
Woman's Day (Aus.)
Woman's Own
Woman's Realm
Woman's Way (Ire.)
Woman's Weekly
Yours

Gossip paragraphs

Art Business Today
Australian Bookseller & Publisher
Big!
The Big Issue
Bliss
Broadcast
Campaign

Car
Church of England Newspaper
Classical Music
Country Life
Cycling Weekly
Dirt Bike Rider
Drapers Record
Electrical Times
Eventing
Farming News
Film Review
Flicks
FW (Fashion Weekly)
Financial Weekly
FourFourTwo
Fresh Produce Journal
Garden News
Geographical Magazine
Gibbons Stamp Monthly
Goldlife 50-Forward
Golf Weekly
Golf World
Hampshire – The County
  Magazine
Health & Efficiency International
Horse & Hound
Irish Farmers Journal
Irish Medical Times
Irish Printer
Journalist
The Lawyer
Making Music
Marketing Week
Men Only
Mojo
Music Week
New Statesman
The New Welsh Review
Nursing Times and Nursing
  Mirror
Opera Now
PC Review
PCS, The Magazine
Pilot
The Pink Paper
Police Review
Pride
Private Eye
Punch
Radio Times
Red Pepper
Retail Week
Rugby World
Runner's World
Satellite Times
The Scottish Farmer
Shoot
Shout
The Stage
Success Now
The Tablet
tate: The Art Magazine

Therapy Weekly
Today's Runner
Total Football
Venue
Woman
Woman's Realm
World Soccer
Writers' Forum

Brief filler paragraphs

Active Life
Africa Confidential
American Markets Newsletter
Angler's Mail
The Architects' Journal
Athletics Weekly
Australian Bookseller &
  Publisher
Babycare and Pregnancy
Ballroom Dancing Times
Bella
Best of British
The Big Issue
Black Beauty & Hair
Bliss
Blueprint
Boards
Bridge Magazine
British Journal of General
  Practice
Broadcast
Cage and Aviary Birds
Car
Cat World
Cencrastus
Classic Cars
Climber
Communicate
Country Garden & Smallholding
Country Life
The Countryman
Current Affairs Bulletin (Aus.)
Cycling Weekly
Dorset Life – The Dorset
  Magazine
Drapers Record
Electrical Times
Eventing
Executive PA
Family Circle
Farming News
The Field
Film Review
Flight International
Fly-Fishing & Fly-Tying
Fortean Times
FourFourTwo
FRANCE Magazine
Freelance Market News
Fresh Produce Journal
FW (Fashion Weekly)

Garden News
Geographical Magazine
Gibbons Stamp Monthly
Gifts International
Goldlife 50-Forward
Golf Illustrated Weekly
Golf Weekly
Golf World
Greetings Magazine
Hampshire – The County
  Magazine
Health & Efficiency International
Health & Fitness
Heritage
Hi-Fi News & Record Review
Horse & Hound
Horticulture Week
Hortus
Hotel and Catering Review (Ire.)
The Illustrated London News
IMAGE (Ire.)
Insurance Age
Inuit Art Quarterly (Can.)
Ireland of the Welcomes
Ireland's Own
Irish Farmers Journal
Irish Medical Times
Irish Printer
Jane's Defence Weekly
Journalist
Justice of the Peace
Kids Out
The Lawyer
Making Music
Marketing Week
Men Only
Model Engineer
Motor Boat and Yachting
Motor Boats Monthly
My Weekly
Nautical Magazine
New Christian Herald
New Scientist
The New Welsh Review
The New Writer
New Zealand Farmer (NZ)
Nursing Times and Nursing
  Mirror
The Oldie
Opera Now
Organic Gardening
Overland (Aus.)
Peninsular Magazine
Picture Postcard Monthly
Pig Farming
Pilot
The Pink Paper
Police Review
Pony
Post Magazine & Insurance Week
Practical Caravan
Practical Fishkeeping

Practical Woodworking
The Press and Journal
Pride
Priests and People
Printing World
Private Eye
QWF
Radio Times
Railway Gazette
Railway Magazine
Reader's Digest
Reader's Digest (Aus.)
Red Pepper
Runner's World
Satellite Times
School Librarian
The Scottish Farmer
Sea Breezes
Shoot
Slimmer Magazine
Snooker Scene
Somerset Magazine
Songwriter (Ire.)
Songwriting and Composing
South African Yachting
Southern Cross (SA)
Squash Player
The Stage
Stamp Lover
Staple New Writing
Steam Classic
Studio Sound
Success Now
The Tablet
tate: The Art Magazine
Technology Ireland
TGO
Therapy Weekly
This England
Today's Runner
Total Football
Toy Trader
Trucking International
TV Quick
Venue
Waterways World
Weight Watchers Magazine
Woman
Woman's Realm
Woman's Weekly
The Woodworker
World Airnews (SA)
World Fishing
World Soccer
Yachts and Yachting
Young People Now
Young Writer
Your Dog

Puzzles and quizzes

*The following take puzzles and/
or quizzes on an occasional or,
in some cases, regular basis.
Ideas must be tailored to suit
each publication; approach in
writing in the first instance.*

Army Quarterly & Defence
    Journal
Art Business Today
Baptist Times
Best of British
The Big Issue in the North
Bird Watching
Bliss
Bridge Magazine
Brownie
Cage and Aviary Birds
Catholic Gazette
Chickadee (Can.)
Choice
Cleo (Aus.)
Country Life
Country-Side
The Cricketer International
The Dandy
Darts World
Dirt Bike Rider
Disability Now
Dolly (Aus.)
East Lothian Life
Electrical Times
Essentials
Everyday with Practical
    Electronics
Fair Lady (SA)
Farmers Weekly (SA)
Film Review
Financial Adviser
Fire
Fishing World Magazine (Aus.)
Football Picture Story Library
Fore!
Garden and Home (SA)
Golf Monthly
Golf World
Guiding
Health & Efficiency International
Here's Health
Hertfordshire Countryside
Horse & Hound
Horse & Pony
Hospital Doctor
Hotel and Catering Review (Ire.)
HouseBuilder
The Illustrated London News
Ireland's Own
Irish Medical Times
J17
Journalist

Kids Alive!
Kids Out
Living and Loving (SA)
Making Music
Men Only
Methodist Recorder
My Weekly Puzzle Time
(Napier) The Daily Telegraph
    (NZ)
New Idea (Aus.)
New Impact
New Scientist
New World
19
Nursing Times and Nursing
    Mirror
Opera
Opera Now
Park Home & Holiday Caravan
PCS, The Magazine
Performing Arts & Entertainment
    in Canada (Can.)
Personality (SA)
Picture Postcard Monthly
Pilot
Practical Photography
The Practitioner
Prospect
Publishing News
Reality (Ire.)
Red Pepper
Runner's World
Satellite Times
The Scottish Farmer
Scottish Homes and Country
She
Shoot
The Short Wave Magazine
Shout
Snooker Scene
South African Yachting
Southern Cross (SA)
The Spectator
The Stage
Steam Classic
Sugar
The Tablet
Take a Break
Take a Break's Take a Puzzle
TGO
Therapy Weekly
The Times Educational
    Supplement
Today's Runner
Total Sport
Toy Trader
Trout and Salmon
TV Quick
Twinkle
The Universe
Vox
War Cry

Waterways World
West Lothian Life
Woman
Woman's Weekly
The Woodworker
The Word (Ire.)
World Soccer
Young People Now
Young Writer
Your Family (SA)

UK ethnic weekly newspapers

Asian Times
Caribbean Times
Eastern Eye
The Voice
The Weekly Journal

Women's interest magazines (see also Health and home)

The Australian Women's Weekly
Bella
Best
Black Beauty & Hair
Bliss
Bona (SA)
Chat
Chatelaine (Can.)
Chic
Company
Cosmopolitan
Country Living
Diva
Elle (Australia)
Elle (UK)
Essentials
Eva
Executive PA
Executive Woman
Fair Lady (SA)
Family Circle
Femina (SA)
For Women
Girl About Town
Good Housekeeping
Hairflair
Harper's Bazaar & Mode (Aus.)
Harpers & Queen
Hello!
Home and Country
Home Words
HQ (Aus.)
IMAGE (Ire.)
IT (Ire.)
Ladies First
The Lady

Living and Loving (SA)
Looks
Marie Claire
Modern Woman (Ire.)
More!
Mother & Baby
Ms London
My Weekly
My Weekly Puzzle Time
New Idea (Aus.)
New Woman
New Woman (Aus.)
New Zealand Woman's Day (NZ)
New Zealand Woman's Weekly
19
Nursery World
Office Secretary
OK! Magazine
ONtheBALL
Options
People's Friend
The Pink Paper
Pride
Prima
Red
Right Start
She
She (Aus.)
She & More (NZ)
Sugar
Take a Break
The Tatler
that's life!
U magazine (Ire.)
Vanity Fair
Vogue
Wedding and Home
Woman
Woman Alive
Woman and Home
Woman's Day (Aus.)
Woman's Journal
Woman's Own
Woman's Realm
Woman's Value (SA)
Woman's Way (Ire.)
Woman's Weekly
World's Children
Your Family (SA)
You & Your Wedding

Men's interest magazines

Arena
Attitude
Country
Esquire
FHM (For Him Magazine)
Gay Times
GQ
Loaded
Masonic Square

Mayfair
Men Only
Men's Health
The Pink Paper

Children's and young adult magazines

Animals and You
Aquila
The Beano
Beano Comic Library
Big!
Brownie
Bunty
Bunty Library
Buster
Chickadee (Can.)
Commando
The Dandy
Dandy Comic Library
Dolly (Aus.)
Football Picture Story Library
Girl Talk
Horse & Pony
Hot Press (Ire.)
i-D Magazine
J17
Live & Kicking Magazine
Looks Magazine
Mandy Library
Mizz
Playdays
Pony
Scouting
Shoot
Shout
Sky Magazine
Smash Hits
Top of the Pops Magazine
Twinkle
Vox
Young Writer

Subject articles

Advertising, design, printing and publishing (see also Literary)

Arena
Australian Bookseller & Publisher
The Author
Blueprint
Books Ireland
The Bookseller
British Journalism Review
British Printer
Campaign
Canadian Interiors

The Face
Freelance Market News
Greetings Magazine
Indexer
InterMedia
Irish Printer
Journalist
Learned Publishing
Market Newsletter
Media Week
New Media Age
PR Week
Press Gazette
Printing World
Publishing News
The World of Interiors
Young Writer

Agriculture, farming and horticulture

Country Garden &
  Smallholding
Country Life
The Countryman
Countryman (Aus.)
Country-Side
Dairy Farmer
Farmer's Weekly
Farmer's Weekly (SA)
Farming News
The Field
Fresh Produce Journal
The Grower
Horticulture Week
Irish Farmers Journal
New Zealand Farmer
Pig Farming
Poultry World
Scottish Farmer
Smallholder
Straight Furrow (NZ)
Town and Country Planning

Architecture and building

The Architects' Journal
Architectural Design
The Architectural Review
Architecture Today
Blueprint
Building
Building Design
Built Environment
Country Homes & Interiors
Country Life
Education
Estates Gazette
Homes and Gardens

House & Garden
HouseBuilder
Ideal Home
International Construction
Local Historian

Art and collecting

AN Magazine
The Antique Dealer &
  Collectors Guide
Apollo
Art and Australia (Aus.)
Art Business Today
Art Monthly
The Art Newspaper
Art Review
The Artist
Artists and Illustrators
ArtsAtlantic (Can.)
BBC Homes & Antiques
Book and Magazine Collector
Burlington Magazine
C Magazine (Can.)
Coin News
contemporary visual arts
Country Life
Creative Camera
Eastern Art Report
Gibbons Stamp Monthly
The Illustrated London News
Inuit Art Quarterly (Can.)
Leisure Painter
Medal News
Modern Painters
Numismatic Chronicle
RA Magazine
Stamp Lover
Stamp Magazine
tate: The Art Magazine
Make: the magazine of women's
  art
World Art (Aus.)
The World of Embroidery
The World of Interiors

Aviation

Aeromodeller
Aeroplane Monthly
Air International
Air Pictorial International
Australian Flying
Flight International
FlyPast
Pilot
Transport
World Airnews (SA)

Blind and partially sighted

*Published by the Royal
National Institute for the Blind
in braille unless otherwise
stated (see under Book
publishers UK and Ireland)*
3-FM
Absolutely Boys (also disk)
Absolutely Girls (also disk)
Access IT (also disk)
After Hours
Aphra (also disk)
BBC on Air (also disk)
Blast Off! (also disk)
Braille Chess Magazine
Braille Journal of Physiotherapy
Braille at Bedtime
Braille Music Magazine (also disk)
Braille Radio Times
Braille TV Times (5 regions)
Broadcast Times (disk only)
Busy Solicitor's Digest (also disk)
Channels of Blessing (also
  abridged in Moon; also disk)
Come Gardening
Compute IT (also disk)
Contention (also disk)
Conundrum (also disk)
Daily Bread (also disk)
Diane (Moon)
Disability Now (print and tape;
  Scope)
Eye Contact (also print)
Good Vibrations (also disk)
High Browse (also print, tape
  and disk)
Light of the Moon (Moon)
The Moon Magazine (Moon)
Money Matters (also disk)
Music Magazine (also disk)
New Beacon (also print, tape
  and disk)
News to You? (also print, tape
  and disk)
Physiotherapists' Quarterly
Piano Tuners' Quarterly
Progress (also disk)
Rhetoric (also disk)
Scientific Enquiry (also disk)
Shaping Up (also disk)
Shop Window (also disk)
Slugs and Snails (also disk)
Spotlight (also print, tape and
  disk)
Sugar and Spice (also disk)
Theological Times (also tape
  and disk)
Upbeat (also disk)
The Weekender (also Moon and
  disk)

You & Your Child (also disk)
VisAbility (also print and tape)
Welcome to a World of ... (also
disk)

Business, industry and management

Achievement
Brewing & Distilling
International
Business Life
Business Scotland
BusinessMatters
Chartered Secretary
Communicate
Cosmetic World News
CWU Voice
Director
Enterprise
The European
European Chemical News
European Drinks Buyer
European Frozen Food Buyer
Executive PA
Executive Woman
Fashion Forecast International
Fasttrack
Financial Director
Fire
Fishing News
FW (Fashion Weekly)
InformationWeek
IPA magazine
Land & Liberty
Leisureweek
Management (NZ)
Management Today
Mobile and Cellular Magazine
Nationwide Magazine
New Impact
Office Secretary
People Management
The Political Quarterly
Success Now
The Sunday Business Post (Ire.)
The Woodworker

Cinema and films

Campaign
Empire
Film Review
Flicks
New Statesman
Screen International
Sight and Sound
Studio Sound
Total Film

Computers

Amiga Format
Computer Weekly
Computing
InformationWeek
Internet
.net The Internet Magazine
New Media Age
PC Direct
PC Review
Personal Computer World
Scientific Computing World

Economics, accountancy and finance

Accountancy
Accountancy Age
Active Life
Africa Confidential
African Business
The Australian Financial Review
The Banker
Business Scotland
Choice
Contemporary Review
Economica
The Economist
Enterprise
The European
Financial Accountant
Financial Adviser
Financial Director
The Grower
Insurance Age
Insurance Brokers' Monthly
Investors Chronicle
Land & Liberty
Local Government Chronicle
MoneyMarketing
Moneywise
New Statesman
Pensions World
Personal Finance
Post Magazine & Insurance
Week
Studies (Ire.)
Tribune
West Africa

Education

Amateur Stage
Aquila
Art & Craft
British Journal of Special
Education
Carousel – The Guide to
Children's Books
Child Education

Education
Guiding
Infant Projects
Junior Education
Junior Focus
Linguist
Local Historian
Modern Language Review
Modus
Music Teacher
New Blackfriars
New Impact
New Statesman
Nursery Projects
Nursery World
Parents
Practical Parenting
Prep School
Reality (Ire.)
Report
Right Start
Safety Education
School Librarian
Scottish Educational Journal
Spoken English
The Teacher
Theology
The Times Educational
Supplement
Times Educational Supplement
Scotland
Times Higher Education
Supplement
Together With Children
Tribune
Under Five Contact
World's Children
Young People Now

Engineering and mechanics (see also Architecture, Aviation, Business, Motor transport, Nautical, Radio, Sciences)

Car Mechanics
Control & Instrumentation
Electrical Review
Electrical Times
Electronics Australia
Electronics Times
The Engineer
Engineering
European Chemical News
Everyday with Practical
Electronics
Fire
International Construction
Mobile and Cellular Magazine
Model Engineer
New Electronics

Petroleum Economist
Practical Woodworking
Rail
Railway Gazette International
Railway Magazine
Transport

Gardening

Amateur Gardening
BBC Gardeners' World Magazine
Country
Country Garden & Smallholding
Country Life
The Field
The Garden
Garden and Home (SA)
Garden Answers
Garden News
Gardens Illustrated
Homestyle
Hortus
House and Garden
Organic Gardening
Your Garden

Health and home (see also Women's interest magazines)

Active Life
Australian Home Beautiful
Australian House and Garden
Babycare and Pregnancy
BBC GoodFood
BBC Homes & Antiques
BBC Vegetarian GoodFood
Canadian Interiors
Choice
Classic Stitches
Country Homes & Interiors
Cycling Today
Garden and Home (SA)
Goldlife 50-Forward
Good Health
Health & Efficiency International
Health & Fitness
Healthy Eating
Here's Health
Home and Family
Homes and Gardens
Homes and Ideas
HomeFlair Magazine
Homestyle
Hospitality
House & Garden
House Beautiful
Ideal Home
Inspirations
Jewish Telegraph
Kids Out

Modus
Our Baby
Parents
Perfect Home
Period Living & Traditional Homes
Practical Householder
Practical Parenting
Running Magazine
Safety Education
Saga
Sainsbury's: The Magazine
Scottish Home and Country
Slimmer Magazine
Slimming Magazine
Today's Runner
Vegan
Weight Watchers Magazine
Wine
Woman's Value (SA)
The World of Embroidery
The World of Interiors
Your Family (SA)
Your Home and Garden (NZ)
Yours
Zest

History and archaeology

Best of British
Coin News
Country Quest
English Historical Review
Geographical Magazine
History
History Today
Illustrated London News
In Britain
Local Historian
The National Trust Magazine
New Blackfriars
Picture Postcard Monthly
Studies (Ire.)

Hotel, catering and leisure

Caterer & Hotelkeeper
European Drinks Buyer
European Frozen Food Buyer
Health Club Management
Hospitality
Hotel and Catering Review (Ire.)
The Leisure Manager
Leisureweek

Humour and satire

Private Eye
Punch
Viz

Inflight magazines

The Australian Way
Business Life
Hot Air

Legal and police

The Criminologist
Family Law
Justice of the Peace
The Lawyer
New Law Journal
Police Journal
Police Review
Solicitors Journal

Leisure interests, pets (see also Nautical, Sports)

ace
Aeromodeller
Astronomy Now
Bird Keeper
Bird Watching
Birding World
Birdwatch
Boards
British Birds
British Philatelic Bulletin
Camping Magazine
Caravan Magazine
City Life – What's on in
   Manchester
Classics
Classic Stitches
Climber
Country Walking
Dogs Today
Family Tree Magazine
The Field
Gibbons Stamp Monthly
Guiding
In Britain
International Stamp &
   Exhibition News
Military Modelling
Model Boats
Model Engineer
Motor Caravan Magazine
Motorcaravan and Motorhome
   Monthly
Needlecraft
Our Dogs
Park Home & Holiday Caravan
Popular Crafts
Practical Caravan
Practical Fishkeeping
Radio Control Models
Rambling Today
Scale Models International

Scottish Field
Scouting
Scuba Diver (Aus.)
Scuba World
Stamp Lover
Stamp Magazine
Steam Classic
Swimming Times
Wine
The Woodworker
Workbox
Your Dog

Literary (see also Poetry)

American Markets Newsletter
Australian Bookseller &
  Publisher
Australian Short Stories
The Author
The Book Collector
Books in Canada
Books Ireland
Books Magazine
The Bookseller
British Journalism Review
Canadian Author
The Canadian Forum
Canadian Literature
Carousel – The Guide to
  Children's Books
Cencrastus
Chapman
Contemporary Review
Critical Quarterly
The Dalhousie Review (Can.)
The Dickensian
The Edge
Edinburgh Review
The Fiddlehead (Can.)
Granta
Hobo (Aus.)
Imago (Aus.)
Index on Censorship
The Indexer
Journal of Canadian Studies
Journalist
Learned Publishing
The Library
The Literary Review
Llais Llyfrau
LOGOS
London Magazine
London Review of Books
The Malahat Review (Can.)
Market Newsletter
Modern Languages
New Library World
New Statesman
The New Welsh Review
The New Writer
The Oldie

Orbis
Outposts Poetry Quarterly
Overland (Aus.)
Peninsular Magazine
Planet
Prospect
Publishing News
Quadrant (Aus.)
Queen's Quarterly (Can.)
Quill & Quire (Can.)
QWF
Reality (Ire.)
Redoubt (Aus.)
Scottish Book Collector
Signal
The Spectator
Springboard
Stand Magazine
Starburst
Studies (Ire.)
Takahe (NZ)
The Times Literary Supplement
Tribune
Wasafiri
Wascana Review (Can.)
Woman Journalist
Writers' Forum
Writers News
Writing Magazine
Young Writer

Local government and civil service

Justice of the Peace
Local Government Chronicle
PCS, The Magazine
Public Service & Local
  Government

Marketing and retailing

Convenience Store
CTN
Drapers Record
FW (Fashion Weekly)
Gifts International
Greetings Magazine
The Grocer
Marketing Week
Off Licence News
Retail Week
Toy Trader
Ulster Grocer

Medicine and nursing

Balance
BMA News Review
The British Deaf News

British Journal of General
  Practice
British Medical Journal
Chemist & Druggist
Community Care
Dental Update
Disability Now
Hospital Doctor
Irish Journal of Medical Science
Irish Medical Times
Journal of Alternative and
  Complementary Medicine
Lancet
Nursery World
Nursing Times
Occupational Health
The Pharmaceutical Journal
The Practising Midwife
The Practitioner
Professional Nurse
Pulse
Therapy Weekly
This Caring Business
The Veterinary Review
Young People Now

Military

Army Quarterly & Defence
  Journal
Jane's Defence Weekly
RUSI Journal

Motor transport and cycling

AA Magazine
Auto Express
Autocar
Back Street Heroes
BBC Top Gear Magazine
Bike
BMW Magazine
Buses
Car
Car (SA)
Car Mechanics
Classic & Sports Car
Classic Cars
Classics
Commercial Motor
Custom Car
Cycling & Mountain Biking
  Today
Cycling Weekly
Dirt Bike Rider
Motor Cycle News
Ride
Truck & Driver
Trucking International
What Car?

Music and recording

Arena
BBC Music Magazine
Classic CD
Classical Music
Early Music
The Face
Gramophone
Hi-Fi News
i-D Magazine
Jazz Journal International
Kerrang!
Making Music
Melody Maker
Mojo
Music and Letters
Music Teacher
Music Week
Musical Opinion
Musical Times
New Musical Express
Opera
Opera Now
The Organ
Q Magazine
Select Magazine
Sky Magazine
Smash Hits
Songwriter (Ire.)
Songwriting and Composing
Studio Sound
Tempo
Top of the Pops Magazine
Vox

Natural history (see also Agriculture, Rural life)

The Aquarist and Pondkeeper
BBC Wildlife Magazine
Bird Keeper
Bird Watching
Birding World
Birdwatch
British Birds
Budgerigar World
Cage and Aviary Birds
Cat World
Chickadee (Can.)
Dogs Today
The Ecologist
Equinox (Can.)
Geo Australasia
Geographical Magazine
Glaucus
Guiding
The National Trust Magazine
Natural World
Naturalist
Nature
Our Dogs

Nautical and marine

Australian Powerboat
Canadian Yachting (Can.)
Classic Boat
Diver
Motor Boat and Yachting
Motor Boats Monthly
Nautical Magazine
Practical Boat Owner
Sea Breezes
Ship & Boat International
Ships Monthly
South African Yachting
Transport
Yachting Monthly
Yachting World
Yachts and Yachting

Photography

Amateur Photographer
Australian Photography
The British Journal of
 Photography
Camcorder User
Creative Camera
Market Newsletter
Photo Answers
Photo Life (Can.)
Photon
Photo Technique
Practical Photography
Professional Photographer
Video Camera

Poetry

Magazines that only take the occasional poem; check with the editor before submitting.

Acumen
Agenda
Ambit
Best of British
British Journal of General
 Practice*
Brownie*
Canadian Author (Can.)
Catholic Pictorial*
Cencrastus
Chapman
Chickadee (Can.)
Contemporary Review*
The Cricketer International*
Critical Quarterly
Cumbria and Lake District
 Magazine
Cyphers (Ire.)
Dalesman*
The Dalhousie Review (Can.)

Day by Day*
East Lothian Life
Edinburgh Review
Envoi
The Fiddlehead (Can.)
Fishing World Magazine
 (Aus.)*
Fortnight (Ire.)
Helicon Poetry Magazine
Herald of the South (Aus.)
Hobo (Aus.)
Home and Country*
HQ Poetry Magazine
HU (The Honest Ulsterman) (Ire.)
Imago (Aus.)
Infant Projects
Jewish Chronicle*
Jewish Quarterly*
Lancet*
Life & Work*
The Literary Review
London Magazine
London Review of Books
The Malahat Review (Can.)
Modern Believing
The Month
New Statesman
The New Welsh Review
Orbis
Organic Gardening*
Outposts Poetry Quarterly
Overland (Aus.)
Oxford Poetry
Peninsular Magazine
Planet
PN Review
Poetry Ireland Review/Éigse
 Éireann
Poetry London Newsletter
Poetry Nottingham International
Poetry Review
Poetry Wales
Pride
Quadrant (Aus.)
Quaker Monthly*
Redoubt (Aus.)
Reform*
The Rialto
The Scots Magazine*
Scuba Diver* (Aus.)
Songwriting and Composing*
Springboard
Stand Magazine
Staple New Writing
Takahe (NZ)
Third Way*
The Times Literary Supplement*
Together with Children*
Traveller*
Tribune*
Wasafiri
Wascana Review (Can.)

West Lothian Life*
Young People Now*
Young Writer
Yours

Politics

Africa Confidential
Australian Journal of
International Affairs
Australian Journal of Politics
and History
The Australian Quarterly
The China Quarterly
The Big Issues (Ire.)
Contemporary Review
Current Affairs Bulletin (Aus.)
The European
Fortnight (Ire.)
The Illustrated London News
International Affairs
Justice of the Peace
Local Government Chronicle
New Blackfriars
New Christian Herald
New Internationalist
New Statesman
Peace News
The Political Quarterly
Prospect
Red Pepper
Studies (Ire.)
Tribune
Voice Intelligence Report
West Africa
The World Today

Radio, TV and video

Broadcast
Campaign
Electronics Australia
Empire
Film Review
Flicks
Gramophone
Hi-Fi News
InterMedia
New Statesman
Opera Now
Practical Wireless
Radio Times
Satellite Times
Short-Wave Magazine
The Stage
Studio Sound
Television
Tribune
TV Quick
TV Times
What's on TV

Religion, philosophy and New Age

Baptist Times
Catholic Gazette
The Catholic Herald
Catholic Pictorial
Catholic Times
Church of England Newspaper
Church of Ireland Gazette
Church Times
Contemporary Review
Day by Day
The Downside Review
Fortean Times
Friend
The Furrow (Ire.)
Herald of the South (Aus.)
Home and Family
Home Words
Inquirer
Jewish Chronicle
Jewish Quarterly
Jewish Telegraph
Kids Alive!
Life & Work
Methodist Recorder
Mind
Modern Believing
The Month
New Blackfriars
New Christian Herald
New Humanist
Priests & People
Quaker Monthly
Reality (Ire.)
Reform
Sign
Southern Cross (SA)
Studies (Ire.)
Tablet
Theology
Third Way
Together with Children
Universe
War Cry
West Africa
Woman Alive
Word (Ire.)

Rural life and country
(see also Natural history)

Aussie Post (Aus.)
Country
Country Life
Country Quest
The Countryman
Country-Side
Cumbria and Lake District
Magazine

Dalesman
Derbyshire Life and Countryside
Dorset Life – The Dorset
Magazine
East Lothian Life
Essex Countryside
The Field
Hampshire – The County
Magazine
Heritage
Hertfordshire Countryside
In Britain
Lancashire Magazine
Lincolnshire Life
The Local Historian
The National Trust Magazine
New Buckinghamshire
Countryside
Rambling Today
The Scots Magazine
Scottish Field
Scottish Home and Country
Shooting Times and Country
Magazine
The Shropshire Magazine
Somerset Magazine
This England
Waterways World
West Lothian Life
Yorkshire Ridings Magazine

Sciences

The Criminologist
Equinox (Can.)
Geological Magazine
Mind
Nature
New Scientist
Science Progress
Scientific Computing World
Technology Ireland

Sports and games (see also Leisure interests, Motor transport, Nautical)

ace
Anglers' Mail
Angling Times
Athletics Weekly
Australian Powerboat
BBC Match of the Day
Bowls International
Bridge International
British Chess Magazine
Chess Monthly
The Cricketer International
Darts World
Eventing
The Field

Fishing World Magazine (Aus.)
Fly-Fishing & Fly-Tying
Fore!
FourFourTwo
Golf Monthly
Golf Weekly
Golf World
Guns Australia
Horse & Hound
Horse and Rider
OntheBALL
Our Dogs
Rugby World
Runner's World
Scottish Field
Scuba Diver (Aus.)
Scuba World
Sea Angler
Shoot
Shooting Times
The Skier and The Snowboarder
Snooker Scene
The Squash Player
Swimming Times
Tennis World
Today's Golfer
Today's Runner
Total Football

Total Sport
Trout and Salmon
When Saturday Comes
Wisden Cricket Monthly
Word (Ire.)
World Fishing
World Soccer

Theatre, drama and dancing (see also Cinema, Music)

Amateur Stage
Ballroom Dancing Times
Canadian Forum
CTR (Canadian Theatre Review)
Dance & Dancers
Dance Australia
Dancing Times
The Illustrated London News
In Britain
New Statesman
New Theatre Quarterly
Performing Arts &
 Entertainment in Canada
Plays & Players Applause
Radio Times

Reality (Ire.)
Speech and Drama
The Stage
Tribune
TV Quick
TV Times

Travel and geography

Australian Geographic
Australian Skiing
Caravan Magazine
Condé Nast Traveller
Equinox (Can.)
FRANCE Magazine
Geo Australasia
Geographical Journal
Geographical Magazine
Heritage
The Illustrated London News
In Britain
In Dublin (Ire.)
Ireland of the Welcomes
The Local Historian
Natal Witness (SA)
Traveller
Wanderlust
Wild (Aus.)

Recent changes to newspapers and magazines

The following changes have taken place since the last edition of the Yearbook.

Changes of name and mergers

Babycare and Your Pregnancy
 now Babycare and Pregnancy
Cycling Today *now* Cycling &
 Mountain Biking Today
Goldlife for 50-Forward *now*
 Goldlife 50-Forward
HQ: The Haiku Quarterly
 Poetry Magazine *now* HQ
 Poetry Magazine (The Haiku
 Quarterly)

Looks Magazine *now* Looks
Plays & Players *now* Plays &
 Players Applause

Titles ceased publication

Art & Design
The Bank of Scotland Magazine
BBC English
Carers World
Clothes Show Magazine
European Bookseller
Inside Edge

Keyboard Review
M&J
Motorcycle International
Parents & Computers
Perspectives on Architecture
Practical Motorist
The Sporting Life (due to be
 relaunched October 1998)
The Mag!

Writing for newspapers

A newspaper may be only ink on paper but it's alive, feeding on topicality, originality and the quality of writing on its pages. The contributors an editor longs to hear from identify with the readers and understand what they want. Such contributors are never short of work and enjoy great personal satisfaction. **Jill Dick** *looks at newspapers from the freelance's point of view.*

Imagine looking at a white space the size of a tennis court and knowing you have to fill it with words and pictures. This is the task editors of newspapers face regularly and it's a wonder any can sleep at night for worrying about how they're going to do it. Not only must the space be filled, it must be temptingly – irresistibly – filled, if existing readers are to be kept happy and new ones attracted.

There have been great changes in the newspaper world in recent times and because staff have been reduced on many newspapers, more freelance work is being accepted than ever before. Although competition is tough, with former staff members now among the competitors, today's freelance writers have many advantages over their predecessors, including being able to benefit from the use of modern technology. But nobody would claim that modern technology makes a good journalist; there is still no substitute for good writing – and never will be.

Use of freelance copy on the Internet without the copyright owners' permission is one of the less welcome changes to the working scene. More and more publishers are asking writers to sign over all rights, i.e. copyright, before freelance work is accepted. There have been many legal cases over allegedly 'stolen' copy appearing elsewhere without extra payment and the battle rumbles on. Copyright is a valuable asset and writers should think very seriously before signing agreements robbing them of it.

Ideas

Newspapers' needs change from day to day or week to week according to the frequency of publication and to provide a list of topics to write about would not be helpful. Furthermore, mere lists of ideas can encourage stultified thinking. Countless writers have stared at similar lists and tried to wrench inspiration from them; countless editors have seen (and rejected) the results. More is needed than an idea. A unique slant on one may be the pointer to a worthwhile venture but an idea is most likely to be successful when it arrives in your head jockeying for priority, albeit loosely at first, with a notion of how you're going to write it.

Fishermen bait their hooks not with what they like, but with what fish like. There are many hard lessons to learn about freelancing and one of the toughest is that you have to write not just the stories that appeal to you, but the stories that will sell.

Reporting

News writing can be dramatic but frequently it is writing about something quite prosaic: a report of a local council meeting, for instance, where an important decision is awaited affecting a keenly felt local issue. Suddenly, perhaps, someone accuses councillors of rigging the ballot on the issue in question – and you will find yourself in the position of not just writing a report but filing a news story. If there is a paper coming out the next morning you, as a freelance, could be the only person able to write it.

Local reporters are hard-working folk at the very root of a paper's activities. They are likely to be out and about collecting information from tip-offs supplied by the office, waiting to file the latest news on a 'running' story or they might be engaged on any one of a dozen duties in the circulation area. A local newspaper is where many a leading journalist began learning the craft. Reporters carry considerable responsibility in a challenging job that should not be undertaken without careful consideration. Being committed to maintaining a flow of news from a small town or village or district can be a chore when you want to go on holiday, or if you are ill, or if you suddenly don't feel like doing it. But the first rule of the job is not to let your community down.

Doing the 'calls' will be a regular task. This means calling on the people or organisations likely to tell you what's going on: the police and fire stations, local hospitals, the town hall, the Citizens Advice Bureau, the morgue, the courts, schools, health clinics, community centres – anywhere and everywhere in the locality where a spokesperson is able and willing to give you news or the basis of a news story to pass on to readers of the paper. Being a reporter will almost certainly bring you more rewards than cash. Your writing skills will benefit by making quick decisions about your copy, learning how to present it clearly in print and over the phone; you will develop an increasing awareness of what is and what is not newsworthy and your confidence will grow.

Market study

What we need to study is not newspapers but readers. Are they treated as serious-minded thinkers or light-heartedly? What are their main interests – domestic, political, adventurous, romantic, creative? Is the language used appropriate for imma-ture youngsters or for folk with more experience of life? Above all, do you know how to talk to them? Picture the very readers the paper is trying to reach and think of someone you know who might be one. For thoughtful market eval-uation read newspaper advertisements carefully. Advertisers don't spend large sums of money without precise reader tar-geting and freelances can benefit from try-ing to see the readers through the same eyes.

There is no better way of finding out who the readers are and how they think and live than making a close, regular and up-to-date study of the papers you'd like to write for. Analyse their content, their page layout and format and discover why they print what they do. Even such atten-tion to detail isn't infallible, for at best it can only reveal what they printed and were interested in yesterday or last week. As for what they'll want tomorrow and next week …

No matter where you live or work, whom you meet, how you spend your time or what your hobbies and interests may be, you'll find a story. Feature, filler, news item, article, review, regular series, specialist column, interview, diary item, letter, anecdote, profile, preview; there is always something to be written. In buying a paper readers instinctively ask them-selves, 'What's in it for me?' You are pro-viding the answer.

There are several well-established mar-ket guides, the best being *Writers' & Artists' Yearbook*, *Willings Press Guide* and *The Media Guide* (see further read-ing, page 145).

Page-stoppers

Written work submitted to editors or fea-tures editors may be referred to as a fea-ture, an article, a piece or just 'copy'. Call it what you wish, it needs to stop them in their tracks or at least intrigue them suffi-ciently to contact you about development of a point here or getting a picture there. So important is this 'must have' factor that such features are called 'page-stop-pers' in newspaper offices. A feature is often tagged to a news event. It may, for instance, give background information on a running story about the progress of hospitalised casualties following a local coach crash, highlight the warnings about a nearby crumbling cliff or reveal some awkward facts following the disappearance of funds from a charity's coffers. Whatever its theme, always be careful your story is not out of date, having been overtaken by more recent events.

Features may be based entirely on facts but it is their relevance to people that makes them viable. Make yourself the bringer of comfort, an inspiration, an instructor or a wallower in nostalgia. Give readers information about education, medical services, local transport, job opportunities – they are all important to people. Above all, be sure not to fill your piece with little more than your own opinion and personal experiences; unless you are famous or well known in the locality, such views are unlikely to be required.

It pays to look ahead, particularly in ways other writers may not. This is not always easy to do and you will have to work hard on an article before ever writing a word. Research can never be skimped. A thinly researched piece quickly lands on the reject pile if another author has taken more time and trouble to delve into the subject than you have. The real value of research lies not in the facts and figures you have unearthed but in the greater understanding you can give your readers from what you have yourself understood.

Reference libraries offer extensive facilities for researching anything and everything, particularly with the aid of highly specialised on-line search engines, but the most comprehensive single volume to help you is *Research for Writers* by Ann Hoffmann (see further reading, page 145). As your pile of researched material grows so will your interest and enthusiasm. To write well you have to be interested in what you're writing, or at least make yourself interested. If you're not, why should anyone else be?

Original freelance copy on an editor's desk is more welcome than a tea-break. A good feature writer can write about virtually anything. When you do so make it strong; make them laugh, cry, want to know more, swear, feel encouraged, understand something or someone better, agree, disagree – or whatever you choose – but make sure they do or feel *something*.

Specialist spots

The many freelances who write a regular page/half page/column/corner know it's not a commission won without effort, often over a number of years. Editors need to know you will be able to sustain an unlimited time at the job, that your copy will constantly be fresh and innovative and, most importantly, that it will always arrive on time. But when satisfied about these criteria, most are only too glad to hand over responsibility for a portion of the paper and know it is being handled efficiently. Making editors aware of your worth by selling them copy is a good basis for seeking a regular column for yourself.

The golden rule that applies for all copy is that (short of real and rare emergencies) it must never be late. To be calm about accepting deadlines you need to plan ahead carefully, to accept your own limits in terms of the research needed for a particular job of work and the time it is likely to take you to write it, and (the best and only true safety net) to have plenty of copy ready in your private store.

What types of regular columns are popular with readers? Their themes are boundless: nature, profiles of famous people, chess, horoscopes, crosswords, competitions, children's and women's pages, young mothers, pop music, pets, food – anything that interests people will make a good column. As a column will get you known and your work constantly read you should be prepared for the feedback from readers. This can be one of the most rewarding aspects of column-running if you don't let it take up too much of your writing time. And at the end of every month you are guaranteed a pre-negotiated fee without having to invoice anyone.

A few topics fall into a separate category: travel, sport, motoring, business and finance among them. These are nearly always covered by staff writers and contributions to these sections have to be exceptional, if not unique.

Reviews

The distinctive task of reviewing books, drama, films, videos, radio and television programmes is seldom work for beginners. Sometimes a person who is not even thought of as a writer but who is famous in another sphere might be invited to contribute – a politician or a top sportsperson, perhaps – to attract readers with the name of the reviewer rather than the quality of the review, but the established papers have their own trained and experienced staff reviewers.

How, then, do you gain experience? For all categories of reviewing it is at the discretion of editors (or features editors) that you may be given a chance. And the only way to build up a solid reputation is to keep writing the copy they want when (or preferably just before) they want it.

Letters, fillers, anecdotes and humour

Writers may complain that computerised page layout leaves fewer spaces for small items but (as in all marketing) it is a matter of finding your own openings. It is sometimes worthwhile amassing a good collection of fillers and filing them to an editor as a single package. Fillers, be they Letters to the Editor, snippets to make readers laugh or small pieces of general interest, are covered by the same copyright protection as their weightier brothers: the original copy belongs to the writer and only an exact copy of it by an unauthorised person infringes that copyright. Other people taking up the ideas in themes or fillers are quite free to develop them as they wish – in fact Letters to the Editor are generally chosen with just this in mind: that the original may generate sufficient interest for other readers to write more letters with their views.

To a freelance writer nothing observed or overheard is ever wasted. Humour is nearly always welcome and the newspaper world is full of surprises: a writer friend persuaded the editor of her evening paper that a 'funny' corner would give readers at least one thing to laugh at every day. That's her column now; it's been running for several years and the readers love it. It's easy to laugh at humour, not easy to write it and virtually impossible to teach someone how to do it. If you can, you're lucky.

Business

Never be deterred by the thought that a freelance writer must also be a seller – or afraid to discuss what you will be paid for work accepted. Bona fide freelances have to deal with tax self-assessment but with this status you can claim many benefits, setting some of your expenses against tax and even working at a tax loss. To satisfy the Inland Revenue you must demonstrate that you are a professional writer, that you are trying to make a profit and that you are eligible to be taxed under Schedule D (see *Income tax* on page 659). This means your taxable income from writing will be the amount you receive in fees less expenses wholly and exclusively incurred in the pursuit of your writing. If you hold another full-time job it may not be easy to substantiate your writing credentials, but being able to produce genuine records and receipts and to demonstrate a proper businesslike approach to your writing work will be to your advantage.

Freelances sometimes fear their work will not be accepted because there is not enough room in the paper after the staff have filled all the editorial space available for each edition. Write what editors want – that's the simple recipe for success; do that and space will always be found. Perhaps that last sentence sums up all we writers need to know.

Jill Dick has spent many years working for national, regional and local newspapers as a feature writer, columnist, reviewer and departmental editor. Her published books include *Freelance Writing for Newspapers* and *Writing for Magazines*, both published by A & C Black.

Writing magazine articles

For the would-be writer there can be little doubt that magazine articles offer the easiest way to get into print. **John Hines** *offers guidance to potential contributors.*

The magazine market is vast and is growing steadily. *Willings Press Guide 1998* recorded no less than 12,928 UK periodicals, and the majority of these rely on freelance contributions to fill their pages. New magazines appear almost daily and, although some founder, most of them survive. The subject material covered by these magazines is so varied that few writers would find their special interests not included.

The magazines range from the modest budget publications to the expensive glossies. Beginners can cut their teeth on the lower end of the market, knowing that, although the fees are modest, the competition is small. These publications provide an excellent start for building skills, self-confidence and credibility. The opportunity for steadily moving up-market is there for the taking, until the writer reaches the level which fulfils his or her ambitions.

The idea

Established article writers usually have files bulging with ideas. They will include newspaper and magazine clippings, jottings from television and radio programmes and personal observations. Almost anything which intrigues the writer or fires the imagination is worth a place in the ideas file. There is an adage in the writing world that it pays to write about what you know. Certainly this is a good idea, for you write more comfortably and competently on a familiar subject, but the wise diversify as well.

In selecting subjects, it is most rewarding to pick those which interest you or, better still, fascinate you. They provide absorbing research and can result in articles rich in original thought with your enthusiasm showing through. As a freelance, you have the luxury of being able to pick and choose, so why not select those articles which are a pleasure to write?

Market study

Successful writers know that effective market study is vital. Any editor will tell you that the vast majority of unsolicited material which lands on their desk is quite unsuitable. The material may be wrong in length, style or choice of subject. Yet studying a copy of the magazine could have helped to avoid these mistakes.

Try to read at least two recent copies of the magazine for which you are aiming to write. Analyse it carefully. Check the number of articles which are staff written (the staff are usually listed in the front of the magazine). By studying several issues you may also discover that there are contributors with regular slots and so deduce the opportunities which exist for the freelance.

The pathway to successful article writing

- have a good idea for a subject;
- find a suitable market;
- produce an interesting and well-written article for that market;
- submit a professional-looking typescript;
- have a sound sales strategy throughout.

If the magazine looks promising, study the type of subject which the editor favours. Check the approximate length of the average article. Ask yourself if the magazine's style is one with which you would be comfortable or to which you could adapt.

Few writers seem to study the advertisements and this is a big mistake. Advertising agencies spend a great deal of money on painstaking expert research, aimed at identifying the typical reader. By studying the advertisements you can benefit from this valuable information which can be most helpful when slanting your article to the readers' interests.

Willings Press Guide, Vol. 1 is an excellent comprehensive source of information on the UK print media. In particular, its classified index can be invaluable for finding a market for those difficult-to-place articles. If you are interested in selling to foreign markets, *Vol. 2* gives international coverage, apart from the UK.

Studying the *Writers' & Artists' Yearbook* can give you a good insight into the requirements of many magazines, even including the fees they pay.

Freelance Market News is the best market newsletter for the freelance writer (see further reading, page 145). However, the finest market information is that which freelances compile for themselves from personal experience. A card filing system is useful here but, like all market information, its value depends on its being kept up to date.

Research and accuracy

Although some articles can be written from personal experience or knowledge, most articles require some sound current research. Public libraries can be very helpful, particularly if you enlist the help of a qualified librarian rather than a library assistant. The copyright libraries, of which the British Library is the best known, are superb. Would-be researchers must establish their bona fides before being issued with a ticket. (See also *Books, research and reference* on page 599.)

All facts should be checked for accuracy,

going back to the source wherever possible. The books of others are not infallible, even reference books. Errors can be embarrassing and inevitably attract unwelcome letters from readers. File your researched material away for future use; an effective filing system is essential. The best book on the subject is *Research for Writers* by Ann Hoffmann (see further reading, page 145).

The Internet can offer a vast amount of research material, particularly in the form of published articles. As some Internet sources may include information of dubious quality, your routine check for accuracy should be made conscientiously.

Research may entail interviewing people and this is a skill which the freelance should consider developing. For effective interviews, sound preparation is important. Research in advance as much as possible about the interviewee and their field of interest. Make a list of important questions in logical sequence. But be prepared to divert from your questions and follow any unexpected revelations. If you use a tape recorder, test it beforehand and always carry spare batteries and tapes. It is essential to have a notebook as a back-up and to carry spare pens.

Sensitivity and courtesy should be the criteria for all interviewing for normal articles. Start with easy general questions. Guide the interview gently, but firmly. Wind up the interview as you began, on an easy note. The interviewee should be left with the feeling that it has been an enjoyable experience. Some interviewees ask if they can vet the finished article. You should always politely refuse, but do offer to allow them to withdraw anything they may regret saying.

For more information on interviewing technique, see *Tape-recording interviews* on page 147, and *Freelance Writing for Newspapers* and *The Way to Write Magazine Articles* in the further reading list on page 145.

Non-linear thinking

A stumbling block for many inexperienced writers is beginning their article, particularly when faced with a daunting mass of notes, clippings and research references. Related research material must be associated and the various aspects considered in order of importance. However, when marshalling material, we often tend to arrange it in a linear fashion, rather like a shopping list. This tends to restrict our thinking on each point.

It has been found that non-linear thinking stimulates ideas and their logical development. I use this method as a framework for my articles, particularly those which are complex. Non-linear flow-of-thought patterns are easy to compile and to use. The subject is written in the centre of a large sheet of paper with the major aspects to be covered radiating from it. From these, further spurs are drawn, filling in other important material. Less significant points are added on minor spurs until all aspects are covered. Never discard these patterns; file them away for future use as a valuable concise reference to your research material.

A detailed explanation of this method, together with illustrations of typical non-linear patterns, is given in *The Way to Write Magazine Articles*; and more general coverage can be found in *Use Your Head* (see further reading, page 145).

The article structure

We all develop our own style, but it is important to learn to modify it to suit the requirements of our market. The majority of articles are relatively short and must put over their story crisply without wasting words. Often this can best be done with fairly short sentences and relatively short paragraphs. Never write long convoluted sentences which require reading more than once to understand.

The opening

The first paragraph of an article has special importance. It must grip the editor's attention immediately, its purpose being to force the editor to read on. You can often make your opening irresistible by selecting a point from your article which is intriguing, startling or even audacious.

The body

You will not sell an article on the strength of its opening. The body of the article must fulfil the promise of that good first paragraph. It is here that the main text or message of your article will be unfolded. Your thought patterns will help you to move logically from one aspect to the next in a smooth progression and ensure that nothing important is left out.

The end

The poor article appears to finish when the writer runs out of ideas. A good ending must aim to tie up any loose ends positively. The way it does this depends a great deal on the subject. It can be speculative – a look into the future, perhaps. It might go back to answer a question posed in the beginning. Avoid a mere recap of the main text for this gives a weak ending. Try to set aside some 'meat' to include in the ending; this could leave the reader with a strong point to ponder over.

Dialogue

Dialogue can breathe life into an article and give it sparkle. It must be used judiciously, for over-use may unbalance the article. It is often effective when used appropriately as the first sentence of an article.

The typescript

The conventional layout of a typescript is described in *Preparing and submitting a manuscript* on page 551. However, an article for the British magazine market needs the addition of a typed cover sheet with the writer's name and address in the top right-hand corner, the article's title centred halfway down the page followed by the writer's name. If you are using a pseudonym it goes here, not at the top.

About two-thirds down the page on the left should be the number of words in the article and two or three lines' space below, the rights which you are offering the editor. For normal practical purposes this would be First British Serial Rights, usually abbreviated to 'FBSR offered' – see below. The cover sheet is not used for USA markets.

An increasing number of editors are asking writers to submit their articles on disk. It pays you to provide this facility if you can. You should always verify with the editor that your system and theirs are compatible before submission. You will find that most editors also require a hard copy (printout) in addition to the disk. For more information, see *The Professional Typescript for Magazine Articles* (further reading, page 145).

Illustrations

Good illustrations enhance an article, making it more saleable. The writer/illustrator also receives an extra fee. It is self-evident that all article writers should try to produce that editors' delight – the words and pictures package. If you are a reasonable photographer, you are halfway there. If you are not, there is little excuse for not trying with one of the fully automatic cameras which are available today.

Study magazines to see, not only whether they use black and white or colour, but also the way they use illustrations. Do they tend to be small and plentiful to assist in the understanding of the text? Does the editor favour large dramatic pictures, sometimes covering as much as a whole page or even two? Finally, can your pictures match those in the magazine?

Your pictures must be pin-sharp and properly exposed. They must avoid all the basic mistakes of composition which are outlined in any photographic primer. For black and white you should submit glossy, borderless prints, 254 x 203mm (10 x 8in). Transparencies are demanded by most quality magazines for their colour illustrations, although a small but growing number of periodicals will consider colour prints. You must always confirm that a magazine uses colour prints before submitting them. For covers, most magazines use 35mm transparencies, but many prefer a larger format. Illustrations are covered in depth in *The Way to Write Magazine Articles* (see further reading, page 145.)

Writers who turn to supplementing their writing with photography rarely look back. They report better sales and increased earnings.

Rights

By offering First British Serial Rights you are inviting the magazine to publish your article once and for the first time in Britain. You are retaining the right to sell it elsewhere in the world. Some editors will try to wring all rights from you. Do not give way as it leaves the magazine free to sell your article worldwide and pocket the proceeds.

Second British Serial Rights are rarely sold, but a magazine may ask to buy them if they see your article in print and wish to reproduce it themselves. You would normally accept, but as Second Rights earn lower fees than First Rights, it is not worth making a particular effort to sell them. It pays to rewrite the original article, reslanting it to suit the new market and possibly introducing some new material. This effectively makes it a new article for which the First Rights may be legitimately offered.

The sales strategy

Probably the most common reason for good articles failing to get published is lack of a sound sales strategy. A surprisingly large number of writers complete a good article and then peddle it hopefully around the markets. This is quite the wrong way. Your article must always be written specifically for the market you have in mind. Your sales strategy should begin the moment you look at your material and can say: 'Yes, there is enough here for a good article.' You then use your market study to find a number of likely magazines which might publish such an article.

Query letters

The sound query letter is essential for sustained success in the article-writing field. Examine your list of possible magazines and arrange them in order of your preference. Select the top one and write your query letter to its editor. Keep it brief and state your idea for the article, mentioning any special slant you have in mind. If you are qualified in any way to write such an article or if you have a 'track-record' of writing in that field, you should say so. Also mention if you have suitable illustrations.

Ask the editor how many words he or she would like to see. It is particularly important to ask for the magazine's rates for contributors. Always enclose an sae. The query letter is your initial shop-window and its quality should be the best of which you are capable. If the editor turns down the idea, write immediately to the next magazine on your list and so on.

If the editor likes your idea, you may get a commission, but if you are unknown it is more likely that you will be asked to submit the article on spec. Some editors try to side-step divulging their rates in advance, but you must be professional and insist on knowing them.

An acceptance is the usual outcome from an editor's expression of interest. As you become better at matching subject to magazine, writing shrewd query letters and producing sound articles, your rejections should drop to virtually nil.

On acceptance, the professional freelance looks around for another outlet. Writing is easy, it is the research which takes the time. Make sure you get the maximum from your research (see above).

Payment

Some magazines pay on acceptance, but the majority pay on publication. Avoid those magazines which hold your material on spec with no guarantee of ultimate publication. They are not worthy of consideration. Never be afraid to question offers of low rates, for many editors will negotiate. If low rates are not improved upon, be professional and withdraw the offer of your article. See *Getting paid for writing* on page 146.

Fresh fields

When you have written articles extensively on a subject, it may be worth considering whether the subject is suitable for a non-fiction book (see *The Way to Write Non-fiction*, below). If so, your articles could be valuable as evidence of your writing skills, your knowledge of the subject and the wide interest the subject can generate. Many writers have used their published articles as a means of gaining an advance contract for a non-fiction book.

John Hines is a freelance writer and lecturer covering a wide range of interests, but specialises in health and the environment. He lectures extensively on writing, both in the UK and abroad.

Further reading

Buzan, Tony, *Use Your Head*, BBC, revised edn, 1995

Dick, Jill, *Freelance Writing for Newspapers*, A & C Black, 2nd edn, 1998

Dick, Jill, *Writing for Magazines*, A & C Black, 2nd edn, 1996

Freelance Market News, Sevendale House, 7 Dale Street, Manchester M1 1JB (on subscription)

Hines, John, *The Professional Typescript for Magazine Articles*, Tanglewood, 1995

Hines, John, *The Way to Write Magazine Articles*, Hamish Hamilton, repr. 1995

Hines, John, *The Way to Write Non-fiction*, Hamish Hamilton, 1990. o.p.

Hoffmann, Ann, *Research for Writers*, A & C Black, 5th edn, 1996

Howard, Godfrey, *The Good English Guide*, Pan Macmillan, 1994

Legat, Michael, *The Nuts and Bolts of Writing*, Robert Hale, repr. 1993

Peak, Steve (ed.), *The Media Guide*, Fourth Estate, annual

The Oxford Writers' Dictionary, Oxford Reference, 1990

Willings Press Guide, Hollis Directories Ltd, annual

Getting paid for writing

A common complaint of writers is that of not getting paid. **John Hines** *offers the benefit of his experience of dealing with unpaid invoices to assess whether to pursue payment, and how to go about it.*

Most writers who read this *Yearbook* are serious about their work and expect to get paid for it. It is not unreasonable to look for adequate and prompt payment as a matter of course. Unfortunately, one of the common complaints of writers is that of payment problems – and not all the complainants are beginners.

The majority of the offenders are magazine publishers. Established magazines rarely create problems, although payment may not be particularly prompt. It is the struggling magazines with low circulations which account for most complaints.

Chasing payments is stressful and time consuming. It is obviously preferable to avoid these situations than to rely on overcoming them when they occur.

Professionalism

A businesslike approach to your work is vital and the key to this is professionalism. Neat, unostentatious headed paper and headed invoices are a sound investment, whether produced using your own word processor or commissioned from your local print shop. Typescripts must be clean and the layout conventional (i.e. typed double spaced with good margins).

A sound sales strategy together with an understanding of rights is essential; this is covered in *Writing magazine articles* on page 141. The question of rights is particularly relevant to current trends. When discussing rates of payment, be prepared to negotiate. Any agreements made over the phone should be confirmed in writing. Keep copies of all correspondence and note details of all phone conversations.

Payment on acceptance is increasingly rare; it is usually made on publication. Seek an agreement on a probable publication date, and impose a deadline if the subject of the piece is topical. Do not permit work to be held indefinitely without a clear agreement to publish. If work is returned unpublished after acceptance, demand a 'kill fee' – this is usually 50%. You can then sell the material elsewhere.

Some writers submit an invoice to the editor with their typescript, others submit one if the agreed payment has not been made promptly. Send a second invoice to the accounts department if payment is not made by, say, four weeks after publication.

Never be in a hurry to chase a payment without good reason. A number of reputable magazines are slow to pay, but they do always pay. Get to know the payment methods of your regular markets and try to accept them philosophically. In cases where payment is unduly late, particularly when the market is new and untried, send a letter stating that payment is overdue and ask for settlement within 14 days.

Try to resolve problems amicably, although firmer action may be required. The Society of Authors provides invaluable advice and support for its members, particularly relating to book contracts. I have found its help highly effective.

Office of Fair Trading

A sound, no-cost course of action is to refer the matter to your local Office of Fair Trading. These Offices vary in their effectiveness. They normally pass the matter to their counterpart in the debtor's area. I have even had them call at a magazine's office and collect the cheque for me.

Small Claims Court

If all else fails, you could turn to the Small Claims Court; but there are several points to consider first. For example, does the debtor have resources? Some magazines are launched on a shoestring with borrowed money and a rented office with hired furniture and equipment. Your Office of Fair Trading may be prepared at least to hint about the debtor's financial standing and whether there are other creditors in the queue.

Is the sum significant enough for your time and trouble? If the debtor defends the case, it is usually transferred to their nearest court. This might be hundreds of miles away, and it is important for you to appear in person. If you win, you can claim all reasonable expenses, including interest on the debt. If you lose, you may be liable for the debtor's expenses, which could be considerable.

Small Claims Courts are informal departments of the County Courts. Your County Court will send you explanatory leaflets and will answer questions on the phone. Currently, the scale of charges for establishing a claim range from £10 for a debt up to £100, to £80 for a debt of £3000

Publishers rarely let a case reach court, but they may offer a defence and wait until the eleventh hour to test your resolve. A publisher once phoned me late in the evening to settle out of court when the case was due to be heard the following morning. If you do settle out of court, you must advise the court as soon as possible.

Is it worth it?

Only you can judge. Beginners are often grateful for modest payments and are prepared to write off losses as experience. But when a writer does press for his or her dues, their action may well help writers elsewhere to be paid.

John Hines is a freelance writer and lecturer covering a wide range of interests, but specialises in health and the environment. He lectures extensively on writing, both in the UK and abroad.

Tape-recording interviews

Tape-recording interviews can both liberate and protect journalists in their craft. Freed of the notepad, they can engage more directly with the interviewee and come away with a fuller and more interesting interview. And having a recording of what was said can solve disputes which may arise at a later date. **John Crace** *describes how to use a tape recorder for successful interviewing.*

Ask any journalist to name his or her most important item of equipment – word processor excepted – and the chances are that the answer will be a tape recorder. Few writers, save for some hard-nosed old pros on the news desk, are familiar with speedwriting or shorthand techniques and, in any case, most interviews these days are better conducted using a tape machine. For the aspiring writer, a tape recorder is an absolute must. Almost every commission will involve talking to someone, be it a celebrity, an expert or an ordinary member of the public. Don't panic about the expense, though. You don't need broadcast quality – something cheap, cheerful and audible will do fine, and will solve most of your interviewing problems. Just don't imagine that it will solve them all.

Using a tape recorder

The first thing to remember about tape recorders is that they can go wrong. Sometimes this will be the machine's fault; most of the time it will be yours. My first-ever interview was with a woman whose son was in prison for murder. While pouring her heart out she cried frequently over the course of our 30-minute conversation, and it was only as we were winding to a close that I noticed I had left the pause button on. So, I guiltily blamed the machine and asked if she would start again. Fortunately, she agreed. Not everybody will be so considerate or have the time, and a few precautionary checks before each interview will avert most potential disasters.

More than anything else, journalists fear their batteries running out on them. So it is not a bad idea always to use fresh ones when starting an interview. This isn't necessary if you're only planning a short chat and you know that your last interview took only 15 minutes. If you know the interview will take a long time, the most practical solution is to test the machine before you start, to see if there is any sign of the machine running slow. If not, you will probably be OK, but have a spare set of batteries in reserve, just in case.

Positioning the recorder is vital. Try to find a quiet spot, where there are few outside disturbances, and place the machine as near to the subject as possible. Get your interviewee to say a few words into the microphone, and play them back to make sure you can hear clearly what has been said. I always find that no matter how well I position the machine I can always hear myself far better than the other person, but as long as I can understand my subject I don't worry too much.

Never use unfamiliar and untried equipment for an interview. I once bought a gadget that would enable me to record telephone conversations. I carefully followed the instructions for setting it up but when I came to play back the interview I couldn't hear anything. I've never dared to use it again. So, the message is: never use any item you haven't tested at home first, and only then if you feel confident with it.

The benefits of a tape recorder

Conducting an interview involves far more than the mere asking of questions and the writing down or recording of replies. It's about the facial expressions and body language of the subject. Most interviews and profiles depend on the journalist picking up nuances of behaviour to give the article colour and depth. So if you have your head buried in a notepad as you struggle to jot down your subject's *bons mots* word for word, you will end up with a one-dimensional piece of writing. It will probably be factual and accurate, but it will also be excruciatingly dull.

A good interview should flow like a normal conversation. This can be tricky when your subject is on his or her fourth interview of the day or when time is tight, but at least a tape recorder allows an approximation of it. Before starting, make a list of questions to ask, but do not be too dogmatic about sticking to it. Watch your interviewee for signs of interest, boredom or discomfort and follow up appropriately. Sometimes, the conversation can flow into other more interesting areas, and allowing your interviewee to wander off the point can help to put him or her at ease, and may even engender more honest answers to difficult questions. As long as you make sure you cover the ground you had planned, just let your subject speak.

Interviews and the law

Occasionally, an interviewee may let something slip in an unguarded moment, or give a surprisingly candid answer. What you do with this is up to you. A tape recorder can be a powerful tool, and it can present you with some moral dilemmas. Do you use a quote that is certain to upset and humiliate your interviewee later? I try to respect the spirit in which the interview has been given. If it has been antagonistic, I feel that anything is fair game. If not, I attempt to allude to the sense of what has been said, but in an inoffensive and unembarrassing manner. Most importantly, if someone says something that they ask me not to use, I never do so.

If you do decide to use what has been said, a taped interview can be a formidable ally against libel threats that may arise – providing you have quoted the person verbatim. With written notes it is your word against that of the interviewee, but a tape can deter even the most eager litigant. I once interviewed a person about the Hillsborough disaster who bitterly regretted having been so outspoken about his feelings. On the day the piece was published he phoned, threatening to sue me. I was able to play back to him the relevant passage to prove I had not misquoted, and he was pacified – if not entirely happy. Remember, though, just because someone says he won't sue doesn't mean that he may not change his mind. Legal proceedings can be started at any time up

to seven years from the date of publication. So always use a new tape when you are interviewing, and keep your old ones safely stored away.

And finally ...

Above all, try not to get over-anxious about an interview. Come well prepared, and concentrate on enjoying it. The more relaxed you are, the more relaxed your subject will be, and the better the conversation will go. Remember – doing the interview should be the fun part of the process. The really hard work starts with the writing.

John Crace is a feature writer regularly working for *The Guardian*, *The Independent* and the *Evening Standard*. He also contributes to many magazines, including the *New Statesman* and *GQ*, and has written five books.

Syndicates, news and press agencies

Before submitting material, you are strongly advised to make preliminary enquiries and to ascertain terms of work. Strictly speaking, syndication is the selling and reselling of previously published work although some news and press agencies handle original material.

Academic File
Eastern Art Publishing Group, PO Box 13666, 27 Wallorton Gardens, London SW14 8WF
tel 0181-392 1122 *fax* 0181-392 1422
e-mail easternart@compuserve.com
Managing Editor Sajid Rizvi, *Executive Editor* Shirley Rizvi
Feature and photo syndication with special reference to the developing world and immigrant communities in the West. Founded 1985.

Advance Features
Stubbs Wood Cottage, Hammerwood, East Grinstead, West Sussex RH19 3QE
tel/fax (01342) 850480
Managing Editor Peter Norman
Supplies text and visual services to the national and regional press in Britain and newspapers overseas. Instructional graphic panels on a variety of subjects.

Text services (weekly); stars, nature and royalty articles. Crosswords: daily, weekly and theme; general puzzles. Daily and weekly cartoons for the regional and national press (not single cartoons).

ALI Press Agency Ltd
Boulevard Anspach 111-115, Bte 9, B9-1000 Brussels, Belgium
tel 02 512 73 94 *fax* 02 512 03 30
Director George Lans
All types of feature services except information and news: cartoons, puzzles, strips, comics, illustrations, picture stories, transparencies, articles of general interest, etc. for magazines, newspapers and books, especially illustrated books for children and adults. Syndication in all major countries. Commissions: 35%. Syndication: 50%. Founded 1948.

Alpha incorporating London News Service

63 Gee Street, London EC1V 3RS
tel 0171-336 0632 *fax* 0171-253 8419
Editor John Rodgers
Worldwide syndication of features and photos.

The Associated Press Ltd

(News Department), The Associated Press House, 12 Norwich Street, London EC4A 1BP
tel 0171-353 1515 *fax* 0171-353 8118

Australian Associated Press

12 Norwich Street, London EC4A 1EJ
tel 0171-353 0153 *fax* 0171-583 3563
News service to the Australian, New Zealand and Pacific Island press, radio and TV. Founded 1935.

Neil Bradley Puzzles

Linden House, 34 Hardy Barn, Shipley, Derbyshire DE75 7JA
tel/fax (01773) 768960
e-mail bradcart@aol.com
Director Neil Bradley
Supplies visual puzzles to national and regional press; emphasis placed on variety and topicality with work based on current media listings. Work supplied on disk or prints to Mac or PC. Daily single frame and strip cartoons. Contact for free booklet and disk demo. Founded 1981.

Bulls Presstjänst AB

Tulegatan 39, Box 6519, S-11383 Stockholm, Sweden
tel (08) 23 40 20 *fax* (08) 15 80 10
e-mail kontakt@bulls.se
web site http://www.bulls.se

Bulls Pressedienst GmbH

Eysseneckstrasse 50, D-60322 Frankfurt am Main, Germany
tel (069) 959 270 *fax* (069) 959 27111
e-mail sales@bullspress.de

Bulls Pressetjeneste A/S

Ebbells Gate 3, N-0183 Oslo, Norway
tel 22 20 56 01 *fax* 22 20 49 78
e-mail bullsosl@online.no

Bulls Pressetjeneste

Östbanegade 9, 1th, DK-2100 Copenhagen, Denmark
tel 31 38 90 99 *fax* 31 38 25 16
e-mail kjartan@bulls.dk

Bulls Finskaförsäljnings AB

Isonniitynkatu 7, Box 180, FIN-00521, Helsinki, Finland
tel (09) 757 13 11 *fax* (09) 757 06 34
e-mail ilkka@bullsress.fi

Bulls Press ul.

Chocimska 28, Pokoj 509, 00-791 Warsawa, Poland
tel/fax (22) 49 80 18
e-mail krzysztof@bulls.com.pl

Bulls Press

Pikk 29 A, EE 0001 Tallinn, Estonia
tel (2) 501 84 85 *fax* (2) 631 41 65
e-mail meelik@division.ee
Market newspapers, magazines, weeklies and advertising agencies in Sweden, Denmark, Norway, Finland, Iceland, Poland, The Baltic States, Germany, Austria and German-speaking Switzerland.
Syndicates human interest picture stories; topical and well-illustrated background articles and series; photographic features dealing with science, people, personalities, glamour; genre pictures for advertising; condensations and serialisations of best-selling fiction and non-fiction; cartoons, comic strips, film and TV rights, merchandising and newspaper graphics on-line via modem or ISDN.

The Canadian Press

Associated Press House, 12 Norwich Street, London EC4A 1EJ
tel 0171-353 6355 *fax* 0171-583 4238
Chief Correspondent Helen Branswell
London Bureau of the national news agency of Canada. Founded 1919.

Central Press Features

Temple Way, Bristol BS99 7HD
tel 0117-934 3600 *fax* 0117-934 3639
e-mail mail@central-press.co.uk
Editor Ken Elkes
Supplies features, cartoons, crosswords, horoscopes and graphics strips to newspapers, magazines and other publications (including Internet sites) in 50 countries. Included in over 100 daily and weekly services are columns of international interest on health and beauty, medicine, employment, sports, house and home, motoring, computers, film and video, children's features, gardening, celebrity profiles, food and drink, finance and law. Also runs a parliamentary service and TV listings service, as well as supplying editorial material for advertising features.

J.W. Crabtree and Son

Cheapside Chambers, 43 Cheapside, Bradford BD1 4HP
tel (01274) 732937 (office), (01535) 655288 (home)
fax (01274) 732937

News, general, trade and sport; information and research for features undertaken. Founded 1919.

Daily & Sunday Telegraph Syndication

Ewan MacNaughton Associates, Alexandra Chambers, 6 Alexandra Road, Tonbridge, Kent TN9 2AA
tel (01732) 771116 *fax* (01732) 771160
e-mail ema@dial.pipex.com

News, features, photography; worldwide distribution and representation.

Environmental & Occupational Health Research Foundation

Penrose House, Birtles Road, Whirley, Cheshire SK10 3JQ
tel/fax (01625) 615323
e-mail eorhfl@aol.com
Managing Editor Peggy Bentham

Undertakes individual commissions and syndicates articles to diverse science and technology journals and general consumer media. Peer reviewed and accredited contributors from academia and professional institutions.

Europa-Press

Saltmätargatan 8, 1st Floor, Box 6410, S-113 82, Stockholm, Sweden
tel 8-34 94 35 *fax* 8-34 80 79
e-mail red.led@europapress.se
Managing Director Tord Steinsvik

Market: newspapers, magazines and weeklies in Sweden, Denmark, Norway and Finland. Syndicates high quality features of international appeal such as topical articles, photo-features – b&w and colour, women's features, short stories, serial novels, non-fiction stories and serials with strong human interest, crime articles, popular science, cartoons, comic strips.

Europress Features (UK)

18 St Chads Road, Didsbury, Nr Manchester M20 9WH
tel 0161-445 2945

Representation of newspapers and magazines in Europe, Australia, United States. Syndication of top-flight features with exclusive illustrations – human interest stories – showbusiness personalities. 30-35% commission on sales of material successfully accepted; 40% on exclusive illustrations.

Express Enterprises

(division of Express Newspapers plc)
Ludgate House, 245 Blackfriars Road, London SE1 9UX
tel 0171-922 7902 *fax* 0171-922 7871

Text and pictures from all Express titles. Archive from 1900. Numerous strips and political cartoons. Material handled worldwide for freelance journalists.

Features International

Tolland, Lydeard St Lawrence, Taunton TA4 3PS
tel (01984) 623014 *fax* (01984) 623901
Editorial Director Anthony Sharrock

Syndicates features to magazines and newspapers throughout the world. The agency produces a wide range of material – mainly from freelance sources – including topical articles, women's features and weekly columns. Distributes directly to all English-language countries. Agents throughout the Common Market countries, Japan, the Americas and Eastern Europe. Buys copy outright and welcomes story ideas. Sae essential.

Frontline Photo Press Agency

18 Wall Street, Norwood, Australia 5067
postal address PO Box 162, Kent Town, Australia 5071
tel (08) 8333 2691 *fax* (08) 8364 0604
e-mail info@frontline.net.au
web site http://www.frontline.net.au
Director Carlo Irlitti

Photographic press agency specialising in sports coverage. Services provided: news, interviews, features, articles and photos for newspapers, magazines and other media. Digital photo wire services.

Syndicates sports, celebrity, travel, women's and general interest features and articles with photos. Welcomes approaches from individuals and organisations abroad. Assignments undertaken. Rates negotiable. Founded 1988.

Gemini News Service

9 White Lion Street, London N1 9PD
tel 0171-833 4141 *fax* 0171-837 5118
e-mail Gemini@gn.apc.org
Editor Daniel Nelson, *Managing Director* Bethel Njoku

Network of freelance contributors and specialist writers all over the world. Specialists in news-features of international, topical and development interest. Preferred length 800-1200 words.

Graphic Syndication

4 Reyntiens View, Odiham, Hants RG29 1AF
tel (01256) 703004
e-mail flanagan@argonet.co.uk
web site http://www.argonet.co.uk/users/
mike.flanagan
Manager M. Flanagan

Cartoon strips and single frames supplied to newspapers and magazines in Britain and overseas. Terms: 50%. Founded 1981.

India-International News Service

Head office Jute House, 12 India Exchange Place, Calcutta 700001, India
tel 2209563, 4791009
Proprietor Ing H. Kothari BSc, DWP(Lond), FIMechE, FIE, FVI. FInstD

'Calcutta Letters' and Air Mail news service from Calcutta. Specialists in industrial and technical news.

INS (International News Service)/ Irish International News Service

7 King's Avenue, Minnis Bay, Birchington-on-Sea, East Kent CT7 9QL
tel (01843) 845022
Editor and Managing Director Barry J. Hardy PC,
Photo Editor Jan Vanek

News, sport, book and magazine reviews (please forward copies), TV, radio, photographic department; also equipment for TV films, etc.

International Fashion Press Agency

Penrose House, Birtles Road, Whirley,
Cheshire SK10 3JQ
tel/fax (01625) 615323
e-mail IFPressAgy@aol.com
Directors P. Bentham (managing), P. Dyson, S. Fagette, L.C. Mottershead, L.B. Fell, T.R. Fox

Monitors and photographs international fashion collections and developments in textile and fashion industry. Specialist writers on health, fitness, beauty and personalities. Undertakes individual commissioned features. Supplies syndicated columns/pages to press, radio and TV (NUJ staff writers and photographers).

International Press Agency (Pty) Ltd

PO Box 67, Howard Place 7450, South Africa
tel (021) 531 1926 *fax* (021) 531 8789
e-mail inpra@iafrica.com
Manager Mrs T. Temple
UK office 19 Avenue South, Surbiton, Surrey KT5 8PJ
tel/fax 0181-390 4414
Managing Editor Mrs U.A. Barnett PhD

South African agents for many leading British, American and continental press firms for the syndication of comic strips, cartoons, jokes, feature articles, short stories, serials, press photos for the South African market. Founded 1934.

Joker Feature Service (JFS)

PO Box 253, 6040 AG, Roermond,
The Netherlands
tel (0475) 337338 *fax* (0475) 315663
e-mail j.f.s@tip.nl
Managing Director Ruud Kerstens

Feature articles, serial rights, tests, cartoons, comic strips and illustrations, puzzles. Handles TV-features and books; also production for merchandising.

Knight Features

20 Crescent Grove, London SW4 7AH
tel 0171-622 1467 *fax* 0171-622 1522
Director Peter Knight, *Associates* Ann King-Hall, Gaby Martin, Andrew Knight, Giovanna Farrell-Vinay, Rochelle Fry

Worldwide selling of strip cartoons and major features and serialisations. Exclusive agent in UK and Republic of Ireland for United Feature Syndicate and Newspaper Enterprise Association of New York. Founded 1985.

London News Service – see Alpha incorporating London News Service

London Sports Reporting Agency

2nd Floor, 13-16 Faro Close, Coates Hill Road, Bromley, Kent BR1 2RR
tel 0181-467 1951 *fax* 0181-295 0190
e-mail 100654.463@compuserve.com
Editor Christopher Harte, *Managers* Michael Latham (Northern Region), David Fox (South West Region), Diana Harding (South East Region)

News and reporting service for sporting events. Research facilities for radio and TV, particularly sports documentaries. Commission: NUJ rates. Founded 1994.

Maharaja Features Pvt. Ltd

5-226 Sion Road East,
Bombay 400022, India
tel 22-4097951 *fax* 22-4097801
e-mail mahafeat@bom2.vsnl.net.in
Editor K.R.N. Swamy, *Managing Editor* K.R. Padmanabhan

Syndicates feature and pictorial material, of interest to Asian readers, to newspapers and magazines in India, UK and abroad. Specialists in well-researched articles on India by eminent authorities for publication in prestige journals throughout the world. Also topical features 1000-1500 words. Illustrations: b&w prints and colour transparencies.

Mirror Syndication International
22nd Floor, 1 Canada Square, Canary Wharf, London E14 5AP
tel 0171-293 3700 *fax* 0171-293 2712
e-mail desk@mirpix.com
web site http://www.mirpix.com
Supplies publishing material and international rights for news text and pictures from Mirror Group Newspapers and other large publishing houses. Extensive picture library of all subjects.

National Association of Press Agencies (NAPA)
41 Lansdowne Crescent, Leamington Spa, Warwickshire CV32 4PR
tel (01926) 424181 *fax* (01926) 424760
Directors Denis Cassidy, Chris Johnson, Barrie Tracey, Peter Steele, John Quinn, Richard Reed
NAPA is a network of independent, established and experienced press agencies serving newspapers, magazines, TV and radio networks. Founded 1980.

New Zealand Press Association
12 Norwich Street, London EC4A 1EJ
tel 0171-353 5430 *fax* 0171-583 3563
Chief Correspondent Kip Brook

News Blitz International
c/o G. Piccione, Via Tonezza 14, 00191 Rome, Italy
tel/fax 36 30 9179
President Vinicio Congiu, *Sales Manager* Gianni Piccione, *Graphic, Literary and Television Depts* Giovanni Congiu
Syndicates cartoons, comic strips, humorous books with drawings, feature and pictorial material, environment, travels, throughout the world. Average rates of commission 60-40%, monthly report of sales, payment 60 days after the date of monthly report.

Chandra S. Perera
Cinetra, 437 Pethiyagoda, Kelaniya-11600, Sri Lanka
tel 94-1-911885 *fax* 94-1-541414/332867/323910
ATTN CHANDRA PERERA
Press and TV news, news films on Sri Lanka and Maldives, colour and b&w photo news and features, photographic and film coverages, screenplays and scripts for TV and films, press clippings.

Broadcasting, TV and newspapers; journalistic features, news, broadcasting and TV interviews.

Pixfeatures
5 Latimer Road, Barnet, Herts. EN5 5NU
tel 0181-449 9946 *fax* 0181-441 2725
Contact Peter Wickman
Spanish office tel 647 6379
Contact Roy Wickman
News agency and picture library. Specialises in selling Spanish pictures and features to British and European press.

The Press Association
292 Vauxhall Bridge Road, London SW1V 1AE
tel 0171-963 7000 *fax* 0171-963 7192
web site http://www.pa.press.net
Chief Executive Robert Simpson, *Editor-in-Chief* Paul Potts, *Commercial Directors* Sally-Anne Murray (print and broadcast), Vivienne Adshead (new media)
PA News Fast and accurate news, photography and information to print, broadcast and electronic media in the UK and Ireland.
PA Sport In-depth coverage of national and regional sports, transmitting a huge range of stories, results, pictures and updates every day.
PA Listings Page- and screen-ready information from daily guides to 7-day supplements on sports results, TV and radio listings, arts and entertainment, financial and weather listings tailored to suit requirements.
PA New Media Top quality content including news and sport for a wide range of multimedia customers.
PA WeatherCentre Continuously updated information on present and future weather conditions; consultancy services for media and industry. Founded 1868.

Press Features Syndicate
9 Paradise Close, Eastbourne, East Sussex BN20 8BT
tel (01323) 728760
Editor Harry Gresty
Specialises in photo-features, both b&w and colour. Seek human interest, oddity, glamour, pin-ups, scientific, medical, etc., material suitable for marketing through own branches in London, San Francisco, Paris, Hamburg, Milan, Stockholm, Amsterdam (for Benelux), Helsinki.

Rann Communication

6th Floor, 117 King William Street, Adelaide,
SA 5000, Australia
postal address GPO Box 958, Adelaide, SA 5001
tel (08) 8211 7771 *fax* (08) 8212 2272
Proprietor C.F. Rann

Full range of professional PR, press
releases, special newsletters, commercial
intelligence, media monitoring.
Welcomes approaches from organisations
requiring PR representation or press
release distribution. Founded 1977.

Republican Press (London)

Suite 15-17, The Outer Temple, 222-225 Strand,
London WC2R 1BA
tel 0171-353 2580 *fax* 0171-353 2578

Acquires material for publication in
South Africa.

Reuters Limited

85 Fleet Street, London EC4P 4AJ
tel 0171-250 1122

Singer Media Corporation

Seaview Business Park, 1030 Calle Cordillera,
Unit 106, San Clemente, CA 92673, USA
tel 714-498-7227
e-mail singer@deltanet.com
Vice-President Helen J. Lee

Features (celebrity interviews and profiles, business, health, fitness, beauty,
diet, self-help, how-to, etc), cartoons,
puzzles and quizzes of international
appeal for international and domestic
syndication. Represented in most countries abroad. No local or national material; no comic strips. Query first.

Solo Syndication Ltd

49-53 Kensington High Street, London W8 5ED
tel 0171-376 2166 *fax* 0171-938 3165
Chairman Don Short

Worldwide syndication of newspaper
features, photos, cartoons, strips and
book serialisations. Professional journalists only. Commission: 50%. Agency represents the international syndication of
Associated Newspapers (*Daily Mail, Mail
on Sunday, Evening Standard*), *The
European*, News Ltd of Australia, *New
Idea* and *TV Week*, Australia. Founded
1978.

Syndicated International Network (SIN)

Unit 4, 2 Somerset Road, London N17 9EJ
tel 0181-808 8660 *fax* 0181-808 1821
e-mail 101457.1516@compuserve.com
Managing Director Marianne Lassen

Worldwide syndication of interview texts
and photos, primarily of music and cinema
artists. Unsolicited material always considered. Commission: 50%. Founded 1984.

Universal Pictorial Press & Agency Ltd

29-31 Saffron Hill, London EC1N 8FH
tel 0171-421 6000 *fax* 0171-421 6006
Managing Director T.R. Smith

Photographic news agency and picture
library: the UK's leading archive for British
and international personalities from 1944
to present. Digital archive from 1994 with
full ISDN facilities. Founded 1929.

UPI (UK) Ltd

4 Ingate Place, London SW8 3NS
tel 0171-579 0852 (news), 0171-579 0860 (admin),
0171-579 0879 (business development)
fax 0171-579 0871

Visual Humour

5 Greymouth Close, Stockton-on-Tees TS18 5LF
tel (01642) 581847/0121-705 4087
fax (01642) 581847
Contact Peter Dodsworth

Daily and weekly humorous cartoon
strips; also single panel cartoon features
(not single cartoons) for possible syndication in the UK and abroad. Picture
puzzles also considered. Submit photocopy samples only initially, with sae.
Founded 1984.

Worldwide Media Ltd

PO Box 3821, London NW2 4DQ
tel 0181-452 6241 *fax* 0181-452 7258
e-mail wm@icr1.demon.co.uk
Director Robert Wallis

Specialises in unusual, often bizarre, features for the international magazine market. Purchases outright text and photos.
Write or fax ideas first. Founded 1995.

Yaffa Syndicate Pty Ltd

17-21 Bellevue Street, Surry Hills, NSW 2010,
Australia
tel (02) 9213-8209 *fax* (02) 9281-2750

Books

Submitting material

Each year, thousands of manuscripts are submitted to publishers by hopeful authors but only a small proportion are accepted for publication. Some manuscripts are needlessly rejected either because they were sent to the wrong publisher, or because the publisher's submission procedure was not followed. We give here some guidelines to consider before submitting a manuscript.

First of all, choose the right publisher. It is a waste of time and money to send the manuscript of a novel to a publisher who publishes no fiction, or poetry to one who publishes no verse. By studying the entries in the *Yearbook*, examining publishers' lists of publications, or by looking for the names of suitable publishers in the relevant sections in libraries and bookshops, you will find the names of several publishers which might be interested in seeing your material.

Secondly, approach the publisher in the way they prefer. Many publishers will not accept unsolicited material – you must enquire first if they would be willing to read the whole manuscript. A few publishers are prepared to speak on the telephone, allowing you to describe, briefly, the work on offer. Most prefer a preliminary letter; and many publishers, particularly of fiction, will only see material submitted through a literary agent. It has to be said that some publishing houses, the larger ones in particular, may well employ all three methods!

Enclose a synopsis of the work, and two or three sample chapters, with your preliminary letter, plus return postage (International Reply Coupons if you are writing from outside the country or if you are submitting material from the UK to the Irish Republic). Writers have been known to send out such letters in duplicated form, an approach unlikely to stimulate a publisher's interest. Remember, also, that whilst every reasonable care will be taken of material in the publishers' possession, responsibility cannot be accepted if material is lost or damaged. Never send your only copy of the manuscript. For more information, see *Preparing and submitting a manuscript* on page 551. An alphabetical listing of publishers' names and addresses follows on page 157. For classified lists, see below.

Fiction

See page 226 for a list of *Publishers of fiction*, by fiction genre. A full list of *Literary agents* starts on page 350.

Poetry

Publishers which consider poetry for adults are listed in *Publishers of poetry* on page 290. See also the article *Poetry into print* on page 279 and *Poetry organisations* on page 284.

Children's books

The market for children's books is considered in *Writing and illustrating children's books* on page 256 and is followed by a list of *Children's book publishers and packagers* on page 260, which includes publishers of poetry for children. A list of *Literary agents for children's books* is on page 369.

Small presses

It is beyond the scope of the *Yearbook* to list all the many smaller publishers which have either a limited output, or that specialise in poetry, avant-garde or other fringe publishing. We include details of some of the better-known small poetry houses but for a comprehensive listing refer to *Small Presses & Little Magazines in the UK and Ireland* (available from the Stationery Office Oriel Bookshop, The Friary, Cardiff CF1 4AA *tel* (01222) 395548.

Self-publishing

Authors are strongly advised not to pay for the publication of their work. A reputable firm of publishers will undertake publication at its own expense, except possibly for works of an academic nature. See *Doing it on your own* on page 266 for an introduction to self-publishing, *Vanity publishing* on page 270, and *Publishing agreements* on page 625.

See also ...

Book publishers UK and Ireland

*Member of the Publishers Association or Scottish Publishers Association
†Member of the Irish Book Publishers' Association

AA Publishing*

Automobile Association, Fanum House,
Basingstoke, Hants RG21 2EA
tel (01256) 20123 *fax* (01256) 22575
web site http://www.theaa.co.uk
Managing Director John Howard, *Marketing and International Sales Director* S.J. Mesquita,
Editorial Manager Michael Buttler

Travel, atlases, maps, leisure interests, including Baedeker, Essential, Thomas Cook and Explorer Travel Guides. Founded 1979.

Abacus – see Little, Brown and Company (UK)*

ABC-Clio Ltd

(formerly Clio Press Ltd)
Old Clarendon Ironworks,
35A Great Clarendon Street,
Oxford OX2 6AT
tel (01865) 311350 *fax* (01865) 311358
e-mail tsloggett@abc-clio.ltd
web site http://www.abc-clio.com
Directors Tony Sloggett (managing), Bob Neville (UK editorial and production)

General and academic reference: history, art, photography, mythology, literature, ethnic studies; bibliography. Publishes *World Bibliographical Series* (comprehensive guides to individual countries), *World Photographers Reference Series*, *The Clio Montessori Series*, *International Organisations Series* (annotated bibliographies), *Electronic Library* (CD-Roms of abstracting services in modern art, American studies and history). Subsidiary of ABC-CLIO Inc. Founded 1971.

Absolute Press

Scarborough House, 29 James Street West,
Bath BA1 2BT
tel (01225) 316013 *fax* (01225) 445836
e-mail sales@absolutepress.demon.co.uk

Publisher Jon Croft, *Directors* Amanda Hawkins (sales), Bronwen Douglas (marketing)

General list: cookery, food-related topics, wine, lifestyle, travel. Streetwise maps, accordian fold, and laminated city maps. No fiction. *Outlines* is a series of monographs on gay and lesbian artists. No unsolicited MSS. Founded 1979.

Academic Press – see Harcourt Brace & Co. Ltd*

Academy Editions – acquired by Wiley Europe Ltd

Access Press – see HarperCollins Publishers*

Ace Books – see Age Concern Books

Acorn Editions – see James Clarke & Co. Ltd*

Actinic Press – see Cressrelles Publishing Co. Ltd

Addison Wesley Longman Ltd*

Edinburgh Gate, Harlow, Essex CM20 2JE
tel (01279) 623623 *fax* (01279) 431059
e-mail enq.order@awl.co.uk
web site http://www.awl.co.uk
Chairman/Chief Executive Peter Jovanovich,
Directors Steve Dowling, T.C. Davy

Addison Wesley Longman was established in 1995 with the merger of Longman and Addison-Wesley, both Pearson companies. It publishes materials for pupils and students from nursery-school to post-graduate level globally.

Adlard Coles Nautical – see A & C Black (Publishers) Ltd*

Adlib – former imprint of Scholastic Children's Books*

Age Concern Books

(formerly Ace Books)
Age Concern England, 1268 London Road,
London SW16 4ER
tel 0181-679 8000 *fax* 0181-679 6069
e-mail books@ace.org.uk
Publisher Richard Holloway, *Marketing* Michael
Addison

Health and care, advice, finance, geron-
tology. Founded 1973.

Airlife Publishing Ltd

101 Longden Road, Shrewsbury,
Shropshire SY3 9EB
tel (01743) 235651 *fax* (01743) 232944
Directors Alastair Simpson (chairman and
managing), Robert Pooley, Andrew Johnston
(sales), John Gibbs, Peter Holmes (finance)

Aviation, technical and general, military.
Founded 1976.

Swan Hill Press (imprint)
Managing Editor P. Coles

Natural history, wildlife, arts, travel,
equestrian, fishing, country sports and
pursuits.

Waterline Books (imprint)
Managing Editor P. Coles

Sailing.

Aladdin/Watts – see The Watts Publishing Group*

Ian Allan Ltd

Riverdene, Molesey Road, Hersham,
Surrey KT12 4RG
tel (01932) 266600 *fax* (01932) 266601
Publishing Manager Peter Waller

Transport: railways, aircraft, shipping,
road; naval and military history; reference books and magazines; sport and
walking guides; no fiction.

George Allen & Unwin Publishers Ltd – acquired by HarperCollins Publishers*

J.A. Allen & Co. Ltd

1-4 Lower Grosvenor Place, Buckingham Palace
Road, London SW1W 0EL
tel 0171-834 0090/5606 *fax* 0171-976 5836
e-mail allen_books
Chief Executive Caroline Burt

Specialist publishers of books on the
horse and equestrianism including
bloodstock breeding, racing, polo, dres-
sage, horse care, carriage driving, breeds,
veterinary and farriery. Technical books
usually commissioned but willing to

consider any serious, specialist MSS on
the horse and related subjects. No fiction
or autobiography. Founded 1926.

W.H. Allen – acquired by Virgin Publishing Ltd

Allen Lane – see Penguin UK*

Allison & Busby Ltd

114 New Cavendish Street, London W1M 7FD
tel 0171-636 2942 *fax* 0171-323 2023
e-mail aandbuk@aol.com
Publisher Peter Day, *Publicity and Marketing*
Susan Herbert, *Editorial* Vanessa Unwin, David
Shelley

Biography and memoirs, and new crime,
fiction, Spanish language translations,
writers' guides. Unsolicited MSS welcome (synopsis and 2 sample chapters
initially) but sae essential.

The Alpha Press – see Sussex Academic Press

AN Publications

PO Box 23, Sunderland SR4 6DG
tel 0191-567 3589 *fax* 0191-564 1600
e-mail edit@anpubs.demon.co.uk
Programme Director Julie Crawshaw

Model contracts for visual and applied
artists covering residencies, permissions,
exhibitions and agents. Founded 1980.

Anchor – see Transworld Publishers Ltd*

Andersen Press Ltd

20 Vauxhall Bridge Road, London SW1V 2SA
tel 0171-840 8700 (editorial) *fax* 0171-233 6263
e-mail 101370.533@compuserve.com
Managing Director/Publisher Klaus Flugge,
Directors Philip Durrance, Janice Thomson
(editorial), Joëlle Flugge (company secretary)

Children's picture books, novelties and
fiction (send synopsis and full MS with
sae); no short stories. International co-
productions. Founded 1976.

Andromeda Oxford Ltd

11-15 The Vineyard, Abingdon,
Oxon OX14 3PX
tel (01235) 550296 *fax* (01235) 550330
e-mail books@andromeda.co.uk
web site http://www.andromeda.co.uk
Directors Mark Ritchie (managing), Graham
Bateman (publishing), Clive Sparling
(production), Andrew Flatt (finance)

Publishes adult and junior reference
books: history, science, natural history,

medicine; children's information and activity books. Founded 1986.

Anness Publishing
88-89 Blackfriars Road, London SE1 8HA
tel 0171-401 2077 *fax* 0171-633 9499
Managing Director Paul Anness, *Publisher* Joanna Lorenz
Practical illustrated books on crafts, cookery and gardening, and children's non-fiction. Founded 1989.
Hermes House (imprint)
Illustrated promotional and bargain books on practical subjects.
Lorenz Books (imprint)
Lifestyle, cookery, crafts, gardening, and all practical illustrated subjects.

Antique Collectors' Club
5 Church Street, Woodbridge,
Suffolk IP12 1DS
tel (01394) 385501 *fax* (01394) 384434
Managing Director Diana Steel
Fine art, antiques, gardening and garden history, architecture. Founded 1966.

Anvil Books/The Children's Press†
45 Palmerston Road, Dublin 6, Republic of Ireland
tel (01) 4973628 *fax* (01) 4968263
Directors Rena Dardis (managing), Margaret Dardis (editorial)
Anvil: history, biography; Children's Press: adventure, fiction, ages 9-14. Founded 1964.

Anvil Press Poetry
Neptune House, 70 Royal Hill,
London SE10 8RF
tel 0181-469 3033 *fax* 0181-469 3363
e-mail anvil@cix.co.uk
Director Peter Jay
Poetry. Submissions only with sae. Founded 1968.

Apple Press
The Fitzpatrick Building, 188-194 York Way,
London N7 9QR
tel 0171-700 2929 *fax* 0171-609 6695
Publisher Oliver Salzmann, *Sales Director* Stuart Henderson
Imprint of **Quarto Publishing plc**, book packagers. Leisure, domestic and craft pursuits; cookery, gardening, sport, transport, militaria, fine and decorative art, children's. Founded 1984.

Appletree Press Ltd†
19-21 Alfred Street, Belfast BT2 8DL
tel (01232) 243074 *fax* (01232) 246756
e-mail frontdesk@appletree.ie
web site http://www.irelandseye.ie
Director John Murphy
Gift books, biography, cookery, guide-books, history, Irish interest, literary criticism, music, photographic, social studies, sport, travel. Founded 1974.

Arc Publications
Nanholme Mill, Shaw Wood Road, Todmorden,
Lancs. OL14 6DA
tel (01706) 812338 *fax* (01706) 818948
Partners Rosemary Jones, Tony Ward (general editor), Angela Jarman, *Associate Editors* Michael Hulse (international), David Morley (UK)
Poetry. MSS with sae only.

Arcadia Books Ltd
15-16 Nassau Street, London W1N 7RE
tel/fax 0171-436 9898
Directors Gary Pulsifer (managing), J.M. Bull (editorial)
Original paperback fiction, fiction in translation, autobiography, biography, travel, gender studies, gay books. No unsolicited MSS. Enquiry letters must include sae. Founded 1996.

Architectural Press – see Reed Educational and Professional Publishing Ltd

Arden Shakespeare – see Thomas Nelson & Sons Ltd*

Arkana – see Penguin UK*

Arms & Armour Press – see Cassell plc

E.J. Arnold Publishing Division – acquired by Thomas Nelson & Sons Ltd*

Edward Arnold – now Arnold, see Hodder Headline plc*

Arrow Books Ltd – see Random House UK Ltd*

Art Trade Press Ltd
9 Brockhampton Road, Havant, Hants PO9 1NU
tel (01705) 484943
Editorial Director J.M. Curley
Publishers of *Who's Who in Art*.

Ashgate Publishing Ltd
Gower House, Croft Road, Aldershot,
Hants GU11 3HR
tel (01252) 331551 *fax* (01252) 344405
e-mail gower@cityscape.co.uk
Chairman Nigel Farrow

Editors Sarah Markham (social sciences), Kate Trew (social work and public service), John Hindley (aviation management), Alec MacAulay (history, economic and general), Pamela Edwardes (art and art history), Rachel Lynch (music and literary studies)

Publishes a wide range of academic research in the social sciences and humanities, and professional practice in the management of business and public services. Founded 1967.
Dartmouth (imprint)
Editor John Irwin
Law and legal studies.
Gower (imprint)
Editor Julia Scott
Business and management.
Variorum (imprint)
Editor John Smedley
History.

Ashmolean Museum Publications
Beaumont Street, Oxford OX1 2PH
tel (01865) 278009/278010 *fax* (01865) 278018
web site http://www.ashmol.ox.ac.uk/
Publications Officer Ian Charlton
Fine and applied art, archaeology, history, numismatics. Founded 1972.

Aslib
(The Association for Information Management)
Staple Hall, Stone House Court,
London EC3A 7PB
tel 0171-903 0000 *fax* 0171-903 0011
e-mail pubs@aslib.co.uk
web site http://www.aslib.co.uk/
Head of Publications Sarah Blair
Information management, librarianship, information science, general reference, computing. Founded 1924.

Aspire Publishing
8 Betony Rise, Exeter,
Devon EX2 5RR
and 9 Wimpole Street, London W1M 8LB
tel (01392) 252516 *fax* (01392) 252517
e-mail aspire@xcentrex.force9.net
Directors Patricia Kay (managing and financial), Alexander Kay (marketing)
Fiction (all genres), autobiography and biography. Founded 1997.
Greenzone Publishing (imprint)
tel 0171-637 1065
Non-fiction, especially political. No unsolicited MSS. Send sae for guidelines.

Associated University Presses – see
Golden Cockerel Press

The Athlone Press Ltd
1 Park Drive, London NW11 7SG
tel 0181-458 0888 *fax* 0181-201 8115
e-mail athlonepress@btinternet.com
Directors Brian Southam (chairman), Doris Southam (managing), Tristan Palmer (editorial), Gill Davies
Anthropology, archaeology, architecture, art, economics, film studies, history, Japan, language, law, literature, medical, music, oriental, philosophy, politics, psychology, religion, science, sociology, cultural studies. Founded 1949.

Atlantic Europe Publishing Co. Ltd
Greys Court Farm, Greys Court,
Henley on Thames, Oxon RG4 4PG
tel (01491) 628188 *fax* (01491) 628189
e-mail info@atlanticeurope.com
web sites http://www.AtlanticEurope.com
http://www.CurriculumVisions.com
Directors Dr B.J. Knapp, D.L.R. McCrae
Children's colour information books: science, geography, history, design and technology, mathematics. Associate company: **Earthscape Editions** (see Book packagers). Founded 1989.

Attic Press†
Crawford Business Park, Crosses Green, Cork, Republic of Ireland
tel (021) 321725 *fax* (021) 315329
e-mail s.wilbourne@ucc.ie
web site http://www.iol.ie/~atticirl/
Publisher Sara Wilbourne
Books by and about women in the areas of social and political comment, fiction, women's studies, humour, reference guides and handbooks. Imprint of **Cork University Press**. Founded 1984.
Basement Press (imprint)
Fiction and non-fiction by men and women.

Éditions Aubrey Walter – see GMP Publishers Ltd

Aureus Publishing
144 Marlborough Road, Cardiff CF2 5BZ
tel/fax (01222) 455200
e-mail meurynhughes@aureus.co.uk
web site http://www.aureus.co.uk
Proprietor Meuryn Hughes
Fiction, education, fine art, autobiography, sport, religion; also publishes music. Founded 1993.

Aurum Press Ltd
25 Bedford Avenue, London WC1B 3AT

tel 0171-637 3225 *fax* 0171-580 2469
Directors André Deutsch (chairman), Bill McCreadie (managing), Piers Burnett (editorial), Sheila Murphy (editorial), Ken Banerji
General, illustrated and non-illustrated adult non-fiction: biography and memoirs, visual arts, film, home interest, travel. Founded 1977.

Award Publications Ltd
1st Floor, 27 Longford Street, London NW1 3DZ
tel 0171-388 7800 *fax* 0171-388 7887
Managing Director Ron Wilkinson
Children's books: full colour picture story books; early learning, information and activity books. Founded 1954.

Bernard Babani (Publishing) Ltd
The Grampians, Shepherds Bush Road, London W6 7NF
tel 0171-603 2581/7296 *fax* 0171-603 8203
Directors S. Babani, M.H. Babani BSc(Eng)
Practical handbooks on radio, electronics and computing.

Baillière Tindall Ltd – see Harcourt Brace & Co. Ltd*

Duncan Baird Publishers
Sixth Floor, Castle House, 75-76 Wells Street, London W1P 3RE
tel 0171-323 2229 *fax* 0171-580 5692
Directors Duncan Baird (managing), Bob Saxton (editorial), Roger Walton (art), Alex Mitchell (international sales), Nick Foster (financial)
Non-fiction, illustrated reference. Founded 1994.

The Bankers' Almanac – see Reed Business Information

Bantam – see Transworld Publishers Ltd*

Barefoot Books Ltd
PO Box 95, Kingswood, Bristol BS30 5BH
tel 0117-932 8885 *fax* 0117-932 8881
e-mail sales@barefoot-books.com
web site http://www.barefoot-books.com
Publisher Tessa Strickland
Children's picture books: myth, legend, fairytale. No unsolicited MSS. Founded 1993.

Barrie & Jenkins – see Random House UK Ltd*

Bartholomew – see HarperCollins Publishers*

Basement Press – see Attic Press†

B.T. Batsford Ltd
583 Fulham Road, London SW6 5BY
tel 0171-471 1100 *fax* 0171-471 1101
web site http://www.batsford.com
Chairman Gerard Mizrahi, *Chief Executive* Jules Perel, *Director* R.E. Huggins (managing director of Batsford Distribution), *Managers* Naomi Roth (editorial), Alan Ritchie (sales), John Andrews (finance), Cathy Slater (foreign rights/export)
Archaeology, architecture, bridge, building, art techniques, film, chess, fashion, costume, craft, pottery, needlecraft, lace, embroidery, horticulture, business and personal finance, graphic design, woodworking. Founded 1843.

BBC Worldwide Ltd*
Woodlands, 80 Wood Lane, London W12 0TT
tel 0181-576 2000
BBC Worldwide
fax 0181-576 2628
Head of Books Tracey Smith
Books tied in to BBC television and radio programmes of all subjects.
BBC Radio Collection
tel 0181-576 2230 *fax* 0181-576 3851
Publisher Jan Paterson
Audio cassettes and CDs of BBC Radio and Television comedy, readings and dramatised serials for adults and children.
Network Books (imprint of BBC Worldwide)
Range of non-fiction titles tied in to non-BBC television programmes.
BBC Children's Publishing
Head of Children's Books Helen Jacobs
Range of fiction and non-fiction titles tied in to BBC television programmes.

Belitha Press
London House, Great Eastern Wharf, Parkgate Road, London SW11 4NQ
tel 0171-978 6330 *fax* 0171-223 4936
Contact Peter Osborn
Illustrated children's non-fiction for international co-editions: art, atlases, geography, history, natural history, reference, science. Subsidiary of C&B Publishing plc. Founded 1980.

Bell & Hyman Ltd – acquired by HarperCollins Publishers*

Bellew Publishing Co. Ltd
The Nightingale Centre, 8 Balham Hill, London SW12 9EA

tel 0181-673 5611 *fax* 0181-675 2142
Chairman Ian McCorquodale, *Managing Director* Ib Bellew

Sociology, politics, art and art criticism, some fiction, poetry. Founded 1983.

David Bennett Books Ltd
15 High Street, St Albans, Herts. AL3 4ED
tel (01727) 855878 *fax* (01727) 864085
Publisher David Bennett, *Managing Director* Peter Osborn

Highly illustrated children's fiction and non-fiction; baby books, interactive play books and gift books for the young. Subsidiary of C&B Publishing plc. Founded 1989.

Berg Publishers
150 Cowley Road, Oxford OX4 1JJ
tel (01865) 245104 *fax* (01865) 791165
e-mail enquiry@berg.demon.co.uk
Editorial Director Kathryn Earle

Social anthropology, cultural studies, dress and fashion studies, European studies, politics and economics, literature. Founded 1983.

Berghahn Books Ltd
3 Newtec Place, Magdalen Road, Oxford OX4 1RE
tel (01865) 250011 *fax* (01865) 250056
e-mail berghahnuk@aol.com
Publisher/Managing Director Dr Marion Berghahn

Academic publishers in humanities: history (especially German and European), politics and economics, anthropology, Jewish studies, cultural studies, gender studies. Founded 1993.

Berkswell Publishing Co. Ltd
PO Box 420, Warminster, Wilts. BA12 9XB
tel/fax (01985) 840189
Directors J.N.G. Stidolph, S.A. Abbott

Books of local interest in Wessex, field sports, royalty. Ideas and MSS welcome. Also provide editorial, design, research, picture research, exhibition organisation and design.

Berlitz Publishing Co. Ltd
4th Floor, 9-13 Grosvenor Street, London W1X 9FB
tel 0171-518 8300 *fax* 0171-518 8310
Managing Director Roger Kirkpatrick

Travel, language and related multimedia. Founded 1970.

Bible Society
Stonehill Green, Westlea, Swindon, Wilts. SN5 7DG
tel (01793) 418100 *fax* (01793) 418118
e-mail info@bfbs.org.uk

Bibles, testaments, portions and selections in English and over 2000 other languages; also books and audiovisual material on use of Bible for personal, education and church groups.

Clive Bingley Ltd – see Library Association Publishing Ltd*

Birnbaum – see HarperCollins Publishers*

A & C Black (Publishers) Ltd*
35 Bedford Row, London WC1R 4JH
tel 0171-242 0946 *fax* 0171-831 8478
e-mail enquiries@acblack.co.uk
Chairman and Joint Managing Director Charles Black, *Joint Managing Director* Jill Coleman, *Directors* Paul Langridge (rights), Janet Murphy (Adlard Coles Nautical), Terry Rouelett (distribution), Oscar Heini (production), Robert Kirk (Christopher Helm, ornithology), Susan Kodicek (sales)

Children's and educational books (including music) for 3-15 years (preliminary enquiry appreciated – fiction guidelines available on request); ceramics, calligraphy, drama (*New Mermaid* series), fishing, ornithology, reference (*Who's Who*), sport, theatre, travel (*Blue Guides*), books for writers. Subsidiary of A & C Black plc. Founded 1807.

Adlard Coles Nautical (imprint)
Editorial Director Janet Murphy
Nautical.

Christopher Helm (imprint)
Editorial Director Robert Kirk
Ornithology.

The Herbert Press (imprint)
Visual arts.

Black Ace Books*
PO Box 6557, Forfar DD8 2YS
tel (01307) 465096 *fax* (01307) 465494
Publisher Hunter Steele, *Art, Publicity and Sales* Boo Wood

New fiction, Scottish and general; new editions of outstanding recent fiction. Non-fiction: biography, history, psychology and philosophy. No unsolicited MSS or submissions from outside the UK. Send only: one-page covering letter, one-page synopsis, one full page of text and large sae. Imprints: Black Ace Books, Black Ace Paperbacks. Founded 1991.

Black Butterfly – see Writers & Readers Ltd*

Black Lace – see Virgin Publishing Ltd

Black Swan – see Transworld Publishers Ltd*

Blackie Academic and Professional – acquired by Wolters Kluwer Group of Companies

Blackstaff Press Ltd[†]
3 Galway Park, Dundonald BT16 0AN
tel (01232) 487161 *fax* (01232) 489552
e-mail books@blkstaff.dnet.co.uk
Managing Director Anne Tannahill
Fiction, poetry, biography, history, politics, natural history, humour, education. Founded 1971.

Blackstone Press Ltd
9-15 Aldine Street, London W12 8AW
tel 0181-740 2277 *fax* 0181-743 2292
Directors Alistair MacQueen (managing), Heather Saward (editorial), Jeremy Stein (sales & marketing)
Law books for practitioners and students. Contact Alistair MacQueen with ideas, or send MSS. Founded 1988.

The Blackwater Press[†] – see Folens Publishing Company

Blackwell Publishers*
(Basil Blackwell Ltd)
108 Cowley Road, Oxford OX4 1JF
tel (01865) 791100 *fax* (01865) 791347
Directors Nigel Blackwell (chairman), René Olivieri (managing), Philip Carpenter, Sue Corbett, Mark Houlton, John Davey, Stephan Chambers, Carolyn Dougherty
Economics, education (academic), geography, history, industrial relations, linguistics, literature and criticism, politics, psychology, social anthropology, social policy and administration, sociology, theology, business studies, professional, law, reference, feminism, information technology, philosophy. Founded 1922.
InfoSource International (division)
InfoSource House, 54 Marston Street, Oxford OX4 1JU
tel (01865) 244068 *fax* (01865) 791347
Directors René Olivieri, Mark Houlton
Computer-based training, skills assessment and instructor manuals. Specialist areas include: PC applications (e.g. Microsoft Excel, WordPerfect, Lotus 1-2-3), networks and Internet.
Shakespeare Head Press (imprint)
Finely printed books; scholarly works.

Blackwell Science Ltd*
Osney Mead, Oxford OX2 0EL
tel (01865) 206206 *fax* (01865) 721205
web site http://www.blackwell-science.com
Chairman Nigel Blackwell, *Managing Director* Robert Campbell, *Directors* Jonathan Conibear, Peter Saugman (editorial), Martin Wilkinson (finance), John Strange (production), Bill Gibson (Boston)
Medicine, nursing, dentistry, veterinary medicine, life sciences, earth sciences, chemistry, professional including construction, allied health. Founded 1939.

Blake Publishing
(incorporating Smith Gryphon Ltd)
3 Bramber Court, 2 Bramber Road, London W14 9PB
tel 0171-381 0666 *fax* 0171-381 6868
Chairman David Blake, *Managing Director* John Blake, *Deputy Managing Director* Rosie Ries, *Executive Editor* Adam Parfitt, *Production Editor* Charlotte Helyar
Popular fiction and non-fiction, including biographies and true crime. No unsolicited fiction. Founded 1991.

Blandford Press – see Cassell plc

Bloodaxe Books Ltd
PO Box 1SN,
Newcastle upon Tyne NE99 1SN
tel (01830) 520590 *fax* (01830) 520596
e-mail editor@bloodaxebooks.demon.co.uk
Directors Neil Astley, Simon Thirsk
Poetry, literary criticism. Founded 1978.

Bloodlines – see The Do-Not Press

Bloomsbury Publishing plc*
38 Soho Square, London W1V 5DF
tel 0171-494 2111 *fax* 0171-434 0151
web site http://www.bloomsbury.com
Chairman and Managing Director Nigel Newton, *Directors* David Reynolds (deputy managing and publishing), Liz Calder (publishing), Alan Wherry (publishing), Kathy Rooney (reference), Sarah Beal (marketing), Becky Shaw (publicity), Ruth Logan (rights), Penny Edwards (production), Matthew Hamilton (paperbacks), Sarah Odedina (children's), Colin Adams (finance)
Fiction, biography, illustrated, reference, travel, children's, trade paperback and mass market paperback. Founded 1986.

Boatswain Press Ltd*
Dudley House, 12 North Street, Emsworth, Hants PO10 7DQ
tel (01243) 377977 *fax* (01243) 379136
Directors Piers Mason, Anthea Mason
Yachting titles, nautical almanacs.

Bodley Head – see Random House UK Ltd*

Bodley Head Children's – see Random House UK Ltd*

Bounty – see Reed Books

Bowker-Saur
Maypole House, Maypole Road, East Grinstead, West Sussex RH19 1HU
tel (01342) 330100 *fax* (01342) 330191
e-mail custserv@bowker-saur.com
web site http://www.bowker-saur.com/service/
Group Publishing Director Gerard Dummett, *Managing Director* Charles Halpin
Bibliographies, trade and reference directories, library and information science, electronic publishing, abstracts and indexes. Division of **Reed Business Information**.
Headland Business Information (imprint)
Business information newsletters, journals and directories.

Boxtree Ltd*
25 Eccleston Place, London SW1W 9NF
tel 0171-881 8000 *fax* 0171-881 8001
Publishing Director Adrian Sington, *Editorial Directors* Susanna Wadeson, Clare Hulton
TV and film tie-ins (adult and children's non-fiction); illustrated and general non-fiction; mass market paperbacks linked to TV, film, rock and sporting events; humour. Imprint of **Macmillan Publishers Ltd**. Founded 1986.

Marion Boyars Publishers Ltd*
24 Lacy Road, London SW15 1NL
tel 0181-788 9522 *fax* 0181-789 8122
Directors Marion Boyars, Arthur Boyars
Belles-lettres and criticism, fiction, sociology, psychology, feminism, history of ideas, music, drama, cinema, dance, biography.

Boydell & Brewer Ltd
PO Box 9, Woodbridge, Suffolk IP12 3DF
Medieval studies, history, literature, archaeology, art history. No unsolicited MSS. Founded 1969.

BPP (Letts Educational) Ltd
(trading as Letts Educational)
Aldine House, Aldine Place, London W12 8AW
tel 0181-7402266 *fax* 0181-743 8451
Managing Director Jonathan Harris, *Publishing Directors* Richard Carr, Edward Peppitt
Revision and exam preparation, and course books for the school, college and home study markets. Founded 1979.

Brandon Book Publishers Ltd – see Mount Eagle Publications Ltd[†]

Bradt Publications
41 Nortoft Road, Chalfont St Peter, Gerrards Cross, Bucks. SL9 0LA
tel/fax (01494) 873478
e-mail bradtpublications@compuserve.com
Managing Director Hilary Bradt
Guides for the adventurous traveller who seeks off-beat places and 'the dreamer who would like to travel there but never will'. Bradt series: *Country Guides, Hiking Guides, Rail Guides, Road Guides, Wildlife Guides*. Founded 1973.

Brandon Book Publishers Ltd – see Mount Eagle Publications Ltd

Brassey's (UK) Ltd
583 Fulham Road, London SW6 5BY
tel 0171-471 1100 *fax* 0171-471 1101
Editorial Caroline Bolton
Defence and national security, international relations, weapons technology, military affairs, military biography, military history, reference. Publisher to the Centre for Defence Studies. Subsidiary of **B.T. Batsford Ltd**. Founded 1886.
Conway Maritime Press (imprint)
Maritime and naval history, ship modelling.
Putnam Aeronautical Books (imprint)
Technical and historical aviation reference.

Nicholas Brealey Publishing Ltd*
36 John Street, London WC1N 2AT
tel 0171-430 0224 *fax* 0171-404 8311
web site http://www.nbrealey-books.com
Managing Director Nicholas Brealey
Business, management, training, economics, Asia, international affairs. Founded 1992.

Breedon Books Publishing Co. Ltd
44 Friar Gate, Derby DE1 1DA
tel (01332) 384235 *fax* (01332) 292755
Directors Anton Rippon (chairman and editorial), Patricia Rippon, Graham Hales
Autobiographies, biographies, sports, heritage, local history. Preliminary letter essential. Founded 1981.

Brewin Books
Doric House, 56 Alcester Road, Studley, Warks. B80 7LG
tel (01527) 854228/853624 *fax* (01527) 852746

Publishing Director K.A.F. Brewin

Non-fiction: Midland regional history (Birmingham, Warwickshire, Worcs. etc), transport history, biography (with Midlands connection). Founded 1976.

Brilliant Publications*
The Old School Yard, Leighton Road, Northall, Dunstable, Beds. LU6 2HA
tel (01525) 222844 *fax* (01525) 221250
e-mail brilliantpublications@compuserve.com
Managing Director Priscilla Hannaford

Books for teachers and others concerned with the education of 3-13 year-olds. Subjects covered include English, mathematics, science, geography and history. Founded 1993.

Brimax Books – see Reed Books

Bristol Classical Press – see Gerald Duckworth & Co. Ltd

British Academic Press – see I.B. Tauris & Co. Ltd

The British Library (Publications)*
Marketing & Publishing Office, Public Affairs, 96 Euston Road, London NW1 2DB
tel 0171-412 7704 *fax* 0171-412 7768
Director Jane Carr, *Managers* David Way (publishing), Anne Young (product development), Jenny McKinley (marketing)

Bibliography, book arts, music, maps, oriental, manuscript studies, history, literature, facsimiles, audio-visual, and multimedia CD-Rom. Founded 1973.

British Museum Press*
46 Bloomsbury Street, London WC1B 3QQ
tel 0171-323 1234 *fax* 0171-436 7315
Managing Director Patrick Wright, *Head of Publishing* Emma Way

Art history, archaeology, numismatics, history, oriental art and archaeology, horology. Division of The British Museum Company Ltd. Founded 1973.

Brockhampton Press – see Hodder Headline plc*

Brown, Son & Ferguson, Ltd*
4-10 Darnley Street, Glasgow G41 2SD
tel 0141-429 1234 (24 hours) *fax* 0141-420 1694
e-mail info@skipper.co.uk
web site http://www.skipper.co.uk
Editorial Director L. Ingram-Brown

Nautical books; Scottish poetry and plays; Scout, Cub Scout, Brownie Guide and Guide story books. Founded 1860.

Brown Wells & Jacobs Ltd
Foresters Hall, 25-27 Westow Street, London SE19 3RY
tel 0181-771 5115 *fax* 0181-771 9994
e-mail postmaster@popking.demon.co.uk
web site http://www.bwj.org
Managing Director Graham Brown

Children's non-fiction novelty and pop-ups. Founded 1979.

Bryntirion Press
(formerly Evangelical Press of Wales)
Bryntirion, Bridgend, Mid Glamorgan CF31 4DX
tel (01656) 655886 *fax* (01656) 656095
e-mail press@draco.uk.com
Chief Executive Gerallt Wyn Davies, *Managing Editor* David Kingdon

Theology and religion (in English and Welsh). Founded 1955.

Buildings of England – see Penguin UK*

Burns & Oates Ltd
(Publishers to the Holy See)
Wellwood, North Farm Road, Tunbridge Wells, Kent TN2 3DR
tel (01892) 510850 *fax* (01892) 515903
Director Charlotte de la Bedoyere

Theology, philosophy, spirituality, church history, Catholic interest, craft books with religious themes. Founded 1847.

Butterworth & Co. (Publishers) Ltd
Halsbury House, 35 Chancery Lane, London WC2A 1EL
tel 0171-400 2500 *fax* 0171-400 2842
e-mail neville.cusworth@butterworths.co.uk
Chairman and Chief Executive Neville Cusworth

Law, tax and accountancy publishing. Division of Reed Elsevier (UK) Ltd.
British and Irish Legal Division
Legal books, journals, loose leaf and electronic services; tax and accountancy books, journals and loose leaf and electronic services.

Butterworth Heinemann UK – see Reed Educational and Professional Publishing Ltd

Cadogan Guides
29 Berwick Street, London W1V 3RF
tel 0171-287 6555 *fax* 0171-734 1733
e-mail guides@cadogan.co.uk
Publisher Rachel Fielding

Travel guides. Founded 1982.

Calder Publications Ltd*
126 Cornwall Road, London SE1 8TQ
tel 0171-633 0599

Director John Calder

European, international and British fiction and plays, art, literary, music and social criticism, biography and autobiography, essays, humanities and social sciences, European classics. No unsolicited MSS. Inquiry letters must include an sae. Series include: *English National Opera Guides, New Paris Editions, Scottish Library, New Writing and Writers, Platform Books, Opera Library, Historical Perspectives.*

Calmann and King Ltd – see Laurence King Publishing*

Cambridge University Press*

The Edinburgh Building, Shaftesbury Road, Cambridge CB2 2RU
tel (01223) 312393 *fax* (01223) 315052
e-mail information@cup.cam.ac.uk
web site http://www.cup.cam.ac.uk
Chief Executive of the Press and University Printer Anthony K. Wilson MA, *Deputy Chief Executive and Managing Director (Publishing Division)* Jeremy Mynott MA, PhD

Anthropology and archaeology, art and architecture, astronomy, biological sciences, classical studies, computer science, earth sciences, economics, educational (primary, secondary, tertiary), educational software, engineering, film, English language teaching, history, language and literature, law, mathematics, medical sciences, music, oriental, philosophy, physical sciences, politics, psychology, reference, technology, social sciences, theology, religion. Journals (humanities, social sciences, science technology and medicine). The Bible and Prayer Book. Founded 1534.

Campbell Books – see Macmillan Publishers Ltd*

Canongate Books Ltd*

14 High Street, Edinburgh EH1 1TE
tel 0131-557 5111 *fax* 0131-557 5211
e-mail info@canongate.co.uk
web site http://www.canongate.co.uk/
Directors Jamie Byng, Hugh Andrew, Ronnie Shanks, Neville Moir

Adult general non-fiction and fiction: Canongate Classics, Kelpie Paperbacks (children's fiction), art, travel, Canongate Audio (audio books). Founded 1973.

Payback Press (imprint)
Publishing Director Jamie Byng
e-mail payback@canongate.co.uk

Afro-American and Jamaican culture: non-fiction, fiction, music, poetry, biography.

Rebel Inc. (imprint)
Publishing Director Jamie Byng, *Chief Editor* Kevin Williamson
e-mail rebelinc@canongate.co.uk
Counter cultural fiction and non-fiction.

The Canterbury Press Norwich

St Mary's Works, St Mary's Plain, Norwich, Norfolk NR3 3BH
tel (01603) 616563/612914 *fax* (01603) 624483
Chief Executive G.A. Knights, *Publisher* Christine Smith

Book publishing imprint of **Hymns Ancient and Modern Ltd**, music publishers. C of E doctrine, theology, history and associated topics, music and liturgy.

Jonathan Cape – see Random House UK Ltd*

Jonathan Cape Children's Books – see Random House UK Ltd*

Carcanet Press Ltd

4th Floor, Conavon Court,
12-16 Blackfriars Street,
Manchester M3 5BQ
tel 0161-834 8730 *fax* 0161-832 0084
e-mail pnr@carcanet.u-net.com
Director Michael Schmidt

Poetry, *Fyfield* series, translations. Founded 1969.

Carlton Books

20 St Anne's Court, Wardour Street,
London W1V 3AW
tel 0171-734 7338 *fax* 0171-434 1196/734 7371
e-mail editorial@carltonbooks.co.uk
Directors Jonathan Goodman (managing), John Maynard (operations), Piers Murray Hill (publishing), Russell Porter (design), Adrian Whitton (finance), Keith Allen-Jones (international sales), Alan Jessop (trade sales)

Popular music, sport, games, film, video, popular science, lifestyle, New Age, TV tie-ins, criminology. Founded 1992.

Cartermill International

Technology Centre, St Andrews,
Fife KY16 9EA
tel (01334) 477660 *fax* (01334) 477180
Managing Director M. Campbell

Print and electronic research and information management products and services on science, technology and industry; health and social care reference; business intelligence and current affairs. Member of FT Group, Pearson plc.

Frank Cass & Co. Ltd
Newbury House, 890-900 Eastern Avenue,
Newbury Park, Ilford, Essex IG2 7HH
tel 0181-599 8866 *fax* 0181-599 0984
Directors Frank Cass (managing), Stewart Cass,
A.E. Cass, M.P. Zaidner

History, economic and social history,
military and strategic studies, politics,
international affairs, development studies, African studies, Middle East studies,
law, business management and academic
journals in all of these fields.

Vallentine Mitchell (imprint)
Jewish interest. Founded 1958.

Woburn Press (imprint)
Educational.

Cassell plc
Wellington House, 125 Strand, London WC2R 0BB
tel 0171-420 5555 *fax* 0171-240 7261
e-mail cassell.poole@virgin.net
web site http://cassell.co.uk
Chairman and Chief Executive Philip Sturrock

Founded 1848.

Arms & Armour Press (imprint)
Director Alison Goff
Military history (land, sea, air, weapon-
ry), military reference, military adventure
non-fiction, modern defence/intelligence.

Blandford Press (imprint)
Director Alison Goff
Aviculture, history, hobbies, music, nat-
ural history, practical handbooks, sport,
New Age/mind, body, spirit.

Cassell (general imprint)
Editorial Director Alison Goff
Cookery, lifestyle, gardening, word reference, art and craft, popular science, current affairs.

Cassell (general reference list)
Commissioning Editor Nigel Wilcockson
General interest reference.

Cassell (academic reference list)
Director Janet Joyce
Foreign language, humanities, social sci-
ence reference.

Cassell (professional lists)
Director Ruth McCurry
Education, hotel and catering management, psychology and counselling, business and professional reference.

Cassell (contemporary studies lists)
Director Janet Joyce
Gender studies, global issues, film
studies.

Geoffrey Chapman (imprint)
Director Ruth McCurry
Religion and theology, particularly
Roman Catholic.

Victor Gollancz Ltd (imprint)
Director Jane Blackstock
Biography and autobiography, current
affairs, history, travel; fiction, literary fiction, crime, science fiction, fantasy. In
association with Peter Crawley: *Master
Bridge Series*. No unsolicited submissions.

Indigo (imprint)
Editorial Director Mike Petty
Literary fiction and general non-fiction.
No unsolicited submissions.

Leicester University Press (imprint)
Director Janet Joyce
Academic books, especially medieval
history, museum studies, political
theory.

Mansell Publishing (imprint)
Director Janet Joyce
Bibliographies in all academic subject
areas and monographs in urban and
regional planning, Islamic studies,
librarianship, history.

Mowbray (imprint)
Director Ruth McCurry
Religion and theology, both Anglican and
non-denominational.

New Orchard Editions (imprint)
Director Finbarr McCabe
Antiques and collecting, children's,
cookery, wines and spirits, gardening,
history and antiquarian, illustrated and
fine editions, military and war, natural
history, reference and dictionaries, transport, travel and topography.

Pinter (imprint)
Director Janet Joyce
Academic and professional publishers
specialising in social sciences including
international relations, politics, economics, new technology, linguistics, communications and religious studies.

Vista (imprint)
Editorial Director Humphrey Price
Popular fiction and commercial non-fic-
tion. No unsolicited submissions.

Ward Lock (imprint)
Director Alison Goff
Cookery, gardening, equestrian and out-
door pursuits, popular reference books,
DIY, health.

Wisley Handbooks (imprint)
Trade Publisher Barry Holmes
Gardening.

Castle House Publications Ltd
3 Linden Close, Tunbridge Wells, Kent TN4 8HH
tel (01892) 539606 *fax* (01892) 517773
Director D. Reinders
Medical. Founded 1973.

Kyle Cathie Ltd
20 Vauxhall Bridge Road, London SW1V 2SA
tel 0171-840 8400 *fax* 0171-821 9258
Publisher and Managing Director Kyle Cathie
Natural history, health, beauty, food and
drink; craft; gardening; reference, style.
Founded 1990.

Catholic Truth Society
40-46 Harleyford Road, London SE11 5AY
tel 0171-640 0042 *fax* 0171-640 0046
Chairman Rt Rev. Peter Smith DCL, LLB, *General
Secretary* Fergal Martin LLB, LLM
General books of Roman Catholic and
Christian interest, bibles, prayer books
and pamphlets of doctrinal, historical,
devotional or social interest. MSS of
11,000-15,000 words with up to 6 illustrations considered for publication as
pamphlets. Founded 1868.

Cavendish Publishing Ltd*
The Glass House, Wharton Street,
London WC1X 9PX
tel 0171-278 8000 *fax* 0171-278 8080
e-mail info@cavendishpublishing.com
web site http://www.cavendishpublishing.com
Publishing Director Sonny Leong, *Managing
Editor* Jo Reddy
A wide range of legal and medico-legal
books and journals. Founded 1990.

CBD Research Ltd
15 Wickham Road, Beckenham, Kent BR3 5JS
tel 0181-650 7745 *fax* 0181-650 0768
e-mail 100702.32@compuserve.com
Directors G.P. Henderson, S.P.A. Henderson,
C.A.P. Henderson, A.J.W. Henderson
Directories, reference books, bibliographies, guides to business and statistical
information. Founded 1961.

Chancery House Press (imprint)
Unusual non-fiction/reference works.
Preliminary letter and synopsis with
return postage essential.

Centaur Press
Fontwell, Arundel, West Sussex BN18 0TA
tel (01243) 543302
Directors Jon Wynne-Tyson, Jennifer Wynne-Tyson

Philosophy, environment, humane education, biography. Principal series: *The
Kinship Library*. Send a preliminary letter with sae before submitting MS.
Founded 1954.

Century – see Random House UK Ltd*

Chadwyck-Healey Ltd*
The Quorum, Barnwell Road, Cambridge CB5 8SW
tel (01223) 215512 *fax* (01223) 215514
e-mail marketing @chadwyck.co.uk
Chairman Sir Charles Chadwyck-Healey,
Directors Steven Hall (managing), Steve Sidaway
(sales and marketing), Don McCrae (finance),
Alison Worthington (publishing)
CD-Roms: News and business information, bibliographies and reference works,
literature, arts, statistics, cartography and
climate. Founded 1973.

Chambers Harrap Publishers Ltd
7 Hopetoun Crescent, Edinburgh EH7 4AY
tel 0131-556 5929 *fax* 0131-556 5313
e-mail chambersharrap.co.uk
Managing Director Maurice Shepherd, *Chambers
Publishing Manager* Elaine Higgleton, *Harrap
Publishing Manager* Patrick White
English language and bilingual dictionaries, reference. Subsidiary of Larousse SA.

Chameleon – see André Deutsch Ltd*

Chancery House Press – see CBD
Research Ltd

Chansitor Publications Ltd
St Mary's Works, St Mary's Plain, Norwich,
Norfolk NR3 3BH
tel (01603) 615995 *fax* (01603) 624483
Chief Executive G.A. Knights, *Publisher* Mary Mears
Church Pulpit Year Book.
**Religious and Moral Education Press
(RMEP)** (imprint)
Books for teachers, primary and sec-
ondary schools on religious, moral, per-
sonal and social education.

Chapman & Hall – acquired by Wolters
Kluwer Group of Companies

Geoffrey Chapman – see Cassell plc

Paul Chapman Publishing Ltd
6 Bonhill Street, London EC2A 4PU
tel 0171-374 0645 *fax* 0171-374 8741
Consultant P.R. Chapman, *Commissioning Editor*
Marianne Langrange
Education. Subsidiary of **Sage
Publications Ltd.**

Chapmans Publishers – now incorporated into The Orion Publishing Group Ltd

Chatham Publishing – see Gerald Duckworth & Co. Ltd

Chatto & Windus – see Random House UK Ltd*

Chester House Publications – see Methodist Publishing House

Child's Play (International) Ltd
Ashworth Road, Bridgemead, Swindon, Wilts. SN5 7YD
tel (01793) 616286 fax (01793) 512795
Chairman and Publishing Director Michael Twinn
Children's educational books: board picture, activity and play books; fiction and non-fiction. Founded 1972.

Churchill Communications Europe Ltd
7th Floor, Lynton House, 7-12 Tavistock Square, London WC1H 9JY
tel 0171-874 7000 fax 0171-383 7800
Managing Director William Priddy, *Director* John Lyttle
Full-service communications agency providing medical communications, multimedia, exhibition and PR activities for the pharmaceutical industry.

Churchill Livingstone – see Harcourt Brace & Co. Ltd*

Cicerone Press
2 Police Square, Milnthorpe, Cumbria LA7 7PY
tel (015395) 62069 fax (015395) 63417
e-mail info@cicerone.demon.co.uk
Directors Dorothy Unsworth (managing and sales), Walt Unsworth (editorial), R.B. Evans (production)
Guidebooks to the great outdoors – walking, climbing, etc – Britain, Europe, and worldwide; general books about the North of England. No fiction or poetry. Founded 1969.

Clarendon Press – see Oxford University Press*

T. & T. Clark
59 George Street, Edinburgh EH2 2LQ
tel 0131-225 4703 fax 0131-220 4260
e-mail SusanNichol@compuserve.com
Managing Director Geoffrey F. Green MA, PhD
Theology, philosophy, law. Founded 1821.

James Clarke & Co. Ltd*
PO Box 60, Cambridge CB1 2NT
tel (01223) 350865 fax (01223) 366951
e-mail lutterworth.pr@dial.pipex.com
web site http://dialspace.dial.pipex.com/lutterworth.pr/
Managing Director Adrian Brink
Theology, academic, reference books. Founded 1859.
Acorn Editions (imprint)
Sponsored books.
Patrick Hardy Books (imprint of Lutterworth Press)
Children's fiction.
Lutterworth Press (subsidiary)
The arts, biography, children's books (fiction, non-fiction, picture, rewards), educational, environmental, general, history, leisure, philosophy, science, sociology, theology and religion.

Cló Iar-Chonnachta Teo.†
Indreabhán, Conamara, Co. Galway, Republic of Ireland
tel (091) 593307 fax (091) 593362
e-mail cic@iol.ie
web site http://www.wombat.ie/cic
Director Micheál Ó Conghaile, *General Manager* Deirdre O'Toole
Mostly Irish-language publications – novels, short stories, plays, poetry, songs, history; cassettes (writers reading from their works in Irish and English). Promotes the translation of contemporary Irish fiction and poetry into other languages. Founded 1985.

Richard Cohen Books
Basement Offices, 7 Manchester Square, London W1M 5RE
tel 0171-935 2099 fax 0171-935 2199
Directors Richard Cohen (managing), Peter Heydon (USA); *Company Secretary* H. Stuart Hughes, *Managing Editor* Patricia Chetwyn
Fiction, biography, current affairs, travel, history, politics, the arts, sport. Founded 1995.

Peter Collin Publishing Ltd
1 Cambridge Road, Teddington, Middlesex TW11 8DT
tel 0181-943 3386 fax 0181-943 1673
e-mail general@pcp.co.uk
web site http://www.pcp.co.uk
Directors P.H. Collin (managing), S.M.H. Collin, F. Collin
Specialised dictionaries covering many subjects – from business to computing,

medicine to tourism, law to banking. Bilingual language dictionaries in various subjects and languages. Founded 1985.

Collins – see HarperCollins Publishers*

Collins & Brown
London House, Great Eastern Wharf, Parkgate Road, London SW11 4NQ
tel 0171-924 2575 *fax* 0171-924 7725
Publisher Mark Collins, *Art Director* Roger Bristow, *Editorial Directors* Susan Berry, Sarah Hoggett, Cindy Richards, Colin Ziegler
Lifestyle and interiors, gardening, photography, practical arts, health and beauty, hobbies and crafts, natural history, history, ancient civilisation and astrology, fantasy art and general interest. Subsidiary of C&B Publishing plc. Founded 1989.
Paper Tiger (imprint)
Contact Cindy Richards
Fantasy art.
Belitha Press
See page 161.
David Bennett Books
See page 162.
Parkgate Books
Ground Floor, Kiln House, 210 New Kings Road, London SW6 4NZ
tel 0171-371 9955 *fax* 0171-371 9151
Publisher Suneel Jaitly
Promotional books.
Pavilion Books
See page 198.

The Collins Press†
Carey's Lane, The Huguenot Quarter, Cork, Republic of Ireland
tel 021 271346 *fax* 021 275489
e-mail info@collins-bookshop.ie
Managing Director Con Collins, *Editor* Maria O'Donovan
Archaeology, biography, fiction, general non-fiction, health, history, mind, body and spirit, poetry, photographic and travel guides. Unsolicited MSS, synopses and ideas for books welcome. No British stamps – please send IRCs.

The Columba Press†
55A Spruce Avenue, Stillorgan Industrial Park, Blackrock, Co. Dublin, Republic of Ireland
tel (1) 2942556 *fax* (1) 2942564
e-mail columba@indigo.ie
Publisher and Managing Director Seán O'Boyle
Religion (Roman Catholic and Anglican) including pastoral handbooks, spirituali-

ty, theology, liturgy and prayer; counselling and self-help. Founded 1985.

Condé Nast Books – see Random House UK Ltd*

Conran Octopus – see Reed Books

Conservative Policy Forum
(formerly the Conservative Political Centre)
32 Smith Square, London SW1P 3HH
tel 0171-896 4161 *fax* 0171-896 4163
Director Michael Simmonds
Politics, current affairs. Founded 1945 as the Conservative Political Forum.

Constable & Co. Ltd*
3 The Lanchesters, 162 Fulham Palace Road, London W6 9ER
tel 0181-741 3663 *fax* 0181-748 7562
Chairman and Managing Director Benjamin Glazebrook, *Directors* Richard Tomkins, Carol O'Brien, Anthony McConnell
Crime fiction; general non-fiction: literature, biography, memoirs, history, military history, politics, current affairs, food, travel, mountaineering, guidebooks, social sciences, psychology and psychiatry, counselling, social work, sociology. Founded 1890.

Consumers' Association – see Which? Ltd*

Conway Maritime Press – see Brassey's (UK) Ltd

Leo Cooper – see Pen & Sword Books Ltd

Corgi – see Transworld Publishers Ltd*

Corgi Children's Books – see Transworld Publishers Ltd*

Cork University Press†
Crawford Business Park, Crosses Green, Cork, Republic of Ireland
tel (021) 902980 *fax* (021) 315329
e-mail corkunip@www.ucc.ie
Publisher Sara Wilbourne
Irish literature, history, cultural studies, medieval studies, English literature, musicology, poetry and translations. Founded 1925.

Cornwall Books – see Golden Cockerel Press

Coronet – see Hodder Headline plc*

Council for British Archaeology
Bowes Morrell House, 111 Walmgate,
York YO1 9WA
tel (01904) 671417 *fax* (01904) 671384
e-mail archaeology@compuserve.com
web site http://www.britac.ac.uk/cba/
Director Richard Morris, *Managing Editor*
Christine Pietrowski
British archaeology – academic; practical
handbooks; general interest archaeology.
Founded 1944.

Countryside Books
2 Highfield Avenue, Newbury,
Berks. RG14 5DS
tel (01635) 43816 *fax* (01635) 551004
Partners Nicholas Battle, Suzanne Battle
Books of local or regional interest, usually on a county basis, walking, outdoor
activity, local history; genealogy.
Founded 1976.

Crescent Moon Publishing
PO Box 393, Maidstone,
Kent ME14 5XY
tel (01622) 729593
Director Jeremy Robinson, *Editors* Cassidy
Hughes, B.D. Barnacle
Literature, poetry, fine art, cultural studies, media, feminism. Founded 1988.

Cressrelles Publishing Co. Ltd
10 Station Road Industrial Estate,
Colwall, Malvern, Worcs. WR13 6RN
tel (01684) 540154 *fax* (01684) 540154
Directors Leslie Smith, Simon Smith
General publishing. Founded 1973.
Actinic Press (imprint)
Chiropody.
Kenyon-Deane (imprint)
Plays and drama textbooks, especially for
amateur dramatic societies. Specialists in
plays for women.

The Crowood Press
The Stable Block, Ramsbury, Marlborough,
Wilts. SN8 2HR
tel (01672) 520320 *fax* (01672) 520280
Directors John Dennis (chairman), Ken Hathaway
(managing)
Sport, motoring, aviation, military,
climbing and walking, fishing, country
sports, farming, natural history, gardening, DIY, crafts, dogs, equestrian, games.
Founded 1982.
Helmsman (imprint)
Nautical.

Current Science Group
34-42 Cleveland Street, London W1P 6LB
tel 0171-323 0323 *fax* 0171-580 1938
Chairman Vitek Tracz
Biological sciences, medicine, chemistry,
pharmaceutical science, general science,
law, Internet communities, electronic
publishing.

James Currey Ltd
73 Botley Road, Oxford OX2 0BS
tel (01865) 244111 *fax* (01865) 246454
Directors James Currey, Clare Currey, Keith
Sambrook, Douglas H. Johnson
Academic studies of Africa, Caribbean,
Third World: history, archaeology, economics, agriculture, politics, literary criticism, sociology. Founded 1985.

Curzon Press Ltd
15 The Quadrant, Richmond,
Surrey TW9 1BP
tel 0181-948 4660 *fax* 0181-332 6735
e-mail publish@curzonpress.demon.co.uk
web site http://nias.ku.dk/curzonpress.html
Managing Director/Publisher Malcolm Campbell
Academic/scholarly books on humanities
and social sciences in the context of
Asia. Imprints: Japan Library, Caucasus
World. Founded 1970.

Cygnus Arts – see Golden Cockerel Press

Dalesman Publishing Co. Ltd
Stable Courtyard, Broughton Hall, Skipton,
North Yorkshire BD23 3AE
tel (01756) 701381 *fax* (01756) 701326
Chairman T.J. Benn, *Managing Director* C.G.
Benn, *General Manager* R. Flanagan
Countryside books and magazines covering the North of England. Founded 1939.

Terence Dalton Ltd
Water Street, Lavenham, Sudbury,
Suffolk CO10 9RN
tel (01787) 247572 *fax* (01787) 248267
Directors T.A.J. Dalton, E.H. Whitehair
Maritime and aeronautical history, East
Anglian interest and history. Contract
publisher for the Chartered Institution of
Water and Environmental Management.
Founded 1966.

The C.W. Daniel Company Ltd
1 Church Path, Saffron Walden, Essex CB10 1JP
tel (01799) 521909 *fax* (01799) 513462
e-mail daniel_publishing@dial.pipex.com
Directors Ian Miller, Jane Miller

Natural healing, Bach Flower Remedies, homoeopathy, aromatherapy, mysticism. Founded 1902.
Health Science Press (imprint)
Directors Ian Miller, Jane Miller
Homeopathy.
Neville Spearman Publishers (imprint)
Editorial Director Sebastian Hobnut
Mysticism, metaphysical.

Dartmouth Publishing Co. Ltd –
subsidiary of Ashgate Publishing Ltd

Darton, Longman & Todd Ltd*
1 Spencer Court, 140-142 Wandsworth High Street, London SW18 4JJ
tel 0181-875 0155 *fax* 0181-875 0133
Editorial Director Morag Reeve
Religious books and bibles, including the following themes: bible study, spirituality, prayer and meditation, anthologies, daily readings, healing, counselling and pastoral care, bereavement, personal growth, mission, political, environmental and social issues, biography/autobiography, theological and historical studies. Founded 1959.

Darwen Finlayson Ltd – see Phillimore & Co. Ltd

David & Charles Ltd
Brunel House, Newton Abbot, Devon TQ12 4PU
tel (01626) 323200 *fax* (01626) 323317
Directors Neil A. Page (managing), Piers Spence (publishing)
High quality illustrated non-fiction specialising in crafts, hobbies, art techniques, cookery, gardening, natural history, equestrian, DIY. Founded 1960.

Christopher Davies Publishers Ltd
PO Box 403, Swansea SA1 4YF
tel (01792) 648825 *fax* (01792) 648825
Directors Christopher Talfan Davies (editorial), K.E.T. Colayera, D.M. Davies
History, leisure books, sport and general of Welsh interest, Welsh dictionaries, *Triskele Books*. Founded 1949.

Dedalus Ltd
24 St Judith's Lane, Sawtry, Cambs. PE17 5XE
tel/fax (01487) 832382
e-mail DedalusLimited@compuserve.com
Chairman Juri Gabriel, *Directors* Eric Lane (managing), Robert Irwin (editorial), Lindsay Thomas (marketing), Mike Mitchell (translations)

Original fiction in English and in translation; Empire of the Senses, Dedalus European Classics, Surrealism and Literary Fantasy Anthologies. Founded 1983.

Delta – see Hodder Headline plc*

J.M. Dent – now incorporated into The Orion Publishing Group Ltd

André Deutsch Ltd*
76 Dean Street, London W1V 5HA
tel 0171-316 4450 *fax* 0171-316 4499
web site http://www.vci.co.uk
Managing Director Tim Forrester, *Editorial Manager* Louise Dixon
Subsidiary of VCI plc. Founded 1950.
Chameleon (imprint)
Film/TV, popular entertainment, music, comedy, sport.
André Deutsch (imprint)
Biography, history and current affairs, popular culture, cookery/craft.
André Deutsch Classics (imprint)
Children's hardback classic books.
Madcap (imprint)
Innovative, fun and accessible children's titles.
Manchester United Books (imprint)
Publishing interests of Manchester United Football Club.

André Deutsch Children's Books –
see Scholastic Children's Books*

diehard
3 Spittal Street, Edinburgh EH3 9DY
tel (0131) 229 7252
Directors Ian William King (managing), Sally Evans King (marketing)
Contemporary drama; literature and historic reprints. Founded 1993.

Discovery Walking Guides Ltd
10 Tennyson Close, Dallington, Northampton NN5 7HJ
tel/fax (01604) 752576
e-mail wiwg@walking.demon.co.uk
web site http://www.walking.demon.co.uk/
Chairman Rosamund C. Brawn
'Warm island' walking guides and plant and flower guides to European holiday destinations. Founded 1994.

The Do-Not Press
PO Box 4215, London SE23 2QD
tel 0171-277 7757 *fax* 0171-652 0466

e-mail thedonotpress@zoo.co.uk
web site http://www.thedonotpress.co.uk
Publisher Jim Driver
'Fiercely independent publishing'. Contemporary fiction, humour, music, non-fiction. No unsolicited MSS. Preliminary letter and sae essential. Founded 1995.
Bloodlines (imprint)
Crime fiction.

John Donald Publishers Ltd
73 Logie Green Road, Edinburgh EH7 4HF
tel 0131-558 8282 *fax* 0131-558 8383
Directors Gordon Angus, D.L. Morrison, J. Elder
British history, archaeology, ethnology, local history, vernacular architecture, general non-fiction. Founded 1973.

Dorling Kindersley Ltd
9 Henrietta Street, London WC2E 8PS
tel 0171-836 5411 *fax* 0171-836 7570
web site http://www.dk.com
Chairman Peter Kindersley, *Deputy Chairman and Publisher* Christopher Davis, *Group Directors* Rod Hare (managing), David Houston (finance), Anita Fulton (legal), David Holmes (marketing) *Subsidiary Directors* Stuart Jackman (group design), Peter Stafford (managing, UK publishing), Daphne Razazan, David Lamb, Jackie Douglas (adult editorial), Anne-Marie Bulat, Peter Luff (adult art), Ruth Sandys (managing, children's), Fiona Macmillan (children's fiction), Roger Priddy, Linda Cole (children's art), Sue Unstead, Sophie Mitchell (children's editorial), Simon Jollands, David Oldfield (managing, Vision), Alan Buckingham, Jonathan Reed (managing, Multimedia), Peter Cartwright (managing, DKFL-Int.), Mike Ward (managing, DKFL-UK)
High quality illustrated books on non-fiction subjects, including health, atlases, travel, cookery, gardening, crafts and reference; also children's non-fiction, picture books and fiction. Specialists in international co-editions, CD-Rom and television/video creation. Founded 1974.

Doubleday (UK) – see Transworld Publishers Ltd*

Doubleday Children's Books – see Transworld Publishers Ltd*

Dragon's World Ltd – acquired by Collins & Brown

Dref Wen
28 Church Road, Whitchurch, Cardiff CF4 2EA
tel (01222) 617860 *fax* (01222) 610507
Directors Roger Boore, Anne Boore

Original Welsh language novels for children and adult learners. Original, adaptations and translations of foreign and English language full-colour picture story books for children. Educational material for primary/secondary schoolchildren in Wales. Founded 1970.

Dryden Press – see Harcourt Brace & Co. Ltd*

Dublar Scripts
204 Mercer Way, Romsey, Hants SO51 7QJ
tel (01794) 501377 *fax* (01794) 502538
Managing Director Robert Heather
One-act and full-length plays. Drama and comedy. Founded 1994.
Sleepy Hollow Pantomimes (imprint)
Pantomime scripts.

Gerald Duckworth & Co. Ltd
48 Hoxton Square, London N1 6PB
tel 0171-729 5986 *fax* 0171-729 0015
Directors Stephen Hill (chairman), Robin Baird-Smith (publisher and managing), Deborah Blake (editorial), John Betts (academic)
General trade publishers with a strong academic division. Imprints: Bristol Classical Press and Chatham Publishing; naval and maritime history. Founded 1898.

Martin Dunitz Ltd
The Livery House, 7-9 Pratt Street, London NW1 0AE
tel 0171-482 2202 *fax* 0171-267 0159
e-mail info@dunitz.co.uk
web site http://www.dunitz.co.uk
Directors Martin Dunitz, Ruth Dunitz, John Slaytor, Rosemary Allen
Books, journals and slide atlases in: cardiology, dentistry, dermatology, gastroenterology, gynaecology, haematology, metabolic bone disease, neurology, obesity, oncology, ophthalmology, orthopaedics, otorhinolaryngology, pathology, plastic surgery, psychiatry, radiology, respiratory medicine, rheumatology, sports medicine, surgery, ultrasound, urology. Founded 1978.

Earthlight – see Simon & Schuster*

Earthscan Publications Ltd – see Kogan Page Ltd*

East-West Publications (UK) Ltd
134 Clock Tower Road, Isleworth, Middlesex TW7 6DT
tel 0181-758 0999 *fax* 0181-758 9777

Chairman L.W. Carp

General non-fiction, Eastern studies, sufism. No unsolicited MSS; please write first. Founded 1977.

Gallery Children's Books (imprint)
Quality children's books.

Ebury Press – see Random House UK Ltd*

Edinburgh University Press*
22 George Square, Edinburgh EH8 9LF
tel 0131-650 4218 fax 0131-662 0053
Chairman David Martin, Editorial Director Ms Jackie Jones

Academic and general publishers. Archaeology, botany, cultural studies, Islamic studies, geography, history, linguistics, literature (criticism), philosophy, politics, Scottish studies, American studies, religious studies, women's studies.

Polygon (imprint)
tel 0131-650 8436
New international fiction and poetry, oral history, general, Scottish, social and political (Determinations series). Preliminary enquiry preferred.

The Educational Company of Ireland
PO Box 43A, Ballymount Road, Walkinstown, Dublin 12, Republic of Ireland
tel (01) 4500611 fax (01) 4500993
e-mail info@edco.ie
web site http://www.edco.ie
Executive Directors F.J. Maguire (chief executive), R. McLoughlin, Financial Director B. Egan, Sales and Marketing Director O. Mulcahy

Trading unit of Smurfit Services Ltd. Educational MSS on all subjects in English or Irish language.

Educational Explorers
11 Crown Street, Reading, Berks. RG1 2TQ
tel (01734) 873101 fax (01734) 873103
Directors M.J. Hollyfield, D.M. Gattegno

Educational, mathematics: Numbers in colour with Cuisenaire Rods, languages: The Silent Way, literacy, reading: Words in Colour; educational films. Please do not send unsolicited material. Founded 1962.

Eel Pie – see Plexus Publishing Ltd

Egmont Children's Books
Michelin House, 81 Fulham Road, London SW8 6RB
tel 0171-581 9393 fax 0171-225 9731

Chairman Ian Findlay, Managing Director Jane Winterbotham, Deputy Managing Director Gill Evans

Hamlyn Children's Non-fiction (imprint)
Illustrated non-fiction and reference books for children.

Heinemann Young Books (imprint)
Books for children including quality picture books, novels, anthologies.

Mammoth (imprint)
Children's paperbacks, licensed characters and tie-ins.

Methuen Children's Books (imprint)
Books for children including picture books and fiction for babies to early teens.

Element Books
The Old School House, The Courtyard, Bell Street, Shaftesbury, Dorset SP7 8BP
tel (01747) 851448 fax (01747) 855721
Directors Michael Mann (chairman and publisher), David Alexander (chief executive), Julia McCutchen (managing/editorial), Roger Lane (production), Barry Cunningham (children's books, managing), Elinor Bagenal (children's books, editorial)

Complementary health, personal development, self-help, psychology, philosophy, religion, colour illustrated books. Children's non-fiction, fiction, picture books and board books. Founded 1978.

Edward Elgar Publishing Ltd
8 Lansdown Place, Cheltenham, Glos. GL50 2HU
tel (01242) 226934 fax (01242) 262111
e-mail info @e-elgar.co.uk
web site http://www.e-elgar.co.uk
Managing Director Edward Elgar

Economics and other social sciences. Founded 1986.

Elliot Right Way Books
Kingswood Buildings, Brighton Road, Lower Kingswood, Tadworth, Surrey KT20 6TD
tel (01737) 832202 fax (01737) 830311
Managing Directors Clive Elliot, Malcolm Elliot

Independent publishers of practical non-fiction 'how to' paperbacks. The low-price Right Way series includes games, pastimes, horses, pets, motoring, sport, health, business, public speaking and jokes, financial and legal, cookery and etiquette. Similar subjects are covered in the Clarion series of large-format paperbacks, sold in supermarkets and bargain bookshops. Welcomes new ideas. Founded 1946.

Aidan Ellis Publishing
Whinfield, Herbert Road, Salcombe,
Devon TQ8 8HN
tel (01548) 842755 *fax* (01548) 844356
e-mail aidan@aepub.demon.co.uk
web site http://www.demon.co.uk/aepub
Publisher Aidan Ellis
Non-fiction: gardening, maritime, art,
general. Founded 1971.

ELM Publications
Seaton House, Kings Ripton, Huntingdon,
Cambs. PE17 2NJ
tel (01487) 773238 *fax* (01487) 773359
Managing Director Sheila Ritchie
Educational books and resources; books
and training aids (tutor's packs and software) for business and management; software simulations; library and information studies. Telephone in the first
instance, rather than send MSS. Please
note: we publish mainly to curricula and
course syllabi. Founded 1977.

Elm Tree Books – former imprint of Hamish Hamilton/Penguin

Elsevier Science Ltd
The Boulevard, Langford Lane, Kidlington,
Oxford OX5 1GB
tel (01865) 843000 *fax* (01865) 843010
Managing Director C. Blake, *Editorial Director
(Primary and Reference)* B. Barret, *Publishing
Director (Magazines and Newsletters)* D.
Bousfield
Journal, magazine and book publishers in
science, technology and medicine.
Imprints: Pergamon, Elsevier Applied
Science, Elsevier Trends Journals,
Butterworth Heinemann Journals.

Encyclopaedia Britannica International Ltd
Chancery House, St Nicholas Way, Sutton,
Surrey SM1 1JB
tel 0181-770 7766 *fax* 0181-642 9090
Managing Director Tim Pethick

Enitharmon Press
36 St George's Avenue, London N7 0HD
tel 0171-607 7194 *fax* 0171-607 8694
Director Stephen Stuart-Smith
Poetry, literary criticism, translations,
artists' books. No unsolicited MSS.
Founded 1967.

Epworth Press
c/o Methodist Publishing House, 20 Ivatt Way,
Peterborough PE3 7PG
tel (01733) 332202 *fax* (01733) 331201
Editorial Committee Rev. Gerald Burt (editorial
secretary), Dr Valerie Edden, Dr E. Dorothy
Graham, Rev. Dr Ivor H. Jones, Rev. Dr John
A. Newton (chairman), Rev. Dr Cyril S. Rodd,
Rev. Michael J. Townsend
Religion, theology, church history, wor-
ship, Bible commentaries.

Eros Plus – see Titan Books Ltd

Eurobook Ltd – see Peter Lowe (Eurobook Ltd)

Euromonitor plc
60-61 Britton Street, London EC1M 5NA
tel 0171-251 8024 *fax* 0171-608 3149
e-mail info@euromonitor.com
web site http://www.euromonitor.com
Directors T.J. Fenwick (managing), R.N. Senior
(chairman)
Business and commercial reference, marketing information, European and
International Surveys, directories.
Founded 1972.

Europa Publications Ltd
18 Bedford Square, London WC1B 3JN
tel 0171-580 8236 *fax* 0171-636 1664
e-mail editorial@europapublications.co.uk
Directors C.H. Martin (chairman), P.A. McGinley
(managing), J.P. Desmond, R.M. Hughes, P.G.C.
Jackson, P. Kelly, M.R. Milton
Directories, international relations, reference, yearbooks.

Evangelical Press of Wales – see Bryntirion Press

Evans Brothers Ltd*
2A Portman Mansions, Chiltern Street,
London W1M 1LE
tel 0171-935 7160 *fax* 0171-487 5034
Directors S.T. Pawley (managing), Brian D. Jones
(international publishing), A.O. Ojora (Nigeria),
A.E. Solly, J.D. Solly, *UK Publisher* Su Swallow
Educational books, particularly
preschool, school library and teachers'
books for the UK, including the
Rainbows series of graded information
books for 5-8-year-olds; primary and secondary for Africa, the Caribbean and
Brazil. Founded 1908.

Everyman – see The Orion Publishing Group Ltd

Everyman's Library
Gloucester Mansions, 140A Cambridge Circus,
London WC2H 8PA

tel 0171-287 0035 *fax* 0171-287 0038
Publisher David Campbell, *Finance Director*
Mark Bicknell
Everyman's Library (clothbound reprints of the classics); *Everyman's Library Children's Classics*; *Everyman's Library Pocket Poets*; *Everyman Guides*; *Everyman City Guides*; *Everyman-EMI Music Companions*; *Cadogan Chess*.

Exley Publications Ltd

16 Chalk Hill, Watford,
Herts. WD1 4BN
tel (01923) 250505 *fax* (01923) 818733/800440
Directors Dalton Exley, Helen Exley (editorial), Lincoln Exley, Richard Exley
Popular colour gift books for an international market. 60 new titles a year. No unsolicited MSS. Founded 1976.

Faber & Faber Ltd*

3 Queen Square, London WC1N 3AU
tel 0171-465 0045 *fax* 0171-465 0034
Chairman and Managing Director Matthew Evans,
Directors John Bodley, Patrick Curran, Giles de la Mare, Valerie Eliot, T.E. Faber, Tom Kelleher, Joanna Mackle, Peter Simpson (company secretary)
High quality general fiction and non-fiction; all forms of creative writing, including plays. Write to Sales Department for current lists. For information on submission procedure ring 0171-465 9070. For practical and security reasons submissions by fax or on disk cannot be accepted, except by special arrangement. Please allow 6-8 weeks for a response. Freelance readers and proofreaders without in-house experience need not apply.

Fabian Society

11 Dartmouth Street,
London SW1H 9BN
tel 0171-222 8877 *fax* 0171-976 7153
e-mail fabian-society@geo2.poptel.org.uk
General Secretary Michael Jacobs
Current affairs, political thought, economics, education, environment, foreign affairs, social policy. Also controls NCLC Publishing Society Ltd. Founded 1884.

Facts on File

c/o Roundhouse Publishing Group, PO Box 140,
Oxford OX2 7FF
tel (01865) 512682 *fax* (01865) 559594
e-mail roundhse@compuserve.com
Contact Alan Goodworth
Non-fiction reference and information books in a broad range of disciplines. No unsolicited MSS.

C.J. Fallon

Lucan Road, Palmerstown, Dublin 20,
Republic of Ireland
tel (01) 6265777 *fax* (01) 6268225
Executive Directors H.J. McNicholas (managing),
P. Tolan (financial), N. White (editorial)
Educational text books. Founded 1927.

Farming Press

2 Wharfedale Road, Ipswich, Suffolk IP1 4LG
tel (01473) 241122 *fax* (01473) 240501
e-mail farmingpress@dotfarming.com
web site http://www.dotfarming.com
Manager Alison Stevens
Technical agriculture, farm machinery, veterinary; books, videos, audio. Founded 1951.

Fernhurst Books

Duke's Path, High Street, Arundel,
West Sussex BN18 9AJ
tel (01903) 882277 *fax* (01903) 882715
Publisher Tim Davison
Sailing, watersports. Founded 1979.

Financial Times Management

(formerly Pitman Publishing)
128 Long Acre, London WC2E 9AN
tel 0171-447 2000 *fax* 0171-240 5771
Managing Director Rod Bristow, *Product Development Director* Simon Lake
Business education, management, professional studies. Member of FT Group, Pearson plc.

First and Best in Education Ltd*

(incorporating Hamilton House Publishing)
Earlstrees Court, Earlstrees Road, Corby,
Northants. NN17 4AX
tel (01536) 399004 *fax* (01536) 399012
e-mail FirstBest9@aol.com
Directors Tony Attwood, Philippa Attwood
Contacts Katy Charge, Julia Perkins (editors)
Education-related books. Currently actively recruiting new writers for schools; ideas welcome. Sae must accompany submissions. Founded 1992.

Fishing News Books Ltd

Osney Mead, Oxford OX2 0EL
tel (01865) 206206 *fax* (01865) 206096
Manager Philip Saugman
Commercial fisheries, aquaculture and allied subjects. Founded 1953.

Fitzroy Dearborn Publishers

310 Regent Street, London W1R 5AJ
tel 0171-636 6627 *fax* 0171-636 6982
e-mail postroom@fitzroydearborn.demon.co.uk
web site http://www.fitzroydearborn.com
Managing Director Daniel Kirkpatrick, *Senior*

Commissioning Editor Lesley Henderson, *Publisher* Roda Morrison, *Marketing Executive* Vikki Cookson

Reference books: history, design, art, literature, gender, business, science. Founded 1994.

Flamingo – see HarperCollins Publishers*

Flicks Books
29 Bradford Road, Trowbridge, Wilts. BA14 9AN
tel (01225) 767728 *fax* (01225) 760418
Partners Matthew Stevens (publisher), Aletta Stevens

Cinema, TV, related media. Founded 1986.

Flint River – see Philip Wilson Publishers Ltd

Floris Books*
15 Harrison Gardens, Edinburgh EH11 1SH
tel 0131-337 2372 *fax* 0131-346 7516
Editor Christopher Moore

Religion, science, Celtic studies, craft; children's books: picture and board books, activity books. Founded 1978.

Focal Press – see Reed Educational and Professional Publishing Ltd

Fodor Guides – see Random House UK Ltd*

Folens Ltd
Albert House, Apex Business Centre, Boscombe Road, Dunstable LU5 4RL
tel (01582) 472788 *fax* (01582) 472575
e-mail folens@folens.com
web site http://www.folens.com
Managing Director Malcolm Watson

Primary and secondary educational books, learn at home books. Founded 1987.

Folens Publishing Company
Unit 8, Broomhill Business Park, Broomhill Road, Tallaght, Dublin 24, Republic of Ireland
tel (01) 4515311 *fax* (01) 4515306
Chairman Dirk Folens, *Directors* John O'Connor (managing), Anna O'Donovan (secondary), Deirdre Whelan (primary)

Educational (primary, secondary, comprehensive, technical, in English and Irish), educational children's magazines.
The Blackwater Press[†] (imprint)
General non-fiction, Irish interest.

Fontana – now HarperCollins Paperbacks*

Fontana Press – see HarperCollins Publishers*

Forest Books
20 Forest View, Chingford, London E4 7AY
tel 0181-529 8470 *fax* 0181-524 7890
Managing Director Brenda Walker

Only international literature in English translation; poetry, plays, novels and short stories, especially East European literature. No unsolicited material please. Founded 1984.

G.T. Foulis & Co. – see Haynes Publishing

W. Foulsham & Co. Ltd
The Publishing House, Bennetts Close, Slough, Berks. SL1 5AP
tel (01753) 526769 *fax* (01753) 535003
Managing Director B.A.R. Belasco, *Editorial Director* W. Hobson

General know-how, cookery, health and alternative therapies, hobbies and games, gardening, sport, travel guides, DIY, collectibles, popular new age. Founded 1819.
Quantum (imprint)
Editor Ian Fenton
Mind, body and spirit, popular philosophy and practical psychology.
Raphael's (imprint)
Editor Ian Fenton
Astrology.

The Foundational Book Company
(for The John W. Doorly Trust)
PO Box 659, London SW3 6SJ
tel 0171-584 1053
Trustee for Publications Mrs Peggy M. Brook
Spiritual Science.

Foundery Press – see Methodist Publishing House

Fount – see HarperCollins Publishers*

Four Courts Press[†]
Fumbally Court, Fumbally Lane, Dublin 8, Republic of Ireland
tel (01) 4534668 *fax* (01) 4534672
e-mail info@four-courts-press.ie
Managing Director Michael Adams

Academic books in the humanities, especially history and Celtic and medieval studies. Founded 1969.

Fourmat Publishing – see Tolley Publishing Co. Ltd

Fourth Estate Ltd*
6 Salem Road, London W2 4BU
tel 0171-727 8993 *fax* 0171-792 3176
Directors Victoria Barnsley (managing), Patric
Duffy (financial), Christopher Potter (publishing),
Kate Shaw (publicity), Stephen Page (sales and
deputy managing), James Kellow (marketing),
Susie Dunlop (rights)
Current affairs, literature, popular cul-
ture, fiction, humour, politics, science,
popular reference, TV tie-ins. No unso-
licited MSS. Founded 1984.
Fourth Estate Paperbacks (imprint)
Publishes paperback editions of Fourth
Estate hardback titles.
Guardian Books (imprint)
Books stemming from the *Guardian*
newspaper.

Framework Press Educational Publishers Ltd*
Albert House, Apex Business Centre,
Boscombe Road, Dunstable LU5 4RL
tel (01582) 478110 *fax* (01582) 475524
Commissioning Editor Liz Cartmell
School and college management, staff
development, vocational, English, PSE.
Founded 1983.

Franklin Watts – see the Watts Publishing Group*

Free Association Books
57 Warren Street, London W1P 5PA
tel 0171-388 3182 *fax* 0171-388 3187
e-mail fab@melmoth.demon.co.uk
Managing Director T.E. Brown, *Publisher* Gill
Davies
Psychoanalysis, psychotherapy, counselling, cultural studies, social sciences,
social welfare, addiction studies, child
and adolescent studies. Founded 1984.

W.H. Freeman
Macmillan Press Ltd, Houndmills, Basingstoke,
Hants RG21 6XS
tel (01256) 332807 *fax* (01256) 330688
Sales Director E. Warner
Science, medicine, economics, psycholo-
gy, archaeology.

Samuel French Ltd*
52 Fitzroy Street, London W1P 6JR
tel 0171-387 9373 *fax* 0171-387 2161
Directors Charles Van Nostrand (chairman), John
Bedding (managing), Amanda Smith, Paul Taylor
Publishers of plays and agents for the
collection of royalties. Founded 1830.

FT Law & Tax – incorporated into Sweet & Maxwell*

David Fulton Publishers Ltd
Ormond House, 26-27 Boswell Street,
London WC1N 3JD
tel 0171-405 5606 *fax* 0171-831 4840
e-mail mail@fultonbooks.co.uk
Managing Director David Fulton, *Editorial
Director* John Owens, *Marketing Director* Pamela
Fulton
Initial and continuing teacher education
(special needs, primary and secondary),
educational management and psychology,
geography (for undergraduates). Unsolicited MSS not returned. Founded 1987.

Funfax Ltd
Marsh House, Tide Mill Way, Woodbridge,
Suffolk IP12 1AN
tel (01394) 380622 *fax* (01394) 380618
Managing Director Roger Priddy, *Managing
Editor* Lisa Telford
Children's books for the international mass
markets: non-fiction information, fun
activity and novelty, preschool and stick-
ers. Wholly owned subsidary Dorling
Kindersley Holdings plc. Founded 1990.

Gaia Books Ltd
66 Charlotte Street, London W1P 1LR
tel 0171-323 4010 *fax* 0171-323 0435 and
20 High Street, Stroud, Glos. GL5 1AS
tel (01453) 752985 *fax* (01453) 752987
Directors Joss Pearson (managing), David
Pearson, Lars Kjeldsen, Tor Svensson
Illustrated reference books on ecology,
natural living, health, mind. Submissions
(outline and sample chapter) to managing director.

Gairm Publications
(incorporating Alex MacLaren & Sons)
29 Waterloo Street, Glasgow G2 6BZ
tel/fax 0141-221 1971
Editorial Director Derick Thomson
(Gaelic and Gaelic-related only) dictionaries, language books, novels, poetry,
music, children's books, quarterly magazine, *Gairm*. Founded 1875.

Gallery Children's Books – see East-West Publications (UK) Ltd

The Gallery Press
Loughcrew, Oldcastle, Co. Meath,
Republic of Ireland
tel/fax (049) 41779
e-mail gallery@indigo.ie
Editor/Publisher Peter Fallon

Poetry, drama, occasionally fiction, by Irish authors. Allied company: Deerfield Publications Inc., USA. Founded 1970.

Garnet Publishing Ltd
8 Southern Court, South Street, Reading RG1 4QS
tel (01189) 597847 *fax* (01189) 597356
Managing Director Kenneth Banerji
Art, architecture, photography, fiction religious studies and general, mainly on Middle and Far East, and Islam. Founded 1991.
Ithaca Press (imprint)
Post-graduate academic works, especially on the Middle East.

Gateway Books
The Hollies, Wellow, Nr Bath BA2 8QJ
tel (01225) 835127 *fax* (01225) 840012
e-mail info@gatewaybooks.com
web site http://www.gatewaybooks.com
Publisher Alick Bartholomew
Popular psychology, spirituality, health and healing, earth mysteries, ecology, self help, metaphysics and alternative science. No unsolicited MSS; outline and sample welcome. Founded 1982.

The Gay Men's Press – see GMP Publishers Ltd

Geddes & Grosset Ltd*
David Dale House, New Lanark ML11 9DJ
tel (01555) 665000 *fax* (01555) 665694
Directors Ron Grosset, Mike Miller
Popular reference including cookery; children's picture books, non-fiction and activity books. Founded 1988.

Gee & Son (Denbigh) Ltd
Chapel Street, Denbigh, Denbighshire LL16 3SW
tel (01745) 812020 *fax* (01745) 812825
Directors E. Evans, E.M. Evans
Oldest Welsh publishers. Books of interest to Wales, in Welsh and English. Founded 1808.

Geographia – now Bartholomew – see HarperCollins Publishers*

GeoInformation International – see Pearson Professional Ltd*

Stanley Gibbons Publications*
Parkside, Christchurch Road, Ringwood, Hants BH24 3SH
tel (01425) 472363 *fax* (01425) 470247
e-mail sales@stangib.demon.co.uk
Chief Executive A.M. McQuillan

Philatelic handbooks, stamp catalogues and albums, *Gibbons Stamp Monthly*. Founded 1856.

Robert Gibson & Sons Glasgow Ltd
17 Fitzroy Place, Glasgow G3 7SF
tel 0141-248 5674 *fax* 0141-221 8219
web site http://robert.gibsons@btinternet.com
Directors R.G.C. Gibson, M. Pinkerton, H.C. Crawford, N.J. Crawford (editorial)
Educational and textbooks. Founded 1885.

Gill & Macmillan Ltd[†]
Goldenbridge, Inchicore, Dublin 8, Republic of Ireland
tel (01) 4531005 *fax* (01) 4541688
Biography or memoirs, educational (secondary, university), history, mind, body and spirit, popular psychology, literature, cookery, current affairs, guidebooks. Founded 1968.

Ginn & Co. – see Reed Educational and Professional Publishing Ltd

Mary Glasgow Publications – now incorporated into Stanley Thornes (Publishers) Ltd

GMP Publishers Ltd
PO Box 247, Swaffham, Norfolk PE37 8PA
tel (01366) 328101 *fax* (01366) 328102
e-mail gmppubs.co.uk
Publishers Aubrey Walter, David Fernbach
Founded 1979.
The Gay Men's Press (imprint)
Modern, popular, historical/literary fiction, including translations from European languages, biography and memoir, history, drama, health, social and political questions, literary criticism. *Gay Modern Classics* – reprints of gay fiction/non-fiction from the past 100 years.
Éditions Aubrey Walter (imprint)
Male photography both art and glamour, fine art editions of gay artists.
Heretic Books (imprint)
Ecology, animal liberation, green politics, Third World.

Godsfield Press Ltd
Laurel House, Station Approach, New Alresford, Hants SO24 9AT
tel (01962) 735633 *fax* (01962) 735320
Directors John Hunt, Debbie Thorpe
Highly illustrated books for adults in the area of mind, body and spirit with an

emphasis on practical application and personal spiritual awareness. Founded 1994.

Golden Age Editions – see New Cavendish Books

Golden Cockerel Press
16 Barter Street, London WC1A 2AH
tel 0171-405 7979 *fax* 0171-404 3598
e-mail lindesay@btinternet.com
Contact Tamar Lindesay
Academic.
Associated University Presses (imprint)
Literary criticism, art, music, history, film, theology, philosophy, Jewish studies, politics, sociology.
Cornwall Books (imprint)
Antiques, history, film.
Cygnus Arts (imprint)
The arts.

The Goldsmith Press
Newbridge, Co. Kildare, Republic of Ireland
tel (045) 433613 *fax* (045) 434648
e-mail De@iol.ie
Directors D. Egan, V. Abbott, *Secretary* Brenda Eves
Literature, art, Irish interest, poetry. Founded 1972.

Victor Gollancz Ltd – see Cassell plc

Gomer Press
Llandysul, Dyfed SA44 4BQ
tel (01559) 362371 *fax* (01559) 363758
Directors Jonathan Lewis, John H. Lewis, Dyfed Elis-Gruffydd, *Editors* Mairwen Prys Jones, Gordon Jones
Literature and non-fiction with a Welsh background or relevance: biography, history, aspects of Welsh culture, children's books. No unsolicited MSS; preliminary letter essential. Founded 1892.

Government Supplies Agency
Publications Division, 4-5 Harcourt Road, Dublin 2, Republic of Ireland
tel (01) 6613111 *fax* (01) 4752760
Government and international publications including EU, OECD, UN, World Trade Organisation, Nordic Council, ILO and Council of Europe.

Gower Publishing Ltd – subsidiary of Ashgate Publishing Ltd

Grafton – now HarperCollins Paperbacks*

Graham & Whiteside Ltd
Tuition House, 5-6 Francis Grove, London SW19 4DT
tel 0181-947 1011 *fax* 0181-947 1163
e-mail sales@major-co-data.com
Directors A.M.W. Graham, H.C.H. Whiteside, R.M. Whiteside, P.L. Murphy
Directories for international business and professional markets. Founded 1995.

Granta Publications
2-3 Hanover Yard, Noel Road, London N1 8BE
tel 0171-704 9776 *fax* 0171-704 0474
Book Publisher Frances Coady, *Publishing Director* Neil Belton, *Magazine Editor* Ian Jack
Literary fiction, autobiography, political non-fiction. Founded 1982.

Green Books
Foxhole, Dartington, Totnes, Devon TQ9 6EB
tel/fax (01803) 863843
Managing Director John Elford
Environment (practical and philosophical). No fiction or children's books. No MSS; synopsis and covering letter please. Founded 1987.

Green Print – see Merlin Press Ltd

Greenhill Books/Lionel Leventhal Ltd
Park House, 1 Russell Gardens, London NW11 9NN
tel 0181-458 6314 *fax* 0181-905 5245
Managing Director Lionel Leventhal
Military history. Founded 1984.

Gresham Books Ltd
The Gresham Press, PO Box 61, Henley-on-Thames, Oxon RG9 3LQ
tel/fax (01189) 403789
e-mail greshambks@aol.com
Chief Executive Mrs M.V. Green
Hymn books, Prayer books, and Service books.

Grub Street
The Basement, 10 Chivalry Road, London SW11 1HT
tel 0171-924 3966/738 1008 *fax* 0171-738 1009
Principals John B. Davies, Anne Dolamore
Adult non-fiction: aviation history, cookery, health and reference. Founded 1989.

Guardian Books – see Fourth Estate Ltd

Guild of Master Craftsman Publications Ltd
Castle Place, 166 High Street, Lewes, East Sussex BN7 1XU
tel (01273) 477374/478449 *fax* (01273) 487692
Managing Director Alan Phillips

Practical, illustrated crafts, including needlecrafts, dolls' houses, woodworking and other leisure and hobby subjects. Founded 1979.

Guinness Publishing Ltd*
338 Euston Road, London NW1 3BD
tel 0171-891 4567 *fax* 0171-891 4501
Publishing Director Ian Castello-Cortes, *Director of Television* Michael Feldman
The Guinness Book of Records, general reference, music and sports reference. Founded 1954.

Gwasg Bryntirion Press – see **Bryntirion Press**

Gwasg y Dref Wen – see **Dref Wen**

Gwasg Gee – see **Gee & Son (Denbigh) Ltd**

Peter Halban Publishers Ltd
42 South Molton Street, London W1Y 1HB
tel 0171-491 1582 *fax* 0171-629 5381
Directors Martine Halban, Peter Halban
General non-fiction; history and biography; Jewish subjects and Middle East. No unsolicited MSS considered; preliminary letter essential. Founded 1986.

Robert Hale Ltd
Clerkenwell House, 45-47 Clerkenwell Green, London EC1R 0HT
tel 0171-251 2661 *fax* 0171-490 4958
Directors John Hale (managing and editorial), Robert Kynaston (financial), Martin Kendall (marketing), Betty Weston (rights)
Adult general non-fiction and fiction. Founded 1936.

Hamish Hamilton – see **Penguin UK***

Hamish Hamilton Children's – see **Penguin UK***

Hamilton House Publishing – see **First and Best in Education Ltd***

Hamlyn – see **Reed Books**

Hamlyn Children's Non-fiction – see **Egmont Children's Books**

Harcourt Brace & Co. Ltd*
24-28 Oval Road, London NW1 7DX
tel 0171-424 4200 *fax* 0171-482 2293/485 4752
Managing Director Peter H. Lengemann
Scientific and medical.
Academic Press (division)
Managing Director Jan Velterop
Academic and reference.

Baillière Tindall Ltd (division)
Managing Director Andrew Stevenson
Medical, veterinary, nursing, pharmaceutical books and journals.
Churchill Livingstone (division)
Managing Director Andrew Stevenson
Medical, nursing, pharmaceutical books and journals.
Dryden Press (division)
Managing Director Peter H. Lengemann
Educational books (college, university), economics, business.
Holt Rhinehart & Winston (division)
Managing Director Peter Lengemann
Educational books.
W.B. Saunders Co. Ltd (division)
Managing Director Andrew Stevenson
Medical and scientific.

Patrick Hardy Books – see **James Clarke & Co. Ltd***

Harlem River Press – see **Writers & Readers Ltd***

Harlequin Mills & Boon Ltd*
Eton House, 18-24 Paradise Road, Richmond, Surrey TW9 1SR
tel 0181-288 2800 *fax* 0181-288 2899
Directors Fredrik Gejrot (managing), Alan Boon (Editor Emeritus), Stuart Barber (financial), Angela Meredith (production), Alan Dawson (retail sales and marketing), Karin Stoecker (editorial), Deborah Scott (direct marketing), Mike Creffield (information technology), Janet Oldham (human resources)
Founded 1908.
Medical & Historical (series)
Senior Editor E. Johnson
Romance fiction.
Mills & Boon (imprint)
Senior Editors T. Shapcott, S. Hodgson
Contemporary romance fiction in paperback and hardback.
Mira Books (imprint)
Senior Editor L. Fildew
Women's fiction.
Silhouette (imprint)
Senior Editor L. Stonehouse
Popular romantic women's fiction.

HarperCollins Publishers*
77-85 Fulham Palace Road, London W6 8JB
tel 0181-741 7070 *fax* 0181-307 4440
Executive Chairman and Publisher Eddie Bell, *Group Managing Director* Les Higgins, *Divisional Managing Directors* Adrian Bourne (trade), Eileen Campbell (Thorsons/religious), Stephen Bray

(cartographic/general reference), Kate Harris (education/children's/dictionaries)

All fiction and trade non-fiction must be submitted through an agent. Unsolicited submissions should be made in the form of a typewritten synopsis. Founded 1819.

Access Press (imprint)
Travel guides.

Bartholomew (imprint)
Maps, atlases, electronic products.

Birnbaum (imprint)
Travel guides.

Collins (imprints)
Collins Crime, Collins Classics, Collins Educational, Collins bibles, Collins Liturgical Books, Collins Dictionaries, Collins Cobuild, Collins Gems, Collins New Naturalist Library, Collins Willow, Collins Longman.

Collins (children's imprint)
Publishing Directors Gail Penston, Domenica de Rosa
Includes Jets, Yellow Storybooks, Red Storybooks, fiction for older children and toddler books.

Collins Children's Audio (imprint)
Collins Children's Books (imprint)
Collins Picture Lions (imprint)
Children's picture paperbacks.

Collins Tracks (imprint)
Young adult books.

Flamingo (imprint)
Editorial Director Philip Gwyn Jones
Literary fiction in hardback and paperback.

Fontana Press (imprint)
Editorial Director Philip Gwyn Jones
Paperback intellectual non-fiction.

Fount (imprint)
Managing Director Eileen Campbell
Religious.

HarperCollins (imprints)
Audiobooks, hardbacks (fiction and non-fiction), paperbacks (fiction and non-fiction), religious.

HarperCollins Broadcasting Consultancy
Contact Cresta Norris
Exploits TV and film rights across the company.

HarperCollins Electronic Products
Managing Director Kate Harris
CD-Rom, floppy disk and on-line.

Specialises in special interest, children's, reference and interactive fiction.

HarperCollins World
Managing Director Robin Wood
General trade titles imported into the UK market.

Lions (imprint)
Publishing Director Gail Penston
Children's books.

Marshall Pickering (imprint)
Managing Director Eileen Campbell
Theology, music, popular religion, illustrated children's, wide range of Christian books.

Nicholson (imprint)
Managing Director Stephen Bray
London maps, atlases and guidebooks. Waterways maps and guidebooks.

Thorsons (imprint)
Managing Director Eileen Campbell
Complementary medicine, health and nutrition, business and management, self-help and positive thinking, popular psychology, parenting and childcare, astrology, tarot and divination, mythology and psychic awareness.

Times Books (imprint)
Managing Director Stephen Bray
World atlases and maps, thematic atlases, reference, guides and crosswords.

Tolkien (imprint)
Projects Director David Brawn, *Editorial Director* Jane Johnson

Voyager (imprint)
Editorial Director Jane Johnson
Science fiction, fantasy fiction and media tie-ins.

Harrap – see Chambers Harrap Publishers Ltd

The Harvill Press
2 Aztec Row, Berners Road, London N1 0PW
tel 0171-704 8766 *fax* 0171-704 8805
Publisher and Chairman Christopher MacLehose, *Directors* John Mitchinson (managing), Guido Waldman (editorial), Rachael Kerr (marketing), *Rights Manager/Sales* Katharina Bielenberg
English-language and world literature in translation (mainly literary fiction, but including non-fiction and some first-class narrative thrillers); monographs in the fields of ethnography, art, horticulture and natural history. Unsolicited MSS only accepted with sae. Founded 1946.

Hawk Books

Suite 309, Canalot Studios, 222 Kensal Road,
London W10 5BN
tel 0181-969 8091 *fax* 0181-968 9012
Director Patrick Hawkey
Comics, nostalgia, juveniles, art.
Founded 1986.

Haynes Publishing

Sparkford, Yeovil, Somerset BA22 7JJ
tel (01963) 440635 *fax* (01963) 440023
Directors J.H. Haynes (chairman), A.C. Haynes,
I.P. Mauger, D.J. Reach (editorial), A.J. Sperring,
K.C. Fullman (managing), C. Davies, D.J.
Hermelin, C.G. Magnus
Car and motorcycle owners workshop
manuals, car handbooks/servicing
guides, do-it-yourself books, aircraft,
trains, nautical.

G.T. Foulis & Co. (imprint)
Editor Darryl Reach
Motoring/motorcycling, marque and
model history, practical maintenance and
renovation, related biographies, aircraft,
nautical, aviation.

Haynes (imprint)
Director Alan Sperring
Home DIY and leisure activities (e.g.
cycling).

Oxford Illustrated Press (imprint)
Editor Darryl Reach
Well-illustrated non-fiction books, sport,
leisure and travel guides, car books, art
books, general.

Oxford Publishing Company (OPC
Railbooks) (imprint)
Editor Darryl Reach
Railway transport.

Patrick Stephens Ltd (imprint)
Editorial Director Darryl Reach
Aviation, biography, maritime, military
and wargaming, model making, motorcy-
cling, motoring and motor racing, railways and railway modelling.

Hazar Publishing Ltd

147 Chiswick High Road,
London W4 2DT
tel 0181-742 8578 *fax* 0181-994 1407
Managing Director Greg Hill, *Editor* Marie Clayton
Children's picture and novelty books;
adult non-fiction: architecture and
design. Founded 1992.

Headland Business Information – see
Bowker-Saur

Headland Publications

Editorial office Ty Coch, Galltegfa, Llanfwrog,
Ruthin, Clwyd LL15 2AR
and 38 York Avenue, West Kirby, Wirral,
Merseyside L48 3JF
Director and Editor Gladys Mary Coles
Poetry, anthologies of poetry and prose.
No unsolicited MSS. Founded 1970.

Headline – see Hodder Headline plc*

Headline Book Publishing Ltd – see
Hodder Headline plc*

Headline Feature – see Hodder
Headline plc*

Headway – see Hodder Headline plc*

Health Science Press – see The C.W.
Daniel Company Ltd

William Heinemann – see Random
House UK Ltd*

Heinemann Educational – see Reed
Educational and Professional Publishing Ltd

**Heinemann English Language
Teaching** – see Macmillan Publishers Ltd*

Heinemann Young Books – see
Egmont Children's Books

Helicon Publishing Ltd

42 Hythe Bridge Street, Oxford OX1 2EP
tel (01865) 204204 *fax* (01865) 204205
e-mail admin@helicon.co.uk
web site http://www.helicon.co.uk
Directors David Attwooll (managing), Michael
Upshall (publishing), Edward Knighton (finance),
Anne-Lucie Norton (editorial, subject reference),
Hilary McGlynn (editorial, general reference),
Tony Ballsdon (production), Sheila Lambie (sales
and marketing), Clare Painter (rights)
General trade reference, hardback and
paperback: *Hutchinson Encyclopedias*,
history, science, the arts; electronic reference. Founded 1992.

Christopher Helm – see A & C Black
(Publishers) Ltd*

Helmsman – see The Crowood Press

Henderson Publishing Ltd – now
Funfax Ltd

The Herbert Press – see A & C Black
(Publishers) Ltd*

Heretic Books – see GMP Publishers Ltd

Hermes House – see Anness Publishing

Nick Hern Books Ltd
The Glasshouse, 49A Goldhawk Road,
London W12 8QP
tel 0181-749 4953 *fax* 0181-746 2006
e-mail info@nickhernbooks.demon.co.uk
Publisher Nick Hern
Theatre, professionally produced plays,
screenplays. Initial letter required.
Founded 1988.

Hilmarton Manor Press
Calne, Wilts. SN11 8SB
tel (01249) 760208 *fax* (01249) 760379
Editorial Director Charles Baile de Laperriere
Fine art, photography, antiques, visual
arts, wine. Founded 1964.

Hippo – see Scholastic Children's Books*

Hippopotamus Press
22 Whitewell Road, Frome, Somerset BA11 4EL
tel/fax (01373) 466653
Editors Roland John, Anna Martin
Poetry, essays, criticism. Publishes
Outposts Poetry Quarterly. Poetry sub-
missions from new writers welcome.
Founded 1974.

HMSO Books – see The Stationery Office/National Publishing*

Hobsons Publishing plc
Bateman Street, Cambridge CB2 1LZ
tel (01223) 460366 *fax* (01223) 323154
Non-executive Director Charles Sinclair,
Chairman Martin Morgan, *Directors* Chris
Letcher (managing), Frances Halliwell, David
Harrington, Nicola Anson
Database publisher of educational and
careers information under licence to CRAC
(Careers Research and Advisory Centre).
Also publishes accommodation guides
under Johansens brand. Founded 1974.

Hodder Headline plc*
338 Euston Road, London NW1 3BH
tel 0171-873 6000 *fax* 0171-873 6024
Chairman Christopher Weston (non-executive),
Group Chief Executive Tim Hely Hutchinson,
Deputy Chief Executive Mark Opzoomer CA Canada,
MBA, *Directors* Martin Neild (managing, Hodder &
Stoughton General), Sue Fletcher (deputy
managing, Hodder & Stoughton General), John
Lloyd (non-executive), Mary Tapissier (managing,
Children's; chairman, Religious), Amanda Ridout
(managing, Headline), Malcolm Edwards
(managing, Australia and New Zealand), Philip

Walters (managing, Educational), Richard Stileman
(managing, Edward Arnold), Mandy Warnford-
Davis (non-executive), Richard Adam (finance)
Founded 1986.

Arnold (division)
Managing Director Richard Stileman, *Humanities*
Chris Wheeler, *Medical, Science and Engineering*
Nicki Dennis
Academic and professional books and
journals.

Brockhampton Press (division)
Managing Director John Maxwell, *Sales Director*
Jack Cooper
Promotional books.

Headline Book Publishing Ltd (division)
Managing Director Amanda Ridout, *Non-fiction*
Heather Holden-Brown, *Fiction* Jane Morpeth
Publishes under **Headline, Headline
Feature, Review**.
Publishers Anne Williams (Headline), Bill
Massey (Feature), Geraldine Cooke (Review)
Commercial and literary fiction (hard-
back and paperback); popular non-fiction
including sport and sports yearbooks,
cookery, autobiography and biography,
popular culture, TV tie-ins, crafts, gar-
dening, health and beauty, humour, refer-
ence and travel guides.
Delta, Liaison, Man2Man (imprints)
Associate Publisher Mike Bailey
Erotica.

Hodder Children's Books (division)
Managing Director Mary Tapissier, *Editorial
Director* Margaret Conroy
Publishes under **Hodder Children's Books**.
Picture books, fiction and non-fiction.

Hodder & Stoughton Educational
(division)
Managing Director Philip Walters, *Humanities,
Science, Mathematics and Catering* Elisabeth
Tribe, *Languages, Business and Psychology* Tim
Gregson-Williams, *Teach Yourself and Trade
Education* Lucy Purkis
Publishes under **Hodder & Stoughton
Educational, Teach Yourself, Headway**.
Textbooks for the primary, secondary,
tertiary and further education sectors
and for self-improvement.

Hodder & Stoughton General (division)
Managing Director Martin Neild, *Deputy
Managing Director* Sue Fletcher, *Non-fiction*
Roland Philipps, *Sceptre* Carole Welch, Neil
Taylor, *Fiction* Carolyn Mays, Carolyn Caughey,
Audio Rupert Lancaster
Publishes under **Hodder & Stoughton,
Coronet, New English Library, Sceptre,**

Lir. Commercial and literary fiction; biography, autobiography, history, self-help, humour, travel and other general interest non-fiction; audio.
Lir (imprint))
Fiction and non-fiction Irish writing.

Hodder & Stoughton Religious
(division)
Managing Director Charles Nettleton, *Editorial Directors* Emma Sealey (bibles and liturgical), Judith Longman (religious trade)
Publishes under **New International Version of the Bible, Hodder Christian** paperbacks. Bibles, commentaries, liturgical works (both printed and software), wide range of Christian paperbacks.

Hodder & Stoughton – see Hodder Headline plc*

Hodder Children's Books Ltd – see Hodder Headline plc*

Hogarth Press – imprint of Random House UK Ltd*

Hollis Directories Ltd
Harlequin House, 7 High Street, Teddington, Middlesex TW11 8EL
tel 0181-977 7711 *fax* 0181-977 1133
e-mail gary@hollis-pr.co.uk
web site http://www.hollis-pr.co.uk
Managing Director Gary Zabel
Publications include *Willings Press Guide, Hollis Press & PR Annual, Hollis Sponsorship Yearbook* and *Advertisers Annual.*

Holt, Rhinehart & Winston – see Harcourt Brace & Co. Ltd*

Honno Ltd (Welsh Women's Press)
Pen Roc, Rhodfa'r Môr, Aberystwyth, Ceredigion SY23 2AZ
tel/fax (01970) 623150
Secretary Rosanne Reeves *tel* (01222) 515014
Literature written by women in Wales or with a Welsh connection. All subjects considered – fiction, non-fiction, poetry, autobiographies. Honno is a collective. Founded 1986.

How To Books Ltd
3 Newtec Place, Magdalen Road, Oxford OX4 1RE
tel (01865) 793806 *fax* (01865) 248780
e-mail info@howtobooks.co.uk
web site http://www.howtobooks.co.uk
Managing Director Giles Lewis, *Secretary* Derek Phillips

How To series of personal achievement paperbacks covering student life, careers, education, training, management, employment, creative writing, general reference, business enterprise, personal development, health, living and working overseas. Outline proposals and ideas welcome. New and experienced authors receive personal attention and careful guidance. Founded 1991.

Hugo's Language Books Ltd
9 Henrietta Street, London WC2E 8PS
tel 0171-836 5411 *fax* 0171-836 7570
Editorial Director Robin Batchelor-Smith
Hugo's language books and courses. Acquired by Dorling Kindersley Ltd. Founded 1864.

Hunt & Thorpe
Deershot Lodge, Park Lane, Ropley, Nr Alresford, Hants. SO24 0BE
tel (01962) 773063 *fax* (01962) 772475
e-mail 106620.1267@compuserve.com
Director John Hunt
Children's and adult religious, full colour books for the international market. MSS welcome; send sae. Founded 1989.

C. Hurst & Co. (Publishers) Ltd*
38 King Street, London WC2E 8JZ
tel 0171-240 2666, (night) 0181-852 9021
fax 0171-240 2667
e-mail hurst@atlas.co.uk
web site http://www.hurstpub.co.uk
Directors Christopher Hurst, Michael Dwyer
Scholarly 'area studies' covering contemporary history, politics, social studies and the religions of Asia and Africa. Founded 1967.

Hutchinson – see Random House UK Ltd*

Hutchinson Children's – see Random House UK Ltd*

ICSA Publishing
Campus 400, Maylands Avenue, Hemel Hempstead, Herts. HP2 7EZ
tel (01442) 881900 *fax* (01442) 882074
e-mail michelle_long@prenhall.co.uk
Marketing Manager Michelle Long
Professional business books for the private, public and voluntary sectors. Publish titles for The Institute of Chartered Secretaries and Administrators. Founded 1981.

Idol – see Virgin Publishing Ltd

In Print Publishing Ltd
Montpelier House, 99 Montpelier Road,
Brighton BN1 3BE
tel (01273) 720891 *fax* (01273) 778244
Directors Michael Forster, Sarie Forster
Special interest travel (including literary guides), Japan, Southeast Asia, guides to teaching English. Founded 1990.

Indigo – see Cassell plc

InfoSource International – see Blackwell Publishers*

Institute of Personnel and Development
IPD House, 35 Camp Road, London SW19 4UX
tel 0181-971 9000 *fax* 0181-263 3333
e-mail publish@ipd.co.uk
web site http://www.ipd.co.uk/newbooks
Head of Publishing Judith Dennett
Personnel management, training and development.

Institute of Physics Publishing
Dirac House, Temple Back, Bristol BS1 6BE
tel 0117-929 7481 *fax* 0117-930 1186
e-mail margaret.ogorman@ioppublishing.co.uk
web site http://www.iop.org
Books and Reference Works Publisher Margaret O'Gorman
Monographs, graduate texts, conference proceedings and reference works in physics and physics-related science and technology; also popular science titles.

Institute of Public Administration†
Vergemount Hall, Clonskeagh, Dublin 6,
Republic of Ireland
tel (01) 2697011 *fax* (01) 2698644
e-mail tmcnamara@ipa.ie
web site http://www.ipa.ie
Head of Publishing Tony McNamara
Government, economics, politics, law, social policy and administrative history. Founded 1957.

Inter-Varsity Press*
38 De Montfort Street, Leicester LE1 7GP
tel 0116-255 1754 *fax* 0116-254 2044
e-mail ivp@uccf.org.uk
Managing Editor Mrs S.J. Heald
Theology and religion.

Irish Academic Press Ltd†
44 Northumberland Road, Ballsbridge, Dublin 4,
Republic of Ireland
tel (01) 6688244 *fax* (01) 6601610
e-mail info@iap.ie
web site http://www.iap.ie
Directors Stewart Cass, Frank Cass, Michael Philip Zaidner
Publishes under the imprints **Irish University Press** and **Irish Academic Press**. Scholarly books especially in 19th and 20th century history and literature. Founded 1974.

Ithaca Press – see Garnet Publishing Ltd

Arthur James Ltd
40 Lower Kings Road, Berkhamsted,
Herts. HP4 2AA
tel (01442) 877511 *fax* (01442) 873019
e-mail arthurjames@compuserve.com
Editorial Director John Hunt, *Managing Director* Ian Carlile
Religion, sociology, psychology, meditation. Founded 1935.

Jane's Information Group
163 Brighton Road, Coulsdon, Surrey CR5 2NH
tel 0181-700 3700 *fax* 0181-700 3704
web site http://www.janes.com/janes.html
Managing Director Alfred Rolington
Professional publishers in hardcopy and multimedia of military, aviation, naval, defence, non-fiction, reference, police, geo-political; CD-Rom games in association with Electronic Arts; consumer books in association with **HarperCollins Publishers**.

Jarrold Publishing
Whitefriars, Norwich NR3 1TR
tel (01603) 763300 *fax* (01603) 662748
Managing Director Antony Jarrold, *Publishing Director* Caroline Jarrold
UK and French travel guidebooks, pictorial books, gift books and calendars. About 30 titles a year. Unsolicited MSS, synopses and ideas welcome but approach in writing before submitting to Donald Greig, Managing Editor. Division of Jarrold & Sons Ltd. Founded 1770.

Jewish Chronicle Publications
c/o Vallentine Mitchell, Newbury House,
900 Eastern Avenue, Ilford, Essex IG2 7HH
tel 0181-599 8866 *fax* 0171-405 9040
e-mail vm@frankcass.com
web site http://www.frankcass.com/um
Theology and religion, reference; *Jewish Year Book*, *Jewish Travel Guide*.

Johnson Publications Ltd
130 Wigmore Street, London W1H 0AT
tel 0171-486 6757 *fax* 0171-487 5436
Directors M.A. Murray-Pearce, Z.M. Pauncefort

Perfume, aromachology, cosmetics, beauty culture, aromatherapy and essential oils, including dictionaries, *objets d'art*, advertising, marketing, beauty business, biography and memoirs. Send return postage with unsolicited MSS. Founded 1946.

John Jones Publishing Ltd

Unit 12, Clwydfro Business Centre, Ruthin, Denbighshire LL15 1NJ
tel/fax (01824) 705272
Directors John Idris Jones (managing), Denise Idris Jones

Paperbacks in English with a Welsh background: topography, biography, travel, children's, history of the Celts and the Elizabethan period. Founded 1979.

Jordan Publishing Ltd

21 St Thomas Street, Bristol BS1 6JS
tel 0117-923 0600 *fax* 0117-925 0486
web sites http://www.jordanpublishing.co.uk
http://www.familylaw.co.uk
Managing Director Richard Hudson

Law and business administration. Also specialist Family Law imprint (including the *Family Law Journal*). Books, looseleaf services, serials, CD-Roms and on-line.

Michael Joseph – see Penguin UK*

The Journeyman Press – see Pluto Press

Karnak House

300 Westbourne Park Road,
London W11 1EH
tel/fax 0171-243 3620
Directors Dimela Yekwai (chairman), Amon Saba Saakana (editorial), Gloria Flaxman (administration), Seheri Sujai (art)

Specialists in African/Caribbean studies worldwide: anthropology, education, Egyptology, fiction, history, language, linguistics, literary criticism, music, parapsychology, philosophy, prehistory. Founded 1979.

Kelly's – see Reed Business Information

The Kenilworth Press Ltd

Addington, Buckingham MK18 2JR
tel (0129 671) 5101 *fax* (0129 671) 5148
e-mail mail@kenilworthpress.co.uk
Directors David Blunt, Deirdre Blunt

Equestrian, including official publications for the British Horse Society. Founded 1989. Incorporates Threshold Books; founded 1970.

Kenyon-Deane – see Cressrelles Publishing Co. Ltd

Laurence King Publishing*

71 Great Russell Street, London WC1B 3BN
tel 0171-831 6351 *fax* 0171-831 8356
e-mail calmann_king@compuserve.com
Directors Robin Hyman (chairman), Laurence King (managing), Lesley Ripley Greenfield (editorial: college and fine arts), Judith Rasmussen (production), John Stoddart (financial)

Illustrated books on design, art, architecture, carpets and textiles. Imprint of **Calmann & King Ltd**, book packagers. Founded 1991.

Kingfisher Publications plc*

(formerly Larousse plc)
New Penderel House, 283-288 High Holborn,
London WC1V 7HZ
tel 0171-903 9999 *fax* 0171-242 4979
Chairman Bertil Hessel, *Directors* Marc Zagar (finance), Robert Snuggs (sales and marketing), John Richards (production)

Kingfisher (imprint)

Publishing Directors Gill Denton (non-fiction), Ann-Janine Murtagh (fiction)

Children's books.

Larousse (imprint)

Reference books and bilingual dictionaries.

Jessica Kingsley Publishers*

116 Pentonville Road, London N1 9JB
tel 0171-833 2307 *fax* 0171-837 2917
e-mail post@jkp.com
web site http://www.jkp.com
Director Jessica Kingsley

Psychology, psychotherapy, psychiatry, arts therapies, social work, higher education policy, regional studies, education, law, anthropology. Founded 1987.

Kingsway Publications

Lottbridge Drove, Eastbourne,
East Sussex BN23 6NT
tel (01323) 437740 *fax* (01323) 411970
Managing Director John Paculabo, *Director of Publishing* Richard Herkes

Christian theology for the lay person. Submissions must have Evangelical Christian content. Please send synopsis/2 sample chapters only with return postage.

Kluwer Publishing

Croner House, London Road,
Kingston-upon-Thames, Surrey KT2 6SR
tel 0181-547 3333 *fax* 0181-547 2637
Managing Director Hans Staal

Law, taxation, finance, insurance, looseleaf information services. Subsidiary of Croner Publications Ltd. Founded 1972.

Knight – now Hodder Children's Books, see Hodder Headline plc*

Charles Knight Publishing – see Tolley Publishing Co. Ltd

Knockabout Comics
10 Acklam Road, London W10 5QZ
tel 0181-969 2945 *fax* 0181-968 7614
Editors Tony Bennett, Carol Bennett
Humorous and satirical comic strips for an adult readership. Founded 1975.

Kogan Page Ltd*
120 Pentonville Road, London N1 9JN
tel 0171-278 0433 *fax* 0171-837 6348
Managing Director Philip Kogan, *Directors* Pauline Goodwin (editorial), Peter Chadwick (production and editorial), Gordon Watts (financial), Philip Mudd (editorial), Jonathan Sinclair-Wilson (Earthscan, editorial), Julie McNair (sales)
Education, training, educational and training technology, journals, business and management, human resource management, transport and distribution, marketing, sales, advertising and PR, finance and accounting, directories, small business, careers and vocational, personal finance, environment. Founded 1967.

Earthscan Publications Ltd (subsidiary)
Directors Philip Kogan, Jonathan Sinclair-Wilson (editorial)
Third World and environmental issues including politics, sociology, environment, economics, current events, geography, health.

Kompass – see Reed Business Information

Ladybird Books Ltd*
Beeches Road, Loughborough,
Leics. LE11 2NQ
tel (01509) 268021 *fax* (01509) 234672
Managing Director Laurence James, *Publishing Director* Michael Herridge
Children's books for 0-10 year-olds – babies, toddlers, preschoolers, general and home educational (infants, primary, junior and secondary). Subsidiary of the Penguin Group. Founded 1924.

Lampada Press – see The University of Hull Press

Larousse – see Kingfisher Publications plc*

Lawrence & Wishart Ltd
99A Wallis Road, London E9 5LN
tel 0181-533 2506 *fax* 0181-533 7369
e-mail lw@l-w-bks.demon.co.uk
web site http://www.l-w-bks.co.uk
Directors S. Davison (editorial), J. Rodrigues, B. Kirsch, M. Seaton, M. Perryman, A. Greenaway, G. Andrews
Cultural studies, current affairs, history, socialism and Marxism, political philosophy, politics, popular culture.

Legend – see Little, Brown and Company (UK)*

Leicester University Press – see Cassell plc

Lennard Publishing
Windmill Cottage, Mackerye End, Harpenden, Herts. AL5 5DR
tel (01582) 715866 *fax* (01582) 715121
e-mail lennard@lenqap.demon.co.uk
Directors K.A.A. Stephenson, R.H. Stephenson
Media tie-ins, sponsored books, special commissions. No unsolicited MSS. Division of Lennard Associates Ltd.

Letts Educational – see BPP (Letts Educational) Ltd

Levinson Books Ltd
Winchester House, 259-269 Old Marylebone Road, London NW1 5XJ
tel 0171-616 7200 *fax* 0171-616 7201
Managing Director Neil A. Page, *Publisher* Neil Burden, *Art Director* Paula Burgess
Picture books, novelty books, toy books, activity books for under-7 age group. Division of **David & Charles Ltd**. Founded 1994.

Lewis Masonic
Riverdene, Molesey Road, Hersham,
Surrey KT12 4RG
tel (01932) 266600 *fax* (01932) 266601
Masonic books; *Masonic Square Magazine*. Founded 1870.

Liaison – see Hodder Headline plc*

John Libbey & Co. Ltd
13 Smiths Yard, Summerley Street,
London SW18 4HR
tel 0181-947 2777 *fax* 0181-947 2664
e-mail libbey@earlsfield.win-uk.net
Directors John Libbey, G. Cahn

Medical: nutrition, obesity, epilepsy, neurology, nuclear medicine, oncology. Film/cinema. Founded 1979.

Library Association Publishing*
7 Ridgmount Street, London WC1E 7AE
tel 0171-636 7543 *fax* 0171-636 3627
e-mail lapublishing@la-hq.org.uk
Managing Director Janet Liebster
Library and information science, information technology, reference works, directories, bibliographies.
Clive Bingley Ltd (imprint)
Library and information science, reference works.

Libris Ltd
10 Burghley Road, London NW5 1UE
tel 0171-482 2390 *fax* 0171-485 4220
Directors Nicholas Jacobs, S.A. Kitzinger
Literature, literary biography, German studies, bilingual poetry. Founded 1986.

The Lilliput Press Ltd[†]
62-63 Sitric Road, Dublin 7, Republic of Ireland
tel (01) 6711647 *fax* (01) 6711233
e-mail lilliput@indigo.ie
web site http://indigo.ie/~lilliput
Managing Director Antony T. Farrell
General and Irish literature: essays, biography/autobiography, fiction, criticism; Irish history; philosophy; contemporary culture; nature and environment. Founded 1984.

Frances Lincoln Ltd
4 Torriano Mews, Torriano Avenue, London NW5 2RZ
tel 0171-284 4009 *fax* 0171-485 0490
Directors Frances Lincoln (managing), Erica Hunningher (editorial, adult books), Janetta Otter-Barry (editorial, children's books)
Illustrated, international co-editions: gardening, interiors, health, cookery, art, gift, children's books. Founded 1977.

Lion Publishing plc*
Peter's Way, Sandy Lane West, Oxford OX4 5HG
tel (01865) 747550 *fax* (01865) 747568
web site http://lion-publishing.co.uk
Directors David Alexander, Denis Cole, Tony Wales, Rebecca Winter (editorial), Paul Clifford (managing), Dy Leyland, Peter Young, John O'Nions
Reference, paperbacks, illustrated children's books, educational, gift books, religion and theology; all reflecting a Christian position. No adult fiction. Send preliminary letter before submitting MSS. Founded 1971.

Lions – see HarperCollins Publishers*

Lir – see Hodder Headline plc*

Little, Brown and Company (UK)*
Brettenham House, Lancaster Place, London WC2E 7EN
tel 0171-911 8000 *fax* 0171-911 8100
Chief Executive and Publisher Philippa Harrison, *Directors* David Young (managing), B. Boote (editorial), A. Samson (editorial), David Kent (home sales), Nigel Batt (financial), Charles Viney (export sales), Terry Jackson (marketing)
Hardback and paperback fiction, general non-fiction and illustrated books. No unsolicited MSS. Founded 1988.
Abacus (division)
Editorial Director Richard Beswick
Trade paperbacks.
Illustrated (division)
Editorial Director Julia Charles
Hardback photographic and art books.
Orbit/Legend (imprint)
Editorial Director Tim Holman
Science fiction and fantasy paperbacks.
Virago (division)
Publisher Lennie Goodings, *Senior Editor* Sally Abbey
Fiction, including Modern Classics Series, biography, autobiography and general non-fiction which highlight all aspects of women's lives.
Warner (division)
Editorial Directors Barbara Boote, Alan Samson, Hilary Hale, Imogen Taylor
Paperbacks: original fiction and non-fiction; reprints.
X Libris (imprint)
Editor Hilary Hale
Erotic fiction for women.

Liverpool University Press*
Senate House, Abercromby Square, Liverpool L69 3BX
tel 0151-794 2233/7 *fax* 0151-794 2235
e-mail sandrob@liverpool.ac.uk
Publisher Robin Bloxsidge
Academic and scholarly books in a range of disciplines. Special interests: art history, education, European and American literature, science fiction criticism, social, political, economic and ancient history, archaeology, veterinary science, urban and regional planning. New series established include *Modern French Writers* and *Public Sculpture of Britain*. Founded 1899.

Livewire – see The Women's Press

Y Lolfa Cyf.
Talybont, Ceredigion SY24 5AP
tel (01970) 832304 *fax* (01970) 832782
e-mail ylolfa@ylolfa.com
web site http://www. ylolfa.com
Directors Robat Gruffudd, Enid Gruffudd,
Garmon Gruffudd, *Editor* Lefi Gruffudd
Welsh-language popular fiction and non-
fiction, music, children's books; Welsh-
language tutors; English-language political
books and a range of Welsh-interest books
for the tourist market. Founded 1967.

Lonely Planet Publications
10A Spring Place, London NW5 3BH
tel 0171-428 4800 *fax* 0171-428 4828
e-mail go@lonelyplanet.co.uk
web site http://www.lonelyplanet.com/
Directors Tony Wheeler, Jim Hart, Maureen
Wheeler, *General Manager UK* Charlotte Hindle
Travel guidebooks, atlases, phrasebooks,
walking guides, diving guides, travel literature. Founded 1973.

Longman Group – see Addison Wesley
Longman Ltd*

Longman Training – now Training
Direct – see Pearson Professional Ltd*

Lorenz Books – see Anness Publishing

Peter Lowe (Eurobook Ltd)
PO Box 52, Wallingford, Oxon OX10 0XU
tel (01865) 858333 *fax* (01865) 858263
e-mail eurobook@compuserve.com
Director P.S. Lowe
Publishers of popular science and related
subjects (including natural history) as
illustrated non-fiction. Age 12+ but no
general or teen fiction. Founded 1968.

Lund Humphries Publishers Ltd
Park House, 1 Russell Gardens,
London NW11 9NN
tel 0181-458 6314 *fax* 0181-905 5245
Managing Director Lionel Leventhal, *Editorial
Director* Lucy Myers
Art, architecture, photography, graphic
art and design.

Lutterworth Press – see James Clarke
& Co. Ltd*

Macdonald Young Books
61 Western Road, Hove, East Sussex BN3 1JD
tel (01273) 722561 *fax* (01273) 329314
e-mail wayland1@fastnet.co.uk

Publishing Director Stephen White-Thomson
Fiction, non-fiction, picture books and
story books for children from preschool
to teenage. Imprint of **Wayland
Publishers Ltd**. Founded 1994.

**McGraw-Hill Book Company
Europe***
McGraw-Hill House, Shoppenhangers Road,
Maidenhead, Berks. SL6 2QL
tel (01628) 502500 *fax* (01628) 770224
Group Vice President Italo Raimondi, *Directors*
Alfred Waller (publishing), Brian Newson
(operations), Peter Kitley (financial)
Technical, scientific, professional refer-
ence.

Macmillan Interactive Publishing –
see Macmillan Publishers Ltd*

Macmillan Press Ltd – see Macmillan
Publishers Ltd*

Macmillan Publishers Ltd*
25 Eccleston Place, London SW1W 9NF
tel 0171- 881 8000 *fax* 0171-881 8001
Chairman N.G. Byam Shaw, *Chief Executive*
Richard Charkin, *Directors* R. Barker, M. Barnard,
C.J. Paterson, A. Soar, A.J. Sutherland, G.R.U. Todd
Macmillan Children's Books Ltd
(division)
Managing Director Kate Wilson, *Editorial
Director (Picture Books and Properties)* Alison
Green, *Editorial Director* Marion Lloyd
Publishes under **Macmillan, Pan,
Campbell Books**. Picture books, fiction,
poetry, non-fiction, early learning, pop-
up, novelty. No unsolicited material.
Macmillan General Books (division)
Managing Director Ian S. Chapman
Publishes under **Macmillan, Pan,
Papermac, Sidgwick & Jackson**.
Boxtree
See page 164.
Macmillan
Publisher Jeremy Trevathan, *Editorial Directors*
Suzanne Baboneau (fiction), Beverley Cousins
(crime), Peter Lavery (thrillers)
Novels, crime, science fiction, fantasy
and horror.
Editorial Director (Non-fiction) Georgina Morley
Autobiography, biography, business, gift
books, health and beauty, history,
humour, natural history, travel, philoso-
phy, politics and world affairs, psycholo-
gy, theatre and film, gardening and cook-
ery, encyclopedias. Founded 1865.

Pan
Publisher Clare Harington
Fiction: novels, crime, science fiction, fantasy and horror. Non-fiction: sports, theatre and film, travel, gardening and cookery, encyclopedias, general. Founded 1947.

Papermac
Senior Editor Tanya Stobbs
Serious non-fiction: history, biography, science, political economy, cultural criticism and art history. Founded 1965.

Picador
Publisher Peter Straus, *Editorial Director* Ursula Doyle
Literary international fiction and non-fiction, poetry. Founded 1972.

Sidgwick & Jackson
Senior Editor Gordon Wise
Military and war, music, pop and rock. MSS, synopses and ideas welcome. Send to submissions editor, with return postage. Founded 1908.

Macmillan Interactive Publishing (division)
New Media Development Director Michael Barnard
CD-Rom and on-line.

Macmillan Reference Ltd (division)
Managing Director Ian Jacobs, *Publishing Directors* Gina Fullerlove (science), Margot Levy (Grove), *Marketing Director* Emma Hardcastle, *Production Director* John Peacock, *Art Publisher* Diane Fortenberry
Reference works in academic, professional and vocational subjects. Founded 1998.

Macmillan Education (division)
Houndmills, Basingstoke, Hants RG21 6XS
tel (01256) 329242 *fax* (01256) 479985
Managing Director Christopher Harrison, *Publishing Director* Alison Hubert, *Sales Director* John G. Watson, *Director (Latin America)* Christopher West
International School and College books in all subjects for all ages.

Macmillan Press Ltd (division)
Managing Director D. Knight, *Publishing Directors* J. Marks (journals), T.M. Farmiloe (academic), S. Kennedy (college), S. Rutt (economics and business), F. Arnold (humanities and social sciences)
Textbooks and monographs in academic, professional and vocational subjects; medical and scientific journals.

Macmillan Heinemann English Language Teaching (division)
Halley Court, Jordan Hill, Oxford OX2 8EJ
tel (01865) 311366 *fax* (01865) 314193
Managing Directors Mike Esplen, Chris Harrison, *Director, ELT Publishing* Sue Bale
English language teaching materials and curriculum publishing for international markets.

Julia MacRae Books – see Random House UK Ltd*

Madcap – see André Deutsch Ltd*

Magi Publications
22 Manchester Street, London W1M 5PG
tel 0171-486 0925 *fax* 0171-486 0926
e-mail mb@magi-publication.demon.co.uk
Publisher Monty Bhatia, *Editor* Linda Jennings
Quality children's picture books and novelty books. New material will be considered from authors and illustrators, but please enquire first. Founded 1987.

Magpie – see Robinson Publishing Ltd

Mainstream Publishing Co. (Edinburgh) Ltd*
7 Albany Street, Edinburgh EH1 3UG
tel 0131-557 2959 *fax* 0131-556 8720
Directors Bill Campbell, Peter MacKenzie
Biography, autobiography, art, photography, sport, health, guidebooks, humour, literature, current affairs, history, politics. Founded 1978.

Mammoth – see Egmont Children's Books

Management Books 2000 Ltd
(incorporating Mercury Books)
Cowcombe House, Cowcombe Hill, Chalford, Glos. GL6 8HP
tel (01285) 760722 *fax* (01285) 760708
e-mail mb2000@compuserve.com
Directors N. Dale-Harris (publisher), R. Hartman
Business and life skills books.

Manchester United Books – see André Deutsch Ltd*

Manchester University Press*
Oxford Road, Manchester M13 9NR
tel 0161-273 5539 *fax* 0161-274 3346
e-mail mup@man.ac.uk
web site http://www.man.ac.uk/mup
Editorial Director Vanessa Graham
Works of academic scholarship: literary criticism, cultural studies, media studies, art history, design, architecture, history, politics, economics, international law, modern language texts. Textbooks and monographs. Founded 1912.

Mandarin – acquired by Random House UK Ltd

Mandrake of Oxford
PO Box 250, Oxford OX1 1AP
tel (01865) 243671 *fax* (01865) 432929
e-mail krm@mandrake.cix.co.uk
web site http://www.compulink.co.uk/~mandrake/welcome.htm
Directors Kris Morgan, Shantidevi Nath
Occult and bizarre. Founded 1986.

Mansell Publishing – see Cassell plc

Manson Publishing Ltd*
73 Corringham Road, London NW11 7DL
tel 0181-905 5150 *fax* 0181-201 9233
e-mail manson@man-pub.demon.co.uk
Managing Director Michael Manson
Medical, scientific, veterinary. Founded 1992.

Mantra Publishing
5 Alexandra Grove, London N12 8NU
tel 0181-445 5123 *fax* 0181-446 7745
e-mail mantrapub@aol.com
web site http://www.mantrapublishing.com
Managing Director M. Chatterji
Children's multicultural picture books; dual language books/cassettes; South Asian literature/teenage fiction; CD-Roms and videos. Founded 1984.

Man2Man – see Hodder Headline plc*

Marino Books – see The Mercier Press†

Marshall Publishing*
170 Piccadilly, London W1V 9DD
tel 0171-629 0079 *fax* 0171-834 8844
e-mail info@mediakey.u-net.com
web site http://www.marshallmedia.com
Directors Richard Harman (chairman), Nick Croydon (Ceo), Barbara Anderson Marshall, Barry Baker (operations), John Christmas, David Rivers, Andrew Lee (financial)
Highly illustrated non-fiction: health, gardening, home and DIY, physical fitness, travel, natural history, children's information reference. Founded 1997.

Marshall Pickering – see HarperCollins Publishers*

Martin Books
Grafton House, 64 Maids Causeway, Cambridge CB5 8DD
tel (01223) 366733 *fax* (01223) 461428
Editorial Director Janet Copleston
Cookery, gardening, illustrated non-fiction and sponsored publishing. Imprint

of Simon & Schuster Consumer Group.

Kenneth Mason Publications Ltd
Dudley House, 12 North Street, Emsworth, Hants PO10 7DQ
tel (01243) 377977 *fax* (01243) 379136
Directors Kenneth Mason (chairman), Piers Mason (managing), Michael Mason, Anthea Mason
Nautical, slimming, health, fitness; technical journals. Founded 1958.

Kevin Mayhew Ltd
Buxhall, Suffolk IP14 3DJ
tel (01449) 737978 *fax* (01449) 737834
e-mail kevinmayhewltd@msn.com
Directors Kevin Mayhew (chairman), Gordon Carter (managing) Ray Gilbert (production), Jonathan Bugden (sales)
Christianity: prayer and spirituality, pastoral care, preaching, liturgy worship, *Springboard* series, children's, youth work, drama, instant art. Music: hymns, organ and choral, piano and instrumental. Contact Editorial Dept before sending MSS/synopses. Founded 1976.

Medical & Historical – see Harlequin Mills & Boon Ltd*

Medici Society Ltd
34-42 Pentonville Road, London N1 9HG
tel 0171-837 7099 *fax* 0171-837 9152
Publishers of Medici Prints, greetings cards and other colour reproductions. Art, nature and illustrated children's books. Send preliminary letter with brief details of the work marked for the attention of the Art Director.

Melrose Press Ltd
3 Regal Lane, Soham, Ely, Cambs. CB7 5BA
tel (01353) 721091 *fax* (01353) 721839
e-mail tradesales@melrosepress.co.uk
Directors R.A. Kay, J.M. Kay, B.J. Wilson, N.S. Law (editorial), C. Emmett FCA, V.A. Kay, J.E. Pearson
International biographical reference works, including *International Authors & Writers Who's Who*, *International Who's Who in Poetry* and *Poets' Encyclopedia*. Founded 1969.

The Mercat Press*
James Thin Ltd, 53-59 South Bridge, Edinburgh EH1 1YS
tel 0131-556 6743 *fax* 0131-557 8149
e-mail mercat@jthin.co.uk
web site http://www.jthin.co.uk/merchome.htm
Chairman D. Ainslie Thin, *Editorial Managers* Tom Johnstone, Seán Costello

Scottish books of general and academic interest. No fiction or new poetry. Founded 1970.

The Mercier Press†
PO Box 5, 5 French Church Street, Cork, Republic of Ireland
tel (021) 275040 *fax* (021) 274969
e-mail books@mercier.ie
web site http://www.mercier.ie/mercier
Directors G. Eaton (chairman), J.F. Spillane (managing), M.P. Feehan, D.J. Keily, A. O'Donnell, J. O'Donoghue
Irish literature, folklore, history, politics, humour, ballads, education, theology, law. Founded 1944.

Marino Books (imprint)
16 Hume Street, Dublin 2, Republic of Ireland
tel (01) 6615299 *fax* (01) 6618583
e-mail books@marino.ie
Publisher Jo O'Donoghue
Fiction, children's fiction, current affairs, health, mind and spirit, general non-fiction.

Merehurst Ltd
Ferry House, 51-57 Lacy Road, London SW15 1PR
tel 0181-355 1480 *fax* 0181-355 1499
Publisher/Ceo Anne Wilson, *Group General Manager* Mark Smith, *International Sales Director* Mark Newman, *General Manager* David Meads, *Key Accounts Manager* Debbie Kent
Crafts and hobbies, cake art, cookery, homes and interiors, children's non-fiction, gardening, DIY.

Merlin Press Ltd
2 Rendlesham Mews, Rendlesham, Nr Woodbridge, Suffolk IP12 2SZ
tel (01394) 461313 *fax* (01394) 461314
Directors M.W. Eve, P.M. Eve
Radical history and social studies. Letters/synopses only please.

Green Print (imprint)
Green politics and the environment.

Seafarer Books (imprint)
Commissioning Editor Martin Eve
Books on traditional sailing, mainly narrative.

Merrell Holberton Publishers Ltd
Willcox House, 42 Southwark Street, London SE1 1UN
tel 0171-403 2047 *fax* 0171-407 1333
e-mail merrholb@dircon.co.uk
Publishing Director Hugh Merrell, *Editorial Director* Paul Holberton
Illustrated fine art books. Founded 1993.

Merrow Publishing Co. Ltd
22 Abbey Road, Darlington, Co. Durham DL3 8LR
tel (01325) 351661 *fax* (01325) 351661
Directors Dr J.G. Cook (editorial), M. Cook, J.A. Verdon, A.M. Creasey
Textiles, plastics, popular science, scientific. Founded 1951.

Methodist Publishing House
20 Ivatt Way, Peterborough PE3 7PG
tel (01733) 332202 *fax* (01733) 331201
Chief Executive Brian Thornton
Hymn and service books, general religious titles, church supplies. Founded 1773.

Chester House Publications (imprint)
Children and youth titles.

Foundery Press (imprint)
Ecumenical titles.

Methuen – see Random House UK Ltd*

Methuen Academic – now incorporated into Routledge*

Methuen Children's Books – see Egmont Children's Books

Metro Publishing Ltd
19 Gerrard Street, London W1V 7LA
tel 0171-734 1411 *fax* 0171-734 1811
Chairman Alan Brooke, *Managing Director* Susanne McDadd, *Editorial Manager* Mary Remnant, *Sales Director* Les Phipps, *Publicity Manager* Becke Parker

Metro Books (imprint)
'Books to help you get the most out of life.' Non-fiction: popular psychology, cookery, gardening childcare, self-help, health, travel, leisure, biography, autobiography. Founded 1995.

Michelin Tyre plc
Tourism Department, The Edward Hyde Building, 38 Clarendon Road, Watford, Herts. WD1 1SX
tel (01923) 415000 *fax* (01923) 415052
Head of Tourism Department J. Lewis
Tourist guides, maps and atlases, hotel and restaurant guides; children's activity books.

Milestone Publications
62 Murray Road, Horndean, Waterlooville PO8 9SL
tel (01705) 597440 *fax* (01705) 591975
Managing Director Nicholas J. Pine
Heraldic china, antique porcelain, business, economics. Founded 1967.

Millennium – see The Orion Publishing Group Ltd

J. Garnet Miller Ltd
10 Station Road Industrial Estate, Colwall, Malvern, Worcs. WR13 6RN
tel (01684) 540154 *fax* (01684) 540154
Directors Leslie Smith, Simon Smith
Plays and theatre textbooks, especially for amateur dramatic societies. Division of **Cressrelles Publishing Ltd**. Founded 1951.

Harvey Miller Publishers*
197 Knightsbridge, London SW7 1RB
tel 0171-584 7676 *fax* 0171-823 7969
e-mail elly.miller@gbhap.com
Editor-in-Chief Elly Miller
Art history. Imprint of G+B Arts International.

Miller Freeman Information Services
Riverbank House, Angel Lane, Tonbridge, Kent TN9 1SE
tel (01732) 362666 *fax* (01732) 367301
Over 20 directories for business and industry, including *Benn's Media* and *The Knowledge*, guides for the media and film and TV markets respectively. Subsidiary of Miller Freeman plc.

Millers – see Reed Books

Mills & Boon (Publishers) Ltd – now Harlequin Mills & Boon Ltd*

Mira Books – see Harlequin Mills & Boon Ltd*

The MIT Press – see under USA in Overseas book publishers, page 230

Mitchell Beazley – see Reed Books

Monarch Publications
Broadway House, The Broadway, Crowborough, East Sussex TN6 1HQ
tel (01892) 652364 *fax* (01892) 663329
e-mail monarch@dial.pipex.com
Publisher Tony Collins, Jane Collins
Christian books: (Monarch) issues of faith and society; (MARC) leadership, mission, evangelism. Submit synopsis/2 sample chapters only with return postage please.

Mosby International
5th Floor, Lynton House, 7-12 Tavistock Square, London WC1H 9LB
tel 0171-388 7676 *fax* 0171-391 6555

Mosby (imprint)
International student textbooks and postgraduate works of reference in full colour in medicine, nursing and bio-medical sciences.

Mosby Wolfe (imprint)
International colour atlases in medicine, biomedical science, dentistry and veterinary medical.

Mosby Wolfe Medical Communications (division)
Managing Director Derrick Holman
Supplies the global pharmaceutical industry with medically relevant educational and promotional programmes in support of ethical drugs. Produces books, slide sets and multimedia programmes for the clinical and consumer health markets. Also runs the co-editions and translation rights businesses.

Mount Eagle Publications Ltd†
(incorporating Brandon Book Publishers Ltd)
PO Box 32, Dingle, Co. Kerry, Republic of Ireland
tel (353) 66 51463 *fax* (353) 66 51234
Publisher Steve MacDonogh
Fiction, biography and current affairs. No unsolicited MSS. Founded 1997.

Mowbray – see Cassell plc

MQ Publications Ltd
254-258 Goswell Road, London EC1V 7EB
tel 0171-490 7732 *fax* 0171-253 7358
Chief Executive Officer Susan Jenkins
Craft, style and gift books. Founded 1993.

Multimedia Books Ltd – now Prion Books

John Murray (Publishers) Ltd*
50 Albemarle Street, London W1X 4BD
tel 0171-493 4361 *fax* 0171-499 1792
Chairman John R. Murray (general books marketing), *Managing Director* Nicholas Perren, *Directors* Grant McIntyre (general editorial), Judith Reinhold (educational marketing), *Company Secretary* Philip Carter
General: art and architecture, biography and autobiography, letters and diaries, travel, exploration and guidebooks, Middle East, Asia, India and sub-continent, general history, health education, aviation, craft and practical. No unsolicited MSS please.
   Educational: biology, chemistry, physics, business studies, economics, management and law, English, geography

and environmental studies, history and social studies, mathematics, modern languages, special educational needs, technical subjects. Also self teaching in all subjects in *Success Studybook* series. Founded 1768.

National Christian Education Council*

(incorporating International Bible Reading Association)
1020 Bristol Road, Selly Oak, Birmingham B26 6LB
tel 0121-472 4242 *fax* 0121-472 7575
e-mail ncec@netlink.co.uk
web site http://www.netlink.co.uk/users.ncec/
Resource materials for worship and learning in Church. Training material for children and youth workers in the Church. Worship resources for use in primary schools. Christian drama and musicals, Activity Club material and Bible reading resources.

National Poetry Foundation

27 Mill Road, Fareham,
Hants PO16 0TH
tel (01329) 822218
Founder/Trustee Johnathon Clifford
Poetry. Founded 1981.

The National Trust

36 Queen Anne's Gate, London SW1H 9AS
tel 0171-222 9251 *fax* 0171-222 5097
Publisher Margaret Willes
History, cookery, architecture, gardening, guidebooks, children's non-fiction. No unsolicited MSS. Founded 1895.

The Natural History Museum Publishing Division

Cromwell Road, London SW7 5BD
tel 0171-938 9048 *fax* 0171-938 8709
e-mail j.hogg@nhm.ac.uk
Head of Publishing Jane Hogg
Natural sciences; entomology, botany, geology, palaeontology, zoology. Founded 1881.

Nautical Books – now Adlard Coles Nautical – see A & C Black (Publishers) Ltd*

NCVO Publications

(incorporating Bedford Square Press)
Regent's Wharf, 8 All Saints Street,
London N1 9RL
tel 0171-713 6161 *fax* 0171-713 6300
Imprint of the National Council for Voluntary Organisations. Practical guides, reference books, directories and policy studies on voluntary sector concerns including management and trustee development, legal, finance and fundraising, self-help and Europe. No unsolicited MSS accepted.

Thomas Nelson & Sons Ltd*

Nelson House, Mayfield Road,
Walton-on-Thames, Surrey KT12 5PL
tel (01932) 252211 *fax* (01932) 246109
e-mail nelinfo@nelson.co.uk
Directors Nigel Hall (managing), Ben Stringer (financial)
Print and electronic publishers for educational market (primary, secondary and college). Imprint: Arden Shakespeare. Member of the Thomson Corporation. Founded 1798.

Network Books – see BBC Worldwide Ltd*

New Adventures – see Virgin Publishing Ltd

New Beacon Books

76 Stroud Green Road, London N4 3EN
tel 0171-272 4889
Directors John La Rose, Sarah White, Michael La Rose, Janice Durham
Small specialist publishers: general non-fiction, fiction, poetry, critical writings, mainly concerning the Caribbean, Africa, African-America, Black Britain and Europe. No unsolicited MSS. Founded 1966.

New Cavendish Books

3 Denbigh Road, London W11 2SJ
tel 0171-229 6765/792 9984 *fax* 0171-792 01027
e-mail narisa@new-cav.demon.co.uk
Specialist books for the collector; art reference, Thai guidebooks. Founded 1973.

Golden Age Editions (imprint)
Contact Chris Shelley
Limited edition books on fine toys.

White Mouse Editions Ltd (imprint)
Contact Chris Shelley
Transport.

New English Library – see Hodder Headline plc*

New Holland (Publishers) Ltd*

Chapel House, 24 Nutford Place, London W1H 6DQ
tel 0171-724 7773 *fax* 0171-724 6184
e-mail vobis@nhpub.u-net.com
Managing Director John Beaufoy, *Publishing*

Directors Charlotte Parry-Crooke, Yvonne McFarlane (lifestyle)

Illustrated books on natural history, travel, cookery, needlecrafts and handicrafts, interior design, DIY, gardening.

New Orchard Editions – see Cassell plc

New Playwrights' Network

10 Station Road Industrial Estate, Colwall, Nr Malvern. Worcs. WR13 6RN
tel/fax (01684) 540154
Publishing Director Leslie Smith

General plays for the amateur, one-act and full length.

Nexus – see Virgin Publishing Ltd

Nexus Special Interests Ltd

Nexus House, Azalea Drive, Swanley, Kent BR8 8HU
tel (01322) 660070 *fax* (01322) 668421
Manager B. Burkinshaw

Modelling, model engineering, woodworking, aviation, railways, military, crafts, electronics, home brewing and winemaking.

NFER-NELSON Publishing Co. Ltd*

Darville House, 2 Oxford Road East, Windsor, Berks. SL4 1DF
tel (01753) 858961 *fax* (01753) 856830
e-mails edu&hsc@nfer-nelson.co.uk
ase@nfer-nelson.co.uk
web site http://www.nfer.nelson.co.uk

Testing, assessment and management publications and services for education, business and health care. Founded 1981.

Nia – see the X Press

Nicholson – see HarperCollins Publishers*

James Nisbet & Co. Ltd

78 Tilehouse Street, Hitchin, Herts. SG5 2DY
tel (01462) 438331 *fax* (01462) 431528
Directors Miss E.M. Mackenzie-Wood, Mrs A.A.C. Bierrum

Dictionaries, educational (infants, primary, secondary), business management. Founded 1810.

Northcote House Publishers Ltd

Plymbridge House, Estover Road, Plymouth, Devon PL6 7PY
tel (01752) 202368 *fax* (01752) 202330
Directors B.R.W. Hulme, A.V. Hulme (secretary)

Careers, education and education management, educational dance and drama, English literature (*Writers and their Work*). Founded 1985.

W.W. Norton & Company

10 Coptic Street, London WC1A 1PU
tel 0171-323 1579 *fax* 0171-436 4553
Managing Director Alan Cameron

History, biography, current affairs, sailing, English and American literature, economics, music, psychology, science. Founded 1980.

Notting Hill Electronic Publishers

31 Brunswick Gardens, London W8 4AW
tel 0171-229 0591 *fax* 0171-727 6641
e-mail 100444.232 @compuserve.com
Chairman Andreas Whittam Smith, *Directors* Ben Whittam Smith, Rachael Broughton (sales and marketing)

Electronic publishing on-line and off-line on CD-Rom platform: food and wine, sport, popular science, music, art and biography. Founded 1995.

Oak Tree Press†

Merrion Building, Lower Merrion Street, Dublin 2, Republic of Ireland
tel (01) 6761600 *fax* (01) 6761644
e-mail oaktreep@iol.ie
web site http://www.oaktreepress.com
Directors Brian O'Kane, Rita O'Kane, *General Manager* David Givens

Law, accountancy, business management. Founded 1991.

O'Brien Educational

20 Victoria Road, Rathgar, Dublin 6, Republic of Ireland
tel (01) 4923333 *fax* (01) 4922777
e-mail books@obrien.ie
web site http://www.obrien.ie
Directors Michael O'Brien, Bride Rosney

Humanities, science, environmental studies, history, geography, English, Irish, art, commerce, music, careers, media studies. Founded 1976.

The O'Brien Press Ltd†

20 Victoria Road, Rathgar, Dublin 6, Republic of Ireland
tel (01) 4923333 *fax* (01) 4922777
e-mail books@obrien.ie
web site http://www.obrien.ie
Directors Michael O'Brien, Ide Ni Laoghaire, Ivan O'Brien

History, biography, general fiction and non-fiction, politics, architecture, topography, humour, music, true crime, travel, walking guides, Irish interest, children's (fiction and non-fiction), tapes/CDs. Series include *Pocket Books*, *Another Ireland*, *Other World* (science fiction, fantasy, horror), *Pandas* (age 5-6), *Fliers* (age 6+). Founded 1974.

The Octagon Press Ltd
PO Box 227, London N6 4EW
tel 0181-348 9392 *fax* 0181-341 5971
e-mail octagon@schredds.demon.co.uk
web site http://www.clearlight.com/octagon/
Managing Director George R. Schrager
Psychology, philosophy, Eastern religion. Unsolicited MSS not accepted. Founded 1972.

Octopus – now Hamlyn/Octopus – see Reed Books

The Oleander Press
17 Stansgate Avenue, Cambridge CB2 2QZ
tel (01223) 244688
Managing Director P. Ward
Travel, language, literature, Libya, Arabia and Middle East, Cambridgeshire, humour, reference. Preliminary letter required before submitting MSS; please send sae for reply. Founded 1960.

Michael O'Mara Books Ltd
9 Lion Yard, Tremadoc Road,
London SW4 7NQ
tel 0171-720 8643 *fax* 0171-627 8953
Chairman Michael O'Mara, *Managing Director* Lesley O'Mara
General non-fiction: Royal books, history, ancient history, humour, anthologies and biography. Founded 1985.

Omnibus Press/Music Sales Ltd*
8-9 Frith Street, London W1V 5TZ
tel 0171-434 0066 *fax* 0171-439 2848
e-mail music@musicsales.co.uk
Sales and Marketing Manager Hilary Power
Rock music biographies, books about music. Founded 1976.

On Stream Publications Ltd
Currabaha, Cloghroe, Blarney, Co. Cork, Republic of Ireland
tel/fax (021) 385798
e-mail onstream@indigo.ie
Owner Rosalind Crowley
Cookery, wine, travel, human interest non-fiction, local history, academic and practical books. Founded 1986.

Oneworld Publications
185 Banbury Road, Oxford, Oxon OX2 7AR
tel (01865) 310597 *fax* (01865) 310598
e-mail oneworld@cix.co.uk
web site http://www.oneworld-publications.com
Directors Juliet Mabey (editorial), Novin Doostdar (marketing)

Social issues, psychology, self-help, religion, world religion, inter-religious dialogue, Islamic studies, philosophy. Founded 1984.

Onlywomen Press Ltd
40 St Lawrence Terrace, London W10 5ST
tel 0181-960 7122 *fax* 0181-960 2817
e-mail 100756.1242@compuserve.com
Managing Director Lilian Mohin
Lesbian feminist: theory, fiction, poetry, crime fiction and cultural criticism. Founded 1974.

Open Books Publishing Ltd
Higher Folly Cottage, Crewkerne,
Somerset TA18 8PN
tel/fax (01460) 78706
Directors P. Taylor (managing), C. Taylor
Gardening. Founded 1974.

Open University Press*
Celtic Court, 22 Ballmoor,
Buckingham MK18 1XW
tel (01280) 823388 *fax* (01280) 823233
e-mail enquiries@openup.co.uk
Directors John Skelton (managing), Jacinta Evans (editorial), Sue Hadden (production), Barry Clarke (financial)
Education, management, psychology, sociology, criminology, counselling, health and social welfare, women's studies. Founded 1977.

Orbit/Legend – see Little, Brown and Company (UK)*

Orchard Books – see The Watts Publishing Group*

The Orion Publishing Group Ltd
Orion House, 5 Upper St Martin's Lane,
London WC2H 9EA
tel 0171-240 3444 *fax* 0171-379 6158
Directors Nicholas Barber (chairman), Anthony Cheetham (chief executive), Peter Roche (managing)
No unsolicited MSS; approach in writing in first instance. Founded 1992.

Illustrated (division)
fax 0171-240 4823 *fax* 0171-240 4823
Contact Michael Dover
Illustrated non-fiction: design, cookery, wine, gardening, art and architecture, natural history and personality based books.

Mass Market (division)
Managing Director Susan Lamb
Mass market fiction and non-fiction under **Everyman**, **Orion** and **Phoenix** imprints.

Millennium (imprint of Orion)
Contact Caroline Oakley
Science fiction and fantasy.
Orion (division)
Directors Malcolm Edwards (managing),
Rosemary Cheetham (publisher), Jane Wood
Hardcover fiction and non-fiction.
Orion Children's Books (division)
fax 0171-379 6158
Managing Director and Publisher Judith Elliott
Children's fiction and non-fiction.
Phoenix House (imprint of Weidenfeld &
Nicolson)
Director Maggie McKernan
Literary fiction.
Weidenfeld & Nicolson (division)
fax 0171-240 4823
Managing Director Ion Trewin
General non-fiction, biography, autobiography, history and travel.

Osprey Publishing Ltd
1st Floor, Elms Court, Chapel Way, Botley,
Oxford OX2 9LP
tel (01865) 727022 *fax* (01865) 727017
e-mail osprey@osprey-publishing.co.uk
web site http://www.osprey.co.uk
Managing Director Jonathan Parker, *Financial
Director* Sarah Lough, *Vice-President, North
American Operations* Bill Corsa
Military history, uniforms, battles, civil
and military aviation, cars, motorcycles.
Founded 1969.

Peter Owen Ltd
73 Kenway Road, London SW5 0RE
tel 0171-373 5628/370 6093 *fax* 0171-373 6760
e-mail admin@peterowen.u-net.com
Directors Peter L. Owen (managing), Antonia
Owen (editorial)
Art, belles-lettres, biography, literary fiction, general non-fiction, sociology, theatre.

Oxford Illustrated Press – see Haynes
Publishing

**Oxford Publishing Company (OPC
Railbooks)** – see Haynes Publishing

Oxford University Press*
Great Clarendon Street, Oxford OX2 6DP
tel (01865) 556767 *fax* (01865) 556646
Chief Executive and Secretary to the Delegates
Henry Reece, *Group Finance Director* Roger
Boning, *Academic Division Managing Director*
Ivon Asquith, *Educational Division Managing
Director* Peter Mothersole, *ELT Division
Managing Director* Bill Andrewes, *Group
Personnel Director* Martin Havelock

Anthropology, archaeology, architecture,
art, belles-lettres, bibles, bibliography, children's books (fiction, non-fiction, picture),
commerce, current affairs, dictionaries,
drama, economics, educational (infants,
primary, secondary, technical, university),
English language teaching, electronic publishing, essays, general history, hymn and
service books, journals, law, maps and
atlases, medical, music, oriental, philosophy, poetry, political economy, prayer
books, reference, science, sociology, theology and religion, educational software.
Academic books published under the
imprint **Clarendon Press**. Trade paperbacks published under the imprint of
Oxford Paperbacks. Founded 1478.

Paladin – now Flamingo – see
HarperCollins Publishers*

Pan – see Macmillan Publishers Ltd*

Pan Macmillan Ltd – now Macmillan
General Books*

Pan Macmillan Children's Books Ltd
– now Macmillan Children's Books Ltd*

Pandora Press – see Rivers Oram Press

Paper Tiger – see Collins & Brown

Papermac – see Macmillan Publishers
Ltd*

Parkgate Books – see Collins & Brown

Partridge Press – see Transworld
Publishers Ltd*

Paternoster Publishing
PO Box 300, Carlisle, Cumbria CA3 0QS
tel (01228) 512512 *fax* (01228) 593388
e-mail patprod@aol.com
Managing Director Pieter Kwant
Biblical studies, Christian theology, ethics,
history, mission. Imprints: Paternoster Press,
Partnership, Regnum, Rutherford House,
OM Publishing, Solway, Hunt & Thorpe (co-
publishing partners), Challenge, Paternoster
Periodicals, SP Media, Alpha Books.

Stanley Paul – see Random House UK
Ltd*

Pavilion Books
London House, Great Eastern Wharf,
Parkgate Road, London SW11 4NQ

tel 0171-924 2575 *fax* 0171-924 7725
Publisher Colin Webb, *Editorial Directors* Vivien
James (adult), Pam Webb (children's)
Cookery, gardening, travel, humour,
sport, art, children's. Subsidiary of C&B
Publishing plc. Founded 1980.

Pavilion Publishing (Brighton) Ltd
8 St George's Place, Brighton BN1 4GB
tel (01273) 623222 *fax* (01273) 625526
e-mail pavpub@pavilion.co.uk
web site http://www.pavpub.com
Directors Jan Alcoe, Chris Parker
Health and social care training: learning
disability, mental health, community
care management, older people, young
people. Founded 1987.

Payback Press – see Canongate Books
Ltd*

Pelham Books – former imprint of
Michael Joseph/Penguin

Pen & Sword Books Ltd
47 Church Street, Barnsley,
South Yorkshire S70 2AS
tel (01226) 734222 *fax* (01226) 734438
e-mail charles@pen-and-sword.demon.co.uk
web site http://www.yorkshire-web.co.uk/ps/
Chairman Sir Nicholas Hewitt, Bt, *Director and
Company Secretary* T.G. Hewitt
Military history. Imprints: Leo Cooper,
Pen & Sword Paperbacks.
Wharncliffe* (imprint)
Local history.

Penguin UK*
27 Wrights Lane, London W8 5TZ
tel 0171-416 3000 *fax* 0171-416 3099
web site http://www.penguin.co.uk
Chairman Michael Lynton, *Managing Director*
Anthony Forbes Watson
Adult and children's lists include fiction,
non-fiction, poetry, drama, classics, refer-
ence and special interest areas. Reprints
and new work. Owned by Pearson plc.
Penguin General Books (division)
Managing Director Helen Fraser
Publishing Directors Tony Lacey (Penguin), Tom
Weldon (Michael Joseph/Penguin), Juliet Annan
(Viking/Hamish Hamilton/Penguin)
Publishers Simon Prosser (Hamish Hamilton),
Louise Moore (Michael Joseph/Penguin fiction)
No unsolicited MSS or synopses.
Hamish Hamilton (imprint)
Fiction, belles-lettres, biography and
memoirs, current affairs, general, history,

literature, politics, travel. No unsolicited
MSS or synopses.
Michael Joseph (imprint)
Biography and memoirs, current affairs,
fiction, history, humour, travel, health,
spirituality and relationships, sports,
general leisure, illustrated books. No
unsolicited MSS or synopses.
Penguin (imprint)
Adult paperback books – wide range of
fiction, non-fiction, TV and film tie-ins.
No unsolicited MSS or synopses.
Viking (imprint)
Fiction, general non-fiction; literature,
biography, autobiography, current
affairs, popular science, travel, popular
culture, reference. No unsolicited MSS
or synopses.
Penguin Press (division)
Managing Director Andrew Rosenheim
Publishing Directors Alastair Rolfe, Stuart
Proffitt, Nigel Wilcockson
Serious adult non-fiction, reference, spe-
cialist and classics. Imprints: Allen Lane,
Arkana (mind, body and spirit list);
Buildings of England; Classics; Penguin
Books. Approach in writing only.
Frederick Warne (division)
Publisher/Managing Director Sally Floyer
Chief Editor Diana Syrat
web site http://www.peterrabbit.com
Classic children's publishing and mer-
chandising including *Beatrix Potter*™,
Flower Fairies, *Orlando*. No unsolicited
MSS or synopses.
Ventura (division)
Publisher/Managing Director Sally Floyer
Chief Editor Diana Syrat
Producer and packager of *Spot* titles by
Eric Hill. No unsolicited MSS or synopses.
Penguin Children's Books (division)
Managing Director Philippa Milnes-Smith
web site http://www.puffin.co.uk
Children's paperback list, publishing in
virtually all fields including fiction, non-
fiction, poetry, picture books, media-
related titles. Imprints: Hamish Hamilton
Children's, Viking Children's (hardback);
Puffin (paperback). No unsolicited MSS
or synopses.
Penguin Audiobooks (division)
Contact Anna Hopkins

Pergamon – see Elsevier Science Ltd

Peterloo Poets
2 Kelly Gardens, Calstock, Cornwall PL18 9SA
tel (01822) 833473
Publishing Director Harry Chambers, *Trustees*
Rosemarie Bailey, Brian Perman, David Selzer,
Honorary President Charles Causley CBE
Poetry. Founded 1976.

Phaidon Press Ltd
Regent's Wharf, All Saints Street, London N1 9PA
tel 0171-843 1000 *fax* 0171-843 1010
Chairman Richard Schlagman, *Managing Director*
Andrew Price, *Directors* Neil Palfreyman
(production), David Jenkins (editorial), Amanda
Renshaw (international editions)
Fine art, architecture, design, decorative
arts, photography, music.

Philips – see Reed Books

Phillimore & Co. Ltd
(incorporating Darwen Finlayson Ltd)
Shopwyke Manor Barn, Chichester,
West Sussex PO20 6BG
tel (01243) 787636 *fax* (01243) 787639
e-mail bookshop@phillimore.co.uk
web site http://www.phillimore.co.uk
Directors Philip Harris JP (chairman), Noel
Osborne MA, FSA (managing), Hilary Clifford
Brown (marketing)
Local and family history; architectural
history, archaeology, genealogy and heraldry; also Darwen County History series
and History from the Sources series.
Founded 1897.

Phoenix House – see The Orion Publishing Group Ltd

Piatkus Books
5 Windmill Street, London W1P 1HF
tel 0171-631 0710 *fax* 0171-436 7137
e-mail info@piatkus.co.uk
Managing Director Judy Piatkus, *Directors* Philip
Cotterell (marketing), Gill Cormode (editorial)
Fiction, self-help, health, mind, body
and spirit, business, careers, women's
interest, how-to and practical, popular
psychology, cookery, parenting and
childcare, biography and paranormal.
Founded 1979.

Picador – see Macmillan Publishers Ltd*

Piccadilly Press
5 Castle Road, London NW1 8PR
tel 0171-267 4492 *fax* 0171-267 4493
Directors Brenda Gardner (chairman and
managing), Philip Durrance (secretary)
Character picture books and parental
advice trade paperbacks; trade paperback
teenage information and humorous fiction. Founded 1983.

Pimlico – see Random House UK Ltd*

Pinter – see Cassell plc

Pitkin Unichrome Ltd
Healey House, Dene Road, Andover,
Hants SP10 2AA
tel (01264) 334303 *fax* (01264) 334110
e-mail guides@pitkin.u-net.com
Managing Director Heather Hook, *Managing
Editor* Shelley Grimwood
Illustrated souvenir guides.

Pitman Publishing – see Financial Times Management

The Playwrights Publishing Company
70 Nottingham Road, Burton Joyce,
Notts. NG14 5AL
tel 0115-931 3356
Proprietor Liz Breeze, *Consultant* Tony Breeze
One-act and full-length drama: serious
work and comedies, for mixed cast, all
women or schools. Reading fee and sae
required. Founded 1990.

Plexus Publishing Ltd
55A Clapham Common Southside,
London SW4 9BX
tel 0171-622 2440 *fax* 0171-622 2441
Directors Terence Porter (managing), Sandra
Wake (editorial)
Film, music, biography, popular culture,
fashion. Founded 1973.
Eel Pie (imprint)
Film, music, biography, popular culture,
fashion.

Pluto Press
345 Archway Road, London N6 5AA
tel 0181-348 2724 *fax* 0181-348 9133
e-mail pluto@plutobks.demon.co.uk
web site http://www.leevalley.co.uk/plutopress
Directors Roger van Zwanenberg (managing),
Anne Beech (editorial)
Sociology, social and political science
including economics, history; cultural,
international, women's studies, legal
studies, Irish studies, Black studies,
Third World and development, anthropology, media studies. Founded 1968.
The Journeyman Press (trade imprint)
Feminist, social history, media handbooks.

Pocket Books – see Simon & Schuster*

Point – see Scholastic Children's Books*

The Policy Press
University of Bristol, Rodney Lodge,
Grange Road, Bristol BS8 4EA
tel 0117-9738797 *fax* 0117-9737308
e-mail tpp@bris.ac.uk
Publishing Manager Alison Shaw, *Editorial
Manager* Dawn Louise Pudney, *Marketing and
Sales Manager* Julia Mortimer, *Production Editor*
Karen Bowler

Ageing, criminal justice, family policy
and child welfare, governance, housing
and planning, race and ethnicity, voluntary sector, community care, education,
gender, health policy, labour markets and
training, urban policy, welfare and
poverty. Founded 1996.

Polity Press
65 Bridge Street, Cambridge CB2 1UR
tel (01223) 324315 *fax* (01223) 461385
Directors Anthony Giddens, David Held, John
Thompson

Social and political theory, politics, sociology, history, economics, psychology,
media and cultural studies, philosophy,
theology, literary theory, feminism, human
geography, anthropology. Founded 1983.

Polygon – see Edinburgh University
Press*

Poolbeg Press Ltd†
123 Baldoyle Industrial Estate,
Baldoyle, Dublin 13,
Republic of Ireland
tel (01) 8321477 *fax* (01) 8321430
e-mail poulbeg@iol.ie
Directors Philip MacDermott (managing), Kieran
Devlin, Kate Cruise O'Brien

Fiction, public interest, women's inter-
est, history, politics, current affairs.
Imprints: Business Poolbeg, Children's
Poolbeg, Beachwood. Founded 1976.

Portland Press Ltd
59 Portland Place, London W1N 3AJ
tel 0171-580 5530 *fax* 0171-323 1136
e-mail edit@portlandpress.co.uk
web site http://www.portlandpress.co.uk
Directors Glyn D. Jones (managing), Chris J.
Finch (finance), Rhonda C. Oliver (publishing),
John Day (IT)

Biochemistry and molecular life science
books for graduate, post-graduate and
research students. Illustrated science
books for children: Making Sense of
Science series. Founded 1990.

Prentice Hall Europe/Academic
Campus 400, Maylands Avenue,
Hemel Hempstead, Herts. HP2 7EZ
tel (01442) 881900 *fax* (01442) 882099
President Simon Allen, *Editorial Director*
Penelope Woolf, *Sales Director* Chris Bunting,
Marketing Director Jane Mackarell, *Rights
Manager* Jean Spurr

Business and economics, computer science, engineering, physics, mathematics,
politics, sociology and social policy, psychology, health studies, literature, trade
computing. Imprints: Allyn & Bacon,
Appleton & Lange, Ellis Horwood,
Prentice Hall, Prentice Hall Europe,
Prentice Hall/Harvester Wheatsheaf,
Woodhead-Faulkner.

Prentice Hall Europe/CPTR
(Computer Professional Trade Reference)
Campus 400, Maylands Avenue,
Hemel Hempstead, Herts. HP2 7EZ
tel (01442) 881900 *fax* (01442) 882099
President Jim Donohue, *Editorial Director* Clare
Grist Taylor, *Sales Director* Simon Beale, *Trade
Editor* Jason Dunne

Divisions: Macmillan Computer
Publishing (USA), Prentice Hall PTR
(Professional Technical Reference),
Jossey-Bass Publishers, ICSA Publishing,
New York Institute of Finance, Prentice
Hall Direct, Prentice Hall Europe.

Prion Books
(formerly Multimedia Books Ltd)
Unit L, 32-34 Gordon House Road,
London NW5 1LP
tel 0171-482 4248 *fax* 0171-482 4203
e-mail books@prion.co.uk
Managing Director Barry Winkleman

Food and drink, historical and literary
reprints, humour, popular culture, psychology and health. Founded 1986.

Prism Press Book Publishers Ltd
The Thatched Cottage, Partway Lane, Hazelbury
Bryan, Sturminster Newton, Dorset DT10 2DP
tel (01258) 817164 *fax* (01258) 817635
Directors Julian King, Diana King

Non-fiction, including health, food, psychology, politics, ecology. Synopses and
ideas welcome, but no complete MSS.
Founded 1974.

Profile Books Ltd
58A Hatton Garden, London EC1N 8LX
tel 0171-404 3001 *fax* 0171-404 3003
e-mail info@profilebooks.co.uk
web site http://www.profilebooks.co.uk/books/

Publisher and Managing Director Andrew Franklin, *Editorial Director* Stephen Brough

Non-fiction: current affairs, politics, social sciences, history, psychology, business and management; *The Economist* books. No unsolicited MSS; phone or send preliminary letter. Founded 1996.

PSI
(Policy Studies Institute)
100 Park Village East, London NW1 3SR
tel 0171-468 0468 *fax* 0171-388 0914
e-mail postmaster@psi.org.uk

Economic, industrial and social policy, political institutions, social sciences.

Puffin – see Penguin UK*

Putnam Aeronautical Books – see Brassey's (UK) Ltd

Quadrille Publishing
5th Floor, Alhambra House, 27-31 Charing Cross Road, London WC2H 0LS
tel 0171-839 7117 *fax* 0171-839 7118
Directors Alison Cathie (managing), Anne Furniss (publishing), Jane O'Shea (editorial), Mary Evans (art), Marlis Ironmonger (commercial), Vincent Smith (production)

Illustrated non-fiction: cookery, craft, health and medical, gardening, interiors, magic. Founded 1994.

Quantum – see W. Foulsham & Co. Ltd

Quartet Books Ltd
27 Goodge Street, London W1P 2LD
tel 0171-636 3992 *fax* 0171-637 1866
e-mail quartetbooks@easynet.co.uk
Chairman N.I. Attallah, *Managing Director* Jeremy Beale, *Publishing Director* Stella Kane

General fiction and non-fiction, foreign literature in translation, classical music, jazz, contemporary music, biography. Member of the Namara Group. Founded 1972.

Queen Anne Press
Windmill Cottage, Mackerye End, Harpenden, Herts. AL5 5DR
tel (01582) 715866 *fax* (01582) 715121
e-mail queenanne@lenqap.demon.co.uk
Directors K.A.A. Stephenson, R.H. Stephenson

Sport and leisure activities. No unsolicited MSS. Division of Lennard Associates Ltd.

Quiller Press Ltd
46 Lillie Road, London SW6 1TN
tel 0171-499 6529 *fax* 0171-381 8941
e-mail quiller@premierservicesdemon.co.uk
Directors J.J. Greenwood, A.E. Carlile

Publishers of sponsored books: guide-books, history, industry, humour, architecture, cookery, collectables, country sports.

Radcliffe Medical Press Ltd
18 Marcham Road, Abingdon, Oxon OX14 1AA
tel (01235) 528820 *fax* (01235) 528830
e-mail medical@radpress.win.uk.net
Directors Andrew Bax (managing), Gill Nineham (editorial), Margaret McKeown (financial), *Head of Marketing* Gregory Moxon

Medicine: management in primary care; management in secondary care; health service development; palliative and cancer care; clinical management. Dentistry: practice management. Pharmacy. Founded 1987.

Ragged Bears Ltd
Ragged Appleshaw, Andover, Hants SP11 9HX
tel (01264) 772269 *fax* (01264) 772391
e-mail books@ragged-bears.co.uk
web site http://www.ragged-bears.co.uk
Managing Director Mrs C. Shirley, *Rights and Editorial Director* Henrietta Stickland

Publisher and distributor of children's fiction and non-fiction. Imprints: Ragged Bears, Spindlewood. Founded 1984.

Random House UK Ltd*
20 Vauxhall Bridge Road, London SW1V 2SA
tel 0171-840 8400 *fax* 0171-233 6058
e-mail randomhouse.co.uk
Chairman and Chief Executive Gail Rebuck, *Directors* Simon Master (deputy chairman), Simon King (publishing), Ian Hudson (commercial), Amelia Thorpe (managing, Ebury Press), Mike Broderick (UK sales), Anthony McConnell (finance), Susan Sandon (publicity and marketing), Katherine Mulders (rights), Stephen Esson (production), Joanna Page (human resources)

Subsidiary of Bertelsmann AG.

Arrow Books Ltd (imprint)
tel 0171-840 8516 *fax* 0171-233 6127
Directors Andy McKillop (publishing), Kate Farquhar-Thomson (publicity)

Fiction, non-fiction, fantasy, crime, humour, film tie-ins.

Barrie & Jenkins (imprint of **Ebury Press**)
tel 0171-840 8400 *fax* 0171-233 6057
Associate Publisher, Ebury Press Julian Shuckburgh

Art, antiques and collecting, architecture, decorative and applied arts.

Jonathan Cape (imprint)
tel 0171-840 8576 *fax* 0171-233 6117
Directors Dan Franklin, Robin Robertson, Tom Maschler, Kate Harbinson (publicity)

Biography and memoirs, current affairs, drama, fiction, history, poetry, travel.

Imprints: **Bodley Head**, **Yellow Jersey Press** (sport).

Century (imprint)
tel 0171-840 8555 *fax* 0171-233 6127
Directors Kate Parkin (publisher), Mark Booth, Oliver Johnson, Katie White (publicity), *Business Editor* Simon Wilson

Fiction, classics, romance, biography, autobiography, general non-fiction, film tie-ins; *Century Business Books*.

Chatto & Windus (imprint)
tel 0171-840 8522 *fax* 0171-233 6123
Directors Alison Samuel (publishing), Penny Hoare

Art, belles-lettres, biography and memoirs, current affairs, drama, essays, fiction, history, poetry, politics, philosophy, translations, travel, hardbacks and paperbacks. No unsolicited MSS.

Condé Nast Books (imprint of **Ebury Press**)

Ebury Press Special Books (division)
tel 0171-840 8400 *fax* 0171-840 8406
Directors Amelia Thorpe (managing) Fiona MacIntyre (publisher), Julian Shuckburgh (associate), Isabel Duffy (publicity)

Art and antiques, biography, buddhism, cookery, gardening, health and beauty, homes and interiors, personal development, spirituality, sport, entertainment, travel guides, TV tie-ins. Unsolicited MSS welcome.

Fodor Guides (imprint of **Ebury Press**)
Worldwide annual travel guides.

William Heinemann (imprint)
tel 0171-840 8517 *fax* 0171-233 6127
Publishing Director Maria Rejt

Fiction and general non-fiction: crime, thrillers, women's fiction, history, biography, science. No unsolicited MSS and synopses considered.

Hutchinson (imprint)
tel 0171-840 8564 *fax* 0171-233 7870
Directors Sue Freestone (publishing), Anthony Whittome, Paul Sidey (editorial), Alex Hippisley-Cox (publicity)

Belles-lettres, biography, memoirs, thrillers, crime, current affairs, general history, politics, translations, travel, film tie-ins.

Methuen (imprint)
tel 0171-840 8638 *fax* 0171-233 6117
Publishing Director Michael Earley

Drama, humour, film, performing arts, plays. No unsolicited MSS or synopses considered.

Stanley Paul (imprint of **Ebury Press**)
tel 0171-840 8400 *fax* 0171-233 6057

Pimlico (imprint)
tel 0171-840 8630 *fax* 0171-233 6117
Publishing Director Will Sulkin

History, biography, literature.

Random House Audio Books
tel 0171-840 8400
Manager Kate Elton

Random House Children's Books (division)
tel 0171-840 8400
Directors Debbie Sandford (managing), Caroline Roberts, Anne McNeil, Tom Maschler, Pilar Jenkins

Publishes under **Bodley Head Children's**, **Jonathan Cape Children's Books**, **Hutchinson Children's**, **Julia MacRae Books**, **Red Fox**, **Tellastory**. Picture books, fiction, poetry, music, non-fiction, audio cassettes.

Rider (imprint of **Ebury Press**)
Publishing Director Fiona MacIntyre, *Editorial Consultant* Judith Kendra

Buddhism, religion and philosophy, psychology, ecology, health and healing, mysticism, meditation and yoga.

Secker and Warburg (imprint)
tel 0171-840 8649 *fax* 0171-233 6117
Directors Geoff Mulligan (editorial), Hannah Corbett (publicity)

Literary fiction, general non-fiction. No unsolicited MSS/synopses.

Vermilion (imprint of **Ebury Press**)

Vintage (imprint)
tel 0171-840 8400
Publisher Caroline Michel, *Associate Publishing Director* Will Sulkin, Susie Craigie Halkett (publicity)

Quality fiction and non-fiction.

Raphael's – see W. Foulsham & Co. Ltd

Rapid Science – acquired by Wolters Kluwer Group of Companies

The Reader's Digest Association Ltd*
11 Westferry Circus, Canary Wharf, London E14 4HE
tel 0171-715 8000 *fax* 0171-715 8181
Managing Director S.N. McRae, *Editorial Directors* R.G. Twisk (magazine), Cortina Butler (general books), Nigel Begbie (condensed books and reading services)

Monthly magazine, condensed and series books; also DIY, car maintenance, gardening, medical, handicrafts, law, touring guides, encyclopedias, dictionaries, nature, folklore, atlases, cookery, music; videos; merchandise catalogue.

Reader's Digest Children's Books –
see Victoria House Publishing Ltd

Reaktion Books
11 Rathbone Place, London W1P 1DE
tel 0171-580 9928 *fax* 0171-580 9935
e-mail reaktionbooks@compuserve.com
General Editor Michael R. Leaman

Art history, design, architecture, history, cultural studies, Asian studies, travel and photography. Founded 1985.

Rebel Inc. – see Canongate Books Ltd*

Red Fox – see Random House UK Ltd*

Reed Books
Michelin House, 81 Fulham Road,
London SW3 6RB
tel 0171-581 9393 *fax* 0171-225 9424
e-mail name@reedbooks.co.uk
Chief Executive John Holloran, *Executive Directors* Derek Freeman, John Philbin, Ross Clayton

Consumer book publishing subsidiary of Reed Elsevier (UK) Ltd.

Bounty (imprint)
fax 0171-225 9031
Publisher/Managing Director Laura Bamford

Promotional publishing, children's and adult books.

Brimax Books (imprint)
Units 4-5, Studland Park Industrial Estate,
Exning Road, Newmarket,
Suffolk CB8 7AU
tel (01638) 664611 *fax* (01638) 665220
Managing Director Patricia Gillette

Mass market picture books for children.

Conran Octopus (imprint)
37 Shelton Street,
London WC2H 9HN
tel 0171-240 6961 *fax* 0171-836 9951
Managing Director John Wallace

Quality illustrated books, particularly lifestyle, cookery, gardening.

Hamlyn/Octopus (imprint)
fax 0171-225 9458
Publisher/Managing Director Laura Bamford

Popular illustrated non-fiction, particularly cookery, gardening, craft, sport, film tie-ins, rock'n'roll.

Millers (imprint)
The Cellars, High Street, Tenterden,
Kent TN30 6BN
tel (01580) 766411 *fax* (01580) 766100
Publisher/Managing Director Jane Aspden

Quality illustrated books on antiques and collectibles.

Mitchell Beazley (imprint)
fax 0171-225 9458
Publisher/Managing Director Jane Aspden

Quality illustrated books, particularly antiques, gardening, craft and interiors, wine.

Philips (imprint)
fax 0171-225 9458
Publisher/Managing Director John Gaisford

Atlases, maps, astronomy, encyclopaedias, globes.

Reed Business Information
Windsor Court, East Grinstead House,
East Grinstead, West Sussex RH19 1XA
tel (01342) 326972 *fax* (01342) 335612
e-mail jwoodger@reedinfo.co.uk
web site http://www.reedbusiness.com
Chief Executive Keith Jones, *Joint Managing Directors* John Minch and Charles Halpin

Directories and reference books covering professional and industrial sectors, including *Kompass, Kelly's, Dial* and *The Bankers' Almanac*. Part of Reed Elsevier plc. Founded 1983.

William Reed Directories
Broadfield Park, Crawley, West Sussex RH11 9RT
tel (01293) 613400 *fax* (01293) 610322
e-mail directories@william-reed.co.uk
web site http://www.foodanddrink.co.uk
Managing Director Maria Farmery, *Editorial Manager* Helen Turner, *Group Sales Manager* Colin Martin

Publishers of leading business-to-business directories and reports, including *The Grocer Marketing Directory* and *The Grocer Food & Drink Directory*.

Reed Educational and Professional Publishing Ltd*
Halley Court, Jordan Hill, Oxford OX2 8EJ
tel (01865) 311366 *fax* (01865) 314641
Chief Executive William Shepherd

Architectural Press (imprint)
Editorial Director Peter Dixon, *Publisher* Neil Warnock-Smith

Architecture, the environment, planning, townscape, building technology; general.

Butterworth Heinemann UK (imprint)
Linacre House, Jordan Hill, Oxford OX2 8EJ
tel (01865) 311366 *fax* (01865) 310898
Managing Director Philip Shaw

Books and electronic products across business, technical, medical and open learning fields for students and professionals.

Focal Press (imprint)
fax (01865) 314572
Publishing Director Peter Dixon, *Senior Commissioning Editor* Margaret Riley
Professional, technical and academic books on photography, broadcasting, film, television, radio, audiovisual and communication media.

Ginn & Co. (imprint)
Prebendal House, Parson's Fee, Aylesbury, Bucks. HP20 2QY
tel (01296) 394442 *fax* (01296) 393433
Textbook/other educational resources for primary and secondary schools.

Heinemann Educational (imprint)
fax (01865) 314140
Managing Director Bob Osborne
Textbooks/literature/other educational resources for all levels.
See also **Butterworth & Co. (Publishers) Ltd.**

Religious and Moral Education Press (RMEP) – see Chansitor Publications Ltd

Review – see Hodder Headline plc*

Rider – see Random House UK Ltd*

Rivelin Grapheme Press
Merlin House, Church Street, Hungerford, Berks. RG17 0JG
tel (01488) 684645 *fax* (01488) 683018
Director Snowdon Barnett
Poetry. Please send introductory letter enclosing one short poem. Founded 1984.

Rivers Oram Press
144 Hemingford Road, London N1 1DE
tel 0171-607 0823 *fax* 0171-609 2776
Directors Elizabeth Rivers Fidlon (managing), Anthony Harris
Non-ficton: social and political science, current affairs, social history, gender studies, sexual politics, cultural studies and photography. Founded 1991.

Pandora Press (imprint)
Managing Editor Katharine Bright-Holmes
Feminist press publishing. General non-fiction: biography, arts, media, health, current affairs, reference and sexual politics.

Robinson Publishing Ltd
7 Kensington Church Court, London W8 4SP
tel 0171-938 3830 *fax* 0171-938 4214
e-mail 100560.3511 @compuserve.com
Publisher Nicholas Robinson, *Publishing Director*

Jan Chamier, *Commissioning Editor* Krystyna Green
Fiction: anthologies; general non-fiction includes health, self-help, psychology, true crime, puzzles, military history. Children's: humour, games, puzzles. Do not send MSS; letters/synopses only. No unsolicited fiction. Founded 1983.

Magpie (imprint)
Publishing Director Nova Jayne Heath
Promotional paperbacks: fiction and non-fiction.

Scarlet (imprint)
Editor Sue Curran
Women's fiction: 100,000-word MSS with a strong central romance. Contemporary (present day) setting. Will look at Regency and medical romances, provided they are sensuous in tone. Guidelines are available.

Robson Books
Bolsover House, 5-6 Clipstone Street, London W1P 8LE
tel 0171-323 1223/637 5937 *fax* 0171-636 0798
Managing Director Jeremy Robson
General, biography, music, humour, sport. Founded 1973.

George Ronald
46 High Street, Kidlington, Oxon OX5 2DN
tel (01865) 841515 *fax* (01865) 841230
e-mail sales@grpubl.demon.co.uk
Managers W. Momen, E. Leith
Religion, specialising in the Baha'i Faith. Founded 1939.

Barry Rose Law Publishers Ltd
Little London, Chichester, West Sussex PO19 1PG
tel (01243) 775552/779174 *fax* (01243) 779278
e-mail jp@barry-rose-law.co.uk
Law, local government, police, legal history. Founded 1972.

Rosendale Press Ltd
Premier House, 10 Greycoat Place, London SW1P 1SB
tel 0171-222 8866 *fax* 0171-799 1416
Chairman Timothy S. Green, *Editorial Director* Maureen P. Green
Food and drink, gourmet guides/travel, business and investment, health and lifestyle. Founded 1987.

Round Hall Sweet & Maxwell
Brehon House, 4 Upper Ormond Quay, Dublin 7, Republic of Ireland
tel (01) 8730101 *fax* (01) 8720078
Chairman Anthony Kinahan, *Director and General Manager* Elanor McGarry
Law.

Roundhouse Publishing Ltd
PO Box 140, Oxford OX2 7FF
tel (01865) 512682 *fax* (01865) 559594
e-mail roundhse@compuserve.com
Publisher Alan T. Goodworth
Film, cinema, and performing arts; reference books. No unsolicited MSS. Founded 1991.

Routledge*
11 New Fetter Lane, London EC4P 4EE
tel 0171-583 9855 *fax* 0171-842 2298
web site http://www.routledge.com
Directors David Hill (managing), Peter Sowden (publishing), David Tebbutt (finance)
Addiction, anthropology, archaeology, Asian studies, business, classical studies, counselling, criminology, development and environment, dictionaries, economics, education, geography, health, history, Japanese studies, library science, language, linguistics, literary criticism, media and culture, nursing, performance studies, philosophy, politics, psychiatry, psychology, reference, social administration, social studies/sociology, women's studies. Routledge is an independent company.

E. & F. Spon (imprint)
Architecture, civil engineering, construction, leisure and recreation management, sports science.

Royal National Institute for the Blind
PO Box 173, Peterborough, Cambs. PE2 6WS
tel (0345) 023153 *fax* (01733) 371555
textphone (0345) 585 691
Magazines and books for blind and partially sighted people, to support daily living, leisure, learning and employment reading needs. Produced in braille, audio, large/legible print, disk and Moon. For complete list of magazines see page 130. Founded 1868.

Ryland Peters & Small
Cavendish House, 51-55 Mortimer Street, London W1N 7TD
tel 0171-436 9090 *fax* 0171-436 9790
e-mail louise.sherwin-stark@rps.co.uk
Directors David Peters (managing), Anne Ryland (publishing), Jacqui Small (art)
Highly illustrated books on cookery, craft, interiors and gardening. Founded 1995.

Sage Publications Ltd*
6 Bonhill Street, London EC2A 4PU
tel 0171-374 0645 *fax* 0171-374 8741
e-mail info@sagepub.co.uk

web site http://www.sagepub.co.uk
Directors Stephen Barr (managing), Lynn Adams, Ian Eastment, Mike Birch, Matt Jackson, Ziyad Marar, Richard Fidczuk, David F. McCune (USA), Sara Miller McCune (USA)
Social sciences, behavioural sciences, humanities, software. Founded 1971.

The Saint Andrew Press*
121 George Street, Edinburgh EH2 4YN
tel 0131-225 5722 *fax* 0131-220 3113
e-mail cofs.standrew@dial.pipex.com
Publishing Manager Lesley A. Taylor
Theology and religion, church and local history. Section of Church of Scotland Board of Communication.

St Pauls
St Pauls (Publishing), Morpeth Terrace, London SW1P 1EP
tel 0171-828 5582 *fax* 0171-828 3329
Theology, ethics, spirituality, biography, education, general books of Roman Catholic and Christian interest. Founded 1948.

St Paul's Bibliographies
West End House, 1 Step Terrace, Winchester, Hants SO22 5BW
tel (01962) 860524 *fax* (01962) 842409
e-mail stpauls@stpaulsbib.com
Publishing Director Robert S. Cross
Bibliography and scholarly works on the history of the Book and the book trade. Founded 1974.

Salamander Books Ltd
8 Blenheim Court, Brewery Road, London N7 9NT
tel 0171-700 7799 *fax* 0171-700 3918
Directors David Spence (managing), Colin Gower (sales)
Cookery, crafts, military, natural history, music, gardening, hobbies, transport, sports. Imprint: Vega. Founded 1973.

Salvationist Publishing and Supplies Ltd
117-121 Judd Street, London WC1H 9NN
tel 0171-387 1656 *fax* 0171-383 3420
Managing Director Lt.-Col. Michael Williams
Devotional books, theology, biography, worldwide Christian and social service, children's books, music.

W.B. Saunders Co. Ltd – see Harcourt Brace & Co. Ltd*

S.B. Publications
c/o 19 Grove Road, Seaford, East Sussex BN25 1TP
tel (01323) 893498. Proprietor Stephen Benz

Local history (illustrated by postcards/ old photographs), local themes (e.g. walking books, guides), maritime history, transport, specific themes. Founded 1987.

Scala – see Philip Wilson Publishers Ltd

Scarlet – see Robinson Publishing Ltd

Sceptre – see Hodder Headline plc*

Schofield & Sims Ltd
Dogley Mill, Fenay Bridge, Huddersfield HD8 0NQ
tel (01484) 607080 *fax* (01484) 606815
e-mail 100641.252@compuserve.com
Directors John S. Nesbitt (chairman), J. Stephen Platts (managing), J. Brierley (sales), M.S. Nesbitt (marketing)
Educational: infants, primary, secondary, children's books; posters. Founded 1901.

Scholastic Children's Books*
Commonwealth House, 1-19 New Oxford Street, London WC1A 1NU
tel 0171-421 9000 *fax* 0171-421 9001
Publishing Director David Fickling, *Character and Preschool Publisher* Penny Morris
Imprint of **Scholastic Ltd**.
André Deutsch Children's Books (imprint)
Publishing Director David Fickling
Children's fiction and non-fiction.
Hippo (imprint)
Publishing Director David Fickling
Children's paperbacks – fiction and non-fiction. No unsolicited MSS.
Point (imprint)
Commissioning Editor Julia Moffatt
Fiction for 11+: horror, crime, romance.
Scholastic Press (imprint)
Publishing Director David Fickling
Quality teenage fiction.

Scholastic Ltd*
Villiers House, Clarendon Avenue, Leamington Spa, Warks. CV32 5PR
tel (01926) 887799 *fax* (01926) 883331
e-mail scholastic@compuserve.com
web site http://www.scholastic.co.uk
London office Commonwealth House, 1-19 New Oxford Street, London WC1A 1NU
tel 0171-421 9000 *fax* 0171-421 9001
Directors D.M.R. Kewley (managing), M.R. Robinson (USA), R.M. Spaulding (USA), D.J. Walsh (USA)
Children's Division
Publishing Director David Fickling
See **Scholastic Children's Books***
Direct Marketing
Managing Director, Book Fair Division Will Oldham, *Managing Director, School Book Clubs*

and Continuities Victoria Birkett, *Managing Director, Consumer Book Clubs and Party Plan* David Teale, *Sales and Marketing Director* Gavin Lang
Children's book clubs and school book fairs.
Educational Division
Publishing Director Anne Peel
Publishers of books for teachers (*Bright Ideas* and other series), primary classroom resources and magazines for teachers (*Child Education, Junior Education* and others). Founded 1964.

Scholastic Press – see Scholastic Children's Books*

Science Museum Publications
Science Museum, Exhibition Road, London SW7 2DD
tel 0171-938 8136 *fax* 0171-938 8169
e-mail e.ginalska@nmsi.ac.uk
web site http://www.nmsi.ac.uk
Publications Manager Ela Ginalska
History of science and technology, public understanding of science, including books for children.

SCM Press Ltd*
9-17 St Albans Place, London N1 0NX
tel 0171-359 8033 *fax* 0171-359 0049
Managing Director and Editor John Bowden, *Directors* Margaret Lydamore (associate editor and company secretary), Roger Pygram (finance)
Theological books with special emphasis on biblical, philosophical and modern theology; books on sociology of religion and religious aspects of current issues. Founded 1929.

Scottish Academic Press*
56 Hanover Street, Edinburgh EH2 2DX
tel 0131-225 7483 *fax* 0131-225 7662
Editor Dr Douglas Grant
All types of academic books and books of Scottish interest. Founded 1969.

Scottish Cultural Press*
Unit 14, Leith Walk Business Centre, 130 Leith Walk, Edinburgh EH6 5DT
tel 0131-555 5950 *fax* 0131-555 5018
e-mail scp@sol.co.uk
web site http://www.taynet.co.uk/users/scp
Director Jill Dick
Literature, poetry, history, archaeology, biography and environmental history. Founded 1992.
Scottish Children's Press (imprint)
Children's Administrator Avril Gray

Scottish fiction, Scottish non-fiction and Scots language, children's writing.

The Scout Association
Baden-Powell House, Queen's Gate, London SW7 5JS
tel 0171-584 7030 *fax* 0171-590 5103
e-mail scoutingmag@enterprise.net
Acting Editor Ron Crabb
Technical books dealing with all subjects relevant to Scouting and monthly journal *Scouting*.

Scripture Union*
207-209 Queensway, Bletchley, Milton Keynes, Bucks. MK2 2EB
tel (01908) 856000 *fax* (01908) 856111
e-mail postmaster@scriptureunion.org.uk
Christian books and Bible reading materials for people of all ages; educational and worship resources for churches; children's fiction and non-fiction; adult non-fiction. Founded 1867.

Seafarer Books – see Merlin Press Ltd

Search Press Ltd
Wellwood, North Farm Road, Tunbridge Wells, Kent TN2 3DR
tel (01892) 510850 *fax* (01892) 515903
e-mail searchpress@serachpress.com
Directors Martin de la Bedoyère (managing), Rosalind Dale (editorial), Ruth B. Saunders
Arts, crafts, leisure, gardening. Founded 1962.

Secker and Warburg – see Random House UK Ltd*

Seren Books
First Floor, 2 Wyndham Street, Bridgend CF31 1EF
tel/fax (01656) 767834
Director Mick Felton
Poetry, fiction, drama, history, film, literary criticism, biography, art – mostly with relevance to Wales. Founded 1981.

Serif
47 Strahan Road, London E3 5DA
tel/fax 0181-981 3990
e-mail threshold.demon.co.uk
Editorial Director Stephen Hayward
Politics, history, Irish studies, cookery; no fiction. Synopses only; no unsolicited MSS. Founded 1993.

Serpent's Tail
4 Blackstock Mews, London N4 2BT
tel 0171-354 1949 *fax* 0171-704 6467
e-mail info@serpentstail.com
web site http://www.serpentstail.com

Director Peter Ayrton
Modern fiction in paperback: literary and experimental work, and work in translation. Approach with query letter please; do not send complete MSS. Sae essential as is familiarity with list. Founded 1986.

Settle Press
10 Boyne Terrace Mews, London W11 3LR
tel 0171-243 0695
Managing Director D. Settle
Travel guidebooks. Founded 1983.

Severn House Publishers
9-15 High Street, Sutton, Surrey SM1 1DF
tel 0181-770 3930 *fax* 0181-770 3850
web site http://www.severnhouse.com
Chairman Edwin Buckhalter, *Editorial Director* Sara Short
Hardcover adult fiction for the library market: romances, thrillers, detective, adventure, war, science fiction; film and TV tie-ins. No unsolicited MSS.

Shakespeare Head Press – see Blackwell Publishers*

Sheed & Ward Ltd
14 Coopers Row, London EC3N 2BH
tel 0171-702 9799 *fax* 0171-702 3583
Directors M.T. Redfern, K.G. Darke, A.M. Redfern
History, philosophy, theology, catechetics, scripture and religion titles, mostly by Catholic authors. Founded 1926.

Sheldon Press – see Society for Promoting Christian Knowledge*

Sheldrake Press
188 Cavendish Road, London SW12 0DA
tel 0181-675 1767 *fax* 0181-675 7736
Publisher J.S. Rigge
History, travel, architecture, cookery, music; stationery. Founded 1979.

Shepheard-Walwyn (Publishers) Ltd
Suite 34, 26 Charing Cross Road, London WC2H 0DH
tel 0171-240 5992 *fax* 0171-379 5770
Directors A.R.A. Werner, M.M. Werner
History, political economy, philosophy; illustrated gift books, some originated in calligraphy; Scottish interest. Founded 1971.

John Sherratt & Son Ltd
Hotspur House, 2 Gloucester Street, Manchester M1 5QR
tel 0161-236 9963 *fax* 0161-236 2026
Managing Director P.A. Westaway

Educational (primary, secondary, technical, university), medical, practical handbooks, collectors' books.

Shire Publications Ltd
Cromwell House, Church Street,
Princes Risborough, Bucks. HP27 9AA
tel (01844) 344301 *fax* (01844) 347080
e-mail shire@shirebooks.co.uk
web site http://www.shirebooks.co.uk
Director J.W. Rotheroe
Discovering paperbacks, Shire Albums,
Shire Archaeology, Shire Natural History,
Shire Ethnography, Shire Egyptology,
Shire Garden History. Founded 1966.

Sidgwick & Jackson – see Macmillan
Publishers Ltd*

Sigma Press
1 South Oak Lane, Wilmslow, Cheshire SK9 6AR
tel (01625) 531035 *fax* (01625) 536800
e-mail sigma.press@zetnet.co.uk
web site http://www.sigmapress.co.uk
Partners Graham Beech, Diana Beech
Leisure (country walking, cycling, regional heritage, sport, cookery, folklore); popular science. Founded 1979.

Signet Books – former imprint of
Michael Joseph/Penguin

Silhouette – see Harlequin Mills &
Boon Ltd*

Simon & Schuster*
Africa House, 64-78 Kingsway,
London WC2B 6AH
tel 0171-316 1900 *fax* 0171-316 0333
Directors Nick Webb (managing), Clare Ledingham
(editorial, fiction), Martin Fletcher (editorial, mass-
market fiction and Touchstone), Diane Spivey
(rights), Helen Gummer (editorial, non-fiction),
Bob Kelly (international sales and marketing)
Fiction; non-fiction: reference, music, travel, mass-market paperbacks. Founded 1986.
Earthlight (imprint)
Science fiction and fantasy.
Pocket Books (imprint)
Mass-market fiction and non-fiction paperbacks.
Touchstone (imprint)
Quality upmarket non-fiction paperbacks.

Skoob Books Ltd
76A Oldfield Road, London N16 0RS
tel/fax 0171-275 9811

e-mail books@skoob.com
Director I.K. Ong, *Editorial* M. Lovell
Literary guides, cultural studies, esoterica/occult, oriental literature. No unsolicited MSS or synopses considered. Founded 1979.

Sleepy Hollow Pantomimes – see
Dublar Scripts

Slow Dancer Press
Flat 2, 59 Parliament Hill, London NW3 2TB
Director John Harvey
Poetry and fiction, especially crime fiction with jazz associations. Study writings published by Slow Dancer first; send letter before submitting material. Unsolicited MSS will not be read. Founded 1977.

Smith Gryphon Ltd – see Blake
Publishing

Colin Smythe Ltd*
PO Box 6, Gerrards Cross, Bucks. SL9 8XA
tel (01753) 886000 *fax* (01753) 886469
Directors Colin Smythe (managing and editorial),
Peter Bander van Duren, A. Norman Jeffares, Ann
Saddlemyer, Leslie Hayward
Biography, phaleristics, heraldry, Irish literature and literary criticism, folklore, crafts and history. Founded 1966.

Society of Genealogists
14 Charterhouse Buildings, Goswell Road,
London EC1M 7BA
tel 0171-251 8799 *fax* 0171-250 1800
e-mail info@sog.org.uk
web site http://www.sog.org.uk/
Director Robert I.N. Gordon, *Finance Officer*
Roger Lawson, *Sales and Marketing Manager*
Robert Thompson
Genealogy and family history books, and guides to records. Founded 1911.

Society for Promoting Christian Knowledge*
Holy Trinity Church, Marylebone Road,
London NW1 4DU
tel 0171-387 5282 *fax* 0171-388 2352
e-mail publishing@spck.co.uk
Director of Publishing Simon Kingston
Founded 1698.
Sheldon Press (imprint)
Editorial Director Joanna Moriarty
Popular medicine, health, self-help, psychology, business.
SPCK (imprint)
Editorial Director Joanna Moriarty

Theology and academic, liturgy, prayer, spirituality, biblical studies, educational resources, mission, gospel and culture.
Triangle (imprint)
Editor Alison Barr
Popular Christian paperbacks.

Souvenir Press Ltd
43 Great Russell Street, London WC1B 3PA
tel 0171-580 9307-8 and 637 5711/2/3
fax 0171-580 5064
Managing Director Ernest Hecht BSc(Econ), BCom
Archaeology, biography and memoirs, educational (secondary, technical), fiction, general, humour, practical handbooks, psychiatry, psychology, sociology, sports, games and hobbies, travel, supernatural, parapsychology, illustrated books.

SPCK – see Society for Promoting Christian Knowledge*

Neville Spearman Publishers – see The C.W. Daniel Company Ltd

Specialist Crafts Ltd
(formerly Dryad)
PO Box 247, Leicester LE1 9QS
tel 0116-251 0405 *fax* 0116-251 5015
e-mail post@speccrafts.co.uk
web site http://www.speccrafts.co.uk
Joint Managing Director P.A. Crick
'How to' booklets on various art and craft skills. *Specialist Crafts 500* series full colour craft booklets and patterns. Suppliers of over 9000 art and craft items.

Spellmount Ltd
The Old Rectory, Staplehurst, Kent TN12 0AZ
tel (01580) 893730 *fax* (01580) 893731
Proprietor Jamie A.G. Wilson
Ancient, 15th-20th century history/military history. Send sae with submissions please. Founded 1984.

Spindlewood – see Ragged Bears Ltd

E. & F. Spon – see Routledge*

Springboard Fiction – see Yorkshire Art Circus

Springer-Verlag London Ltd
Sweetapple House, Catteshall Road, Godalming, Surrey GU7 3DJ
tel (01483) 418800 *fax* (01483) 415151
e-mail postmaster@svl.co.uk
web site http://www.springer.co.uk
Managing Director John Watson, *Executive Directors* C. Michaletz, D. Goetz

Medicine, computing, engineering, astronomy, mathematics. Founded 1972.

Stacey International
128 Kensington Church Street, London W8 4BH
tel 0171-221 7166 *fax* 0171-792 9288
e-mail 106463.424@compuserve.com
Directors Tom Stacey (managing), S.F.A. Stacey, *Publishing Executive* Mark Petre
Illustrated non-fiction, encyclopedic books on regions and countries, Islamic and Arab subjects, world affairs, art, travel, belles-lettres. Founded 1974.

Stainer & Bell Ltd
PO Box 110, Victoria House, 23 Gruneisen Road, London N3 1DZ
tel 0181-343 3303 *fax* 0181-343 3024
e-mail post@stainer.co.uk
Directors Keith Wakefield (joint managing), Carol Wakefield (joint managing and secretary), John Hosier CBE, Antony Kearns
Books on music, religious communication. Founded 1907.

Harold Starke Publishers Ltd*
Pixey Green, Stradbroke, Eye, Suffolk IP21 5NG
tel (01379) 388334 *fax* (01379) 388335
203 Bunyan Court, Barbican, London EC2Y 8DH
tel 0171-588 5195
Directors Harold K. Starke, Naomi Galinski (editorial)
Specialist, scientific, medical, reference.

The Stationery Office/National Publishing*
Head Office St Crispins, Duke Street, Norwich NR3 1PD
tel (01603) 695532 *fax* (01603) 695317
Distribution and Order Point The Stationery Office Publication Centre, PO Box 276, London SW8 5DT
tel 0171-873 0011
Chief Executive, National Publishing Fred Perkins, *Business Development Director* Kevan Lawton
Archaeology, architecture, art, business, current affairs, directories and guide-books, educational (primary, secondary, technical, university), general, heritage, history, naval and military, medical, pharmaceutical, professional, practical handbooks, reference, science, sociology, yearbooks (including *Whitaker's Almanack*).

Stationery Office (Ireland) – see Government Supplies Agency

Patrick Stephens Ltd – see **Haynes Publishing**

Sterling Publishing Group plc
PO Box 839, 86-88 Edgware Road,
London W2 2YW
tel 0171-258 0066 *fax* 0171-723 5766
Chairman Christopher Haines, *Chief Executive* Simone Kesseler, *Directors* R. Harrison, D. Watson, L.S. Garman, C. Gillings, R. Panton Corbett
International business-to-business publishing. Reference, management and technology directories, leisure, commemorative publishing, exhibition organising. Founded 1978.

Stride Publications
11 Sylvan Road, Exeter, Devon EX4 6EW
e-mail rml@madbear.demon.co.uk
Managing Editor Rupert M. Loydell
Poetry, short story collections, literary experimental novels, contemporary music and visual arts, interviews. Submissions in writing only. Founded 1980.

Summersdale Publishers
46 West Street, Chichester, West Sussex PO19 1RP
tel (01243) 771107 *fax* (01243) 786300
e-mail summersdale@summersdale.com
Editors Alastair Williams, Stewart Ferris
Travel, humour, gift books, TV/film tie-ins, cookery. Seeking strong, commercial non-fiction. Founded 1990.

Sunflower Books
12 Kendrick Mews, London SW7 3HG
tel 0171-589 1862 *fax* 0171-589 1862
web site http://www.sunflowerbooks.co.uk/
Directors P.A. Underwood (editorial), J.G. Underwood, S.J. Seccombe
Travel guidebooks.

Sussex Academic Press
PO Box 2950, Brighton BN2 5SP
tel (01273) 699533 *fax* (01273) 621262
e-mail edit@sussex-academic.co.uk
web site http://www.sussex-academic.co.uk
Editorial Director Anthony Grahame
British history and Middle East studies. Founded 1994.
The Alpha Press (imprint)
Religion and sport.

Sutton Publishing Ltd
Phoenix Mill, Thrupp, Stroud,
Glos. GL5 2BU
tel (01453) 731114 *fax* (01453) 731117
Directors David Prigent, Peter Clifford (publishing), Christopher Sackett, David Hogg, Nick Carter (sales and marketing)
General and academic publishers of high quality illustrated books: history, military, biography, transport, archaeology. Founded 1978.

Swan Hill Press – see **Airlife Publishing Ltd**

Swedenborg Society
20-21 Bloomsbury Way, London WC1A 2TH
tel 0171-405 7986 *fax* 0171-831 5848
e-mail swed.soc@netmatters.co.uk
The Writings of Swedenborg.

Sweet & Maxwell*
100 Avenue Road, London NW3 3PF
tel 0171-393 7000 *fax* 0171-393 7010
Directors Mike Dixon (managing), Jackie Rhodes, Barbara Grandage, Alina Lourie, Derek Sturdy, Antonia Rodgers, Anthony Kinahan, Kevin Waterman, Anne Hayes, Christine Miskin, Janson Woodhall, Alan Wells, Paul Riddle
Law. Part of Thomson Professional Information UK. Founded 1799; incorporated 1889.

Take That Ltd
PO Box 200, Harrogate,
North Yorkshire HG1 2YR
tel (01423) 507545 *fax* (01423) 526035
e-mail sales@takethat.co.uk
web site http://www.takethat.co.uk
Managing Director Chris Brown
Internet/computing, business, finance, gambling. Send sae with synopsis/samples. Founded 1986.

Tamarind Ltd
PO Box 296, Camberley,
Surrey GU15 4WD
tel (01276) 683979 *fax* (01276) 685365
Managing Director Verna Wilkins
Multicultural children's picture books and educational material. Publications give a high positive profile to black children. Unsolicited material welcome with return postage. Founded 1987.

Tango Books – imprint of **Sadie Fields Productions Ltd, book packagers**

Tarquin Publications
Stradbroke, Diss, Norfolk IP21 5JP
tel (01379) 384218 *fax* (01379) 384289
Partners Gerald Jenkins, Margaret Jenkins
Mathematics and mathematical models; paper cutting, paper engineering and pop-up books for intelligent children. No unsolicited MSS; send suggestion or synopsis in first instance. Founded 1970.

Tate Gallery Publishing Ltd

Millbank, London SW1P 4RG
tel 0171-887 8869/70 *fax* 0171-887 8878
Managing Director Celia Clear, *Senior Manager*
Brian McGahon, *Retail Manager* Rosemary
Bennett, *Marketing Manager* Mark Eastment,
Production Manager Tim Holton

Publishers for the Tate Gallery in
London, Liverpool and St Ives.
Exhibition catalogues, general and educational books, diaries, calendars, posters
and stationery in the field of British and
modern art. Founded 1996.

I.B. Tauris & Co. Ltd

Victoria House, Bloomsbury Square,
London WC1B 4DZ
tel 0171-831 9060 *fax* 0171-831 9061
e-mail mail@ibtauris.com
Directors I. Bagherzade (chairman and publisher),
Jonathan McDonnell (managing)

History, politics, international relations,
economics, current affairs, Middle East,
cultural and media studies, film. Founded
1983.

British Academic Press (imprint)
Academic monographs and research dissertations in history, political science
and social sciences.

Tauris Academic Studies (imprint)
Academic monographs on history, politics, international relations, economics,
international law.

Tauris Parke Books (imprint)
Illustrated books on architecture, design,
cultural history and travel.

Taylor & Francis Group plc*

1 Gunpowder Square, London EC4A 3DE
tel 0171-583 0490 *fax* 0171-583 0581
Group Publishing Director (Editorial) Stephen Neal

Educational (university), science: physics,
mathematics, chemistry, electronics, natural history, pharmacology and drug
metabolism, toxicology, technology, history of science, ergonomics, production
engineering, remote sensing, geographic
information systems, psychology.

Teach Yourself – see Hodder Headline plc*

Telegraph Books

The Daily Telegraph, 1 Canada Square,
Canary Wharf, London E14 5DT
tel 0171-538 6826 *fax* 0171-538 6064
Manager Susannah Charlton

Business, personal finance, crosswords,
sport, travel and guides, cookery and
wine, general, gardening, history – all by
Telegraph journalists and contributors,
and co-published with major publishing
houses. Founded 1920.

Tellastory – see Random House UK Ltd*

Thames and Hudson Ltd*

30-34 Bloomsbury Street, London WC1B 3QP
tel 0171-636 5488 *fax* 0171-636 4799
e-mail mail@thbooks.demon.co.uk
Chairman E.U. Neurath, *Managing Director*
T.M. Neurath, *Directors* E. Bates (company
secretary), J.R. Camplin (editorial), T.L. Evans
(sales and marketing), C.A. Ferguson
(production), W. Guttmann, C.M. Kaine (design),
N. Stangos (editorial), T.J. Flood (finance), P.
Hughes CBE

Illustrated non-fiction for an international audience, especially art, architecture,
graphic design, garden and landscape
design, archaeology, cultural history, historical reference, fashion, photography,
ethnic arts, mythology and religion.

Thames Publishing

14 Barlby Road, London W10 6AR
tel 0181-969 3579 *fax* 0181-969 1465
Publishing Manager John Bishop

Books about music (not pop), particularly British composers and musicians. Preliminary letter essential. Founded 1970.

D.C. Thomson & Co. Ltd – Publications

Dundee DD1 9QJ
tel (01382) 223131 *fax* (01382) 322214
London office 185 Fleet Street,
London EC4A 2HS
tel 0171-242 5086 *fax* 0171-404 5694

Publishers of newspapers and periodicals. Children's books (annuals), based
on weekly magazine characters; fiction.

Thomson Science – acquired by Wolters Kluwer Group of Companies

Stanley Thornes (Publishers) Ltd

(incorporating Mary Glasgow Publications)
Ellenborough House, Wellington Street,
Cheltenham, Glos. GL50 1YW
tel (01242) 228888 *fax* (01242) 221914
Directors David Smith (managing), Brian Carvell,
Paul Vinson, Dominic Richardson

Educational: primary, secondary, further
education books, higher education, professional.

Thorsons – see HarperCollins Publishers*

Times Books – see HarperCollins Publishers*

Times Mirror International Publishers Ltd (TMIP Ltd) – see Mosby International

Titan Books Ltd
42-44 Dolben Street, London SE1 0UP
tel 0171-620 0200 *fax* 0171-620 0032
e-mail 101447.2455@compuserve.com
Publisher and Managing Director Nick Landau, *Editorial Director* Katy Wild
Graphic novels, including Aliens and Batman, featuring comic strip material; film and TV tie-ins and reference books, including *Star Wars* and *Star Trek*. Erotic fiction under the Eros Plus imprint. No fiction or children's proposals and no unsolicited material without preliminary letter please; send large sae for current author guidelines. Founded 1981.

Tolkien – see HarperCollins Publishers*

Tolley Publishing Co. Ltd
Tolley House, 2 Addiscombe Road, Croydon, Surrey CR9 5AF
tel 0181-686 9141 *fax* 0181-686 3155
e-mail sales@tolley.co.uk
Directors Neville Cusworth (chairman), Kelvin D. Ladbrook (managing), Gareth Taylor (editorial, tax/ accountancy), Carol Doyle-Linden (editorial, legal/business), Jill Howis (finance and operations)
Law, taxation, accountancy, business. Founded 1916.
Fourmat Publishing (division)
Director Carol Doyle-Linden, *Commissioning Editor* Irene Kaplan
Books and legal forms for lawyers, business and the professions.
Charles Knight Publishing (division)
Director Carol Doyle-Linden, *Managing Editor* S.C. Cotter
Looseleaf legal works and periodicals on local government law, construction law and technical subjects.

Touchstone – see Simon & Schuster*

Town House and Country House†
Trinity House, Charleston Road, Ranelagh, Dublin 6, Republic of Ireland
tel (01) 4972399 *fax* (01) 4970927
e-mail books@townhouse.ie

Directors Treasa Coady, Jim Coady
General illustrated non-fiction, popular fiction, art, archaeology and biography. Founded 1981.

Training Direct – see Pearson Professional Ltd*

Transworld Publishers Ltd*
61-63 Uxbridge Road, London W5 5SA
tel 0181- 579 2652 *fax* 0181-579 5479
e-mail info@transworld-publishers.co.uk
Chairman Jack Hoeft, *Managing Director* Mark Barty-King, *Deputy Managing Director* Barry Hempstead (operations), *Publishers* Patrick Janson-Smith (adult trade books), Ursula Mackenzie (hardbacks), Larry Finlay (paperbacks), Philippa Dickinson (children's books)
Subsidiary of Bertelsmann AG.
Anchor (imprint)
Publisher John Saddler
Literary fiction and non-fiction.
Bantam (imprint)
Publishing Director Francesca Liversidge
Paperback general fiction and non-fiction.
Bantam Press (imprint)
Publishing Director Sally Gaminara
Fiction, general, cookery, business, crime, health and diet, history, humour, military, music, paranormal, self-help, science, travel and adventure, biography and autobiography.
Bantam Children's Books (division)
Publisher Philippa Dickinson
Paperback young adult books and series.
Black Swan (imprint)
Editorial Director Bill Scott-Kerr
Paperback quality fiction.
Corgi (imprint)
Editorial Director Bill Scott-Kerr
Paperback general fiction and non-fiction.
Corgi Children's Books (division)
Publisher Philippa Dickinson
Children's paperback picture books, fiction and poetry.
Doubleday (UK) (imprint)
Publisher Marianne Velmans
General fiction and non-fiction.
Doubleday Children's Books (imprint)
Publisher Philippa Dickinson
Hardback picture books, fiction and poetry for children.
Partridge Press (imprint)
Senior Editor Alison Barrow
Sport and leisure.

Also: IDG Computer Books and Expert Gardening Books.

Treehouse Children's Books Ltd
Page Farm, Newtown, West Pennard, Glastonbury, Somerset BA6 8NN
tel (01458) 835757 *fax* (01458) 835758
Editorial Director Richard Powell
Preschool children's books and novelty books. Founded 1989.

Trentham Books Ltd*
Westview House, 734 London Road, Oakhill, Stoke-on-Trent, Staffs. ST4 5NP
tel (01782) 745567/844699 *fax* (01782) 745553
e-mail tb@trentham.books.co.uk
web site http://www.trentham-books.co.uk
Directors Prof S.J. Eggleston (managing), Dr Gillian Klein (editorial), Barbara Wiggins (executive)
Editorial office 28 Hillside Gardens, London N6 5ST
tel 0181-348 2174
Education (including specialist fields – multicultural issues, equal opportunities, bullying, design and technology, early years), social policy, sociology of education, European education, women's studies. Does not publish books for use by children or fiction, biography, reminiscences and poetry. Founded 1968.

Triangle – see Society for Promoting Christian Knowledge*

Trotman & Company Ltd
12 Hill Rise, Richmond, Surrey TW10 6UA
tel 0181-940 5668 *fax* 0181-948 9267
web site http://www.trotmanpublishing.co.uk
Chairman A.F. Trotman, *Publishing Director* Morfydd Jones
Higher education guidance, careers, classroom resources. Founded 1970.

Two Heads Publishing
9 Whitehall Park, London N19 3TS
tel 0171-561 1606 *fax* 0171-561 1607
e-mail twoheads.demon.co.uk
Publisher Charles Frewin
Sport, especially cricket and football. Founded 1992.

Two-Can Publishing*
346 Old Street, London EC1V 9NQ
tel 0171-684 4000 *fax* 0171-613 3371
e-mail info@two-can.co.uk
Directors Andrew Jarvis (chairman), Ian Grant (marketing), Sara Lynn (creative), Damian Kelleher (editorial)
Children's: reference and non-fiction

books, magazines, video and multimedia products. Founded 1987.

UCL Press Ltd
1 Gunpowder Square, London EC4A 3DE
tel 0171-583 0490 *fax* 0171-583 0581
web site http://www.tandf.co.uk
Group Publishing Director (Editorial) Stephen Neal
History, philosophy, politics, cultural studies, planning and geography, social research methods, sociology. Member of the Taylor & Francis Group. Founded 1991.

Unicorn Books
16 Laxton Gardens, Paddock Wood, Kent TN12 6BB
tel (01892) 833648 *fax* (01892) 833577
Director R. Green
Militaria, music, transport.

University of Exeter Press*
Reed Hall, Streatham Drive, Exeter, Devon EX4 4QR
tel (01392) 263066 *fax* (01392) 263064
e-mail uep @exeter.ac.uk
web site http://www.ex.ac.uk/uep/
Publisher Simon Baker
Academic and scholarly books on history, local history (Exeter and the South West), archaeology, classical studies, English literature, film history, medieval studies, linguistics, modern languages, European studies, maritime studies, mining history, politics, American studies. Founded 1958.

The University of Hull Press & Lampada Press
Cottingham Road, Hull, North Humberside HU6 7RX
tel (01482) 465322 *fax* (01482) 466857
Publisher Glen Innes
General interest: economic and social history, history, local history, modern languages, English, geography, law, music, literature, poetry, art history. Founded 1983/1991.

University of Wales Press
6 Gwennyth Street, Cathays, Cardiff CF2 4YD
tel (01222) 231919 *fax* (01222) 230908
e-mail press@press.wales.ac.uk
web site http://www.swan.ac.uk/uwp/home.htm
Editorial Director Ned Thomas
Academic and educational (Welsh and English). Publishers of *Welsh History Review, Studia Celtica, Llên Cymru, Y Gwyddonydd, Efrydiau Athronyddol, Contemporary Wales, Welsh Journal of Education, Journal of Celtic Linguistics, ALT-J (Association for Learning Technology*

Journal), Borderlines, Kantian Review, Education and Ethos. Founded 1922.

Merlin Unwin Books
Palmers House, 7 Corve Street, Ludlow, Shropshire SY8 1DB
tel (01584) 877456 *fax* (01584) 877457
web site http://www.merlinunwin.co.uk
Proprietor Merlin Unwin
Fishing and country books. Founded 1990.

Unwin Hyman Ltd – acquired by HarperCollins Publishers*

Unwin Hyman Academic – now incorporated into Routledge*

Usborne Publishing*
Usborne House, 83-85 Saffron Hill, London EC1N 8RT
tel 0171-430 2800 *fax* 0171-430 1562
Directors Peter Usborne, Jenny Tyler (editorial), Robert Jones, David Lowe, Keith Ball, David Harte, Lorna Hunt
Children's books: reference, practical, craft, natural history, science, languages, history, geography, fiction. Founded 1973.

V&A Publications
160 Brompton Road, London SW3 1HW
tel 0171-938 9663 *fax* 0171-938 8370
web site http://www.vam.ac.uk
Head of Publications Mary Butler
Popular and scholarly books on fine and decorative arts, architecture, contemporary design, fashion and photography. Founded 1980.

Vallentine Mitchell – see Frank Cass & Co. Ltd

Van Nostrand Reinhold – acquired by John Wiley & Sons Inc. – see Overseas book publishers, page 230

Variorum – see Ashgate Publishing Ltd

Ventura – see Penguin UK*

Veritas Publications†
Veritas House, 7-8 Lower Abbey Street, Dublin 1, Republic of Ireland
tel (01) 8788177 *fax* (01) 8786507
UK Veritas Book & Video Distribution Ltd, Lower Avenue, Leamington Spa, Warks. CV31 3NP
tel (0926) 451 730 *fax* (0926) 451 733
Religion, including social and educational works, and material relating to the media of communication. Division of the Catholic Communications Institute of Ireland, Inc.

Vermilion – see Random House UK Ltd*

Verso Ltd
6 Meard Street, London W1V 3HR
tel 0171-437 3546 *fax* 0171-734 0059
e-mail verso@verso.co.uk
Directors Lucy Heller (executive chairman), Colin Robinson, Robin Blackburn, Tony Stevenson, Mike Sprinker, Mike Davis, Tariq Ali, Perry Anderson
Politics, sociology, economics, history, philosophy, cultural studies. Founded 1970.

Victoria House Publishing Ltd
King's Court, Parsonage Lane, Bath BA1 1EF
tel (01225) 463401 *fax* (01225) 460942
Managing Director Clyde Hunter
Reader's Digest Children's Books (imprint)
Mass market children's and novelty information books. Fully owned subsidiary of Reader's Digest Association Inc. Founded 1980.

Viking – see Penguin UK*

Viking Children's – see Penguin UK*

Vintage – see Random House UK Ltd*

Virago – see Little, Brown and Company (UK)*

Virgin Publishing Ltd
Thames Wharf Studios, Rainville Road, London W6 9HT
tel 0171-386 3300 *fax* 0171-386 3360
Chairman Robert Devereux, *Directors* Robert Shreeve (managing), Richard Branson, *Management* Peter Darvill-Evans (publisher, fiction), Carolyn Thorne (publisher, illustrated), K.T. Forster (international sales), Amy Nelson-Bennett (marketing), Susan Atkinson (publicity), Ray Mudie (sales), Nigel Williams (financial), Rod Green (senior editor, general)
Virgin (imprint)
Editorial Carolyn Thorne (illustrated), Rod Green (general, film and TV tie-ins, humour), Peter Darvill-Evans (fiction, cult TV), Louise Cavanagh (travel)
Popular culture: entertainment, showbiz, arts, film and TV, music, humour, biography and autobiography, popular reference, true crime, sport, travel.

Black Lace (imprint)
Editor Kerri Sharp
Erotic fiction by women for women.

Idol (imprint)
Editor Rebecca Levene
Homoerotic fiction for men.

New Adventures (imprint)
Editor Simon Winstone
Science fiction.

Nexus (imprint)
Publisher Peter Darvill-Evans
Erotic fiction.

Virtue Books Ltd
Edward House, Tenter Street, Rotherham S60 1LB
tel (01709) 365005 *fax* (01709) 829982
Directors Peter E. Russum, Margaret H. Russum, Michael G. Virtue (editorial)
Books for the professional chef, catering and drink.

Vista – see Cassell plc

VNR – see Wiley Europe Ltd*

Voyager – see HarperCollins Publishers*

Walker Books Ltd
87 Vauxhall Walk, London SE11 5HJ
tel 0171-793 0909 *fax* 0171-587 1123
e-mail mail@walkerbooks.co.uk
Directors David Heatherwick, Wendy Boase, David Lloyd, Amelia Edwards, Judy Burdsall, Harold G. Gould OBE, Henryk Wesolowski, Sarah Foster, Gary Gentel
Children's – mainly picture books; junior and teenage fiction. Founded 1979.

Warburg Institute
University of London, Woburn Square, London WC1H 0AB
tel 0171-580 9663 *fax* 0171-436 2852
Cultural and intellectual history, with special reference to the history of the classical tradition.

Ward Lock – see Cassell plc

Ward Lock Educational Co. Ltd
BIC Ling Kee House, 1 Christopher Road, East Grinstead, West Sussex RH19 3BT
tel (01342) 318980 *fax* (01342) 410980
Directors Au Bak Ling (chairman, Hong Kong), Au King Kwok (Hong Kong), Au Wai Kwok (Hong Kong), Albert Kw Au (Hong Kong), Au Chun Kwok (Hong Kong), *General Manager* Penny Kitchenham
Primary and secondary pupil materials, Kent Mathematics Project: KMP BASIC for primary and KMP Main for sec-

ondary, Reading Workshops, Take Part Series and Take Part Starters, teachers' books, music books, Target Series for the National Curriculum: Target Science and Target Geography, religious education, environmental studies. Founded 1952.

Frederick Warne – see Penguin UK*

Warner – see Little, Brown and Company (UK)*

Warner/Chappell Plays Ltd
Griffin House, 161 Hammersmith Road, London W6 8BS
tel 0181-563 5888 *fax* 0181-563 5801
Editorial Director Michael Callahan
Stage plays only, in both acting and trade editions. Preliminary letter essential.

Waterline Books – see Airlife Publishing Ltd

The Watts Publishing Group*
96 Leonard Street, London EC2A 4RH
tel 0171-739 2929 *fax* 0171-739 2318
Directors Francesca Dow (publishing, Orchard), Philippa Stewart (publishing, Franklin Watts), Marlene Johnson (managing), George Spicer (sales), Elaine Ward (production)
Division of Grolier Ltd.

Franklin Watts (division)
Publishing Director Philippa Stewart
Children's illustrated non-fiction, reference, education. Imprint: Aladdin/Watts.

Orchard Books (division)
Publishing Director Francesca Dow
Children's picture books, fiction, poetry, novelty books, board books.

Wayland Publishers Ltd
61 Western Road, Hove, East Sussex BN3 1JD
tel (01273) 722561 *fax* (01273) 329314
Managing Director D.J. Smith, *Directors* R. Bailey (general manager), S. White-Thomson (product development), N. Padbury (finance), Gerry Frost (sales)
Children's information books for ages 4-18. Includes the imprint **Macdonald Young Books**. Founded 1969.

Websters International Publishers Ltd
2nd Floor, Axe & Bottle Court, 70 Newcomen Street, London SE1 1YT
tel 0171-407 2846 *fax* 0171-407 6437
Chairman and Publisher Adrian Webster, *Managing Director* Jean-Luc Barbanneau, *Publishing Director* Susannah Webster
Wine, food, travel, health. Founded 1983.

Weidenfeld & Nicolson – see The Orion Publishing Group Ltd

Wharncliffe* – see Pen & Sword Books Ltd

Which? Ltd*
2 Marylebone Road, London NW1 4DF
tel 0171-830 6000 *fax* 0171-830 7660
e-mail books@which.net
Chief Executive Sheila McKechnie, *Assistant Director* Kim Lavely, *Head of Publishing* Gill Rowley
Part of Consumers' Association. Founded 1957.

Which? Books (imprint)
Travel, restaurant, hotel and wine guides, medicine, law and personal finance for the layman, gardening, careers, DIY – all branded *Which? Books.*

J. Whitaker & Sons Ltd*
12 Dyott Street, London WC1A 1DF
tel 0171-420 6000 *fax* 0171-836 2909
Directors Peter Allsop, Robin Baum (non-executive chairman), John Lycett, Jonathan Nowell, Chris Ostrom, Paul Pounsford, Tom Sweetman, Sally Whitaker (deputy chairman), Martin Whitaker (managing)
Reference including *The Bookseller* (1858), *Whitaker's Books in Print* (1874), and other book trade directories.

White Mouse Editions Ltd – see New Cavendish Books

Whittet Books Ltd
Hill Farm, Stonham Road, Cotton, Stowmarket, Suffolk IP14 4RQ
tel (01449) 781877 *fax* (01449) 781898
Directors Annabel Whittet, John Whittet
Natural history, countryside, transport, pets, horses. Founded 1976.

Whurr Publishers Ltd*
19B Compton Terrace, London N1 2UN
tel 0171-359 5979 *fax* 0171-226 5290
Managing Director Colin Whurr
Disorders of human communication, medicine, psychology, psychiatry, occupational therapy, physiotherapy, nursing, business. Founded 1987.

Wiley Europe Ltd*
(incorporating Interscience Publishers)
Baffins Lane, Chichester, West Sussex PO19 1UD
tel (01243) 779777 *fax* (01243) 775878
e-mail europe@wiley.co.uk
web site http://www.wiley.co.uk
Chairman The Duke of Richmond, *Managing*

Director J.H. Jarvis, *Publishing Director* S. Mair
Physics, chemistry, mathematics, statistics, engineering, architecture, computer science, biology, medicine, earth science, psychology, business, economics, finance, law. Imprints: Chancery Law, Halsted Press, Interscience, Wiley Heyden, Wiley-Interscience, Wiley-Liss, Wiley Valusource, Wiley-VCH, VNR.

Neil Wilson Publishing Ltd*
303A The Pentagon Centre, 36 Washington Street, Glasgow G3 8AZ
tel 0141-221 1117 *fax* 0141-221 5363
e-mail nwp@cqm.co.uk
web site http://www.nwp.co.uk
Managing Director Neil Wilson
Scottish interest, biography, history, food and drink, hill walking, travel, humour, true crime, whisk(e)y and real ale.

Philip Wilson Publishers Ltd
143-149 Great Portland Street,
London W1N 5FB
tel 0171-436 4490 *fax* 0171-436 4403
Chairman P. Wilson, *Managing Director* A. White, *Publishing Director* A. Jackson
Fine and applied art, architecture, museums. Founded 1975.

Flint River (imprint)
Countries.

Scala (imprint)
Museums.

The Windrush Press
Little Window, High Street, Moreton-in-Marsh, Glos. GL56 0LL
tel (01608) 652012/652025 *fax* (01608) 652125
e-mail windrush@netcomuk.co.uk
Managing Director Geoffrey Smith, *Publishing Director* Victoria Huxley
History, military history, *The Traveller's History* series, ancient mysteries, humour. Founded 1987.

Wisley Handbooks – see Cassell plc

Woburn Press – see Frank Cass & Co. Ltd

Wolfhound Press†
68 Mountjoy Square, Dublin 1, Republic of Ireland
tel (01) 8740354 *fax* 8720207
Publisher Seamus Cashman, *Editor* Susan Houlden
Literary studies and criticism, fiction, art, biography, history, young readers, children's and teenage fiction, law, gift titles, cookery, general non-fiction. Founded 1974.

The Women's Press
34 Great Sutton Street, London EC1V 0DX
tel 0171-251 3007 *fax* 0171-608 1938
Directors Kathy Gale (publishing), Mary Hemming (sales)

Books by women in the areas of literary fiction, crime novels, biography and autobiography, health, politics, handbooks, literary criticism, psychology and self-help, the arts. Founded 1978.

Livewire (imprint)
Books for young women.

Woodhead Publishing Ltd
Abington Hall, Abington, Cambridge CB1 6AH
tel (01223) 891358 *fax* (01223) 893694
e-mail woodhead @dial.pipex.com
web site http://www.woodhead-publishing.com
Managing Director Martin Woodhead

Materials engineering, welding, textiles, finance, investment, banking, business, food science and technology. Founded 1989.

Wordsworth Editions Ltd
6 London Street, London W2 1HL
tel 0171-706 8822 *fax* 0171-706 8833
e-mail 100434.276@compuserve.com
Directors Michael Trayler (managing), Helen Trayler (operations), Marcus Clapham (editorial), Clive Reynard (sales and company secretary)

Reprints of classic books: literary, children's, American, women's, military, erotica, poetry; reference. Founded 1987.

World International Ltd
Deanway Technology Centre, Wilmslow Road, Handforth, Cheshire SK9 3FB
tel (01625) 650011 *fax* (01625) 650040
Directors Ian Findlay (managing), Peter Balderson (production), Robin Howard (sales), Peter Hey, Andrew Maddock

Books for children of all ages; early learning, activity, annuals; character publishing including *Mr Men.*

Writers & Readers Ltd
35 Britannia Row, London N1 8QH
tel 0171-226 3377 *fax* 0171-359 1454
e-mail faye@writersandreaders.com/
web site http://www.writersandreaders.com
Publisher Glenn Thompson

African/Black studies, architecture, performing arts, media, history, music, philosophy, photography, poetry, political studies, psychology, religion, science, social issues, spirit and body, US studies, women/gender studies, *For Beginners* documentary comic book series. Founded 1974.

Black Butterfly (imprint)
Children's books.

Harlem River Press (imprint)
Poetry anthologies and spiritual writing by Black women writers, Black political studies.

X Libris – see Little, Brown and Company (UK)*

The X Press
6 Hoxton Square, London N1 6NU
tel 0171-729 1199 *fax* 0171-729 1771
e-mail x@xpress.co.uk
Editorial Director Dotun Adebayo, *Marketing Director* Steve Pope

Black interest popular novels, particularly reflecting contemporary ethnic experiences. *Black Classics* series: reprints of American classic novels by black writers. Founded 1992.

Nia (imprint)
Literary black fiction.

Yale University Press London*
23 Pond Street, London NW3 2PN
tel 0171-431 4422 *fax* 0171-431 3755
e-mail firstname.lastname@yale.co.uk
Managing Director John Nicoll

Art, architecture, history, economics, political science, literary criticism, Asian and African studies, religion, philosophy, psychology, history of science. Founded 1961.

Yellow Jersey Press – see Random House UK Ltd

Yorkshire Art Circus
School Lane, Glass Houghton, Castleford, West Yorkshire WF10 4QH
tel (01977) 550401 *fax* (01977) 512819
e-mail books@artcircus.org.uk
Contact Ian Daley

Specialises in new writing by first-time authors. Publishes autobiography, community books and local interest (Yorkshire/Humberside). On the lookout for worker-writers and book editors. No local history, children's, reference or nostalgia. Unsolicited MSS discouraged; send for fact sheet first. Founded 1986.

Springboard Fiction (imprint)
Novels (80,000 words) and short stories (5000 words) of a contemporary nature by first-time authors (Yorkshire/Humberside). Send for fact sheet. Founded 1993.

Young Library (Assetpulse Ltd)

PO Box 2231, Reading RG4 9YP
tel (01734) 722805 *fax* (01734) 722544
Director Roger Bonnett

Highly illustrated non-fiction for children's libraries, including geography, history, natural history, social and urban studies, science and technology, comparative religion. Founded 1982.

Zed Books Ltd*

7 Cynthia Street, London N1 9JF
tel 0171-837 4014 (general), 0171-837 0384
(editorial) *fax* 0171-833 3960
e-mail zed @ zedbooks.demon.co.uk
web site http://www.zedbooks.demon.co.uk
Editors Robert Molteno, Louise Murray

Social sciences on international issues; women's studies, cultural studies, development and environmental studies; area studies (Africa, Asia, Caribbean, Latin America, Middle East and the Pacific). Founded 1976.

Zoë Books Ltd

15 Worthy Lane, Winchester, Hants SO23 7AB
tel (01962) 851318 *fax* (01962) 843015
Directors I.Z. Dawson (managing publishing),
A.R. Davidson

Publishers of children's information books for the school and library markets in the UK; specialists in co-editions for world markets. Founded 1990.

Book packagers

Many modern illustrated books are created by book packagers, whose special skills are in the areas of book design and graphic content. In-house desk editors and art editors match up the expertise of specialist writers, artists and photographers who usually work on a freelance basis.

Packaged books are often expensive to produce, beyond the cost parameters set by traditional publishers for their own markets. The packager recoups the expense by pre-selling titles to publishers in various countries. The usual subject areas are children's interests and informational how-to, such as crafts and cookery. Thus packaged books are usually international in content and approach, avoiding local interests such as cricket or Cornish cream teas.

The working style in most packagers' offices is more akin to magazine publishing than to traditional book publishing, with creative groups concentrating on the complexities of integrating words and pictures for individual titles rather than merely manuscript editing for a broad publishing list.

The many opportunities for freelance writers, specialist contributors and consultants, photographers and illustrators will usually be short-term and high pressure; packagers rarely spend more than a year on any title.

The Book Packagers Association

93A Blenheim Crescent, London W11 2EQ
Secretary Rosemary Pettit
tel 0171-221 9089
e-mail rosemarypettit@msn.com

The forum for the exchange of creative and commercial experience in this branch of the publishing industry. The BPA has devised standard contracts to cover members' relationships with contributors and customers.

Payment

As packaged books are frequently the work of more than one 'author' and because of the complications of the overseas rights deals that will be made and the formulae for a packager's earnings, which are obviously only a proportion of a book's retail price, flat fees are often suggested rather than royalty agreements. Where royalties are appropriate, they will be based on the packager's receipts but the expectation is that there will be more foreign language editions than a traditional publisher can achieve.

*Member of the Book Packagers Association

Aladdin Books Ltd

28 Percy Street, London W1P 0LD
tel 0171-323 3319 *fax* 0171-323 4829
e-mail aladdin@dircon.co.uk
Directors Charles Nicholas, Bibby Whittaker

Full design and book packaging facility specialising in children's non-fiction and reference. Founded 1980.

Albion Press Ltd

Spring Hill, Idbury, Oxon OX7 6RU
tel (01993) 831094 *fax* (01993) 831982

Directors Emma Bradford, Neil Philip
Quality integrated illustrated titles. Specialises in children's books. Supply finished books. Publishers' commissions undertaken. Founded 1984.

Alphabet & Image Ltd

Marston House, Marston Magna, Yeovil, Somerset BA22 8DH
tel/fax (01935) 851331
Directors Anthony Birks-Hay, Leslie Birks-Hay
Complete editorial, picture research, pho-

tographic, design and production service for illustrated books on ceramics, fine art, horticulture, architecture, history, etc. Imprint: Marston House. Founded 1972.

Amber Books Ltd

Bradley's Close, 74-77 White Lion Street, London N1 9PF
tel 0171-520 7600 *fax* 0171-520 7606/7607
Managing Director Stasz Gnych, *Rights and Operations Director* Sara Ballard, *Managing Editor* Sally Harper, *Head of Production* Gary Grant, *Military Editor* Peter Darman, *Picture Manager* Samantha Nunn

Illustrated non-fiction. Subject areas include military, aviation, transport, crime, unexplained, sport and maritime. Opportunities for freelances. Imprints: Brown Books Ltd. Founded 1989.

Andromeda Oxford Ltd

11-15 The Vineyard, Abingdon, Oxon OX14 3PX
tel (01235) 550296 *fax* (01235) 550330
e-mail books@andromeda.co.uk
web site http://www.andromeda.co.uk
Directors A. Flatt, J.G. Bateman, C. Sparling

Illustrated reference titles for the international market for children and adults. Founded 1986.

BCS Publishing Ltd

1 Bignell Park Barns, Kirtlington Road, Chesterton, Bicester, Oxon OX6 8TD
tel (01869) 324423 *fax* (01869) 324385
e-mail bcs-publishing@dial.pipex.com
Managing and Art Director Steve McCurdy, *Managing Editor* Jo Newson

Specialises in the preparation of illustrated general interest books; provides a full creative, design, editorial and production service. Opportunities for freelances. Founded 1993.

Bellew Publishing Co. Ltd

The Nightingale Centre, 8 Balham Hill, London SW12 9EA
tel 0181-675 2142 *fax* 0181-675 2142
Chairman Ian McCorquodale, *Managing Director* Ib Bellew

Adult and children's illustrated titles from origination of idea through concept and design to production. Founded 1983.

Bender Richardson White

PO Box 266, Uxbridge, Middlesex UB9 5NX
tel (01895) 832444 *fax* (01895) 835213
e-mail brw@brw.co.uk
Partners Lionel Bender, Kim Richardson, Ben White

Book and multimedia packaging, specialising in children's natural history, sci-

ence and family information. Opportunities for freelances. See also **Lionheart Books**. Founded 1990.

BLA Publishing Ltd

BIC Ling Kee House, 1 Christopher Road, East Grinstead, West Sussex RH19 3BT
tel (01342) 318980 *fax* (01342) 410980
Directors Au Bak Ling (chairman, Hong Kong), Au King Kwok (Hong Kong), Au Chun Kwok (Hong Kong), Albert Kw Au (Hong Kong), Au Wai Kwok (Hong Kong). *Contact* Penny Kitchenham

High quality illustrated reference books, particularly science dictionaries and encyclopedias, for the international market. Founded 1981.

Book Packaging and Marketing*

3 Murswell Lane, Silverstone, Towcester, Northants. NN12 8UT
tel/fax (01327) 858380
Proprietor Martin F. Marix Evans

Illustrated general and informational non-fiction and reference for adults, especially travel, military history, countryside, health and fitness. Product development and project management; editorial and marketing consultancy. Limited opportunities for freelances. Founded 1990.

Breslich & Foss Ltd*

20 Wells Mews, London W1P 3FJ
tel 0171-580 8774 *fax* 0171-580 8784
Directors Paula G. Breslich, K.B. Dunning

Books produced from MS to bound copy stage from in-house ideas. Specialising in the arts, crafts, gardening, health, gift and novelty, children's. Founded 1978.

Brown Packaging Books Ltd

Bradley's Close, 74-77 White Lion Street, London N1 9PF
tel 0171-520 7600 *fax* 0171-520 7606/7607
Managing Director Stasz Gnych, *Rights and Operations Director* Sara Ballard, *Managing Editor* Sally Harper, *Head of Production* Gary Grant, *Military Editor* Peter Darman

Highly illustrated non-fiction. Subject areas include military, aviation, transport, crime, unexplained, sport and maritime. Opportunities for freelances. Imprints: Brown Books Ltd. Founded 1989.

Brown Partworks Ltd

255-257 Liverpool Road, London N1 1LX
tel 0171-607 9039 *fax* 0171-700 5673
Director Sharon Hutton

Book, partwork and continuity set packaging services for trade, promotional and international publishers. Opportunities for freelances. Founded 1989.

Brown Wells & Jacobs Ltd
Foresters Hall, 25-27 Westow Street, London SE19 3RY
tel 0181-771 5115 *fax* 0181-771 9994
e-mail postmaster@popking.demon.co.uk
web site http://www.bwj.org
Director Graham Brown
Design, editorial, illustration and production of high quality non-fiction illustrated children's books. Specialities include pop-ups and novelties. Opportunities for freelances. Founded 1979.

Calmann & King Ltd
71 Great Russell Street, London WC1B 3BN
tel 0171-831 6351 *fax* 0171-831 8356
e-mail calmann_king@compuserve.com
Directors Robin Hyman, Laurence King, Judy Rasmussen, Lesley Ripley Greenfield, John Stoddart
Illustrated books on design, art, history, carpets and textiles, and architecture for international co-editions. Imprint: **Laurence King**. Founded 1976.

Cambridge Language Services Ltd
64 Baldock Street, Ware, Herts. SG12 9DT
tel/fax (01920) 486526
e-mail paul@oakleaf.demon.co.uk
Managing Director Paul Procter
Suppliers to publishers, societies and other organisations of customised database management systems, with advanced retrieval mechanisms, and electronic publishing systems for the preparation of dictionaries, reference books, encyclopedias, catalogues, journals, archives. PC (windows) based. Founded 1982.

Cameron Books
PO Box 1, Moffat, Dumfriesshire DG10 9SU
tel (01683) 220808 *fax* (01683) 220012
Directors Ian A. Cameron, Jill Hollis
Illustrated non-fiction including fine arts (including environmental and land art), film, the decorative arts and crafts, architecture, design, antiques, collecting, natural history, environmental studies, social history, food. Founded 1976.

Edition
Design, editing, typesetting, production work from concept to finished book for galleries, museums, institutions and other publishers. Founded 1975.

Carroll & Brown Ltd*
20 Lonsdale Road, London NW6 6RA
tel 0171-372 0900 *fax* 0171-372 0460
e-mail 100675.1470@compuserve.com
Directors Amy Carroll (managing), Denise Brown (creative)
Editorial and design through to final film and printing of cookery, health, craft and lifestyle titles. Opportunities for freelances. Founded 1989.

Philip Clark Ltd*
53 Calton Avenue, London SE21 7DF
tel 0181-693 5605 *fax* 0181-299 4647
Director Philip Clark
Illustrated non-fiction for the international co-edition market. Titles include the *Travellers Wine Guides* series; consultancy service; sponsored publications. Founded 1981.

Roger Coote Publishing
Gissing's Farm, Fressingfield, Eye, Suffolk IP21 5SH
tel (01379) 588044 *fax* (01379) 588055
e-mail 101577.1530@compuserve.com
Director Roger Goddard-Coote
High quality illustrated children's non-fiction titles for trade, institutional and international markets. Commissions undertaken. Freelance opportunities for editors and designers. Founded 1989.

D & N Publishing
Membury Business Park, Lambourn Woodlands, Hungerford, Berks. RG17 7TJ
tel (01488) 71210 *fax* (01488) 71220
Partners David and Namrita Price-Goodfellow
Production from MS to printed book. Specialises in taking raw MS and doing all necessary liaison, editorial, design and production work up to when book is ready to print, but can also organise printing. Opportunities for freelances. Founded 1991.

Diagram Visual Information Ltd
195 Kentish Town Road, London NW5 2JU
tel 0171-482 3633 *fax* 0171-482 4932
Director Bruce Robertson
Research, writing, design and illustration of reference books, supplied as film, on disk or as manufactured copies. Opportunities for freelances. Founded 1967.

Earthscape Editions
Greys Court Farm, Greys Court, Henley on Thames, Oxon RG9 4PG
tel (01491) 628188 *fax* (01491) 628189

Partners B.J. Knapp, D.L.R. McCrae

High quality, full colour, illustrated children's books, including co-editions, for education and library market. Sae with MSS essential. Opportunities for freelances. Associate company: Atlantic Europe Publishing Co. Ltd. Founded 1987.

Eddison Sadd Editions Ltd*

St Chad's House, 148 King's Cross Road, London WC1X 9DH
tel 0171-837 1968 *fax* 0171-837 2025
Directors Nick Eddison, Ian Jackson, David Owen, Elaine Partington, Charles James, Susan Cole

Illustrated non-fiction books for the international co-edition market. Founded 1982.

Equinox (Oxford) Ltd – acquired by Andromeda Oxford Ltd

First Rank Publishing

23 Ditchling Rise, Brighton, East Sussex BN1 4QL
tel (01273) 279934 *fax* (01273) 297128
e-mail 100772.3566@compuserve.com
web site http://www.netivity.co.uk/firstrank
Partners Byron Jacobs and Andrew Kinsman

Packager and publisher of sports, games and leisure books. No unsolicited MSS but ideas and synopses welcome. Payment usually fees. Also provides editorial, production and typesetting services. Founded 1996.

Geddes & Grosset Ltd

David Dale House, New Lanark ML11 9DJ
tel (01555) 665000 *fax* (01555) 665694
Directors R. Michael Miller, Ron Grosset

Production, editorial project and joint venture management. Publishers of children's and mass market books and popular reference books. Opportunities for freelances. Founded 1988.

Graham-Cameron Publishing

The Studio, 23 Holt Road, Sheringham, Norfolk NR26 8NB
tel (01263) 821333 *fax* (01263) 821334
Directors Mike Graham-Cameron, Helen Graham-Cameron

Educational and children's books; sponsored publications. Illustration agency, editorial and production services. No unsolicited MSS please. Founded 1984.

Haldane Mason Ltd*

59 Chepstow Road, London W2 5BP
tel 0171-792 2123 *fax* 0171-221 3965
e-mail haldane.mason@dial.pipex.com
Directors Ron Samuels, Sydney Francis

Illustrated and reference books for the international market, for both trade and promotional publishers. Opportunities for freelances. Founded 1992.

Angus Hudson Ltd

Concorde House, Grenville Place, London NW7 3SA
tel 0181-959 3668 *fax* 0181-959 3678
Directors Angus Hudson (chairman), Nicholas Jones (managing), Stephen Price (production), Geoffrey Benge, William Brooks

Children's and religious international co-editions, from concept to finished copies. Publishing imprints: Candle Books and Concorde House Books. Founded 1971.

Lennard Books

Windmill Cottage, Mackerye End, Harpenden, Herts. AL5 5DR
tel (01582) 715866 *fax* (01582) 715121
e-mail lennard@lenqap.demon.co.uk
Directors K.A.A. Stephenson, R.H. Stephenson

Sport, personalities, TV tie-ins, humour. Division of Lennard Associates Ltd.

Lexus Ltd

13 Newton Terrace, Glasgow G3 7PJ
tel 0141-221 5266 *fax* 0141-226 3139
e-mail pt@lexus.win-uk.net
Director P.M. Terrell

Reference book publishing (especially bilingual dictionaries) as contractor, packager, consultant; translation. Founded 1980.

Lionheart Books

10 Chelmsford Square, London NW10 3AR
tel 0181-459 0453 *fax* 0181-451 3681
Partners Lionel Bender (editorial), Madeleine Bender (editorial), Ben White (design)

Handle all aspects of editorial and design packaging of, mostly, children's illustrated science, natural history and history projects. See also **Bender Richardson White**. Founded 1985.

Market House Books Ltd*

2 Market House, Market Square, Aylesbury, Bucks. HP20 1TN
tel (01296) 484911 *fax* (01296) 437073
e-mail mhb_aylesbury@compuserve.com
Directors Dr Alan Isaacs, Dr John Daintith, P.C. Sapsed

Compilation of dictionaries, encyclopedias, and reference books. Founded 1970.

Marshall Cavendish Books
119 Wardour Street, London W1V 3TD
tel 0171-734 6710 *fax* 0171-439 1423
Head of Books Liz Dennis

Cookery, crafts, gardening, do-it-yourself, general illustrated non-fiction. Founded 1969.

Marshall Editions Ltd
The Orangery, 161 New Bond Street,
London W1Y 9PA
tel 0171-291 8222 *fax* 0171-291 8233
e-mail info@mediakey.u-net.com
web site http://www.marshallmedia.com
Directors Richard Harman (chairman), Barbara Anderson (publisher), Nick Croydon (managing), Barry Baker (Coo), Ellen Dupont (editorial, adult), Cindy O'Brien (editorial, children's), Anne-Marie Bulat (creative), Janice Storr (production), Andy Lee (finance), David Rivers (UK sales and marketing), Belinda Ioni Rasmussen (international rights)

Highly illustrated non-fiction for adults and children, including health, gardening, lifestyle, self-improvement, leisure, popular science and visual information for children. Founded 1977.

Orpheus Books Ltd
2 Church Green, Witney, Oxon OX8 6AW
tel (01993) 774949 *fax* (01993) 700330
e-mail post@orpheusbooks.demon.co.uk
Executive Directors Nicholas Harris (editorial, design and marketing), Joanna Turner (production and administration)

Children's illustrated non-fiction/reference. Opportunities for freelance artists. Founded 1992.

Oyster Books
Unit 4, Kirklea Farm, Badgworth, Axbridge, Somerset BS26 2QH
tel (01934) 732251 *fax* (01934) 732514
Directors Jenny Wood, Tim Wood, Ali Brooks, Donna Webber

Specialises in high-quality children's books and book/toy gift items. Founded 1985.

Playne Books Ltd
Chapel House, Trefin, Haverfordwest,
Pembrokeshire SA62 5AU
tel (01348) 837073 *fax* (01348) 837063
Design and Production David Playne, *Editor* Gill Davies

Specialises in highly illustrated adult non-fiction and books for very young children. All stages of production undertaken from initial concept (editorial, design and manufacture) to delivery of completed books. Founded 1987.

Mathew Price Ltd
The Old Glove Factory, Bristol Road, Sherborne, Dorset DT9 4HP
tel (01935) 816010 *fax* (01935) 816310
Chairman Mathew Price

Illustrated fiction and non-fiction children's books for all ages for the international market. Specialist in flap, pop-up, paper-engineered titles. Founded 1983.

Quarto Children's Books Ltd
3rd Floor, The Fitzpatrick Building,
188-194 York Way, London N7 9QP
tel 0171-607 3322 *fax* 0171-700 2951
Publisher Andrew Farrow

Highly illustrated non-fiction children's books.

Quarto Publishing plc/Quintet Publishing Ltd
The Old Brewery, 6 Blundell Street,
London N7 9BH
tel 0171-700 6700 *fax* 0171-700 4191
Directors L.F. Orbach, R.J. Morley, M.J. Mousley

International co-editions. Founded 1976/1984.

Sadie Fields Productions Ltd
3D West Point, 36-37 Warple Way,
London W3 0RG
tel 0181-746 1171 *fax* 0181-746 1170
e-mail sadiefields@compuserve.com
Directors Sheri Safran, David Fielder

Creates and produces international co-editions of pop-up, hologram, touch-and-feel, and other novelty books for children. Imprint: Tango Books. Founded 1983.

Savitri Books Ltd*
115J Cleveland Street,
London W1P 5PN
tel 0171-436 9932 *fax* 0171-580 6330
Director Mrinalini S. Srivastava

Packaging, design, production. Founded 1983.

The Templar Company plc
Pippbrook Mill, London Road, Dorking,
Surrey RH4 1JE
tel (01306) 876361 *fax* (01306) 889097
Directors Richard Carlisle, Amanda Wood, Ruth Huddleston, Graeme East

Children's gift, novelty, picture and illustrated information books; most titles aimed at international co-edition market. Established links with major co-publishers in USA, Australia and throughout Europe.

Toucan Books Ltd*

Fourth Floor, 32-38 Saffron Hill,
London EC1M 8BS
tel 0171-404 8181 *fax* 0171-404 8282
Directors Robert Sackville West, Adam Nicolson,
Jane MacAndrew

International co-editions; editorial, design and production services. Founded 1985.

Touchstone Publishing Ltd

Gissing's Farm, Fressingfield, Eye,
Suffolk IP21 5SH
tel (01379) 588044 *fax* (01379) 588055
Directors Roger Goddard-Coote (managing),
Edwina Conner (publishing)

High quality, illustrated children's non-fiction for trade and institutional markets worldwide. Supply CRC, film or finished books. Publishers' commissions undertaken. Founded 1989.

Tucker Slingsby

5th Floor, Berkeley House, 73 Upper Richmond Road, London SW15 2RZ
tel 0181-874 3400 *fax* 0181-874 3004
Directors Janet Slingsby, Del Tucker

Creation, editorial and design to disk, film or finished copy of children's books, maga-zines and general interest adult books. Commissioned work undertaken. Opportu-nities for freelances. Founded 1993.

Ventura Publishing Ltd

27 Wrights Lane, London W8 5TZ
tel 0171-416 3000 *fax* 0171-416 3070
Publisher Sally Floyer

Specialises in production of the *Spot* books by Eric Hill.

Webb & Bower (Publishers) Ltd

9 Duke Street, Dartmouth,
Devon TQ6 9PY
tel (01803) 835525 *fax* (01803) 835552
Director Richard Webb

Specialises in licensing illustrated non-fiction books. Founded 1975.

Wordwright Books*

25 Oakford Road, London NW5 1AJ
tel 0171-284 0056 *fax* 0171-284 0041
Director Charles Perkins

Full packaging/production service – from original concept to delivery of film or fin-ished copies. Produces illustrated non-fiction. Also assesses and prepares MSS for the US market. Founded 1987.

Publishers of fiction

Addresses for Book publishers UK and Ireland start on page 157.

Adventure/thrillers

Allison & Busby
Bantam
Bantam Press
Black Ace Books
Black Swan
Blackstaff Press (Ire.)
Blake Publishing
Bloomsbury Publishing
Marion Boyars Publishers
Brandon Book Publishers
Chatto & Windus
Richard Cohen Books
Corgi
Coronet
Doubleday (UK)
Fourth Estate
Gairm Publications
Robert Hale
HarperCollins Publishers
Headline Book Publishing
William Heinemann
Hodder & Stoughton
Hutchinson Books
Jane's Information Group
Michael Joseph
Little, Brown
Macmillan Publishers
New English Library
Onlywomen Press
Orion
Pan
Penguin Books
Piatkus Books
Random House UK
Sceptre
Severn House Publishers
Simon & Schuster
Souvenir Press
Vintage
Virago Press
Warner

Crime/mystery/suspense

Allison & Busby
Arrow Books
Bantam

Bantam Press
Black Swan
Blake Publishing
Bloomsbury Publishing
Marion Boyars Publishers
Canongate Books
Carlton Books
Richard Cohen Books
Collins Crime
Constable & Co.
Corgi
Coronet
The Do-Not Press
Faber & Faber
Fourth Estate
Gairm Publications
Robert Hale
Hamish Hamilton
HarperCollins Publishers
Headline Book Publishing
William Heinemann
Hodder & Stoughton
Hutchinson Books
Michael Joseph
Little, Brown
Macmillan Publishers
New English Library
The O'Brien Press (Ire.)
Michale O'Mara Books
Onlywomen Press
Orion
Pan
Penguin Books
Piatkus Books
Polygon
Random House UK
Sceptre
Serpent's Tail
Severn House Publishers
Souvenir Press
Town House and Country
   House (Ire.)
Viking
Vintage
Virago Press
Warner – Futura
Wolfhound Press (Ire.)
The Women's Press
The X Press

Gay/lesbian

Arcadia Books
Bantam
Black Swan
Marion Boyars Publishers
Richard Cohen Books
Corgi
Faber & Faber
Fourth Estate
GMP Publishers
Hamish Hamilton
HarperCollins Publishers
Little, Brown
Macmillan Publishers
The O'Brien Press (Ire.)
Michael O'Mara Books
Onlywomen Press
Penguin Books
Polygon
Serpent's Tail
Vintage
Virago Press
The Women's Press

General

Abacus
Allison & Busby
Arcadia Books
Aureus Publishing
Bantam
Bantam Press
Basement Press (Ire.)
Black Ace Books
Black Swan
Blackstaff Press (Ire.)
Blake Publishing
Bloomsbury Publishing
Marion Boyars Publishers
Brandon Book Publishers (Ire.)
Jonathan Cape
Carlton Books
Century
Chatto & Windus
Cló Iar-Chonnachta Teo. (Ire.)
Richard Cohen Books
The Collins Press (Ire.)
Corgi

Doubleday (UK)
Gerald Duckworth & Co.
Faber & Faber
Fourth Estate
Gairm Publications
The Gallery Press (Ire.)
Garnet Publishing
Gee & Son (Denbigh)
Victor Gollancz
Robert Hale
Hamish Hamilton
HarperCollins Publishers
Headline Book Publishing
William Heinemann
Hodder & Stoughton
Honno
Hutchinson Books
Michael Joseph
Karnak House
Little, Brown
Y Lolfa Cyf. (Welsh language)
Macmillan Publishers
Marino Books (Ire.)
The Mercier Press
New English Library
The O'Brien Press (Ire.)
Michael O'Mara Books
Orion
Pan Books
Paternoster Publishing
Penguin Books
Piatkus Books
Pimlico
Pocket Books
Poolbeg Press (Ire.)
Quartet Books
Random House UK
Sceptre
Secker and Warburg
Seren Books
Serpent's Tail
Severn House Publishers
Simon & Schuster
Souvenir Press
Springboard Fiction
Touchstone
Town House and Country
   House (Ire.)
Viking
Vintage
Virago
Vista
Warner
Wolfhound Press (Ire.)
Worldwide Books

Historical

Allison & Busby
Bantam
Bantam Press
Black Ace Books

Blackstaff Press (Ire.)
Canongate Books
Jonathan Cape
Richard Cohen Books
Doubleday (UK)
Everyman's Library
Fourth Estate
Gee & Son (Denbigh)
Victor Gollancz
Robert Hale
HarperCollins Publishers
Headline Book Publishing
William Heinemann
Hodder & Stoughton
C. Hurst & Co. (Publishers)
Hutchinson Books
Michael Joseph
Karnak House
Kingsway Publications
Little, Brown
Macmillan Publishers
The O'Brien Press (Ire.)
Michael O'Mara Books
Onlywomen Press
Orion
Pan
Penguin Books
Piatkus Books
Pimlico
Random House UK
Sceptre
Severn House Publishers
Simon & Schuster
Souvenir Press
Vintage
Virago Press
Warner
Wolfhound Press (Ire.)

Literary

Abacus
Allison & Busby
Anchor
Arcadia Books
Bantam
Bantam Press
Bellew Publishing Co.
Black Ace Books
Black Swan
Blackstaff Press (Ire.)
Bloomsbury Publishing
Marion Boyars Publishers
Calder Publications
Canongate Books
Jonathan Cape
Chatto & Windus
Richard Cohen Books
Corgi
Dedalus
Doubleday (UK)
Gerald Duckworth & Co.

Enitharmon Press
Everyman's Library
Faber & Faber
Flamingo
Forest Books
Fourth Estate
Gee & Son (Denbigh)
Victor Gollancz
Granta Publications
Robert Hale
Hamish Hamilton
HarperCollins Publishers
Harvill
Headland Publications
William Heinemann
Hodder & Stoughton
Honno
Hutchinson Books
Indigo
Karnak House
Libris
Little, Brown
Macmillan Publishers
Methuen
The O'Brien Press (Ire.)
Onlywomen Press
Orion
Peter Owen
Pan
Paternoster Publishing
Penguin Books
Phoenix
Piatkus Books
Picador
Pimlico
Polygon
Poolbeg Press (Ire.)
Random House UK
Sceptre
Scottish Cultural Press
Secker and Warburg
Seren Books
Serpent's Tail
Skoob Books
Souvenir Press
Springboard Fiction
Stride Publications
Viking
Vintage
Virago Press
Wolfhound Press (Ire.)
The Women's Press
The X Press

Romantic

Bantam
Bantam Press
Black Swan
Blake Publishing
Corgi
Coronet

Doubleday (UK)
Robert Hale
Harlequin Mills & Boon
Headline Book Publishing
William Heinemann
Hodder & Stoughton
Kingsway Publications
Little, Brown
Macmillan Publishers
Monarch Publications
Onlywomen Press
Orion
Pan
Piatkus Books
Random House UK
Scarlet
Severn House Publishers
Silhouette
Town House and Country
  House (Ire.)
Warner

Science fiction/fantasy

Arrow Books
Bantam
Bantam Press
Black Swan
Blake Publishing
Marion Boyars Publishers
Carlton Books
Corgi
Coronet
Victor Gollancz
HarperCollins Publishers
Headline Book Publishing
Hodder & Stoughton
Kingsway Publications
Legend
Little, Brown
Macmillan Publishers
Millennium
New Adventures
New English Library
The O'Brien Press (Ire.)
Onlywomen Press
Orbit
Orion
Pan
Penguin Books
Random House UK
Severn House Publishers
Souvenir Press
Voyager
Wolfhound Press (Ire.)
The Women's Press

Short stories

Allison & Busby
Arcadia Books
Blackstaff Press (Ire.)
Marion Boyars Publishers
Jonathan Cape
Chatto & Windus
Canongate Books
Everyman's Library
Forest Books
Fourth Estate
Gairm Publications
Gee & Son (Denbigh)
Granta Publications
Hamish Hamilton
William Heinemann
Hodder & Stoughton
Honno
Karnak House
Y Lolfa Cyf.
Macmillan Publishers
Onlywomen Press
Pan
Penguin Books
Polygon
Random House UK
Scottish Cultural Press
Secker and Warburg
Seren Books
Severn House Publishers
Springboard Fiction

Other

Ethnic

Allison & Busby
Marion Boyars Publishers
Canongate Books
C. Hurst & Co. (Publishers)
Souvenir Press
The Women's Press
The X Press

Erotic

Black Lace
Marion Boyars Publishers
Eros Plus
Headline Delta
Headline Liaison
Idol
Nexus
Michael O'Mara Books
Souvenir Press
X Libris
The X Press

Graphic

Knockabout Comics
Titan Books

Horror

Black Ace Books
Chapman
Robert Hale
Severn House Publishers
Warner

Humour

Black Swan
Canongate Books
Corgi
Forest Books
Victor Gollancz
Robert Hale
Michael O'Mara Books
Paternoster Publishing
Piccadilly Press
Souvenir Press
Warner

New/experimental

Arcadia Books
Black Ace Books
Marion Boyars Publishers
Canongate Books
Polygon
Serpent's Tail
Stride Publications
The X Press

Translations

Allison & Busby
Arcadia Books
Marion Boyars Publishers
Canongate Books
Dedalus
Enitharmon Press
Everyman's Library
Forest Books
Granta Publications
The Harvill Press
Peter Owen
Quartet Books
Serpent's Tail
Souvenir Press

War

Canongate Books
Robert Hale
Severn House Publishers
Souvenir Press

Westerns

Robert Hale

Publishers of multimedia

Addresses for Book publishers UK and Ireland start on page 157 and for Book packagers on page 220.

AA Publishing
ABC-Clio
Addison Wesley Longman
Andromeda Oxford (book packager)
Ashmolean Museum Publications
BBC Worldwide
Berlitz Publishing
Blackwell Publishers (InfoSource International)
The British Library (Publications)
Butterworth & Co. (Publishers)
Cavendish Publishing
Chadwyck-Healey

Current Science Group
Dorling Kindersley Multimedia
Encyclopaedia Britannica
W.H. Freeman
Harcourt Brace & Co. (Academic Press)
Helicon Publishing
Hodder Headline
Jane's Information Group
McGraw Hill
Macmillan Interactive Publishing
Market House Books (book packager)
Mosby Wolfe Medical

Communications
Thomas Nelson
Notting Hill Electronic Publishers
Oxford University Press
Reed Educational and Professional Publishing
Routledge
St Pauls
Sterling Publishing Group
Training Direct (Pearson Professional)
Two-Can Publishing
Usborne Publishing
The Watts Publishing Group

Book publishers overseas

Listings are given for book publishers in Australia (below), Canada (page 233), New Zealand (page 236), South Africa (page 238) and the USA (page 240).

Australia

Member of the Australian Publishers Association

Access Press
35 Stuart Street, Northbridge,
Western Australia 6003
postal address PO Box 132, Northbridge,
Western Australia 6865
tel (08) 9328 9188 *fax* (08) 9328 4605
e-mail ctomlins@omen.com.au
Managing Editor Helen Weller
Australiana, poetry, children's, history, general. Privately financed books published and distributed. Founded 1979.

Addison Wesley Longman Australia Pty Ltd*
95 Coventry Street, South Melbourne,
Victoria 3205
tel (03) 9697 0666 *fax* (03) 9699 2041
e-mail robert.fisher@awl.com.au
Managing Director Robert W. Fisher
Educational, academic and trade.

Allen & Unwin Pty Ltd*
9 Atchison Street, PO Box 8500, St Leonards,
NSW 2065
tel (02) 8425 0100 *fax* (02) 9906 2218
e-mail frontdesk@allen.unwin.com.au
web site http://www.allen-unwin.com.au
General trade, including fiction and children's books, academic, especially social science and history.

The Australian Council for Educational Research Ltd*
19 Prospect Hill Road, Private Bag 55,
Camberwell, Victoria 3124
tel (03) 9277 5555 *fax* (03) 9277 5500
e-mail info@acer.edu.au
Range of books and kits: for teachers, trainee teachers, parents, psychologists, counsellors, students of education, researchers.

Blackwell Science Asia Pty Ltd
54 University Street, South Carlton, Victoria 3053
tel (03) 9347 0300 *fax* (03) 9347 5001
e-mail Dimi-Katsieris@blacksci-asia.comau
web site http://www.blackwell-science.com/australi
Managing Director Mark Robertson
Medical, healthcare, life, earth sciences, professional.

Butterworths*
271-273 Lane Cove Road, North Ryde, NSW 2113
tel (02) 9335 4444 *fax* (02) 9335 4655
web site http://www.butterworths.com.au
Managing Director Murray Hamilton, *Editorial/Deputy Managing Director* J. Broadfoot
Legal, tax and commercial. Division of Reed International Books Australia Pty Ltd.

Cambridge University Press Australian Branch*
10 Stamford Road, Oakleigh, Melbourne,
Victoria 3166
tel (03) 9568 0322 *fax* (03) 9563 1517
Director Kim W. Harris
Academic, educational, reference, English as a second language.

Craftsman House
Level 1, Tower A, 112 Talavera Road,
North Ryde, NSW 2113
tel (02) 9878 8222 *fax* (02) 9878 8122
Directors Nevill Drury (publishing), Martin Gordon (chairman), Anna Mayo (marketing manager)
Australian and European fine arts. Division of Fine Arts Press Pty Ltd. Founded 1981.

Dominie Pty Ltd
Drama Department, 8 Cross Street, Brookvale,
NSW 2100
tel (02) 9905 0201 *fax* (02) 9905 5209
Australian representatives of publishers of plays and agents for the collection of

royalties for Samuel French Ltd, incorpo-rating Hanbury Plays and Samuel French Inc., The Society of Authors, ACTAC, and Bakers Plays of Boston.

Samuel French Ltd – see Dominie Pty Ltd

Harcourt Brace & Co. Australia Pty Ltd*

30-52 Smidmore Street, Marrickville, NSW 2204
tel (02) 9517 8999 *fax* (02) 9550 6007
Managing Director Brian M. Brennan

Novels, children's, academic, medical and scientific books. Imprints: Harcourt Brace & Company; Holt, Rinehart and Winston; W.B. Saunders/Ballière Tindall; Dryden Press; Saunders College; The Psychological Corporation; Academic Press, Churchill Livingstone; Morgan Kaufmann; Industrial Press; Technomic Publishing. Established 1972.

HarperCollins Publishers (Australia) Pty Limited Group*

25-31 Ryde Road, Pymble, NSW 2073
postal address PO Box 321, Pymble, NSW 2073
tel (02) 9952 5000 *fax* (02) 9952 5555
Managing Director Barrie Hitchon

Literary fiction and non-fiction, popular fiction, reference, biography, autobiogra-phy, current affairs, sport, lifestyle, health/self-help, humour, true crime, travel, Australiana, history, business, gift/stationery, religion.

Hill of Content Publishing Co. Pty Ltd*

86 Bourke Street, Melbourne, Victoria 3000
tel (03) 9662 2282 *fax* (03) 9662 2527
Directors M. Slamen, M.G. Zifcak, Michelle Anderson

Health, philosophy, and mind, body and spirit. Founded 1965.

Hodder Headline Australia Pty Ltd*

10-16 South Street, (Locked Bag 386), Rydalmere, NSW 2116
tel (02) 9841 2800 *fax* (02) 9841 2810
e-mail hsales@hha.com.au
Directors Malcolm Edwards (managing), Tim Hely Hutchinson, Lisa Highton, Mary Howell, Sandra McComb, David Cocking, Mark Opzoomer

General, illustrated non-fiction, chil-dren's, religious, educational books.

Jacaranda Wiley Ltd*

33 Park Road, Milton, Queensland 4064
tel (07) 3859 9755 *fax* (07) 3859 9715 and
38-40 Prospect Street, Box Hill, Victoria 3128
tel (03) 9898 0255 *fax* (03) 9898 4255 and
Suite 4A, 113 Wicks Road, North Ryde, NSW 2113
tel (02) 9805 1100 *fax* (02) 9805 1597
e-mail headoffice @jacwiley.com.au
Managing Director P. Donoughue

Educational, technical, atlases, profes-sional, reference, trade. Imprints: Brooks Waterloo, John Wiley & Sons, Jacaranda Press. Founded 1954.

Kangaroo Press*

20 Barcoo Street, East Roseville, NSW 2069
postal address PO Box 507, East Roseville, NSW 2069
tel (02) 9415 9912 *fax* (02) 9417 4292
e-mail kangaroo@parramatta.starway.net.au
Publisher David Rosenberg, *Publicist* Priscilla Rosenberg

Gardening, craft, Australian history and natural history, collecting, fitness, trans-port, children's non-fiction. Imprint of Simon & Schuster Australia. Founded 1980.

LBC Information Services*

PO Box 3502, Rozelle, NSW 2039
tel (02) 8587 7000 *fax* (02) 8587 7100
e-mail lbccustomer@lbc.com.au
web site http://www.lbc.com.au

Accountancy and taxation, law.

Lonely Planet Publications*

Head office PO Box 617, Hawthorn, Victoria 3122
tel (03) 9819 1877 *fax* (03) 9819 6459
e-mail talk2us@lonelyplanet.com.au
web site http://www.lonelyplanet.com

Travel guidebooks, walking guides, travel atlases, phrasebooks, travel literature and audio packs. Offices in London, Paris and Oakland, USA. Founded 1973.

Lothian Books Pty Ltd*

11 Munro Street, Port Melbourne, Victoria 3207
tel (03) 9645 1544 *fax* (03) 9646 4882
e-mail books@lothian.com.au
Chairman/Managing Director P. Lothian,
Directors E. McDonald, B. Hilliard

Juveniles, health, gardening, general lit-erature, craft, educational, reference, Australian history, business.

Macmillan Education Australia Pty Ltd*

Melbourne office 107 Moray Street, South Melbourne, Victoria 3205
tel (03) 9699 8922 *fax* (03) 9690 6938

e-mail meapl@macmillan.com.au
Sydney office Suite 310, Henry Lawson Business Centre, Birkenhead Point, Carey Street, Drummoyne, NSW 2047
tel (02) 9719 8944 *fax* (02) 9719 8613
e-mail measyd@macmillan.com.au
Directors N. Byam Shaw (UK), Brian Stonier (executive chairman), John Rolfe (managing), Margaret Brownie (primary publishing), Peter Debus (tertiary publishing), Peter Huntley (sales), Rex Parry (secondary publishing), George Smith (production), Kay Watts (marketing), *Company Secretary/Financial Controller* Terry White
Educational books.

Melbourne University Press*

268 Drummond Street, Carlton, Victoria 3053
postal address PO Box 278, Carlton South, Victoria 3053
tel (03) 9347 3455 *fax* (03) 9349 2527
Chairman Prof Barry Sheeham, *Director* John Meckan
Academic, scholastic and cultural; educational textbooks and books of reference. Imprint: Miegunyah Press. Founded 1922.

Mimosa Publications Pty Ltd – see Weldon International Pty Ltd*

Nelson ITP*

102 Dodds Street, South Melbourne, Victoria 3205
tel (03) 9685 4111 *fax* (03) 9685 4199
Educational books.

Oxford University Press, Australia*

253 Normanby Road, South Melbourne, Victoria 3205
postal address GPO Box 2784Y, Melbourne, Victoria 3001
tel (03) 9934 9123 *fax* (03) 9934 9100
Managing Director Marek Palka
Australian history, biography, literary criticism, general, but excluding fiction; school books in all subjects.

Pan Macmillan Australia Pty Ltd*

Level 18, 31 Market Street, Sydney, NSW 2000
tel (02) 9261 5611 *fax* (02) 9261 5047
Directors Ross Gibb (managing), James Fraser (publishing), Roxarne Burns (publishing), Siv Toigo (finance), Peter Phillips (sales), Jeannine Fowler (publicity)
Fiction, non-fiction, children's.

Penguin Books Australia Ltd*

(PO Box 257), 487 Maroondah Highway, Ringwood, Victoria 3134
tel (03) 9871 2400 *fax* (03) 9870 9618
Managing Director P.J. Field, *Publishing Director* R.P. Sessions

Fiction, general non-fiction, current affairs, sociology, economics, environmental, travel guides, anthropology, politics, children's, health, cookery, gardening, pictorial and general books relating to Australia under Penguin Books and Viking imprints. Founded 1946.

Random House Australia Pty Ltd*

20 Alfred Street, Milsons Point, NSW 2061
tel (02) 9954 9966 *fax* (02) 9954 9008
e-mail random@randomhouse.com.au
Managing Director Juliet Rogers, *Publishing Director* Jane Palfreyman, *Children's Publishing Director* Mark Macleod, *Illustrated Publishing Director* Gordon Cheers
General fiction and non-fiction, illustrated children's. Telephone before submitting MSS. Imprints: Arrow, Ballantine, Barrie & Jenkins, Bodley Head, Business Books, Century, Chatto & Windus, Del Rey, Ebury Press, Fawcett, Fodor Travel Guides, Happy House, Hogarth Press, Hutchinson, Ivy, Jonathan Cape, Julia MacRae Books, Knopf, Pantheon, Pimlico, Rider, Stanley Paul, Times Books, Villard, Vintage. Subsidiary of Bertelsmann AG.

Reed Educational & Professional Publishing Australia*

22 Salmon Street, Port Melbourne, Victoria 3207
tel (03) 9245 7111 *fax* (03) 9245 7333
Managing Director Jack Mulcahy
Art, chemistry, chemical engineering, environmental studies, geography, geology, health, nutrition, history, mathematics, physics, languages. Primary, Secondary; electronic publishing. Division of Reed Elsevier Australia. Founded 1982.

Reeve Books

35 Stuart Street, Northbridge, Western Australia 6003
postal address PO Box 132, Northbridge, Western Australia 6865
tel (08) 9328 9188 *fax* (08) 9328 4605
e-mail ctomlins@omen.com.au
Managing Director/Editor Helen Weller
Biography, local history, general non-fiction. Commissioned works only. Founded 1987.

Rigby Heinemann – see Reed Education & Professional Publishing Australia*

Scholastic Australia Pty Ltd*
PO Box 579, Gosford, NSW 2250
tel (02) 4328 3555 *fax* (02) 4323 3827
Managing Director Ken Jolly
Children's fiction/non-fiction; educational materials for elementary schools, teacher reference. Founded 1968.

Transworld Publishers (Aust) Pty Ltd*
Ground Floor, 40 Yeo Street, Neutral Bay, NSW 2089
tel (02) 9908 9900 *fax* (02) 9953 8563
Managing Director Geoffrey Rumpf, *Publisher* Shona Martyn
Bio, self-help, personal awareness, health, parenting and childcare, sports, current affairs, social history, popular culture, fiction, autobiography, biography, humour, romance, juvenile, children's. Imprints: Anchor, Bantam, Black Swan, Corgi, Dell, Doubleday. Founded 1981.

University of Queensland Press
PO Box 42, St Lucia, Queensland 4067
tel (07) 3365 2127 *fax* (07) 3365 7579
e-mail uqpbris@peg.apc.org.au
General Manager L.C. Muller
Scholarly works, tertiary texts, Australian fiction, young adult fiction, poetry, history, general interest. Founded 1948.

University of Western Australia Press*
Tuart House, Nedlands 6907, Western Australia
tel (08) 9380 3670 *fax* (08) 9380 1027
e-mail uwap@cyllene.uwa.edu.au
web site http://www.uwa.edu.au/cyllene/uwap
History, natural history, literary criticism, Asian studies, Aboriginal studies, biography, children's picture books. Imprints: Cygnet Books, Tuart House, UWA Press. Founded 1954.

Viking – see Penguin Books*

Weldon International Pty Ltd*
43-45 Victoria Street, North Sydney, NSW 2060
tel (02) 9955 0091 *fax* (02) 9955 9390
Chairman Kevin Weldon
Mimosa Publications Pty Ltd (division)
Primary school education.
Weldon Owen (division)
Cookery, natural science, aerial photography, encyclopedic reference works, young readers' non-fiction.
Weldon Russell (division)
Illustrated non-fiction including natural

history, cookery, gardening, ancient history, general reference books and gift books.

Wild & Woolley P*
PO Box 41, Glebe, NSW 2037
tel (02) 692 0166 *fax* (02) 552 4320
web site http://www.fastbooks.com.au
Director Pat Woolley
Offers short-run paperback printing for self-publishing writers. Founded 1974.

Wrightbooks Pty Ltd*
5 Horne Street, Elsternwick, Victoria 3185
Postal address PO Box 270, Elsternwick, Victoria 3185
tel (03) 9532 7082 *fax* (03) 9532 7084
e-mail wbooks@ozemail.com.au
web site http://wwwwrightbooks.com.au
Managing Director/Publisher Geoff Wright, *Editorial Director* Lesley Beaumont
Finance, investment, money management, personal development, business management. Unsolicited MSS welcome. Founded 1988.

Canada

*Member of the Canadian Publishers' Council
†Member of the Association of Canadian Publishers

Annick Press Ltd†
15 Patricia Avenue, Willowdale, Ontario M2M 1H9
tel 416-221-4802 *fax* 416-221-8400
e-mail annickpress@powerwindows.ca
Co-editors Anne Millyard, Rick Wilks
Juvenile fiction. Founded 1975.

Butterworths Canada Ltd
75 Clegg Road, Markham, Ontario L6G 1A1
tel 905-479-2665 *fax* 905-479-2826
e-mail name@butterworths.ca

Canada Publishing Corporation†
164 Commander Boulevard, Scarborough, Ontario M1S 3C7
tel 416-293-8141 *fax* 416-293-9009
Publishers of elementary and secondary school textbooks; general trade/consumer publications including cookbooks, business, sport and fiction; professional and reference materials; annual publications, including *Canadian Global Almanac* and *Who's Who in Canada*. Founded 1844.

Canadian Stage and Arts Publications Ltd
104 Glenrose Avenue, Toronto, Ontario M4T 1K8
tel 416-484-4534 *fax* 416-484-6214

President/Publisher George Hencz

Primarily interested in children's books of an educational nature, art books. Also publishes quarterly *Performing Arts & Entertainment in Canada*, (Editor: Karen Bell).

The Charlton Press
2040 Yonge Street, Suite 208, Toronto, Ontario M4S 1Z9
tel 416-488-1418 *fax* 416-488-4656
e-mail chpress@charltonpress.com
web site http://www.charltonpress.com
President W.K. Cross

Collectibles, numismatics, Sportscard price catalogues. Founded 1952.

Copp Clark Professional
200 Adelaide Street West, 3rd Floor, Toronto, Ontario M5H 1W7
tel 416-597-1616 *fax* 416-597-1617
President/Ceo Frederick Wardle

Professional publishers. Subsidiary of Pearson Professional Ltd.

Doubleday Canada Ltd*
105 Bond Street, Toronto, Ontario M5B 1Y3
tel 416-340-0777 *fax* 416-340-1069
Chairman Abraham Simkin, *President/Publisher* John Neale

General trade non-fiction: current affairs, politics; fiction; children's fiction and illustrated. Founded 1942.

Douglas & McIntyre Ltd†
1615 Venables Street, Vancouver, BC V5L 2H1
tel 604-254-7191 *fax* 604-254-9099
e-mail dm@douglas-mcintyre.com

General list, including Greystone Books imprint: Canadian biography, art and architecture, natural history, history, native studies, Canadian fiction. Children's division (Groundwood Books) specialises in fiction and illustrated flats. No unsolicited MSS. Founded 1964.

ECW Press†
2120 Queen Street E, Toronto, Ontario M4E 1E2
tel 416-694-3348 *fax* 416-698-9906
e-mail ecw@sympatico.ca
President Jack David, *Secretary-Treasurer* Robert Lecker

Literary criticism, general trade books, biographies, guidebooks. Founded 1979.

Fitzhenry & Whiteside Limited†
195 Allstate Parkway, Markham, Ontario L3R 4T8
tel 905-477-9700 *fax* 905-477-9179
toll free 1-800-387-9776
e-mail godwit@fitzhenry.ca

Director Sharon Fitzhenry
Trade, educational, college books. Founded 1966.

Gage Educational Publishing Company – see Canada Publishing Corporation

Gold Eagle Books – see Harlequin Enterprises Ltd*

Harcourt Brace & Company Canada, Ltd*
55 Horner Avenue, Toronto, Ontario M8Z 4X6
tel 416-255-4491 *fax* 416-255-4046

Educational materials from K-College, medical texts, psychological testing products.

Harlequin Enterprises Ltd*
225 Duncan Mill Road, Don Mills, Ontario M3B 3K9
tel 416-445-5860 *fax* 416-445-8655
President/Ceo Brian E. Hickey

Romance, action adventure, mystery. Founded 1949.

Gold Eagle Books (imprint)
Senior Editor/Editorial Co-ordinator Feroze Mohammed
Series action adventure fiction.

Harlequin Books (imprint)
Editorial Director Randall Toye
Contemporary and historical romance fiction in series.

Mira Books (imprint)
Senior Editor/Editorial Co-ordinator Dianne Moggy
Women's fiction: contemporary and historical dramas, family sagas, romantic suspense and relationship novels.

Silhouette Books (imprint)
Editorial Director Isabel Swift
Contemporary romance fiction in series.

Worldwide Library (imprint)
Senior Editor/Editorial Co-ordinator Feroze Mohammed
Contemporary mystery fiction. Reprints only.

HarperCollins Publishers Ltd*
Suite 2900, Hazelton Lanes, 55 Avenue Road, Toronto, Ontario M5R 3L2
tel 416-975-9334 *fax* 416-975-9884

Publishers of literary fiction and non-fiction, business books, history, politics, biography, spiritual and children's books. Founded 1989.

Irwin Publishing[†]
325 Humber College Blvd, Toronto,
Ontario M9W 7C3
tel 416-798-0424 *fax* 416-798-1384
e-mail irwin@irwin-pub.com
President Brian O'Donnell, *Chairman* Jack
Stoddart
Educational books at the elementary,
high school and college levels. Division
of General Publishing Co. Ltd.

ITP Nelson*
(formerly Nelson Canada)
1120 Birchmount Road, Scarborough,
Ontario M1K 5G4
tel 416-752-9100 *fax* 416-752-9646
President/Ceo George W. Bergquist, *Vice-President of Finance/Cfo* Lesley Gouldie, *Director of Human Resources* Marlene Fedorkow, *Director of Communications* Jim Black, *Vice-President, Media Services* Susan Cline, *Vice-President, Operations* Ed Bierman, *Publishers* Michael Young (arts and humanities), Mark Cobham (humanities and reference), Jackie Wood (business and career education), David Steele (science and mathematics)
School (K-12), college and university,
career education, measurement and guidance, professional and reference, and
ESL titles. Founded 1914.

Key Porter Books[†]
70 The Esplanade, 3rd Floor, Toronto,
Ontario M5E 1R2
tel 416-862-7777 *fax* 416-862-2304
e-mail aporter@keyporter.com
web site http://www.keyporter.com
Publisher/ceo Anna Porter, *President/Editor-in-Chief* Susan Renouf, *Vice-President/Director of Publishing* Clare McKeon
Fiction, nature, history, Canadian politics, conservation, humour, biography,
autobiography, health, children's books.
Founded 1981.

Kids Can Press Ltd[†]
29 Birch Avenue, Toronto, Ontario M4V 1E2
tel 416-925-5437 *fax* 416-960-5437
Publisher Valerie Hussey
Juvenile/young adult books.

Alfred A. Knopf Canada*
33 Yonge Street, Suite 210, Toronto,
Ontario M5E 1G4
tel 416-777-9477 *fax* 416-777-9470
web site http://www.randomhouse.com
Publisher, Vice-President Louise Dennys
Literary fiction and non-fiction. Division
of **Random House of Canada Ltd**.
Founded 1991.

Lone Pine Publishing
206, 10426-81 Avenue, Edmonton,
Alberta T6E 1X5
tel 403-433-9333 *fax* 403-433-9646
Publisher and Founder Grant Kennedy, *President* Shane Kennedy
Natural history, recreation and wildlife
guidebooks, gardening, popular history.
Founded 1980.

McClelland & Stewart Inc.[†]
481 University Avenue, Suite 900, Toronto,
Ontario M5G 2E9
tel 416-598-1114 *fax* 416-598-7764
Chairman/President/Ceo Avie Bennett
General. Founded 1906.

McGill-Queen's University Press[†]
3430 McTavish Street, Montreal,
Quebec H3A 1X9
tel 514-398-3750 *fax* 514-398-4333
e-mail mqup@printing.lan.mcgill.ca and
Queen's University, Kingston,
Ontario K7L 3N6
tel 613-545-2155 *fax* 613-545-6822
e-mail mqup@qucdn.queensu.ca
web site http://www.mcgill.ca/mqupress
Academic. Founded 1969.

McGraw-Hill Ryerson Ltd*
300 Water Street, Whitby, Ontario L1N 9B6
tel 905-430-5000 *fax* 905-430-5020
web site http://www.mcgrawhill.ca
Educational and trade books.

Macmillan Canada
29 Birch Avenue, Toronto, Ontario M4V 1E2
tel 416-963-8830 *fax* 416-923-4821
Trade book publishers. Division of
Canada Publishing Corporation.
Founded 1905.

Maxwell Macmillan Canada –
acquired by Prentice Hall Canada Inc.*

Mira Books – see Harlequin
Enterprises Ltd

Nelson Canada – see ITP Nelson

Oberon Press
400-350 Sparks Street, Ottawa, Ontario K1R 7S8
tel/fax 613-238-3275
General.

Oxford University Press, Canada
70 Wynford Drive, Don Mills, Ontario M3C 1J9
tel 416-441-2941 *fax* 416-444-0427
web site http://www.oupcan.com
Managing Director Susan Froud
General, educational and academic.

Pippin Publishing Corporation

Suite 232, 85 Ellesmere Road, Toronto,
Ontario M1R 4B9
tel 416-510-2918 fax 416-510-3359
President/Editorial Director Jonathan Lovat
Dickson
ESL/EFL, teacher reference, adult basic
education, school texts (all subjects).

Prentice Hall Canada Inc.*

1870 Birchmount Road, Scarborough,
Ontario M1P 2J7
tel 416-293-3621 fax 416-299-2529
web site http://www.phcanada.com
President Brian Heer
Academic, technical, educational, children's and adult, trade. Founded 1960.

Random House of Canada Ltd*

33 Yonge Street, Suite 210, Toronto,
Ontario M5E 1G4
tel 416-777-9477 fax 416-777-9470
web site http://www.randomhouse.com
President and Publisher David Kent
Imprints: Ballantine Canada, Knopf
Canada, Random House Canada, Vintage
Canada. Subsidiary of Bertelsmann AG.
Founded 1944.

Silhouette Books – see Harlequin Enterprises Ltd*

Stoddart Publishing Co. Ltd†

34 Lesmill Road, Don Mills, Ontario M3B 2T6
tel 416-445-3333 fax 416-445-5967
e-mail stoddart@genpub.com
web site http://www.genpub.com/stoddart
Fiction and non-fiction.

Tundra Books Inc.†

481 University Avenue, Suite 802, Toronto,
Ontario M5G 2E9
tel 416-598-4786 fax 416-598-0247
High quality children's picture books.

University of Toronto Press Inc.†

10 St Mary Street, Suite 700, Toronto,
Ontario M4Y 2W8
tel 416-978-2239 fax 416-978-4738
e-mail bookstore@utpress.utoronto.ca
web site http://www.utpress.utoronto.ca
President/Publisher George L. Meadows

Worldwide Library – see Harlequin Enterprises Ltd*

New Zealand

*Member of the New Zealand Book Publishers' Association

Addison Wesley Longman*

Private Bag 102908, North Shore Mail Centre,
Glenfield, Auckland 10
tel (09) 444-4968 fax (09) 444-4957
e-mail rosemary.stagg@awl.co.nz
NZ educational books.

Ashton Scholastic Ltd – see Scholastic New Zealand Ltd

Auckland University Press*

University of Auckland, Private Bag 92019,
Auckland
tel (09) 373-7528 fax (09) 373-7465
e-mail aup@auckland.ac.nz
Director Elizabeth Caffin
NZ history, NZ poetry, Maori and Pacific
studies, politics, sociology, literary criticism, art history, biography, media studies, women's studies. Founded 1966.

David Bateman Ltd*

30 Tarndale Grove, Albany Business Park,
Bush Road, Albany, Auckland
postal address PO Box 100242, North Shore Mail
Centre, Auckland 10
tel (09) 415-7664 fax (09) 415-8892
Chairman/Publisher David L. Bateman, Directors
Janet Bateman, Paul Bateman (joint managing),
Paul Parkinson (joint managing)
Natural history, gardening, encyclopedias, sport, art, cookery, historical, juvenile, travel, motoring, maritime history,
business. Founded 1979.

Bush Press Communications Ltd

4 Bayview Road, Hauraki Corner, Takapuna,
Auckland 1309
postal address PO Box 33-029, Takapuna,
Auckland 1309
tel/fax (09) 486-2667
Governing Director/Publisher Gordon Ell
NZ non-fiction, particularly outdoor,
nature, travel, architecture, crafts, Maori,
popular history; children's non-fiction.
Founded 1979.

Butterworths of New Zealand Ltd*

205-207 Victoria Street, Wellington 1
postal address PO Box 472, Wellington !
tel (04) 385-1479 fax (04) 385-1598
e-mail Hellen.Papadopoulos@butterworths.co.nz
web site http://www.butterworths.co.nz
Publishing Director Hellen Papadopoulos
Law, accountancy.

The Caxton Press
113 Victoria Street, Christchurch,
PO Box 25-088
tel (03) 366-8516 *fax* (03) 365-7840
Director E.B. Bascand
Fine printers and publishers since 1935
of NZ books of many kinds, including
biography, history, natural history, travel,
gardening.

Dunmore Press Ltd*
PO Box 5115, Palmerston North
tel (06) 358-7169 *fax* (06) 357-9242
e-mail dunmore@xtra.co.nz
Directors Murray Gatenby, Sharmian Firth
Education, history, sociology, business
studies, general non-fiction. Founded 1970.

Godwit Publishing Ltd
PO Box 34-683, Birkenhead, Auckland
tel (09) 480-5410 *fax* (09) 480-5930
e-mail godwit@godwit.co.nz
Publisher Jane Connor, *Executive Director* Brian
Phillips
Art, gardening, lifestyle, literature and
natural history. Founded 1994.

Grantham House Publishing
PO Box 17-256, Wellington 6033
tel (04) 476-4625 *fax* (04) 476-3048
e-mail gstewart@iconz.co.nz
Publisher/Chief Executive Graham C. Stewart,
Editorial Anna Rogers, Lorraine Olphert
Antiques and collecting, architecture and
design, aviation, gardening, history and
antiquarian, illustrated and fine editions,
military and war, nautical, transport, railways, tramways. Founded 1984.

HarperCollins Publishers (New
Zealand) Ltd*
PO Box 1, Auckland
tel (09) 443-9400 *fax* (09) 443-9403
Publishers of general literature, teen fiction, non-fiction, reference books, trade
paperbacks.

Hodder Moa Beckett Publishers Ltd*
PO Box 100-749, North Shore Mail Centre,
Auckland 1330
tel (09) 478-1000 *fax* (09) 478-1010
e-mail admin@hoddermoa.co.nz
Managing Director Neil Aston, *Publisher* Sarah
Beresford
Sport, gardening, cooking, travel, atlases,
general, fiction, children's.

Mallinson Rendel Publishers Ltd*
Level 5, 15 Courtney Place, PO Box 9409,
Wellington
tel (04) 802-5012 *fax* (04) 802-5013
Directors Ann Mallinson, David Rendel
Children's books. Founded 1980.

Nelson Price Milburn Ltd*
1 Te Puni Street, Petone
postal address PO Box 38-945,
Wellington Mail Centre, Wellington
tel (04) 568-7179 *fax* (04) 568-2115
Children's fiction, primary school texts,
especially school readers and maths, secondary educational.

New Zealand Council for
Educational Research*
Box 3237, Education House,
178-182 Willis Street, Wellington 1
tel (04) 384-7939 *fax* (04) 384-7933
Director Anne Meade, *Publisher* Bev Webber
Education, including educational policy
and institutions, early childhood education, educational achievement tests,
Maori education, curriculum and assessment, etc. Founded 1933.

Oxford University Press*
PO Box 11-149, Ellerslie, Auckland 5
tel (09) 525-8020 *fax* (09) 525-1072
e-mail casselll@oup.com.au
web site http://www.oup.com.au
NZ Academic/Trade Publisher Linda Cassells

Random House New Zealand Ltd*
Private Bag 102950, North Shore Mail Centre,
Auckland 10
tel (09) 444-7197 *fax* (09) 444-7524
Managing Director B. Phillips
Fiction, general non-fiction, gardening,
cooking, art, business, health.
Subsidiary of Bertelsmann AG. Founded
1977.

Reed Publishing (New Zealand) Ltd*
(incorporating Reed Consumer Books and
Heinemann Education)
39 Rawene Road, Private Bag 34901, Birkenhead,
Auckland 10
tel (09) 480-4950 *fax* (09) 480-4999
Chairman John Holloran, *Managing Director* Alan
Smith
NZ literature, specialist and general
titles, primary, secondary and tertiary
textbooks. Imprints: George Philip,
Conran Octopus, Mitchell Beazley, Reed
Publishing Group Australia Pty Ltd,
Heinemann Young Books, Secker &
Warburg, Hamlyn, Bounty, Dean, Buzz,
Minerva, Mandarin, Cedar, Methuen
Drama, Brimax, Budget Books, Octopus

Publishing Group, Ginn & Company, Heinemann Education Books, Rigby Heinemann (Australia), Rigby (USA), Heinemann Education Books Inc. (USA).

Scholastic New Zealand Ltd*
21 Lady Ruby Drive, East Tamaki, Auckland
postal address Private Bag 94407, Greenmount, Auckland
tel (09) 274-8112 *fax* (09) 274-8114
e-mail jbaker@scholastic.co.nz
Managing Director/Publisher Joan Baker, *Finance and Operations Director* David Peagram
Children's books. Founded 1962.

Shortland Publications Ltd*
2B Cawley Street, Ellerslie, Auckland 5
Submissions Heather Peach, Shortland Publications Ltd, Private Bag 11904, Ellerslie, Auckland 5
tel (09) 526-6200 *fax* (09) 526-4499
International primary reading market: potential authors should familiarise themselves with Shortland products. Currently seeking submissions for: *Junior novels* (ages 9-13) – Fictional MSS 800-20,000 words long; non-fiction MSS significantly shorter. Topic suggestions – humour (what makes us laugh), action stories (dare-devil sports), animal stories, communication (media, language, space and beyond), disasters in history, famous people and events in history, social issues.
Emergent/early and fluency reading material, 8-24pp – Stories need to be predictable and to feature supports for the child learning to read, e.g. repetition of vocabulary and sentence structure. *Cocky's Circle* – 24pp read-to books for 2-6 year-olds. Stories must lend themselves to a different illustration on each page. Fantasy and humour are always good sellers. All submissions should cater for an international market; include sae. Founded 1984.

University of Otago Press*
University of Otago, PO Box 56, Dunedin
tel/fax (03) 479-8807 *fax* (03) 479-8385
e-mail university.press@otago.ac.nz
Managing Editor Wendy Harrex
Student texts and scholarly works in all disciplines and general books, including Maori and women's studies, natural history and environmental studies, health and fiction. Also publishes journals including *Landfall* and the *Women's Studies Journal*. Founded 1958.

Victoria University Press*
Victoria University of Wellington, PO Box 600, Wellington
tel (04) 496-6580 *fax* (04) 496-6581
e-mail victoria-press@vuw.ac.nz
web site http://www.vup.vuw.ac.nz
Publisher Fergus Barrowman
Academic, scholarly books on NZ history, sociology, environment, law, biology; Maori language; fiction, plays, poetry. Founded 1974.

Viking Sevenseas Ltd
23B Ihakara Street, Paraparaumu
tel (04) 297-1990 *fax* (04) 297-1990
Managing Director M.B. Riley
Factual books on New Zealand only.

South Africa

Member of the Publishers' Association of South Africa

Jonathan Ball Publishers (Pty) Ltd*
10-14 Watkins Street, Denver Ext. 4, Johannesburg
postal address Box 33977, Jeppestown 2043
tel (011) 622-2900 *fax* (011) 622-3553
Ad Donker (division)
Africana, literature, history, academic.
Jonathan Ball/HarperCollins (division)
General publications, reference books, business, history, politics.
Delta Books (division)
General non-fiction.

Cambridge University Press
1 The Moorings, Portswood Ridge, Victoria & Alfred Waterfront, Cape Town 8001
tel (021) 419-8414
Director Tony Seddon
Educational, ELT and academic publishers serving primary and secondary schools, further education, technikons and universities.

Ad Donker (Pty) Ltd – see Jonathan Ball Publishers (Pty) Ltd

HarperCollins Publishers (SA) (Pty) Ltd – see Jonathan Ball Publishers (Pty) Ltd

Jacklin Enterprises (Pty) Ltd
Private Bag 16, Centurion 0046
tel (011) 652-1800 *fax* (011) 314-2984
Managing Director M.A.C. Jacklin

Children's fiction and non-fiction; Afrikaans large print books. Subjects include aviation, natural history, romance, general science, technology and transportation. Imprints: Mike Jacklin, Kennis Onbeperk, Daan Retief.

Juta & Company Ltd*
PO Box 14373, Kenwyn 7790, Cape Town
tel (21) 797-5101 *fax* (21) 762-7424
e-mail books@juta.co.za
web site http://www.juta.co.za
Managing Director R.J.H. Cooke
School, academic, professional, law and electronic. Founded 1853.

Lovedale Press
Private Bag X1346, Alice 5700, Eastern Cape
tel (040) 653-1135 *fax* (040) 653-1871
Educational, religious and general book publications for African and overseas market.

Maskew Miller Longman (Pty) Ltd*
Howard Drive, Pinelands 7405
postal address PO Box 396, Cape Town 8000
tel (021) 531-7750 *fax* (021) 531-4049
Educational and general publishers.

Oxford University Press Southern Africa*
Vasco Boulevard, NI City,
Goodwood 7460
postal address PO Box 12119, NI City 7463
tel (021) 595-4400 *fax* (021) 595-4430
e-mail oxford@oup.co.za
Managing Director Kate McCallum

David Philip Publishers (Pty) Ltd*
PO Box 23408, Claremont 7735,
Western Cape
tel (21) 644-136 *fax* (21) 643-358
e-mail dpp@iafrica.com
web site http://www.twisted.co.za/dpp
Managing Directors David Philip, Marie Philip,
Directors Russell Martin, Bridget Impey
Academic, history, social sciences, politics, theology, biography, belles-lettres, reference books, fiction, educational, children's books. Founded 1971.

Ravan Press (Pty) Ltd*
4th Floor, Randhill, 104 Bordeaux Drive,
Randburg
postal address PO Box 145, Randburg 2125
tel (011) 789-7636 *fax* (011) 789-7653
Executive Chairman G.E. de Villiers
South African studies: history, politics, social studies; fiction, literature, children's, educational. Founded 1972.

Shuter and Shooter (Pty) Ltd*
230 Church Street *and* 199 Pietermaritz Street,
Pietermaritzburg 3201, KwaZulu-Natal
postal address PO Box 109,
Pietermaritzburg 3200, KwaZulu-Natal
tel (0331) 946-830/948-881
fax (0331) 943-096/427-419
e-mail dryder@shuter.co.za
web site http://www.shuter.co.za
Publishing Director D.F. Ryder
Primary and secondary educational, science, biology, history, maths, geography, English, Afrikaans, biblical studies, music, teacher training, agriculture, accounting, school readiness, dictionaries, African languages. Founded 1925.

Southern Book Publishers (Pty) Ltd*
PO Box 3103, Halfway House, Gauteng 1685
tel (011) 315-3633/7 *fax* (011) 315-3810
Publishers of general non-fiction books, especially natural history, as well as those of South African interest. Subsidiary of Struik New Holland Publishing (Pty) Ltd.

Struik Publishers (Pty) Ltd*
Cornelius Struik House, 80 Mckenzie Street,
Cape Town 8001
tel (021) 462-4360 *fax* (021) 461-9378
Managing Director John Schoeman
General illustrated non-fiction. Division of The Struik Publishing Group (Pty) Ltd.

Unisa Press*
PO Box 392, Pretoria 0003
tel (012) 429-3051 *fax* (012) 429-3221
e-mail unisa-press@unisa.ac.za
web site http://www.unisa.ac.za/dept/press/index.html
Head Mrs P. Van Der Walt
Theology and all academic disciplines. Publishers of University of South Africa. Imprint: UNISA. Founded 1957.

J.L. Van Schaik Publishers*
PO Box 12681, Hatfield, Pretoria 0028
tel (012) 342-2765 *fax* (012) 433-563
e-mail mbotha@jlvanschaik.com
web site http://www.naspers.co.za
Publishers of books in English, Afrikaans and African languages. Specialists in non-fiction, religion, textbooks and fiction in 11 official languages. Founded 1914.

William Waterman Publications Pty Ltd*
(incorporating Ashanti Publishing, Justified Press, Justified Press for Juniors)
PO Box 5091, Rivonia 2128
tel (011) 882-1408 *fax* (011) 882-1559

Directors Murray J. Bolton, Nicholas W. Combrinck (managing)

General non-fiction, military history, literature, poetry, children's educational.

Witwatersrand University Press*
PO Wits, Johannesburg 2050
tel (011) 484-5910 *fax* (011) 484-5971
e-mail wup@iafrica.com
web site http://www.wits.ac.za/wup.html

USA

Member of the Association of American Publishers Inc.

Abbeville Press
488 Madison Avenue, 23rd Floor, New York, NY 10022
tel 212-888-1969 *fax* 212-644-5085
Publisher/President Robert Abrams

Art and illustrated books. Founded 1977.

Abingdon Press
PO Box 801, Nashville, TN 37202-0801
tel 615-749-6404 *fax* 615-749-6512
web site http://www.abingdon.org
Editorial Director Harriett Jane Olson

General interest, professional, academic and reference – primarily directed to the religious market.

Harry N. Abrams, Inc.
100 Fifth Avenue, New York, NY 10011
tel 212-206-7715 *fax* 212-645-8437
Ceo/President/Editor-in-Chief Paul Gottlieb

Art and architecture, photography, natural sciences, performing arts, children's books. No fiction. Founded 1950.

Addison Wesley Longman*
One Jacob Way, Reading, MA 01867-3999
tel 781-944-3700 *fax* 781-942-3022
web site http://www2.awl.com
Chairman/Ceo Peter Jovanovich

Natural history and sciences, outdoors, travel, environment and ecology, children's fiction and non-fiction, picture books and novelty books. Founded 1892.

Andrews McMeel Publishing*
4520 Main Street, Kansas City, MO 64111
tel 816-932-6700 *fax* 816-932-6706
Vice-President/Editorial Director Christine Schillig

General trade publishing; emphasis on humour, how-to, self-help, women's issues.

Applause Theatre Book Publishers
1841 Broadway, New York, NY 10023
tel 212-765-7880 *fax* 212-765-7875

President/Publisher Glenn Young

Plays, theatre, cinema, entertainment. Founded 1983.

Arcade Publishing
141 Fifth Avenue, New York, NY 10010
tel 212-475-2633 *fax* 212-353-8148
e-mail arcadepub@aol.com
President/Publisher Richard Seaver, *Associate Publisher/Marketing Director* Jeannette Seaver, *General Manager* Cal Barksdale

General, including adult hard cover and paperbacks.

Atlantic Monthly Press – see Grove/Atlantic Inc.

Avon Books
The Hearst Corporation, 1350 Avenue of the Americas, New York, NY 10019
tel 212-261-6800 *fax* 212-261-6895
web site http://www.avonbooks.com/
Senior Vice-President/Publisher Lou Aronica

All subjects, fiction and non-fiction. Founded 1941.

Walter H. Baker Company
100 Chauncy Street, Boston, MA 02111
tel 617-482-1280 *fax* 617-482-7613
web site http://www.bakersplays.com
President Charles Van Nostrand, *Editor* John B. Welch
UK Agent Samuel French Ltd

Plays and books on the theatre. Also agents for plays. Founded 1845.

The Ballantine Publishing Group
210 East 50th Street, New York, NY 10022
tel 212-751-2600 *fax* 212-940-7539
e-mail bfi@randomhouse.com
web site http://www.randomhouse.com
President Linda Grey

Trade and mass-market general fiction, science fiction and non-fiction. Imprints: Ballantine, Del Rey, Fawcett, Ivy, House of Collectibles, One World. Division of **Random House Inc.** Founded 1952.

Bantam Doubleday Dell Publishing Group Inc.*
1540 Broadway, New York, NY 10036
tel 212-782-9000 *fax* 212-302-7985
web site http://www.bdd.cp
President/Coo BDD, North America Erik Engstrom, *Senior Vice-President/Publisher, Bantam Books* Irwyn Applebaum, *Senior Vice-President/Publisher, Doubleday* Stephen Rubin, *Senior Vice-President/Publisher, Dell Publishing* Carole Baron, *President/Publisher, Books for Young Readers* Craig Virden, *President/Publisher,*

BDD Audio Publishing Jenny Frost, *Vice-President/Editorial Director, The Dial Press* Susan Kamil, *Executive Editor, Delacorte Press* Jackie Farber

General fiction and non-fiction, children's books. Divisions: Bantam Books, Bantam Doubleday Dell Books for Young Readers, Doubleday, Dell Publishing; Subsidiaries: Delacorte Press, The Dial Press. Subsidiary of Bertelsmann AG.

Barron's Educational Series Inc.

250 Wireless Boulevard, Hauppage, NY 11788
tel 516-434-3311 *fax* 516-434-3723
President Manuel H. Barron, *Executive Vice President* Ellen Sibley

Test preparation, juvenile, cookbooks, crafts, business, pets, gardening, family and health, art, study guides, school guides. Founded 1941.

Beacon Press

25 Beacon Street, Boston, MA 02108
tel 617-742-2110 *fax* 617-723-3097
Director Helene Atwan

General non-fiction in fields of religion, ethics, philosophy, current affairs, gender studies, environmental concerns, African-American studies, anthropology and women's studies, nature.

Berkley Publishing Group

200 Madison Avenue, New York, NY 10016
tel 212-951-8800 *fax* 212-213-6706
e-mail webmaster@putnam.com
web site http://www.penguinputnam.com
President David Shanks, *Publisher/Senior Vice-President/Editor-in-Chief* Leslie Gelbman, *Senior Vice-President/Executive Director, Trade Paperbacks* Louise Burke

General fiction and non-fiction for adults and young adults. Imprints: Ace Science Fiction & Fantasy, Berkley Books, Berkley Prime Crime, Boulevard, Charter/Diamond, Jove. Subsidiary of Penguin Putnam Inc. Founded 1954.

R.R. Bowker

121 Chanlon Road, New Providence, NJ 07974
tel 908-464-6800 *fax* 908-464-3553
President Ira T. Siegel

Bibliographies and reference tools for the book trade and literary and library worlds, available in hardcopy, on microfiche, on-line and CD-Rom. Reference books for music, art, business, computer industry, cable industry and information industry. A Reed Reference Publishing company.

Boyds Mills Press

815 Church Street, Honesdale, PA 18431
tel 717-253-1164 *fax* 717-253-0179
Publisher Kent Brown Jr, *President* Clay Winters, *Editorial Director* Larry Rosler, *Art Director* Tim Gillner

Fiction, non-fiction, and poetry trade books for children. Founded 1990.

Brassey's Inc.

22883 Quicksilver Drive, Dulles, VA 20166
tel 703-260-0602
Managing Director Jim Sutton

Foreign policy, defence, national and international affairs, military history, intelligence, biography, sports. Founded 1984.

George Braziller Inc.

171 Madison Avenue, New York, NY 10016
tel 212-889-0909 *fax* 212-689-5405
Publisher George Braziller, *Assistant to the Publisher* Mary Taveras

Art, architecture, history, biography, fiction, poetry, science. Founded 1955.

Cambridge University Press (North American branch)*

40 West 20th Street, New York, NY 10011
tel 212-924-3900 *fax* 212-691-3239
Director Barbara Colson

Candlewick Press

2067 Massachusetts Avenue, Cambridge, MA 02140
tel 617-661-3330 *fax* 617-661-0565
Editor-in-Chief Liz Bicknell, *Senior Editor* Mary Lee Donovan, *Editor* Gale Pryor, *Editor-at-Large* Amy Ehrlich

Children's books – 6 months to 14 years: board books, picture books, novels, non-fiction, novelty books. Submit material through a literary agent. Subsidiary of **Walker Books Ltd**, UK. Founded 1991.

Carroll & Graf Publishers Inc.

19 West 21st Street, Suite 601, New York, NY 10010
tel 212-889-8772
Publisher/Editor Kent Carroll, *Subrights* Martine Ballen, *Foreign Rights* Henry Lincoln

Mystery and crime, popular fiction, history, biography, literature, business, sports. Founded 1983.

Chronicle Books

85 Second Street, San Francisco, CA 94105
tel 415-777-7240 *fax* 415-777-2289
web site http://www.chronbooks.com
Publisher Jack Jensen, *Associates* Christine Carswell, Caroline Herter, Nion McEvoy, Victoria Rock

Cooking, art, fiction, general, children's, gift, new media, gardening, regional, nature. Founded 1967.

Coffee House Press
27 N 4th Street, Suite 400, Minneapolis, MN 55401
tel 612-338-0125 *fax* 612-338-4004
Publisher Allan Kornblum
UK agent Patrick Walsh, Christopher Little Agency
Literary fiction and poetry; collectors' editions. Founded 1984.

Columbia University Press*
562 West 113th Street, New York, NY 10025
tel 212-666-1000 *fax* 212-316-3100
Editor-in-Chief Kate Wittenberg
UK 1 Oldlands Way, Bognor Regis, West Sussex PO22 9SA
tel (0243) 842165 *fax* (0243) 842167
General reference works in print and electronic formats, translations and serious non-fiction of more general interest.

Concordia Publishing House
3558 S Jefferson Avenue, St Louis, MO 63118
tel 314-268-1000 *fax* 314-268-1329
Executive Vice-President, Editorial Barry Bobb
Religious books, Lutheran perspective. Few freelance MSS accepted; query first. Founded 1869.

The Continuum Publishing Company Inc.
370 Lexington Avenue, New York, NY 10017-6503
tel 212-953-5858 *fax* 212-953-5944
e-mail contin@tiac.net
web site http://www.continuum-books.com
Chairman/Publisher Werner Mark Linz
General non-fiction, education, literature, psychology, politics, sociology, literary criticism, religious studies. Founded 1980.

Cornell University Press*
(including ILR Press and Comstock Publishing Associates)
Sage House, 512 East State Street, Ithaca, NY 14850
tel 607-277-2338 *fax* 607-277-2374
e-mail cupressinfo@cornell.edu
web site http://www.cornellpress.cornell.edu
Director John G. Ackerman.
Scholarly books. Founded 1869.

Council Oak Books
1350 East 15th Street, Tulsa, OK 74120-5801
tel 918-587-6454 *fax* 918-583-4995
e-mail oakie@ionet.net
Chief Operating Officer David Kanbar, *Publishers*

Sally Dennison PhD, Paulette Millichap
Non-fiction: native American, multicultural, life skills, life accounts, Earth awareness, meditation. Founded 1984.

The Countryman Press
PO Box 748, Rte 12N, Mount Tom, Woodstock, VT 05091
tel 802-457-4826 *fax* 802-457-1678
e-mail countrymanpress@wwnorton.com
web site http://www.countrymanpress.com
Editor-in-Chief Helen Whybrow
Outdoor recreation guides for anglers, hikers, cyclists, canoeists and skiers, US travel guides, New England non-fiction, how-to books, country living books, books on nature and the environment, classic reprints and general non-fiction. No unsolicited MSS. Division of **W.W. Norton & Co. Inc.** Founded 1973.

Crown Publishing Group
201 East 50th Street, New York, NY 10022
tel 212-572-2408 *fax* 212-940-7408
President/Publisher Chip Gibson
General fiction, non-fiction, illustrated books. Affiliate of **Random House Inc.**
Crown Publishers Inc. (imprint)
Editorial Director Steve Ross
General ficiton and non-fiction.
Clarkson Potter Publishers (imprint)
Editorial Director Laureen Shakely
Illustrated books, cookbooks.
Harmony Books (imprint)
Editorial Director Steve Magnuson
New Age, spirituality, religion, fiction.
Three Rivers Press (imprint)
Publisher Steve Magnuson
Non-fiction general paperbacks.
Living Language (imprint)
Publisher Kathy Mintz
Foreign language books and audiotapes.

DAW Books, Inc.
375 Hudson Street, 3rd Floor, New York, NY 10014
tel 212-366-2096 *fax* 212-366-2090
e-mail daw@penguin.com
President/Publisher Elizabeth R. Wollheim,
Executive Vice-President/Publisher Sheila E. Gilbert
Science fiction, fantasy, horror, mainstream thrillers. Affiliate of Penguin Putnam Inc. Founded 1971.

Devin-Adair Publishers Inc.
PO Box A, Old Greenwich, CT 06870
tel 203-531-7755

Conservative politics, health and ecology, Irish topics, gardening and travel, homeopathy and holistic health books, original photography publications. Founded 1911.

Dial Books for Young Readers
345 Hudson Street, New York, NY 10014
tel 212-366-2000 *fax* 212-414-3394
e-mail webmaster@penguin.com
web site http://www.penguinputnam.com
President/Publisher Phyllis Fogelman
Children's fiction and non-fiction, trade paperbacks, picture books, board books, interactive books, novels. Imprint of **Penguin USA**.

Doubleday – see Bantam Doubleday Dell Publishing Group Inc.*

Dover Publications Inc.
31 E 2nd Street, Mineola, NY 11501
tel 516-294-7000 *fax* 516-873 1401
Vice-President, Editorial Paul Negri
Art, architecture, antiques, crafts, juvenile, food, history, folklore, literary classics, mystery, language, music, math and science, nature, design and ready-to-use art. Founded 1941.

Dryden Press
City Center Tower II, 301 Commerce Street, Suite 3700, Fort Worth, TX 76102
tel 817-334-7711 *fax* 817-334-8059
web site http://www.dryden.com
Publisher George E. Provol
College textbooks.

Dutton/Signet
375 Hudson Street, New York, NY 10014
tel 212-366-2000 *fax* 212-366-2666
e-mail webmaster@penguin.com
web site http://www.penguin.com
President Elaine Koster
General publishers. General non-fiction, including biographies, adventure, history, travel, fiction, mysteries, juveniles, quality paperbacks. Imprint of **Penguin USA**. Founded 1852.

Dutton Children's Books
375 Hudson Street, 3rd Floor, New York, NY 10014
tel 212-366-2600 *fax* 212-366-2011
e-mail webmaster@penguin.com
web site http://www.penguin.com
President/Publisher Karen Lotz, *Editor-in-Chief/Associate Publisher* Lucia Monfried, *Editorial Director* Donna Brooks
Picture books, young adult novels, non-

fiction photographic books. Imprint of **Penguin USA**. Founded 1852.

Faber and Faber Inc.
53 Shore Road, Winchester, MA 01890
tel 781-721-1427 *fax* 781-729-2783
Publisher Tom Kelleher, *Senior Editor* Dan Weaver
Adult non-fiction: biographies, popular history, film, popular music, ethnic and cultural works, travelogues, anthologies, popular science, women's issues, gay and lesbian fiction and non-fiction. Founded 1976.

Facts On File Inc.
11 Penn Plaza, 15th Floor, New York, NY 10001-2006
tel 212-967 8800 *fax* 212-967 9196
President Mark McDonnell
General reference books and services for colleges, libraries, schools and general public. Founded 1940.

Farrar, Straus & Giroux Inc.
19 Union Square West, New York, NY 10003
tel 212-741-6900 *fax* 212-633-9385
Executive Vice-President/Editor-in-Chief Jonathan Galassi
General publishers.

Firebrand Books
141 The Commons, Ithaca, NY 14850
tel 607-272-0000
Editor/Publisher Nancy K. Bereano
Feminist and lesbian fiction and non-fiction. Founded 1986.

Four Walls Eight Windows
39 West 14th Street, Room 503, New York, NY 10011
tel 212-206-8965 *fax* 212-206-8799
e-mail eightwind@aol.com
web site http://www.fourwallseightwindows.com
Publisher John Oakes
Fiction, graphic works, novels, memoirs, art, African-American studies, current affairs, biography, environment, health. No unsolicited submissions accepted. Founded 1987.

Samuel French Inc.
45 West 25th Street, New York, NY 10010
tel 212-206-8990 *fax* 212-206-1429
Play publishers and authors' representatives (dramatic).

David R. Godine, Publisher Inc.
9 Hamilton Place, Boston, MA 02108
tel 617-451-9600 *fax* 617-350-0250

e-mail info@godine.com
web site http://www.godine.com
President David R. Godine, *Editorial Director*
Mark Polizzotti
Fiction, photography, poetry, art, biography, children's, essays, history, typography, architecture, nature and gardening, music, cooking, words and writing, and mysteries. Founded 1970.

Golden Books Family Entertainment
888 Seventh Avenue, New York,
NY 10106
tel 212-583-6700 *fax* 212-371-1091
Chairman/Ceo Richard E. Snyder, *Executive Vice-President* Phillip Rowley
Children's and adult books, educational workbooks and products, electronic books and software, children's videos. Founded 1907.

Greenwillow Books
1350 Avenue of the Americas, New York,
NY 10019
tel 212-261-6500 *fax* 212-261-6619
Senior Vice-President/Editor-in-Chief Susan Hirschman
Children's books. Division of **William Morrow & Co. Inc.**

Grosset & Dunlap Inc.
200 Madison Avenue, New York, NY 10016
tel 212-951-8700
President/Publisher Jane O'Connor
Children's mass market: easy-to-reads, series books, activity books, board books. No unsolicited MSS. Division of The Putnam & Grosset Group.

Grove/Atlantic Inc.
841 Broadway, New York, NY 10003-4793
tel 212-614-7850 *fax* 212-614-7886
Publisher Morgan Entrekin
MSS of permanent interest, fiction, biography, autobiography, history, current affairs, social science, belles-lettres, natural history. Imprints: Atlantic Monthly Press, Grove Press.

Grove Press – see Grove/Atlantic Inc.

Harcourt Brace Trade Publishers*
525 B Street, Suite 1900, San Diego, CA 92101
tel 619-231-6616 *fax* 619-699-6320
President Rubin Pfeffer, *Vice President/Publisher, Children's Books* Louise Pelan, *Vice President/Publisher, Adult Books* Dan Farley
General publishers. Fiction, history, biography, etc.

HarperCollins Publishers*
10 East 53rd Street, New York, NY 10022
tel 212-207-7000
President/Ceo Jane Friedman
HarperCollins San Francisco 1160 Battery Street, San Francisco, CA 94111
tel 415-477-4400 *fax* 415-477-4444
London office 77-85 Fulham Palace Road, London W6 8JB
Fiction, history, biography, poetry, science, travel, juvenile, educational, business, technical and religious. No unsolicited material; all submissions must come through a literary agent. Founded 1817.

Harvard University Press*
79 Garden Street, Cambridge, MA 02138-1499
tel 617-495 2600 *fax* 617-495-5898
web site http://www.hup.harvard.edu
Director William P. Sisler, *Editor-in-Chief/Assistant Director* Aida D. Donald
History, philosophy, literary criticism, politics, economics, sociology, music, science, classics, social sciences.

Hastings House – see United Publishers Group

D.C. Heath and Co. – acquired by Houghton Mifflin Company*

Hill & Wang
19 Union Square West, New York, NY 10003
tel 212-741-6900 *fax* 212-633-9385
Publisher Elisabeth Sifton, *Editor* Lauren M. Osborne, *Consulting Editor* Arthur W. Wang
General non-fiction, history, drama. Division of **Farrar, Straus & Giroux Inc.** Founded 1956.

Hippocrene Books Inc.
171 Madison Avenue, New York, NY 10016
tel 212-685-4371 *fax* 212-779-9338
President/Editorial Director George Blagowidow, *Publisher/Director of Marketing* Jacek Galazka
Foreign language books, international cookbooks, foreign language dictionaries, love poetry, travel, military history, Polonia, general trade. Founded 1971.

Holiday House
425 Madison Avenue, New York, NY 10017
tel 212-688-0085 *fax* 212-421-6134
President John Briggs, *Vice-President/Editor-in-Chief* Regina Griffin
General children's books. Send query letter before submitting MSS. Always include sae. No multiple submissions, please. Founded 1935.

Holmes & Meier Publishers Inc.

160 Broadway, New York, NY 10038
tel 212-374-0100 *fax* 212-374-1313
Executive Editor Katharine Turok
History, biography, political science, art, costume, Jewish studies, international affairs, Latin American studies, sociology, theatre (history), women's studies, fiction and poetry in translation, Africana publishing. Founded 1969.

Henry Holt and Company Inc.*

115 West 18th Street, New York, NY 10011
tel 212-886-9200 *fax* 212-633-0748
Associate Publisher, Editor-in-Chief Adult Books William Strachan, *Associate Publisher, Editor-in-Chief Books for Young Readers* Marjorie Cuyler, *Associate Publisher, Editorial Director Reference Books* Ken Wright, *Publisher, Twenty-First Century Books* Jeanne Vestal, *Editorial Director MIS Press and M&T Books* Paul Farrell, *Associate Publisher, Editorial Director Metropolitan Books* Sara Bershtel, *Associate Publisher, Editorial Director Owl Books* Gregory Hamlin
History, biography, nature, science, self-help, novels, mysteries; books for young readers; trade paperback line, computer books. Founded 1866.

Houghton Mifflin Company*

222 Berkeley Street, Boston, MA 02116
tel 617-351-5000
Executive Vice-President/Publisher, Trade and Reference Division Wendy J. Strothman
Fiction and non-fiction – history, political science, biography, nature (Peterson Guides), and gardening guides; both adult and juvenile. Imprints: Mariner (original and reprint paperbacks); Chapters (cookbooks). Best length: 60,000-180,000 words; juveniles, any reasonable length. Founded 1832.

Hyperion

114 Fifth Avenue, New York, NY 10011
tel 212-633-4400 *fax* 212-633-4811
Vice-President/Publisher Robert Miller, *Vice-President/Publisher (Hyperion Books for Children)* Lisa Holton
General fiction and non-fiction, children's books. Division of Buena Vista Publishing, formerly Disney Book Publishing Inc. Founded 1990.

Indiana University Press

601 North Morton Street, Bloomington, IN 47404-3797
tel 812-855-4203 *fax* 812-855-7931
e-mail iuorder@indiana.edu
web site http://www.indiana.edu/~iupress
Director John Gallman
African studies, Russian and East European studies, semiotics, literary criticism, music, history, women's studies, Jewish studies, African-American studies, film, folklore, philosophy, medical ethics, archaeology, anthropology. Reference and high level trade books. Founded 1950.

The Johns Hopkins University Press*

2715 North Charles Street, Baltimore, MD 21218-4319
tel 410-516-6971 *fax* 410-516-6968
Director Dr Willis Regier
History, literary criticism, classics, politics, economic development, environmental studies, biology, medical genetics, consumer health, history, religion. Founded 1878.

Keats Publishing Inc.

27 Pine Street, PO Box 876, New Canaan, CT 06840
tel 203-966-8721
President/Publisher Richard Gallen
Natural health, alternative medicine, nutrition and medical books. Founded 1971.

Alfred A. Knopf Inc.*

201 East 50th Street, New York, NY 10022
tel 212-751-2600 *fax* 212-572-2593
web site http://www.randomhouse.com
General literature, fiction, belles-lettres, sociology, politics, history, nature, science, etc. Subsidiary of **Random House Inc.** Founded 1915.

Krause Publications

700 East State Street, Iola, WI 54990-0001
tel 715-445-2214 *fax* 715-445-4087
e-mail info@Krause.com
web site http://www.Krause.com
Acquisitions Editor Paul Kennedy
Antiques and collectibles, sewing and crafts, ceramics.

Lippincott-Raven Publishers

227 East Washington Square, Philadelphia, PA 19106
tel 215-238-4200
President/Ceo Mary M. Rogers, *President* J.W. Lippincott, III, *Publishers* Kathey Alexander (medical), Donna Hilton (nursing)
Medical and nursing books and journals. A Wolters Kluwer company. Founded 1792.

Little, Brown & Company
3 Center Plaza, Boston, MA 02108
tel 617-227-0730
Chief Executive Larry Kirshbaum
General literature, especially fiction, non-fiction, biography, history, trade paperbacks, books for boys and girls. Art and photography books under the Bulfinch Press imprint.

Lothrop, Lee & Shepard Books
1350 Avenue of the Americas, New York, NY 10019
tel 212-261-6641 *fax* 212-261-6648
Vice-President/Editor-in-Chief Susan Pearson
Children's books only. Division of **William Morrow & Co. Inc.** Founded 1904.

Lyons & Burford, Publishers
31 West 21st Street, New York, NY 10010
tel 212-620-9580 *fax* 212-929-1836
Publishers Nick Lyons, Peter Burford
Outdoor sport, natural history, general sports, art.

McGraw-Hill*
11 West 19th Street, New York, NY 10011
tel 212-337 4098
Group Vice-President Theodore Nardin
Professional and reference: engineering, scientific, business, architecture, encyclopedias; college textbooks; high school and vocational textbooks: business, secretarial, career; trade books; training materials for industry. Division of The McGraw-Hill Companies.

McPherson & Company
PO Box 1126, Kingston, NY 12402
tel/fax 914-331-5807
e-mail bmcpher@ulster.net
web site http://www.mcphersonco.com
Publisher Bruce R. McPherson
Literary fiction; non-fiction: art criticism, writings by artists, film-making, etc; occasional general titles (e.g. anthropology). No poetry. No unsolicited MSS; query first. Founded 1974.

Macmillan General Reference USA
1633 Broadway, New York, NY 10019
tel 212-654-8500
Senior Vice-President/Publisher Lloyd Short
General trade reference: travel, horticulture, cookery. Imprints: Alpha, ARCO, Audel, Baedeker's, Betty Crocker, Burpee, Cassell's Spectrum, Frommer's, Horticulture, Howell Book House, J.K. Lasser, Macmillan Cooking and

Gardening, Macmillan Travel, Monarch, The Unofficial Guides, Webster's New World, Weight Watchers. Division of Simon & Schuster Inc.

Macmillan Publishing USA
201 West 103rd Street, Indianapolis, IN 46290
tel 800-545-5914 *fax* 317-581-3550
web site http://www.mcp.com
President Scott N. Flanders
Computer science, general and mass-market non-fiction, high school and college reference and text books. Divisions: Macmillan Computer Publishing, Macmillan Digital Publishing, Macmillan Reference USA. Division of Simon & Schuster Inc.

Mercury House
785 Market Street, Suite 1500, San Francisco, CA 94103
tel 415-974-0729 *fax* 415-974-0832
web site http://www.wenet.net/~mercury/
Executive Editor Thomas Christensen
Fiction; non-fiction: biography/memoirs, contemporary issues, translations, nature/ environment, literary travel, women's issues, philosophy and personal growth. Material only accepted through agents. Founded 1985.

Microsoft Press
One Microsoft Way, Redmond, WA 98052-6399
tel 425-882-8080 *fax* 425-936-7329
Publisher James Brown, *Editorial Director* Kim Fields
Computer books. Division of Microsoft Corp. Founded 1983.

Milkweed Editions
430 First Avenue North, Suite 400, Minneapolis, MN 55401
tel 612-332-3192 *fax* 612-332-6248
Publisher/Editor Emilie Buchwald
Fiction, poetry, essays, literature, children's novels (ages 8-14). Founded 1979.

The MIT Press*
5 Cambridge Center, Cambridge, MA 02142-1493
tel 617-253-5646 *fax* 617-258-6779
web site http://mitpress.mit.edu
Director Frank Urbanowski, *Editor-in-Chief* Laurence Cohen
Architecture, art and design, cognitive sciences, neuroscience, linguistics, computer science and artificial intelligence, economics and finance, philosophy, environment and ecology, natural history. Founded 1961.

Morehouse Publishing Co.

PO Box 1321, Harrisburg, PA 17105
tel 717-541-8130 *fax* 717-541-8128
President Kenneth Quigley, *Publisher* Harold Rast
Religious books, religious education, texts, seminary texts, children's books.

Morrow Jr. Books

1350 Avenue of the Americas, New York, NY 10019
tel 212-261-6500 *fax* 212-261-6689
Vice-President/Editor-in-Chief vacant
Children's books only. No unsolicited material accepted. Division of **William Morrow & Co. Inc.**

William Morrow & Co. Inc.

1350 Avenue of the Americas, New York, NY 10019
tel 212-261-6500 *fax* 212-261-6595
Publisher Michael Murphy
General literature, fiction and juveniles. Imprints: Greenwillow Books, Lothrop, Lee & Shepard, Morrow Jr Books, Tambourine Books, Mulberry/Beech Tree/Tupelo.

The Naiad Press Inc.

PO Box 10543, Tallahassee, FL 32302
tel 904-539-5965 *fax* 904-539-9731
web site http://www.naiadpress.com
Ceo Barbara Grier
Lesbian fiction; non-fiction: bibliographies, biographies, essays. Founded 1973.

Thomas Nelson Publisher

501 Nelson Place, Nashville, TN 37214-1000
tel 615-889-9000 *fax* 615-391-5225
President of Publishing Byron Williamson
Bibles, religious, non-fiction and fiction general trade books. Founded 1798.

W.W. Norton & Company Inc.

500 Fifth Avenue, New York, NY 10110
tel 212-354-5500 *fax* 212-869-0856
e-mail ftp@wwnorton.com
web site http://www.wwnorton.com
General fiction and non-fiction, music, boating, psychiatry, economics, family therapy, social work, reprints, college texts, science.

NTC/Contemporary Publishing Company

4255 West Touhy Avenue, Lincolnwood, IL 60646
tel 847-679-5500 *fax* 847-679-2494
Vice President/Publisher Christine Albritton, *Editorial Director* John Nolan
Non-fiction.

Orchard Books

95 Madison Avenue, New York, NY 10016
tel 212-951-2600 *fax* 212-213-6435
e-mail JWilson@grolier.com
web site http://Grolier.com
President/Publisher Judy V. Wilson
Books for children and young adults; picture books, fiction. Founded 1987.

Ottenheimer Publishers Inc.

10 Church Lane, Baltimore, MD 21208
tel 410-484-2100 *fax* 410-486-8301
Directors Allan T. Hirsh, Jr, Allan T. Hirsh, III
Juvenile and adult non-fiction, reference. Founded 1890.

The Overlook Press*

386 West Broadway, 4th Floor, New York, NY 10012
tel 212-965-8400 *fax* 212-965-9834
President Peter Mayer, *Publishing Director* Tracy Carns
Non-fiction, fiction, children's books.

Oxford University Press Inc.*

198 Madison Avenue, New York, NY 10016
tel 212-726-6000 *fax* 212-726-6455
web site http://www.oup-usa.org
Scholarly, professional, reference, bibles, college textbooks, religion, medicals, music.

Pantheon Books*

201 East 50th Street, New York, NY 10022
tel 212-572-2838 *fax* 212-572-6030
web site http://www.randomhouse.com
Senior Editor Shelley Wanger
Fiction, mysteries, belles-lettres, translations, philosophy, history and art, sociology, psychology. Division of **Random House Inc.**

Peachtree Publishers Ltd

494 Armour Circle NE, Atlanta, GA 30324-4088
tel 404-876-8761 *fax* 404-875-2578
President and Publisher Margaret Quinlin, *Editorial Director* Kathy Landwehr
Children's picture books and novels. Non-fiction subjects include self-help, parenting, education, health, the American South, cookbooks and gardening; also gift books and fiction. Founded 1977.

Pelican Publishing Company*

PO Box 3110, Gretna, LA 70054
tel 504-368-1175 *fax* 504-368-1195
e-mail office@pelicanpub.com
Publisher/President Milburn Calhoun
Art and architecture, cookbooks, travel, music, business, children's. Founded 1926.

Penguin USA

375 Hudson Street, New York, NY10014
tel 212-366-2000 *fax* 212-366-2666
e-mail webmaster@penguin.com
web site http://www.penguinputnam.com
Chairman Michael Lynton, *President* Phyllis
Grann, *Coo* David Shanks

Mass market fiction and non-fiction for adults and children. Imprints: Allen Lane, Akana, Cobblehill Books, Dial Books for Young Readers, Donald I. Fine Books, Dutton, Dutton Children's Books, Ladybird Books, Lodestar Books, Looney Tunes Books, Mentor, Meridian, Onyx, Penguin, Penguin Audiobooks, Penguin Classics, Penguin HighBridge Audio, The Penguin Press, Penguin Reference, Penguin Studio, Playskool Books, Plume, Puffin, ROC Books, Signet, Signet Classics, Topaz, Truman M. Talley Books, Viking, Viking Children's Books, Frederick Warne, William Abrahams Books. Member of Penguin Putnam Inc.

Penn State University Press*

820 North University Drive, USB1, Suite C,
University Park, PA 16802
tel 814-865-1327 *fax* 814-863-1408
web site http://www.psu.edu/psupress
Senior Editor, Humanities Philip Winsor, *Editor,
History and Social Science* Peter Potter

Art history, literary criticism, religious studies, philosophy, political science, sociology, history, Russian and East European studies, Latin American studies and medieval studies. Founded 1956.

The Permanent Press and Second Chance Press

4170 Noyac Road, Sag Harbor, NY 11963
tel 516-725-1101
web site http://www.thepermanentpress.com
Directors Martin Shepard, Judith Shepard

Quality fiction. Founded 1978.

Pocket Books*

1230 Avenue of the Americas, New York,
NY 10020
tel 212-698-7000 *fax* 212-698-7007
web site http://www.SimonSays.com
President/Publisher Gina Centrello, *Vice-
President/Editorial Director* Emily Bestler

General fiction and non-fiction, trade hardcovers and paperbacks, mass market paperbacks. Imprints: Archway Paperbacks, Minstrel Books, Washington Square Press, MTV Books. Division of Simon & Schuster Consumer Group. Founded 1939.

Praeger Publishers

Greenwood Publishing Group Inc.,
88 Post Road West, Westport, CT 06881
tel 203-226-3571 *fax* 203-222-1502

Non-fiction on international relations, social sciences, economics, contemporary issues, urban affairs, psychology, education.

Prentice Hall – imprint of Simon & Schuster Education Group*

Price Stern Sloan Inc.

345 Hudson Street, New York, NY 10014
tel 212-366-2000
Editorial Director Lara Bergen

Children's books: novelty/lift-flaps, activity books, middle-grade fiction, mid-grade and YA non-fiction, cutting-edge graphic readers, picture books, books plus. Division of Penguin Putnam Books for Young Readers. Founded 1963.

Princeton University Press*

Princeton, NJ 08540
Mailing address 41 William Street, Princeton,
NJ 08540
tel 609-258-4900 *fax* 609-258-6305
web site http://www.pup.princeton.edu
Director Walter Lippincott, *Editor-in-Chief* Ann
Wald

Scholarly and scientific books on all subjects. Founded 1905.

Puffin Books

395 Hudson Street, New York, NY 10014
tel 212-414-3475 *fax* 212-414-3399
web site http://www.penguinputnam.com
President/Publisher Tracy Tang, *Associate
Publisher/Managing Editor* Gerard Mancini

Children's paperback books. Imprint of **Penguin Putnam Inc.**

The Putnam Berkley Group Inc.

200 Madison Avenue, New York, NY 10016
tel 212-951-8400

All types of literature; history, economics, political science, natural science, and standard literature; fiction; children's books.

Rand McNally

PO Box 7600, Chicago, IL 60680
tel 847-329-2178
Chairman/President/Ceo Henry J. Feinberg

Maps, guides, atlases, educational publications, globes and children's geographical titles and atlases in print and electronic formats.

Random House Inc.*
201 East 50th Street, New York, NY 10022
tel 212-751-2600 *fax* 212-572-8700
Chairman/Ceo Alberto Vitale, *President/Coo*
Philip M. Pfeffer
Adult and children's fiction and non-fiction. Imprints include Ballantine, Crown, Del Rey, Fawcett, Ivy, Alfred A. Knopf, Pantheon, Random House, Times Books, Villard Books, Vintage Books. Subsidiary of Bertelsmann AG. Founded 1925

Rawson Associates
1230 Avenue of the Americas, New York, NY 10020
tel 212-632-4941 *fax* 212-632-4918
Publisher Eleanor S. Rawson
Adult non-fiction of wide general interest.

Rizzoli International Publications Inc.
300 Park Avenue South, New York, NY 10010
tel 212-387-3400 *fax* 212-387-3535
Publisher Solveig Williams
Art, architecture, photography, fashion, gardening, design, gift books, cookbooks. Founded 1976.

Rodale Press Inc.
33 East Minor Street, Emmaus, PA 18098
tel 610-967-5171 *fax* 610-967-8961
President, Book Division Pat Corpora, *Vice-President/Editorial Director, Health and Fitness* Deborah Yost
General health, women's health, men's health, senior health, alternative health, fitness, healthy cooking, gardening, pets, spirituality/inspiration, trade health. Founded 1930.

Ronin Publishing Inc.
Box 1035, Berkeley, CA 94701
tel 510-540 6278 *fax* 510-548-7326
e-mail roninpub@dnai.com
web site http://www.roninpub.com
New Age business, psychedelics, marijuana, visionary, underground comix. Preliminary letter essential; no unsolicited MSS or artwork.

Routledge Inc.
29 West 35th Street, New York, NY 10001
tel 212-244-3336 *fax* 212-563-2269
President and Publisher Colin Jones, *Vice-President and Associate Publisher* Kenneth Wright
Literary criticism, history, philosophy, psychology and psychiatry, politics, women's studies, education, anthropology, religion, lesbian and gay studies, classical studies, reference.

Running Press Book Publishers
125 S 22 St, Philadelphia, Pennsylvania 19103
tel 215-567-5080 *fax* 215-568 2919
Publisher Stuart Teacher, *Associate Publisher/Editorial Director* Brian Perrin, *Director of Acquisitions* Nancy Steele, *Design Director* Ken Newbaker, *Production Director* Bob Passantino, *Associate Publisher/Sales and Marketing* Carlo DeVito
Art, craft/how-to, general non-fiction, children's books. Imprints: Courage Books, Running Press Miniature Editions. Founded 1972.

Rutgers University Press*
100 Joyce Kilmer Avenue, Piscataway, NJ 08854-8099
tel 732-445-7762 *fax* 732-445-7039
web site http://www.rutgerspress.rutgers.edu
Directors Marlie Wasserman, *Editor-in-Chief* Leslie Mitchner
Women's studies, anthropology, sociology, health, cultural studies, literature, religion, science, medicine, psychology, Asian-American studies, African-American studies, history, American studies, art history. Founded 1936.

Rutledge Hill Press
211 Seventh Avenue North, Nashville, TN 37219
tel 615-244-2700 *fax* 615-244-2978
e-mail bjayne@compuserve.com
President William E. Jayne, *Publisher* Lawrence M. Stone
Regional books, cookbooks, books on quilts, gift books. Founded 1982.

St Martin's Press Inc.*
175 Fifth Avenue, New York, NY 10010
tel 212-674-5151 *fax* 212-420-9314
Trade, reference, college.

Saunders College Publishing
The Public Ledger Building, 150 South Independence Mall West, Suite 1250, Philadelphia, PA 19106
tel 215-238-5500 *fax* 215-238-5660
College textbooks.

Schocken Books*
201 East 50th Street, New York, NY 10022
tel 212-572-2559 *fax* 212-572-6030
web site http://www.randomhouse.com
Editorial Director Arthur Samuelson
Cultural studies, education, health, history, Judaica, psychology, race and ethnici-

ty, religion, women's studies. Division of **Random House Inc.**

Scholastic Inc.*

555 Broadway, New York, NY 10012
tel 212-343-6100 *fax* 212-343-6930
web site http://www.scholastic.com/
Chairman/President/Ceo M. Richard Robinson,
Executive Vice- President (Children's) Barbara
Marcus, *Executive Vice-President (Instructional)*
Margery Mayer

Fiction and non-fiction for children and young adults, including picture books; instructional material for preschool, elementary and high school. Founded 1920.

Scribner – imprint of Simon & Schuster Trade Division*

Simon & Schuster Children's Publishing Division*

1230 Avenue of the Americas, New York, NY 10020
tel 212-698-7200 *fax* 212-605 3068
President/Publisher Rick Richter

Preschool to young adult, fiction and non-fiction, trade, library and mass market. Imprints: Aladdin Paperbacks, Atheneum Books for Young Readers, Little Simon, Margaret K. McElderry Books, Simon & Schuster Books for Young Readers, Simon Spotlight. Division of Simon & Schuster Consumer Group. Founded 1924.

Simon & Schuster Trade Division*

1230 Avenue of the Americas, New York, NY 10020
tel 212-698-7000 *fax* 212-698-7007
President/Publisher Carolyn K. Reidy

General fiction and non-fiction. Imprints: H&R Block, Lisa Drew Books, Fireside, The Free Press, Free Press Paperbacks, Hudson River Editions, Kaplan, Rawson Associates, Scribner, Scribner Classics, Scribner Paperback Fiction, Scribner Poetry, S&S Libros en Espanol, S&S Editions, Simon & Schuster, Touchstone. Division of Simon & Schuster Consumer Group. Founded 1924.

Soho Press Inc.

853 Broadway, New York, NY 10003
tel 212-260-1900 *fax* 212-260-1902
web site http://www.sohopress.com
Publisher Juris Jurjevics, *Associate Publisher* Laura Hruska

Literary fiction, commercial fiction, mystery, thrillers, travel, memoir, general non-fiction. Founded 1986.

Stanford University Press*

Stanford, CA 94305-2235
tel 415-723-9434 *fax* 415-725-3457
Director Norris Pope

Scholarly non-fiction.

Strawberry Hill Press

3848 SE Division Street, Portland, OR 97202
tel 503-235-5989
President Jean-Louis Brindamour PhD, *Executive Vice-President/Art Director* Ku Fu-Sheng, *Treasurer* Edward E. Serres

Health, self-help, cookbooks, philosophy, religion, history, drama, science and technology, biography, mystery, Third World. No unsolicited MSS; preliminary letter and return postage essential. Founded 1973.

Theatre Arts Books

29 West 35th Street, New York, NY 10001
tel 212-244-3336
President Colin Jones, *Publishing Director* William Germano

Successor to the book publishing department of Theatre Arts (1921-1948). Theatre, performance, dance and allied books – acting techniques, voice, movement, costume, etc; a few plays. Division of **Routledge Inc.**

Time Life Inc.*

2000 Duke Street, Alexandria, VA 22314
tel 703-838-7000 *fax* 703-838-7225
President, Chairman/Ceo George Artandi

Non-fiction: art, cooking, crafts, food, gardening, health, history, home maintenance, nature, photography, science. Subsidiary of Time Warner Inc. Founded 1961.

Tor Books

175 Fifth Avenue, 14th Floor, New York, NY 10010
tel 212-388-0100 *fax* 212-388-0191
President/Publisher Tom Doherty

Fiction: general, historical, western, suspense, mystery, horror, science fiction, fantasy, humour, juvenile, classics (English language); non-fiction: adult and juvenile. Subsidiary of **St Martin's Press Inc.** Founded 1980.

Tuttle Publishing/Periplus Editions

153 Milk Street, Boston, MA 02109
tel 617-951-4080 *fax* 617-951-4045
Suido I-chome, 2-6 Bunkyo-ku, Tokyo 112, Japan
tel 813-3811-7741 *fax* 813-5689 4926
Periplus Editions, 5 Little Road 08-01, Singapore 536983

tel 65-280-3320 *fax* 65-280-6290
President Eric Oey
Asian art, culture, cooking, gardening, Eastern philosophy, martial arts, health. Founded 1948.

United Publishers Group
50 Washington Street, Norwalk, CT 06854
tel 203-838-4083 *fax* 203-838 4084
e-mail info@upub.com
web site http://www.upub.com
Publisher Henno Lohmeyer
Hastings House (imprint)
Editor-in-Chief Hy Steirman
Gates & Bridges (imprint)
Judd Publishing (imprint)
Editor Rue Judd
Rosset-Morgan Books (imprint)
Editors Barney Rosset, Gabriel Morgan
Non-fiction, general, consumer, travel, cooking, controversy and how-to. Founded 1936.

The University of Alabama Press
Box 870380, Tuscaloosa, AL 35487
tel 205-348-5180 *fax* 205-348-9201
Director Nicole Mitchell, *Managing Editor* Elizabeth May
American and Southern history, African-American studies, religion, rhetoric and communication, Judaic studies, literary criticism, anthropology and archaeology. Founded 1945.

The University of Arkansas Press
The University of Arkansas, 201 Ozark Street, Fayetteville, AR 72701
tel 501-575-3246 *fax* 501-575-6044
Director John Coghlan
History, literary criticism, biography, poetry, fiction. Founded 1980.

University of California Press*
2120 Berkeley Way, Berkeley, CA 94720
tel 510-642-4247 *fax* 510-643-7127
Director James H. Clark
Publishes scholarly books, books of general interest, series of scholarly monographs and scholarly journals.

University of Chicago Press*
5801 South Ellis Avenue, Chicago, IL 60637
tel 773-702-7700 *fax* 773-702-9756
Director Morris Philipson
Scholarly books and monographs, religious and scientific books, general trade books, and 54 scholarly journals.

University of Illinois Press
1325 South Oak Street, Champaign, IL 61820
tel 217-333-0950 *fax* 217-244-8082
Director Richard L. Wentworth
American studies (history, music, literature), poetry, working-class and ethnic studies, communications, regional studies, architecture, philosophy and women's studies. Founded 1918.

The University of Massachussetts Press
PO Box 429, Amherst, MA 01004-0429
tel 413-545-2217 *fax* 413-545-1226
web site http://www.umass.edu/umpress
Director Bruce G. Wilcox
Scholarly books and works of general interest: American studies and history, black and ethnic studies, women's studies, cultural criticism, architecture and environmental design, literary criticism, poetry, fiction, philosophy, political science, sociology, books of regional interest. Founded 1964.

The University of Michigan Press
839 Greene Street, PO Box 1104, Ann Arbor, MI 48106
tel 734-764-4388 *fax* 734-936-0456
e-mail um.press@umich.edu
web site http://www.press.umich.edu/
Director Colin Day, *Assistant Director* Mary Erwin, *Executive Editor* LeAnn Fields, *Managing Editor* Christina Milton
Scholarly works in literature, classics, history, theatre, women's studies, political science, law, anthropology, economics, archaeology; textbooks in English as a second language; regional trade titles, health policy and management. Founded 1930.

University of Missouri Press
2910 LeMone Boulevard, Columbia, MO 65201
tel 573-882-7641 *fax* 573-884-4498
web site http://www.system.missouri.edu/upress
Director/Editor-in-Chief Beverly Jarrett, *Acquisitions Editor* Clair Willcox
American and European history, American, British and Latin American literary criticism, journalism, political philosophy, art history, regional studies; short fiction. Founded 1958.

University of New Mexico Press
1720 Lomas Boulevard NE, Albuquerque, NM 87131-1591
tel 505-277-2346 *fax* 505-277-9270

e-mail unmpress@unm.edu
Director Elizabeth C. Hadas

Western history, anthropology and archaeology, Latin American studies, photography, multicultural literature. Founded 1929.

The University of North Carolina Press*

PO Box 2288, 116 South Boundary Street, Chapel Hill, NC 27514
tel 919-966-3561 *fax* 919-966-3829
Director Kate Douglas Torrey

American history, American studies, Southern studies, European history, women's studies, Latin American studies, political science, anthropology and folklore, classics, regional trade. Founded 1922.

University of Oklahoma Press*

1005 Asp Avenue, Norman, OK 73019-0445
tel 405-325-5111 *fax* 405-325-4000
Director John N. Drayton

History of American West, American Indian studies, Mesoamerican studies, classical studies, women's studies, natural history, political science. Founded 1928.

University of Pennsylvania Press

4200 Pine Street, Philadelphia, PA 19104-4011
tel 215-898-6261 *fax* 215-898-0404
Director Eric Halpern

American and British history, anthropology, art, architecture, business, cultural studies, economics, folklore, ancient studies, human rights, literature, medicine, Pennsylvania regional studies, women's studies. Founded 1890.

University of Tennessee Press*

293 Communications Building, Knoxville, TN 37996-0325
tel 423-974-3321 *fax* 423-974-3724
e-mail gadair@utk.edu
web site http://www.sunsite.utk.edu/utpress
Director Jennifer Siler

American studies: women's studies, African-American studies, ethnomusicology, folklore, history, religion, anthropology, political science, vernacular architecture, material culture, literature. Native American studies; cultural and ethnic studies; studies in most disciplines on Appalachia and the Southeast; Caribbean studies; regional fiction. Founded 1940.

University of Texas Press*

PO Box 7819, Austin, TX 78713-7819
tel 512-471-7233 *fax* 512-320-0668
e-mail utpress@uts.cc.utexas.edu
web site http://www.utexas.edu/utpress/
Director Joanna Hitchcock, *Assistant Director and Executive Editor* Theresa May, *Assistant Director and Financial Officer* Joyce Lewandowski

Scholarly non-fiction: anthropology, classics and the Ancient World, conservation and the environment, film and media studies, geography, Latin American and Latino studies, Middle Eastern studies, natural history, ornithology, Texas and Western studies. Founded 1950.

University of Washington Press

PO Box 50096, Seattle, WA 98145-5096
tel 206-543-4050 *fax* 206-543-3932
Director Patrick Soden, *Associate Director/Editor-in-Chief* Naomi B. Pascal

Anthropology, Asian-American studies, Asian studies, art and art history, aviation history, environmental studies, forest history, Jewish studies, literary criticism, marine sciences, Middle East studies, music, regional studies, including history and culture of the Pacific Northwest and Alaska, Native American studies, resource management and public policy, Russian and East European studies, Scandinavian studies. Founded 1909.

University Press of Kansas

2501 West 15th Street, Lawrence, KS 66049-3905
tel 913-864-4155 *fax* 913-864-4586
e-mail upkansas@kuhub.cc.ukans.edu
Director Fred Woodward, *Editor-in-Chief* Michael Briggs, *Senior Production Editor* Melinda Wirkus, *Assistant Director/Marketing Manager* Susan K. Schott

American history, military history, American political thought, American presidency studies, law and constitutional history, political science and philosophy. Founded 1946.

Van Nostrand Reinhold – acquired by John Wiley & Sons

Viking Children's Books

345 Hudson Street, New York, NY 10014
tel 212-366-2000 *fax* 212-414-3399
e-mail webmaster@penguinputnam.com
web site http://www.penguinputnam.com
President/Publisher Regina Hayes, *Executive Editor* Deborah Brodie

Fiction, non-fiction, picture books.
Member of Penguin Putnam Inc.

Viking Penguin
375 Hudson Street, New York, NY 10014
tel 212-366-2000 *fax* 212-366-2666
e-mail webmaster@penguin.com
web site http://www.penguin.com
President Susan Petersen, *Publisher/Editor-in-Chief* Kathryn Court
Fiction, general non-fiction. Imprint of
Penguin USA.

Walker & Co.
435 Hudson Street, New York, NY 10014
tel 212-727-8300 *fax* 212-727-0984
Publisher George Gibson, *Mystery* Michael
Seidman, *Juvenile* Emily Easton
General publishers, biography, popular
science, health, business, mystery, history, juveniles. Founded 1960.

Warner Books Inc.*
1271 Avenue of the Americas, New York,
NY 10020
tel 212-522-7200 *fax* 212-522-7991
Ceo Laurence K. Kirshbaum, *President/Coo/
Publisher* Maureen Mahon Egen
Paperback originals and reprints, fiction
and non-fiction, trade paperbacks and
hardcover books, audio books, gift books.
Subsidiary of Time Warner Inc. Founded
1961.

Watson-Guptill Publications
1515 Broadway, New York, NY 10036
tel 212-764-7300 *fax* 212-536-5359
President/Publisher Glenn Heffernan, *Vice-President, Marketing and Sales* Harriet Pierce,
Senior Editor Candy Raney
Art, architecture, crafts, entertainment,
drama, film, interior design, photography, popular culture, music, theatre.
Imprints: Amphoto, Back Stage Books,
Billboard Books, Radio Amateur
Callbook, Watson-Guptill, The Whitney
Library of Design. Founded 1937.

Franklin Watts
Sherman Turnpike, Danbury, CT 06813
tel 203-797-3500 *fax* 203-797-6986
School and library books for grades K-12.

Westminster John Knox Press
100 Witherspoon Street, Louisville,
KY 40202-1396

tel 502-569-5043 *fax* 502-569-5113
e-mail wjk@ctr.pcusa.org
web site http://www.pcusa.org
web site http://www.pcusa.org/ppc
Editorial Manager Stephanie Egnotovich
Religious, academic, reference, general.

John Wiley & Sons Inc.*
605 Third Avenue, New York, NY 10158
tel 212-850-6000 *fax* 212-850-6088
e-mail info@wiley.com
web site http://www.wiley.com
President/Ceo William Pesce
Specialises in scientific and technical
books and journals, textbooks and educational materials for colleges and universities, as well as professional and consumer books and subscription services.
Subjects include business, computer science, electronics, engineering, environmental studies, reference books, science,
social sciences, multimedia, and trade
paperbacks. Founded 1807.

Writer's Digest Books
1507 Dana Avenue, Cincinnati, OH 45207
tel 513-531-2690 *fax* 513-531-7107
Market Directories, books for writers,
photographers and songwriters.

North Light Books (imprint)
Fine art and graphic arts instruction
books.

Betterway Books (imprint)
How-to in home building, remodelling,
woodworking, sports, home organisation,
theatre, genealogy.

Yale University Press*
302 Temple Street, New Haven, CT 06511
postal address PO Box 209040, New Haven,
CT 06520
tel 203-432-0960 *fax* 203-432-0948/2394
e-mail firstname.lastname@yale.edu
web site http://www.yale.edu/yup/
Director John G. Ryden
Scholarly books and art books.

Zoland Books Inc.
384 Huron Avenue, Cambridge,
MA 02138
tel 617-864-6252 *fax* 617-661-4998
Publisher Roland F. Pease Jr., *Managing Editor*
Michael Lindgren
Fiction, poetry, art criticism, memoirs.
Founded 1987.

A timeline of British publishers

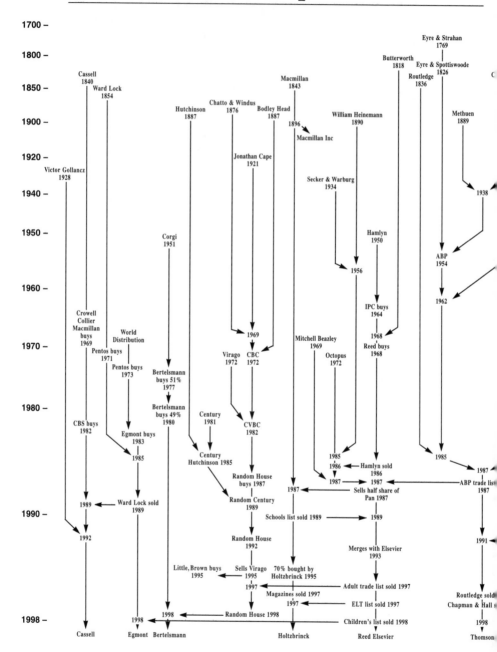

Sponsored by **KPMG**

*The chart below, **A timeline of British publishers – a simplified history of the main trade publishing groups**, first appeared in **Who Owns Whom in British Book Publishing**, a supplement to the Bookseller (12 June 1998).*

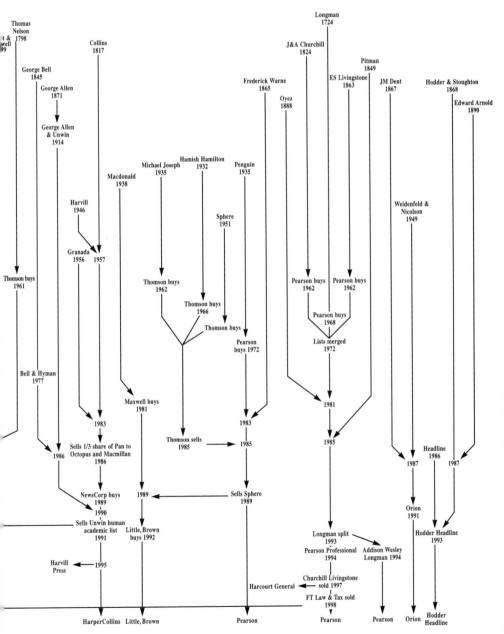

Source: *Who Owns Whom in British Book Publishing*, compiled by Christopher Gasson, published by Bookseller Publications, sponsored by KPMG.   Sponsored by **KPMG**

Writing and illustrating children's books

Sammy the Squirrel, Cyril the Slug, Teddy the Traffic Light ... mention such titles to a group of children's book editors and they all recognise yesterday's pile of rejected manuscripts. Editors are looking for something with more originality and punch. **Caroline Sheldon** *guides the potential children's author and/or illustrator in the direction of success.*

The best way to get a feel of what children's publishers are publishing today is to read a large range of children's books published now and over the last 30 years. They cover an enormous spectrum in length and content – from simple, highly illustrated picture book stories to full length novels for teenagers, and most children's publishers' lists cover the whole range.

Writing children's books

Observe all the rules of submitting any other manuscript – a doubled-spaced, attractively presented manuscript; a covering letter giving information about yourself and your writing; return postage; no bulky ring binders that burst open in the post. Mention any experience you have had of working with children.

Picture books

There is limited opportunity for authors to get involved in bath books or board books, and therefore picture books are generally the youngest end of the age range for writers.

The high cost of printing in full colour necessitates a long print run of copies to keep the unit cost down. To achieve this, collaboration with an American, European or other foreign publisher is essential. Thus a publisher has to believe a book is really going to make its mark in the international market before taking it

on. It is a very competitive field but, when asked what they are short of, most publishers will say good picture book texts – which just proves how difficult they are to write successfully.

Almost all picture books are 32 pages long with 12-14 spreads (i.e. double pages) of full colour illustration. The number of words varies from none (it has been done; the author provided the storyline to which the artist worked) to a maximum of about 2500. The book has to encompass a big enough idea to make it something of an event, yet not deal with issues too wide to resolve within the limits of the page size and design. A narrative with a strong beginning, middle and end is needed to encourage the reader to turn the pages. Even some successful authors in the area find their publisher or agent may reject five stories before one magically slips into place. So be warned, it's tough ...

Picture book manuscripts should be typed as a series of numbered pages each with its own text. Detailed descriptions of the illustrations and instructions to the illustrator are almost always a mistake. However, if there is something that should be included in the picture, but it is not clear from the text, it should be pointed out.

Younger fiction

This area of publishing is designed for children who are reading their first whole novels. Texts tend to be anything from

Publisher	Series name	Length	Age group	Comments
Andersen Press	Tigers	3000-5000 words 64 pages	6-9	B&w illustrations throughout
A & C Black	Jets	2000 words 64 pages	6-9	B&w illustrations throughout
	Chillers	4500 words 64 pages	8-10	Spooky texts; b&w illustrations throughout
	Graffix	4000 words 80 pages	9-12	B&w graphic novels
Bloomsbury	Young Fiction	2500 words 64 pages	5-7	B&w illustrations throughout
	Middle Fiction	6000 words 64 pages	7-9	B&w illustrations throughout
Doubleday/Corgi	Corgi Pups	2000-2500 words 64 pages	5-8	B&w illustrations throughout
	Young Corgi	3000-7500 words 64/80 pages	6-9	B&w illustrations throughout
HarperCollins	Yellow Storybooks	2000 words 64 pages	5-7	B&w illustrations throughout
	Red Storybooks	6000-8000 words	7-9	B&w illustrations throughout
	Colour Jets	2000 words 64 pages	7-10	
Hodder & Stoughton	My First Read Alone	1500 words 48/64 pages	5	B&w illustrations throughout
	Read Alone	2000-4000 words	6-7	B&w illustrations throughout
	Story Book	8000-12,000 words 96/128 pages	7-9	B&w illustrations throughout
Kingfisher	I Am Reading	1500-2000 words 48 pages	5-6	Colour illustrations throughout
Macdonald Young Books	First Story Books	900 words 32 pages	5-7	Colour illustrations throughout
	Yellow Story Books	2000 words 48 pages	6-8	Colour and b&w illustrations
	Red Story Books	2500 words 48 pages	7-9	Colour and b&w illustrations
	Tremors	2500 words 48 pages	7-10	Colour and b&w illustrations
	Scientists	2500 words 48 pages	7-10	Colour and b&w illustrations
	Historical Story Books	2500 words 48 pages	7-10	Colour and b&w illustrations
Orchard	Crunchies	1000-1500 words	5-7	B&w line illustrations
	Super Crunchies	5000 words	7-9	B&w line illustrations
Penguin Group	First Young Puffin	1500 words 32 pages	5-6	Colour illustrations
	Colour Young Puffin	3000 words 64 pages	6-7	Colour illustrations
	Surfers	13,000 words	9-12	B&w chapter heads
Reed Children's Books	Blue Bananas	1000-1500 words 48 pages	5-7	Colour illustrations

Publisher	Series name	Length	Age group	Comments
Reed Children's Books (cont.)	Yellow Bananas	3000 words 48 pages	7-9	
	Story Books	6000 words 64 pages	5-7	4 linked stories about one character
	Reads	1500 words 48 pages	9-11	B&w illustrations throughout
	Epix		9-11	B&w graphic novels
Scholastic Children's Books	Young Hippo	3500-10,000 words 64-128 pages	5-9	Spooky, magic, adventure, funny, school
	Hippo	20,000-25,000	8-11	Mystery, funny, ghost, animal, sports
	Point	40,000	12+	
Walker Books	Story Books	6000-10,000 words	4-7	Stories around central character
	Sprinters	2000	6-8	B&w illustrations throughout
	Racers	7,500-15,000 words	7-10	B&w illustrations throughout

1500 to 7500 words long; in many cases the books will be illustrated with line illustrations to break up the words on the page. Generally, publishers don't want a use of restricted vocabulary, but writers should remember that, particularly at the bottom end of the age range, they are writing for children who have just learnt to read. Novels for this age range can be published as individual books but often publishers put them out under an umbrella series name. Investigate a series before approaching the publisher and check that your book fits in to that series in terms of length and interest level. You can indicate in a covering letter that you have planned that it will be illustrated, but don't give illustration notes in the manuscript.

The table oppposite shows some currently published series with the approximate word length of the manuscript and the age group at which the books are aimed.

General fiction

Children's novels for the over nine age group are mainly published as individual books. Generally, they are shorter than children's books read by previous generations. Any books over 40,000 words will have to face the problems of a higher price than the publisher would like. Each book stands on its own merits and publishers are looking for authors whose work they like and whom they believe will go on to write a number of books for their list.

There are also a number of extremely successful fiction series for older children that have recently become established. For example, Scholastic commission books for their *Point* series with genres including horror, romance, crime and science fiction. Sample material submitted to a publisher should consist of the first three chapters, a brief synopsis and a covering letter.

Non-fiction

Non-fiction is an area almost exclusively covered by specialists. Some publishers have much of their non-fiction written by their own staff. If you are interested in this area, nothing can replace a research trip to a good children's library or bookshop to establish who is publishing what, and how your work or field of interest could fit in.

Illustrating children's books

Illustrating children's books is a highly professional field but one in which there is always room for new talent. Most illustrators working in children's books have an art school background but there are also those who have come to it without formal training. The work available varies from illustrations for full-colour picture books, to jackets and black and white line illustrations for novels, to non-fiction illustration.

Illustrators looking for work in this area should try to make appointments to show their portfolios to either the Art Director or Children's Book Editor at a publishing house and to show their work to suitable agents. A portfolio should show as wide a range of work as possible – it is well worth working up some black and white line illustrations for children's novels for the 6-10 age range since so much bread-and-butter work is commissioned in this area. Once you have achieved this, people are more likely to be interested in spending time with you developing your special picture book project. The main complaints of those who look at prospective illustrators' portfolios is that the work shown is too stylised and sophisticated, and there is not an obvious application to children's book illustration.

If you find it difficult to get an appointment, send in a folder of photocopied samples of your work together with a letter outlining the type of work for which you are looking. Always send photocopies of work, never the original artwork; even if the photocopies don't do full justice to the colour, publishers are experienced at spotting the sort of quality that makes them want to see more.

Words/pictures – which come first?

Unless you are best buddies with a best-selling illustrator or writer, it is best to present your work individually. It is an unwanted complication to have wonderful artwork tied in to an amateurish text, or a nice text illustrated by an artist whose work won't stand up in the very competitive picture book market. Publishers are experienced in matching the work of writers and artists, and the individual work should stand on its own. Having said that, at the younger end of children's publishing, life is much simpler if you are a writer/illustrator.

Caroline Sheldon is an established literary agent who represents writers and artists working in children's books and adult fiction.

Children's book publishers and packagers

A quick reference guide to children's book publishers and packagers by subject area. Listings for Book publishers UK and Ireland start on page 157 and listings for Book packagers start on page 220.

Picture books

Book publishers
Andersen Press
Award Publications
Bantam
Barefoot Books
BBC Children's Publishing
David Bennett Books
A & C Black
Black Butterfly
Bloomsbury Publishing
Bodley Head Children's Books
Brimax Books
Brown Wells & Jacobs
Jonathan Cape Children's Books
Child's Play (International)
David & Charles
J.M. Dent
André Deutsch Children's Books
Dorling Kindersley
Element Books
Floris Books
Gairm Publications (Gaelic)
Gallery Children's Books
Gomer Press
Hamish Hamilton Children's
 Books
HarperCollins Publishers
Hawk Books
Hazar Publishing
Heinemann Young Books
Hippo Books
Hodder & Stoughton
Hunt & Thorpe
Hutchinson Children's Books
Kingfisher
Ladybird Books
Levinson Books
Frances Lincoln
Lion Publishing
Little, Brown
Peter Lowe (Eurobook Ltd)
Lutterworth Press
Macdonald Young Books
Macmillan Children's Books

Julia MacRae Books
Magi Publications
Mammoth
Mantra Publishing
Medici Society
Methuen Children's Books
The O'Brien Press (Ire.)
Michael O'Mara Books
Orchard Books
Orion Children's Books
Oxford University Press
Paternoster Publishing
Pavilion Books
Piccadilly Press
Poolbeg Press (Ire.)
Puffin
Ragged Bears
Reader's Digest Children's Books
Red Fox
Scholastic Children's Books
Scripture Union
Tamarind
Tango Books
Transworld Publishers
Two-Can Publishing
Usborne Publishing
Ventura Publishing
Viking Children's Books
Walker Books
Frederick Warne
Wolfhound Press (Ire.)
World International

Book packagers
Aladdin Books
Albion Press
Bellew Publishing
Brown Wells & Jacobs
Geddes & Grosset
Graham-Cameron Publishing
Angus Hudson
Marshall Editions
Orpheus Books
Oyster Books
Mathew Price
Sadie Fields Productions

The Templar Company
Tucker Slingsby
Ventura Publishing

Fiction

Book publishers
Andersen Press
Anvil Books/The Children's
 Press (Ire.)
Attic Press (Ire.)
Award Publications
Bantam
BBC Children's Publishing
A & C Black
Black Butterfly
Bloomsbury Publishing
Bodley Head Children's Books
Brimax Books
Brown, Son & Ferguson
Canongate Books
Jonathan Cape Children's Books
Child's Play (International)
David & Charles
J.M. Dent
André Deutsch Children's Books
Dorling Kindersley
Element Books
Evans Brothers
Everyman's Library
Faber & Faber
Gairm Publications (Gaelic)
Gallery Children's Books
Gomer Press (English/Welsh)
Hamish Hamilton Children's
 Books
Patrick Hardy Books
HarperCollins Publishers
Hawk Books
Heinemann Young Books
Hippo
Hodder & Stoughton
Honno
Hutchinson Children's Books
Kingfisher

Ladybird Books
Lion Publishing
Y Lolfa Cyf. (Welsh)
Peter Lowe (Eurobook Ltd)
Lutterworth Press
Macdonald Young Books
Macmillan Children's Books
Julia MacRae Books
Mammoth
Mantra Publishing
Marino Books (Ire.)
Kevin Mayhew
Methuen Children's Books
Michael O'Mara Books
The O'Brien Press (Ire.)
Orchard Books
Orion Children's Books
Oxford University Press
Pavilion Books
Piccadilly Press
Point
Poolbeg Press (Ire.)
Puffin
Ragged Bears
Reader's Digest Children's Books
Red Fox
Robinson Publishing
Schofield & Sims
Scholastic Press
Scottish Children's Press
Scripture Union
Seren Books
Tamarind
Tango Books
D.C. Thomson
Transworld Publishers
Usborne Publishing
Viking Children's Books
Walker Books
Wolfhound Press (Ire.)
World International
The X Press

Book packagers
Albion Press
Oyster Books
Mathew Price

Non-fiction

Book publishers
Aladdin/Watts
Andromeda Oxford
Anness Publishing
Anvil Books/The Children's
Press (Ire.)
Apple Press
Atlantic Europe Publishing Co.
Award Publications
Bantam
BBC Children's Publishing
Belitha Press

David Bennett Books
A & C Black
Black Butterfly
Boxtree (film/TV tie-ins)
Brimax Books
Brown Wells & Jacobs
Child's Play (International)
J.M. Dent
André Deutsch Children's Books
Dorling Kindersley
Element Books
Evans Brothers
Exley Publications
First and Best in Education
Folens (Ire.)
Funfax
Geddes & Grosset
Gomer Press (English/Welsh)
Hamlyn Children's Non-Fiction
HarperCollins Publishers
Heinemann Young Books
Hippo
Hodder & Stoughton
Kingfisher
Ladybird Books
Frances Lincoln
Lion Publishing
Little, Brown
Y Lolfa Cyf. (Welsh)
Peter Lowe (Eurobook Ltd)
Lutterworth Press
Macdonald Young Books
Macmillan Children's Books
Julia MacRae Books
Madcap
Mantra Publishing
Marshall Publishing
Medici Society
Merehurst
Michelin Tyre
The National Trust
New Orchard Editions
The O'Brien Press (Ire.)
Michael O'Mara Books
Oxford University Press
Paternoster Publishing
Pavilion Books
Piccadilly Press
Poolbeg Press (Ire.)
Puffin
Ragged Bears
Reader's Digest Children's Books
Salamander Books
Science Museum Publications
Schofield & Sims
Scholastic Children's Books
Scottish Children's Press
Scripture Union
Studio Editions
Tango Books
Transworld Publishers
Two-Can Publishing
Usborne Publishing

Walker Books
Frederick Warne
Wayland Publishers
Wolfhound Press (Ire.)
World International
Young Library
Zoë Books

Book packagers
Aladdin Books
Alphabet & Image
Andromeda Oxford
Bellew Publishing
Bender Richardson White
Breslich & Foss
Brown Wells & Jacobs
Philip Clark
Roger Coote Publishing
Diagram Visual Information
Earthscape Editions
Geddes & Grosset
Graham-Cameron Publishing
Lionheart Books
Marshall Editions
Orpheus Books
Oyster Books
Mathew Price
Quarto Children's Books
The Templar Company
Toucan Books
Touchstone Publishing
Tucker Slingsby
Wordwright Books

Other

Activity and novelty
Book publishers
Andersen Press
Andromeda Oxford
Apple Press
Award Publications
BBC Children's Publishing
David Bennett Books
Bloomsbury Publishing
Brimax Books
Brown Wells & Jacobs
Child's Play (International)
David & Charles
André Deutsch
Dorling Kindersley
Exley Publications
First and Best in Education
Floris Books
Funfax
Geddes & Grosset
Hamlyn Children's Non-Fiction
Hazar Publishing
Heinemann Young Books
Hippo
Kingfisher

Ladybird Books
Levinson Books
Frances Lincoln
Lion Publishing
Lutterworth Press
Macmillan Children's Books
Magi Publications
Mammoth
Kevin Mayhew
Methuen Children's Books
Michelin Tyre
The O'Brien Press (Ire.)
Michael O'Mara Books
Orchard Books
Orion Children's Books
Oxford University Press
Pavilion Books
Puffin
Ragged Bears
Reader's Digest Children's Books
Robinson Publishing
Salamander Books
Scholastic Children's Books
Scripture Union
Studio Editions
Tango Books
Tarquin Publications
Transworld Publishers
Treehouse Children's Books
Two-Can Publishing
Usborne Publishing
Walker Books
Frederick Warne
World International

Book packagers
Aladdin Books
Andromeda Oxford
Bellew Publishing
Breslich & Foss
Brown Wells & Jacobs
Roger Coote Publishing
Geddes & Grosset
Graham-Cameron Publishing
Angus Hudson
Lionheart Books
Orpheus Books
Oyster Books
Playne Books
Mathew Price
Quarto Children's Books
Sadie Fields Productions
The Templar Company
Touchstone Publishing
Tucker Slingsby

Audiobooks

Book publishers
Award Publications
BBC Children's Publishing
Child's Play (International)

André Deutsch
Funfax
HarperCollins Publishers
Hodder Headline
Ladybird Books
Mantra Publishing
The O'Brien Press (Ire.)
Random House Audio Books
St Pauls
Scholastic Children's Books
Scottish Children's Press
Scripture Union
Tellastory
Usborne Publishing

Multimedia

Book publishers
BBC Children's Publishing
Dorling Kindersley
Ginn
HarperCollins
Heinemann Educational
Hodder Headline
Macmillan
Mantra Publishing
Oxford University Press
Paternoster Publishing
Puffin
Random House
St Pauls
Thomas Nelson
Two-Can Publishing
Usborne Publishing
Frederick Warne
Wayland Publishers

Book packagers
Roger Coote Publishing
Touchstone Publishing
Oyster Books

Poetry

Book publishers
Andersen Press
Award Publications
Bantam
Barefoot Books
A & C Black
Bloomsbury Publishing
Bodley Head Children's Books
Jonathan Cape Children's Books
André Deutsch Children's Books
Evans Brothers
Everyman's Library
Faber & Faber
Gallery Children's Books
Gairm Publications
Gomer Press (English/Welsh)
HarperCollins Publishers

Heinemann Young Books
Hutchinson Children's Books
Kingfisher
Frances Lincoln
Lutterworth Press
Macmillan Children's Books
Mammoth
Methuen Children's Books
Orchard Books
Oxford University Press
Paternoster Publishing
Puffin
Ragged Bears
Red Fox
Scholastic Children's Books
Scottish Children's Press
Transworld Publishers
Usborne Publishing
Viking Children's Books
Walker Books
Wolfhound Press (Ire.)

Religion

Book publishers
Award Publications
Child's Play (International)
Dorling Kindersley
Element Books
Gallery Children's Books
Hamlyn Children's Non-Fiction
HarperCollins Publishers
Hunt & Thorpe
Kingsway Publications
Lion Publishing
Frances Lincoln
Lutterworth Press
Mantra Publishing
Kevin Mayhew
Marshall Pickering
Medici Society
National Christian Education
  Council
Oxford University Press
Paternoster Publishing
Ragged Bears
Reader's Digest Children's Books
George Ronald
St Pauls
Salvationist Publishing and
  Supplies
Scottish Children's Press
Scripture Union
Society for Promoting Christian
  Knowledge

Book packagers
Graham-Cameron Publishing
Angus Hudson
Lionheart Books
Marshall Editions
Oyster Books

Pictures into print

More and more writers wish to supply their own photographs to illustrate their written work, and in many cases they are well placed to do so. The requirements of a publisher must be understood to avoid basic mistakes. **David Askham** *gives some useful pointers for starting out.*

Imagine completing a book-length manuscript, accompanied by a fine selection of your own photographs, only to discover that the publisher requires colour transparencies, whereas your illustrations are in the form of colour prints!

To an author such a setback can be highly demoralising. Apart from the frustrations of lost time and opportunities, there is the daunting prospect of a major re-shoot of the photography, a costly conversion of negatives into transparencies, or facing up to hiring photographs from a picture library at a cost probably not included in the original budget.

Interestingly, had our author produced a short article for a popular consumer magazine, colour prints may well have been an acceptable alternative to colour transparencies. This is where a photographer experienced in producing pictures for the media would have either known what was required or would have clarified the requirement with the editor.

Increasingly, more and more writers are undertaking the provision of their own photographs to illustrate their written work. And why not? Modern cameras are well-endowed with automatic features to simplify the task and are quite capable of yielding results perfectly acceptable for reproduction.

It should be stressed, however, that you should know and respect the upper limits of your photographic capabilities. A publisher will not thank you for second-rate results. If in doubt, consider engaging a talented colleague, though your agreement needs to take account of the ultimate division of labour. At all times be honest with your editor about the degree of confidence you have in providing acceptable photography. It is sensible to submit samples of your best photographic work so that your commissioning editor can consider its standard and suitability and advise you accordingly.

On the positive side, many authors have acquired and developed photographic skills to the point where their work is highly accomplished in its own right. But first – back to basics.

Basic requirements

Before embarking on any photography it is essential first to elicit a publisher's or editor's requirements. In the case of a book-length project the contract should set out, precisely, what the author accepts and is obliged to produce in terms of numbers of pictures and their breakdown, where appropriate, into colour and monochrome images. Check also whether colour pictures are required in the form of colour transparencies (slides) or colour prints. With illustrated features, it is less usual to have a written contract prior to production. Nevertheless, a letter should spell out the salient facts concerning the provision of pictures.

The question of fees and reproduction rights should also be addressed, not only for text but also for the illustrations. Publishers have budgets for their editorial needs and prior agreement on fees is essential if the contributing author is not to finish the commitment unwittingly well out of pocket. While photographic film may appear a relatively inexpensive item, travel to distant locations can inflate overall costs. Thought, therefore, must be given to the question of expenses.

Where colour is concerned, transparencies (derived from colour reversal or slide film) provide the better source for high quality reproduction than do colour prints. Gradually this situation may change as reproduction techniques continue to develop. To be safe, however, always check with your publisher before deviating from industry standards. If in any doubt when, for example, you are producing pilot material to form the basis of a book proposal, do use colour slide film. Then, if the proposal is accepted, you have already made a valuable start with your photography.

Editors rarely influence the choice of pictorial content of images produced by authors, provided the pictures offered meet certain criteria and accepted standards. So, while the author would appear to enjoy unbridled freedom in deciding what pictures to take and supply to the publisher, the editor will only be satisfied if your pictures are truly relevant to the manuscript and the aim of your work, and are also of a satisfactory quality. Let us now look at these aspects in more detail.

Picture relevance

Images should complement and help to clarify the text. In addition, they can beautify and add interest. Picture subjects often suggest themselves. However, there is a potential trap in sacrificing relevance when the most appropriate pictures are unavailable or difficult to acquire.

Take an example of a non-fiction book about London Midland and Scottish Railway locomotives which would clearly require illustrations of some, if not all, of the models described. It would be quite misleading to intermix pictures of the London and North Western Railway locomotives unless a specific point of comparison or contrast was being made. Without such justification, readers could become confused, misled and eventually lose

interest in the book. The author's credibility would suffer. Fortunately, such lack of relevance should be spotted at the editorial stage and the author would be required to rectify the error.

A biographer seeking to illustrate the boyhood home environment of an historical figure would be lucky indeed to find the actual dwelling, let alone the atmosphere of the period, unless immortalised in a museum. In the absence of contemporary artwork, it becomes acceptable to show the current locale provided captions clearly account for the time-shift.

Occasionally a publisher will have preferences or fixed ideas on the need for certain illustrations. Provided these ideas are feasible and reasonable they should be respected and added to the author's list of picture requirements.

Picture quality

Picture quality is vitally important; photographs should be sharp and clear. Modern cameras are capable of yielding high definition results provided the lens is correctly focused on the principal subject and the camera is held steady at the time of exposure. The latter calls for practice and suggestions for success appear in instruction manuals and books.

Paradoxically, a photograph may appear to be sharp but at the same time suffer from lack of clarity. Why should this be? Usually the cause of such obfuscation is conflict and confusion in the picture area, caused by lack of thought at the time of exposure. Remedies lie in isolating the main subject by using certain simple techniques such as careful framing, differential focus or employing contrasting tones or colour.

It should be realised that no amount of camera automation will substitute for skill on the part of the photographer. Only the photographer can compose the picture in such a way as to communicate his or her ideas clearly and unambiguously to the reader.

Quality results also depend on reliable equipment, films, processing and presentation. Avoid skimping in any of these areas. It is not necessary to invest a small fortune in photographic equipment. A modern 35mm camera of a reputable make will serve an author well. Choose wisely, taking counsel from a learned colleague or trusted dealer. Use fresh films and have them processed by a professional laboratory rather than a cut-price corner shop.

While the emphasis has been on colour photography, most of the principles apply equally to monochrome pictures. Black and white photography will continue to be an important source of illustration in publishing.

It is becoming more and more difficult to find good processors of black and white films so many photographers print their own 10 x 8in or whole plate ($6^{1}/_{2}$ x $8^{1}/_{2}$in) enlargements. However, impressive black and white illustrations can be derived from colour transparency originals, albeit at a cost.

Administration

Once you start producing your own pictures for publication, it is important to consider their administration.

Each picture should be presented in such a way that your name, address, telephone number, reference and caption is clearly related to the subject. Captions should include all relevant information and answer the classic journalistic questions such as who? what? where? when? and why? Records should be kept of pictures stored in your library and of those held by publishers. Despite all reasonable care losses will occasionally occur. Depending on circumstances, compensation should be claimed.

Colour transparencies need to be mounted, handled and stored with extreme care if damage is to be avoided. Never mount colour transparencies in glass if they are intended for publication.

Depending on urgency, pictures can be dispatched by post or courier services. In all cases they should be carefully packed and insured, if so inclined, according to their value.

In general, an author retains copyright both of his or her literary and artistic works unless these are assigned to a publisher. It is customary to assign only limited rights – e.g. First British Serial Rights for an article, or Single Reproduction Rights (qualified by territory and time if appropriate) – for pictures unless special circumstances prevail. See *British copyright law* on page 641 for more detail.

Occasionally problems arise in the reproduction of historic photographs, such as those produced, for example, by Henry Fox Talbot and other pioneering practitioners. By any definition these old pictures would be out of copyright by virtue of the time elapsed since the photographer's death. However, trustees or independent commercial libraries often levy hire charges if material in their possession is subsequently reproduced.

In summary, authors are well placed to produce their own photography to illustrate their literary works. With sensible understanding of publishers' requirements and thoughtful application with the camera, writers will derive extra pleasure and profit from seeing their pictures, as well as words, in print.

David Askham is author of *Photo Libraries and Agencies* (BFP Books) and has been illustrating his written work for over 35 years. His photographs have been published worldwide in books, brochures, magazines and newspapers, many through international agencies.

Doing it on your own

Reasons for self-publishing are varied. Many highly respected comtemporary and past authors have published their own works. **Peter Finch** *introduces the concept and outlines the implications of such an undertaking.*

Why bother?

You've tried all the usual channels and been turned down; your work is uncommercial, specialised, technical, out of fashion; you are concerned with art while everyone else is obsessed with cash; you need a book out quickly; you want to take up small publishing as a hobby; you've heard that publishers make a lot of money out of their authors and you'd like a slice – all reason enough. But be sure you understand what you are doing before you begin.

But isn't this cheating? It can't be real publishing – where is the critical judgement? Publishing is a respectable activity carried out by firms of specialists. Writers of any ability never get involved.

But they do. Start self-publishing and you'll be in good historical company: Horace Walpole, Balzac, Walt Whitman, Virginia Woolf, Gertrude Stein, John Galsworthy, Rudyard Kipling, Beatrix Potter, Lord Byron, Thomas Paine, Mark Twain, Upton Sinclair, W.H. Davies, Zane Grey, Ezra Pound, D.H. Lawrence, William Carlos Williams, Alexander Pope, Robbie Burns, James Joyce, Anaïs Nin and Lawrence Stern. All these at some time in their careers dabbled in doing it themselves. William Blake did nothing else. He even made his own ink, handprinted his pages and got Mrs Blake to sew on the covers.

But today it's different?

Not necessarily. This is not vanity publishing we're talking about although if all you want to do is produce a pamphlet of poems to give away to friends then self-

publishing will be the cheapest way. Doing it yourself today can be a valid form of business enterprise. Being twice shortlisted for the Booker Prize sharpened Timothy Mo's acumen. Turning his back on mass-market paperbacks, he published *Brownout on Breadfruit Boulevard* on his own. Michael Tod's badger trilogy, *The Silver Tide*, has been paperbacked by Orion, Susan Hill self-produced her short stories, *Listening to the Orchestra*, and as an example to us all Jill Paton Walsh's self-published *Knowledge of Angels* was shortlisted for the Booker Prize.

Can anyone do it?

Certainly. If you are a writer then a fair number of the required qualities will already be in hand. If, in addition, you can put up a shelf then the manufacture of the book to go on it will not be beyond you. The more able and practical you are then the cheaper the process will be. The utterly inept will need to pay others to help them, but it will still be self-publishing in the end.

Where do I start?

With research. Read up on the subject. Make sure you know what the parts of a book are. Terms like *verso, recto,* prelims, typeface and point size all have to lose their mystery. You will not need to become an expert but you will need a certain familiarity. Don't rush. Learn.

What about ISBN numbers?

International Standard Book Numbers – a standard bibliographic code, individual to each book published, are used by booksellers and librarians alike. They are issued free of charge by the Standard Book Numbering Agency, 12 Dyott Street, London WC1A 1DF. Write giving the basic details of your proposed book and, if appropriate, you will receive an ISBN by return.

Next?

Put your book together – be it the typed pages of your novel, your selected poems or your story of how it was in the forces – and see how large a volume it will make. See *Preparing and submitting a manuscript* on page 551 for guidelines on how to lay out the text.

No real idea of what your book should look like? Anything will not do. Go to your local bookshop and hunt out a few contemporary examples of volumes produced in a style you would like to emulate. Ask the manager for advice. Take your manuscript and your examples round to a number of local printers (find these through *Yellow Pages*) and ask for a quote. This costs nothing and will give you an idea of what the enterprise is likely to involve. Some examples of printers who are specialists in low print runs are given in the box above. A number of others advertise their services in the writers' magazines. Many are worth a look but tread with care. Don't rush.

Low print run printers

Start by asking a few local printers for quotes. It is also worth trying:

Anthony Rowe Ltd
Bumper's Way, Bristol Road,
Chippenham SN14 6LM
Specialist in low print runs from camera ready copy.

Book-in-Hand Ltd
20 Shepherds Hill, London N6 5AH

Evergreen Graphics
Meadow Lane, West Wittering, Chichester,
West Sussex PO20 8LR

Ex-Libris Press Book Production
1 The Shambles, Bradford on Avon,
Wilts. BA15 1JS
Contact Roger Jones

How much?

It depends. How long is a piece of string? You will not get a pamphlet of poems out for less than a few hundred pounds while a hardbacked work of prose will cost several thousand. Unit cost is important. The larger the number of copies you have printed the less each will cost. Print too many and the total bill will be enormous. Books are no longer cheap; perhaps they never were.

Can I make it cost less?

Yes. Do some of the work yourself. If you want to publish poems and you are prepared to use a text set by a home word processor, you will make a considerable saving. Many word processing programs today have desktop publishing (DTP) facilities which will enhance the look of your text. See *Desktop publishing* on page 559. Could you accept home production, run the pages off on an office photocopier, then staple the sheets? Editions made this way can be very presentable. For longer texts keyed in on a word processor, savings can be made by supplying the work on disk to an operator of a more sophisticated DTP program. They can import your text into their program without the need for any retyping.

Home binding, if your abilities lie in that direction, can save a fair bit. What it all comes down to is the standard of production you want and indeed at whom your book is aimed. Books for the commercial marketplace need to look like their fellows; specialist publications can afford to be more eccentric.

Who decides how it looks?

You do. No one should ever ask a printer simply to produce a book. You should plan the design of your publication with as much care as you would a house extension. Books which sell are those which stand out in the bookshop. Spend as much time and money as you can on the cover. It is the part of the book your buyer will see first. Look at the volumes in bookshop displays, especially those in the window. Imitate British paperback design – it's the best in the world.

How many copies should I produce?

Small press poetry pamphlets sell about 300 copies, new novels sometimes manage 1000, literary paperbacks 10,000, mass-market blockbusters over a million. But that is generally where there is a sales team and whole distribution organisation behind the book. You are an individual. You must do everything yourself. Do not, on the one hand, end up with a prohibitively high unit cost by ordering too few copies. One hundred of anything is usually a waste of time. On the other hand can you really sell 3000? Will shops buy in dozens? They will probably only want twos and threes. Take care. Research your market first.

How do I sell it?

With all your might. This is perhaps the hardest part of publishing. It is certainly as time consuming as both the writing of the work and the printing of it put together. To succeed here you need a certain flair and you should definitely not be of a retiring nature. If you intend selling through the trade (and even if you don't you are bound to come into contact with bookshop orders at some stage), your costing must be correct and worked out in advance. Shops will want at least 33% of the selling price as discount. You'll need about the same again to cover your distribution, promotion and other overheads, leaving the final third to cover production costs and any profit you may wish to make. Multiply your unit production cost by at least four. Commerical publishers often multiply by as much as nine.

Do not expect the trade to pay your carriage costs. Your terms should be 33% post free on everything bar single copy orders. Penalise these by reducing your discount to 25%. Some shops will suggest that you sell copies to them on sale or return. This means that they only pay you for what they sell and then only after they've sold it. This is a common practice with certain categories of publications and often the only way to get independent books into certain shops; but from the self-publisher's point of view it should be avoided if at all possible. Cash in hand is best but expect to have your invoices paid by cheque at a later

Useful organisations

Association of Little Presses (ALP)

Chairperson Lawrence Upton,
32 Downside Road, Sutton, Surrey SM2 5HP
web site http://www.melloworld.com/alp

Offers advice, publishes a catalogue of small independent publications, produces a newsletter, organises book fairs. Publishes a booklet: *Self-Publishing: Not So Difficult After All.* Membership £12.50.

Author-Publisher Network

6 Kelvinbrook, West Molesey, Surrey KT8 1R2
tel 0181-979 3060

A self-publishers' self-help organisation. Runs courses and lectures; publishes *Write to Publish*, an essential self-publisher's newsletter; compiles a catalogue of members' publications; and a directory of services. Self-publishers should certainly join the A-PE. Membership £15.

date. Buy a duplicate pad in order to keep track of what's going on. Phone the shops you have decided should take your book or turn up in person and ask to see the buyer. Letters and sample copies sent by post will get ignored. Get a freelance distributor to handle all of this for you if you can. Check the trade section of Cassell's *Directory of Publishing* or advertise for one in *The Bookseller*. If you can contract one they will want another 12% or so commission on top of the shops' discount – but expect to have to go it alone.

What about promotion?

A vital aspect often overlooked by beginners. Send out as many review copies as you can, all accompanied by slips quoting selling price and name and address of the publisher. Never admit to being that person yourself. Invent a name: it will give your operation a professional feel. Ring up newspapers and local radio stations ostensibly to check that your copy has arrived but really to see if they are prepared to give your book space. Try to think of an angle for them, anything around which they can write a story.

Buying advertising space rarely pays for itself but good local promotion with 100% effort will generate dividends.

What about depositing copies at the British Library?
Under the Copyright Acts the British Library, the Bodleian Library, Oxford, The University Library, Cambridge, The National Library of Scotland, the Library of Trinity College Dublin and the National Library of Wales are all entitled to a free copy of your book which must be sent to them within one month of publication. One copy should go direct to the Legal Deposit Office at The British Library, Boston Spa, Wetherby, West Yorkshire LS23 7BY. The other libraries use an agent, Mr A.T. Smail, at 100 Euston Street, London NW1 2HQ *tel* 0171-388 5061. Contact him directly to find out how many copies he requires. Many self-publishers object to sending books out for nothing but there are advantages. Data on your title will be used by the libraries as part of their bibliographic services and the book itself will eventually form part of a comprehensive national archive and be made available to the public.

What if I can't manage all this myself?
You can employ others to do it for you. If you are a novelist and you opt for a package covering everything, it could set you back more than £10,000. A number of publishers and associations advertise such services in writers' journals and in the Sunday classifieds. 'Authors. Publish with us.' is a typical ploy. They will do a competent job for you, certainly, but you will still end up having to do the bulk of

the selling yourself. It is a costly route, fraught with difficulty. Do the job on your own if you possibly can.

And what if it goes wrong?
Put all the unsolds under the bed or give them away. It has happened to lots of us. Even the big companies who are experienced at these things have their regular flops. It was an adventure and you did get your book published. On the other hand you may be so successful that you'll be at the London Book Fair selling the film rights and wondering if you've reprinted enough. Whichever way it goes – good luck.

Can the Internet help?
Certainly. The World Wide Web, with which many authors are now dabbling, offers unrivalled opportunity for self-promulgation. This rapidly developing and highly flexible medium enables participants to promote themselves and their work internationally for as little as £10 per month. Initial investment may be high – you need a decent computer, a modem and a set of software – but the benefits can be enormous. And it's fun. Some authors are happy simply to advertise their books while others produce complete on-line electronic versions for the world to read. The process may at first appear difficult but it is actually no more complex than traditional publishing. If you'd like to try then read up before investing.

Peter Finch is a poet, bookseller and former small publisher. His best-selling *How to Publish Yourself* (Allison & Busby) has just gone into a third, completely revised edition. His web site contains further advice for self-publishers: dialspace.dial.pipex.com/peter.finch/

Further reading
Bride, Mac, *Teach Yourself the Internet*, Hodder & Stoughton, 3rd edn, 1998

Domanski, Peter and Irvine, Philip, *A Practical Guide to Publishing Books Using Your PC*, Domanski-Irvine Books, 1997

Finch, Peter, *How To Publish Yourself*, Allison & Busby, 3rd edn, 1997

Foster, Charles, *Editing, Design and Book Production*, Journeyman, 1993

Godber, Bill, Webb, Robert, and Smith, Keith, *Marketing For Small Publishers*, Journeyman, 1992

Kennedy, Angus J., *The Internet & World Wide Web: The Rough Guide*, Rough Guides Ltd, 1997

Ross, Tom and Marilyn, *The Complete Guide to Self-Publishing*, Writer's Digest Books, 1994

Spicer, Robert, *Publishing A Book*, How To Books, 3rd edn, 1998

Vanity publishing

Vanity publishers produce copies of a book in return for a fee paid by its author. The job they undertake is very different from that carried out by a publisher, which invests its own money in the whole publishing process. Authors considering vanity publishing should exercise caution.

Publishers very rarely ask authors to pay for the production of their work, to contribute to its cost, or to undertake purchase of copies. Exceptions may be a book of an extremely specialised nature with a very limited market, or perhaps the first book of poems by a talented new writer. In such cases, especially if the book makes a significant contribution to its subject, an established and reliable publisher may be prepared to accept a subvention from the author to make publication possible, and such financial grants often come from scientific or other academic foundations or funds. This is a very different procedure from that of the vanity publisher who claims to perform, for a fee to be paid by the author, all the many functions involved in publishing a book.

Manufacture *v.* publication

Some vanity publishers clearly state the services they provide and are open in all their dealings. However, the promotional material sent out by many vanity publishers makes claims which prove to be lacking in substance and foundation. The Advertising Standards Authority, with the support of the Committee of Advertising Practice, has issued revised guidelines to advertisers in an endeavour to reduce misleading claims made by some vanity publishers in their follow-up material. Several national newspaper and magazine groups are now refusing advertisements from vanity publishers. In their effort to secure business, vanity publishers may give exaggerated praise to an author's work and arouse equally unrealistic hopes of its commercial success. True publishers invest their own money in the whole publishing process: editorial, design, manufacturing, selling and distribution. The vanity publisher usually invests the author's money in but one part of this process: manufacture.

The distressing reports the *Writers' & Artists' Yearbook* office has received from embittered victims of vanity publishers underlines the importance of reading with extreme care the contracts offered by such publishers. It is worth asking a solicitor to check over this paperwork. The Publishers Association (see page 490)

Vanity publishing considerations

Any author who wants to use their money to publish their own books through a vanity publisher should:
• not immediately believe all the claims of a vanity publisher's promotional material
• treat with caution enthusiastic praise by a vanity publisher of a manuscript submitted
• take any contract to a solicitor to be read
• not sign anything without first consulting a solicitor
• ask to see examples of reviews which they have obtained in the national press
• ask to see a sample of a book published by them to assess the standard of publication
• make sure that the vanity publisher is connected with a distributor
• remember that the publishing business in general is risky, so never part with more money than he or she can afford to lose.

may also be able to provide useful advice. Often, these contacts will provide for the printing of, say, 2000 copies of the book, usually at a quite exorbitant cost to the author, but will leave the 'publisher' under no obligation to bind more than a very limited number. Alternatively, the vanity publisher may promise to print any number of copies for an author, but actually print only 100 copies or fewer.

Frequently, too, the author will be expected to pay extra for the cost of any effective advertising, while the 'publisher' makes little or no effort to promote the distribution and sale of the book. The names and imprints of vanity publishers are well known to literary editors and, with some worthy exceptions, their productions are rarely reviewed in any important periodical. Such books are unlikely to be stocked by major booksellers.

Mainstream publishers receive a very large number of unsolicited manuscripts, only a small percentage of which are published. Manuscripts may be rejected because they are not of an acceptable standard, because they do not fit in with the kind of books the publisher normally produces or because the market for them is too small or too local. In any case, getting a manuscript accepted by a mainstream publisher requires careful targeting and perseverance.

If you are unable to persuade a mainstream publisher to take your manuscript and decide to publish at your own expense, you could consider the possibility of self-publishing (see page 266). If you decide to approach a vanity publisher do so with caution and do not expect any commercial gain from your investment.

Having checked that the sum asked for is a reasonable one, and the publisher will provide the services you require, take the attitude that you are paying simply for the pleasure of seeing your work in print. You are less likely to be disappointed.

Top hundred chart of 1997 paperback fastsellers

*Every year since 1979, **Alex Hamilton** has compiled for the Guardian an annual survey comprising a table of the 100 topselling paperbacks published for the first time during that year by British publishers. For readers new to the chart he describes here its terms of reference and indicates certain limitations.*

Bestsellers and fastsellers

An important distinction has first to be made between 'bestsellers' and the term used here – 'fastsellers'. Bestsellers have the real commercial pedigree. Sometimes, but not always, they have made a very visible showing in the fastseller lane, but among bestselling authors there are hundreds whose books have made a slow start and only through the cumulative sales over many years vindicate the faith of the original publisher. Among many examples of those whose sales in their lifetimes were modest but the posthumous interest spectacular, two durable cases are D.H. Lawrence and George Orwell.

Poetry

While serious poets never repeat Lord Byron's success in becoming a bestseller and 'famous overnight', and the only two works with short lines in a decade of fastsellers were collections of comic verse, a poet such as T.S. Eliot – not to mention Shakespeare and Chaucer – will over the long haul rack up sales in millions. And an outside event, such as the award of the Nobel Prize to Seamus Heaney in 1995, produces an immediate selling bonanza.

Fiction and non-fiction

The bread and butter of publishing has long been Bibles, classic authors, cookbooks, dictionaries and other reference books, and these are also the bridge for the trade into CD-Rom. Although the larger bulk of counter sales, and of library borrowings, consists of fiction, the topselling individual titles for this century, with figures of over 20 million copies, include most of these categories. However, the gross figures worldwide for hardcover and paperback, with translations, of prolific authors such as Agatha Christie, Alistair MacLean, Mickey Spillane, Stephen King and Catherine Cookson are claimed to be between 50 million and 300 million copies.

Individual titles of such popular authors would generally show up in topical bestseller lists, but not always. Dennis Wheatley, for instance, had a big following in Britain, but the 'British' quality he prided himself on did not travel; overseas he was hardly read. Something like it happens also with Barbara Cartland who, with more than 500 titles, is so prolific as to compete with herself: her individual books are never bestsellers but all together they do loom large.

The fastselling list which follows is limited to paperbacks which have appeared for the first time in that year from British publishers (regardless of their hardcover provenance). It is tempting to include old titles revived to synchronise with film releases and television serials, because these tie-ins have a strong influence (a good example for 1997 is Michael Ondaatje's *The English Patient*, which sold 437,760 more) but except when the figure is very large, I try to exclude them.

Looking at the figures

Since 1979 there were always, until the 1990s recession, between 102 and 125 titles that passed the 100,000 mark – a convenient round figure for those who like to make comparisons. (This year there were 123.) While publishers inevitably highlight the performances of their own authors, it was never my aim to make the list look like a competition. Nor should it be seen as a yardstick of publishing efficiency, or solvency. The high-profile books which achieve six-figure sales are a vital part of the trade, but the list has little significance in the assessment of quality, policy and financial acumen in any one publishing house. It is possible to go broke with a runaway fast-seller – on more than one occasion the success of a single book has led to an unrealistic expansion – but on the other hand, there are many attractive and profitable imprints which never come within hailing distance of having a title in this list. The best way to look at it is as a reflection of popular taste accentuated by aggressive marketing.

A distortion for titles published at the end of the period may naturally be suspected but in actual fact it rarely makes much difference. The widespread use of electronic stock control by booksellers now enables them to more closely match their ordering to demand. The significant sale of new paperbacks, particularly by authors with a regular following, takes place within a few weeks of their appearance on the racks. Having said this, however, a few do enter the magic circle of bestsellers: during the 1980s the highest cumulative sales were for books by Sue Townsend and Jeffrey Archer, each passing five million, having sold 400,000 and a million respectively in their first year.

The authors

Surveyed over a period, the fastseller lists indicate a rather conservative attitude on the part of buyers. It is not very common for a book to appear in the top 20 (which earn between them much the same as the rest of the list put together) which has not appeared somewhere on the list in previous years. (1996 provided three exceptions to the rule, 1997 only two.) Once established on the list, an author has only to turn in a regular supply of similar works to stay on it. Being comfortable with a formula is therefore a psychological asset for those wanting to compete in this market; however, like actors who are typecast, authors may find too late that the market will then not allow them to escape. One among several stories of authors corralled in their own fantasies relates that thriller writer Peter Cheyney gave his publisher a book unlike the rest of his oeuvre and was told to bury it, lest its publication confuse his loyal following.

The dominant figures of the 1980s were Wilbur Smith (now with more than 20 novels past the million), Barbara Taylor Bradford, Dick Francis, Len Deighton, Stephen King, Catherine Cookson, Jeffrey Archer, Danielle Steel and Victoria Holt, with Jilly Cooper coming through at the end, particularly in the UK market. The 1990s have not seen any very significant shift, save the arrival as front-runners of John Grisham and Maeve Binchy. It is the author's name that matters most, as shown by the fact that of 1900 titles only seven have been volumes of short stories, two with sales over 750,000 copies, because they were by Frederick Forsyth and Jeffrey Archer, and two with 500,000 (Archer again, and Rosamund Pilcher).

More than half the buyers of books have always been women but for most of the 1980s hardly more than a quarter of the authors were women. However, in the 1990s they have had a steadily increasing presence, from 25% rising to settle at a new level of between 35% and 40%.

Genres

Some 80% of the bulk is usually fiction. The regular elements of the non-fiction remainder are diet books, the horoscope division of astrology, joke books, showbiz lives and exploitations based on big movies (anything by Spielberg, for instance). Of fiction, genres take up most of the slots, particularly adventure yarns, thrillers, horror stories, family sagas and a mixed bag of romances, from historical to 'Gothic' to the now faded bodice-rippers and 'sex'n'shopping' (which has dropped

the shopping), and career conflict stories under the vague umbrella of 'women's fiction'. There seems to be no overt category of 'men's fiction' that might once have included authors like Mickey Spillane and Harold Robbins, or today would correspond to the focus and tone of laddish magazines. Perhaps there is a slight hint of this in the popularity of heroics by SAS men, war commanders and pilots who have been shot down, but it is not yet a developed genre, and has run into a problem with the Ministry of Defence objecting to the revelation of secret techniques.

Science fantasy is more likely to show than science fiction of a harder, more experimental kind. Westerns have never featured at all, despite the sometime fame of authors such as Zane Grey, Louis L'Amour and J.T. Edson. Travellers' tales have had no significant presence until the American Bill Bryson's flattering farewell journey around Britain sold more copies in one year (1996) than any other travelogue has in 20.

Heavyweight to juvenile

There are rarely more than 10-12 titles in any list that could count on reviews from serious book pages, and most of these appear some way down. However, in recent years, broadly since the television focus on it, the Booker Prize has taken winners into the fastseller list. When it does happen, this award seems to establish the book rather than the author, and the only winners to keep a pace with subsequent books are Anita Brookner and Roddy Doyle. No other literary award has yet resulted in a 100,000 paperback sale for the author.

The highest selling title for the 1980s happens to have been a juvenile, *The Secret Diary of Adrian Mole Aged 13¾*, whose author Sue Townsend is said to have been embarrassed when she heard that the publishers had a print run of 70,000 in hand, and begged them to reduce it because she could not bear to think of them risking so much on her behalf. With this and a sequel she very nearly equals the total sale for 11 titles of

No	Title	Genre	Author	Imprint
1	The Runaway Jury	Thriller	John Grisham (US)	Arrow
2	Evening Class	Novel	Maeve Binchy (Ire.)	Orion
3	Angela's Ashes	Memoir	Frank McCourt (Ire.)	Flamingo
4	Bridget Jones's Diary	Novel	Helen Fielding (Br.)	Picador
5	Fourth Estate	Novel	Jeffrey Archer (Br.)	HarperCollins
6	Icon	Thriller	Frederick Forsyth (Br.)	Corgi
7	Cause of Death	Thriller	Patricia Cornwell (US)	Warner
8	Appassionata	Novel	Jilly Cooper (Br.)	Corgi
9	The Upstart	Novel	Catherine Cookson (Br.)	Corgi
10	Malice	Novel	Danielle Steel (US)	Corgi
11	The Branded Man	Novel	Catherine Cookson (Br.)	Corgi
12	To the Hilt	Thriller	Dick Francis (Br.)	Pan
13	Silent Honour	Novel	Danielle Steel (US)	Corgi
14	Desperation	Horror	Stephen King (US)	NEL
15	Hogfather	Fantasy	Terry Pratchett (Br.)	Corgi
16	Next of Kin	Novel	Joanna Trollope (Br.)	Black Swan
17	Executive Orders	Thriller	Tom Clancy (US)	HarperCollins
18	The Dilemma	Novel	Penny Vincenzi (Br.)	Orion
19	The Tailor of Panama	Thriller	John le Carré (Br.)	Coronet
20	The Bonny Dawn	Novel	Catherine Cookson (Br.)	Corgi
21	Airframe	Thriller	Michael Crichton (US)	Arrow
22	The Art Book	Art	Various (Br.)	Phaidon
23	Feet of Clay	Fantasy	Terry Pratchett (Br.)	Corgi
24	Vendetta	Novel	Jackie Collins (Br.)	Pan
25	Her Own Rules	Novel	Barbara T. Bradford (Br.)	HarperCollins
26	The Keys to the Street	Crime	Ruth Rendell (Br.)	Arrow
27	Op-Centre: Acts of War	Thriller	Clancy/Pieczenik (US)	HarperCollins
28	The Third Twin	Thriller	Ken Follett (Br.)	Pan
29	Woman Who Walked Into Doors	Novel	Roddy Doyle (Ire.)	Minerva
30	48 Horror	Horror	James Herbert (Br.)	HarperCollins
31	Death Is Now My Neighbour	Crime	Colin Dexter (Br.)	Pan
32	Last Orders	Novel	Graham Swift (Br.)	Picador
33	Popcorn	Novel	Ben Elton (Br.)	Pocket
34	Cradle of Thorns	Saga	Josephine Cox (Br.)	Headline
35	Sole Survivor	Thriller	Dean Koontz (US)	Headline
36	Mad Cows	Novel	Kathy Lette (Aus.)	Picador
37	Cry of the Halidon	Thriller	Robert Ludlum (US)	HarperCollins
38	Shockwave	Thriller	Clive Cussler (US)	Pocket
39	The Regulators	Horror	Richard Bachman (US)	NEL
40	A Time For Us	Saga	Josephine Cox (Br.)	Headline
41	SSN	Thriller	Tom Clancy (US)	HarperCollins
42	Politika	Thriller	Tom Clancy (US)	Penguin
43	The Midden	Humour	Tom Sharpe (Br.)	Pan
44	Every Woman Knows a Secret	Romance	Rosie Thomas (Br.)	Mandarin
45	Birds of Prey	Thriller	Wilbur Smith (SA)	Pan
46	Alias Grace	Novel	Margaret Atwood (Can.)	Virago
47	Ticktock	Thriller	Dean Koontz (US)	Headline
48	A Crack in Forever	Novel	Jeannie Brewer (US)	Bantam
49	Spring Collection	Novel	Judith Krantz (US)	Bantam
50	The Last Don	Novel	Mario Puzo (US)	Mandarin

Price £	Month	Home	Export	Total	Gross £	No
£5.99	April	670,810	344,446	1,015,256	£6,081,383	1
£6.99	May	702,211	300,465	1,002,676	£7,008,705	2
£7.99	May	383,046	340,513	723,559	£5,781,236	3
£5.99	June	635,011	44,331	679,342	£4,069,259	4
£6.99	April	389,401	279,962	669,363	£4,678,847	5
£5.99	July	325,639	293,228	618,867	£3,707,013	6
£5.99	June	421,282	169,018	590,300	£3,535,842	7
£6.99	April	443,849	132,013	575,862	£4,025,275	8
£5.99	Feb	456,986	111,993	568,979	£3,408,184	9
£5.99	May	426,569	131,469	558,038	£3,342,648	10
£5.99	Sept	420,005	106,595	526,600	£3,154,334	11
£5.99	Nov	370,547	146,368	516,915	£3,096,321	12
£5.99	Oct	364,935	112,827	477,762	£2,861,794	13
£6.99	July	320,922	148,697	469,619	£3,282,637	14
£5.99	Nov	328,918	62,820	391,738	£2,346,511	15
£6.99	June	316,511	65,002	381,513	£2,666,776	16
£7.99	June	155,210	225,737	380,947	£3,043,767	17
£6.99	July	249,006	126,819	375,825	£2,627,017	18
£6.99	May	236,830	135,445	372,275	£2,602,202	19
£4.99	Nov	281,365	90,514	371,879	£1,855,676	20
£5.99	Oct	209,408	132,136	341,544	£2,045,849	21
£6.95	April	133,712	206,995	340,707	£2,367,914	22
£5.99	May	259,985	65,886	325,871	£1,951,967	23
£6.99	June	220,171	96,355	316,526	£2,212,517	24
£5.99	July	222,741	86,717	309,458	£1,853,653	25
£5.99	Sept	212,585	91,704	304,289	£1,822,691	26
£6.99	Mar	170,532	131,798	302,330	£2,113,287	27
£5.99	Oct	142,999	148,228	291,227	£1,744,450	28
£6.99	May	240,874	50,018	290,892	£2,033,335	29
£5.99	June	253,903	27,773	281,676	£1,687,239	30
£5.99	Sept	224,172	55,507	279,679	£1,675,277	31
£5.99	Feb	184,843	92,729	277,572	£1,662,656	32
£5.99	May	221,459	50,009	271,468	£1,626,093	33
£5.99	Aug	239,143	29,771	268,914	£1,610,795	34
£5.99	Oct	180,646	86,310	266,956	£1,599,066	35
£5.99	June	197,810	60,501	258,311	£1,547,283	36
£6.99	Nov	117,324	138,447	255,771	£1,787,839	37
£5.99	April	145,897	96,511	242,408	£1,452,024	38
£6.99	June	131,597	89,039	220,636	£1,542,246	39
£5.99	Mar	187,265	33,054	220,319	£1,319,711	40
£6.99	Nov	126,294	92,503	218,797	£1,529,391	41
£5.99	Nov	103,511	113,755	217,266	£1,301,423	42
£5.99	Apr	159,197	53,281	212,478	£1,272,743	43
£5.99	July	191,303	17,505	208,808	£1,250,760	44
£9.99	Oct	204,582	1,000	205,582	£2,053,764	45
£6.99	Sept	141,620	60,323	201,943	£1,411,582	46
£5.99	Jan	125,844	74,646	200,490	£1,200,935	47
£5.99	July	153,330	37,537	190,867	£1,143,293	48
£5.99	Mar	111,720	77,536	189,256	£1,133,643	49
£5.99	July	82,353	104,236	186,589	£1,117,668	50

No	Title	Genre	Author	Imprint
51	A Secret Affair	Novel	Barbara T. Bradford (Br.)	HarperCollins
52	The Poet	Thriller	Michael Connelly (US)	Orion
53	Laws of our Fathers	Thriller	Scott Turow (US)	Penguin
54	Jack and Jill	Thriller	James Patterson (US)	HarperCollins
55	Danger Zones	Novel	Sally Beauman (Br.)	Bantam
56	Hide and Seek	Thriller	James Patterson (US)	HarperCollins
57	Absolute Power	Thriller	David Baldacci (US)	Pocket
58	The Final Judgement	Thriller	Richard N. Patterson (US)	Arrow
59	The Cauldron	Thriller	Colin Forbes (Br.)	Pan
60	Lucy Sullivan's Getting Married	Novel	Marian Keyes (Ire.)	Mandarin
61	Unnatural Exposure	Thriller	Patricia Cornwell (US)	Warner
62	It's a Magical World	Humour	Bill Watterson (US)	Warner
63	Beyond Recall	Novel	Robert Goddard (Br.)	Corgi
64	Grand Affair	Novel	Charlotte Bingham (Br.)	Bantam
65	Cold Blood	Crime	Lynda La Plante (Br.)	Pan
66	Mr Bean's Scrapbook	Humour	Rowan Atkinson (Br.)	Boxtree
67	Making History	Novel	Stephen Fry (Br.)	Arrow
68	The Beach	Novel	Alex Garland (Br.)	Penguin
69	Deep End of the Ocean	Novel	Jacquelyn Mitchard (US)	HarperCollins
70	The Man Who Listens to Horses	Autobiog.	Monty Roberts (US)	Arrow
71	Drums of Autumn	Novel	Diana Gabaldon (US)	Arrow
72	Undone	Thriller	Michael Kimball (US)	Headline
73	Enemy of God	Myth	Bernard Cornwell (Br.)	Penguin
74	Going the Distance	Romance	Christina Jones (Br.)	Orion
75	Year of the Tiger	Thriller	Jack Higgins (Br.)	Penguin
76	Solitaire Mystery	Novel	Jostein Gaarder (Nor)	Phoenix
77	Charity	Thriller	Len Deighton (Br.)	HarperCollins
78	Strand of Dreams	Saga	Audrey Howard (Br.)	Coronet
79	The Clinic	Thriller	Jonathan Kellerman (US)	Warner
80	Debutantes	Novel	Charlotte Bingham (Br.)	Bantam
81	3001: The Final Odyssey	Science	Arthur C. Clarke (Br.)	Voyager
82	Wizard and Glass	Fantasy	Stephen King (US)	Hodder
83	Servant of the Bones	Thriller	Anne Rice (US)	Arrow
84	Accordion Crimes	Novel	E. Annie Proulx (US)	Fourth Estate
85	New Body Plan	Health	Rosemary Conley (Br.)	Arrow
86	X-Files: Ruins	TV Tie-in	Kevin Anderson (US)	Voyager
87	Reading in the Dark	Novel	Seamus Deane (Ire.)	Vintage
88	Shadowed Hills	Saga	Audrey Howard (Br.)	Coronet
89	Stand By, Stand By	Yarn	Chris Ryan (Br.)	Arrow
90	Ecstasy	Stories	Irving Welsh (Br.)	Vintage
91	The Partner	Thriller	John Grisham (US)	Century
92	Bestseller	Novel	Olivia Goldsmith (US)	HarperCollins
93	Superplonk	Wine	Malcolm Gluck (Br.)	Coronet
94	Time For Bed	Novel	David Baddiel (Br.)	Warner
95	Well Groomed	Romance	Fiona Walker (Br.)	Coronet
96	Java Spider	Thriller	Geoffrey Archer (Br.)	Arrow
97	Headless Ghost	Juv.	R.L. Stine (US)	Hippo
98	Choices	Novel	Susan Sallis (Br.)	Corgi
99	Johnny and the Bomb	Juv.	Terry Pratchett (Br.)	Corgi
100	Tarnished Gold	Saga	'Virginia Andrews' (US)	Pocket

Price £	Month	Home	Export	Total	Gross £	No
£5.99	Nov	125,322	58,908	184,230	£1,103,538	**51**
£5.99	Jan	116,890	66,118	183,008	£1,096,218	**52**
£5.99	Aug	102,895	79,342	182,237	£1,091,600	**53**
£6.99	Nov	101,370	80,455	181,825	£1,270,957	**54**
£5.99	Jan	140,337	39,141	179,478	£1,075,073	**55**
£5.99	Feb	119,819	58,892	178,711	£1,070,479	**56**
£5.99	April	122,499	56,018	178,517	£1,069,317	**57**
£5.99	Mar	110,338	66,497	176,835	£1,059,242	**58**
£5.99	Dec	109,884	64,912	174,796	£1,047,028	**59**
£6.99	Feb	140,136	32,638	172,774	£1,207,690	**60**
£9.99	Oct	22,948	147,996	170,944	£1,707,731	**61**
£9.99	Sept	114,031	55,556	169,587	£1,694,174	**62**
£5.99	Dec	123,482	39,550	163,032	£976,562	**63**
£5.99	Aug	137,702	23,393	161,095	£964,959	**64**
£5.99	July	96,046	61,715	157,761	£944,988	**65**
£7.99	July	152,518	4,852	157,370	£1,257,386	**66**
£5.99	Oct	116,449	39,608	156,057	£934,781	**67**
£5.99	June	133,414	21,491	154,905	£927,881	**68**
£5.99	Aug	46,661	108,040	154,701	£926,659	**69**
£6.99	Oct	109,503	42,861	152,364	£1,065,024	**70**
£5.99	July	42,542	109,446	151,988	£910,408	**71**
£5.99	Jan	97,405	53,759	151,164	£905,472	**72**
£5.99	April	103,485	45,960	149,445	£895,176	**73**
£5.99	Feb	136,391	12,500	148,891	£891,857	**74**
£5.99	June	98,037	50,704	148,741	£890,959	**75**
£6.99	June	78,292	70,309	148,601	£1,038,721	**76**
£5.99	Sept	90,340	53,339	143,679	£860,637	**77**
£5.99	Oct	116,140	27,276	143,416	£859,062	**78**
£5.99	Aug	86,874	56,240	143,114	£857,253	**79**
£5.99	Mar	111,800	29,758	141,558	£847,932	**80**
£5.99	Nov	99,566	41,210	140,776	£843,248	**81**
£14.99	Nov	79,545	60,553	140,098	£2,100,069	**82**
£5.99	Aug	71,256	65,398	136,654	£818,557	**83**
£6.99	June	111,987	21,360	133,347	£932,096	**84**
£4.99	Jan	127,717	5,220	132,937	£663,356	**85**
£5.99	May	64,366	65,902	130,268	£780,305	**86**
£6.99	April	104,612	24,382	128,994	£901,668	**87**
£5.99	Apr	101,951	26,693	128,644	£770,578	**88**
£5.99	July	88,044	39,613	127,657	£764,665	**89**
£5.99	Sept	94,212	33,080	127,292	£762,479	**90**
£9.99	Nov	125,334	0	125,334	£1,252,087	**91**
£5.99	May	80,306	43,081	123,387	£739,088	**92**
£5.99	Nov	123,250	0	123,250	£738,268	**93**
£5.99	Oct	120,125	2,923	123,048	£737,058	**94**
£5.99	June	100,351	22,025	122,376	£733,032	**95**
£5.99	May	68,448	53,314	121,762	£729,354	**96**
£3.99	Feb	119,876	0	119,876	£478,305	**97**
£5.99	Dec	117,507	2,308	119,815	£717,692	**98**
£3.99	Feb	85,727	33,439	119,166	£475,472	**99**
£5.99	July	94,939	23,457	118,396	£709,192	**100**

the best known author in children's fiction, the late Roald Dahl. The latter's death left the role of natural market leader vacant, a position apparently now being being filled by Terry Pratchett.

Horror books that can be racked at children's eye level, such as Scholastic's *Point Horror* series (which can usually muster several titles that reach 90,000) are examples of a perennially popular genre.

The year 1997

On the whole, 1997 was a better year for children's books than 1996, though educational titles, particularly at primary level, have suffered badly from the weakness of government subsidy.

The new element for the trade over the past three years has been its adaptation to the price flexibility resulting from the collapse of the Net Book Agreement (whereby booksellers maintained the cover price fixed by the publisher), the 'sheet-anchor' of fair trading since 1899. At present, although one major chain does reduce prices on some paperbacks, it seems that discounting is felt more among about 200 top hardcover titles. Indeed the fastsellers list is one feature that remains almost eerily stable, as if these books had an independent orbit.

The most common price point is now £5.99 (67 examples), but the average price paid by the buyer appears to have risen from £5.96 to £6.47. (This apparent leap is in part the result of an increasing number of popular books being offered in the larger 'trade paperback' format, whose cover price is midway between that of the hardcover and the mass market paperback format. The large bookselling chains, and the retailers in Australia and South Africa increasingly ask for trade paperbacks, and more and more of them are likely to figure in fastseller lists of the future.)

However the rest of the book business may have fared, the fastsellers' performance seems to be the most stable element in it. Even though 1997 was not an outstanding commercial year, with the aggregate falling back from 30 million units to the 1996 figure of 26.4 million,

with a corresponding decrease in turnover from £178.8 million to £170.3 million (the first 25 titles accounting for 13 million books and £83.4 million). Export turnover was improved with its relative share rising from 30.5% to 33.8%.

Casting about for evidence of those genres which have been spoken of optimistically in recent times, it seems few fulfil their promise. Those that do are new subdivisions in the major categories of thriller, horror and romance. The Western has disappeared into the sunset; the modest flutter in travel writing in the late 1980s subsided; fantasy now does better than hardcore science fiction, though the veteran Arthur C. Clarke, and the relatively young Iain Banks still have an appeal which goes beyond the narrow specialisation. *X-Files* books, which featured so prominently in 1996, have all but vanished over the horizon. 'Green books', after looking as if they would be as uplifting commercially as sermons in the late 19th century, have not much expanded their original niche market. The much heralded wave of books related to the millennium has not yet broken in full force, though there is quite an undercurrent of metaphysical speculation and divination and challenges to religious orthodoxy. Oddly enough, and unpredictably, at the more trivial level of horoscopes, 1997 was the first year in which there was no salient book on astrology.

The current vogue for courtroom drama stems from the success of American lawyer John Grisham, who has the top spot almost as of right. However, in 1997 there was one newcomer to the fastseller list who appeared to represent a new style, but immediately recognisable as needed. This was Helen Fielding, whose first novel, *The Diary of Bridget Jones*, seemed to speak for her generation of 'thirty-something' independent women as pithily and entertainingly as Kingsley Amis once did for his in *Lucky Jim*, and likewise to be the precursor of a genre.

Alex Hamilton is a journalist and award-winning travel writer, and the author of several novels and volumes of short stories.

Poetry

Poetry into print

John Whitworth has submitted hundreds of poems and has had dealings with a number of publishers of poetry. He gives advice here 'from the handle end of the long spoon that poets use to sup with those they would persuade or bamboozle into printing, even paying for, their work.'

There are two things to say at the outset. Do not expect to make more than pin money *directly* from publication of your work. You may, in the fullness of time, make quite a tidy sum *indirectly* – I mean you get work because you are a published poet: readings, workshops, reviewing and so forth, if you like any of that sort of thing. But if you get £50 for a poem from a national magazine you may feel very satisfied, and as for your published slim volumes – they will not sell in four figures, nor do the publishers, except in a very few instances, expect them to. In a sense, nearly all poetry publishing is vanity publishing. Nobody is in it for the money.

And, secondly, as one poet put it to me, do not have too much respect for the taste of individual literary editors. She is right. An editor is not God (whatever he or she thinks). Remember that, though it can be hard if you are diffident (and most poets are). But this person is just like you; the fact that he or she (nearly always he) is warming an editorial chair may mean many things. It certainly does not mean papal infallibility. If Snooks of the *Review* sends back your work, despatch it immediately to Snurd of the *Supplement.* And if Snurd concurs with Snooks, they may both be wrong, indeed neither may actually have read through (or at all) what you sent. Grit your teeth and send to Snarl and then to Snivel. Do not be discouraged by rejection. If your poems are as good as you can make them and have been submitted in as professional a way as you can manage, then just keep on sending them out. I

started writing poems in 1968, wrote my first good one in 1972, and was paid my first proper money (£40 from the Arts Council) in 1976. The first book was published in 1980. So patience and a thick skin are big advantages.

It does help, of course, to have read the magazine you are making submissions to. This will prevent you sending your bawdy ballad to *The Times Literary Supplement (TLS)* or concrete poetry to *The Literary Review.* And I am assuming that you actually are interested in the craft of poetry and the names of, say, Milton, Tennyson and Eliot mean something to you. You will also be interested to know what Heaney, Hughes, Harrison and Hannah actually do. You don't have to like it, but you ought to want to know about it. If no one is writing anything remotely like your work, perhaps you should ask yourself why that might be. On the other hand, remember the words of Charlie Coburn, the old music-hall singer: 'I sang my song to them, and they didn't like it. So I sang it again, and they still didn't like it. So I sang it a third time and one of them thought he might just get to like it if I changed the tune and altered the words. So I sang it again, just exactly the same way, and after a bit they all liked it.'

Submitting your work to magazines

I asked a number of poets about this. Some of them said they never submitted to magazines at all, because they disliked being rejected. I must say I think that a rather craven attitude, but you *can* carve out a poetic reputation through work-shops and readings. You must be good at putting yourself about in public and have the time and energy to expend on it. All who did submit work regularly agreed on a number of basics:

• Submit your poem on an A4 sheet, typed or printed out from a word processor. One poet, David Phillips, reckoned his percentage of successful submissions had gone up appreciably since he bought his word processor, and he assumed it was because his work now looked much more professional. It might be, of course, that it has just got better. Do not type it in italic, capitals or mock cursive. Keep it simple.

• Put your name and address at the bottom of each poem. Editors, reasonably, do not keep your letters, only the poems that interest them. You might consider one of those rubber stamps. I know a number of poets who have them, though I don't myself.

• Fold the poem once and put it into the sort of envelope designed to take A4 folded once. I don't know why poets like to scrunch their verses into tiny envelopes, but don't do it. Don't go to the other extreme either and send it decorated with admonitions not to bend, etcetera. Include a stamped, self-addressed envelope of the same size. This really is important. Shakespeare himself would be consigned to the wpb without an appropriate sae.

• Do not send just one poem. Do not send 20 poems. Send enough to give a reasonable flavour of your work – say about four or five. Long poems are less likely to be accepted than short poems. If you write different kinds of things, then make sure your selection covers a fair few of these kinds. Send what you think of as your best work, but do not be surprised if what is finally accepted is the one you put in at the last minute, 'to make the others look better' as Larkin lugubriously puts it. And if an editor says he or she likes your work and would like to see more, then send more as soon as possible. The editor wasn't just being polite. Editors aren't. It was

---

Submitting poems

• Submit poems on an A4 sheet, simply typed.
• Put your name and addess at the bottom of each sheet.
• Fold the sheet only once and use an A5 envelope.
• Send about four or five poems.
• Consider whether to submit the same poem simultaneously to more than one editor.
• Always keep copies of your poems.
• Include a short covering letter.

---

said because it was meant.

• At this point there is generally some po-faced stuff about never sending the same poem to more than one editor simultaneously. As it happens, I don't do this, but some well-known poets do. And indeed, if Snurd of the *Supplement* sits on your poems for six months, what are you supposed to do, since the polite follow-up letter recommended will, almost certainly, have no effect at all, except to waste your time and your stamps? The real reason for not making multiple submissions is the embarrassment when the same poem is accepted by two editors at once. I once, inadvertently, won two microscopic prizes in poetry competitions for the same poem. What did I do? I kept my mouth shut and cashed the cheques, that's what I did.

• You wouldn't have been daft enough to send off your *only* copies of poems to Snurd, would you? *Of course* he lost them and it's all your own silly fault. No you can't sue him but you'll know better next time. Send photocopies and keep your originals. Editors don't mind photocopies. Why should they? They look a lot better than the original all covered in Tippex.

• Keep your covering letter short, but if you have been published in reputable places then it will do no harm to say so. This advice comes from Duncan Forbes. Selling poems is very like selling anything else, so blow your own trumpet, but don't blow for too long. Don't ask the editor for help in the advancement of your poetic career. Being rude won't help either. Artists are supposed to be rude and a lot of them are, too, but it hasn't actually helped them to anything except an ulcer or a punch on the nose.

Which magazines?

You could start with the *TLS* but I wouldn't advise it. One editor (not from the *TLS*) said honestly that he tended to reject, more or less unread, poems from anyone he had never heard of. Before you play with the big boys perhaps you ought to have some sort of a record in the little magazines. Some pay and some do not. What matters is not the cash but whether you feel proud or ashamed to be seen in the thing. The Poetry Library at the South Bank Centre (Royal Festival Hall, London SE1 8XX) publishes a list of poetry magazines, and if you can get along there (very convenient for Waterloo Station and open 11am-8pm except Mondays), you can nose around among the back numbers and see what is appealing to you. If you can't do that, then a letter with an sae will get you the list (see also page 285).

Judge where you think you will fit in, and buy yourself a big sheet of second-class stamps. Send off your work and be prepared to be reasonably patient. Most editors reply in the end. Little magazines have a high mortality rate, so be prepared for a particularly crushing form of disappointment – having your work accepted by a magazine which promptly ceases publication. It happens to us all; it goes on happening to me. The Poetry Library also sends out for an sae of 75p a satisfying wodge of bumph about poetry publishing in general. Worth the money.

Some inexperienced poets seem very worried that editors will filch their 'ideas' and pay them nothing, but poems are not made up of ideas; they are made up of words, and if anyone prints your poem without permission they are infringing your copyright and you can threaten them with all sorts of horrible things. But, honestly, this is a buyer's market, and even the editor of that badly photocopied rag

has more material than can be used.

There seems to be a new kind of organisation that solicits poems. Often with names like Global or International, they don't ask for money up front, so are not exactly vanity presses. But they encourage you in marketers' prose to buy super-duper anthologies for £40 or so. Harmless, I suppose, but I'd rather appear in something less pretentious along with some poets I had actually heard of.

Subscribe to *Poetry Review*, the magazine of the Poetry Society. It's quarterly, expensive and the best poetry magazine. *Poetry Wales* and *The New Welsh Review* are both beautifully produced. Earlier remarks about 'relentless celticity' may now be unfair. Particularly since Robert Minhinnick has taken over at *Poetry Wales*. *HU (The Honest Ulsterman)* is unpretentious to look at, but consistently interesting and intelligent – you don't have to be at all Irish to contribute either. *Ambit* is lively with good artwork; the editors take ages to look at submissions. *Iron* is run by a relic of the Sixties (Peter Mortimer who has a little boy called Dylan). The quality of the work has steadily improved along with the quality of the production. Mortimer is a most conscientious editor too, and replies promptly and individually. *Stand* has a wide distribution – a rather *Guardian*-y feel to the poems and opinions. *London Magazine* is as good as ever – Alan Ross scribbles cryptic encouragement on poems that don't quite make it. *PN Review* has rude reviewers, an offshoot of the publisher Carcanet (or the other way round) and prints a wide range of poems. *Edinburgh Review* also has rude reviewers. *The Rialto* is well spoken of. This is a personal list – magazines I read from time to time. (See the list on page 134 for the poetry magazines listed in this *Yearbook*.)

Of the national newspapers, the *Express* prints a poem every day. You can send to Harry Eyres and you may get £25 – I didn't but Michael Conaghan did. The *Independent* prints a daily poem from published collections; they don't pay. The *Observer* and the *Sunday Times* print poems; the *Sunday Telegraph* and the *Independent on Sunday* don't.

The two literary heavyweights are the *Times Literary Supplement* and the *London Review of Books*, and both publish poetry. The *TLS* does not publish Fiona Pitt-Kethley's ruderies.

Book publication

Every poet wants to get a book out. How do you do it? One pretty sure way is to win a big prize in a competition, the National or the biennial Arvon or Harry Chambers' Peterloo. Otherwise, you wait until you have reached the stage of having had two or three dozen poems published in reputable places; then you type out enough poems for a collection, traditionally 64pp but collections seem to be getting longer, and send them out, keeping your own copy and including return postage. I suppose you do. I first got published by talking to Anthony Thwaite in a pub; everybody needs a slice of luck. I know some excellent poets who are still trying to place their first book and, contrariwise, there are books … Poetry, like most things, goes in fashions. But don't be in a hurry. Wait until you have a reputation in the magazines and small presses. Neil Astley at Bloodaxe reckons more than 90% of what comes through his letterbox he sends back, and he has usually had an eye on the successful ones before they got around to submitting.

Who do you send out to? Faber are still out in front (though they did turn down Larkin's *The Less Deceived*, the most influential book of English poems in the last 50 years). It is not that their poets are better, but Faber promote them heavily and care about them. And being a Faber poet puts you in the company of Eliot and Larkin. Penguin have revived their excellent *Modern Poets* series and have 12 titles so far. Most other big publishers do poetry – fortunes wax and wane with the person, often a poet, nearly always a man, in the editorial chair.

But being published by a household name does not mean selling thousands – hundreds are more common. Publishers

Small press information

Association of Little Presses (ALP)
Chairperson Lawrence Upton,
32 Downside Road, Sutton, Surrey SM2 5HP
web site http://www.melloworld.com/alp
They put out a newsletter and a catalogue for £3.00 plus 75p p&p.

The Stationery Office Oriel Bookshop
The Friary, Cardiff CF1 4AA
Publishes *Small Presses and Little Magazines of the UK and Ireland.*

The National Small Press Centre
BM BOZO, London WC1N 3XX
Publishes *Small Press Listings* quarterly.

Photon Press
The Light House, 37 The Meadows, Berwick-upon-Tweed, Northumberland TD15 1NY
Light's List is a list of over 1200 small press magazines in the UK and overseas. It costs £1.50 plus A5 sae.

The Poetry Library
Royal Festival Hall, South Bank Centre,
London SE1 8XX
tel 0171-921 0943/0664 *fax* 0171-921 0939
Lists of poetry magazines, poetry bookshops, current competitions, etc. See also page 285.

like to have poetry on their list as a badge of virtue, but often they don't want to know much about it, they don't promote it and they don't persist with it. The book sinks or swims, and usually it sinks. (Publishers that consider poetry for adults are listed in *Publishers of poetry* on page 290; *Children's book publishers and packagers* on page 260 includes publishers of poetry for children.)

Specialist poetry presses (some, though not all of which, publish nothing but poetry) produce books that look every bit as good and, in most cases, sell every bit as well (or badly). Bloodaxe, Peterloo and Carcanet, none of them London-based, are leaders in the field.

Bloodaxe sounds fearsomely dismissive, but the name is from a Viking who conquered Northumbria. They have more titles and possibly better poets than

Faber but they still fail the railway bookstall test. 'From traditional formalists to post-modernists', says Neil Astley. Half the poets on his list are women – good if you are a woman. Carcanet publish both Elizabeth Jennings and John Ashberry, which indicates Michael Schmidt's catholicity and willingness to go outside this country. He welcomes manuscripts, though he wishes people would read some of the books on his list first. This is good advice; every publisher has a style, just as every magazine has. His latest find is Sophie Hannah, the infant phenomenon.

If infancy is long past, then Harry Chambers at Peterloo is worth a try. He published a first book by Kirkpatrick Dobie in the poet's 84th year. Dana Gioia, the American 'new formalist' and Ursula Fanthorpe are his biggest guns.

Anvil are based in London and do a lot of poetry in translation. Enitharmon's books are as well produced as anyone's and it's a good list (Anthony Thwaite, Jeremy Reed, Duncan Forbes), unfashionable perhaps, but none the worse for that. Stephen Stuart-Smith doesn't get a lot of Arts money for some unfathomable reason. Seren, the imprint of Poetry Wales, publishes the lively Sheena Pugh and Headland Simon Rae of the *Guardian* fame. There are a lot more excellent small presses and information on them can be obtained through the organisations listed in the box.

Competitions

Some poets are snooty about these. Of course they are popular because they make money for the organisers: a biggish competition may attract 10,000 entries paying £3 a time. That gives an income of £30,000, enough to pay for some good prizes, a fair bit of promotion, fees for the judges and running costs, and still leave a nice bit in the kitty. But, from the poet's end, it is a good deal too. Though unknowns (everybody starts as an unknown, don't they?) only occasionally win the big prizes, they do pick up the smaller ones quite often, and that can be a

great encouragement when you need it. If you are just starting out, then enter the competitions with first prizes of hundreds rather than thousands of pounds. The big guns probably won't enter these.

You might consider subscribing to *Writers News*. Their Poetry Competitions specifically exclude published poets like me and their stuff on poetry is good, if elementary. For more information on current competitions, see page 286 and *Prizes and awards* on page 510.

Getting on radio

Michael Conaghan, who has had many poems broadcast, says BBC local radio – more talk than its commercial equivalent – is the place to start. Find out who is responsible for Arts programming and contact them. 'Short punchy, topical work is probably what they want, and events/festivals concentrate their minds wonderfully. Nationally, Radio 1's Mark Radcliffe is a notable friend to poets.'

Poetry on the Internet

To get on the Internet you need a computer (PC or Mac, not an Amstrad word processor), a modem and a phone line. Any of the service providers are eager to give you an Internet connection for a few pounds per month. You can then e-mail anywhere or surf the World Wide Web.

The poet Peter Howard writes an Internet column for *Poetry Review* and suggests you can submit to electronic magazines or set up your own site and get people to visit it. You can even set up your own magazine – there's no extra charge. 'Everything's up for grabs – there are no real reputations yet, though they're forming', he says.

Poetry for children

Not (repeat *not*) a dustbin for grow-up rejects. The publishing grapevine says there is a shortage of good poetry for children, and schools pay poets (some with more brass-neck than talent) to perform in book weeks. Poet Lindsay MacRae thinks it helps to be young and a woman. But Roger McGough is oldish and a man. *Words and Pictures*, a quarterly newsletter, will tell you where to send your poems, often in the USA (Elizabeth Wein, 41A Oak Tree Road, Marlow, Bucks. SL7 3ED). See also page 288.

Vanity/subsidy publishing

Never give a publisher money. That is what they give to you. If you want your work in print and nobody will do it for you without a cheque, then do it yourself. See *Doing it on your own* on page 266. You could buy yourself a second-hand word processor with the money you save by not answering that advertisement!

A last word

Invest some time, invest some money. Buy yourself, if not a word processor, at least a decent typewriter and some nice paper. Buy some books of poetry and try to see how your favourites do it. If you're a joiner, join a local group. Your local Regional Arts Board (see page 491) will know who they are. The Muse chooses her favourites, but be a bit welcoming.

John Whitworth has published six books of poetry, including *Landscape With Small Humans* (Peterloo) and, for children, *The Complete Poetical Works of Phoebe Flood* (Hodder). He has been a Faber anthologist, both judge and prizewinner in national poetry competitions, and has been published in national newspapers and on radio and television.

Poetry organisations

Britain probably has more publicly funded poetry organisations than any other country. These are all committed to helping poets and poetry in different ways and are useful ports of call for the aspiring poet. **Mary Enright**, *Chair of the Poetry Society, introduces the most important of these organisations.*

Societies

The Poetry Society
22 Betterton Street, London WC2H 9BU
tel 0171-420 9880 *fax* 0171-240 4818
e-mail poetrysoc@dial.pipex.com
web site http://www.poetrysoc.com
The Poetry Society has been operating for nearly 90 years and works to help poets and poetry thrive in Britain today. Its principal activities include:
• the publication of *Poetry Review* and *Poetry News*;
• involvement in promotions such as Poetry Places, a 2-year scheme of placements, residencies and projects throughout the country, and the annual National Poetry Day;
• running an information and training service;
• administration of the annual National Poetry Competition;

• provision of 'The Script' critical service;
• 'the Poetry Surgery', offering immediate one-to-one feedback on work.
  Its London centre – the Poetry Place – includes a café, reading room, meeting space and access to the Internet. It is also a venue for a wide variety of readings, workshops and other poetry events, and is open to members and friends of the Society, which is open to all. You can also visit the Place via the Society's web site.

Poetry Ireland
Bermingham Tower, Upper Yard, Dublin Castle, Dublin 2, Republic of Ireland
tel (01) 6714632 *fax* (01) 6714634
Poetry Ireland acts as the Irish Poetry Society and also runs the Austin Clarke Library, a reference library of over 10,000 titles. It publishes a quarterly magazine, *Poetry Ireland Review*, organises readings in Dublin and nationally, and runs the Writers in Schools scheme.

European Association for the Promotion of Poetry

European Poetry Centre, 'The Seven Sleepers', J.P. Minckelersstraat 168, B-3000 Louvain, Belgium
tel (16) 235351

The British Haiku Society

35 Downs Park West, Westbury Park, Bristol BS6 7QH
tel 0117-962 1035

With an international membership, BHS promotes the appreciation and writing of haiku, senyen, tenka, and renga. It organises tutorials, workshops, critical comment and information, as well as formal and informal meetings. It publishes a quarterly journal *Blithe Spirit* and occasional books, as well as providing the *Haiku Kit* for schools, which covers all Key stages through to adult. Founded 1990.

The Poetry Book Society

Book House, 45 East Hill, London SW18 2RX
tel 0181-870 8403 *fax* 0181-877 1615

The PBS is a unique book club for readers of poetry, founded in 1953 by T.S. Eliot, and funded by the Arts Council of England. Every quarter, selectors choose one outstanding publication (the PBS Choice), and make 4 recommendations. Members can receive some or all of these books free and are also offered substantial discounts on other poetry books. The PBS also runs the T.S. Eliot Prize (see page 517), and has recently launched an education service providing teaching materials for secondary schools. Write for membership details.

Regional Arts Boards (RABs)

Information Service, The Arts Council of England, 14 Great Peter Street, London SW1P 3NQ

The officers responsible for literature in the Regional Arts Boards can provide information on local poetry groups, workshops and societies. Many RABs give grant aid to local publishers and magazines and help fund festivals and readings, etc; some run critical services. A list of the relevant officers is available on receipt of an sae. See also page 491.

Libraries

The Poetry Library

Royal Festival Hall, South Bank Centre, London SE1 8XX
tel 0171-921 0943/0664 *fax* 0171-921 0939
web site http://www.poetrylibrary.org.uk

The Poetry Library is situated on Level 5 of the Royal Festival Hall. Its principal roles are to collect and preserve all poetry published in the UK in this century, and to act as a public lending library. Two copies of all titles are purchased, allowing one to be available for consultation and the other to go out on loan. Books may be borrowed by those outside London through the national Inter-Library Lending network. The collection of about 38,000 titles is all in the English language, although it includes translations from all over the world. There is a large children's section, as well as poetry on cassette, record and video.

As well as the normal functions of all libraries, the Poetry Library also runs an active information service on all poetry-related activities, and offers advice to the new poet. Current awareness lists are produced and are available by post on receipt of a large sae. They include lists of magazines, competitions, bookshops, groups and workshops, evening classes, festivals, etc and are updated regularly. The Library also stocks the full range of British poetry magazines as well as a large selection from abroad.

Membership of the Library is free, and is open to all on production of proof of identity and current address. Founded in 1953 by the Arts Council of Great Britain.

The British Haiku Society Library

Longholm, East Bank, Wingland, Sutton Bridge, Spalding, Lincs. PE12 9YS

The BHS Library is a collection of books, magazines and cassettes in haiku and related forms. It is a mail-order, members-only lending library. Write for membership details.

Northern Poetry Library

County Library, The Willows, Morpeth, Northumberland NE61 1TA
tel (01670) 512385 *fax* (01670) 518012

The Northern Poetry Library serves the

area covered by the Northern Regional Arts Board, i.e. Tyne and Wear, Durham, Northumberland, Cumbria and Cleveland. Its collection contains over 14,000 titles of mostly British material and includes magazines and poetry in translation. There is a full information service, access to a database of pre-20th-century poetry, and a postal lending service to members. Full membership is free to those living in the region and associate membership is free to those outside. It is run by Northumberland County Library as one of its special services. Founded in 1968.

The Scottish Poetry Library
Tweeddale Court, 14 High Street,
Edinburgh EH1 1TE
tel 0131-557 2876
e-mail spl_queries@presence.co.uk
The Scottish Poetry Library is run along similar lines to the Poetry Library in London, specialising in 20th-century poetry written in Scotland, in Scots, Gaelic and English. It also collects some pre-20th-century poetry and contemporary poetry from all over the world. Information and advice on all poets is given and visits by individuals, groups and schools are welcome. Borrowing is free of charge and there is a membership scheme at £10.00 p.a., which includes use of the members' reading room and a regular newsletter. It has branches in libraries and arts centres throughout Scotland and also runs a mobile library service. Readings and exhibitions are regularly organised, particularly during the Edinburgh Festival. Founded in 1984.

During 1999 the library will be moving to new, larger purpose-built premises at 5 Crichton court, Canongate, Edinburgh.

Public libraries

Public libraries can be an invaluable source of information on writing activities in the area in addition to having collections of modern poetry for loan. Some also have literature field workers or writers-in-residence, who can be very helpful to beginners. Promotions such as 'Brave New Words' by Well Worth Reading help to encourage a greater interest in, and better access to, modern poetry in public libraries.

Competitions and awards

There are literally hundreds of poetry competitions going on throughout the year, varying widely in quality and quantity of entries and prizes. The two most important are the National Poetry Competition run by the Poetry Society and the biennial Arvon Foundation International Poetry Competition. Details of these and other competitions can be found under *Prizes and awards* (page 510). The Poetry Library produces a free list, updated monthly, of these and other competitions, and is available on receipt of a large sae.

There are several prestigious awards for poetry, most awarded annually to published poets, and therefore non-competitive. A complete list of prizes is included in the *Guide to Literary Prizes*, published by Book Trust at £3.99 (which also produces a free leaflet on grants and awards).

Bookshops

Not all general bookshops have a strong modern poetry section but there are some which specialise in poetry. The principal ones are listed below. These and other good bookshops stocking a range of poetry are listed by the Poetry Library; this list is divided into London and outside London areas and can be obtained by sending a large sae.

The Stationery Office Oriel Bookshop
The Friary, Cardiff CF1 4AA
tel (01222) 395548

Peter Riley
27 Sturton Street, Cambridge CB1 2QG
tel (01223) 576422

Festivals

Literature festivals have become increasingly popular and prestigious in the past few years and are now held in almost every part of the country. Information on what is happening in your area should be readily available from your local library and Regional Arts Board. A selection of literature festivals is listed on page 545.

The British Council

Information Officer, Literature Department,
British Council, 11 Portland Place,
London W1N 4EJ
web site http://www.britcoun.org/literature
/litfest.htm

For a list of forthcoming literature festivals, send an A4 or A5 size sae or visit the web site. See also page 465.

Performance venues

In London the best way to keep up to date with readings and poetry events is through the weekly listing magazines, *Time Out* and *What's On in London*. The main London venues are given below.

Outside London, local listings magazines should be helpful and Regional Arts Boards and public libraries will have details of all literature events happening in their area.

Apples and Snakes Performance Poetry

Battersea Arts Centre, Lavender Hill,
London SW11
tel 0181-692 0393 (information), 0181-223 2223 (tickets)

Blue Nose Poetry

tel (0958) 402657
web site http://www.netkonect.co.uk/~athelstan/
Workshop venue Golden Square Books,
16 Golden Square, London W1R 3AR

Phone for details of readings and residential weekend workshops.

The Poetry Place

The Poetry Society, 22 Betterton Street,
London WC2H 9BU
tel 0171-420 9880 (tickets and information)

Terrible Beauty

Troubadour Coffee House,
265 Old Brompton Road, London SW5

Alternate Mondays 8pm-10pm.

Voice Box

Level 5, Royal Festival Hall, London SE1 8XX
tel 0171-921 0906 (information), 0171-960 4242 (tickets)

Poetry groups and workshops

Joining a poetry group can be an excellent way to get useful help and advice on writing and publishing. Groups vary enormously; if possible, try a few in your area to find the one most congenial to your style. They tend to wax and wane, but your Regional Arts Board and local library should have up-to-date information on those currently active, or you could consult *Poetry Groups Register*, published by Blaxland Family Press (Blaxland Tan, 12 Matthews Road, Taunton, Somerset TA1 4NH *tel* (01823) 324423).

The Poetry Library compiles a list of groups and workshops for the Greater London area; this is updated regularly and available on receipt of a large sae.

Writing courses

There is currently much more available than ever before in the area of short-term creative writing courses, as writers-in-residence are appointed by Regional Arts Boards, and by libraries, colleges, prisons, etc. There is also a choice of residential writing courses, of which the long established ones are run by the Arvon Foundation and the Ty Newydd. All areas of writing are covered, as well as poetry.

Information on other courses not listed here can be obtained from the Regional Arts Boards, local libraries or the Poetry Library.

The Arvon Foundation

The Arvon Foundation at Lumb Bank
Hebden Bridge, West Yorkshire HX7 6DF
The Arvon Foundation at Totleigh Barton
Sheepwash, Beaworthy, Devon EX21 5NS
The Arvon Foundation at Moniack Mhor
Teavarran, Kiltarlity, Beauly,
Inverness-shire IV4 7HT

Runs 3 centres and has wide experience of residential writing courses. Most last for about 5 days and offer tuition by working writers.

The Poetry School

130c Evering Road, London N16 7BD
tel 0181-985 0090

Using London venues, the Poetry School offers a core programme of tuition in reading and writing poetry. It provides a forum to share experience, develop skills and extend appreciation of both traditional and innovative aspects of poetry.

The Poets' House/Teach na hÉigse

Clonbarra, Falcarragh, Co. Donegal, Ireland
tel (74) 65470 *fax* (74) 65471
e-mail walledgarden@msn.com

The Poets' House runs courses in poetry only. Three 2-week courses are offered over the summer months; an MA in creative writing is also available.

Ty Newydd
Taliesin, Ty Newydd, Llanystumdwy, Criccieth, Gwynedd LL52 0LW
Courses here are run along similar lines to the Arvon Houses with a wide variety of courses offered. Some of the tutors used are Welsh writers though there is a good mix.

Write Away, East Midlands Arts
Mountfields House, Epinal Way, Loughborough, Leics. LE11 0QE
East Midlands Arts runs 4 residential writing courses from July 1998 to April 1999 located at Leicester University. A variety of types of writing is covered.

Poetry for children and young adults

Children's Section, The Poetry Library
Royal Festival Hall, London SE1 8XX
The Poetry Library has a large children's section of about 4000 books incorporating the SIGNAL Collection of Children's Poetry. It runs an education service for teachers and schools, and from time to time special projects for other groups in the community. A teachers' information file covering all aspects of poetry in education is available, as are selected reading lists for different age groups. There is a special collection of books and materials for teachers and poets involved in education; the teachers' membership scheme offers special loan facilities to use books in the classroom.

National Association of Writers in Education (NAWE)
PO Box 1, Sheriff Hutton, York YO60 7YU
tel/fax (01653) 618429
e-mail paul@nawe.co.uk
web site http://www.nawe.co.uk
A national organisation which aims to widen the scope of writing in education, and co-ordinate activities between writers, teachers and funding bodies. It publishes a magazine, *Writing in Education*, and a national directory of writers who work in schools, colleges and the community. Write for membership details.

Poetry Society Education
The Poetry Society, 22 Betterton Street, London WC2H 9BU
tel 0171-420 9894 *fax* 0171-240 4818
Poetry Society Education promotes poetry through schools, youth clubs, libraries and community centres. It sponsors poets in residence in educational settings from the BBC Education to festivals and playgroups. A publication celebrating National Poetry Day is sent free to every school, giving an insight into the best of contemporary verse.

Poetry Society publications for schools include primary and secondary guidebooks produced in association with the Year of Reading, a young poet's pack, posters ranging from 'riddles for early years' to longer narrative verse for key stage 2, to 'poets on poets' linked to GCSE requirements.

Schools can become members of the Poetry Places scheme, which offers publications, training opportunities to teachers and poets, a consultancy service matching poets to places, discounts and display materials. Member schools can apply for a grant of £500 in order to employ a poet.

Young poets can join the Society at a reduced rate of £10 a year. Youth membership offers regular performance opportunities, a national network of criticism and advice, and copies of the quarterly *Poetry News* with a special section devoted to youth events.

The Young National Competition, sponsored by the Arvon Foundation, is free to any poet aged between 11 and 18, and the closing date is the end of July. The 12 winners spend a week as apprentice poets alongside the judges at the Arvon Foundation centre at Lumb Bank.

A full catalogue of poetry resources, details of youth membership and the Young National Competition, Poetry Places in Schools registration, and details of education residencies are available from The Education Development Officer.

Young Book Trust
Book House, 45 East Hill, London SW18 2QZ
The children's division of Book Trust, the aims of Young Book Trust are to promote reading and offer advice and information on all aspects of children's reading and

books. It runs a library of all children's books published over the last two years. It organises Children's Book Week, held usually in October, co-ordinating national activities throughout the week. It also offers an information service, including information on authors (Authorbank), and publishes a newsletter. A subscription service is available for schools, libraries, colleges, bookshops and publishers.

Competitions

The number of good poetry competitions for children are limited. The main annual ones are listed here.

BBC Radio 4 Young Poetry Competition

BBC Broadcasting House, Whiteladies Road, Bristol BS8 2LR

First launched in 1994, there are 3 age categories between 8 and 21 years for poems written for radio.

The Roald Dahl Foundation Poetry Competition

PO Box 1375, 20 Vauxhall Bridge Road, London SW1V 2SA

Competition divided into 4 age groups, between 7 and 17 years.

W.H. Smith Young Writers Competition

Strand House, 7 Holbein Place, Sloane Square, London SW1W 8NR

An open competition for original writing – poems, stories, plays or articles – by children aged 16 and under.

Welsh Academy Young Writers Competition

PO Box 328, Cardiff CF2 4XL

A national competition for poetry and prose in 3 categories, the upper limit being 18. The closing date is usually July.

Young National Poetry Competition

The Poetry Society, 22 Betterton Street, London WC2H 9BU

A new competition free to everyone between the ages of 11 and 18. Twelve winners will spend a week at the Arvon Foundation.

Mary Enright has been Librarian at the Poetry Library, London, since 1988 and is Chair of the Poetry Society.

Further reading

ALP, *Catalogue of Little Press Books in Print*, Association of Little Presses, 1998

Baldwin, Michael, *The Way to Write Poetry*, Elm Tree Books, 1982

Bolton, Marjorie, *The Anatomy of Poetry*, Routledge, 1990, o.p.

Chisholm, Alison, *The Craft of Writing Poetry*, Allison & Busby, 1992

Chisholm, Alison, *A Practical Poetry Course*, Allison & Busby, 1994

Clifford, Johnathon, *Metric Feet and Other Gang Members*, Johnathon Clifford, 1993

Clifford, Johnathon, *Vanity Press & The Proper Poetry Publishers*, Johnathon Clifford, 1994

Corti, Doris, *Writing Poetry*, Writers News, 1994

Fairfax, John and Moat, John, *The Way to Write*, Elm Tree Books, 1981

Fergusson, Rosalind, *The Penguin Rhyming Dictionary*, Penguin Books, 1992

Finch, Peter, *How to Publish Your Poetry*, Allison & Busby, 2nd edn, 1998

Finch, Peter, *The Poetry Business*, Seren Books, 1994

Finch, Peter, *Small Presses and Little Magazines of the UK and Ireland: an address list*, Oriel

Fulton, Len, *Directory of Poetry Publishers*, 11th edn, Dustbooks, USA

Fulton, Len, *The International Directory of Little Magazines and Small Presses*, 30th edn, Dustbooks, USA

Gortschacher, Wolfgang, *Little Magazines Profiles*, University of Salzburg, 1993

Guide to Literary Prizes, Book Trust, 45 East Hill, London SW18 2QZ, 9th edn, 1997

Hamilton, Ian, *The Oxford Companion to Twentieth-Century Poetry in English*, Oxford University Press, 1994

Hyland, Paul, *Getting into Poetry*, Bloodaxe, 2nd edn, 1996

Jerome, Judson, *Poet's Market: Where and How to Publish Your Poetry*, Writer's Digest Books, USA, 1998

Livingstone, Dinah, *Poetry Handbook for Readers & Writers*, Macmillan, 1992

Myers, Jack and Simms, Michael, *Longman Dictionary and Handbook of Poetry*, Longman, o.p.

PALPI Poetry and Little Press Information, Association of Little Presses

Preminger, Alex, *New Princeton Encyclopedia of Poetry and Poetics*, Princeton University Press, USA, 3rd rev. edn, 1993

Riggs, Thomas (ed.), *Contemporary Poets*, St James Press, 6th edn, 1996

Roberts, Philip Davies, *How Poetry Works: the Elements of English Poetry*, Penguin Books, 1991

Sansom, Peter, *Writing Poems*, Bloodaxe, 1994, repr. 1997

Scannell, Vernon, *How to Enjoy Poetry*, Piatkus, 1987, o.p.

Sweeney, Matthew and Williams, John Hartley, *Teach Yourself Writing Poetry*, Hodder & Stoughton, 1997

Publishers of poetry

Addresses for Book publishers UK and Ireland start on page 157. See Children's book publishers and packagers on page 260 for publishers of poetry for children.

Anvil Press Poetry
Arc Publications
Bellew Publishing
Blackstaff Press (Ire.)
Bloodaxe Books
Marion Boyars Publishers
Brown, Son & Ferguson
Jonathan Cape
Carcanet Press
Chatto & Windus
Cló Iar-Chonnachta Teo. (Ire.)
    (Irish language only)
The Collins Press (Ire.)
Enitharmon Press
Everyman's Library
Faber & Faber

Forest Books
Gairm Publications
The Gallery Press (Ire.)
Gee & Son (Denbigh)
The Goldsmith Press (Ire.)
Headland Publications
Hippopotamus Press
Honno
Libris
Liverpool University Press
Kevin Mayhew
National Poetry Foundation
New Beacon Books
Onlywomen Press
Oxford University Press
Payback Press

Penguin Books
Peterloo Poets
Polygon
Random House UK
Rivelin Grapheme Press
St Pauls
Scottish Cultural Press
Seren Books
Slow Dancer Press
Stride Publications
The University of Hull Press &
    Lampada Press
Wolfhound Press (Ire.)
Writers & Readers

Television and film

Writing for television

Writing for television can be an extremely rewarding career and one that can be started at virtually any age. **Anji Loman Field** *says anyone with the right aptitude and attitude can succeed. Here she gives sound advice for the potential screenwriter.*

The markets

There are various openings for new writers in television, but apart from competitions and special projects these are hardly ever advertised. The openings fall into four categories:

Single drama

There are fewer slots nowadays for the one-off single play. However, a strong script fitting the remit of a particular series like BBC's Screen One or Screen Two, or the recent Love Bites & Obsession seasons, could well succeed. There have also been cases of new writers selling feature film projects to broadcasters. Ask television companies for their current guidelines on single drama and film.

Series and serials

Although it has been known for a new writer to sell an original series or serial, it is a relatively rare occurrence. Writers with a track record of writing for existing strands are far more likely to be taken seriously. Long-running soaps like *EastEnders* and *Emmerdale*, or series such as *The Bill*, are often in the market for new writers, but check first. If the door is open, a good 'calling card script' is usually the way in. Submit an original piece of work in a similar genre that is at least an hour long and shows your ability to create believable characters, write sparkling dialogue and tell a compelling story. You may be invited to try out for one of these long-running shows.

Dramatisations/adaptations

A new writer is extremely unlikely to be commissioned to adapt or dramatise someone else's work for television. However, if there's something you really want to adapt and you can afford to take out an 'option' on the rights (or already own them, if it is your own novel or play) then write the script on spec. If you have a good script and can show that you own the rights, you could succeed.

Situation comedy

This is the one area where production companies and broadcasters are desperate for new talent, and there are several competitions open to new writers. If you are a good comedy writer and market your work well, you will undoubtedly succeed (see 'Writing situation comedy' below).

Aptitude and attitude

The first prerequisite in writing for television is that you enjoy the medium, and actually watch the kinds of shows that you would be interested in writing for. A cynical approach will always show through. And before sitting down to write that first television script, arm yourself with the appropriate skills by examining the medium as a whole.

• **Tape the kind of show you'd like to write for and analyse it.** How many scenes are there? What length are they? How much of the story happens 'off camera'? Knowing the answers to these questions will help you to understand the grammar of screen, and enable you to write a more professional script.

• **Study the structure of story telling.** There are plenty of books on the subject, and although it is never a good idea to follow structural paradigms to the letter, absorb as much information as possible so that the essential 'rules' on character, motivation and plot filter through into your writing.

• **Read scripts.** Some are published in book form, but a huge variety of scripts are also available from specialist book shops such as Offstage (*tel* 0171-485 4996), The Screenwriter Store (*tel* 0181-469 2244), and the British Film Institute (*tel* 0171-928 3535).

• **If you want to write sitcom, see as many live recordings of shows as possible.** This enables you to understand the techniques involved in television production, and particularly the physical constraints imposed by the studio. Free tickets for sitcom recordings are always available – phone the broadcasters for information.

• **Be realistic.** Don't make your first project too ambitious in terms of screen time, locations or special effects. If you can 'contain the action' and make your first script affordable to shoot, it is far more likely to be taken seriously.

Learning the craft

Even the most successful and experienced screenwriters say they never stop learning. Some have been lucky enough to learn the skill of writing for the screen in a subliminal way. For example, Lynda La Plante (*Prime Suspect*) was an actress with plenty of opportunity for studying scripts and production techniques before she turned her hand to writing; John Sullivan (*Only Fools and Horses*) worked in the props department at the BBC on countless sitcoms, and used to take the scripts home to study. But there are other ways to learn. Script workshops are particularly useful.

There are many courses and workshops available. These range from small self-help groups, where writers give each

other feedback on their work, to full- and part-time Screenwriting MA courses at universities (e.g. in London, Sheffield, Bournemouth, Manchester and Leeds). Evening classes are springing up in local colleges, and there are even script workshops on the Internet. Workshops can help in the following ways:

• **Discipline.** The hardest thing most writers ever have to do is sit down and face that blank screen or page. Joining a script workshop – where you *have* to deliver an outline or a treatment, or the next 20 pages of your script by a certain date – provides the push that so many writers need.

• **Feedback.** Reading and giving feedback on other people's work helps you to focus on getting your own script right. It is also good to get used to the idea of showing your own work to others and getting their feedback. Television writing is generally a collaborative process and writers need to be pleasant to work with, and receptive to ideas. Knowing when to argue a point and when to concede are crucial skills which can be developed in good writing workshops.

• **Rewriting.** Learn to Love the Rewrite. It is such a major achievement to get to the end of a first draft that it is all too easy to rush to the post box and send it off to several production companies at once. *Four Weddings and a Funeral*, a Channel 4-funded project, went through 17 rewrites before finally reaching the screen. So before you post your masterpiece:

• Leave it to 'settle' for a few days and do something completely different – allow your head to clear completely. Then re-read the script from beginning to end – from as objective a viewpoint as possible – and make necessary changes.

• Get feedback so that you're sure your script is ready to send. Be warned: knowing how to read and analyse a script properly is a particular skill. Unless they are equipped in this area, *never* ask your friends or relations to read your script. Their comments could either lull you into a false sense of security or destroy your confidence for ever. Feedback from other writers in your workshop group is best. There are some organisations (including

Useful information

Euroscript
PO Box 81, Shepperton, Middlesex TW19 9ND
tel/fax (01932) 267522
web site http://www.euroscript.co.uk
A media project of the EU to advance European scriptwriting in the form of distance training that develops scripts; reads, selects and promotes scripts and writers; and runs workshops and supports writers' groups.

London Film & Video Development Agency
tel 0171-383 7755
(incorporating the London Production Fund *tel* 0171-383 7766)
Offers grants that enable writers, producers and directors to make their projects.

The London Screenwriters' Workshop
114 Whitfield Street, London W1P 5RW
tel/fax 0171-387 5511
web site http://www.lsw.org.uk
Educational charity that runs regular courses, workshops and events, and publishes a quarterly newsletter. (See also page 495.)

National Association of Television Program Executives (NATPE)
450 Oakleigh Road North, London N20 0RZ
tel 0181-361 3793 *fax* 0181-368 3824
web site http://www.natpe.org
Contact Pam Smithard
Non-profit TV programming and software association dedicated to the continued growth and success of the global TV marketplace. Year-round activities include the annual conference and exhibition, which reaches tens of thousands of key decisionmakers in virtually every sector of the TV industry.

PACT (Producers' Alliance for Cinema and Television)
45 Mortimer Street, London W1N 7TD
tel 0171-331 6000 *fax* 0171-331 6700
Serves the feature film and independent TV production sector. The *PACT Guide* lists contacts in all areas (£25 to non-members). (See also page 486.)

Regional Arts Boards
Many RABs offer grants that enable writers, producers and directors to make their projects. Contact your local Arts Board for details (see page 491).

The Spotlight
7 Leicester Place, London WC2H 7BP
tel 0171-437 7631
Publishes a book called *Contacts*, which contains useful information and contact addresses. The 1998-99 edition is available from October.

The Writers' Guild of Great Britain
430 Edgware Road, London W2 1EH
tel 0171-723 8074
web site http://www.writers.org.uk/guild
Trade organisation for professional writers. Negotiates rates for TV drama with the BBC and the ITV Network Centre. (See also page 506.)

---

the London Screenwriters' Workshop) which offer a professional script feedback service for a moderate fee.

Writing situation comedy

Situation comedy writing is the most lucrative area of television, and deservedly so. Have you ever tried making an audience laugh several times a minute for 25 minutes for at least six weeks running, and maybe (in the case of *Last of the Summer Wine*) for 20 long years?

Despite its name, sitcom is less about situation and much more about character.

It is better to start with funny and engaging characters in mind and then (if it isn't part and parcel of the character) find the perfect situation in which to place them than it is to begin with the premise 'nobody's ever set a sitcom in a nuclear power station before'. It is not the setting that makes the audience laugh, it is the characters.

A good exercise in seeing if you can write funny material is to write an episode of an existing sitcom. If *Fawlty Towers* is your all-time favourite, study a few episodes and then try your own. It will never get made, but you'll learn a lot in the process – and sample scripts like this are often useful as calling card scripts.

Some of the broadcast companies issue guidelines on writing situation comedy. Phone the comedy departments at the BBC, LWT and Carlton for information, or the Programme Support Unit at Channel 4 (0171-396 4444) for their excellent 'beginner's guide to sitcom writing' pack – available for a small fee.

Competitions and courses

Comedy. For the past four years Channel 4 has run a Sitcom Festival at the Riverside Studios in Hammersmith. Several projects and new writers have been picked up from this showcase. The BBC also runs occasional comedy courses and competitions, and Carlton Television has a regular sitcom course which involves paying writers to write a pilot episode.

Drama. There are various initiatives for drama writing: the Denis Potter Screenwriting Award, the PAWS (People's Awareness of Science) Award, The Carlton Drama Course, The Lloyds Bank Film Challenge, Brief Encounters and various others.

For both comedy and drama competitions and initiatives, phone the major broadcasters and ask for details of their opportunities for new writers, and watch the trade press for announcements. See also *Prizes and awards* section on page 510.

Breaking in

Do you need an agent?

Many new writers are keen to get an agent before they attempt to sell anything, but this can be an arduous process and there are few agents prepared to take on a completely untried writer.

The best way to get an agent is to first get an offer of a deal on a project. Most *bona fide* production companies and broadcasters will happily recommend a selection of agents to writers they want to do business with. If you can phone an agent and say 'so-and-so wants to option/commission my project and has recommended you as an agent' s/he is far more likely to be interested. And at that point you can pick and choose the agent who is right for you, rather than going with the first one to say "yes".

Selling yourself

Once you are sure you have a good script, where do you send it? If you've done your homework, you will already know which channel is the most likely to be interested. But often it is better to send to an independent production company rather than directly to a broadcaster, so do a bit more research. Check out the companies that are making the kind of show you've written and approach them first.

A preliminary letter or phone call can save you time and money because some smaller companies simply don't have the resources to read unsolicited material. If you feel that a certain production company is absolutely right for your project, write a letter giving a brief synopsis of the project and asking if they will read the script. If they agree, your script will join the 'solicited' pile. And if it fits the bill, they may even pick it up and develop it. But don't expect overnight results. It can sometimes take many months before scripts are even read by small and/or busy companies.

Sending your script directly to a broadcaster can lead to a commission, but unless you target a particular producer whose work you admire you will probably have less control over who you work with.

Being 'discovered'

If you can get your work 'rehearse-read' by actors in front of an audience it will help your writing, and may even lead to discovery. Many script readings are attended by development executives from television and production companies and there are many stories of individuals being picked up from such projects. TAPS (Television Arts Performance Showcase) (0181-977 3252), Player-Playwrights (0181-883 0371) and the London Screenwriters' Workshop, all organise rehearsed readings.

Development hell

This is the place between finding someone who wants to produce your script and waiting for the 'suits' at the television companies to give the final go-ahead for the project. In the meantime you will have been paid, perhaps just an option fee, or maybe a commission fee for a script or two. Either way, *never put all your eggs in one development basket.* Aim eventually to have several projects bubbling under for every one that comes to the boil.

A realistic optimism is required for this game. Don't believe anything wonderful will happen until you actually have that signed contract in front of you. In the meantime keep writing, keep marketing and, if you possibly can, keep making contacts in the industry. If you're good at schmoozing, go to as many industry events as possible and make new contacts. If you can send a script to a producer with a covering letter saying 'I heard your talk the other day ...' you will immediately arouse interest.

Coping with rejection

The standard rejection letter is the worst part of this business. When it is accompanied by your returned script – looking decidedly un-read – it is very easy to become disillusioned. The trick is this: change your mental attitude to the point where if you don't receive at least one rejection letter in the post every day, you feel rejected! So long as you are absolutely sure that your work is good, keep sending it out. Sooner or later you'll get a nicer, more personalised rejection letter, and then eventually perhaps even a cup of tea with the producer ...

Selling ideas

Completely new writers do occasionally sell ideas but are much more likely to sell the idea alone, i.e. the 'format rights', and will probably end up not writing the script. If you have a great calling card script or two, or have had a few episodes of something produced, your ideas will be taken much more seriously. At this stage you might well sell a project on the basis of a short outline or synopsis, and be paid to write the script(s).

Summary

Writing for television is not generally something that can be taken up as a hobby. It may look easy but a huge amount of work and commitment are required in order to succeed. If that doesn't put you off, and it is what you really want to do, then go for it. And good luck!

Anji Loman Field worked as a television producer for several years before turning to writing. She has since written drama, comedy drama and animation for film and television, and has taught writing at the London Screenwriters' Workshop, the Royal College of Art and the London Institute.

Further reading

Friedmann, Julian, *How to Make Money Scriptwriting*, Boxtree, 1995, o.p.

Kelsey, Gerald, *Writing for Television*, A & C Black, 2nd edn, 1995

Seger, Linda, *Making a Good Script Great*, Samuel French Inc. (pbk), 1994

Vogler, Christopher, *The Writer's Journey*, Boxtree, revised edn due 1999

Wolfe, Ronald, *Writing Comedy*, Robert Hale, 1996

Writing Long-Running Television Series (lectures by various writers/producers), University of Luton Press, 1996, *tel* (01702) 552912

BBC national television

The BBC commissions from both BBC Production and independent producers (page 308), as well as from BBC regional centres.

BBC Broadcast

BBC Broadcast, Television Centre, Wood Lane, London W12 7RJ
tel 0181-743 8000
web site www.bbc.co.uk

BBC Broadcast is the commissioning, scheduling, marketing and broadcast directorate of the BBC – both for TV and radio. Almost 14,000 hours of TV programmes are broadcast each year on its two current channels, BBC1 and BBC2. The great majority of programmes are commissioned from BBC Production, but BBC Broadcast has a statutory obligation to ensure that 25% of its network programmes are made by independent producers and, further, that a significant proportion are made in the regions outside London.
Chief Executive Will Wyatt
Director of Television Alan Yentob
Deputy Director of Television David Docherty
Controller, BBC1 Peter Salmon
Controller, BBC2 Mark Thompson
Director of Regional Broadcasting Mark Byford
Controller, Programme Acquisition Alan Howden
Head of Purchased Programmes Sophie Turner Laing
Head of Independent Commissioning Group Jane Root
Head of Children's Commissioning Roy Thompson
Head of Daytime Commissioning Liz Barron
Head of Commissioning, Education for Adults Glenwyn Benson
Head of Commissioning, Schools and Colleges Frank Flynn

BBC Production

BBC Production, Television Centre, Wood Lane, London W12 7RJ
tel 0181-743 8000
Chief Executive, Production Ronald Neil
Director, Production Jana Bennett
BBC Production is the largest single programme maker in Europe. There are 16 bi-media programme departments based in London and the English regions, including BBC Sport, the Natural History Unit, Classical Music, Drama Production, Features and Events, Religion, Education, Children's, Entertainment, Science, Documentaries and History, and Arts. Addresses are given for individual departments if they are different from above.

Drama Production

Centre House, 56 Wood Lane, London W12 7SB
tel 0181-743 8000
Controller, Drama Production Colin Adams
Head of Drama Series Mal Young
Head of Films and Single Drama David Thompson
Senior Executive Producer, BBC1 Films and Serials Jane Tranter
Senior Executive Producer, BBC2 Serials Hilary Salmon
Head of Radio Drama and New Services Kate Rowland
Head, Production Development, Birmingham, Drama Toni Charlton
Executive Producer, London Production Development Centre Richard Fell

Unsolicited scripts for BBC Films, Singles and Radio Drama should be sent to the New Writing Initiative (see below); Series and Serials should go to the Head of Series or the relevant Senior Executive Producer. Please note that unsolicited scripts have to compete with regularly commissioned work for BBC Drama, so the competition is fierce. Scripts may also be submitted to the regional Drama departments – for addresses see page 298.

New Writing Initiative

Room 6059, Broadcasting House, Portland Place, London W1A 1AA

BBC Drama Production has recently launched a New Writing Initiative to encourage new writers. The initiative, headed by Kate Rowland, will launch various schemes to encourage writers for both radio and TV. These will be advertised in appropriate publications during the year.

Entertainment

fax 0181-743 9459
Controller of Entertainment Paul Jackson
Head of Comedy Geoffrey Perkins
Head of Light Entertainment Michael Leggo
Head of Comedy Entertainment Jon Plowman
Head of Music Entertainment Trevor Dann

The Comedy Department Script Development Unit in Entertainment welcomes new 30-minute comedy series. Only original formats, preferably mainly studio based, are required. The script editors prefer to see a completed half-hour script rather than an idea or outline, novel or treatment, etc. They do not read sketch material but they will read and respond to all comedy script submissions, although it is a highly competitive market. For brief sitcom writing guidelines send an A4 sae.

Arts

Head of BBC Arts Kim Evans
Managing Editor Alex Graham
Editors Gillian Greenwood, Anthony Wall, Basil Comely, Michael Poole, Nicholas Rossiter

Classical Music

Head of Classical Music Roger Wright
Head of Classical Music (Television) Peter Maniura

Documentaries and History

White City, 201 Wood Lane, London W12 7TS
tel 0181-752 5252 *fax* 0181-752 6060
Head of Documentaries Paul Hamman
Executive Producers Clare Paterson, Edward Mirzoeff

Science

White City, 201 Wood Lane, London W12 7RJ
tel 0181-752 6178
Head of Science Glenwyn Benson
Deputy Head and Executive Editor John Lynch

Features and Events

White City, 201 Wood Lane, London W12 7TS
tel 0181-752 5252
Head of Features and Events Anne Morrison
Deputy Head and Editor, Holiday Jane Lush
Executive Editor, Events Mike Ward

Children's

Head, Children's Programmes Lorraine Heggessey
Executive Producer, Drama tba
Head, Children's Entertainment Chris Bellinger
Programme Executive, New Media Greg Childs
Editor, Children's News and Factual Roy Milani
Editor, Blue Peter Oliver Macfarlane

Sport

Head, Sport Bob Shennan
Executive Editor, Football and Deputy Head of Sport, Production Niall Sloane
Executive Editor, TV Dave Gordon
Executive Editor, Continuous News Graeme Reid Davies

Features, Bristol

Broadcasting House, Whiteladies Road, Bristol BS8 2LR
tel 0117-9732211
Head, Features, Bristol Jeremy Gibson
Deputy Head, Managing Editor, Radio and Television Sam Organ
Managing Editor, Television Andy Batten-Foster

Natural History Unit, Bristol

Broadcasting House, Whiteladies Road, Bristol BS8 2LR
tel 0117-9732211
Head, Natural History Unit Keith Scholey
Director of Development Michael Bright

Network Production, Birmingham

Broadcasting Centre, Pebble Mill Road, Birmingham B5 7QQ
tel 0121-414 8888
Head, Network Production, Birmingham Rod Natkeil
Editor, Motoring and Leisure Sports Jon Bentley
Editor, Rural Affairs Paul Cannon
Editor Leisure and Lifestyle Roger Casstles
Editor, Entertainment Richard Lewis
Editor, Consumer Affairs and Features Huw Marks

Entertainment and Features (Manchester)

New Broadcasting House, Oxford Road, Manchester M60 1SJ
tel 0161-200 2020
Head, Entertainment and Features (Manchester) Wayne Garvie
Managing Editor John Drury
Editor, Entertainment and Popular Music Bridget Boseley
Editor, Archive, Media and Sport Gaynor Vaughan-Jones
Editor, African Caribbean Unit Dele Oniya

Open University Production Centre

Walton Hall, Milton Keynes, Bucks. MK7 6BH
tel (01908) 274033 *fax* (01908) 653744
Head, OUPC Ian Rosenbloom
Executive Producer Andrew Law

Religion

New Broadcasting House, Oxford Road, Manchester M60 1SJ
tel 0161-200 2020
Head, Religion Rev Ernie Rea
Managing Editor, Religious Programmes Helen Alexander

Production Executives Fiona Breslin, Anita Walsh
Executive Producer, Factual Programmes David Coomes

BBC Production, Education

Head, Production Education Marilyn Wheatcroft
Managing Editor Clare Brigstocke
Executive Producer, Schools Television Clare Elstow
Executive Producer Schools Television and Signed Language Programmes Sue Nott

BBC News

Television Centre, Wood Lane, London W12 7RJ
tel 0181-743 8000
Chief Executive, BBC News Tony Hall
Controller, Programme Policy Peter Bell
Head of News Programmes Richard Clemmow
Head of Current Affairs tba
Head of Political Programmes Mark Damazer
Head of News Gathering Richard Sambrook
World Affairs Editor John Simpson
Economics Editor Peter Jay
Editor, Breakfast News Andrew Thompson
Editor, One O'Clock/Six O'Clock News tba
Editor, Nine O'Clock News Jonathan Baker
Editor, Newsnight Sian Kevill
Editor, Public Eye Mark Wakefield

Editor, Panorama Peter Horrocks
Editor, The Money Programme Diarmuid Jeffreys
Editor, On the Record David Jordan
Editor, Ceefax Peter Clifton

Education

White City, 201 Wood Lane, London W12 7TS
tel 0181-752 5252
Director of Education Jane Drabble
Head of Education Policy Lucia Jones
Head of Commissioning, Schools and Colleges Frank Flynn
Head of Commissioning, Education for Adults Fiona Chesterton
Head of Marketing Dafna Israeli
Head of Digital Media/Learning Channel Jonathan Drori
Head of Learning Support Steve Pollock

Independent Commissioning Group

Television Centre, Wood Lane, London W12 7RJ
tel 0181-743 8000
Head, ICG Jane Root
The BBC commissions independent productions via the Independent Commissioning Group (ICG).

BBC regional television

The regions are responsible for producing both television and radio programmes.

BBC regions

BBC Northern Ireland
Broadcasting House, Belfast BT2 8HQ
tel (01232) 338000
Regular programmes include *Country Times, Newsline 6.30, Home Truths, Hearts and Minds, Sportsnight from Northern Ireland, Spotlight* and *Ballykissangel*. All programme-making departments are bi-media.
Controller Patrick Loughrey
Head of Broadcast Anna Carragher
Head of Production Paul Evans
Head of News and Current Affairs Tony Maddox
Editor, Current Affairs Andrew Colman
Head of Drama Robert Cooper
Political Editor Jim Dougal
Chief Producer, Agriculture Veronica Hughes

Chief Producer, Education Michael McGowan
Chief Producer, Entertainment Charlie Warmington
Chief Producer, Magazines Kathleen Carragher
Chief Producer, Irish Language Kiera Hegarty
Chief Producer, Music and Arts tba
Chief Producer, Documentaries Bruce Batten
Chief Producer, Religion Rev. Bert Tosh
Chief Producer, Music Sequences tba
Chief Producer, Sport Terry Smith

BBC Scotland
Broadcasting House, Queen Margaret Drive, Glasgow G12 8DG
tel 0141-339 8844
Headquarters of BBC Scotland with opt-out stations based in Aberdeen, Dundee, Edinburgh and Inverness. Regular programmes include the nightly *Reporting Scotland* plus *Friday Sportscene, Frontline Scotland* and *Landward* (bi-

monthly farming news).
Controller John McCormick
Head of Production Colin Cameron
Head of Broadcast Ken McQuarrie
Head of News and Current Affairs Ken Cargill
Head of Arts and Entertainment Mike Bolland
Head of Drama Andrea Calderwood
Head of Sport and Leisure Neil Fraser
Head of Children's and Features Liz Scott
Head of Education and Religion Andrew Barr

Aberdeen
Broadcasting House, Beechgrove Terrace,
Aberdeen AB9 2ZT
tel (01224) 625233

Dundee
Nethergate Centre, 66 Nethergate, Dundee DD1 4ER
tel (01382) 202481

Edinburgh
Broadcasting House, Queen Street,
Edinburgh EH2 1JF
tel 0131-469 4200

Inverness
7 Culduthel Road, Inverness IV2 4AD
tel (01463) 221711

BBC Wales
Broadcasting House, Llandaff, Cardiff CF5 2YQ
tel (01222) 322000 *fax* (01222) 552973
Headquarters of BBC Wales; regional TV
centres in Bangor and Swansea. All Welsh
language programmes are transmitted by
S4C and produced in Cardiff or Swansea.
Regular programmes include *Wales
Today*, *Wales on Saturday* and *Pobol y
Cwm* (Welsh language drama series).
Controller Geraint Talfan Davies
Head of Broadcast (Welsh Language) Gwynn
  Pritchard
Head of Broadcast (English Language) Dai Smith
Head of Production John Geraint
Head of News and Current Affairs Aled Eirug
Head of Drama Pedr James
Head of Sport Arthur Emyr
Head of Entertainment Geraint Evans
Head of Arts, Music and Features Phil George
Commissioning Editor, Radio Wales Nick Evans
Commissioning Editor, Radio Cymru Aled
  Glynne Davies
Series Editor, Pobol y Cwm William Gwyn

Bangor
Broadcasting House, Meirion Road, Bangor,
Gwynedd LL57 2BY
tel (01248) 370880 *fax* (01248) 351443
Head of Production Marian Wyn Jones

Swansea
Broadcasting House, 32 Alexandra Road,
Swansea, West Glamorgan SA1 5DZ
Senior Producer Geraint Davies

BBC English regions

BBC Birmingham
Broadcasting Centre, Pebble Mill Road,
Birmingham B5 7QQ
tel 0121-414 8888
Regular programmes include *The Clothes
Show*, *Telly Addicts*, *Top Gear*, *Network
East*, *East*, *Gardener's World*, *Countryfile*,
The Really Useful Show, *Can't Cook,
Won't Cook*, *Kilroy* (TV); *The Archers,
Folk on Two*, *Jazz Notes*, *Farming Today,
Costing the Earth* (radio). Local news
programmes include *Midlands Today*,
Midlands Report and *Out and About*.

Network Production
Head of Network Production Rod Natkiel
Head of Production (Drama) Development Toni
  Charlton
Executive Editor, Radio Chris Marshall
Editor, Asian Programmes Paresh Solanki
Editor, Consumer Affairs and Features Huw Marks
Editor, Entertainment Richard Lewis
Editor, Leisure and Lifestyle Roger Casstles
Editor, Motoring and Leisure Sports Jon Bentley
Editor, Rural Affairs Paul Cannon
Production and Development Executive
  Stephanie Silk
Editor, New Media Programmes Tony Steyger
Head of Regional and Local Programmes Laura
  Dalgleish
Editor, Newsgathering Roger Clark

BBC East Midlands (Nottingham)
East Midlands Broadcasting Centre, York House,
Mansfield Road, Nottingham NG1 3JA
tel 0115-9550500
Head of Local Programmes Richard Lucas
Local news programmes such as *East
Midlands Today*.

BBC East (Norwich)
St Catherine's Close, All Saint's Green, Norwich,
Norfolk NR1 3ND
tel (01603) 619331
Regular programmes include *Look East*
and *Matter of Fact*.
Head of Regional and Local Programmes David
  Holdsworth
Editor, Newsgathering Tim Bishop

BBC Manchester
New Broadcasting House, Oxford Road,
Manchester M60 1SJ
tel 0161-200 2020
Home of BBC Production's Entertainment
and Features and Religion Departments,
it is also headquarters of BBC North
West's local and regional programmes

operation. Regular programmes include *Rough Guides, The Travel Show, Red Dwarf, The Sunday Show; Songs of Praise, Everyman, Heart of the Matter.*
Head of Entertainment and Features Wayne Garvie
Head of Religious Broadcasting Rev. Ernie Rea
Head of Regional and Local Programmes (BBC North West) Martin Brooks
Editor, Newsgathering (BBC North West) Mike Briscoe

Leeds
Broadcasting Centre, Woodhouse Lane, Leeds LS2 9PX
tel (01132) 441188
Also headquarters of local and regional programme operations for the North.
Head of Regional and Local Programmes (BBC North) Colin Philpott
Regional Political Editor Geoff Talbott
Series Producer, Close Up North Ian Cundall

Newcastle upon Tyne
Broadcasting Centre, Barrack Road, Newcastle upon Tyne NE99 2NE
tel 0191-232 1313
Also headquarters of local and regional programme operations for the North East and Cumbria.
Head of Regional and Local Programmes (BBC North East and Cumbria) Olwyn Hocking
Editor, Newsgathering Andrew Hartley
Producers, Look North Iain Williams, Andrew Lambert

BBC Bristol
Broadcasting House, Whiteladies Road, Bristol BS8 2LR
tel 0117-9732211
The home of the BBC's Natural History Unit, which produces regular programmes such as *Wildlife On One, The Natural World* and *The Really Wild Show.* Recent popular series include *Incredible Journeys, Spirits of the Jaguar* and *Big Cat Diary.* The Bristol features department produces a wide range of regular TV programmes, such as *Antiques Roadshow, 999, Picture This, Under the Sun, Great Antiques Hunt* and *Rick Stein.*
Head of Features, Bristol Jeremy Gibson
Head of Natural History Unit Keith Scholey
Head of Regional and Local Programmes John Conway

BBC West
Broadcasting House, Whiteladies Road, Bristol BS8 2LR
tel 0117-9732211

Bristol is also the home of BBC West, which produces nearly 300 hours of TV each year, including the nightly news magazine *News West,* news bulletins throughout the day, the 30-minute local current affairs programme *Close Up West,* the leisure strand *Out and About,* and a weekly parliamentary programme *Out of Westminster.*
Head of Regional and Local Programmes John Conway
Editor, News and Current Affairs Ian Cameron

BBC South (Southampton)
Broadcasting House, Havelock Road, Southampton, Hants SO14 7PU
tel (01703) 226201
Produces nearly 300 hours of TV each year, including the nightly news magazine *South Today,* news bulletins throughout the day, the 30-minute local current affairs programme *Southern Eye,* the leisure strand *Out and About,* and a weekly parliamentary programme *South of Westminster.*
Head, Regional and Local Programmes Andy Griffee
Editor, Newsgathering Mia Costello

BBC South West (Plymouth)
Broadcasting House, Mannamead, Plymouth PL3 5BD
tel (01752) 229201
Produces nearly 300 hours of TV each year, including the nightly news magazine *Spotlight,* news bulletins throughout the day, the 30-minute local current affairs programme *Close Up,* the leisure strand *Out and About,* and a weekly parliamentary programme *Spotlight on Westminster.*
Head, Regional and Local Programmes Eve Turner
Editor, Newsgathering tba
Editor, Current Affairs Simon Willis

BBC South East (Elstree)
Elstree Centre, Clarendon Road, Borehamwood, Herts. WD6 1JF
tel 0181-953 6100
Produces nearly 300 hours of TV each year, including the nightly news magazine *Newsroom South East,* news bulletins throughout the day, the 30-minute local current affairs programme *First Sight,* the leisure strand *Out and About,* and a weekly parliamentary programme *Around Westminster.*
Head, Regional and Local Programmes Jane Mote
Editor, Newsgathering Peter Solomons

BBC broadcasting rights and terms

Contributors are advised to check latest details of fees with the BBC.

Rights and terms

Specially written material

Fees for submitted material are paid on acceptance. For commissioned material, half the fee is paid on commissioning and half on acceptance as being suitable for television. All fees are subject to negotiation above the minima.

- Rates for one performance of a 60-minute original television play are a minimum of £4728 for a play written by a beginner and a 'going rate' of £7450 for an established writer, or *pro rata* for shorter or longer timings.
- Fees for a 50-minute episode in a series during the same period are a minimum of £3900 for a beginner and a 'going rate' of £5634 for an established writer.
- Fees for a 50-minute dramatisation are a minimum of £2721 for a beginner and a 'going rate' of £4010 for an established writer.
- Fees for a 50-minute adaptation of an existing stage play or other dramatic work are a minimum of £1640 for a beginner and a 'going rate' of £2403 for an established writer.

Specially written light entertainment sketch material

- The rates for sketch material range from £31.31 per minute for beginners with a 'going rate' of £62.62 for established writers.
- The fee for a quickie or news item is half the amount of the writer's per minute rate.
- Fees for submitted material are

payable on acceptance and for commissioned material half on signature and half on acceptance.

Published prose and poems

- Prose works: £18.24 per minute.
- Poems: £21.17 per half minute.

Stage plays and source material for television

- Fees for stage plays and source novels are negotiable.

Repeats in BBC programmes

- Further proportionate fees are payable for repeats.

Use abroad of recordings of BBC programmes

If the BBC sends abroad recordings of its programmes for use by overseas broadcasting organisations on their own networks or stations, further payments accrue to the author, usually in the form of additional percentages of the basic fee paid for the initial performance or a royalty based on the percentage of the distributors' receipts. This can apply to both sound and television programmes.

Value Added Tax

A self-billing system for VAT was introduced in January 1978 for programmes made in London. This now covers radio, external services and television.

Talks

Contributors to talks will be offered the standard television talks contract which provides the BBC certain rights to broadcast the material in a complete, abridged and/or translated manner, and which provides for the payment of further fees for additional usage of the material whether by television, domestic radio or external broadcasting. The contract also covers the assignment of material and limited publication rights. Alternatively, a contract taking in all standard rights may be negotiated. Fees are arranged by the contract authorities in London and the Regions.

Independent national, satellite and cable television

BSkyB
Grant Way, Isleworth, Middlesex TW7 5QD
tel 0171-705 3000 *fax* 0171-705 3030/3113
web site http://www.sky.co.uk

Channel 5 Broadcasting Ltd
22 Long Acre, London WC2E 9LY
tel 0171-497 5225 *fax* 0171-497 5222
The fifth and last national 'free to air' terrestrial 24-hour TV channel. Commissions a wide range of programmes to suit all tastes.

Channel 4 Television Corporation
124 Horseferry Road, London SW1P 2TX
tel 0171-396 4444 *fax* 0171-306 8347
web site http://www.channel4.com
Commissions and purchases programmes (it does not make them) for broadcast during the whole week throughout the United Kingdom (except Wales).

GMTV
London Television Centre, Upper Ground, London SE1 9TT
tel 0171-827 7000 *fax* 0171-827 7001
ITV's national breakfast TV service, 6.00-9.25am, 7 days a week.

Independent Television Commission (ITC)
33 Foley Street, London W1P 7LB
tel 0171-255 3000 *fax* 0171-306 7800
e-mail publicaffairs@itc.org.uk
web site http://www.itc.co.uk
Licenses and regulates all commercially funded TV services in the UK, including cable and satellite services as well as terrestrial services.

ITN
200 Gray's Inn Road, London WC1X 8XZ
tel 0171-833 3000
web site http://www.itn.co.uk
Provides the national and international news programmes for ITV, Channel 4 and Channel 5.

ITV Network Centre
200 Gray's Inn Road, London WC1X 8HF
tel 0171-843 8000 *fax* 0171-843 8158

ON TV
NTL National Media, Bristol House,
1 Lakeside Road, Farnborough, Hants GU14 6XP
tel (01252) 402675 *fax* (01252) 402679
e-mail ontv@cabletel.co.uk
National Producer Sally Allen
Operates 24-hour cable TV service, broadcasting to West Scotland, Northern Ireland, Huddersfield/Kirklees, South Wales, Beds., Herts, East Hants/ West Surrey. Caters for all age groups and interests. Ideas for potential programming material welcome.

S4C
Parc Ty Glas, Llanishen, Cardiff CF4 5DU
tel (01222) 747444 *fax* (01222) 754444
Welsh Fourth Channel broadcasting in English and Welsh. Programmes in Welsh provided by the BBC, HTV and independent producers. Most of Channel 4's output is broadcast on S4C with some rescheduling.

Teletext Ltd
101 Farm Lane, London SW6 1QJ
tel 0171-386 5000 *fax* 0171-386 5002
e-mail enquiries@teletext.co.uk
web site http://www.teletext.co.uk

Independent regional television

It is advisable to check before submitting any ideas/material – in all cases, scripts are preferred to synopses. Programmes should be planned with natural breaks for the insertion of advertisements. These companies also provide some programmes for Channel 4.

Anglia Television Ltd
Anglia House, Norwich NR1 3JG
tel (01603) 615151 *fax* (01603) 631032
e-mail angliatv@angliatv.co.uk
web site http://www.anglia.tv.co.uk
48 Leicester Square, London WC2H 7FB
tel 0171-389 8555 *fax* 0171-930 8499
Provides programmes for the East of England, daytime discussion programmes, drama and Survival natural history programmes for the ITV Network. Drama submissions only through an accredited agency or similar source.

Border Television plc
The Television Centre, Carlisle CA1 3NT
tel (01228) 25101
Provides programmes for The Borders and the Isle of Man, during the whole week. Ideas for programmes, but not drama programmes, are considered from outside sources. Suggestions should be sent to Neil Robinson, Controller of Programmes.

Carlton Broadcasting
101 St Martin's Lane, London WC2N 4AZ
tel 0171-240 4000 *fax* 0171-240 4171
Provides ITV programmes for London and the South East from Monday to Friday.

Central Broadcasting
Central Court, Gas Street, Birmingham B1 2JT
tel 0121-643 9898 *fax* 0121-643 4897
Carlton Studios, Lenton Lane,
Nottingham NG7 2NA
tel 0115-986 3322 *fax* 0115-964 5552
Unit 9, Windrush Court, Abingdon Business Park, Abingdon, Oxon OX1 1SA
tel (01235) 554123 *fax* (01235) 524024
Provides ITV programmes for the East, West and South Midlands 7 days a week.

Channel Television
The Television Centre, St Helier, Jersey JE1 3ZD
tel (01534) 816816 *fax* (01534) 816817
e-mail newsroom@channeltv.co.uk
Provides programmes for the Channel Islands during the whole week relating mainly to Channel Islands news and current affairs.

Grampian Television plc
Queens Cross, Aberdeen AB15 4XJ
tel (01224) 846846 *fax* (01224) 846800
e-mail gtv@grampiantv.co.uk
Albany House, 68 Albany Road, West Ferry,
Dundee DD5 1NW
tel (01382) 739363
23-25 Huntly Street, Inverness IV3 5PR
tel (01463) 242624
Seaforth House, 54 Seaforth Road,
Stornoway HS1 2SD
tel (01851) 704433 *fax* (01851) 706406
Provides programmes for North Scotland during the whole week.

Granada Television Ltd
Granada Television Centre, Manchester M60 9EA
tel 0161-832 7211 and
36 Golden Square, London W1R 4AH
tel 0171-734 8080
The ITV franchise holder for the North West of England. Produces programmes across a broad range for both its region and the ITV Network. Writers are advised to make their approach through agents who would have some knowledge of Granada's current requirements.

HTV Ltd
HTV Wales, The Television Centre,
Culverhouse Cross, Cardiff CF5 6XJ
tel (01222) 590590 and
HTV West, The Television Centre,
Bristol BS4 3HG

tel 0117-977 8366

Provides programmes for Wales and West of England during the whole week. Produces programmes for home and international sales.

LWT

The London Television Centre, London SE1 9LT
tel 0171-620 1620

Provides programmes for Greater London and much of the Home Counties area from Friday 5.15pm to Monday 6.00am (excluding 6.00-9.25am on Sat/Sun).

Meridian Broadcasting

Television Centre, Southampton, Hants SO14 0PZ
tel (01703) 222555 *fax* (01703) 335050
web site http://www.meridian.tv.co.uk

The ITV franchise holder for the South and South East. Meridian produces quality drama, factual and children's programming for the ITV network.

Scottish Television Enterprises

Cowcaddens, Glasgow G2 3PR
tel 0141-300 3000 *fax* 0141-300 3030

Wholly owned subsidiary of the Scottish Media Group, making drama and other programmes for the ITV network. Material: ideas and formats for long-form series with or without a Scottish flavour. Approach in the first instance to the Controller of Drama, Robert Love.

Tyne Tees Television Ltd

The Television Centre, City Road, Newcastle upon Tyne NE1 2AL
tel 0191-261 0181 *fax* 0191-261 2302

Serving the North of England 7 days a week, 24 hours a day.

Ulster Television plc

Havelock House, Ormeau Road, Belfast, Northern Ireland BT7 1EB
tel (01232) 328122 *fax* (01232) 246695

Provides programmes for Northern Ireland during the whole week.

Westcountry Television Ltd

Langage Science Park, Plymouth PL7 5BG
tel (01752) 333333 *fax* (01752) 333444

Provides programmes for South West England throughout the week. In-house production mainly news, regional current affairs and topical features; other regional features commissioned from independent producers. Conduit to the Network for independent production packages.

Yorkshire Television Ltd

The Television Centre, Leeds LS3 1JS
tel 0113-243 8283 *fax* 0113-244 5107

Yorkshire Television is a Network Company which produces many programmes for the ITV Network and the Yorkshire area 7 days a week. Material preferred submitted through agents. Wholly owned subsidiary of Granada Media Group.

Presenting scripts for television and film

There is an old saying that the plot of the best movie can be written on a post-card. However, whether your aim is to write a big feature film or a television play to be made on film (as most are nowadays), you must be prepared to write the full screenplay. **Jean McConnell** *describes how to lay out your manuscript and how to submit it for consideration.*

That the decision of the Arts Council to channel lottery money into British films was a wise one is self-evident. The promise of more of the same for another four years should give renewed confidence to everyone involved in the industry. Our quality movies can not only win the prizes but, more importantly, win back a satisfied audience of regular cinema-goers.

What is a screenplay?

A screenplay should tell a story in terms of visual action and dialogue spoken by the characters. A script for a full-length feature film running about one and a half hours will be about 100-130 pages long. Whether it is a feature film, a short film for children, say, or a documentary, it is better to present a version which is too short rather than too long.

Elaborate camera directions are not necessary as a shooting script will be made at a later stage. Your job is to write the master scenes, clearly broken down into each incident and location.

Layout

Individual companies may vary slightly in their house style but the general layout of a screenplay, either for a feature film or television film, is illustrated on page 307. The following points should be noted.
• Each scene should be numbered on the left and given a title which indicates whether the scene is an interior or an exterior, where it takes place, and the lighting

conditions, i.e. day or night. The situation of each scene should be standardised; don't call your 'sitting room' a 'lounge' the next time you come to it, or people will think you mean a different place.
• Note that the dialogue is spaced out, with the qualifying directions such as '(frowning)' on a separate line, slightly inset from the dialogue. Double space each speech from the previous one.
• Always put the names of the characters in CAPITALS, except when they occur in the actual dialogue. Double space the stage directions from the dialogue, but single space the lines of the stage directions themselves.
• Use A4 size paper. Leave at least a 4cm margin on the left and a reasonably wide right-hand margin. It is false economy to cram the page. Use one side of the sheet only.
• Only give the camera directions when you feel it to be essential. For instance, if you want to show something from a particular character's point of view, or if you think you need it to make a point, i.e. 'HARRY approaches the cliff edge and looks down. LONG SHOT – HARRY'S POINT OF VIEW. ALICE fully clad is walking into the sea. CUT TO: CLOSE UP OF HARRY'S HORRIFIED FACE.' Note the camera directions are put in capital letters on a separate line, as in the specimen page.
• Character sketches should appear in the body of the screenplay, e.g. PETE enters. He is a man you wouldn't want to meet in a dark alley.

Preparation of manuscript

The title page should give the name and nature of your piece. Also include your (or your agent's) address. The second page should give a list of the main characters.

Add a front and back cover and bind your screenplay, securing the pages firmly. Make sure you have saved it on disk or retain a master copy. Never part with the only copy you possess. If you do, it will surely get lost.

Submission

Try to get an agent. A good agent will give you a fair opinion of your work and, if your work is worthwhile, he or she will know the particular film company which will want to buy it. Remember that if film companies state that they will only consider material sent through an agent, they definitely mean it.

If you are sending your manuscript to a company direct, it is advisable to first check as far as possible in case it is already working on a similar idea.

Attach a stamped, addressed envelope to your manuscript whether sending it through an agent or direct. Most companies have a story department, to which you should address your material. As story editors are very busy people, you can make their life easier by complying with the submission notes listed in the box.

Accept that this is really a tough market, namely because:
• films cost so much to make today that the decision to go ahead is only taken after a great many important factors have been satisfied and an even greater number of important people are happy about it;
• writing a screenplay calls for knowledge and appreciation of the technicalities of film-making, as well as the ability to combine dialogue, action and pictures, throughout in the language of a visual medium.

The treatment

If a producer likes the idea of your screenplay, he or she may ask to see a treatment.

Submission notes

If you have based your screenplay on someone else's published work you should make the fact clear in a covering letter, stating that:
• the material is no longer in copyright, or
• you yourself own the copyright, or at least an option on it, or
• you have not obtained the copyright but have reason to believe that there would be no difficulty in doing so.

Apart from a note of any relevant credits you may already possess, do not regale the editor with your personal details, unless they bear a direct relation to the material submitted. For instance, if your story concerns a brain surgeon, then it would be relevant for the editor to know that you actually are one. Otherwise, trust your work to stand on its own merit.

There is no need to mention if your work has been turned down by other companies, however regretfully. The comments of others will not influence a story editor one way or the other.

Do not suggest actors or actresses you would like to play your characters. This decision is entirely out of your hands.

Don't pester the company if you don't get a reply, or even an acknowledgement, for some weeks. Most companies will formally acknowledge receipt and then leave you in limbo for at least six weeks. However, after about three months or so, a brief letter politely asking what has happened is in order. A telephone call is unlikely to be helpful. It is possible the company may have liked your work enough to have sent it to America, or to be getting further readers' opinions on it. This all takes time. If they don't like it, you will certainly get your manuscript back in due course.

A treatment can range from a basic outline through to a synopsis of the story with a breakdown of the main characters and some of the key scenes written in detail. Its aim is to demonstrate the style and general flavour of the piece and may be wanted before the whole script is read and/or in order to interest his or her colleagues. It may be no more than half a dozen pages but it is likely to be your major selling document. So do your best to thrill the producer to the core in a couple of minutes flat.

13.   INT.   BARN   DAY

ALAN regards ELIZABETH anxiously. ELIZABETH is staring at the
large wine vat. She backs away from it and crosses to the door,
where she turns.

                    ELIZABETH
          I still think the police ought to know.

She goes out. ALAN listens as her footsteps retreat. the he
crosses quickly to the vat, climbs up and heaves at the lid.

                                                  CUT TO:

14.   EXT.   FARMYARD   DAY

DONALD intercepts ELIZABETH as she crosses the yard.

                    DONALD
          What does he say?

                    ELIZABETH
          Nothing.

                    DONALD
               (frowning)
          Right. Now it's my turn.

He starts for the barn. ELIZABETH watches him go.

                                                  CUT TO:

15.   INT.   BARN   DAY

DONALD'S shadow falls across the threshold. He hesitates, his
eyes getting used to the gloom.

                    DONALD
          Alan?

ALAN lets the lid of the vat fall. He jumps down. He stands
quite still as DONALD crosses to him. The two men eye each other
silently. ALAN turns away.

                    DONALD
               (with sudden realisation)
          You knew it was there ... didn't you?

                                                  CUT TO:

CLOSE-UP OF ALAN'S FACE: IT IS HAGGARD

                    ALAN
          I hoped to God it wouldn't be.

Television and film producers

Jean McConnell advises on submitting a screenplay for consideration.

The recommended approach for placing material is through a recognised literary agent. Most film companies have a story department to which material can be sent for consideration by its editors. If you choose to submit material direct, first check with the company to make sure it is worth your while.

It is a fact that many of the feature films these days are based on already best-selling books. However, there are some companies, particularly those with a television outlet, which will sometimes accept unsolicited material if it seems to be exceptionally original.

When a writer submits material direct to a company, some of the larger ones – usually those based in the United States – may request that a Release Form be signed before they are prepared to read it. This document is ostensibly designed to absolve the company from any charge of plagiarism if they should be working on a similar idea; and also to limit their liability in the event of any legal action. Writers must make up their own minds whether they wish to sign this but, in principle, it is not highly recommended.

It should be noted that there are a number of independent companies making films specifically for television presentation. These are included in the list below of companies currently in active production.

Jean McConnell is a founder member of the Writers' Guild of Great Britain. She has written screenplays, radio and stage plays, and books. She is a member of the Crime Writers' Association and the Society of Women Writers and Journalists.

Aardman Animations
Gas Ferry Road, Bristol BS1 6UN
tel 0117-984 8485 *fax* 0117-984 8486
web site http://www.aardman.com
Producer, Broadcast/Features Michael Rose
Specialists in model animation, looking for treatments for adults and families for cinema and TV. Founded 1972.

Agran Barton Television Ltd
The Yacht Club, Chelsea Harbour,
London SW10 0XA
tel 0171-351 7070 *fax* 0171-352 3528
Contact Development Executive
Screenplays for cinema; drama and factual TV programmes. Founded 1993.

British Lion Screen Entertainment
Pinewood Studios, Iver, Bucks. SL0 0NH
tel (01753) 651700 *fax* (01753) 656391
Contact Peter Snell
Screenplays and treatments for cinema; TV drama and sitcoms. No unsolicited material. Founded 1927.

Brook Lapping Ltd
21-24 Bruges Place, Randolph Street,
London NW1 0TF
tel 0171-428 3100 *fax* 0171-284 0626
Development Executives Anne Lapping, Brian Lapping, Phillip Whitehead, Norma Percy
TV documentaries and current affairs.

Carlton Productions
35-38 Portman Square,
London W1H 0NU
tel 0171-486 6688 *fax* 0171-486 1132
Director of Programmes Andy Allan
Makes and commissions programmes for Central Broadcasting and Carlton Broadcasting to supply ITV and other broadcasters.

Catalyst Television Ltd
Brook Green Studios, 186 Shepherds Bush Road,
London W6 7LL
tel 0171-603 7030 *fax* 0171-603 9519
Contact Head of Drama Development
Screenplays/novels for adaptation for TV.

Will only consider material submitted through an agent or publisher. Founded 1991.

Celador Productions Ltd
39 Long Acre, London WC2E 9JT
tel 0171-240 8101 *fax* 0171-836 1117
Contact Alexandra Monk

Chatsworth Television Ltd
97-99 Dean Street, London W1V 5RA
tel 0171-734 4302 *fax* 0171-437 3301
e-mail 106035,663@compuserve.com
Head of Drama Development Stephen Jeffery-Poulter (film and TV drama scripts)
Head of Entertainment Justin Scroggie (infotainment, entertainment and game show formats)
No sitcoms. All submissions must be accompanied by an sae. Founded 1980.

Children's Film and Television Foundation Ltd
Elstree Film Studios, Borehamwood, Herts. WD6 1JG
tel 0181-953 0844 *fax* 0181-207 0860
Not a production company; finances script development, especially for feature films (principally TV) aimed at children between 5 and 12 years old.

Childsplay Productions Ltd
8 Lonsdale Road, London NW6 6RD
tel 0171-328 1429 *fax* 0171-328 1416
Contact Kim Burke
Children's (not preschool) and family TV programming; chiefly drama. Founded 1984.

The Comic Strip Ltd
Dean House, 102 Dean Street, London W1V 3RA
tel 0171-734 1166 *fax* 0171-734 1105
Contact Rebecca Jeffrey, Peter Richardson
Screenplays for cinema and TV; half-hour comedy and drama series. Founded 1980.

Deep Silver TV
Planet Building, 195 Marsh Wall, London E14 9SG
tel 0171-512 5012 *fax* 0171-345 9185
e-mail bigal@dircon.co.uk
Managing Director Alex Connock
Scripts, synopses and ideas for TV drama and films. Founded 1997 under the Planet 24 umbrella.

The Walt Disney Company Ltd
3 Queen Caroline Street, London W6 9PE
tel 0181-222 1000 *fax* 0181-222 2795
Screenplays not accepted by London office. Must be submitted by an agent to The Walt Disney Studios in Burbank, California.

Feelgood Fiction
(trading name of Diverse Fiction Ltd)
49 Goldhawk Road, London W12 8AP
tel 0181-746 2535 *fax* 0181-740 6177
Managing Director Philip Clarke, *Drama Producer* Laurence Bowen
Film and TV drama. Founded 1982.

Fairwater Films Ltd
68 Vista Rise, Llandaff, Cardiff CF5 2SD
tel/fax (01222) 578488
e-mail tbarnes@netcomuk.co.uk
Managing Director Tony Barnes
Animation for cinema and TV; live action entertainment. All material should be submitted through an agent. Founded 1982.

The First Film Company Ltd
38 Great Windmill Street, London W1V 7PA
tel 0171-439 1640 *fax* 0171-437 2062
Producers Roger Randall-Cutler, Simon Flind, Rob Cheek
Screenplays for cinema. All material should be submitted through an agent. Founded 1984.

Focus Films Ltd
The Rotunda Studios, rear of 116-118 Finchley Road, London NW3 5HT
tel 0171-435 9004 *fax* 0171-431 3562
e-mail focus@pupix.demon.co.uk
Contact Head of Development
Screenplays for cinema. Will only consider material submitted through an agent. Founded 1982.

Mark Forstater Productions Ltd
27 Lonsdale Road, London NW6 6RA
tel 0171-624 1123 *fax* 0171-624 1124
Contact Rosie Homan
Film and TV production. No unsolicited scripts, please.

Front Page Films
23 West Smithfield, London EC1A 9HY
tel 0171-329 6866 *fax* 0171-329 6844
Contact Script Editor
Screenplays for cinema. Material only accepted through agents. Founded 1985.

Gaia Communictions
Sanctuary House, 35 Harding Avenue, Eastbourne, East Sussex BN22 8PL
tel (01323) 727183 *tel/fax* (01323) 734809
Director Robert Armstrong, *Script Editor* Loni von Gruner
Specialises in Southeast regional documentary programmes, particularly historical and tourist. Expanding operation

into programmes for the new multiple satellite stations. Send synopsis in first instance with sae for return of material. Founded 1987.

Noel Gay Television
1 Albion Court, Albion Place, Galena Road, London W6 0QT
tel 0181-600 5200 *fax* 0181-600 5222
Contact Head of Development
Treatments for cinema and TV; entertainment and drama. Founded 1987.

Granada Film
The London TV Centre, Upper Ground, London SE1 9LT
tel 0171-737 8681 *fax* 0171-737 8682
Head of Film Pippa Cross
Screenplays for cinema: major commercial feature films and smaller UK-based films. No unsolicited material. Founded 1989.

Hammer Film Production Ltd
Elstree Studios, Borehamwood, Herts. WD6 1JG
tel 0181-207 4011 *fax* 0181-905 1127
Contact Roy Skeggs
Completed screenplays and published books for cinema and TV development: drama/mystery/horror/ghost. No unsolicited material.

Hartswood Films
Twickenham Studios, The Barons, St Margaret's, Twickenham, Middlesex TW1 2AW
tel 0181-607 8736 *fax* 0181-607 8744
Producer Beryl Vertue, *Development* Elaine Cameron
Screenplays for cinema and TV; comedy and drama. No unsolicited material. Founded 1981.

Hat Trick Productions Ltd
10 Livonia Street, London W1V 3PH
tel 0171-434 2451 *fax* 0171-287 9791
Contact Denise O'Donoghue
Situation and drama comedy series and light entertainment shows. Founded 1986.

The Jim Henson Company
30 Oval Road, London NW1 7DE
tel 0171-428 4000 *fax* 0171-428 4001
Contact Angus Fletcher
Screenplays for cinema and TV; fantasy, family and children's programmes – usually involving puppetry or animatronics. All material should be submitted through an agent. Founded 1979.

Hightimes Productions
7 Anglers Lane, London NW5 3DG
tel 0171-482 5202 *fax* 0171-485 4254
Managing Director Al Mitchell
Screenplays for TV; light entertainment, comedy and drama. Founded 1981.

Mike Hopwood Productions Ltd
Winton House, Stoke Road, Stoke-on-Trent ST4 2RW
tel (01782) 848800 *fax* (01782) 749447
Contact Development Executive
Screenplays for cinema; drama and factual TV programmes. Founded 1991.

Illuminations
19-20 Rheidol Mews, Rheidol Terrace, London N1 8NU
tel 0171-226 0266 *fax* 0171-359 1151
e-mail linda@illumin.co.uk
web site http://www.illumin.co.uk
Contact Linda Zuck
Screenplays for TV; cultural documentaries, arts and entertainment for broadcast TV. All material should be submitted through an agent. Founded 1982.

Kensington Films and Television Ltd
60 Charlotte Street, London W1P 2AX
tel 0171-927 8458 *fax* 0171-927 8798
Screenplays for cinema and TV drama. Send material to Margot Gavan Duffy. Founded 1993.

Brian Lapping Associates – merged with Brook Associates Ltd to form Brook Lapping Ltd

Little Bird Company Ltd
7 Lower James Street, London W1R 3PL
tel 0171-434 1131 *fax* 0171-434 1803
Development Executives J. Cavendish, M. Pope
Screenplays for cinema and TV. Founded 1982.

Little Dancer Ltd
Avonway, 3 Naseby Road, London SE19 3JJ
tel 0181-653 9343
Producer Robert Smith
Screenplays for cinema and TV; drama. Founded 1992.

London Film Productions Ltd
35 Davies Street, London W1Y 1FN
tel 0171-499 7800 *fax* 0171-499 7994
Chairman J. Eliasch
No unsolicited material considered.

Malone Gill Productions Ltd
9-15 Neal Street, London WC2H 9PU
tel 0171-460 4683/4 *fax* 0171-460 4679

e-mail ikonic@compuserve.com
Contact Georgina Denison
TV programmes. Founded 1978.

Maya Vision Ltd
43 New Oxford Street, London WC1A 1BH
tel 0171-836 1113 *fax* 0171-838 5169
Producer/Director Rebecca Dobbs
Features, TV dramas and documentaries.
No unsolicited scripts. Founded 1982/3.

Monogram Productions Ltd
27-29 Berwick Street, London W1V 3RF
tel 0171-734 9873 *fax* 0171-734 9874
Managing Director Eileen Quinn
Screenplays for cinema and TV; drama
series and serials only. All material
should be submitted through an agent.
Founded 1997.

New Blitz TV
Via Guido Banti 34, 00191 Rome, Italy
tel 333 26 41 *fax* 333 26 51
Television Department Giovanni A. Congiu
Importation and dubbing TV series, documentaries, educational films and video
for schools. Material from freelance
sources required.

Penumbra Productions Ltd
80 Brondesbury Road, London NW6 6RX
tel 0171-328 4550 *fax* 0171-328 3844
e-mail 101621.3135@compuserve.com
Contact H.O. Nazareth
Drama for feature films and TV; documentaries for TV; non-broadcast videos
to commissions. Founded 1981.

Picture Palace Films Ltd
19 Edis Street, London NW1 8LE
tel 0171-586 8763 *fax* 0171-586 9048
e-mail 100444.2737@compuserve.com
Contact Malcolm Craddock
Screenplays for cinema and TV; low budget films; TV drama series. Material only
considered if submitted through an
agent. Founded 1971.

Planet 24
The Planet Building, 195 Marsh Wall,
Thames Quay, London E14 9SG
tel 0171-345 2424 *fax* 0171-345 9400
Contact Development Department
Screenplays for cinema and TV; drama
and comedy for TV and radio; factual
entertainment formats. Founded 1992.

Portman Productions Ltd
167 Wardour Street, London W1V 3TA
tel 0171-468 3400 *fax* 0171-468 3499

Head of Development Katherine Butler
TV drama. Founded 1944.

Portobello Pictures Ltd
14-15 D'Arblay Street, London W1V 3FP
tel 0171-379 5566 *fax* 0171-379 5599
Contact Ed Whitmore, Eric Abraham
Screenplays for cinema. Founded 1987.

Primetime Television Associates
Seymour Mews House, Seymour Mews,
Wigmore Street, London W1H 9PE
tel 0171-935 9000 *fax* 0171-935 1992,
0171-487 3975
Contact Victoria Hull
Screenplays for TV and TV programmes
of international interest, especially
drama and documentary series. No unsolicited scripts. Founded 1968.

Red Rooster Film & Television Entertainment Ltd
14-15 D'Arblay Street, London W1V 3FP
tel 0171-439 6969 *fax* 0171-439 6767
Managing Director Jill Green, *Development
Executive* Joanna Anderson
Screenplays for cinema and TV; drama.
All material should be submitted through
an agent. Founded 1982.

Regent Productions Ltd
The Mews, 6 Putney Common, London SW15 1HL
tel 0181-789 5350 *fax* 0181-789 5332
Contact William G. Stewart
Screenplays for TV; drama, situation
comedies. Founded 1982.

Specific Films
25 Rathbone Street, London W1P 1AG
tel 0171-580 7476 *fax* 0171-494 2676
e-mail specificfilms@compuserve.com
Contact Christian Routh
Feature-length screenplays.

Spitting Image Productions Ltd
Cairo Studios, 4 Nile Street, London N1 7ZZ
tel 0171-251 2626 *fax* 0171-251 2066
Head of Development Roger Law, *Managing
Director* Richard Bennett
Projects for puppets and animation.
Founded 1983.

Talisman Films Ltd
5 Addison Place, London W11 4RJ
tel 0171-603 7474 *fax* 0171-602 7422
e-mail talisman_films@dial.pipex.com
Contact Anna Sofroniou
Screenplays for cinema and TV. Material
only considered if submitted through an
agent. Founded 1991.

TalkBack Productions
36 Percy Street, London W1P 0LN
tel 0171-323 9777 *fax* 0171-637 5105
TV situation comedies and comedy dramas. Send unsolicited material to PA to Managing Director; material through an agent to Peter Fincham. Founded 1981.

Tiger Aspect Productions Ltd
5 Soho Square, London W1V 5DE
tel 0171-434 0672 *fax* 0171-287 1448
Contact Lucy Kenwright
TV comedy drama and sitcoms. All material should be submitted through an agent. Founded 1993.

Triple Vision Ltd
Folly Lodge, Folly Lane, North Wooton, Somerset BA4 4ER
tel/fax (01749) 890610
Contact Terry Flaxton
Screenplays for cinema and TV; arts/drama and documentaries, plays. Material only accepted through agents. Founded 1983.

Twentieth Century Fox Productions Ltd
Twentieth Century House, 31-32 Soho Square, London W1V 6AP
tel 0171-437 7766 *fax* 0171-434 2170
Will not consider unsolicited material.

Twenty Twenty Television
20 Kentish Town Road, London NW1 9NX
tel 0171-284 2020 *fax* 0171-284 1810
e-mail twentytwenty@dial.pipex.com
Executive Producer Claudia Milne
Current affairs, documentaries, travel films, science and educational programmes, drama documentaries. Founded 1982.

UBA Ltd
21 Alderville Road, London SW6 3RL
tel 0171-371 0160 *fax* (01984) 623733
Contact Peter Shaw
Screenplays for cinema and TV of international interest. All material should be submitted through an agent. Founded 1983.

United Film and Television Productions
48 Leicester Square, London WC2H 7FB
tel 0171-389 8555 *fax* 0171-930 8499
Managing Director John Willis
Synopses for TV drama or mini-series, comedies, non-factual programme ideas. Founded 1996.

Warner Bros. Productions Ltd
135 Wardour Street, London W1V 4AP
tel 0171-437 5600
Screenplays for cinema. Will only consider material submitted through an agent.

Warner Sisters Film & TV Ltd
Canalot Studios, 222 Kensal Road, London W10 5BN
tel 0181-960 3550 *fax* 0181-960 3880
Screenplays for cinema and TV; TV programmes. All material should be submitted through an agent. Founded 1984.

Michael White
48 Dean Street, London W1V 5HL
tel 0171-734 7707 *fax* 0171-734 7727
e-mail mw@mwents.demon.co.uk
Screenplays for cinema and TV. Founded 1963.

Working Title Films
76 Oxford Street, London W1N 9FD
tel 0171-307 3000 *fax* 0171-307 3001/2/3
Head of Development Debra Hayward (Films), Simon Wright (TV)
Screenplays for film and TV – drama and comedy. Founded 1984.

World Productions Ltd
17 Golden Square, London W1R 4BB
tel 0171-734 3536 *fax* 0171-434 2410
e-mail world-productions.com
Head of Development Serena Cullen
Screenplays for TV; TV drama series and serials.

Zenith Productions Ltd
43-45 Dorset Street, London W1H 4AB
tel 0171-224 2440 *fax* 0171-224 3194
e-mail zenith@zenith.tv.co.uk
Screenplays for cinema; TV drama. No unsolicited scripts.

Television and radio overseas

Opportunities are outlined here for submitting material to television and radio companies in Australia, Canada, Republic of Ireland, New Zealand and South Africa.

Australia

Australian Broadcasting Corporation (ABC)
Box 9994, Sydney, NSW 2001
tel (02) 9333 1500 *fax* (02) 9333 5305
e-mail comments@your.abc.net.au
web site http://www.abc.net.au
Manager for Europe Australian Broadcasting Corporation, 54 Portland Place, London W1N 4DY

Provides TV and radio programmes in the national broadcasting service; operates Radio Australia; operates the international TV news service, Australia Television; and co-ordinates a network of six symphony orchestras and stages concerts throughout Australia.

ABC TV restricts its production resources to work closely related to the Australian environment. ABC radio also looks principally to Australian writers for the basis of its drama output. However, ABC radio is interested in reading or auditioning new creative material of a high quality from overseas sources and this may be submitted in script or taped form. No journalistic material is required. Talks on international affairs are commissioned.

Federation of Australian Commercial Television Stations (FACTS)
44 Avenue Road, Mosman, NSW 2088
tel (02) 9960 2622 *fax* (02) 9969 3520
General Manager Tony Branigan
Represents all 44 commercial TV stations.

Federation of Australian Radio Broadcasters Ltd
PO Box 299, St Leonards, NSW 2065
tel (02) 9906 5944 *fax* (02) 9906 5128

Ceo A.M. King
Association of privately owned radio stations.

Canada

Canadian Broadcasting Corporation
250 Lanark Avenue, PO Box 3220, Stn. 'C', Ottawa, Ontario K1Y 1E4
tel 613-724-1200

CTV Television Network
250 Yonge Street, Suite 1800, Toronto, Ontario M5B 2N8
tel 416-595-4100 *fax* 416-595-5998
President/Ceo John Cassaday
Network of 25 privately owned affiliated TV stations from coast to coast.

Republic of Ireland

Radio Telefís Éireann (RTÉ)
Donnybrook, Dublin 4
tel (01) 2083111 *fax* (01) 2083080
web site http://www.rte.ie
The Irish national broadcasting service operating radio and TV.

Television Ongoing production of both a rural and an urban drama serial. Treatments and character profiles accepted for one-off drama productions, drama series and situation comedies, preferably set in Ireland or of strong Irish interest, with preferred durations of commercial half hour or hour length. Forwarding of fully dialogued submissions not encouraged. Before submitting material to Current Affairs, Drama, Features or Young People's programmes, authors are advised to write to the department in question.
Radio Short stories (length 13-14 min-

utes) in Irish or English suitable for broadcasting; plays (running 30, 60 or 90 minutes) are welcomed and paid for according to merit. Guidelines on writing for radio drama are available from the RTE Radio Drama Department, Radio Centre, Donnybrook, Dublin 4.

Independent Radio and Television Commission (IRTC)

Marine House, Clanwilliam Place, Dublin 2, Republic of Ireland
tel (01) 6760966 *fax* (01) 6760948
e-mail info@irtc.ie

Statutory body with responsibility for independent broadcasting. At present there are 21 local radio stations operating in Ireland, in addition to one special interest/community station and one Irish language station. A further 11 community and community of interest radio stations are currently on air as part of a community radio pilot project.

The IRTC launched a new national radio station, Radio Ireland on 17 March 1997 and negotiations are currently under way for the establishment of a national independent television service.

New Zealand

The Radio Network of New Zealand Ltd

PO Box 3526, Auckland
tel (09) 377-6199 *fax* (09) 367-4619
Chief Executive Stephen Barron

A radio company controlling a NZ-wide groip of 52 commercial radio stations in metropolitan and provincial markets. The station brand groups are Newstalk ZB, Classic Hits, ZM, Easy Listening 1, Rock, Radio Sports Network, and Community.

Television New Zealand Ltd

PO Box 3819, Auckland
tel (09) 377-0630 *fax* (09) 375-0918
Chairman Norman Geary, *Group Chief Executive* Chris Anderson

TVNZ is a state-owned enterprise with production facilities in all four main centres. It owns and operates TV ONE, TV2 and subsidiary companies, South Pacific Pictures Ltd, Avalon Studios Ltd, Broadcast Communications Ltd and Horizon Pacific Television, which operates five regional TV stations.

South Africa

South African Broadcasting Corporation (SABC)

Private Bag X1, Auckland Park 2006
tel (011) 714-9111 *fax* (011) 714-3106
web site http://www.sabc.co.za

Television Operates 3 TV services in 11 languages, SABC1, SABC2 and SABC3. All services accept scripts in English for drama and comedy, either for one-off programmes or series.

Radio Operates 16 internal radio networks and one external radio service. The service which makes the greatest use of written material in English is SAFM.

Drama One-hour plays of all kinds welcomed. Half-hour plays are occasionally broadcast.

Short stories Short stories of all kinds (1500-1800 words) are welcomed.

Children's programmes Short stories, plays and serials (maximum 15 minutes) may be submitted.

Talks Most are locally commissioned, but outstanding material of particular interest may be submitted (3-10 minutes).

Radio

Writing drama for radio

Writing drama for radio allows a freedom which none of the other performing arts can give. **Lee Hall** *guides the radio drama writer to submit a script which will be both well received and merit production.*

With upwards of 300 hours of radio drama commissioned each year, radio is an insatiable medium and, therefore, one which is constantly seeking new blood. It is no surprise to find that many of our most eminent dramatists, such as Pinter and Stoppard, did important radio work early in their careers.

Although the centrality of radio has been eclipsed somewhat by television and fringe theatre, it continues to launch new writers, and its products often find popular recognition in other media (for example, the film version of Anthony Mingella's *Truly Madly Deeply*). Because radio is often cited as the discoverer and springboard of so many talents, this should not obscure the fact that many writers make a living primarily out of their radio writing and the work itself is massively popular, with plays regularly getting audiences of over 500,000 people.

For the dramatist, the medium offers a variety of work which is difficult to find anywhere else: serials, dramatisations, new commissions of various lengths (from a couple of minutes to several hours), musicals, soap operas, adaptations of the classics, as well as a real enthusiasm to examine new forms.

Because it is no more expensive to be in the Hindu Kush than to be in a laundrette in Deptford, the scope of the world is only limited by the imagination of the writer. However, though radio drama in the 'Fifties and 'Sixties was an important conduit for absurdism, there is a perceived notion that radio drama on the BBC is domestic, Home Counties and endlessly trotting out psychological trauma in a rather naturalistic fash-

ion. This is not a fair assessment of the true range of work presented. The BBC itself is anxious to challenge this idea and as the face of broadcasting changes, there is a conscious move to attract new audiences with new kinds of work.

Get to know the form

Listen to as many plays as possible, read plays that are in print, and try to analyse what works, what doesn't and why. This may seem obvious, but it is easy to fall back on your preconceived notions of what radio plays are. The more you hear other people's successes and failures, the more tools you will have to discriminate when it comes to your own work.

Plays on radio tend to fit into specific time slots: 30, 60, 75, 90 minutes, and each slot will have a different feel – an afternoon play will be targeted at a different audience from one at 10.30pm.

A radio play will be chosen on artistic grounds but nevertheless a writer should be familiar with the market. This should not be seen as an invitation merely to copy forms or to try to make your play 'fit', but an opportunity to gain some sense of what the producers are dealing with. Producers are looking for new and fresh voices, ones which are unique, open new areas or challenge certain preconceptions. This is not to suggest you should be wilfully idiosyncratic but to be aware that it is the individuality of your 'voice' that people will notice.

Write what you feel strongly about, in the way that most attracts you. It should be bold, personal, entertaining, challenging and stimulating. Radio has the scope to explore drama that wouldn't get produced in theatres or on television, so treat it as the most radical forum for new writing. How many times have you listened to the radio with the sense that you've heard it all before? Never feel limited by what exists but be aware how your voice can enrich the possibilities of the future.

Who to approach

Opportunities for writing for radio in the UK are dominated by the BBC. Whilst there are increasing opportunities with independent stations, BBC Radio Drama overwhelms the field. Its output is huge. The variety of the work – from soaps to the classics – makes it the true national repertory for drama in its broadest sense. However, the BBC is increasingly commissioning productions from independent producers, so you can:
• send your unsolicited script to the BBC Radio Drama Department (see page 318) where it will be assessed by a reader. If they find it of interest they will put you in contact with a suitable producer.
• approach a producer directly. This may be a producer at the BBC or at an independent company (see page 333). Both will give a personal response based on their own taste, rather than an institutional one.

Producers have a broad role: they find new writers, develop projects, edit the script, cast the actors, record and edit the play, and even write up the blurb for the *Radio Times*. Because of this intense involvement, the producer needs to have a strong personal interest in the writer or writing when they take on a project.

The system of commissioning programmes at the BBC is such that staff producers or independent production companies offer projects to commissioning editors to decide upon. Thus, a writer must be linked to a producer in the first instance to either get their play produced or get a commission for a new piece of work. Therefore, going direct to a producer can be a convenient short cut, but it requires more preparation.

Approaching a producer

Discovering and developing the work of new writers is only a small part of a producer's responsibilities, so be selective. Do your homework – there is little point in sending your sci-fi series to a producer who exclusively produces one-off period comedies.

To help decide which producer will be the most receptive to your work, become familiar with the work of each producer you are intersted in and the type of writers they work with. Use the *Radio Times* to help with your research and listen to as many of their plays as possible. It is well worth the effort in order to be sure to send your play to the right person. If you can quote the reasons why you've chosen them in particular, it can only help to get a congenial reception. It will also give you confidence in their response, as the comments – good or bad – will be from someone you respect.

Submitting your work

Don't stuff your manuscript into an envelope as soon as you've written 'The End'. You owe it to yourself to get the script into the best possible state before anyone sees it. First impressions matter and time spent refining will pay dividends in attracting attention.

Ask a person you trust to give you some feedback. Try to edit the work yourself, cutting things that don't work and spending time revising and reinventing anything which you think could be better. Make sure that what you send is the best you can possibly do.

Producers have mountains of scripts to read. The more bulky your tome the less enthusiastically it will be received. (It's better to send a sparkling 10-page sample than your whole 300-page masterpiece.) Try to make the first scene excellent. The more you can surprise, engage or delight in the first few pages, the more chance the rest will be carefully read. The adage that a reader can tell whether a play is any good after the first three pages might be wholly inaccurate but it reflects a cynicism versed by the practice of script reading. The reader will probably approach your script with the expectation that it is unsuitable, and part of getting noticed is jolting them out of their complacency.

Have your script presentably typed. Make sure your letter of introduction is well informed and shows that you haven't just picked a name at random. Do not send it to more than one producer at a time, as this is considered bad etiquette. And don't expect an instantaneous response – it may take a couple of months before you receive a reply. Don't be afraid of calling up if they keep you waiting for an unreasonable length of time, but don't badger people as this will inevitably be counterproductive.

Finally

Don't be discouraged by rejection and *don't* assume that because one person has rejected your script that it is no good. It is all a question of taste. Use the criticism positively to help your work, not as a personal attack.

Lee Hall's first radio play, *I Luv U, Jimmy Spud*, won the Alfred Bradley Bursary Award, The Richard Imison Award, and the Society of Authors/Sony Award in 1996. He has written several other plays for BBC Radio, as well as the series *God's Country*, which included the award-winning play *Spoonface Steinberg*, and a serial dramatisation of Mario Vargas Llosa's *Aunt Julia and the Scriptwriter*.

BBC national radio

The BBC commissions from both BBC Production and independent producers (see page 333), as well as from BBC regional centres.

BBC Broadcast

BBC Broadcast, Broadcasting House,
London W1A 1AA
tel 0171-580 4468
web site http://www.bbc.co.uk

In April 1997 BBC Broadcast came into being as the commissioning, scheduling, marketing and broadcast directorate of the BBC – for both radio and TV.

The BBC has five national radio networks – Radio 1, Radio 2, Radio 3, Radio 4 and Radio 5 Live – broadcasting approximately 42,500 hours of music, comedy, drama, features, news and sport each year.

In 1996-97, BBC Radio commissioned approximately 2900 hours of output from independent radio producers. On every network key programmes are now being made independently.
Director of Radio Matthew Bannister
Controller, Radio 1 Andy Parfitt
Controller, Radio 2 James Moir
Controller, Radio 3 Nicholas Kenyon
Controller, Radio 4 James Boyle
Controller, Radio 5 Live Roger Mosey

Deputy Controller, Radio 5 Live/Controller, Sports Rights, Radio Mike Lewis
Head of Music Policy, Radio 1 Jeff Smith
Head of Music Policy, Radio 2 Geoff Mullin
Managing Editor, Radio 1 Ian Parkinson
Managing Editor, Radio 2 Lesley Douglas
Managing Editor, Radio 3 Brian Barfield
Commissioning Editor, Music (Policy), Radio 3 Hilary Boulding
Commissioning Editor, Music (Live), Radio 3 Martyn Westerman
Network Manager, Radio 4 Caroline Elliot
Commissioning Editors, Radio 4 Elizabeth Burke, Andrew Caspari, Fiona Cooper, Jane Ellison, Caroline Raphael, Mary Sharp
Commissioning Editor, News, Radio 5 Live Stephen Kyte

BBC Production

BBC Production, BBC Television Centre,
London W12 7RJ
tel 0171-743 8000

BBC Production is the largest single programme maker in Europe. There are 16 bi-media programme departments based in London and the English regions, including (for radio) Drama Production,

Entertainment, Science, Features and Events, Classical Music, Arts, Religion, Education, Sport, the Natural History Unit, Features Bristol, Entertainment and Features (Manchester). Addresses are given for individual departments if they are different from above.

Drama Production

Broadcasting House, London W1A 1AA
Controller, Drama Production Colin Adams
Head, Radio Drama Kate Rowland
Executive Producers, London David Hunter, Jeremy Mortimer, Eoin O'Callaghan
Executive Producer, World Service Gordon House
Executive Producer, Birmingham Vanessa Whitburn
Executive Producer, Manchester Susan Roberts

The Radio Drama Department comprises Production teams for London and the World Service, Birmingham (including *The Archers*) and Manchester Drama. The department produces plays, series, serials, readings and features for broadcast on BBC Network Radio. It manages a number of new writing initiatives including the Alfred Bradley Bursary Award, First Bite Young Writers, Black Broadcast, World Service playwriting competition (not open to UK residents) and, in association with the Arts Council, Write Out Loud. A free leaflet, *Writing Drama for BBC Radio*, giving basic guidance on the technique of radio writing and on the drama requirements of Radio 4 and Radio 3 is available from the Editorial Assistant. See also *Writing drama for radio* on page 315.

Scripts can be sent to the Radio Drama Department in London, Birmingham or Manchester (for regional addresses see page 320). Only original radio scripts, submitted with an sae will be considered.

Short stories will be considered for the Afternoon Reading (Radio 4). Stories need to be between 2000 and 2300 words in length. Brief guidelines on the slot are available from Radio 4 Readings, Room 6067.

Entertainment

Controller, Entertainment Paul Jackson
Head, Light Entertainment, Radio Jonathan James-Moore (Broadcasting House)
Head, Music Entertainment Trevor Dann

Entertainment is interested in receiving scripts or ideas for series of half-hour sitcoms or panel games, principally for Radio 4. Before submitting material, send for the writers' guidelines – available from the Senior Producer, Scripts, Entertainment (Radio) enclosing an A4 sae.

Two programmes, *The Way It Is* and *The News Huddlines*, are interested in using unsolicited topical sketches during the course of their run. Details (and times of deadlines) can be obtained by phoning and asking for the production office of the programme concerned. All fees are a matter for negotiation with the Corporation's Copyright Department.

Arts

Head, Arts Kim Evans
Editor, Arts, Radio John Boundy (Broadcasting House)

Classical Music

Head, Classical Music Roger Wright
Head, Radio Classical Music Dr John Evans

At the heart of the BBC's music policy is a commitment to high-quality, live music-making in all its forms and across the full range of styles and periods. The BBC also regularly commissions new works from a wide range of composers both nationally and internationally for all its house orchestras and the BBC Singers as well as for other groups and special occasions. Their range includes jazz, electronic and radiophonic media.

The BBC makes best endeavours to consider all unsolicited scores and tapes for broadcast. This is carried out chiefly by the Classical Music Department's specialist producers.

Science

White City, 201 Wood Lane, London W12 7TS
tel 0181-752 5252
Head, Science Glenwyn Benson
Editor, Science, Radio Deborah Cohen

Features and Events

Head, Features and Events Anne Morrison
Executive Editor, Radio Graham Ellis

Sport

Head, Sport Bob Shennan
Senior Producer, Football, Radio Charlotte Nicol
Executive Editor, Continuous News Graeme Reid Davies
Executive Editor, Radio 1 Gordon Turnbull
Editor, Magazines and Documentaries, Radio Alison Rusted

Religion

New Broadcasting House, Oxford Road,
Manchester M60 1SJ
tel 0161-200 2020
Head of Religion Rev Ernie Rea
Managing Editor, Religious Programmes Helen
  Alexander
Executive Producer, World Service Alison Hilliard

Features, Bristol

Broadcasting House, Whiteladies Road,
Bristol BS8 2LR
tel 0117-9732211
Head, Features, Bristol Jeremy Gibson
*Deputy Head, Managing Editor, Radio and
  Television* Sam Organ

Entertainment and Features, (Manchester)

New Broadcasting House, Oxford Road,
Manchester M60 1SJ
tel 0161-200 2020
Head, Entertainment and Features Wayne Garvie
Managing Editor John Drury
Editor, Entertainment & Pop Music Bridget Boseley
Editor Archive, Media and Sport Gaynor
  Vaughan-Jones
Editor, African Caribbean Unit Dele Oniya

Network Production, Birmingham

Broadcasting Centre, Pebble Mill Road,
Birmingham B5 7QQ
tel 0121-414 8888
*Execuitve Head, Network Production
  Birmingham* Rod Natkiel
Executive Editor, Radio Chris Marshall

Natural History Unit, Bristol

Broadcasting House, Whiteladies Road,
Bristol BS8 2LR
tel 0117-9732211
Head, Natural History Unit Keith Scholey
Editor, Radio Sarah Blunt

BBC Production, Education

Head, BBC Production, Education Marilyn
  Wheatcroft
Managing Editor, Education for Adults Radio
  Ruth Gardiner
Executive Producer, Schools Radio Geoffrey
  Marshall-Taylor
Managing Editor, BBC English World Service
  David Thomas

BBC international radio

BBC World Service

Bush House, Strand, London WC2B 4PH
tel 0171-240 3456 *fax* 0171-557 8258
e-mail worldservice.letters@bbc.co.uk
web site http://www.bbc.co.uk/worldservice
Provides radio services in English and 43
other languages. Its key aims are:
• To deliver objective information
• To help meet the need for education
and English language teaching
• To give access to the best of British
culture and entertainment.

BBC World Service reports and analyses world events around the clock, every day of the year. On-the-spot coverage comes from the full network of 250 BBC correspondents and 50 news bureaux worldwide. In addition to news and analysis, there is a wide choice of other radio programmes in the larger language services. In English, the range includes: the arts, features, religious affairs, drama, music, education, science, entertainment and sport. BBC World Service has the biggest global audience.

Managing Director Sam Younger
Director of News and Programme Commissioning
  Bob Jobbins
Controller, English Network Penny Tuerk
*Commissioning Editor (with responsibility for
  independent productions)* Tim Dean
Head of Resources Commissioning Chris Gill
Head of Region, Africa and Middle East Barry
  Langridge
Head of Region, Americas Jerry Timmins
Head of Region, Asia-Pacific Elizabeth Wright
Head of Region, Europe Benny Ammar
*Head of Region, Former Soviet Union and SW
  Asia* David Morton
Regional Director Andrew Taussig

BBC regional radio

The regions are responsible for producing both television and radio programmes. For addresses, see BBC Regional television section on page 320.

The regions produce a total of over 7250 hours of radio broadcasting on all five networks. BBC Pebble Mill in Birmingham is the source of almost half this output – music for broadcast on Radio 2 and Radio 3, farming and environment programmes for Radio 4, and Asian and motoring magazines for Radio 5 Live. It also produces a wide range of drama, including *The Archers*.

BBC Manchester provides religious programmes for all five networks, features such as Radio 1's *Roadshow* and the *Mark Radcliffe Show*, and Radio 4's *Mastermind* and *The Moral Maze*. It is also home to the BBC Philharmonic Orchestra. BBC Bristol specialises in history, travel, literature and human interest features, mainly for Radio 4, including *Poetry Please* and *A Good Read*.

BBC Scotland contributes programmes to all the networks, including BBC Scottish Symphony Orchestra concerts (Radio 3), *Sherlock Holmes* and dramas and features such as *The Trick is to Keep Breathing*.

BBC Wales and BBC Northern Ireland have both increased their commissions for Network Radio. Programme highlights have included dramas such as *A Clockwork Orange* (Wales), and the Ulster Orchestra (Northern Ireland).

BBC local radio

There are opportunities for writers to submit short stories, plays and poetry to local radio. A number of stations hold play-writing or short story competitions and the winners have their work broadcast. Others consider original work from local writers. Material should be submitted to the Assistant Editor.

English regions

BBC Asian Network
Epic House, Charles Street, Leicester LE1 3SH
tel 0116-251 6688
Pebble Mill Road, Birmingham B5 7SD
tel 0121-414 8484

BBC Radio Bristol
PO Box 194, Bristol BS99 7QT
tel 0117-974 1111

BBC Radio Cambridgeshire
Broadcasting House, 104 Hills Road,
Cambridge CB2 1LD
tel (01223) 259696

BBC Radio Cleveland
PO Box 95FM, Broadcasting House,
Newport Road, Middlesbrough, Cleveland TS1 5DG
tel (01642) 225211

BBC Radio Cornwall
Phoenix Wharf, Truro, Cornwall TR1 1UA
tel (01872) 75421

BBC Coventry and Warwickshire
Holt Court, 1 Greyfriars Road, Coventry CV1 2WR
tel (01203) 860086

BBC Radio Cumbria
Annetwell Street, Carlisle, Cumbria CA3 8BB
tel (01228) 592444

BBC Radio Derby
PO Box 269, Derby DE1 3HL
tel (01332) 361111

BBC Radio Devon
PO Box 5, Broadcasting House, Seymour Road,
Mannamead, Plymouth, Devon PL3 5BD
tel (01752) 260323

BBC Essex
198 New London Road, Chelmsford,
Essex CM2 9XB
tel (01245) 262393

BBC Radio Gloucestershire
London Road, Gloucester GL1 1SW
tel (01452) 308585

BBC GLR
(London)
35C Marylebone High Street, London W1A 4LG
tel 0171-224 2424

BBC GMR
(Manchester)
PO Box 951, Oxford Road, Manchester M60 1SJ
tel 0161-244 3002

BBC Radio Guernsey
Commerce House, Les Banques, St Peter Port,
Guernsey, Channel Islands
tel (01481) 728977

BBC Hereford and Worcester
Hylton Road, Worcester WR2 5WW
tel (01905) 748485

BBC Radio Humberside
9 Chapel Street, Hull, North Humberside HU1 3NU
tel (01482) 323232

BBC Radio Jersey
18 Parade Road, St Helier, Jersey,
Channel Islands JE2 3PL
tel (01534) 870000

BBC Radio Kent
Sun Pier, Chatham, Kent ME4 4EZ
tel (01634) 830505

BBC Radio Lancashire
26 Darwen Street, Blackburn, Lancs. BB2 2EA
tel (01254) 262411

BBC Radio Leeds
Broadcasting House, Woodhouse Lane,
Leeds LS2 9PN
tel 0113-244 2131

BBC Radio Leicester
Epic House, Charles Street, Leicester LE1 3SH
tel 0116-251 6688

BBC Radio Lincolnshire
PO Box 219, Newport, Lincoln LN1 3XY
tel (01522) 511411

BBC Radio Merseyside
55 Paradise Street, Liverpool L1 3BP
tel 0151-708 5500

BBC Radio Newcastle
Broadcasting Centre, Barrack Road,
Newcastle upon Tyne NE99 1RN
tel 0191-232 4141

BBC Radio Norfolk
Norfolk Tower, Surrey Street, Norwich NR1 3PA
tel (01603) 617411

BBC Radio Northampton
Broadcasting House, Abington Street,
Northampton NN1 2BH
tel (01604) 239100

BBC Radio Nottingham
York House, Mansfield Road,
Nottingham NG1 3JB
tel 0115-955 0500

BBC Radio Sheffield
Ashdell Grove, 60 Westbourne Road,
Sheffield S10 2QU
tel 0114-268 6185

BBC Radio Shropshire
2-4 Boscobel Drive, Shrewsbury,
Shropshire SY1 3TT
tel (01743) 248484

BBC Solent
Broadcasting House, Havelock Road,
Southampton SO14 7PW
tel (01703) 631311

BBC Somerset Sound
14-15 Paul Street, Taunton, Somerset TA1 3PF
tel (01823) 252437

BBC Southern Counties Radio
(Sussex and Surrey)
Broadcasting Centre, Guildford, Surrey GU2 5AP
tel (01483) 306306

BBC Radio Stoke
Cheapside, Hanley, Stoke-on-Trent, Staffs. ST1 1JJ
tel (01782) 208080

BBC Radio Suffolk
Broadcasting House, St Matthews Street,
Ipswich, Suffolk IP1 3EP
tel (01473) 250000

BBC Thames Valley
269 Banbury Road, Oxford OX2 7DW
tel (01865) 311444

BBC Three Counties Radio
(Bedfordshire, Hertfordshire and
Buckinghamshire)
PO Box 3CR, Luton, Beds. LU1 5XL
tel (01582) 459111

BBC Wiltshire Sound
Broadcasting House, Prospect Place, Swindon,
Wilts. SN1 3RW
tel (01793) 513626

BBC Radio WM
(West Midlands)
Broadcasting House, Pebble Mill Road,
Birmingham B5 7SD
tel 0121-414 8484

BBC Radio York
20 Bootham Row, York YO3 7BR
tel (01904) 641351

Scotland, Wales and Ireland

BBC Radio Scotland
Broadcasting House, Queen Margaret Drive,
Glasgow G12 8DG
tel 0141-338 2000 fax 0141-334 0614
Castle Street, Kirkwall, Orkney KW15 1DF
tel (01856) 873939 fax (01856) 872908
Municipal Buildings, High Street,
Selkirk TD7 4BU
tel (01750) 21884 fax (01750) 22400
Brentham House, Lerwick, Shetland ZE1 0LR
tel (01595) 694747 fax (01595) 694307
'Elmbank', Lovers' Walk, Dumfries DG1 1NZ
tel (01387) 268008 fax (01387) 252568

BBC Radio Nan Gaidheal
7 Culduthel Road, Inverness IV2 4AD
tel (01463) 720720 fax (01463) 236125
Rosebank, Church Street, Stornoway,
Isle of Lewis PA87 2LS
tel (01851) 705000 fax (01851) 704633

BBC Radio Wales/Cymru
Broadcasting House, Llantrisant Road, Llandaff,
Cardiff CF5 2YQ
tel (01222) 322000 fax (01222) 552973

BBC Radio Foyle
8 Northland Road, Londonderry BT48 7NE
tel (01504) 262244 fax (01504) 378666

BBC Radio Ulster
Broadcasting House, Ormeau Avenue,
Belfast BT2 8HQ
tel (01232) 338000 fax (01232) 338800

BBC broadcasting rights and terms

Contributors are advised to check latest details of fees with the BBC.

Rights and terms

Specially written material

Fees are assessed on the basis of the type of material, its length, the author's status and experience in writing for radio. Fees for submitted material are paid on acceptance. For commissioned material, half the fee is paid on commissioning and half on acceptance as being suitable for broadcasting.

- Rates for specially written radio dramas in English (other than educational programmes) are £39.89 a minute for beginners and a 'going rate' of £60.73 a minute for established writers. This rate covers two broadcasts.

Specially written short stories

- Fees range from £123.00 for 15 minutes.

Published material

Domestic radio
- Dramatic works: £12.04 per minute.
- Prose works: £12.04 per minute.
- Prose works required for dramatisation: £9.39 per minute.
- Poems: £12.04 per half minute.

World Service Radio (English)
- Dramatic works: £6.03 per minute for broadcasts within a seven-day period.
- Prose works: £6.03 per minute for broadcasts within a seven-day period.
- Prose works required for dramatisation: £4.70 per minute for broadcasts within a seven-day period.

- Poems: £6.03 per half minute for broadcasts within a seven-day period.
- Foreign Language Services are approximately one-fifth of the rate for English Language Services.

Repeats in BBC programmes

- Further proportionate fees are payable for repeats.

Use abroad of recordings of BBC programmes

If the BBC sends abroad recordings of its programmes for use by overseas broadcasting organisations on their own networks or stations, further payments accrue to the author, usually in the form of additional percentages of the basic fee paid for the initial performance or a royalty based on the percentage of the distributors' receipts. This can apply to both sound and television programmes.

Value Added Tax

There is a self-billing system for VAT which covers radio, external services and television for programmes made in London.

Talks

Contributors to talks for domestic Radio and World Service broadcasting may be offered either:
- the standard talks contract which takes rights and provides for residual payments, as does the television standard contract; or

• an STC (Short Talks Contract) which takes all rights except print publication rights where the airtime of the contribution does not exceed five minutes and which has set fees or disturbance money payable; or

• an NFC (No Fee Contract) where no payment is made which provides an acknowledgement that a contribution may be used by the BBC.

Independent national radio

Commercial Radio Companies Association (CRCA)

(formerly Association of Independent Radio Companies – AIRC)
77 Shaftesbury Avenue, London W1V 7AD
tel 0171-306 2603 *fax* 0171-470 0062
e-mail info@crca.co.uk
CRCA is the trade body for UK commerical radio. It represents commercial radio to Government, the Radio Authority, copyright societies and other organisations concerned with radio. CRCA is a source of advice to members and acts as a clearing house for radio information.

CRCA runs the Radio Advertising Clearance Centre. It jointly owns Radio Joint Audience Research Ltd (RAJAR) with the BBC, and also owns the Network Chart Show, sponsored by Pepsi.

CRCA is a founder member of the Association of European Radios (AER), which lobbies European institutions on behalf of commercial radio.

Classic FM

Academic House, 24-28 Oval Road, London NW1 7DQ
tel 0171-284 3000 *fax* 0171-713 2630
e-mail enquiries@classicfm.co.uk
web site www.classicfm.co.uk

IRN (Independent Radio News)

6th Floor, 200 Gray's Inn Road, London WC1X 8XZ
tel 0171-430 4090 *fax* 0171-430 4092
e-mail news@irn.co.uk
National news provider to all UK commercial radio stations, including live news bulletins, sport and financial news, and coverage of the House of Commons.

The Radio Authority

Holbrook House, 14 Great Queen Street, London WC2B 5DG
tel 0171-430 2724 *fax* 0171-405 7062
Licenses and regulates Independent Radio. Plans frequencies, awards licences, regulates programming and advertising, and plays an active role in the discussion and formulation of policies which affect the Independent Radio industry and its listeners.

Talk Radio

76 Oxford Street, London W1N 0TR
tel 0171-636 1089 *fax* 0171-636 1053

Virgin 1215

1 Golden Square, London W1R 4DJ
tel 0171-434 1215 *fax* 0171-434 1197
e-mail virgin@vradio.co.uk
web site www.virginradio.co.uk/.

Independent local radio

England

Alton
Wey Valley Radio, Prospect Place, Mill Lane,
Alton, Hants GU34 2SY
tel (01420) 544444 *fax* (01420) 544044
e-mail weyvalley@ukrd.com

Aylesbury
Mix 96, Friars Square Studios,
11 Bourbon Street, Aylesbury, Bucks. HP20 2PZ
tel (01296) 399396 *fax* (01296) 398988

Barnstaple
Lantern FM, The Light House, 17 Market Place,
Bideford, Devon EX39 2DR
tel (01237) 424444 *fax* (01237) 423333

Basingstoke
107.6 Kestrel FM, 2nd Floor, Paddington House,
The Walks Shopping Centre, Basingstoke RG21 7LJ
tel (01256) 694000 *fax* (01256) 694111

Bassetlaw
Trax FM, PO Box 444, Worksop, Notts. S81 9YW
tel (01909) 500611 *fax* (01909) 500445

Bedford
B97 Chiltern FM, 55 Goldington Road,
Bedford MK40 3LT
tel (01234) 272400 *fax* (01234) 218580

Birmingham
96.4 FM BRMB *and* Capital Gold (1152), Radio
House, Aston Road North, Birmingham B6 4BX
tel 0121-359 4481 *fax* 0121-359 1117
e-mail info@brmb.co.uk

Birmingham
Choice FM, 95 Broad Street, Birmingham B15 1AU
tel 0121-616 1000 *fax* 0121-616 1011
e-mail onair@choice1022.co.uk

Blackpool
The Wave 96.5, 965 Mowbray Drive, Blackpool,
Lancs. FY3 7JR
tel (01253) 304965 *fax* (01253) 301965
e-mail any@thewavefm.co.uk

Birmingham
Radio XL 1296 AM, KMS House, Bradford Street,
Birmingham B12 0JD
tel 0121-753 5353 *fax* 0121-753 3111

Bournemouth
Classic Gold 828 *and* 2CR FM, 5 Southcote Road,
Bournemouth BH1 3LR
tel (01202) 259259 *fax* (01202) 255244

Bradford
Sunrise FM, Sunrise House, 30 Chapel Street,
Little Germany, Bradford BD1 5DN
tel (01274) 735043 *fax* (01274) 728534

Bradford, Huddersfield & Halifax
Classic Gold 1278/1530 *and* The Pulse,
Pennine House, Forster Square,
Bradford BD1 5NE
tel (01274) 203040 *fax* (01274) 203130
e-mail general@pulse.co.uk

Brighton
Surf 107, PO Box 107, Brighton BN1 1QG
tel (01273) 386107 *fax* (01273) 273107

Bristol & Bath
Classic Gold 1260 *and* GWR FM, PO Box 2020,
Watershed, Canons Road, Bristol BS99 7SN
tel 0117-984 3200 *fax* 0117-984 3202
e-mail reception@gwrfm@musicradio.com

Cambridge
Cambridge Café Radio, PO Box 1079,
Cambridge CB5 8FX
tel (01223) 722300 *fax* (01223) 577686
e-mail <recipient>@caferadio.com

Cambridge & Newmarket
Q103 FM, Enterprise House, The Vision Park,
Chivers Way, Histon, Cambs. CB4 4WW
tel (01223) 235255 *fax* (01223) 235161
e-mail reception@q103.musicradio.com

Canterbury
106 CTFM Radio, 16 Lower Bridge Street,
Canterbury, Kent CT1 2HQ
tel (01227) 789106 *fax* (01227) 785106
e-mail e-mail@ctfm.co.uk

Carlisle
CFM, PO Box 964, Carlisle CA1 3NG
tel (01228) 818964 *fax* (01228) 819444

Chelmsford
Chelmer FM, Duke House, Victoria Road South,
Chelmsford, Essex CM1 1LN (temporary address)
tel (01245) 259400

Cheltenham
The Cat and Cheltenham Radio, Regent Arcade,
Cheltenham, Glos. GL50 1JZ
tel (01242) 699555 fax (01242) 699666

Chesterfield
Peak 107 FM, Radio House, Foxwood Road,
Chesterfield
tel (01246) 269107

Chichester, Bognor Regis & Littlehampton
Spirit FM, Dukes Court, Bognor Road, Chichester,
West Sussex PO19 2FX
tel (01243) 773600 fax (01243) 786464
e-mail spiritfm@argonet.co.uk

Colchester
SGR Colchester, Abbeygate Two,
9 Whitewell Road, Colchester CO2 7DE
tel (01206) 575859 fax (01206) 561199

Cornwall
Pirate FM102·2/8, Carn Brea Studios,
Wilson Way, Redruth, Cornwall TR15 3XX
tel (01209) 314400 fax (01209) 314345
e-mail enquiries@piratefm102.co.uk

Coventry
Classic Gold 1359 and Mercia FM,
Hertford Place, Coventry CV1 3TT
tel (01203) 868200 fax (01203) 868202
e-mail mercia@musicradio.com

Coventry
Kix 96, St Mark's Church Annexe, Bird Street,
Soney Standon Road, Coventry CV1 4FH
tel (01203) 525656 fax (01203) 551744
e-mail kix962@aol.com

Darlington
Alpha 103.2, Radio House, 11 Woodland Road,
Darlington, Co. Durham DL3 7BJ
tel (01325) 255552 fax (01325) 255551
e-mail admin@alpharadio.demon.co.uk

Derby
Ram FM, The Market Place, Derby DE1 3AA
tel (01332) 292945 fax (01332) 292229

Dover & Folkestone
Neptune Radio, PO Box 1068, Dover CT16 1GB
and PO Box 964, Folkestone CT18 8GG
tel (01304) 202505

East of England
Vibe FM, Reflection House, The Anderson Centre,
Olding Road, Bury St Edmunds IP33 3TA
tel (01284) 718800 fax (01284) 718839
e-mail studios@vibefm.co.uk

East Lancashire
Asian Sound Radio, Globe House, Southall
Street, Manchester M3 1LG

tel 0161-288 1000 fax 0161-288 9000
e-mail asr@aol.com

East Midlands
Century 106 and City Link, Nottingham NG2 4NG
tel 0115-910 6100 fax 0115-910 6107
e-mail century106.co.uk

Eastbourne
Sovereign Radio, 14 St Mary's Walk, Hailsham,
East Sussex BN27 1AF
tel (01323) 442700 fax (01323) 440643
e-mail sovereignradio.co.uk

Exeter & Torbay
Gemini AM and Gemini FM,
Hawthorn House, Exeter Business Park,
Exeter, Devon EX1 3QS
tel (01392) 444444 fax (01392) 444433

Along the M20 towards Folkestone and the Kent channel ports
Channel Travel Radio, Main Control Building,
Eurotunnel UK Terminal, PO Box 2000,
Folkestone, Kent CT18 8XY
tel (01303) 283873 fax (01303) 283874

Gloucester & Cheltenham
Classic Gold 774 and Severn Sound FM,
Old Talbot House, Southgate Street,
Gloucester GL1 2DQ
tel (01452) 423791 fax (01452) 529446
e-mail reception@severnfm.musicradio.com

Great Yarmouth & Lowestoft
The Beach, PO Box 103.4, Lowestoft, Suffolk NR32
tel (07000) 001035 fax (07000) 001036
e-mail 103.4@thebeach.co.uk

Great Yarmouth & Norwich
Broadland 102·4 FM and Classic Gold Amber,
St George's Plain, 47-49 Colegate,
Norwich NR3 1DB
tel (01603) 630621 fax (01603) 666252

Guernsey
Island FM, 12 Westerbrook, St Sampson,
Guernsey GY2 4QQ, Channel Islands
tel (01481) 42000 fax (01481) 49676
e-mail kevin@islandfm.guernsey.net

Guildford
County Sound Radio 1476 AM and
96.4 The Eagle, Dolphin House, North Street,
Guildford, Surrey GU1 4AA
tel (01483) 300964 fax (01483) 531612
e-mails onair@countysound.co.uk,
eagle@countysound.co.uk

Harlow
Ten 17, Latton Bush Centre, Southern Way,
Harlow, Essex CM18 7BU
tel (01279) 432415 fax (01279) 445289
e-mail studios@ten17.co.uk

Harrogate
97.2 Stray FM, PO Box 972, Station Parade,
Harrogate HG1 5YF
tel (01423) 522972 *fax* (01423) 522922
e-mail @972strayfm.co.uk

Haslemere
Delta Radio 97.1 FM, 65 Weyhill, Haslemere,
Surrey GU27 1HN
tel (01428) 651971 *fax* (01428) 658971
e-mail delta@ukrd.com

Hastings
107.8 Arrow FM, Priory Meadow Centre,
Hastings, East Sussex TN34 1PJ
tel (01424) 461177 *fax* (01424) 422662
e-mail info@arrowfm.co.uk

Havering
Active 107.5 FM, Lambourne House,
7 Western Road, Romford, Essex RM1 3LD
tel (01708) 731643 *fax* (01708) 730383

Hereford & Worcester
Classic Gold 954/1530 *and* Wyvern FM,
5 Barbourne Terrace, Worcester WR1 3JZ
tel (01905) 612212 *fax* (01905) 613549
e-mail wyvernfm@musicradio.com

High Wycombe
ElevenSeventy, PO Box 1170, High Wycombe,
Bucks HP13 6YT
tel (01494) 446611 *fax* (01494) 445400

Hinkley & South West Leicestershire
Fosseway Radio, PO Box 107, Hinckley,
Leics. LE10 1WR
tel (01455) 614151
e-mail fossewayradio.co.uk

Huddersfield
Huddersfield FM, The Old Stableblock, Brewery
Drive, Lockwood Park, Huddersfield HD1 3UR
tel (01484) 321107 *fax* (01484) 311107

Humberside
Magic 1161 AM *and* 96.9 Viking FM,
Commercial Road, Hull HU1 2SG
tel (01482) 325141 *fax* (01482) 587067

Ipswich & Bury St Edmunds
Classic Gold Amber (Suffolk) *and* SGR-FM,
Radio House, Alpha Business Park,
White House Road, Ipswich IP1 5LT
tel (01473) 461000 *fax* (01473) 741200
e-mail sgrfm.co.uk

Isle of Wight
Isle of Wight Radio, Dodnor Park, Newport PO30 5XE
tel (01983) 822557 *fax* (01983) 822109
e-mail admin@iwradio.co.uk

Jersey
Channel 103 FM, 6 Tunnell Street, St Helier,
Jersey JE2 4LU, Channel Islands

tel (01534) 888103 *fax* (01534) 887799
e-mail chan103@itl.net

Kent
Capital Gold (1242 and 603) *and* Invicta FM,
Radio House, John Wilson Business Park,
Whitstable, Kent CT5 3QX
tel (01227) 772004 *fax* (01227) 771558
e-mail info@invictaradio.co.uk

Kettering
KCBC, PO Box 1074, Centre 2000, Kettering,
Northants. NN16 8PU
tel (07000) 1074 1074 *fax* (01536) 517390
e-mail fm107.4@kcbc.co.uk

Kings Lynn
KL.FM 96·7, PO Box 77, 18 Blackfriars Street,
Kings Lynn, Norfolk PE30 1NN
tel (01553) 772777 *fax* (01553) 766453
e-mail klfmradio.co.uk

Kingston upon Thames
107.8 FM Thames Radio, Brentham House,
45c High Street, Hampton Wick,
Kingston upon Thames KT1 4DG
tel 0181-288 1300 *fax* 0181-288 1312

Leeds
96.3 Aire FM *and* Magic 828, PO Box 2000,
51 Burley Road, Leeds LS3 1LR
tel 0113-283 5500 *fax* 0113-283 5501

Leicester
Leicester Sound, Granville House,
Granville Road, Leicester LE1 7RW
tel 0116-256 1300 *fax* 0116-256 1303
e-mail leicestersound@musicradio.com

Leicester
Sabras, Radio House, 63 Melton Road,
Leicester LE4 6PN
tel 0116-261 0666 *fax* 0116-266 7776
e-mail sabras1260@sabrasradio.com

Lincoln
Lincs FM, Witham Park, Waterside South,
Lincoln LN5 7JN
tel (01522) 549900 *fax* (01522) 549911
e-mail lincsfm@msn.com

Liverpool
Radio City 96·7 *and* Magic 1548,
8-10 Stanley Street, Liverpool L1 6AF
tel 0151-227 5100 *fax* 0151-471 0330

London (Brixton)
Choice FM, 16-18 Trinity Gardens,
London SW9 8DP
tel 0171-738 7969 *fax* 0171-738 6619

London, Greater
95.8 Capital FM *and* Capital Gold (1548),
30 Leicester Square, London WC2H 7LA
tel 0171-766 6000 *fax* 0171-766 6100

London, Greater
Heart 106·2, The Chrysalis Building,
Bramley Road, London W10 6SP
tel 0171-468 1062 *fax* 0171-470 1062
e-mail (initial.surname)@heart1062.co.uk

London, Greater
Jazz FM 102.2, 26-27 Castlereagh Street,
London W1H 6DJ
tel 0171-706 4100 *fax* 0171-723 9742
e-mail richard@jazzfm.com

London, Greater
Kiss 100 FM, Kiss House, 80 Holloway Road,
London N7 8JG
tel 0171-700 6100 *fax* 0171-700 3979

London, Greater
LBC 1152 AM *and* News Direct 97·3 FM,
200 Gray's Inn Road, London WC1X 8XZ
tel 0171-973 1152 *fax* 0171-973 8833
e-mail jackiek@lnr.uk.co

London, Greater
963/972 Liberty Radio, 7th Floor, Trevor House,
100 Brompton Road, London SW3 1ER
tel 0171-893 8966 *fax* 0171-893 8965

London, Greater
Melody FM, 97 Tottenham Court Road,
London W1 9HF
tel 0171-504 6000 *fax* 0171-504 6021

London, Greater
Premier Radio, Glen House, Stag Place,
London SW1E 5AG
tel 0171-316 1300 *fax* 0171-233 6706
e-mail premier@premier.org.uk

London, Greater
RTL Country 1035 AM, PO Box 1035,
London W1A 2ZT
tel 0171-546 1010 *fax* 0171-546 1020

London, Greater
Spectrum International Radio, International
Radio Centre, 204-206 Queenstown Road,
London SW8 3NR
tel 0171-627 4433 *fax* 0171-627 3409

London, Greater
Sunrise Radio, Sunrise House, Sunrise Road,
Southall, Middlesex UB2 4AU
tel 0181-574 6666 *fax* 0181-813 9800

London, Greater
Virgin 105.8, 1 Golden Square,
London W1R 4DJ
tel 0171-434 1215 *fax* 0171-434 1197
e-mail virgin@vradio.co.uk

London, Greater
Xfm, 97 Charlotte Street, London W1P 1LP
tel 0171-2294000 *fax* 0171-229 4010

London (Lewisham)
FLR 107.3, PO Box 1073, London SE8 4WU
tel 0181-469 3981 *fax* 0181-692 7308
e-mail enquiries@ukrd.com

London (North)
London Greek Radio, Florentia Village,
Vale Road, London N4 1TD
tel 0181-800 8001 *fax* 0181-800 8005
e-mail lgrhgc@globalnet.co.uk

London (North)
London Turkish Radio, 185B High Road,
London N22 6BA
tel 0181-881 0606/2020 *fax* 0181-881 5151

London (Thamesmead)
Millennium Radio, Harrow Manor Way,
Thamesmead, London SE2 9XH
tel 0181-311 3112 *fax* 0181-312 1930

**Loughborough & neighbouring parts of
North West Leicestershire**
Oak FM, 18 Jubilee Drive, Loughborough LE11 5TQ
tel (01509) 217080 *fax* (01509) 264104

Ludlow
Sunshine 855, Sunshine House, Waterside,
Ludlow, Shropshire SY8 1GS
tel (01584) 873795 *fax* (01584) 875900

Luton/Bedford
Chiltern FM *and* Classic Gold 792/828,
Chiltern Road, Dunstable, Beds. LU6 1HQ
tel (01582) 676200 *fax* (01582) 676231/201
e-mail chilternfm@musicradio.com

Macclesfield
Silk FM, Radio House, Bridge Street,
Macclesfield, Cheshire SK11 6DJ
tel (01625) 268000 *fax* (01625) 269010
e-mail mail@silkfm.com

Manchester
Galaxy 102, 127-129 Portland Street,
Manchester M1 6ED
tel 0161-228 0102 *fax* 0161-228 1020

Manchester
Key 103 *and* Piccadilly Radio 1152 AM,
Castle Quay, Castlefield, Manchester M5 4PR
tel 0161-288 5000 *fax* 0161-288 5001

Manchester
1458 Lite AM, PO Box 1458, Quay West,
Trafford Park, Manchester M17 1FL
tel 0161-872 1458 *fax* 0161-872 0206

Mansfield & Ashfield
Radio Mansfield, The Media Suite,
Brunts Business Centre, Samuel Brunts Way,
Mansfield, Notts. NG18 2AH
tel (01623) 646666 *fax* (01623) 660606
e-mail philsmith.radman@btinternet.com

Medway towns
Medway FM, Berkeley House, 186 High Street,
Rochester ME1 1EY
tel (01634) 841111 *fax* (01634) 841122
e-mail studio@medwayfm.com

Merseyside
Crash FM, 27 Fleet Street,
Liverpool L1 4AR
tel 0151-707 3107 *fax* 0151-707 3109
e-mail info@107crashfm.com

Milton Keynes
FM 103 Horizon, The Broadcast Centre,
Vincent Avenue, Crownhill Industry,
Milton Keynes MK8 0AB
tel (01908) 269111 *fax* (01908) 564063
e-mail fm103horizon@musicradio

Morecambe Bay
The Bay 96.9 FM, PO Box 969, St George's Quay,
Lancaster LA1 3LD
tel (01524) 848747 *fax* (01524) 848787
e-mail (staffname)@thebay.co.uk

Newcastle
Magic 1152, Newcastle upon Tyne NE99 1BB
tel 0191-420 3040 *fax* 0191-488 9222

North East England
Century Radio, Century House, PO Box 100,
Gateshead NE8 2YX
tel 0191-477 6666 *fax* 0191-477 1771

North West England
Century 105, Century House, Waterfront Quay,
Salford Quays, Manchester M5 2XW
tel 0161-400 0105 *fax* 0161-400 1105

North West England
Jazz FM 100.4, The World Trade Centre,
Exchange Quay, Manchester M5 3EJ
tel 0161-877 1004 *fax* 0161-877 1005
e-mail jazzinfo@jazzfm.com

Northampton
Classic Gold 1557 *and* Northants 96,
19-21 St Edmunds Road,
Northampton NN1 5DY
tel (01604) 795600 *fax* (01604) 795601
e-mail reception@northants96.musicradio.com

Nottingham & Derby
Classic Gold GEM *and* TRENT FM,
29-31 Castle Gate, Nottingham NG1 7AP
tel 0115-952 7000 *fax* 0115-912 9302
e-mails admin@gemammusicradio.com,
admin@trentfm.musicradio.com

Oxford
Oxygen 107.9 FM, Suite 41, Westgate Centre,
Oxford OX1 1PD
tel (01865) 724442 *fax* (01865) 726161
e-mail mail@oxygen.demon.co.uk

Oxford & Banbury
Fox FM, Brush House, Pony Road,
Oxford OX4 2XR
tel (01865) 871000 *fax* (01865) 871036
e-mail fox@foxfm.co.uk

Peterborough
Classic Gold 1332 AM, PO Box 2020,
Queensgate Centre, Peterborough PE1 1LL
tel (01733) 460460 *fax* (01733) 281445

Peterborough
102·7 Hereward FM, PO Box 225,
Queensgate Centre, Peterborough PE1 1XJ
tel (01733) 460460 *fax* (01733) 281445

Plymouth
Plymouth Sound AM *and* Plymouth Sound FM,
Earl's Acre, Plymouth PL3 4HX
tel (01752) 227272 *fax* (01752) 670730
e-mail plymouth.com

Preston & Blackpool
Red Rose 999 *and* Rock FM,
PO Box 999/PO Box 974, Preston,
Lancs. PR1 1XR
tel (01772) 556301 *fax* (01772) 201917

Reading, Basingstoke & Andover
Classic Gold 1431/1485 *and* 2-TEN FM,
PO Box 2020, Reading RG31 7FG
tel 0118-945 4400 *fax* 0118-928 8483
e-mail mail2tenfm@musicradio.com

Reigate & Crawley
Fame 1521 *and* Mercury FM,
The Stanley Centre, Kelvin Way, Crawley,
West Sussex RH10 2SE
tel (01293) 519161 *fax* (01293) 565663
e-mail studio@mercuryfm.co.uk

Rutland & Stamford
Rutland Radio, Rutland Business Centre, East
Street, Oakham, Rutland LE5 6AQ
tel (01572) 757868
e-mail rutradio@aol.com

St Albans & Watford
96.6 Oasis FM, 9 Christopher Place Shopping
Centre, St Albans, Herts. AL3 5DQ
tel (01727) 831966 *fax* (01727) 834456
e-mail studios@oasisfm.co.uk

Salisbury
Spire FM, City Hall Studios, Malthouse Lane,
Salisbury, Wilts. SP2 7QQ
tel (01722) 416644 *fax* (01722) 416688
e-mail admin@spirefm.co.uk

Scarborough
Yorkshire Coast Radio, PO Box 962,
Scarborough, North Yorkshire YO12 5AX
tel (01723) 500962 *fax* (01723) 501050
e-mail mail@minsterfm.demon.co.uk

Severn Estuary
Galaxy 101, Millennium House,
27 Baldwin Street, Bristol BS1 1SE
tel 0117-901 0101 *fax* 0117-901 4666
e-mail addressee@galaxy101.co.uk

Shaftesbury
97.4 Gold Radio, Longmead, Shaftesbury,
Dorset SP7 8QQ
tel (01747) 855711 *fax* (01747) 855722

Slough, Windsor & Maidenhead
106·6 Star FM, The Observatory Shopping
Centre, Slough, Berks. SL1 1LH
tel (01753) 551066 *fax* (01753) 512277
e-mail enquiries@starfm.co.uk

Solent area
Wave 105.2 FM, 5 Manor Court, Barnes Wallis
Road, Segensworth East, Fareham PO15 5TH
tel (01489) 481050 *fax* (01489) 481060

South Hampshire
Capital Gold (1170 and 1557) *and* Ocean FM *and*
Power FM, Radio House, Whittle Avenue,
Segensworth West, Fareham PO15 5SH
tel (01489) 589911 *fax* (01489) 589453
e-mail info@oceanradio.co.uk

South-East Staffordshire
Centre FM, 5-6 Aldergate, Tamworth,
Staffordshire B79 7DJ
tel (01827) 318000 *fax* (01827) 318002

South Yorkshire
Hallam FM *and* Magic AM, Radio House,
900 Herries Road, Sheffield S6 1RH
tel 0114-285 3333/2121 *fax* 0114-285 3159
e-mail programmes@hallamfm.co.uk,
programmes@magicam.co.uk

Southend & Chelmsford
The Breeze *and* Essex FM, Radio House,
Clifftown Road, Southend-on-Sea, Essex SS1 1SX
tel (01702) 333711 *fax* (01702) 345224
e-mails studios@breeze.co.uk,
studios@essexfm.co.uk

Southport
Dune FM, The Power Station, Victoria Way,
Southport PR8 1RR
tel (01704) 502500 *fax* (01704) 502540
e-mail dunefm@aol.com

Stockport
Signal FM, Regent House, Heaton Lane,
Stockport SK4 1BX
tel 0161-285 4545 *fax* 0161-285 1050
e-mail radio@signal1049.com

Stoke-on-Trent
Signal One *and* Signal Two, Stoke Road,
Stoke-on-Trent ST4 2SR
tel (01782) 747047 *fax* (01782) 744110
e-mail <recipient>@signalradio.com

Stratford upon Avon
FM 102 – The Bear, The Guard House Studios,
Banbury Road, Stratford upon Avon CV37 7HX
tel (01789) 262636 *fax* (01789) 263102
e-mail studio@thebear.co.uk

Stroud
5 Valleys Radio, 6 Lansdown, Stroud GL5 1BE
tel/fax (01453) 759576
e-mail 5vr.g@ukonline.co.uk

Sunderland
Sun FM, PO Box 1034, Sunderland SR1 3YZ
tel 0191-567 3333 *fax* 0191-567 0777

Sussex
Capital Gold (1323 and 945) *and* Southern FM,
Radio House, PO Box 2000, Brighton BN14 2SS
tel (01273) 430111 *fax* (01273) 430098

Swindon & West Wiltshire
Classic Gold 936/1161 AM *and* GWR FM,
PO Box 2000, Swindon SN4 7EX
tel (01793) 842600 *fax* (01793) 842602
e-mail reception@gwrfm.musicradio.com

Teesside
Magic 1170 *and* TFM, Radio House, Yale
Crescent, Thornaby, Stockton-on-Tees TS17 6AA
tel (01642) 888222 *fax* (01642) 868288

Tendring
Mellow 1557 AM, Media Centre,
2 St John's Wynd, Culver Square,
Colchester CO1 1WG
tel (01206) 764466 *fax* (01206) 764672
e-mail mellow@enterprise.net

Thanet
Thanet Local Radio, Imperial House, 2-14 High
Street, Margate, Kent CT9 1DH
(01843) 220222 299666
e-mail paul.mccartney@tlrfm.co.uk

Tunbridge Wells & Sevenoaks
KFM, 1 East Street, Tonbridge, Kent TN9 1AR
tel (01732) 369200 *fax* (01732) 369201
e-mail kfm@cis.compuserve.com

Tyne and Wear
Metro FM, Newcastle upon Tyne NE99 1BB
tel 0191-420 0971 *fax* 0191-488 9222

Warrington
107.2 Wire FM *and* 102.4 Wish FM, The Lodge,
Orrell Road, Wigan WN5 8HJ
tel (01942) 777666 *fax* (01942) 777657 (Wire)
tel (01942) 761024 *fax* (01942) 777694 (Wish)
e-mail mail@wire-fm.u-net.com

Wellingborough
Connect FM, Church Street, Wellingborough,
Northants. NN8 4XX
tel (01933) 224972 *fax* (01933) 442333
e-mail connectfm@web-uk.com

West Cumbria
CFM, PO Box 964, Carlisle CA1 3NG
tel (01228) 818964 *fax* (01228) 819444

West Midlands
100·7 Heart FM, 1 The Square, 111 Broad Street,
Birmingham B15 1AS
tel 0121-626 1007 *fax* 0121-696 1007
e-mail (initial.surname)@heartfm.com

West Somerset
Quay West Radio, Harbour Studios,
The Esplanade, Watchet, Somerset TA23 0AJ
tel (01984) 634900 *fax* (01984) 634811
e-mail quaywestradio@csi.com

Weymouth & Dorchester
Wessex FM, Radio House, Trinity Street,
Dorchester, Dorset DT1 1DJ
tel (01305) 250333 *fax* (01305) 250052

Wirral
MFM 97.1, Media House, Claughton Road,
Birkenhead L45 6EY
tel 0151-650 1700 *fax* 0151-647 5427

Wolverhampton
107.7 The Wolf, 10th Floor, Mander House,
Wolverhampton WV1 3NB
tel (01902) 571070 *fax* (01902) 571079
e-mail studio@thewolf.co.uk

Wolverhampton, Shrewsbury & Telford
Beacon Radio FM *and* Classic Gold WABC,
267 Tettenhall Road, Wolverhampton WV6 0DQ
tel (01902) 838383 *fax* (01902) 838266

Yeovil & Taunton
Orchard FM, Haygrove House, Taunton TA3 7BT
tel (01823) 338448 *fax* (01823) 320444

York
Minster FM, PO Box 123, Dunnington,
York YO1 5ZX
tel (01904) 488888 *fax* (01904) 488878
e-mail mail@minsterfm.demon.co.uk

Yorkshire
Galaxy 105, Josephs Well, Westgate, Leeds LS3 1AB
tel 0113-213 0105 *fax* 0113-213 1055
e-mail name@galaxy105.co.uk

Yorkshire Dales, with Skipton
Yorkshire Dales Radio, YDR House, Gargrave
Road, Skipton, North Yorkshire BD23 1YD
tel (01756) 799991 *fax* (01756) 799771

Scotland

Aberdeen
Northsound One *and* Northsound Two,
45 Kings Gate, Aberdeen AB15 4EL
tel (01224) 337000 *fax* (01224) 637289

e-mails northsound1@srh.co.uk,
northsound2@srh.co.uk

Ayr
West FM *and* West Sound AM, Radio House,
54A Holmston Road, Ayr KA7 3BE
tel (01292) 283662 *fax* (01292) 283665
e-mail wsradio@srh.co.uk

The Borders
Radio Borders, Tweedside Park, Galashiels TD1 3TD
tel (01896) 759444 *fax* (01896) 759494

Central Scotland
Scot FM, 1 Albert Quay, Leith EH6 7DN
tel 0131-554 6677 *fax* 0131-554 2266

Dundee/Perth
Radio Tay AM *and* Tay FM, 6 North Isla Street,
Dundee DD3 7JQ
tel (01382) 200800 *fax* (01382) 593252
e-mail tayam@srh.co.uk, tayfm@srh.co.uk

Edinburgh
Forth AM *and* Forth FM, Forth House,
Forth Street, Edinburgh EH1 3LF
tel 0131-556 9255 *fax* 0131-558 3277
e-mail forth@srh.co.uk

Fife
KingdomFM, Gilmerton House, By St Andrews,
Fife KY16 8NB
tel (01382) 776403 *fax* (01382) 739164
e-mail mediamack@sol.co.uk

Fort William
Nevis Radio, Inverlochy, Fort William PH33 6LU
tel (01397) 700007 *fax* (01397) 701007
e-mail nevisradio@lochaber.co.uk

Glasgow
Clyde 1 FM *and* Clyde 2, Clydebank Business
Park, Clydebank, Glasgow G81 2RX
tel 0141-565 2200 *fax* 0141-565 2265
e-mails clyde1@srh.co.uk, clyde2@srh.co.uk

Inverness
Moray Firth Radio, Scorguie Place,
Inverness IV3 6SF
tel (01463) 224433 *fax* (01463) 243224
e-mail mfr@mfr.uk.com

Inverurie
NECR, Town House, Kintore, Inverurie AB51 0US
tel (01467) 632909 *fax* (01467) 632969

Oban
Oban FM, McLeod Units, Lochavullin Estate,
Oban, Argyll
tel/fax (01631) 570057

Paisley
96.3 QFM, 26 Lady Lane, Paisley PA1 2LG
tel 0141-887 9630 *fax* 0141-887 0963
e-mail requests@qfmclassichits.co.uk

Peterhead
Waves Radio Peterhead, Unit 2, Blackhouse,
Industrial Estate, Peterhead AB42 1BW
tel (01779) 491012 *fax* (01779) 490802

Pitlochry & Aberfeldy
Heartland FM, Atholl Curling Rink,
Lower Oakfield, Pitlochry, Perthshire PH16 5HQ
tel (01796) 474040 *fax* (01796) 474007

Shetland
SIBC, Market Street, Lerwick, Shetland ZE1 0JN
tel (01595) 695299 *fax* (01595) 695696

Stirling
Central FM, 201 High Street, Falkirk FK1 1DU
tel (01324) 611164 *fax* (01324) 611168

Stranraer, Dumfries & Galloway
South West Sound, Campbell House,
Bankend Road, Dumfries DG1 4TH
tel (01387) 250999 *fax* (01387) 265629

Ullapool
Lochbroom FM, Mill Street Industrial Estate,
Ullapool, West Ross IV26 2UN
tel (01854) 613131 *fax* (01854) 613132

Western Isles
Isles FM, PO Box 333, Stornoway,
Isle of Lewis HS1 2PU
tel (01851) 703333 *fax* (01851) 703322

Ireland

Belfast
City Beat 96.7, Lamont Buildings, Stranmills
Embankment, Belfast BT9 5FN
tel (01232) 205967 *fax* (01232) 200023

Cookstown
Gold Beat 828, 2c Park Avenue, Cookstown,
Co. Tyrone, Northern Ireland BT80 8AH
tel (016487) 64828 *fax* (016487) 63828

Craigavon
Heart Beat 1521, Carn Business Park, Craigavon,
Co. Armagh BT63 5RH
tel (01762) 330033 *fax* (01762) 391896

Londonderry
Q102·9 FM, The Riverside Suite,
Old Waterside Railway Station, Duke Street,
Londonderry, BT47 6DH
tel (01504) 344449/346666 *fax* (01504) 311177
e-mail q102@iol.ie

Northern Ireland
Cool FM, PO Box 974, Belfast BT1 1RT
tel (01247) 817181 *fax* (01247) 814974
e-mail music@coolfm.co.uk

Northern Ireland
Downtown Radio, Newtownards, Co. Down,
Northern Ireland BT23 4ES
tel (01247) 815555 *fax* (01247) 818913
e-mail programmes@downtown.co.uk

Wales

Caernarfon
Champion FM, PO Box 103, Caernarfon LL55 1ZD
tel (01978) 752202 *fax* (01978) 758565
e-mail eira@championfm.co.uk

Cardiff & Newport
Red Dragon FM, Radio House, West Canal Wharf,
Cardiff CF1 5XL
tel (01222) 384041 *fax* (01222) 384014
e-mail mail@rdfm.co.uk

Cardiff & Newport
Touch Radio, West Canal Wharf, Cardiff CF1 5XL
tel (01222) 237878 *fax* (01222) 384014
e-mail mail@touchradio.co.uk

Ceredigion
Radio Ceredigion, Yr Hen Ysgol Cymraeg,
Ffordd Alexandra, Aberystwyth,
Ceredigion SY23 1LF
tel (01970) 627999 *fax* (01970) 627206

Heads of South Wales Valleys
Valleys Radio, Festival Park, Victoria,
Ebbw Vale NP3 6XW
tel (01495) 301116 *fax* (01495) 300710
e-mail info@valleysradio.co.uk

Montgomeryshire
Radio Maldwyn, The Studios, The Park,
Newtown, Powys SY16 2NZ
tel (01686) 623555 *fax* (01686) 623666
e-mail radio.maldwyn@ukonline.co.uk

North Wales Coast
Coast FM, Media House, Conway Road,
Colwyn Bay LL28 5AB
tel (01492) 534555 *fax* (01492) 535248

Swansea
Swansea Sound *and* The Wave 96·4 FM,
PO Box 1170/PO Box 964, Victoria Road,
Gowerton, Swansea SA4 3AB
tel (01792) 511170 *fax* (01792) 511171 (Sound)
tel (01792) 511964*fax* (01792) 511965 (Wave)
e-mails admin@swanseasound.co.uk,
admin@thewave.co.uk

Wrexham & Chester
Marcher Gold *and* MFM 103.4, The Studios,
Mold Road, Gwersyllt, Wrexham LL11 4AF
tel (01978) 752202 *fax* (01978) 759701

Independent radio producers

Many writers approach independent production companies direct and, increasingly, BBC Radio is commissioning independent producers to make programmes.

*Member of RADIO

Boom Media Ltd
PO Box 17, Halesworth, Suffolk IP19 0JZ
tel (01986) 781722 *fax* (01986) 781733
e-mail ideas@boom-media.demon.co.uk
Director Nick Patrick
Features and docs with an East Anglian bias, sports' features, popular culture, East Anglian drama. Founded 1993.

Business Sound Ltd*
Unit 9, Bramley Business Centre, Station Road, Bramley, Surrey GU5 0AZ
tel (01483) 898868 *fax* (01483) 894056
Managing Director Michael Bartlett
Ideas and synopses for packages for the corporate training market; docs. No unsolicited material; initial approach by phone, please. Founded 1989.

Fast Forward Productions
A132, Riverside Business Centre, Bendon Valley, London SW18 4LZ
tel 0181-875 9999 *fax* 0181-875 0344
Producer Adrian Quine
Aviation. Founded 1994.

Festival Radio Productions
PO Box 107, Brighton, East Sussex BN1 1QG
tel (01273) 321500 *fax* (01273) 321512
Managing Director Daniel Nathan
Plays, docs, features and programmes. Founded 1989.

The Fiction Factory*
201 Greenwich High Road, London SE10 8NB
tel 0181-853 5100 *fax* 0181-293 3001
e-mail radio@fiction-factory.demon.co.uk
Creative Director John Taylor
Plays, dramatisations, readings, documentaries, arts features and family drama mainly for BBC radio (R4, R2, World Service, etc). Original radio drama scripts and ideas for all radio genres considered. Founded 1993.

The Flying Dutchman Company
5-7 Hughes Mews, 143 Chatham Road, London SW11 6HJ
tel 0171-223 9067 *fax* 0171-585 0459
e-mail info@flyingdutchman.co.uk
Managing Director Michael Cameron
Plays, docs and other programmes on all topics. No unsolicited scripts. Please send synopsis only. Founded 1988.

GRF Christian Radio
342 Argyle Street, Glasgow G2 8LY
tel 0141-221 9447 *fax* 0141-332 9187
e-mail grf.radio@scet.org.uk
Programme Controller Brian W. Muir
Docs on ethical/moral/religious issues; mini-dramas (up to four minutes) on religious themes; one-minute scripts; children's programmes (religious/educational). Founded 1948.

Heavy Entertainment Ltd*
208-209 Canalot Studios, 222 Kensal Road, London W10 5BN
tel 0181-960 9001/2 *fax* 0181-960 9003
e-mail scripts@heavy-entertainment.co.uk
Company Directors David Roper, Nick St George
Full-length plays, docs and comedy programmes. Founded 1992.

Mike Hopwood Productions Ltd
Winton House, Stoke Road, Stoke-on-Trent, Staffs. ST4 2RW
tel (01782) 848800 *fax* (01782) 749447
Editor Mike Hopwood
Plays, docs, comedy, soaps, light entertainment. Founded 1991.

IRDP
PO Box 518, Manningtree, Essex CO11 1XD
tel (01206) 299088
web site www.irdp.co.uk/
New writing schemes for radio and theatre, and professional independent productions.

Mediatracks

93 Columbia Way, Blackburn, Lancs. BB2 7EA
tel/fax (01254) 691197
Contact Steve Johnson

Pop-music and general interest docs for BBC local radio network. Founded 1987.

Mr Punch Productions

4 Hughes Mews, 143 Chatham Road, London SW11 6HJ
tel 0171-924 7767 *fax* 0171-924 7775
Director Stewart Richards

Plays and dramatisations for broadcast on BBC Radio 4 and for audiobooks. Founded 1993.

Partners in Sound Ltd*

The Tower, Church Studios, North Villas, London NW1 9AY
tel 0171-485 0873 *mobile* (0973) 221 479
fax 0171-428 0541
e-mail partners_insound@compuserve.com
Director Ian Willox

Scripts for plays, docs and other programmes.

Penumbra Productions Ltd

80 Brondesbury Road, London NW6 6RX
tel 0171-328 4550 *fax* 0171-328 3844
e-mail 101621.3135@compuserve.com
Contact R. Elsgood

Drama and documentaries for Radio 3 and 4. Founded 1981.

Planet 24*

Norex Court, Thames Quay, 195 Marsh Wall, London E14 9SG
tel 0171-345 2424 *fax* 0171-345 9400
Managing Director Alex Connock

Scripts, synopses and ideas for plays, docs and other programmes. Founded 1991.

Quantam Radio Syndications Ltd

A132, Riverside Business Centre, Haldane Place, London SW18 4UQ
tel 0181-875 9999 *fax* 0181-875 0344
Producer Adrian Quine

Sponsored syndicated radio programmes.

Rewind Productions Ltd*

The Media Centre, 131-151 Great Titchfield Street, London W1P 8AE
tel 0171-577 7770 *fax* 0171-577 7773
Managing Director Simon Hughes

Plays, docs, popular and classical music, comedy and game shows. Founded 1989.

Screenplay Ltd

25 Cleveland Road, Brighton, East Sussex BN1 6FF
tel (01273) 708610 *fax* (01273) 708611
e-mail screenplay@dial.pipex.com
Managing Director Robert J. Shepherd

Scripts for drama and comedy, particularly series and serials. Unsolicited material not considered. Write with synopsis in first instance; sae essential for return of material. Founded 1987.

SH Radio

Robert Symes, Green Dene Cottage, Honeysuckle Bottom, East Horsley, Surrey KT24 5TD
tel/fax (01483) 283223
Mary-Jean Hasler, 22 Carew Road, London W13 9QL
tel 0181-567 2100

Music series, documentary features and broadcast/non-broadcast commercial material, voice over for films. Founded 1988.

Smooth Operations

PO Box 286, Cambridge CB1 4TW
tel (01223) 880835 *fax* (01223) 881647
e-mail smoothop@dial.pipex.com
Contact Nick Barraclough *and*
105 Delph Lane, Delph, Oldham OL3 5UP
tel (01457) 873752 *fax* (01457) 878500
e-mail smoothops@dial.pipex.com
Contact John Leonard

Scripts and ideas for docs and series. Founded 1992.

Testbed Productions*

10 Margaret Street, London W1N 7LF
tel 0171-436 0555 *fax* 0171-436 2800
Directors Viv Black, Nick Baker

Docs and other programmes; ideas for interviews, feature series, magazine, plays and panel/quiz games. Founded 1992.

Theatre

Marketing a stage play

Despite the financial problems facing many subsidised theatres and the mounting costs of commercial productions, there are still plenty of companies interested in producing new plays and supporting new writers. Indeed, the sheer number and variety of such companies can be daunting. **Ben Jancovich** *examines the options.*

Selecting the theatre

Given the financial costs of submitting a play and the emotional strain in waiting for a response, it is important to take the time to research where a submission is most likely to gain a positive response. Start by recognising the disparate nature of contemporary outlets for new plays. Study the box (right) and decide on which kind of theatre company you should concentrate your efforts.

Clearly, the sheer volume of plays submitted to certain companies and the specific requirements of others make a blanket marketing campaign likely to be neither practical nor successful. An in-depth examination is needed on how to give your submission a head start.

Submitting your play

If the subject matter, form or the references in the play are specific enough, start by submitting your play to a theatre company which is likely to be predisposed towards those aspects of your play. For instance, if your play is about disability, you will want to be aware that the *raison d'etre* of the Graeae Theatre Company is to explore this theme. Likewise, if you have written a play for children you should know about the Polka Theatre for Children in Wimbledon. There is a danger of compartmentalising both writers and companies but, if your play has a distinct selling point, do the research and work to that strength.

Similarly, if your play details the life or history of a specific locale or region, send a copy of your script to the repertory theatre for that area – they may well have an interest in plays with a local appeal.

If a character in your play has a specific and discernible quality for which you think a particular actor may be uniquely suitable, it may be worth contacting them

---

Types of theatre companies

- **Metropolitan new writing theatre companies:** Largely London-based theatres which specialise in new writing, such as Hampstead Theatre, Royal Court, Bush Theatre, Soho Theatre, etc.
- **Regional repertory theatre companies:** Theatres based in towns and cities across the country which may do new plays as part of their repertoire.
- **Commercial producing managements:** Unsubsidised profit-making theatre producers who may occasionally be interested in new plays to take on tour or to present in the West End.
- **Small and/or middle-scale touring companies:** Companies – mostly touring – which exist to explore or promote specific themes or are geared towards specific kinds of audiences.
- **Independent theatre practitioners:** For example, actors who may be looking for interesting plays in which to appear.
- **Independent theatre producers:** For example, young directors or producers who are looking for plays to produce at the onset of their career.
- **Drama schools and amateur dramatics companies.**

through their agent. Of course, there is no point in contacting an actor merely because they are famous – they will already receive many more scripts than they could ever read. Therefore, only consider doing this if there is genuinely something specific about the play that demands their attention.

Further options

If your play does not obviously fit any such niche, there are still plenty of companies which are keen to read exciting new writing irrespective of subject matter.

Metropolitan new writing companies, the regional repertory theatres and commercial producers are all, to different degrees, in the market for new plays. Additionally, and often most successfully, are the plethora of young directors and other practitioners who institute productions under the aegis of their own independent theatre companies. An all-inclusive list of these latter organisations would be daunting, so research their interests and be selective. Reading reviews in the national and local press and listings magazines, such as *Time Out*, will give you some idea of which are the most productive and successful companies and practitioners.

Choosing which company to approach can be difficult as past productions and achievements rarely give precise indications of the way a company wants to move forward. Likewise, the notion of a successful 'commercial' company or play is not straightforward. For example, recent new plays with youthful, urban and often violent content have proved big commercial hits despite appearing anathema to the cliché of a well-made West End play.

Amateur companies/drama schools

Two other avenues to consider are amateur theatres and drama schools. Certain amateur theatre companies, such as the Questors Theatre in Ealing, have premiered plays by both new and established writers. The Leisure Department of your local council should be able to give information on groups which exist in your area.

One good reason for approaching such a company is that they are often the only organisations (apart from the RSC and RNT) which can afford to mount large cast plays. It is a reality of modern theatre that, if you write a play requiring a cast of more than 10, it will prove financially problematic for many companies.

Similar considerations are at work regarding drama schools, with the added incentive that the people involved – directors and actors – may form an attachment to the play and want to work on it professionally elsewhere. The publication *Contacts* lists and gives contact details of the drama schools which are recognised by and accredited to the Conference of Drama Schools.

How to approach a company

Although some details may be obvious, they are worth noting and of course much depends on who you are approaching. At the very least, only ever submit a script which is legible, typed and bound, and always include a stamped addressed envelope large enough for its return. Find out the name and position of the best person to receive and assess your script. Do this not only a matter of courtesy but also because it will help if you need to follow up anything at a later date.

Do your best to ensure that you are happy with the script as it stands. Mistakes are inevitable but it is unprofessional to send rewrites before the original draft has even been read. Obviously, always keep a copy of your play.

Some theatres employ a literary manager or dramaturg whose job is specifically to facilitate the passage of plays through the administrative and artistic channels. In such cases, submissions should be simple and, under their management, the theatre should always be willing and ready to read plays by writers previously unknown to them (although some may not be interested in musicals, revues or translations and adaptations).

Useful addresses

The Arts Council of England
14 Great Peter Street,
London SW1P 3NQ
Contact The Drama Director
Publishes a brochure, *Schemes for Writers & Theatre Companies*, which gives details of various forms of assistance available to playwrights and to theatres wishing to commission new plays. The Council awards Bursaries (e.g. the John Whiting Award) and helps writers who are being commissioned or encouraged by a theatre company. A number of Resident Dramatists' Attachment Awards are available. See also page 459.

New Playwrights Trust
Interchange Studios, Dalby Street,
London NW5 3NQ
A useful organisation which provides members with the fruits of its extensive knowledge of the industry through publications, forums and databases.

The Spotlight
7 Leicester Place, London WC2H 7BP
tel 0171-437 7631
Publishes a book, *Contacts*, which contains all the addresses for professional organisations and theatre companies listed in the article. The 1998-99 edition is available from October.

However, in the majority of cases there will be no one person whose main function is to deal with writers and their plays. Therefore, you will need to be particularly rigorous in finding out the theatre's policy (remember that due to the pressure of work, dealing with writers may not be the highest of priorities).
Some companies may only accept submission of scripts through agents or with some sort of recommendation. Others may want a brief description of the play so they can decide whether it is worth their time looking at it. They may want this either sent by post, or they may prefer a brief telephone conversation.

What to expect

Since working practices vary from organisation to organisation, the response you can expect and how long before you get it will also vary. After submitting your script, do not expect any response for two to three months. If you have heard nothing from the company after six months, make a gentle inquiry. Obviously, badgering the company for a response is unlikely to work to your advantage.
The company is likely to give one or more of the following responses:
• an explanation for the rejection of the play;
• the offer of a 'getting to know you' meeting;
• a more formal dramaturgical meeting to discuss possible textual changes or clarifications;
• a reading or workshop on the play;
• advice on where else to send the play;
• an offer of a more formal recommendation for the play to colleagues working elsewhere.

Agents

When you enter into any kind of contractual relationship with a theatre company you should find an agent. An agent can help you on all the legal aspects of selling a play and ensure that your rights are protected. He or she will also help to promote you and your work and in guiding your career. As the relationship between you and your agent is crucial to the long-term development of you as a writer, meet as many agents as possible to seek out someone with whom you feel at ease and have an affinity. See *Literary agents for television, film, radio and theatre* on page 384.

New writing support agencies

Aside from theatre companies and practitioners, there is a burgeoning industry of organisations which exist to help writers develop their craft, their contacts and their appreciation of the industry. One cross-over organisation is the National

Theatre Studio, which is part of the Royal National Theatre but exists more as a service to theatre artists and the industry at large rather than directly for the scheduling of the company's three theatres. The national New Playwrights Trust exists as an information and research organisation.

Attached and supported by most of the Regional Arts Boards are regional forums, such as Stage Coach for the Midlands and North West Playwrights for the north of England. It is worth making contact with these organisations, especially if you are based outside one of the metropolitan areas as they can act on your behalf. Some are very good at the national promotion of the work of their local writers, while others are more active in putting writers and directors in contact with each other. Contact your local Regional Arts Board (see page 491) or repertory theatre for more information.

Bursaries and prizes

There are various schemes run by theatre companies, arts boards, television companies and independent organisations to financially assist writers. These fall into two categories: bursaries and prizes. Bursaries relate to the writer rather than their work, and can sometimes include an attachment to a theatre or arts organisation. Some writers can apply for themselves (e.g. The Arts Council's Writers Bursaries), while for other awards a theatre company applies on the writer's behalf. Prizes usually (though not always) relate to the judging of a play. Because the prize for such a scheme may be either a production or sufficient money to encourage one to happen, it is worth familiarising yourself with the various schemes and their deadlines. This is best done either through membership of New Playwrights Trust or by being in contact with the regional forums, mentioned above. Also, watch out for announcements in the Press, especially the *Observer*, the *Author*, *Amateur Stage* and the *Stage*. A list of magazines dealing with the theatre is on page 136; see also *Prizes and awards* on page 510.

Ben Jancovich is Literary Manager of Hampstead Theatre. Previously Literary Assistant at the Royal Shakespeare Company, he has directed plays in the London fringe and has worked as a freelance theatre critic with *City Limits*.

Theatre producers

This list is divided into London theatres (below), provincial theatres (page 341) and touring companies (page 345). See also Marketing a stage play on page 335.

London

Bush Theatre

Shepherd's Bush Green, London W12 8QD
tel 0171-602 3703 *fax* 0171-602 7614
Literary Manager Tim Fountain
Welcomes unsolicited full-length scripts (plus one small and one large sae); commissions writers at an early stage in their career; produces 6 premieres a year.

Michael Codron Plays Ltd

Aldwych Theatre Offices, Aldwych,
London WC2B 4DF
tel 0171-240 8291 *fax* 0171-240 8467

Ray Cooney Presentations Ltd

Hollowfield Cottage, Littleton, Surrey GU3 1HN
tel (01483) 440 443 *fax* (01483) 532068
Contact H.S. Udwin
Commercial producing management. Comedy/farce scripts only.

English Stage Company Ltd

Royal Court Theatre, Sloane Square,
London SW1W 8AS
tel 0171-730 5174 *fax* 0171-730 4705
Literary Manager Graham Whybrow
New plays.

Flying Machine Theatre

212 Piccadilly, London W1V 9LD

tel 0171-917 6257 *fax* 0171-917 6258
e-mail flyingmachine@aol.com
Contact Tom Downs

Metropolitan new writing theatre company, co-producing in medium-sized venues. 2-3 productions a year. Founded 1996.

Greenwich Theatre Ltd

Greenwich Theatre, Crooms Hill, London SE10 8ES
tel 0181-858 4447 *fax* 0181-858 8042
Contact Artistic Director

Hampstead Theatre

Swiss Cottage Centre, Avenue Road,
London NW3 3EX
tel 0171-722 9224 *fax* 0171-722 3860
Contact Ben Jancovich

New plays and the occasional modern classic. After initial assessment, promising scripts are then read by the literary manager and/or artistic director. It can therefore take 2-3 months to reach a decision.

Bill Kenwright Ltd

55-59 Shaftesbury Avenue, London W1V 8JA
tel 0171-439 4466 *fax* 0171-437 8370
Chief Executive Brett Finnigan

Commercial producing management presenting revivals and new works for the West End and for touring theatres.

King's Head Theatre

115 Upper Street, London N1 1QN
tel 0171-226 8561 *fax* 0171-226 8507
Contact General Manager

Pub theatre producing revivals and some new works. No unsolicited submissions.

Knightsbridge Theatrical Productions Ltd

21 New Fetter Lane, London EC4A 1JJ
tel 0171-583 8687 *fax* 0171-583 1040
Contact Mrs Sheila H. Gray

Lyric Theatre Hammersmith

King Street, London W6 0QL
tel 0181-741 0824 *fax* 0181-741 7694
Chief Executive Sue Storr, *Artistic Director* Neil Bartlett, *Administrative Producer* Simon Mellor

A producing theatre as well as a receiving venue for work by new writers, translators, performers and composers.

Man in the Moon Theatre

392 King's Road, London SW3 5UZ
tel 0171-351 5701 *fax* 0171-351 1873
Administrator Pete Staves

65-seat theatre; medium-scale company. Broad range of plays (24-40 a year), including new writing; scripts from new

writers considered. Plays scheduled in seasons of 3-4 months for in-house productions.

Moral Support

Tabard Theatre, 2 Bath Road, London W4 1LW
tel 0181-994 5985 *fax* 0181-747 8256
e-mail moral-support@tir-nan-og.demon.co.uk
web site http://www.tir-nan-og.demon.co.uk/moral-support.html
Contact Clare L. Price

The company brings together writers, musicians and other freelance practitioners to create new work with the emphasis on producing new writing and performance styles, to be performed in a variety of locations. Its performance technique has been described as 'an utterly original theatrical language'. Available for commissions of new plays, performance and dance. Founded 1993.

The Old Red Lion Theatre

418 St John Street, London EC1V 4QE
tel 0171-833 3053 *fax* 0171-833 3053
Artistic Director Ken McClymont

Interested in contemporary pieces, especially from unproduced writers. No funding: incoming production company pays to rent the theatre. Sae essential with enquiries. Founded 1977.

Orange Tree Theatre

1 Clarence Street, Richmond, Surrey TW9 2SA
tel 0181-940 0141 *fax* 0181-332 0369
Literary Manager Nina Anne Kaye

Producing venue. Patience and sae required!

Polka Theatre for Children

240 The Broadway, London SW19 1SB
tel 0181-542 4258 *fax* 0181-542 7723
e-mail polkatheatre@dial.pipex.com
web site http://www.polkatheatre.com
Artistic Director Vicky Ireland

Exclusively for children, the Main Theatre seats 300 and The Adventure Theatre seats 80. Programmed for 18 months to 2 years in advance. Theatre of new writing, with targeted commissions. Founded 1967.

The Questors Theatre

Mattock Lane, London W5 5BQ
tel 0181-567 0011 *fax* 0181-567 8736
Theatre Manager Elaine Orchard, *Marketing Director* Sonja Garsvo

Annual Student Playwriting Competition with £1000 prize (funds permitting).

Royal National Theatre

South Bank, London SE1 9PX
tel 0171-928 2033 *fax* 0171-620 1197
Little opportunity for the production of
unsolicited material, but submissions
welcomed. Send to Jack Bradley, Literary
Manager, together with an sae.

Royal Shakespeare Company

Barbican Theatre, Barbican, London EC2Y 8BQ
tel 0171-628 3351 *fax* 0171-628 2812
Artistic Director Adrian Noble, *Literary Manager*
Simon Reade
The RSC is a classical theatre company
based in Stratford-upon-Avon, bringing
its repertoire to the Barbican Theatre for
6 months of the year, and with residencies in Newcastle and Plymouth. It also
tours both nationally and internationally.

As well as Shakespeare, English classics and foreign classics in translation,
new plays counterpoint the RSC's repertory, especially those which celebrate language. The Literary Department is proac-
tive rather than reactive, and seeks out the
plays and playwrights it wishes to commission. It will read all translations of
classic foreign works submitted, or of contemporary works where the original writer
and/or translator is known. It is unable to
read unsolicited works from less established writers, and can only return scripts
if an sae is enclosed with the submission.

Soho Theatre Company

21 Dean Street, London W1V 6NE
tel 0171-287 5060 *fax* 0171-287 5061
e-mail sohotheatre.co.uk
Artistic Director Abigail Morris, *Literary Manager*
Paul Sirett
Always on the look out for new plays
and playwrights and welcome unsolicited scripts. These are read by a professional panel who write a detailed critical
report. Also offer various levels of workshop facilities, including rehearsed reading and platform performances, for
promising playwrights, and in-depth
script development with the Artistic
Director and Literary Manager. See also
the Verity Bargate Award on page 512.

The Steam Industry

Finborough Theatre, 118 Finborough Road,
London SW10 9ED
tel 0171-244 7439 *fax* 0171-835 1853
Contact Phil Willmott

Creates and develops large cast productions which deal with 'big' subjects in an
ambitious and innovative way. Founded
1994.

Stoll Moss Theatres

Manor House, 21 Soho Square,
London W1V 5FD
tel 0171-494 5200 *fax* 0171-434 1217
e-mail info@stoll-moss.com
web site http://www.stoll.moss.com
Production Director Nica Burns
Owns 10 West End theatres: Apollo,
Cambridge, Duchess, Garrick, Gielgud,
Her Majesty's, London Palladium, Lyric
Shaftesbury Avenue, Queens and Theatre
Royal Drury Lane. Now commissions
new plays from both established writers
and new talent. Founded 1978.

Tabard Theatre

2 Bath Road, London W4 1LW
tel 0181-995 6035 *fax* 0181-747 8256
e-mail tabard@cmb.dircon.co.uk
Artistic Director Kate Bone
Aims to promote new work of contemporary relevance with particular emphasis on
multimedia events, cross-art forms, new
writing and experimental performance
styles. It hosts workshops, readings,
lunchtime and evening performances, and
is also home to producing company **Moral
Support**. Do not send unsolicited material:
the theatre has no literary department.

Theatre Royal, Stratford East

Gerry Raffles Square, London E15 1BN
tel 0181-534 7374 *fax* 0181-534 8381
Associate Director Mr Kerry Michael

The Tricycle Theatre Company

Tricycle Theatre, 269 Kilburn High Road,
London NW6 7JR
tel 0171-372 6611 *fax* 0171-328 0795
Contact Nicolas Kent
Metropolitan new writing theatre company.

Triumph Proscenium Productions Ltd

Suite 4, Waldorf Chambers, 11 Aldwych,
London WC2B 4DA
tel 0171-343 8800 *fax* 0171-343 8801

Unicorn Theatre for Children

Arts Theatre, 6-7 Great Newport Street,
London WC2H 7JB
tel 0171-379 3280 *fax* 0171-836 5366
Administrative Director Christopher Moxon,
Artistic Director Tony Graham
Six productions a year for children aged
4-12 – new writing and adaptations.

Warehouse Theatre

Dingwall Road, Croydon CR0 2NF
tel 0181-681 1257 *fax* 0181-688 6699
Artistic Director Ted Craig

South London's new writing theatre. Seats 100-120. Produces up to 6 new plays a year and co-produces with companies which share the commitment to new work. It continues to build upon a tradition of discovering and nurturing new writers, with activities including a monthly writers' workshop and the annual International Playwriting Festival (see page 523). Unsolicited scripts are welcome but it is more advisable to submit plays via the Playwriting Festival. The theatre is committed to productions at least 9 months in advance.

Michael White

48 Dean Street, London W1V 5HL
tel 0171-734 7707 *fax* 0171-734 7727
Contact Mac MacKenzie

Provincial

Abbey Theatre

Lower Abbey Street, Dublin 1, Republic of Ireland
tel (01) 8748741 *fax* (01) 8729177
Artistic Director Patrick Mason, *General Manager* Martin Fahy

Mainly produces plays written by Irish authors or on Irish subjects. Foreign classics are however regularly produced.

Yvonne Arnaud Theatre Management Ltd

Millbrook, Guildford, Surrey GU1 3UX
tel (01483) 440077 *fax* (01483) 564071
Contact David Lindsey

Receives and produces Number One touring and pre-West End product.

Belgrade Theatre

Belgrade Square, Coventry CV1 1GS
tel (01203) 256431 *fax* (01203) 550680
Contact Julie Evans

Produces new plays both in the main house and studio.

Birmingham Repertory Theatre Ltd

Broad Street, Birmingham B1 2EP
tel 0121-236 6771 *fax* 0121-236 7883
Artistic Director Bill Alexander, *Associate Director* Tony Clark, *Literary Manager* Ben Payne

Aims to provide a platform for the best work from new writers from both within and beyond the West Midlands region. The development, commissioning and production of new writing takes place across the full range of the theatre's programme including: the Main House (capacity 900); the Studio, a space dedicated to new work; and its biannual Community tours. Unsolicited submissions are welcome largely from the point of view of beginning a relationship with a writer. Priority in such development work is given to writers from the region.

Bristol Old Vic Company

Theatre Royal, King Street, Bristol BS1 4ED
tel 0117-949 3993 *fax* 0117-949 3996
Director's Office Hilary Davis, *Artistic Director* Andy Hay

Programme includes classical and new plays. New writing encouraged. New scripts read by experienced reader for a fee, currently £10.

The Byre Theatre of St Andrews Ltd

Abbey Street, St Andrews KY16 9LA
tel (01334) 476288 *fax* (01334) 475370
Artistic Director Ken Alexander

Currently involved in a major rebuilding programme. On reopening (scheduled for the end of 1999), the theatre will operate a blend of in-house productions and touring productions. The Byre Theatre Company meanwhile maintains a policy of producing a wide variety of new and established work, theatre-in-education projects, youth theatre and community work in Fife. The company also offers support for new writing through the Byre Writers, a well-established and successful playwrights group.

Chester Gateway Theatre Trust Ltd

Hamilton Place, Chester CH1 2BH
tel (01244) 344238 *fax* (01244) 317277
Administrative Director Katy Spicer

Regional repertory company presenting a wide range of small-cast plays, including new works, to a broad audience.

Chichester Festival Theatre Productions Company Ltd

Chichester Festival Theatre, Oaklands Park, Chichester, West Sussex PO19 4AP
tel (01243) 784437 *fax* (01243) 787288
e-mail admin@cft.org.uk
web site http://www.cft.org.uk
Festival Director Andrew Welch, *General Manager* Paul Rogerson

Festival season Apr-Oct in Festival

Theatre and Minerva Theatre; rest of year seasons of touring plays, opera, ballet, dance, jazz, orchestral concerts and Minerva Movies.

Churchill Theatre

High Street, Bromley, Kent BR1 1HA
tel 0181-464 7131 *fax* 0181-290 6968
Contact General Manager

Full-length plays; comedies, thrillers, dramas, new plays considered.

Theatr Clwyd

Mold, Clwyd CH7 1YA
tel (01352) 756331 *fax* (01352) 758323
e-mail drama@celtic.co.uk
Director Terry Hands, *Literary Manager* William James

Lively repertory company producing a season of classics, revivals, contemporary drama and new writing each year, performed in repertoire by a resident company, along with tours throughout Wales (in English and Welsh). Especially interested in new plays by Welsh writers or with Welsh themes.

Colchester Mercury Theatre Ltd

Balkerne Gate, Colchester, Essex CO1 1PT
tel (01206) 577006 *fax* (01206) 769607
e-mail mercury.theatre@virgin.net
Contact (Playwrights' Group) Adrian Stokes

Regional repertory theatre presenting works to a wide audience. Produces some new work, mainly commissioned. Supports local Playwrights' Group for adults with a serious commitment to writing plays.

The Coliseum Theatre

Fairbottom Street, Oldham OL1 3SW
tel 0161-624 1731 *fax* 0161-624 5318
Chief Executive Kenneth Alan Taylor

Special interest in northern plays. Contact by letter initially.

Contact Theatre Company

Oxford Road, Manchester M15 6JA
tel 0161-274 3434 *fax* 0161-273 6286
Artistic Director Benjamin Twist

Interested in exciting, theatrical plays for a younger (under 25) audience.

Derby Playhouse Ltd

Theatre Walk, Eagle Centre, Derby DE1 2NF
tel (01332) 363271 *fax* (01332) 294412
e-mail admin@derbyplayhouse.demon.co.uk
web site http://www.derbyplayhouse.demon.co.uk
Artistic Director Mark Clements

Regional repertory company. In the first instance, send a letter with a synopsis, a resumé of your writing experience and any 10 pages of your script. A review of this material will determine whether a complete copy of the script is required.

Druid Theatre Company

Druid Lane Theatre, Chapel Lane, Galway, Republic of Ireland
tel (091) 568617/568660 *fax* (091) 563109
e-mail druid@iol.ie
General Manager Louise Donlon, *Artistic Director* Garry Hynes

Producing company presenting a wide range of national and international plays. Emphasis on new Irish writing.

The Duke's Playhouse

Moor Lane, Lancaster LA1 1QE
tel (01524) 67461 *fax* (01524) 846817
Artistic Director Ewan Marshall

Dundee Repertory Theatre

Tay Square, Dundee DD1 1PB
tel (01382) 227684
Artistic Director Hamish Glen

Regional repertory theatre company. Its policy is to concentrate resources on commissions for new writers.

Everyman Theatre

5-9 Hope Street, Liverpool L1 9BH
tel 0151-708 0338 *fax* 0151-709 0398
e-mail everyman@liverpool.ac.uk
web site http://everyman.merseyworld.com/
Executive Producer Kevin Fearon, *General Manager* Sharon Duckworth

Regional repertory theatre company.

Everyman Theatre

Regent Street, Cheltenham, Glos. GL50 1HQ
tel (01242) 512515 *fax* (01242) 224305
e-mail admin@everyman.u-net.com
web site http://www.everyman.u-net.com
Chief Executive Philip Bernays, *Associate Director* Sue Colverd

Regional presenting theatre promoting a wide range of plays. Small-scale experimental, youth and educational work encouraged in The Other Place studio theatre. Contact the Associate Director before submitting material.

Grand Theatre

Singleton Street, Swansea SA1 3QJ
tel (01792) 475242 *fax* (01792) 475379
General Manager Gary Iles

Regional receiving theatre.

Haymarket Theatre Company
The Haymarket Theatre, Wote Street,
Basingstoke, Hants RG21 7NW
tel (01256) 355844 *fax* (01256) 357130
Mounts seasons of plays, many of which
are designed for co-production with
London managements.

Leicester Haymarket Theatre
Belgrave Gate, Leicester LE1 3YQ
tel 0116-253 0021 *fax* 0116-251 3310
web site http://www.netpresence.co.uk/leicester
haymarkettheatre/
Regional repertory theatre company.

Library Theatre Company
St Peter's Square, Manchester M2 5PD
tel 0161-234 1913 *fax* 0161-228 6481
Contact Artistic Director
Contemporary drama, classics, plays for
children. Aims to produce drama which
illuminates the contemporary world;
scripts from new writers considered.

New Victoria Theatre
Etruria Road, Newcastle under Lyme ST5 0JG
tel (01782) 717954 *fax* (01782) 712885
Theatre Director Gwenda Hughes
Europe's first purpose built theatre in the
round, presenting major classics, adaptations, contemporary plays, documentaries, new plays.

New Victoria Theatre
Peacocks Arts & Entertainment Centre, Woking,
Surrey GU21 1GQ
tel (01483) 747422 *fax* (01483) 740477
Contact Robert Cogo-Fawcett, Beaufort Cottage,
Grosvenor, Bath BA1 6PZ
tel (01225) 311248
Large-scale touring house. Interested to
co-produce or produce.

Northampton Repertory Players Ltd
The Royal Theatre, Guildhall Road,
Northampton NN1 1EA
tel (01604) 38343 *fax* (01604) 602408
Contact Julie Martell, *Artistic Director* Michael
Napier Brown
Presents plays for main house, studio,
theatre-in-education, community touring
and youth theatre. Please send scripts,
indicating which area of work they are
for, to Artistic Director.

Northcott Theatre
Stocker Road, Exeter, Devon EX4 4QB
tel (01392) 256182
Artistic Director Ben Crocker
Regional repertory theatre company.

Northern Stage Company
Newcastle Playhouse, Barras Bridge,
Newcastle upon Tyne NE1 1RH
tel 0191-232 3366 *fax* 0191-261 8093
e-mail northern.stage@ncl.ac.uk
Artistic Director Alan Lyddiard
Major company producing and present-
ing international work.

Nottingham Playhouse
Nottingham Theatre Trust Ltd, Wellington Circus,
Nottingham NG1 5AF
tel 0115-947 4361 *fax* 0115-947 5759
Artistic Director Martin Duncan
Works closely with communities of Not-
tingham and Nottinghamshire; presents
best of innovative and world theatre.
Takes 6 months to read unsolicited MSS.

Nuffield Theatre
University Road, Southampton SO17 1TR
tel (01703) 315500 *fax* (01703) 315511
Script Executive Penny Gold
Repertory theatre producing straight
plays and musicals, and some small-
scale fringe work. Interested in new
plays.

Octagon Theatre
Howell Croft South, Bolton BL1 1SB
tel (01204) 529407 *fax* (01204) 380110
Administrative Director Amanda Belcham,
Artistic Director Lawrence Till
Repertory season Sept-June, including
new plays and contemporary theatre.

Oxford Stage Company
15-19 George Street, Oxford OX1 2AU
tel (01865) 245781 *fax* (01865) 790625
Contact Marketing Manager

The Palace Theatre Watford Ltd
Clarendon Road, Watford, Herts. WD1 1JZ
tel (01923) 235455 *fax* (01923) 819664
Contact Giles Croft
Regional repertory theatre. Produces 8
plays each year, both classic and contemporary drama. Welcomes scripts from
new writers. Founded 1908.

Palace Theatre Trust Ltd
London Road, Westcliff-on-Sea, Essex SS0 9LA
tel (01702) 347816 *fax* (01702) 435031
Theatre Secretary Iris Stewart
Subsidised repertory theatre producing a
programme of predominantly modern
British drama with some foreign writers,
particularly American. Most new work is
done in small, 100-seater studio.

Peacock Theatre

The Abbey Theatre, Lower Abbey Street,
Dublin 1, Republic of Ireland
tel (01) 8748741 *fax* (01) 8729177
Artistic Director Patrick Mason, *General Manager*
Martin Fahy

Experimental theatre associated with the Abbey Theatre; presents mostly new writing.

Perth Theatre Ltd

185 High Street, Perth PH1 5UW
tel (01738) 472700 *fax* (01738) 624576
e-mail theatre@perth.org.uk
web site http://www.perth.org.uk/perth/theatre.htm
Artistic Director Michael Winter, *General Manager* Paul McLennan

Three-weekly repertory programme Aug-May of plays, musicals, revivals and new writing; also studio and theatre-in-education work.

Plymouth Theatre Royal

Theatre Royal, Royal Parade, Plymouth PL1 2TR
tel (01752) 668282 *fax* (01752) 671179
Chief Executive Adrian Vinken, *Producer* Simon Stokes

Regional repertory theatre company which encourages new writing. All scripts are read and considered for production.

Queen's Theatre Hornchurch

(Havering Theatre Trust Ltd)
Billet Lane, Hornchurch, Essex RM11 1QT
tel (01708) 456118 *fax* (01708) 452348
Artistic Director Bob Carlton, *Admin Director* Tony Hill

Middle-scale regional theatre with permanent company of actors/musicians producing popular comedy, drama and musicals. Scripts from new writers welcome, especially as co-productions with commercial producer or additional funding.

Royal Exchange Theatre Company Ltd

St Ann's Square, Manchester M2 7DH
tel 0161-833 9333 *fax* 0161-832 0881
General Manager Patricia Weller

Varied programme of major classics, new plays, musicals, contemporary British and European drama; also explores the creative work of diverse cultures.

Royal Lyceum Theatre Company

Royal Lyceum Theatre, Grindlay Street,
Edinburgh EH3 9AX
tel 0131-229 7404 *fax* 0131-228 3955
e-mail lyceum@infoser.com
web sites http://www.infoser.com/infotheatre/lyceum *and*
http://www.infoser.com/infotheatre/vtour
Artistic Director Kenny Ireland, *Associate Literary Director* Tom McGrath

Edinburgh's busiest repertory company, producing an all-year-round programme of classic, contemporary and new drama. Interested in work of Scottish writers.

Salisbury Playhouse

Malthouse Lane, Salisbury, Wilts. SP2 7RA
tel (01722) 320117 *fax* (01722) 421991
Artistic Director Jonathan Church

Regional repertory theatre producing a broad programme of classical and modern plays.

Scarborough Theatre Trust Ltd

Stephen Joseph Theatre, Westborough,
Scarborough, North Yorkshire YO11 1JW
tel (01723) 370540 *fax* (01723) 360506
e-mail response@sjt.onyxnet.co.uk
web site http://www.webart.co.uk/clients/sjt/
Literary Manager Connal Orton

Regional repertory theatre company which produces about 10 plays a year, half of which are premieres. The theatre has a particular reputation for comedy. Plays should have a strong narrative and a desire to entertain, though nothing too lightweight will be considered. Please enclose a sae with all submissions.

Sheffield Theatres

(Crucible, Crucible Studio & Lyceum),
55 Norfolk Street, Sheffield S1 1DA
tel 0114-2760621 *fax* 0114-2701532
Artistic Director Deborah Paige

Large-scale producing house with distinctive thrust stage; smallish studio; Victorian proscenium arch theatre used mainly for touring productions.

Sherman Theatre

Senghennydd Road, Cardiff CF2 4YE
tel (01222) 396844 *fax* (01222) 665581
General Manager Margaret Jones

Plays mainly for 15-25 age range. Founded 1974.

Show of Strength Theatre Company Ltd

Hebron House, Sion Road, Bedminster,
Bristol BS3 3BD
tel 0117-953 7735
Administrator Sheila Hannon

Small-scale company committed to producing new and unperformed work.

Theatre season: Oct-Jan. Send sae for return of MSS. Founded 1986.

Sionnach Theatre Company
The New Theatre, Temple Bar, 43 East Essex Street, Dublin 2, Republic of Ireland
tel (1) 6703361 *fax* (1) 6711943
e-mail sionnach@indigo.ie
web site http://indigo.ie/~sionach
Producer/Artistic Director Anthony Fox
Small-scale theatre producing plays by Irish writers whose work deals with issues pertaining to young people in contemporary Irish society. Welcomes scripts from new writers. Founded 1997.

Swan Theatre
The Moors, Worcester WR1 3EF
tel (01905) 726969 *fax* (01905) 723738
Artistic Director Jenny Stephens
Regional repertory company producing a wide range of plays to a mixed audience. A writing group meets at the theatre. Unsolicited scripts are discouraged.

Theatre Royal
Windsor, Berks. SL4 1PS
tel (01753) 863444 *fax* (01753) 831673
Executive Producer Bill Kenwright, *Executive Director* Mark Piper
Regional repertory company presenting a wide range of productions from classics to new plays.

Thorndike Theatre
Church Street, Leatherhead, Surrey KT22 8DF
tel (01372) 376211 *fax* (01372) 362595
Contact Theatre Manager

Traverse Theatre
10 Cambridge Street, Edinburgh EH1 2ED
tel 0131-228 3223 *fax* 0131-229 8443
Literary Director John Tiffany, *Literary Associate* Ella Wildridge
Scotland's new writing theatre.

Watermill Theatre Ltd
Bagnor, Newbury, Berks. RG20 8AE
tel (01635) 45834
Contact Jill Fraser
Small professional theatre. Interested in all types of new work, including drama and musicals, suitable for small stage and auditorium.

The West Yorkshire Playhouse
Playhouse Square, Quarry Hill,
Leeds LS2 7UP
tel 0113-244 2141 *fax* 0113-244 8252
Artistic Director Jude Kelly

Twin auditoria complex – with a policy of encouraging new writing; community theatre; Young People's Theatre programme.

The Wolsey Theatre
Civic Drive, Ipswich, Suffolk IP1 2AS
tel (01473) 218911 *fax* (01473) 212946
Administrative Director Lorna Anderson, *Artistic Director* Andrew Manley

York Citizens' Theatre Trust Ltd
Theatre Royal, St Leonard's Place,
York YO1 2HD
tel (01904) 658162 *fax* (01904) 611534
Executive Director Elizabeth Jones, *Artistic Director* Damian Cruden
Repertory productions, tours.

Touring companies

Actors Touring Company
Alford House, Aveline Street, London SE11 5DQ
tel 0171-735 8311 *fax* 0171-735 1031
Executive Producer Hetty Shand
Small to medium-scale company producing new theatre from old stories, myths and legends.

Black Theatre Co-Operative Ltd
Unit 3P, Leroy House, 436 Essex Road,
London N1 3QP
tel 0171-226 1225 *fax* 0171-226 0223
Artistic Director Felix Cross, *General Manager* Olivia Jacobs
Interested in Black plays, especially those that relate to the experiences of Black people both in Britain and outside Britain.

Bristol Express Theatre Company
Flat 1, Stepney Green Court,
London E1 3LJ
tel 0171-423 9453
Artistic Director Andy Jordan
Most productions are new plays; scripts from new writers considered.

Compass Theatre Company
Carver Street Institute, 24 Rockingham Lane,
Sheffield S1 4FW
tel 0114-275 5328 *fax* 0114-278 6931
General Manager Deborah Rees

Graeae Theatre Company
Interchange Studios, Dalby Street,
London NW5 3NQ
tel 0171 267 1959 *fax* 0171-267 2703
Contact Kevin Dunn
Small-scale company. Welcomes scripts from disabled writers. Founded 1980.

The Hiss & Boo Company

1 Nyes Hill, Wineham Lane, Bolney,
West Sussex RH17 5SD
tel (01444) 881707 *fax* (01444) 882057
e-mail hissboo@msn.com

Not much scope for new plays, but will consider comedy thrillers/chillers and plays/musicals for children. Send synopsis first. Plays/synopses will be returned only if accompanied by an sae.

Hull Truck Theatre Co. Ltd

Hull Truck Theatre, Spring Street, Hull HU2 8RW
tel (01482) 224800 *fax* (01482) 581182
e-mail admin@hulltruck.co.uk
Executive Director Simon Stallworthy

World-renowned small-cast touring company presenting popular and accessible theatre. Produces some new work, mainly commissioned.

The London Bubble

(Bubble Theatre Company)
3-5 Elephant Lane, London SE16 4JD
tel 0171-237 4434 *fax* 0171-231 2366
e-mail londonbubble@gn.apc.org

M6 Theatre Company

Hamer C.P. School, Albert Royds Street,
Rochdale, Lancs. OL16 2SU
tel (01706) 355898 *fax* (01706) 711700
Contact Jane Milne

Theatre-in-education company providing high quality, educational, innovative and relevant live theatre for children and young people, and for audiences who may not normally have access to theatre.

Made in Wales

Chapter, Market Road, Canton, Cardiff CF5 1QE
tel (01222) 344737 *fax* (01222) 344738
Artistic Director Jeff Teare

Three productions per year of new plays relevant to Wales; scripts from new writers always welcome.

New Perspectives Theatre Company

The Old Library, Leeming Street, Mansfield,
Notts. NG18 1NG
tel (01623) 635225 *fax* (01623) 635240
e-mail art@nperspex.demon.co.uk
Artistic Director Gavin Stride

Has a policy of employing writers for new work. Regret unsolicited scripts returned, unless writers are local to the East Midlands region.

NTC Touring Theatre Company

(formerly Northumberland Theatre Company)
The Playhouse, Bondgate Without, Alnwick,
Northumberland NE66 1PQ
tel (01665) 602586 *fax* (01665) 605837
Artistic Director Gillian Hambleton

Performs a wide cross-section of work: new plays, extant scripts, classic and modern. Particularly interested in non-naturalism, physical theatre and plays with direct relevance to rural audiences.

Orchard Theatre Company

108 Newport Road, Barnstaple, Devon EX32 9BA
tel (01271) 371475 *fax* (01271) 371825
e-mail OrchardTheatre@compuserve.com
Administrator Frederica Notley

Produces and tours a range of work, including classics, new plays, and productions for children. Welcomes plays from new writers.

Oxford Stage Company

15-19 George Street, Oxford OX1 2AU
tel (01865) 723238 *fax* (01865) 790625
e-mail info@oxfordstage.co.uk
web site http://www.oxfordstage.co.uk
Contact General Manager

A middle-scale touring company presenting 3 productions per year: Shakespeare, modern classics, and new work. Founded 1989.

Paines Plough

4th Floor, 43 Aldwych, London WC2B 4DA
tel 0171-240 4533 *fax* 0171-240 4534
e-mail paines.plough@dial.pipex.com
Artistic Director Vicky Featherstone, *Literary Director* Mark Ravenhill, *Literary Manager* Jessica Dromgoole

Tours new plays by British writers to a national audience and is increasingly developing an international profile. The company believes that the playwright's voice should be at the centre of contemporary theatre and works with new and experienced writers. A programme of workshops and readings develops new work and approx. 4 playwrights a year are commissioned by the company. A new programme seeks to develop the company's relationship with writers outside London. For script-reading service send 2 saes, one for acknowledgement, and one for return of script with reader's report.

Proteus Theatre Company

Fairfields Arts Centre, Council Road, Basingstoke,
Hants RG21 3DH
tel (01256) 354541
Administrative Director Katherine Ives, *Artistic Director* Chris Baldwin, *Associate Director (Community and Education)* Brendon Burns

Small-scale touring company committed to new writing and new work, education and internationalism. Presents 2-3 touring plays per year plus 2-3 main projects, all of which may include new commissions. Founded 1981.

Quicksilver National Touring Theatre
4 Enfield Road, London N1 5AZ
tel 0171-241 2942 fax 0171-254 3119
e-mail qsilver@easynet.co.uk
web site http://www.ecna.org/qsilver
Artistic Director Guy Holland
A professional touring theatre company which brings live theatre to theatres and schools all over the country. Delivers good stories, original music, kaleidoscopic design and humorous, poignant writing to entertain and make children think. Three new plays a year for 3-5 year-olds, 7-11 year-olds and 6+ years and families. Founded 1978.

Red Ladder Theatre Company
3 St Peters Buildings, York Street, Leeds LS9 8AJ
tel 0113-245 5311 fax 0113-245 5351
e-mail red-ladder@geo2.poptel.org.uk
Artistic Director Kully Thiarai
Theatre performances for young people (14-25) in youth clubs and small-scale theatre venues. Commissions at least two new plays each year. Training/residentials for youth workers/young people.

Red Shift Theatre Company
TRG2 Trowbray House, 108 Weston Street, London SE1 3QB
tel 0171-378 9787 fax 0171-378 9789
Artistic Director Jonathan Holloway
Productions include adaptations, classics, new plays. No commissions planned before 2001.

Shared Experience Theatre
The Soho Laundry, 9 Dufours Place, London W1V 1FE
tel 0171-434 9248 fax 0171-287 8763
e-mail 106250.1562@compuserve.com
Artistic Director Nancy Meckler
Middle-scale touring company presenting 2 productions per year: adaptations or translations of classic texts, and some new writing. Tours nationally and internationally. Founded 1975.

Solent Peoples Theatre
The Heathfield Centre, Valentine Avenue, Sholing, Southampton SO19 0EQ
tel (01703) 443943 fax (01703) 440752
minicom (01703) 434177
Administrative Director Caroline Routh
Produces 3 plays a year, one of which is always a family show and another is generally a new commission. All productions endeavour to be relevant to the communities in which the theatre works. Currently looking to develop cross art form work – in particular video and computer imaging – and also to create work which can tour to non-typical performance spaces. Welcomes plays from new writers.

The Sphinx Theatre Co. Ltd
25 Short Street, London SE1 8LJ
tel 0171-401 9993/4 fax 0171-401 9995
Artistic Director Sue Parrish, General Manager Alison Gagen
Women writers only.

Stage One Theatre Company
34 Jasmine Grove, London SE20 8JW
tel 0181-778 5213 fax 0181-778 1756
e-mail admin@stageone.demon.co.uk
web site http://www.stageone.demon.co.uk
Scripts address Buddy Dalton,
c/o 11 Cannon Place, London NW3 1EH
Scripts from new writers considered.

Talawa Theatre Company
3rd Floor, 23-25 Great Sutton Street, London EC1V 0DN
tel 0171-251 6644 fax 0171-251 5969
e-mail hq@talawa.com
General Manager Anthony Corriette
Scripts from new writers considered. Particularly interested in scripts from black writers and plays portraying a black experience.

Theatre Centre
Toynbee Workshops, 3 Gunthorpe Street, London E1 7RQ
tel 0171-377 0379 fax 0171-377 1376
Administrator Jo Hemmant
National touring theatre for young people – schools, art centres, venues.

Theatre Workshop Company
34 Hamilton Place, Edinburgh EH3 5AX
tel 0131-225 7942 fax 0131-220 0112
Contact Robert Rae
Plays include new writing/community/children's/disabled. Scripts from new writers considered.

Publishers of plays

Playwrights are reminded that it is unusual for a publisher of trade editions of plays to publish plays which have not had at least reasonably successful, usually professional, productions on stage first. See listings beginning on page 157 for addresses.

Marion Boyars Publishers
Brown, Son & Ferguson
Cló Iar-Chonnachta Teo
Cressrelles Publishing Co.
diehard
Dublar Scripts
Everyman's Library
Faber & Faber
Forest Books

Samuel French
The Gallery Press (Ire.)
Gee & Son (Denbigh)
Nick Hern Books
Kenyon-Deane
Kevin Mayhew
Methuen, Random House
J. Garnet Miller
New Playwrights' Network

The O'Brien Press (Ire.)
The Playwrights Publishing
  Company
Scottish Cultural Press
Seren Books
Warner/Chappell Plays
Wolfhound Press (Ire.)

Literary agents

The role of the literary agent

The primary task of a literary agent is to look after a writer's commercial interests and to exploit fully the rights in the material he or she handles. This can mean anything from placing work with a British publisher to the sale of US, translation, dramatic, film, television, audio, electronic or other rights.

Agents can supply editorial guidance, advise on career strategy, and – in the increasingly fluid and unpredictable world of modern publishing – provide the author with a degree of continuity.

What agents cannot be expected to do is comment at length on unsuitable work or sell the unsaleable. Nor can they guarantee that the writer's life is without disappointments.

Approaching an agent

Try to define your needs and choose an agent who seems most likely to meet them. Work from an up-to-date edition of this *Yearbook* and either ring (but check the entry first as some smaller agencies prefer initial contact by letter, perhaps accompanied by a synopsis and the first few pages or chapters), or write a preliminary letter to the agent(s) of your choice to ascertain whether the agent is taking on new clients. Describe as succinctly as possible the nature of your work, your future plans, and give any biographical information that might be relevant to your writing.

Enquire about the agent's terms. Some of this information will be given in the listings that follow, but make sure you understand how the agency operates. Does it use associates for the sale of subsidiary rights, and how does this affect commission? Does it have a letter of agreement for its clients which details its terms of business?

When submitting your work, make sure the manuscript is well presented (see *Preparing and submitting a manuscript*, page 551) and enclose the right-sized stamped addressed envelope for its return. Bear in mind that it is not good practice to send work to more than one agent at the same time.

Code of practice

The Association of Authors' Agents (see page 461) is the trade association of British agents. Members, designated with an asterisk in the following list, meet regularly and are committed to a code of practice. They do not charge authors a reading fee. Agents that do charge a reading fee usually refund the fee (which covers a report on the manuscript) on acceptance of the material by a publisher. This fee is not to be confused with commission, which is the agreed percentage charged by the agent to the author and deducted by the agent from publishers' advances, royalties earned and any other monies paid to the author.

The listings

All the agents listed on the following pages have been sent a *Writers' & Artists' Yearbook* questionnaire designed to provide pertinent information. Each one is asked regularly to update this information. The list is not exhaustive. If any literary agents who are not included would like to receive a copy of the questionnaire and to be considered for inclusion, please contact the publishers.

Literary agents UK and Ireland

Full member of the Association of Authors' Agents

A & B Personal Management Ltd
5th Floor, Plaza Suite, 114 Jermyn Street,
London SW1Y 6HJ
tel 0171-839 4433 *fax* 0171-930 5738
Directors R.W. Ellis, R. Ellis
Full-length MSS. Scripts for TV, theatre, cinema; also novels, fiction and non-fiction (home 12.5%, overseas 15%), performance rights (12.5%). Synopsis required initially from writers submitting work for first time. No reading fee for synopsis, plays or screenplays, but fee charged for full-length MSS. Return postage required. Founded 1982.

The Agency (London) Ltd*
(incorporating Lemon Unna & Durbridge Ltd)
24 Pottery Lane, London W11 4LZ
tel 0171-727 1346 *fax* 0171-727 9037
e-mail info@theagency.co.uk
Directors Stephen Durbridge, Leah Schmidt, Sebastian Born, Julia Kreitman, Girsha Reid, Bethan Evans, Wendy Gresser, Hilary Delamere
Represents writers for theatre, film, TV, radio and children's writers and illustrators. Also film and TV rights in novels and non-fiction. Adult novels represented only for existing clients. Commission: 10% unless sub-agents employed overseas; works in conjunction with agents in USA and overseas. No unsolicited MSS. Preliminary letter including publishing/production history and sae essential. Founded 1995.

Aitken & Stone Ltd*
(and Hughes Massie Ltd)
29 Fernshaw Road, London SW10 0TG
tel 0171-351 7561 *fax* 0171-376 3594
e-mail 100303.1765@compuserve.com
Directors Gillon Aitken, Brian Stone, Sally Riley, Antony Harwood, Emma Parry
Full-length MSS (home 10%, USA 15%, translations 20%). Preliminary letter and return postage essential.

Authors include Pat Barker, Agatha Christie Estate, Sebastian Faulks, Helen Fielding, Germaine Greer, Alan Hollinghurst, Susan Howatch, A.L. Kennedy, Douglas Kennedy, Pauline Melville, V.S. Naipaul, Caryl Phillips.

Michael Alcock Management
5-7 Young Street, London W8 5EH
tel 0171-937 5277 *fax* 0171-937 2833
e-mail michaelalcock@compuserve.com
Director Michael Alcock
Full length MSS. General fiction and non-fiction. Specialises in health and self-development, mind, body and spirit; biography, history, current affairs, lifestyle and media. No reading fee. No unsolicited MSS: send letter, CV and synopsis with sae (home 15%, overseas 20%, performance rights 15%).
Clients include Michael Brunson, Ross Burden, James Burke, James Carleton Paget, Philip Dunn, Kevin Gould, Mark Griffiths, Martin Miller, Jo-Anne Richards, Lynne Robinson.

Jacintha Alexander Associates – see Lucas Alexander Whitley*

Darley Anderson Literary, TV and Film Agency*
Estelle House, 11 Eustace Road, London SW6 1JB
tel 0171-385 6652 *fax* 0171-386 5571
e-mail dander6652@aol.com
Proprietor Darley Anderson, *Associates* Gabi Chase (film/TV scripts), Elizabeth Wright (love stories and 'tear jerkers'/women's fiction), Kerith Biggs (foreign rights/crime)
Full-length MSS. Popular commercial fiction and non-fiction. Special fiction interests: all types of thrillers and crime (American/hard boiled/cosy/historical); women's fiction including contemporary, 20th century romantic sagas, love stories, 'tear jerkers', women in jeopardy and

erotica; thrillers, horror; comedy (TV and books); and all types of American and Irish novels.

Special non-fiction interests: investigative books, revelatory history and science, TV tie-ins, celebrity autobiographies, true life women in jeopardy, diet, beauty, health, cookery, popular psychology, self improvement, inspirational, popular religion and supernatural (home 15%, US/translation 20%, film/TV/radio 20%). No poetry, plays or academic books. Can arrange PR and author publicity and specialist financial advice; editorial guidance on selected MSS. Preliminary letter, synopsis and first 3 chapters. Return postage/sae must accompany submission. No reading fee. Overseas associates: Renaissance-Swanson Film Agency (LA/Hollywood) and leading foreign agents worldwide.

Authors include Tessa Barclay, Paul Carson, Lee Child, Martina Cole, John Connolly, Joseph Corvo, Debbie Frank, Martica Heaner, Joan Jonker, Beryl Kingston, Frank Lean, Deborah McKinlay, Lesley Pearse, Allan Pease, Adrian Plass, Ben Richards, Fred Secombe, Julia Stephenson, Jane Walmsley.

Artellus Ltd
30 Dorset House, Gloucester Place, London NW1 5AD
tel 0171-935 6972 *fax* 0171-487 5957
Director Leslie Gardner, *Chairman* Gabriele Pantucci
Full-length and short MSS; scripts for films (home 10%, overseas 12.5-20%). Crime, science fiction, historical, contemporary and literary fiction; non-fiction: science, art history, current affairs, biography, general history. Works directly in USA and with agencies in Europe, Japan and Russia. Will suggest revision. No reading fee. Founded 1986.

Associated Publicity Holdings Ltd
5-7 Young Street, London W8 5EH
tel 0171-937 5277 *fax* 0171-937 2833
e-mail Jonathan.Harris@aph-agent.demon.co.uk
Managing Director Jonathan G. Harris
Full-length MSS. Fiction and non-fiction, particularly sport, history, archaeology, biographies, thrillers and crime novels (home 10-15%, overseas 20%), perfor-

mance, film and TV rights (15%). Send outline, 2 sample chapters and sae. Works with foreign agencies. No reading fee. Founded 1987.

Authors Representative Co.
3 Behoes Cottage, Behoes Lane, Woodcote, Oxon RG8 0PS
tel (01491) 680169
e-mail Literary@compuserve.com
Proprietor David Sarjent, *Associate* Brenda Ralph Lewis
Popular fiction only: political, military, crime, spy, etc and black comedy (home 15%, overseas 20%). Large return sae essential. Small exclusive agency. No reading fee for synopses. Founded 1997.

Don Baker Associates
25 Eley Drive, Rottingdean, East Sussex BN2 7FH
tel (01273) 386842
Directors Donald Baker, Katy Baker Quayle
Full-length MSS. Fiction, film, TV and theatre scripts (home 12.5%, overseas 15%). No reading fee. Founded 1996.

Yvonne Baker Associates
8 Temple Fortune Lane, London NW11 7UD
tel 0181-455 8687 *fax* 0181-458 3143
Television, film, theatre, radio (10%). Particularly interested in contemporary drama and TV comedy drama series. No books, short stories, articles, poetry. No reading fee but preliminary letter essential with full information and sae. Founded 1987.

Blake Friedmann Literary, TV & Film Agency Ltd*
37-41 Gower Street, London WC1E 6HH
tel 0171-631 4331 *fax* 0171-323 1274
Directors Carole Blake, Julian Friedmann, Barbara Jones, Conrad Williams
Full-length MSS. Fiction: thrillers, women's novels and literary fiction; non-fiction: investigative books, biography, travel; no poetry or plays (home 15%, overseas 20%). Specialises in film and TV rights; place journalism and short stories for existing clients only. Represented worldwide in 26 markets. Preliminary letter, synopsis and first 2 chapters preferred. No reading fee.

Authors include Gilbert Adair, Ted Allbeury, Jane Asher, Teresa Crane, Barbara Erskine, Maeve Haran, John

Harvey, Ken Hom, Glenn Meade, Lawrence Norfolk, Joseph O'Connor, Michael Ridpath, Tim Sebastian, Robyn Sisman. Founded 1977.

David Bolt Associates

12 Heath Drive, Send, Surrey GU23 7EP
tel/fax (01483) 721118

Specialises in biography, fiction, theology. Full-length MSS (home 10%, overseas 19%; all other rights including film, video and TV 10%). No unsolicited short stories or play scripts. Will sometimes suggest revision. Works in association with overseas agencies worldwide. Preliminary letter essential. Reading fee terms on application.

Authors include Chinua Achebe, David Bret, Keith Cory-Jones, Nicci Mackay, James Purdy, Joseph Rhymer, Colin Wilson.

BookBlast Ltd

21 Chesterton Road, London W10 5LY
tel 0181-968 3089 *fax* 0181-932 4087
Director G. de Chamberet

Full-length MSS (home 10%, overseas 20%), TV and radio (15%), film (20%). Fiction and non-fiction; traditional and underground literature. No unsolicited material. Preliminary letter, biographical information and sae essential. No reading fee. Will suggest revision. Founded 1997.

Authors include Jamika Ajalon, Paul Binding, Garth Cartwright, Stuart Hood, Aamer Hussein, S.I. Martin, Onyekachi Wambu.

Alan Brodie Representation Ltd

(incorporating Michael Imison Playwrights)
211 Piccadilly, London W1V 9LD
tel 0171-917 2871 *fax* 0171-917 2872
e-mail alanbrodie@aol.com
Directors Alan Brodie, Caroline Brodie, Sarah McNair
Consultant Michael Imison

Specialises in stage plays, radio, TV, film, stage/film directors (home 10%, overseas 15%); no fiction or general MSS. Represented in all major countries. No unsolicited scripts; recommendation from known professional required.

Rosemary Bromley Literary Agency

Avington, Winchester, Hants SO21 1DB
tel/fax (01962) 779656

Specialises in biography, travel, leisure, cookery, health (home 10%, overseas from

15%.) No poetry. No reading fee. No unsolicited MSS; enquiries unaccompanied by return postage will not be answered. For children's books see **Juvenilia**.

Felicity Bryan*

2A North Parade, Banbury Road,
Oxford OX2 6PE
tel (01865) 513816 *fax* (01865) 310055

Fiction and general non-fiction; no light romance, science fiction, short stories, plays or children's (home 10%, overseas 20%). Translation rights handled by Andrew Nurnberg Associates; works in conjunction with US agents. Return postage essential.

Peter Bryant (Writers)

94 Adelaide Avenue, London SE4 1YR
tel 0181-691 9085 *fax* 0181-692 9107

Special interests: animation, children's fiction and TV comedy; also handles drama scripts for theatre, radio and TV (home/USA 10%). Overseas associate: Hartmann and Stauffacher, Germany. No reading fee for the above categories, but sae essential for all submissions.

Authors include Isabelle Amyes, Roy Apps, Joe Boyle, Andrew Brenner, Lucy Daniel, Jimmy Hibbert, Jan Page, Ruth Silvestre, Peter Symonds, George Tarry. Founded 1980.

Bycornute Books

76A Ashford Road, Eastbourne,
East Sussex BN21 3TE
tel (01323) 726819 *fax* (01323) 649053
Director Asia Haleem

Specialises in illustrated books on sacred art, comparative religion, mythology, cosmology, astrology, iconography, symbolism, metaphysics, art history and popular archaeology/ancient history (not fiction, poetry, children's, psychic studies or psychology) (home 10%, overseas 15%). No unsolicited MSS.

Authors include Peter Clough, June Hager, George Hart, Anne Macaulay, Asia Shepsut, Derek Shiel, Gordon Strachan, Robertson of Strathloch.

Campbell Thomson & McLaughlin Ltd*

1 King's Mews, London WC1N 2JA
tel 0171-242 0958 *fax* 0171-242 2408
Directors John McLaughlin, Charlotte Bruton, Hal Cheetham

Full-length book MSS (home 10%, overseas up to 20% including commission to foreign agent). No poetry, plays or TV scripts, short stories or children's books. USA agents represented: Raines & Raines, The Fox Chase Agency, Inc. Representatives in most European countries. Preliminary letter with sae, please. No reading fee, but return postage required. Subsidiary company: Peter Janson-Smith Ltd.

Casarotto Ramsay Ltd

National House, 60-66 Wardour Street, London W1V 4ND
tel 0171-287 4450 *fax* 0171-287 9128
e-mail carmarsh@dial.pipex.com
Directors Tom Erhardt, Jenne Casarotto
MSS – theatre, films, TV, sound broadcasting only (10%). Works in conjunction with agents in USA and in all foreign countries. Preliminary letter essential. No reading fee.

Authors include Alan Ayckbourn, Peter Barnes, Edward Bond, Caryl Churchill, David Greig, Christopher Hampton, David Harrower, David Hare, Sarah Kane, Larry Kramer, Phyllis Nagy, Mark Ravenhill, Willy Russell, Martin Sherman, David Wood. Founded 1992; formerly Margaret Ramsay Ltd, 1953.

Celia Catchpole

56 Gilpin Avenue, London SW14 8QY
tel 0181-255 7200 *fax* 0181-878 0594
Specialises as agent for children's writers and illustrators (home 10% writers, 15% illustrators; overseas 20%). Phone before sending scripts or artwork. Founded 1996.

Chapman & Vincent

(formerly Media House)
The Mount, Sun Hill, Royston, Herts. SG8 9AT
tel (01763) 247474 *fax* (01763) 243033
Directors Jennifer Chapman, Gilly Vincent
Original non-fiction, quality fiction, works with film or TV potential (but no scripts). Home 15%; overseas 20%. No reading fee. Will help with a revision as appropriate. Most clients come from personal recommendation. For fiction, send synopsis and 2 sample chapters with sae. Associates in Stockholm and Zurich.

Authors include Leslie Geddes-Brown, Sara George, Rowley Leigh, Dorit Peleg. Founded 1995.

Mic Cheetham Literary Agency

11-12 Dover Street, London W1X 3PH
tel 0171-495 2002 *fax* 0171-495 5777
Director Mic Cheetham
General and literary fiction, science fiction, general non-fiction (home 10%, overseas 20%); film, TV and radio rights (10-15%); will suggest revision. Works with The Marsh Agency for foreign rights. No unsolicited MSS. Founded 1994.

Judith Chilcote Agency*

8 Wentworth Mansions, Keats Grove, London NW3 2RL
tel 0171-794 3717 *fax* 0171-794 7431
e-mail judybks@aol.com
Director Judith Chilcote
Fiction, non-fiction – sports, self-help and health, cookery, autobiography and biography, cinema, current affairs, TV tie-ins (home 15%, overseas 20-25%). No short stories, science fiction, children's, poetry. Works in conjunction with overseas agents and New York affiliate. No reading fee but preliminary letter with 3 chapters only, CV and sae essential.

Authors include Jane Alexander, Richard Barber, David Emery, Sarah Gristwood, Maureen Paton, Douglas Thompson. Founded 1990.

Teresa Chris Literary Agency

43 Musard Road, London W6 8NR
tel 0171-386 0633
Director Teresa Chris
All fiction, especially crime, women's commercial, general and literary fiction; all non-fiction, especially health, cooking, arts and crafts. No science fiction, horror, fantasy, short stories, poetry, academic books (home 10%, USA 15%, rest 20%). Own US office: Thompson & Chris Literary Agency. No reading fee. No unsolicited MSS. Send introductory letter describing work, sample chapter and sae. Founded 1988.

Christy & Moore Ltd – see Sheil Land Associates Ltd*

Serafina Clarke*

98 Tunis Road, London W12 7EY
tel 0181-749 6979 *fax* 0181-740 6862
Full-length MSS (home 15%, overseas 20%). Works in conjunction with agents overseas. No submissions considered at present. Founded 1980.

Mary Clemmey*

6 Dunollie Road, London NW5 2XP
tel/fax 0171-267 1290

High quality fiction and non-fiction with an international market (home 10%, overseas 20%), performance rights (15%). No children's books, science fiction or fantasy. Works in conjunction with US agent. No reading fee. Small exclusive agency, approach by letter (including sae) first. Founded 1992.

Jonathan Clowes Ltd*

10 Iron Bridge House, Bridge Approach, London NW1 8BD
tel 0171-722 7674 *fax* 0171-722 7677
Directors Jonathan Clowes, Ann Evans, Brie Burkeman

Full-length MSS fiction and non-fiction; no academic or text books (home/USA 15%, translation 19%). Television, film, theatre and radio. Works in association with agents in most foreign countries. Founded 1960.

Elspeth Cochrane Agency

11-13 Orlando Road, London SW4 0LE
tel 0171-622 0314 *fax* 0171-622 5815
Contact Elspeth Cochrane

Send synopsis with covering letter in first instance (home and overseas 12.5%), performance rights (12.5%). No reading fee.

Authors include Nick Hennegan, Royce Ryton, Robert Tanitch. Founded 1960.

Rosica Colin Ltd

1 Clareville Grove Mews, London SW7 5AH
tel 0171-370 1080 *fax* 0171-244 6441
Directors Sylvie Marston, Joanna Marston

All full-length MSS (excluding sci-fi and poetry); also theatre, film and sound broadcasting (home 10%, overseas 10-20%). No reading fee, but may take 3-4 months to consider full MSS. Send synopsis only in first instance, with letter outlining writing credits and whether MS has been previously submitted, plus return postage.

Authors include Richard Aldington, Simone de Beauvoir (in UK), Samuel Beckett (publication rights), Steven Berkoff, Alan Brownjohn, Donald Campbell, Nick Dear, J.T. Edson, Bernard Farrell, Rainer Werner Fassbinder (in UK), Jean Genet, Franz Xaver Kroetz, Heiner Müller (in UK), Graham Reid,

Botho Strauss (in UK), Wim Wenders (in UK). Founded 1949.

Jane Conway-Gordon*

(in association with Andrew Mann Ltd)
1 Old Compton Street, London W1V 5PH
tel 0171-494 0148 *fax* 0171-287 9264

Full length MSS, performance rights (home 10%, overseas 20%). Represented in all foreign countries. No reading fee but preliminary letter and return postage essential. Founded 1982.

Coombs Moylett Literary Agency

12 Cobbold Road, London W12 9LW
tel 0181-740 0454
Partners Georgina Coombs and Lisa Moylett

Specialises in crime, thrillers, contemporary women's fiction and literary fiction (home 10%; overseas 15%). Send first 3 chapters and synopsis. Will help with revision as appropriate. Return postage essential.

Rupert Crew Ltd*

1A King's Mews, London WC1N 2JA
tel 0171-242 8586 *fax* 0171-831 7914
e-mail rupertcrew@compuserve.com
Directors Kathleen A. Crew, Doreen Montgomery, Caroline Montgomery

International representation, handling volume and subsidiary rights in fiction and non-fiction properties (home 10-15%, elsewhere 20%); no plays, poetry, journalism or short stories. No reading fee, but preliminary letter and return postage essential. Also acts independently as publishers' consultants. Founded 1927 by F. Rupert Crew.

Cruickshank Cazenove Ltd

97 Old South Lambeth Road, London SW8 1XU
tel 0171-735 2933 *fax* 0171-820 1081
Director Harriet Cruickshank

Film, TV and theatre scripts only (home 10%, overseas varies). Works with agents abroad. No reading fee but preliminary letter essential with sae. Also agent for directors, designers and choreographers. Founded 1983.

Curtis Brown*

Haymarket House, 28-29 Haymarket, London SW1Y 4SP
tel 0171-396 6600 *fax* 0171-396 0110
Chairman Paul Scherer, *Managing Director* Jonathan Lloyd, *Directors* Jane Bradish-Ellames, Mark Collingbourne (finance), Tim Curnow (Australia), Sue Freathy, Jonny Geller, Giles

Gordon, Diana Mackay, Nick Marston (managing, Media Division), Anthea Morton-Saner, Peter Murphy, Peter Robinson, Vivienne Schuster, Michael Shaw, Elizabeth Stevens

Agents for the negotiation in all markets of novels, general non-fiction, children's books and associated rights (home 10%, overseas 20%). Preliminary letter required; no reading fee. MSS for films, theatre, TV and radio. Also agents for directors and designers. Return postage essential.

Judy Daish Associates Ltd
2 St Charles Place, London W10 6EG
tel 0181-964 8811 *fax* 0181-964 8966
Agents Judy Daish, Sara Stroud, Deborah Harwood

Theatre, film, TV, radio (rates by negotiation). No unsolicited MSS. Founded 1978.

The Caroline Davidson Literary Agency
5 Queen Anne's Gardens, London W4 1TU
tel 0181-995 5768 *fax* 0181-994 2770

Specialises in literary fiction and non-fiction of all kinds, including highly illustrated books, academic and reference works (12.5%). Will suggest revision and edit if necessary; if the work is extensive, an additional fee may be charged, by mutual agreement. No reading fee, but preliminary letter with book proposal and/or sample text, CV and sae required.

Authors include Robert Baldock, Nigel Barlow, John Brackenbury, Elizabeth Bradley, Stuart Clark, Andrew Dalby, Emma Donoghue, Willi Elsener, Hazel Evans, Anissa Helou, Paul Hillyard, Tom Jaine, Guy Johnson, Andrew King, Bernard Lavery, J.P. McEvoy, Simon Maginn, Huon Mallalieu, Marie O'Connor, Diane Purkiss, Rena Salaman, Roland Vernon, Florence and Kenneth Wood. Founded 1988.

Merric Davidson Literary Agency
12 Priors Heath, Goudhurst, Cranbrook, Kent TN17 2RE
tel/fax (01580) 212041

Specialising in contemporary adult fiction (home 10%, overseas 20%). No unsolicited MSS. Preliminary letter with synopsis, author information and sae, though very few new clients taken on. No initial reading fee, may suggest revision, subsequent editorial advice by arrangement.

Authors include Valerie Blumenthal, Louise Doughty, Alison Habens, Elizabeth Harris, Alison MacLeod, Mark Pepper, Luke Sutherland. Founded 1990.

Felix De Wolfe
Manfield House, 1 Southampton Street, London WC2R 0LR
tel 0171-379 5767 *fax* 0171-836 0337

Theatre, films, TV, sound broadcasting, fiction (home 10-12.5%, overseas 20%). Works in conjunction with many foreign agencies.

Dorian Literary Agency (DLA)
Upper Thornehill, 27 Church Road, St Marychurch, Torquay, Devon TQ1 4QY
tel/fax (01803) 312095
Proprietor Mrs D. Lumley

Full-length MSS. Specialises in women's fiction, science fiction, fantasy and horror, crime, thrillers and mainstream (home 10%, USA 15%, translations 20-25%), performance rights (10%). No poetry, children's or short stories. Works in conjunction with agencies in most countries; negotiates direct with USA. No reading fee. Enquiries or submissions by fax or e-mail are not acceptable. Contact by letter only with first chapter and synopsis; return postage essential.

Authors include Brian Lumley, Dee Williams, Amy Myers, Stephen Jones. Founded 1986.

Anne Drexl
8 Roland Gardens, London SW7 3PH
tel 0171-244 9645

Special interest in women's fiction, glitzy, family sagas, crime fiction and non-fiction. Also illustrated books for young readers, activity titles, and juvenile fiction (home 12.5%, overseas 20-25%). Works in conjunction with foreign agencies and negotiates direct with foreign publishers. No reading fee, but no unsolicited MSS; return postage and preliminary letter essential. Founded 1988.

Toby Eady Associates Ltd
3rd Floor, 9 Orme Court, London W2 4RL
tel 0171-792 0092 *fax* 0171-792 0879
e-mail eadyassociates@compuserve.com
Directors Toby Eady, Alexandra Pringle

Fiction and non-fiction (home 10%, overseas 20%), performance rights (10%). Works with overseas associates. No read-

ing fee, but return postage essential.
Authors include Jung Chang, Bernard Cornwell, Julia Blackburn, Barbara Trapido, Esther Freud, Tim Pears. Founded 1968.

Eddison Pearson Literary Agents

44 Inverness Terrace, London W2 3JA
tel 0171-727 9113 *fax* 0171-727 9143
e-mail box1@eddisonpearson.com
Partners Clare Pearson and Tom Eddison

Literary fiction and non-fiction, some quality commercial fiction, poetry for the literary market, children's books, feature screenplays, stage plays, TV and radio scripts. Commission negotiable but usually 15% of home sales for first 2 books/scripts, 10% thereafter; additional 5% for overseas sales. Unsolicited MSS welcome with sae. No reading fee. May suggest revision where appropriate.
Authors include Gordon Fleming, Abdullah Hussein, Anne Mangan, Brendan O'Brien, Hazel Richardson.

Edwards Fuglewicz*

49 Great Ormond Street, London WC1N 3HZ
tel 0171-405 6725 *fax* 0171-405 6726
e-mail efla@ftech.co.uk
Partners Ros Edwards and Helenka Fuglewicz

Full-length MSS. Fiction: adult (literary and commercial). Non-fiction: quality general interest including music and film. Home 10%, overseas 20%. No reading fee but sae essential. Founded 1996.

Faith Evans Associates*

27 Park Avenue North, London N8 7RU
tel 0181-340 9920 *fax* 0181-340 9410

Small select agency (home 15%, overseas 20%). New clients by recommendation only. Sub-agents in most countries. No phone calls, scripts or unsolicited MSS.
Authors include Melissa Benn, Eleanor Bron, Helen Falconer, Saeed Jaffrey, Helena Kennedy, Seumas Milne, Christine Purkis, Sheila Rowbotham, Lorna Sage, Hwee Hwee Tan, Marion Urch, Harriet Walter, Andrea Weiss, Elizabeth Wilson. Founded 1987.

Fact & Fiction Agency Ltd

16 Greenway Close, London NW9 5AZ
tel 0181-205 5716
Directors Roy Lomax, Vera Lomax

TV and radio – comedy only (home 10%, overseas 15%). Established writers only.

John Farquharson Ltd* – see Curtis Brown*

Film Rights Ltd

483 Southbank House, Black Prince Road, Albert Embankment, London SE1 7SJ
tel 0171-735 8171
Directors Brendan Davis, Joan Potts

Theatre, films, TV and sound broadcasting (10%). Represented in USA and abroad. Founded 1932.

Laurence Fitch Ltd

(incorporating The London Play Company 1922)
483 Southbank House, Black Prince Road, Albert Embankment, London SE1 7SJ
tel 0171-735 8171
Directors F.H.L. Fitch, Joan Potts, Brendan Davis

Theatre, films, TV and sound broadcasting. Also works with several agencies in USA and in Europe.
Authors include The Estate of the Late Dodie Smith, Ray Cooney, John Chapman, Carlo Ardito, John Graham, Edward Taylor, Judy Allen, Dawn Lowe-Watson, Peter Coke, Glyn Robbins.

Jill Foster Ltd

9 Barb Mews, Brook Green, London W6 7PA
tel 0171-602 1263 *fax* 0171-602 9336

Theatre, films, TV, sound broadcasting (12.5%). Particularly interested in film and TV comedy and drama. No novels or short stories. No reading fee. Preliminary letter essential. Founded 1978.

Fox & Howard Literary Agency

4 Bramerton Street, London SW3 5JX
tel 0171-352 8691 *fax* 0171-352 8691
Partners Chelsey Fox, Charlotte Howard

Full-length MSS. General non-fiction: biography, popular culture, current affairs, reference, business, mind, body and spirit, self-help and health (home 10%, overseas 20%); will suggest revision where appropriate. No poetry, plays, short stories, children's, science fiction, fantasy or horror. No reading fee, but preliminary letter and synopsis with sae essential.
Authors include Sarah Bartlett, Sir Rhodes Boyson, Tony Clayton Lea, Jane Struthers. Founded 1992.

Fraser & Dunlop Ltd, Fraser & Dunlop Scripts Ltd – see The Peters Fraser & Dunlop Group Ltd*

French's

9 Elgin Mews South, London W9 1JZ
tel 0171-266 3321 *fax* 0171-286 6716
Director Mark Taylor
All MSS; specialises in novels and screenplays (home/overseas 10%); theatre, films, TV, radio (10%). Reading service available, details on application. Sae must be enclosed with all MSS.

Vernon Futerman Associates*

Administration 159A Goldhurst Terrace, London NW6 3EU
tel/fax 0171-625 9601
Submissions 17 Deanhill Road, London SW14 7DQ
tel 0181-286 4860 *fax* 0181-286 4861
Contacts Vernon Futerman (academic/politics/current affairs), Alexandra Groom (educational/art), Christopher Oxford (theatre scripts), Guy Rose (fiction/biography/show business/TV, film scripts)
Fiction and non-fiction, including academic, art, biography, autobiography, educational, politics, current affairs, show business; also scripts for film, TV and theatre. No short stories, science fiction, crafts or hobbies. No unsolicited MSS; send preliminary letter with a brief biography, detailed synopsis and sae. No reading fee. Literature (home 12.5%, overseas 17.5%); drama, screenplays (home 15%, overseas 20%); translations (20%). Overseas associates: USA, South Africa, France (Lora Fountain), Germany/Austria/Switzerland (Brigitte Axter).

Clients include Stephen Lowe, Valerie Grosvenor Myer, Sir Martin Ewans KCMG, Susan George, Ernie Wise, Lorraine Chase, Kingsley Fielding, Angus Graham-Campbell, Sir Robert McCrindle, Angela Meredith, Sue Lenier, Russell Warren Howe, Judy Upton, Simon Woodham, Dapo Odesanya, Prof Wu Ningkun, Adam Shaw, Brian Milton, Richard Morley. Founded 1984.

Jüri Gabriel

35 Camberwell Grove, London SE5 8JA
tel/fax 0171-703 6186
Quality fiction and non-fiction (current specialisations: medical, military, practical art, popular academic); radio, TV and film, but mainly selling these rights in existing works by existing clients. Full-length MSS (home 10%, overseas 20%), performance rights (10%); will suggest revision where appropriate. No short stories, articles, verse or books for children. No reading fee; return postage essential. Jüri Gabriel is the chairman of Dedalus (publishers) and was a writer/translator for 20 years.

Authors include Nigel Cawthorne, Diana Constance, Stephen Dunn, Miriam Dunne, Pat Gray, James Hawes, Robert Irwin, 'David Madsen', 'Mark Lloyd', David Miller, Prof Cedric Mims, John Outram, Ewen Southby-Tailyour, Dr Terence White, John Wyatt, Dr Robert Youngson.

Eric Glass Ltd

28 Berkeley Square, London W1X 6HD
tel 0171-629 7162 *fax* 0171-499 6780
Director Janet Glass
Full-length MSS only; also theatre, films, TV, and sound broadcasting. No unsolicited MSS. Sole representatives of the French Society of Authors (Societé des Auteurs et Compositeurs Dramatiques). Founded 1932.

David Godwin Associates

14 Goodwins Court, London WC2N 4LL
tel 0171-240 9992 *fax* 0171-240 3007
Directors David Godwin, Heather Godwin
Literary fiction and general non-fiction (home 10%, overseas 20%). No reading fee; send sae for return of MSS. Founded 1996.

Christine Green Authors' Agent*

40 Doughty Street, London WC1N 2LF
tel 0171-831 4956 *fax* 0171-405 3935
Fiction and general non-fiction. Full-length MSS (home 10%, overseas 20%). Works in conjunction with agencies in Europe and Scandinavia. No reading fee, but preliminary letter and return postage essential. Founded 1984.

Greene & Heaton Ltd*

37 Goldhawk Road, London W12 8QQ
tel 0181-749 0315 *fax* 0181-749 0318
Directors Carol Heaton, Judith Murray, Charles Elliott, *Junior Agent* Antony Topping
Full-length MSS, fiction and non-fiction (home 10%, overseas 20%). No plays, TV or film scripts, science fiction, fantasy, or children's books. Works in conjunction with agencies in most countries. No reading fee. No unsolicited MSS without preliminary letter. Founded 1962.

Gregory & Radice Authors' Agents*

3 Barb Mews, London W6 7PA
tel 0171-610 4676 *fax* 0171-610 4686
Partners Jane Gregory, Lisanne Radice (editorial)

Full-length MSS; fiction and non-fiction. Specialises in crime fiction, commercial and literary fiction, thrillers and politics. Particularly interested in books with potential for sales abroad and/or to film and TV (home 15%, articles, USA and translation 20%, film/TV rights 15%). No short stories, plays, film scripts, science fiction, fantasy, poetry, academic or children's books. Represented in all foreign markets. No reading fee, editorial advice given to own authors. No unsolicited MSS: preliminary letter, synopsis and first 3 chapters essential plus return postage. Founded 1987.

David Grossman Literary Agency Ltd

118B Holland Park Avenue, London W11 4UA
tel 0171-221 2770 *fax* 0171-221 1445

Full-length MSS (home 10-15%, overseas 20% including foreign agent's commission), performance rights (15%). Works in conjunction with agents in New York, Los Angeles, Europe, Japan. No reading fee, but preliminary letter required. Founded 1976.

The Rod Hall Agency Ltd

7 Goodge Place, London W1P 1FL
tel 0171-637 0706 *fax* 0171-637 0807
e-mail rod.hall@dial.pipex.com
Directors Rod Hall, Clare Barker

Specialises in writers for stage, screen and radio but also deals in TV and film rights in novels and non-fiction (home 10%, overseas 15%). No reading fee.

Clients include Simon Beaufoy, Jeremy Brock, Arthur Hopcraft, Martin McDonagh, Simon Nye, Andrea Newman, Susan Hill. Founded 1997.

Richard Hatton Ltd

29 Roehampton Gate, London SW15 5JR
tel 0181-876 6699 *fax* 0181-876 8278
Director Richard Hatton

Stage plays; TV, cinema and radio scripts (15%). No reading fee. Preliminary letter with outline and sae only. Founded 1954.

A.M. Heath & Co. Ltd*

79 St Martin's Lane, London WC2N 4AA
tel 0171-836 4271 *fax* 0171-497 2561

Directors William Hamilton, Sara Fisher, Sarah Molloy

Full-length MSS (home 10-15%, USA 20%, translation 20%), performance rights (15%). Agents in USA and all European countries and Japan. No reading fee. Founded 1919.

David Higham Associates Ltd*

(incorporating Murray Pollinger)
5-8 Lower John Street, Golden Square, London W1R 4HA
tel 0171-437 7888 *fax* 0171-437 1072
Directors Bruce Hunter, Jacqueline Korn, Anthony Crouch, Elizabeth Cree, Anthony Goff, Ania Corless

Agents for the negotiation of all rights in fiction, general non-fiction, children's fiction and picture books, plays, film and TV scripts (home 10%, USA/translation 20%). USA associate agency: Harold Ober Associates Inc. Represented in all foreign markets. Preliminary letter and return postage essential. No reading fee. Founded 1935.

Vanessa Holt Ltd*

59 Crescent Road, Leigh-on-Sea, Essex SS9 2PF
tel (01702) 73787 *fax* (01702) 471890

General adult fiction and non-fiction (home 10%, overseas 20%). Works in conjunction with many foreign agencies. No reading fee, but preliminary letter and sae essential. Founded 1989.

Valerie Hoskins Associates

20 Charlotte Street, London W1P 1HJ
tel 0171-637 4490 *fax* 0171-637 4493
e-mail ValerieHoskinsAss@compurserve.com
Proprietor Valerie Hoskins

Film, TV and radio only (12.5% home and maximum 20% overseas). No reading fee, but sae appreciated. Works in conjunction with overseas agents. No unsolicited MSS; preliminary letter essential.

Tanja Howarth Literary Agency*

19 New Row, London WC2N 4LA
tel 0171-240 5553/836 4142 *fax* 0171-379 0969

Full-length MSS. General fiction and non-fiction, thrillers, contemporary and historical women's novels and sagas (home 15%, USA/translation 20%). Represented in the USA by various agents. Please submit preliminary letter, synopsis and 3 sample chapters with return postage. No reading fee. Founded 1970.

ICM Ltd
Oxford House, 76 Oxford Street, London W1N 0AX
tel 0171-636 6565 *fax* 0171-323 0101
e-mail admin@icmlondon.co.uk
Directors Duncan Heath, Susan Rodgers, Ian Amos, Paul Lyon-Maris
Literary Agents Susan Rodgers, Jessica Sykes, Catherine King, Ian Amos, Greg Hunt, Alan Radcliffe
Specialises in scripts for film, theatre, TV, radio (home 10%, overseas 10%). Part of International Creative Management Inc., Los Angeles and New York. No reading fee.

IMG
Pier House, Strand on the Green, London W4 3NN
tel 0181-233 5000 *fax* 0181-233 5001
Chairman Mark H. McCormack, *Agents* Sarah Wooldridge (UK), Carolyn Krupp, David Chalfant, Mark Reiter (US), Fumiko Matsuki (Japan)
Represents sports celebrities, classical musicians and broadcasting personalities (home/US 20%, elsewhere 25%). No reading fee. Please send synopsis, 3 sample chapters and sae.

Intercontinental Literary Agency*
The Chambers, Chelsea Harbour, Lots Road, London SW10 0XF
tel 0171-351 4763 *fax* 0171-351 4809
e-mail nkennedy@pfd.co.uk
jbuckman@pfd.co.uk
Contacts Anthony Guest Gornall, Nicki Kennedy, Jessica Buckman, Mary Esdaile
Represents translation rights for The Peters Fraser & Dunlop Group Ltd, London, Harold Matson Company Inc., New York, The Turnbull Agency (John Irving) Inc., and Lucas Alexander Whitley Ltd. Founded 1965.

International Copyright Bureau Ltd
22A Aubrey House, Maida Avenue, London W2 1TQ
tel 0171-724 8034 *fax* 0171-724 7662
Directors Joy Westendarp, J.C.H. Hadfield
Theatre, films, TV, radio (home 10%, overseas 19%). Works in conjunction with agents in New York and most foreign countries. Preliminary letter essential. Founded 1905.

International Scripts
1 Norland Square, London W11 4PX
tel 0171-229 0736 *fax* 0171-792 3287
Directors H.P. Tanner, J. Lawson
Specialises in full-length contemporary and women's fiction, horror, general non-fiction (home 15%, overseas 20-25%),

performance rights (15-20%); no poetry or short stories. Works with overseas agents worldwide. Preliminary letter and sae required. Return postage required for MSS plus a £30.00 reading fee (for which a report will be provided).
Authors include Richard Laymon, Anna Jacobs, Mary Ryan, Ed Gorman, Julie Harris, Peter Haining, Graham Masterton, Zita Adamson, Simon Clark, John and Anne Spencer. Founded 1979.

Mary Irvine
11 Upland Park Road, Oxford OX2 7RU
tel (01865) 513570
Specialises in women's fiction and family sagas. No plays, scripts, children's books, short stories or poetry (home 10%, USA 15%, translations 20%). Works with agents in USA, Europe, Japan. No unsolicited MSS. Preliminary letter essential and return postage required. No reading fee. Founded 1974.

John Johnson (Authors' Agent) Ltd*
Clerkenwell House, 45-47 Clerkenwell Green, London EC1R 0HT
tel 0171-251 0125 *fax* 0171-251 2172
Full-length MSS (home 10%, overseas direct 15%, with subagent maximum of 20%). Works in conjunction with agents in USA and many European countries. No unsolicited MSS. Founded 1956.

Jane Judd Literary Agency*
18 Belitha Villas, London N1 1PD
tel 0171-607 0273 *fax* 0171-607 0623
Full-length MSS only (home 10%, overseas 20%). Works with agents in USA and most foreign countries. No reading fee, but preliminary letter with synopsis and sae essential. Founded 1986.

Juvenilia
Avington, Winchester, Hants SO21 1DB
tel/fax (01962) 779656
Proprietor Mrs Rosemary Bromley
Full-length MSS for the children's market, fiction and non-fiction (home 10%, overseas from 15%), illustration (20%), performance rights (10%). Short stories only if specifically for picture books, radio or TV. No verse. No unsolicited MSS; preliminary letter with sae and full details essential. No reading fee. Postage for acknowledgement and return of material imperative. Founded 1973.

Michelle Kass Associates*
36-38 Glasshouse Street, London W1R 5RH
tel 0171-439 1624 *fax* 0171-734 3394
Proprietor Michelle Kass
Full-length MSS. Fiction and drama (screen and stage) (home 10%, overseas 15-20%), performance rights (10%); will suggest revision where appropriate. Works with agents overseas. No reading fee. Preliminary letter and return postage required. Founded 1991.

Frances Kelly Agency*
111 Clifton Road, Kingston-upon-Thames, Surrey KT2 6PL
tel 0181-549 7830 *fax* 0181-547 0051
Full-length MSS. Non-fiction: general and academic, reference and professional books, all subjects (home 10%, overseas 20%), TV, radio (10%). No reading fee, but no unsolicited MSS; preliminary letter with synopsis, CV and return postage essential. Founded 1978.

Peter Knight Agency
20 Crescent Grove, London SW4 7AH
tel 0171-622 1467 *fax* 0171-622 1522
Director Peter Knight, *Associates* Ann King-Hall, Gaby Martin, Andrew Knight, Giovanna Farrell-Vinay
Motor sports, cartoon books, business, history, and factual and biographical material. No poetry, science fiction or cookery. Overseas associates: United Media (USA), Auspac Media (Australia). No unsolicited MSS. Send letter accompanied by CV and sae with synopsis of proposed work. Founded 1985.

Labour & Management Ltd – Tricia Sumner Literary Agency
Milton House, Milton Street, Waltham Abbey, Essex EN9 1EZ
tel/fax (01992) 711511
e-mail triciasumner@classic.msn.com
Director Tricia Sumner
Writers for film, theatre, TV, radio. Also full-length MSS, fiction and non-fiction (home 12.5%, overseas 20%). Special interests (not exclusively): multicultural, gay, feminist, anti-establishment. No reading fee. Send preliminary letter, synopsis and sample chapters and return postage.
   Clients include Marion Baraitser, Noel Currer-Briggs, John Gordon, Angela Lanyon, Christopher Moncrieff, Olusola Oyeleye, Clifford Thurlow. Founded 1995.

Cat Ledger Literary Agency*
33 Percy Street, London W1P 9FG
tel 0171-436 5030 *fax* 0171-631 4273
General non-fiction and fiction but no short stories, film/TV scripts, poetry or plays (home 10%, overseas 20%). No reading fee but preliminary letter, synopsis and sae essential. Represented in all foreign countries.

Lemon Unna & Durbridge Ltd – see The Agency (London) Ltd*

Barbara Levy Literary Agency*
64 Greenhill, Hampstead High Street, London NW3 5TZ
tel 0171-435 9046 *fax* 0171-431 2063
Director Barbara Levy, *Associate* John Selby (solicitor)
Full-length MSS only; also films, TV and radio (home 10%, overseas by arrangement). No reading fee, but informative preliminary letter and return postage essential. Founded 1986.

Limelight Management*
33 Newman Street, London W1P 3PD
tel 0171-637 2529 *fax* 0171-637 2538
Directors Fiona Lindsay, Linda Shanks
Full-length and short MSS. Food, wine, health, crafts, gardening, interior design (home 15%, overseas 20%), TV and radio rights (10-20%); will suggest revision where appropriate. No reading fee. Founded 1991.

The Christopher Little Literary Agency*
10 Eel Brook Studios, 125 Moore Park Road, London SW6 4PS
tel 0171-736 4455 *fax* 0171-736 4490
e-mail 100555.3137@compuserve.com
Contacts Christopher Little, Patrick Walsh (fiction, non-fiction); *Office Manager* Emma Schlesinger
Commercial and literary full-length fiction and non-fiction and film/TV scripts. Special interests: crime, thrillers, autobiographies, popular science and narrative and investigative non-fiction. Also packages celebrities for the book market and represents book projects for journalists. Rights representative in the UK for 6 US literary agencies (home 15%; US, translation, motion picture 20%). No reading fee. Send letter giving a summary of present and future intentions together with

track record, if any, plus synopsis and/or first 2 chapters and sae in first instance.

Authors include Simon Beckett, Marcus Berkmann, Colin Cameron, Harriet Castor, Linford Christie, Michael Cordy, Mike Dash, Frankie Dettori, Ginny Elliot, Simon Gandolfi, John Gordon-Davis, Janet Gleeson, Brian Hall, Paula Hamilton, Tom Holland, Charles Kennedy-Scott, Alistair MacNeill, Mark McCormack, Robert Mawson, Sanjida O'Connell, A.J. Quinnell, Alvin Rakoff, Rebbecca Ray, Candace Robb, Peter Rosenberg, J.K. Rowling, Simon Singh, Alan Smith, John Spurling, Laura Thompson, John Watson, James Whitaker, John Wilson, Tiger Woods. Founded 1979.

London Independent Books
26 Chalcot Crescent, London NW1 8YD
tel 0171-706 0486 *fax* 0171-724 3122
Proprietor Carolyn Whitaker

Specialises in commercial and fantasy fiction, cinema, jazz, show business, travel. Full-length MSS (home 15%, overseas 20%), films, TV and sound broadcasting (15%). Will suggest revision of promising MSS. No reading fee.

Authors include Bruce Crowther, Nigel Frith, Keith Grey, Andre Launay, Glenn Mitchell, Connie Monk, Emma Sinclair. Founded 1971.

Andrew Lownie Literary Agency*
17 Sutherland Street, London SW1V 4JU
tel 0171-828 1274 *fax* 0171-828 7608
Director Andrew Lownie

Full-length MSS. Biography, history, reference, current affairs, and packaging journalists and celebrities for the book market (worldwide 15%). No reading fee; will suggest a revision.

Authors include Juliet Barker, Timothy Good, Norma Major, Nick Pope; *The Oxford Classical Dictionary*, *The Cambridge Guide to Literature in English*. Founded 1988.

Lucas Alexander Whitley*
Elsinore House, 77 Fulham Palace Road, London W6 8JA
tel 0181-600 3800 *fax* 0181-600 3810
Directors Mark Lucas, Julian Alexander, Araminta Whitley, Roger Houghton

Full length MSS. Fiction and general non-fiction (home 15%, overseas 20%).

No poetry, plays, science fiction, fantasy, textbooks or children's books. Film or TV scripts for established clients only. Works with agents and publishers worldwide. Preliminary letter, synopsis and 2 chapters with sae required. No reading fee. Founded 1996.

Jennifer Luithlen Agency
88 Holmfield Road, Leicester LE2 1SB
tel 0116-273 8863 *fax* 0116-273 5697
Agent Jennifer Luithlen

Children's books; adult fiction: crime, historical, saga (home 10%, overseas 20%), performance rights (15%). Not looking for new clients. Founded 1986.

Lutyens & Rubinstein*
231 Westbourne Park Road, London W11 1EB
tel 0171-792 4855 *fax* 0171-792 4833
Directors Sarah Lutyens, Felicity Rubinstein

Fiction and non-fiction, commercial and literary (home 10%, overseas 20%). Send outline/two sample chapters and sae. No reading fee. Founded 1993.

Duncan McAra
28 Beresford Gardens, Edinburgh EH5 3ES
tel/fax 0131-552 1558

Literary fiction; non-fiction: art, architecture, archaeology, biography, military, Scottish, travel (home 10%, overseas by arrangement). Preliminary letter with sae essential. No reading fee. Founded 1988.

McLean & Slora Literary Agents
20A Eildon Street, Edinburgh EH3 5JU
tel 0131-556 3368 *fax* 0131-443 9118
Partners Barbara McLean and Annie Slora

Full-length MSS. Literary fiction, biography, cookery, poetry, Scottish interest (home 15%, overseas 25%). No reading fee; will suggest a revision and undertake for a fee.

Authors include Tom Bryan, John Herdman, Ruari McLean.

Eunice McMullen Children's Literary Agent Ltd
38 Clewer Hill Road, Windsor, Berks. SL4 4BW
tel (01753) 830348 *fax* (01753) 833459
Director Eunice McMullen

All types of children's books, particularly picture books (home 10%, overseas 15%). No unsolicited scripts.

Authors include Wayne Anderson, Reg Cartwright, Richard Fowler, Charles Fuge,

Simon James, Moira Maclean, Graham Oakley, Sue Porter, Angela McAllister, Carol Thompson, David Wood. Founded 1992.

Andrew Mann Ltd*
(in association with Jane Conway-Gordon)
1 Old Compton Street, London W1V 5PH
tel 0171-734 4751 *fax* 0171-287 9264
Directors Anne Dewe, Tina Betts
Full-length MSS. Scripts for TV, cinema, radio and theatre (home 15%, USA and Europe 20%). Associated with agents worldwide. No reading fee, but no unsolicited MSS without preliminary enquiry and sae. Founded 1974.

Manuscript ReSearch
PO Box 33, Bicester, Oxon OX6 7PP
tel (01869) 323447 *fax* (01869) 324096
Proprietor T.G. Jenkins
Now concentrating on film/TV and radio scripts. No reading fee, but sae for script return essential. Founded 1988.

The Marsh Agency*
11-12 Dover Street, London W1X 3PH
tel 0171-399 2800 *fax* 0171-399 2801
e-mail enquiries@marsh-agency.co.uk
Partners Paul Marsh, Susanna Nicklin
Specialisation: translation rights (10%). Founded 1994.

Judy Martin
94 Goldhurst Terrace, London NW6 3HS
tel 0171-372 8422 *fax* 0171-372 8423
Fiction, non-fiction, humour (home 15%, overseas 20%; dramatic rights 15%). No plays, poetry, cookery, gardening or children's stories. Translation rights handled by The Marsh Agency. No reading fee, but sae required for all unsolicited MSS, together with details of publishing history. Founded 1990.

Martinez Literary Agency
60 Oakwood Avenue, London N14 6QL
tel 0181-886 5829
Contact F.T. Budd
Fiction, children's books, arts and crafts, interior design, alternative health and complementary medicine, cookery, autobiographies, popular music, sport and business. No unsolicited MSS. No reading fee but an admin fee may be charged where appropriate. Preliminary letter with synopsis and sae required (home 15%; US, overseas and translation 20%; perfor-

mance rights 20%). Telephone first, possible change of address. Founded 1988.

Blanche Marvin
21A St John's Wood High Street, London NW8 7NG
tel/fax 0171-722 2313
Full-length MSS (home 12.5% + 12.5% overseas), performance rights. No reading fee but return postage essential.
Authors include Christopher Bond.

MBA Literary Agents Ltd*
62 Grafton Way, London W1P 5LD
tel 0171-387 2076 *fax* 0171-387 2042
e-mail agent@mbalit.co.uk
Contact Diana Tyler, John Richard Parker, Meg Davis, Ruth Needham, Laura Longrigg
Handles fiction and non-fiction; no poetry (home 10%, overseas 20%; theatre, TV, radio 10%; films 10-15%). Works in conjunction with agents in most countries. Also UK representative for **Writers House Inc.**, the Donald Maass Agency and the **Susan Schulman Literary & Dramatic Agents Inc.** No reading fee. No unsolicited material.
Clients include Campbell Armstrong, A.L. Barker, Harry Bowling, Jeffrey Caine, Glenn Chandler, Andrew Cowan, Patricia Finney, Maggie Furey, Sue Gee, the estate of B.S. Johnson, Paul J. McAuley, Anne McCaffrey, Susan Oudot, Sir Roger Penrose, Anne Perry, Iain Sinclair, E.V. Thompson, Mark Wallington, Douglas Watkinson, Valerie Windsor, Zhang Xianliang. Founded 1971.

Richard Milne Ltd
15 Summerlee Gardens, London N2 9QN
tel 0181-883 3987 *fax* 0181-883 0323
e-mail dsharp121@aol.com
Directors R.M. Sharples, K.N. Sharples
Specialises in scripts for films, TV, sound broadcasting (10%). Unable to represent any additional authors at present. Founded 1956.

Jay Morris & Co. Authors' Agents
PO Box 2926, Brighton BN1 3NR
tel (01273) 240070 *fax* (01273) 240072
Directors Jay Morris (managing), Dr Phillida Kanta, *Assistant Director* Toby Tillyard-Burrows
Full-length MSS (home 10%, overseas 15%). Mainstream commercial adult fiction: racy sagas, gay erotica, horror, children's fantasy, women in power (not women's issues), thrillers and crime. No

reading fee; will suggest a revision. Send preliminary letter with synopsis and sae. *Authors* include Jonathan Douglas, Saxon Hollis, Hon. Joy Parker-Dixon, Elika Rise, Piers de Villias. Founded 1994.

William Morris Agency (UK) Ltd*
1 Stratton Street, London W1X 6HB
tel 0171-355 8500 *fax* 0171-355 8600
e-mail adl@wma.com
Contacts Tanya Cohen, Jim Crabbe, Steve Kenis (film/TV/stage); Stephanie Cabot (books)
Worldwide theatrical and literary agency with offices in New York, Beverly Hills and Nashville, and associates in Munich and Sydney. Handles film, TV, stage and radio scripts; fiction and general non-fiction (film/TV/theatre/UK books 10%, US books and translation 20%). No unsolicited material; MSS only when preceded by letter. No reading fee. Founded 1965.

MS-S
Julia MacRae, 13 Pattison Road, London NW2 2HL
tel/fax 0171-435 7882 and
Christopher Sinclair-Stevenson, 3 South Terrace, London SW7 2TB
tel/fax 0171-581 2550
Julia MacRae: children's fiction and picture books, music, history and the arts. Christopher Sinclair-Stevenson: general. Worldwide 10%. Will suggest a revision (see page 581). Founded 1996.

Judith Murdoch Literary Agency
19 Chalcot Square, London NW1 8YA
tel 0171-722 4197
Full-length fiction only (home 15%, overseas 20%). No genre novels, science fiction/fantasy, poetry, short stories or children's. Don't phone – write! Send first 2 chapters and synopsis with preliminary letter. Return postage/sae essential. Editorial advice given; no reading fee. Translation rights handled by The Marsh Agency. Founded 1993.

Negotiate Ltd
99 Caiyside, Edinburgh EH10 7HR
tel 0131-445 7571 *fax* 0131-445 7572
e-mail gavin@neg1.demon.co.uk
web site http://www.negotiate.co.uk
Contact Gavin Kennedy
Specialises in the negotiation of author's contracts and subsidiary rights. Established authors only or new authors with draft contract from a publisher. Preliminary letter or fax please. Founded 1986.

New Authors Showcase
Rivendell, Kingsgate Close, Torquay TQ2 8QA
tel/fax (01803) 326617
e-mail newauthors@compuserve.com
web site http://ourworld.compuserve.com/home-pages/newauthors
Contact Barrie E. James
An Internet site for new unpublished authors to display their work to publishers, and for published authors to advertise their work. All literary work considered, including poetry (10%). No reading fee. Send preliminary letter and synopsis with sae.

Maggie Noach Literary Agency*
21 Redan Street, London W14 0AB
tel 0171-602 2451 *fax* 0171-603 4712
e-mail maggie.noach@netmatters.co.uk
General fiction and non-fiction, especially biography, travel, history and current events; non-illustrated children's books. Full-length MSS (home 15%, US/translation 20%). No scientific, academic or specialist non-fiction; no poetry, plays, short stories or books for the very young. Very few new clients taken on as it is considered vital to give individual attention to each author's work. Unsolicited MSS not welcome. Approach by letter (not by telephone), giving a brief description of the book and enclosing a few sample pages. Return postage essential. No reading fee. Founded 1982.

Andrew Nurnberg Associates Ltd*
Clerkenwell House, 45-47 Clerkenwell Green, London EC1R 0HT
tel 0171-417 8800 *fax* 0171-417 8812
e-mail au@nurnberg.co.uk
Specialises in the sale of translation rights of English and American authors into European languages.

Alexandra Nye, Writers & Agents
44 Braemar Avenue, Dunblane, Perthshire FK15 9EB
tel (01786) 825114
Director Alexandra Nye
Literary fiction, historical, biographies; no poetry or plays (home 10%, overseas 20%, translation 15%). No unsolicited material. Founded 1991.

David O'Leary Literary Agency
10 Lansdowne Court, Lansdowne Rise, London W11 2NR
tel 0171-229 1623 *fax* 0171-727 9624

Popular and literary fiction and non-fiction: special interests Russia, Ireland, history, science (home 10%, overseas 20%), performance rights (15%). Will suggest revision; no reading fee. Write or call before submitting MSS; please enclose sae.

Authors include Alexander Cordell, David Crackanthorpe, Jim Lusby, Alex Keegan, James Kennedy, Gretta Mulrooney. Founded 1988.

Deborah Owen Ltd*
78 Narrow Street, Limehouse, London E14 8BP
tel 0171-987 5119/5441 *fax* 0171-538 4004
Contact Deborah Owen

Full-length MSS (home 10%, overseas 15%). All types of literary material except plays, scripts, children's books, short stories or poetry. No unsolicited MSS. No new authors at present.

Authors include Ellis Peters, Amos Oz, Delia Smith. Founded 1971.

Mark Paterson & Associates*
10 Brook Street, Wivenhoe, Colchester, Essex CO7 9DS
tel (01206) 825433/4 *fax* (01206) 822990
e-mail markpaterson@compuserve.com

Book-length MSS; general but with special experience in psychoanalysis, psychotherapy, history, copyright and education (20% worldwide including sub-agents' commission). No articles or short stories except for existing clients. Preliminary letter with synopsis, sample material and sae essential.

Authors include Sigmund Freud, Anna Freud, Hugh Brogan, Donald Winnicott, Peter Moss, Sir Arthur Evans, Dorothy Richardson, Hugh Schonfield, Georg Groddeck, Patrick Casement. Founded 1955.

John Pawsey
60 High Street, Tarring, Worthing, West Sussex BN14 7NR
tel (01903) 205167 *fax* (01903) 205167

Full-length popular fiction and non-fiction MSS (home 10-15%, overseas 19%). No unsolicited material, poetry, short stories, journalism or original film and stage scripts. Preliminary letter and return postage with all correspondence essential. Works in association with agencies in the USA, Europe and the Far East. Will suggest revision if MS sufficiently promising. No reading fee.

Authors include Jonathan Agnew, Dr David Lewis, Peter Hobday, Jon Silverman. Founded 1981.

Maggie Pearlstine Associates Ltd*
31 Ashley Gardens, Ambrosden Avenue, London SW1P 1QE
tel 0171-828 4212 *fax* 0171-834 5546

Full-length MSS, fiction and non-fiction. Special interests: commercial fiction, illustrated non-fiction, home and leisure, health, biography, history and politics (home 10-12.5%, overseas, journalism and media 20%). Translation rights handled by Aitken & Stone Ltd. No children's or poetry; only deals with scripts and short stories by authors already on its books. No unsolicited MSS. Preliminary letter required and sae. No reading fee.

Authors include David Aaronovitch, John Biffen, Matthew Baylis, Kate Bingham, Glorafilia, Prof Roger Gosden, Roy Hattersley, Prof Lisa Jardine, Charles Kennedy, Prof Nicholas Lowe, Simon Morris, Dr Raj Persaud, Prof Lesley Regan, Jackie Rowley, Chief Rabbi Jonathan Sacks, Polly Sellar, Lady Henrietta Spencer-Churchill, Jack Straw, Dr Thomas Stuttaford, Prof Robert Winston. Founded 1989.

The Peters Fraser & Dunlop Group Ltd*
(incorporating A.D. Peters & Co. Ltd, Fraser & Dunlop Scripts Ltd, Fraser & Dunlop Ltd, June Hall Literary Agency Ltd, Watergate Film Services Ltd)
503-4 The Chambers, Chelsea Harbour, Lots Road, London SW10 0XF
tel 0171-344 1000 *fax* 0171-352 7356/7351/1756
e-mail rscoular@pfd.co.uk
web site http://www.pfd.co.uk
Joint Chairmen Michael Sissons, Anthony Jones, *Managing Director* Anthony Baring, *Books* Michael Sissons, Pat Kavanagh, Caroline Dawnay, Charles Walker, Rosemary Canter, Sarah Leigh, Robert Kirby, *Serial* Pat Kavanagh, *Film/TV* Anthony Jones, Tim Corrie, Norman North, Charles Walker, Vanessa Jones, St John Donald, Rosemary Scoular, Natasha Galloway *Actors* Maureen Vincent, Ginette Chalmers, Dallas Smith, Lindy King, *Theatre* Kenneth Ewing, St John Donald, Nicki Stoddart, *Children's* Rosemary Canter, *Multimedia* Rosemary Scoular
Translation Rights Intercontinental Literary Agency, *US Illustrators' Representation* Harriet Kasak

Handles the full range of books including fiction, children's and non-fiction as well as scripts for film, theatre, radio and TV, and multimedia projects. Seventy-five years of international experience in all media. Send a full outline for non-fiction and short synopsis for fiction with 2 or 3 sample chapters and autobiographical note. It is preferred that material be submitted on an exclusive basis but in any event it should be made plain if submitting to other agencies or publishers at the same time. Return postage essential. No reading fee. No guaranteed response to submissions by e-mail. Home 10%; US and trranslation 20%.

Laurence Pollinger Limited

18 Maddox Street, London W1R 0EU
tel 0171-629 9761 *fax* 0171-629 9765
e-mail laurence.pollinger@compuserve.com
Directors Gerald J. Pollinger, Heather Chalcroft, Lesley Hadcroft, Juliet Burton, *Secretary* Denzil de Silva, *Dramatic Associate* Micheline Steinberg

All material except original film stories, poetry and freelance journalistic articles. Commission: 15%, except for translation (20%), which may include commission to the associate in the territory concerned. No reading fee. An editorial contribution may be requested.

Murray Pollinger – see David Higham Associates Ltd*

Shelley Power Literary Agency Ltd*

Le Montaud, 24220 Berbiguières, France
tel 53 29 62 52 *fax* 53 29 62 54

General fiction and non-fiction. Full-length MSS (home 10%, USA and translations 19%). No children's books, poetry or plays. Works in conjunction with agents abroad. No reading fee, but preliminary letter with sae for return from UK or France essential.

Authors include Madge Swindells, William Gibson, Elizabeth Hand, Michael Swanwick, Richard Stern, Peter Lambley and Roger Wilkes. Also based in the UK. Founded 1976.

Elizabeth Puttick Literary Agency

46 Brookfield Mansions, Highgate West Hill, London N6 6AT
tel 0181-340 6383 *fax* 0181-340 6384
e-mail liz@puttick.com
web site http://www.btinternet.com/~lizputtick

Director Elizabeth Puttick

General non-fiction and selected fiction with special interest in personal development, religion/supernatural, popular psychology, popular science, health, complementary medicine, childcare, business, women's issues, social issues. Full-length MSS (home 15%, overseas 20%). No reading fee. Editorial service by arrangement. Send preliminary letter with synopsis; return postage essential.

Clients include William Bloom, Anne Baring, Nitya Lacroix. Founded 1995.

PVA Management Ltd

Hallow Park, Worcester WR2 6PG
tel (01905) 640663 *fax* (01905) 641842
e-mail pvamanltd@aol.com
Managing Director Paul Vaughan

Full-length MSS. Non-fiction only (home 15%, overseas 20%, performance rights 15%). Please send synopsis and sample chapters together with return postage.

Radala & Associates

17 Avenue Mansions, Finchley Road, London NW3 7AX
tel 0171-794 4495 *fax* 0171-431 7636
Director Richard Gollner, *Associates* Neil Hornick, Anna Swan, Andy Marino

Full-length MSS (home 10%, overseas 15%). Fiction and non-fiction. Books, TV, sound broadcasting. Submit synopsis in first instance; evaluation of MSS charged (£50 upwards); outlines, proposals, etc at no charge. Founded 1970.

Margaret Ramsay Ltd – now Casarotto Ramsay Ltd

Real Creatives Worldwide

14 Dean Street, London W1V 5AH
tel 0171-437 4188 *fax* 0171-437 4221
Directors F.L. Rasala, M. Rasala, M. Maco

Producers and directors of motion pictures and TV commerials. Also package movie ideas and scripts for submission to Hollywood studios and TV companies worldwide (10-20%). Founded 1984.

Rogers, Coleridge & White Ltd*

20 Powis Mews, London W11 1JN
tel 0171-221 3717 *fax* 0171-229 9084
Directors Deborah Rogers, Gill Coleridge, Patricia White (USA), David Miller, *Consultant* Ann Warnford-Davis
USA Associate International Creative Management, Inc.

Full-length book MSS, including children's books (home 10%, USA 15%, translations 20%). No unsolicited MSS please, and no submissions by fax or e-mail. Founded 1967.

Elizabeth Roy Literary Agency
White Cottage, Greatford, Nr Stamford, Lincs. PE9 4PR
tel/fax (01778) 560672
Contemporary women's fiction, crime fiction, children's books – writers and illustrators (home 10-15%, overseas 20%). Will suggest revision. Preliminary letter, synopsis and sample chapters essential with names of publishers and agents previously contacted. Return postage essential. No reading fee. Founded 1990.

Hilary Rubinstein Books
32 Ladbroke Grove, London W11 3BQ
tel 0171-792 4282 *fax* 0171-221 5291
Director Hilary Rubinstein
Full-length MSS. Fiction and non-fiction (home 10%, overseas 20%); will suggest revision where appropriate. No plays, scripts, children's books or poetry. No reading fee, but no unsolicited MSS without preliminary letter or call.

Authors include Eric Lomax, Donna Williams. Founded 1992.

Uli Rushby-Smith
72 Plimsoll Road, London N4 2EE
tel/fax 0171-354 2718
Directors Uli Rushby-Smith
Full length MSS only. Fiction and non-fiction, literary and commercial (home 10%, USA/foreign 20%). Work in conjunction with foreign sub-agents in some countries. UK representatives of Curtis Brown Ltd, New York (children's books) and Henry Holt & Co. Inc., New York, and Penguin Canada. Send outline, sample chapters and sae; no reading fee. Founded 1993.

Rosemary Sandberg Ltd
6 Bayley Street, London WC1B 3HB
tel 0171-304 4110 *fax* 0171-304 4109
Directors Rosemary Sandberg, Ed Victor, Graham Greene CBE
Children's – writers and illustrators, general fiction and non-fiction (home 10-15%, overseas 20%). Absolutely no unsolicited MSS: client list is full. Founded 1991.

Tessa Sayle Agency*
11 Jubilee Place, London SW3 3TE

tel 0171-823 3883 (5 lines) *fax* 0171-823 3363
Publishing Rachel Calder, *Film, TV* Jane Villiers, Matthew Bates
Full-length MSS (home 10%, overseas 20%), film, TV, theatre (home 10%, overseas 15-20%). USA Associates: Darhansoff & Verrill, 179 Franklin St, New York, NY 10013 and **Elaine Markson Literary Agency**. Represented in all foreign countries. No reading fee, but preliminary letter and return postage essential.

The Sharland Organisation Ltd
9 Marlborough Crescent, Bedford Park, London W4 1HE
tel 0181-742 1919 *fax* 0181-995 7688
Directors Mike Sharland, Alice Sharland
Specialises in film, TV, stage and radio rights throughout the world (home 15%, overseas 20%); also negotiates multimedia, interactive TV deals and computer game contracts. Works in conjunction with overseas agents. Preliminary letter and return postage is essential. Founded 1988.

Sheil Land Associates Ltd*
(incorporating Christy & Moore Ltd 1912 and Richard Scott Simon Ltd 1971)
43 Doughty Street, London WC1N 2LF
tel 0171-405 9351 *fax* 0171-831 2127
Agents Sonia Land, Anthony Sheil, Luigi Bonomi, Vivien Green, Simon Trewin, John Rush (film/drama/TV), Laura Susijn (foreign rights)
Full-length general, commercial and literary fiction and non-fiction, biography, travel, cookery, humour (home 10-15%, USA/translations 20%); theatre, film, radio and TV scripts (home 10-15%, overseas 20%). Sample chapters with return postage essential.

Authors include Peter Ackroyd, Melvyn Bragg, John Banville, Nicky Clarke, Catherine Cookson, Josephine Cox, Seamus Deane, John Fowles, Susan Hill, John Humphrys, HRH The Prince of Wales, Michael Ignatieff, John Keegan, Charlotte Lamb, David Mellor, Andrew Miller, Van Morrison, Esther Rantzen, Pam Rhodes, Tom Sharpe, Alan Titchmarsh, Rose Tremain, Paul Wilson. Founded 1962.

Foreign Rights Department
19 John Street, London WC1N 2DL
tel 0171-405 7473 *fax* 0171-405 5239
Contacts Laura Susijn, Susy Behr
Translation and US rights.

Caroline Sheldon Literary Agency*
71 Hillgate Place, London W8 7SS
tel 0171-727 9102
Proprietor Caroline Sheldon
Full-length MSS. General fiction, women's fiction, and children's books (home 10%, overseas 20%). No reading fee. Synopsis and first 3 chapters with large sae in case of return required initially. Founded 1985.

Jeffrey Simmons
10 Lowndes Square, London SW1X 9HA
tel 0171-235 8852 *fax* 0171-235 9733
Specialises in fiction (no sci-fi, horror or fantasy), biography, autobiography, show business, personality books, law, crime, politics, world affairs. Full-length MSS (home from 10%, overseas from 15%). Will suggest revision. No reading fee, but preliminary letter essential.

Richard Scott Simon Ltd – see Sheil Land Associates Ltd*

Simpson Fox Associates*
52 Shaftesbury Avenue, London W1V 7DE
tel 0171-434 9167 *fax* 0171-494 2887
Directors David Watson, Angela Fox, John Simpson, Anita Land, Georgina Capel, Robert Fox
General fiction and non-fiction, scripts (worldwide 15%). No reading fee. Write to Georgina Capel with synopsis, sample chapter and sae.
Authors include Julie Burchill, Lucy Moore, Henry Porter, Andrew Roberts.

Sinclair-Stevenson
3 South Terrace, London SW7 2TB
tel/fax 0171-581 2550
Directors Christopher Sinclair-Stevenson, Deborah Sinclair-Stevenson
Full-length MSS (worldwide 10%). General – no children's books. No reading fee; will suggest a revision. Founded 1995.

The Carol Smith Literary Agency
22 Adam and Eve Mews, London W8 6UJ
tel 0171-937 4874 *fax* 0171-938 5323
e-mail 100067,1643
Full-length fiction and non-fiction. Specialises in contemporary commercial and literary novels (home 10%, overseas/translation 20%). Please write rather than phone. Send first 3-4 chapters and synopsis with preliminary letter. Return postage essential. No reading fee. MSS submissions by invitation only.

Solo Literary Agency Ltd
49-53 Kensington High Street, London W8 5ED
tel 0171-376 2166 *fax* 0171-938 3165
Directors Don Short (managing), Wendy Short (secretary)
Specialises in celebrity and autobiographical books. Fiction from established authors only (home 15%, overseas 20%). No reading fee.
Authors include Peter Essex, Rosemary Kingsland, Edward Vale. Founded 1978.

Abner Stein*
10 Roland Gardens, London SW7 3PH
tel 0171-373 0456 *fax* 0171-370 6316
Full-length and short MSS (home 10%, overseas 20%). No reading fee, but no unsolicited MSS; preliminary letter and return postage required.

Micheline Steinberg Playwrights' Agent
409 Triumph House, 187-191 Regent Street, London W1R 7WF
tel 0171-287 4383 *fax* 0171-287 4384
Full-length MSS – theatre, films, TV, radio (home 10%, overseas 15%). Dramatic Associate for Laurence Pollinger Ltd; works in conjunction with agents in USA and other countries. No reading fee, but preliminary letter essential and return postage with MSS. Founded 1987.

Rochelle Stevens & Co.
2 Terretts Place, Upper Street, London N1 1QZ
tel 0171-359 3900 *fax* 0171-354 5729
Proprietor Rochelle Stevens, *Associate* Frances Grannum
Drama scripts for film, TV, theatre and radio (10%); will suggest revision where appropriate. No reading fee, but preliminary letter and return postage essential. Founded 1984.

Shirley Stewart Literary Agency*
36 Brand Street, London SE10 8SR
tel 0181-853 1381 *fax* 0181-305 2175
e-mail sstewartlitag@atlas.co.uk
Director Shirley Stewart
Specialises in literary fiction and non-fiction, and crime writing (home 10%, overseas 20%); theatre, film/TV and radio (15%). No poetry, plays, textbooks or children's books. No reading fee. Send

preliminary letter, synopsis and first 3 chapters plus return postage. Founded 1993.

J.M. Thurley Management
30 Cambridge Road, Teddington,
Middlesex TW11 8DR
tel 0181-977 3176 *fax* 0181-943 2678
Contact Jon Thurley

Specialises in commercial and literary full-length fiction and commercial work for film and TV. No plays, poetry, short stories, articles or fantasy. No reading fee but preliminary letter and sae essential. Editorial/creative advice provided to clients (home 15%, overseas 20%). Links with leading US and European agents. Founded 1976.

Lavinia Trevor*
The Glasshouse, 49A Goldhawk Road,
London W12 8QP
tel 0181-749 8481 *fax* 0181-749 7377

Fiction and non-fiction, including popular science for the general trade market. No reading fee. Brief autobiographical letter and approx. first 50 pages required plus sae. Founded 1993.

Jane Turnbull*
13 Wendell Road, London W12 9RS
tel 0181-743 9580 *fax* 0181-749 6079

Fiction and non-fiction (home 10%, USA 15%, translation 20%), performance rights (15%). No science fiction, romantic fiction, children's or short stories. Works in conjunction with Aitken & Stone for sale of translation rights. No reading fee. Preliminary letter and sae essential; no unsolicited MSS. Founded 1986.

Harvey Unna & Stephen Durbridge Ltd – see The Agency (London) Ltd*

Ed Victor Ltd*
6 Bayley Street, Bedford Square,
London WC1B 3HB
tel 0171-304 4100 *fax* 0171-304 4111
Directors Ed Victor, Graham C. Greene cbe, Carol Ryan, Leon Morgan, Margaret Phillips, Sophie Hicks (children's writers and illustrators)

Full-length MSS, fiction and non-fiction, but no short stories, film/TV scripts, poetry or plays (home 15%, USA 15%, translation 20%), performance rights (15%). Represented in all foreign markets. No unsolicited MSS.

Authors include Douglas Adams, Sir Ranulph Fiennes, Frederick Forsyth, Josephine Hart, Jack Higgins, Erica Jong, Kathy Lette, Iris Murdoch, Nigel Nicolson, Lisa St Aubin de Téran, Erich Segal, Will Self, and the estates of Irving Wallace, Raymond Chandler, Sir Stephen Spender. Founded 1976.

Warner/Chappell Plays Ltd
Griffin House, 161 Hammersmith Road,
London W6 8BS
tel 0181-563 5888 *fax* 0181-563 5801
e-mail warner.chappell@dial.pipex.com

Specialises in stage plays. Works in conjunction with overseas agents. Preliminary letter essential. Formerly English Theatre Guild Ltd; part of Warner Chappell Music Ltd. Founded 1938.

Watson, Little Ltd*
Capo Di Monte, Windmill Hill, London NW3 6RJ
tel 0171-431 0770 *fax* 0171-431 7225
Directors Sheila Watson, Amanda Little, Sugra Zaman

Full-length MSS. Special interests: business books, popular science, psychology, all leisure activities, popular culture, fiction; no short stories or play scripts (home 10%, serial 15%, translation 19%, US 24%; electronic rights 20%; all other rights including film, video and TV 10%). Works in association with US agencies and many foreign agencies. Preliminary letter please.

A.P. Watt Ltd*
20 John Street, London WC1N 2DR
tel 0171-405 6774 *fax* 0171-831 2154 (books)
0171-430 1952 (drama)
Directors Caradoc King, Linda Shaughnessy, Derek Johns, Jo Frank, Sam North (associate)

Full-length MSS; dramatic works for all media (home 10%, US and foreign 20% including commission to foreign agent). No poetry. No reading fee. No unsolicited MSS. Founded 1875.

WCA Licensing
18 Beckwith Road, London SE24 9LG
tel 0171-274 6263 *fax* 0171-274 1509
e-mail wca@pro-net.co.uk
Partners Elaine Collins and Arabella Woods

TV tie-ins, thrillers, general fiction; no poetry (home 15%, overseas 20%). No reading fee; will suggest a revision. Founded 1993.

Dinah Wiener Ltd*

12 Cornwall Grove, London W4 2LB
tel 0181-994 6011 *fax* 0181-994 6044
e-mail dinahwiener@enterprise.net

Full-length MSS only, fiction and general non-fiction (home 15%, overseas 20%), film and TV in association (15%). No plays, scripts, poetry, short stories or children's books. No reading fee, but preliminary letter and return postage essential.

Jonathan Williams Literary Agency

2 Mews, 10 Sandycove Avenue West, Sandycove, Co. Dublin, Republic of Ireland
tel/fax (01) 2803482
Director Jonathan Williams

General fiction and non-fiction, preferably by Irish authors (home 10%). Will suggest revision; usually no reading fee. Return postage appreciated (no British stamps – please use International Reply Coupons). Founded 1981.

Elisabeth Wilson

24 Thornhill Square, London N1 1BQ
fax 0171-609 6045

Rights agent and consultant. Founded 1979.

The Wylie Agency (UK) Ltd

36 Parkside, 52 Knightsbridge, London SW1X 3JP
tel 0171-235 6394 *fax* 0171-838 9030
Directors Andrew Wylie (president), Georgia Garrett, Benita Edzard

Literary fiction and non-fiction (home 10%, overseas 20%, USA 15%). No unsolicited MSS; send preliminary letter with 2 sample chapters and sae in first instance. Founded 1996.

Literary agents for children's books

The following literary agents will consider work suitable for children's books, from both authors and illustrators. See also Writing and illustrating children's books on page 256 and Art agents and commercial art studios on page 391.

The Agency (London) Ltd
Peter Bryant (Writers)
Celia Catchpole
Curtis Brown
Anne Drexl
Eddison Pearson Literary Agents
A.M. Heath & Co. Ltd
David Higham Associates Ltd
Juvenilia
Christopher Little Literary Agency

Jennifer Luithlen Agency
McLean & Slora Literary Agents
Eunice McMullen Children's Literary Agent Ltd
Andrew Mann Ltd
Martinez Literary Agency
Jay Morris & Co. Authors' Agents
MS-S (Julia MacRae)
Maggie Noach Literary Agency
The Peters, Fraser & Dunlop Group Ltd (Rosemary Canter)
Laurence Pollinger Limited

Rogers, Coleridge & White Ltd
Elizabeth Roy Literary Agency
Rosemary Sandberg Ltd
Caroline Sheldon Literary Agency
Ed Victor Ltd (Sophie Hicks)
A.P. Watt Ltd

Literary agents overseas

Before submitting material, writers are advised to send a preliminary letter with an sae (or an International Reply Coupon) and to ascertain terms. Listings for overseas literary agents other than in the USA start on page 379.

*Member of the Association of Authors' Representatives

USA

American Play Company Inc.
19 West 44th Street, Suite 1204, New York, NY 10036
tel 212-921-0545 *fax* 212-869-4032
President Sheldon Abend

The Axelrod Agency*
54 Church Street, Lenox, MA 01240
tel 413-637-2000 *fax* 413-637-4725
President Steven Axelrod
Full-length MSS. Fiction and non-fiction, software (home 10%, overseas 20%), film and TV rights (10%); will suggest revision where appropriate. Works with overseas agents. No reading fee. Founded 1983.

The Balkin Agency Inc.*
PO Box 222, Amherst, MA 01004
tel 413-548-9835 *fax* 413-548-9836
e-mail balkin@crocker.com
Director Richard Balkin
European and British Representative Christopher Little Agency
Full-length MSS – adult non-fiction only (home 15%, overseas 20%). Query first. May suggest revision. No reading fee.

Virginia Barber Literary Agency Inc.*
101 Fifth Avenue, New York, NY 10003
tel 212-255-6515 *fax* 212-691-9418
President Virginia Barber, *Contacts* Jennifer Rudolph Walsh, Jay Mandel, Claire Tisne, Cornelius Howland
General fiction and non-fiction (home 15%, overseas 20%), performance rights (15%); will suggest revision. Has co-agents in all major countries; Abner Stein handles UK rights. No reading fee. Founded 1974.

Berman, Boals & Flynn Inc.*
208 West 30th Street, Suite 401, New York, NY 10001
tel 212-868-1068 *fax* 212-868-1052
Agents Lois Berman, Judy Boals, Jim Flynn
Dramatic writing only (and only by recommendation).

Georges Borchardt Inc.*
136 East 57th Street, New York, NY 10022
tel 212-753-5785 *fax* 212-838-6518
Directors Georges Borchardt, Anne Borchardt
Full-length and short MSS (home/British/performance 15%, translations 20%). Agents in most foreign countries. No unsolicited MSS. No reading fee. Founded 1967.

Brandt & Brandt Literary Agents Inc.*
1501 Broadway, New York, NY 10036
tel 212-840-5760 *fax* 212-840-5776
British Representative A.M. Heath & Co. Ltd
Full-length and short MSS (home 15%, overseas 20%), performance rights (10%). No reading fee.

The Helen Brann Agency Inc.*
94 Curtis Road, Bridgewater, CT 06752
tel 203-354-9580 *fax* 203-355-2572

Maria Carvainis Agency Inc.*
235 West End Avenue, New York, NY 10023
tel 212-580-1559 *fax* 212-877-3486
President Maria Carvainis
Fiction: all categories (except science fiction), especially general fiction/literary and mainstream; mystery, thrillers and suspense; fantasy; young adult and children's; historical, Regency and category romance. Non-fiction: political and film biographies; medicine and women's

issues; business, finance, psychology and popular science (home 15%, overseas 20%). Maria Carvainis views the author's editorial needs and career development as integral components of the literary agent's role, in addition to the negotiation of intricate contracts. Works in conjunction with foreign, TV and movie agents. No reading fee. Query first; no unsolicited MSS.

Martha Casselman, Literary Agent*
PO Box 342, Calistoga, CA 94515-0342
tel 707-942-4341 *fax* 707-942-4358
Food and cookbook, other adult non-fiction (combined home/overseas 25%); will suggest revision where appropriate. No fiction, poetry or textbooks; no MSS; include return postage with query. Works with overseas agents. No reading fee. Founded 1978.

Faith Childs Literary Agency Inc.*
915 Broadway, Suite 1009, New York, NY 10010
tel 212-645-4600 *fax* 212-645-4644
Director Faith Hampton Childs, *Associate* Lori A. Pope
Literary fiction; non-fiction (home 15%, overseas 20%). Works in conjunction with overseas agents. Will suggest revision. No reading fee. Founded 1990.

Ruth Cohen Inc. Literary Agency*
PO Box 7626, Menlo Park, CA 94025
tel 415-854-2054
Requires quality writing: women's contemporary fiction; mysteries; juvenile – picture books to middle grade novels (home 15%, overseas 20%), film, TV rights (15%); will suggest revision. Works in conjunction with overseas agents. Send query letter and 25 opening pages; must include sae. No reading fee. Founded 1982.

Frances Collin Literary Agent*
PO Box 33, Wayne, PA 19087-0033
tel 610-254-0555
Full-length MSS (specialisations of interest to UK writers: mysteries, women's fiction, history, biography, science fiction, fantasy) (home 15%, overseas 20%), performance rights (20%). No screenplays. Works in conjunction with agents worldwide. No reading fee. No unsolicited MSS please. Letter queries must include sufficient international postage response coupons. Founded 1948; successor to Marie Rodell-Frances Collin Literary Agency.

Don Congdon Associates Inc.*
156 Fifth Avenue, Suite 625, New York, NY 10010
tel 212-645-1229 *fax* 212-727-2688
e-mail doncongdon@aol.com
Agents Don Congdon, Michael Congdon, Susan Ramer
Full-length and short MSS. General fiction and non-fiction (home 10%, overseas 19%), performance rights (10%); will sometimes suggest revision. Works with co-agents overseas. No reading fee, but no unsolicited MSS – query first. Founded 1983.

Richard Curtis Associates Inc.*
171 East 74th Street, New York, NY 10021
tel 212-772-7363 *fax* 212-772-7393
web site http://curtisagency.com
President Richard Curtis, *Associates* Amy Victoria Meo, Laura Tucker
All types of commercial fiction; also non-fiction (home 15%P overseas 20%), multimedia, film, TV rights (15%). Works in conjunction with overseas agents. Will suggest revision. No reading fee. Founded 1970.

Curtis Brown Ltd*
10 Astor Place, New York, NY 10003
tel 212-473-5400
Chairman Perry Knowlton
Contact Query Department
and 1750 Montgomery Street, San Francisco, CA 94111
tel 415-954-8566
President Peter Ginsberg
Fiction and non-fiction, juvenile, film and TV rights. No unsolicited MSS; query first with sae. No reading fee; no handling fees.

Joan Daves Agency
21 West 26th Street, New York, NY 10010
tel 212-685-2663 *fax* 212-685-1781
Director Jennifer Lyons, *Assistant* Hannah Tinti
Sample chapter or detailed outline of non-fiction projects (home 15%, overseas 20%). No reading fee. No unpublished writers. Subsidiary of **Writers House Inc.** Founded in 1952 by Joan Daves.

Elaine Davie Literary Agency
620 Park Avenue, Rochester, NY 14607
tel 716-442-0830
President Elaine Davie

Full-length MSS. Specialises in books by and for women, especially genre romance (home 15%, overseas 20%); will sometimes suggest revision. Works with overseas agents. No reading fee, but preliminary letter with sae essential. Query or first 100 pages/synopsis. Founded 1986.

Sandra Dijkstra Literary Agency*
1155 Camino del Mar, Suite 515, Del Mar, CA 92014
tel 619-755-3115
President Sandra Dijkstra

Adult fiction, especially literary/contemporary, mystery/suspense; non-fiction: current affairs, memoir/biography, science, health, history and psychology/self-help, business, how-to; selected children's projects (home 15%, overseas 20%). Works in conjunction with foreign agents. Will suggest revision. No reading fee. Send first 50 pages and sae for response/return. No faxed queries. Response period 4-6 weeks; do not call to enquire. Founded 1981.

Donadio & Ashworth Inc.*
121 West 27th Street, Suite 704, New York, NY 10001
tel 212-691-8077 *fax* 212-633-2837

Literary fiction and non-fiction.

Jane Dystel Literary Management*
One Union Square West, New York, NY 10003
tel 212-627-9100 *fax* 212-627-9313
web site http://www.dystel.com
President Jane D. Dystel, *Vice-President* Miriam Goderich

General fiction and non-fiction: literary and commercial fiction; narrative non-fiction; self-help; cookbooks; parenting, etc. Full-length and short MSS (home 15%, overseas 10%); film, TV and radio (15%). No reading fee. Founded 1991.

Peter Elek Associates
PO Box 223, Canal Street Station, New York, NY 10013
tel 212-431-9368/9371 *fax* 212-966-5768
e-mail 73174.2515 @compuserve.com
web site http://www.peterelek@theliteraryagency.com
Directors Peter Elek, Helene W. Elek

Full-length and short MSS. Adult and illustrated adult non-fiction: style, culture, popular history, popular science, current affairs; juvenile picture books (home 15%, overseas 20%), performance rights (20%); will sometimes suggest revision. Works with overseas agents. No reading fee.

Experienced in licensing for multimedia, on-line and off-line. Founded 1979.

Ann Elmo Agency Inc.*
60 East 42nd Street, New York, NY 10165
tel 212-661-2880 *fax* 212-661-2883
Director Lettie Lee

Full-length fiction and non-fiction MSS (home 15%, overseas 20%), theatre (15%). Will suggest revision when MSS is promising. Works with foreign agencies. No reading fee.

Frieda Fishbein Associates
PO Box 723, Bedford, NY 10506
tel 914-234-7232 *fax* 914-234-4196
e-mail fishbein@juno.com
Contacts Heidi Carlson, Douglas Michael

TV, plays, books, screenplays, film and TV rights. No unsolicited MSS; query first. Reading fee for new writers, or published writers in a new genre.

ForthWrite Literary Agency
28990 Pacific Coast Highway, Suite 106, Malibu, CA 90265
tel 310-457-5785 *fax* 310-457-9785
e-mail literaryag@aol.com
Owner Wendy Keller

Only non-fiction: business, self-help popular psychology, how-to. Subjects include: animals, art, horticulture/gardening, archaeology, European history (especially English), biography, health (especially homeopathy and alternative medicines), parenting, coffee table (illustrated) books, crafts (bobbin lace, handicrafts, etc), nature, psychology. Send IRC with query. Response in 8 weeks. Founded 1988.

The Fox Chase Agency Inc.*
5 Radnor Corporate Center, Suite 441, 100 Matsonsford Road, Radnor, PA 19087
tel 610-341-9840 *fax* 610-341-9842

Jeanne Fredericks Literary Agency Inc.
221 Benedict Hill Road, New Canaan, CT 06840
tel/fax 203-972-3011
e-mail jflainc@ix.netcom.com

Quality non-fiction, especially health, science, women's issues, gardening, antiques and decorative arts, biography, cookbooks, popular reference, business, natural history (home 15%, overseas 20%). No reading fee. Query first, enclosing sae. Founded 1997.

Robert A. Freedman Dramatic Agency Inc.*

(Formerly Harold Freedman Brandt & Brandt Dramatic Dept. Inc.)
1501 Broadway, Suite 2310, New York, NY 10036
tel 212-840-5760

Plays, motion picture and TV scripts. Send letter of enquiry first, with sae.

Samuel French Inc.*

45 West 25th Street, New York, NY 10010
tel 212-206-8990 *fax* 212-206-1429
President Charles R. Van Nostrand

Play publishers; authors' representatives.

Jay Garon-Brooke Associates Inc.* – see Pinder, Lane & Garon-Brooke Associates Ltd

Gelfman Schneider Literary Agents Inc.*

250 West 57th Street, Suite 2515, New York, NY 10107
tel 212-245-1993 *fax* 212-245-8678
Directors Jane Gelfman, Deborah Schneider

General adult fiction and non-fiction (home 15%, overseas 20%). Works in conjunction with Curtis Brown, London. Will suggest revision. No reading fee but please send sae for return of material.

Goodman Associates, Literary Agents*

500 West End Avenue, New York, NY 10024
tel 212-873-4806
Partners Arnold P. Goodman, Elise Simon Goodman

Adult book length fiction and non-fiction (home 15%, overseas 20%). No reading fee. Founded 1976.

Sanford J. Greenburger Associates Inc.*

55 Fifth Avenue, New York, NY 10003
tel 212-206-5600 *fax* 212-463-8718
Contacts Heide Lange, Faith Hamlin, Beth Vesel, Theresa Park, Elyse Cheney

Fiction and non-fiction, film and TV rights. No unsolicited MSS; query first. No reading fee.

The Joy Harris Literary Agency Inc.*

156 Fifth Avenue, Suite 617, New York, NY 10010-7002
tel 212-924-6269 *fax* 212-924-6609
e-mail jhlitagent@aol.com
President Joy Harris

John Hawkins & Associates Inc.*

(formerly Paul R. Reynolds Inc.)
71 West 23rd Street, Suite 1600, New York, NY 10010
tel 212-807-7040 *fax* 212-807-9555
President John Hawkins, *Vice-President* William Reiss, *Foreign Rights* Moses Cardona, *Permissions* Gladys Guadalupe, *Other Agents* Elinor B. Sidel, J. Warren Frazier, Anne Hawkins

Fiction, non-fiction, juvenile. Founded 1893.

Heacock Literary Agency Inc.*

1523 Sixth Street, Suite 14, Santa Monica, CA 90401
tel 310-393-6277
President Rosalie G. Heacock, *Associate Agent* Robin Henning

Adult non-fiction: self-help, health/medicine, science/technology, philosophy/ psychology, art, women's studies, biography. Fiction including mystery/suspense, action/adventure, mainstream (home 15%, overseas 15%-25%). Will suggest revision; no reading fee but charges for expenses. Works in conjunction with overseas agents. No unsolicited MSS or facsimile submissions. Send synopsis, say why you wrote the book, include bio and 1-2 sample chapters plus sae. Founded 1978.

The Jeff Herman Agency Inc.*

332 Bleecker Street, Suite 631, New York, NY 10014
tel 212-941-0540

Business, reference, popular psychology, computers, health and beauty, spirituality, general non-fiction (home/overseas 15%); will suggest revision where appropriate. Works with overseas agents. No reading fee. Founded 1986.

Frederick Hill Associates

1842 Union Street, San Francisco, CA 94123
tel 415-921-2910 *fax* 415-921-2802
Branch office 8446½ Melrose Place, Los Angeles, CA 90069
tel 213-852-0830 *fax* 213-852-0426

Full-length fiction and non-fiction (home 15%, overseas 20%). Will suggest revision. Works in conjunction with agents in Scandinavia, France, Germany, Holland, Japan, Spain. No reading fee. Founded 1979.

IMG Bach Literary*

22 East 71st Street, New York, NY 10021
tel 212-772-8900 *fax* 212-772-2617

Fiction (no science fiction) and non-fiction. Send query letter with sae for response.

International Creative Management Inc.*
40 West 57th Street, New York, NY 10019
tel 212-556-5600 *fax* 212-556-5665
No unsolicited MSS, please; send query letters.

JCA Literary Agency Inc.*
27 West 20th Street, Suite 1103, New York, NY 10011
tel 212-807-0888
Contacts Jane Cushman, Jeff Gerecke, Tony Outhwaite
Adult fiction and non-fiction. No unsolicited MSS; query first.

Ben F. Kamsler Ltd
5501 Noble Avenue, Sherman Oaks, CA 91411
tel 818-785-4167 *fax* 818-988-8304
Directors Ben Kamsler, Irene Kamsler
Full-length novel MSS, plays, TV specials, screenplays (home 10%, overseas 20%), performance rights (10%). Will suggest revision on promising MSS. No reading fee, but preliminary letter with sae essential. Founded 1990.

Barbara S. Kouts, Literary Agent*
PO Box 560, Bellport, NY 11713
tel 516-286-1278 *fax* 516-286-1538
Full-length MSS. Fiction and non-fiction, children's and adult (home 10%, overseas 20%); will suggest revision. Works with overseas agents. No reading fee. Query first. Founded 1980.

The Lazear Agency Inc.
430 First Avenue North, Suite 416, Minneapolis, MN 55401
tel 612-332-8640 *fax* 612-332-4648
Contacts Jonathon Lazear, Wendy Lazear, Jeff McGuiness, Christi Cardenas-Roen
Fiction: full-length MSS; non-fiction: proposals. Adult fiction and non-fiction; film and TV rights; foreign language rights; audio, video and electronic rights (home 15%, overseas 20%). No reading fee. No unsolicited MSS; 2-3 page query first with sae for response. No faxed queries. Founded 1984.

Lescher & Lescher Ltd*
47 East 19th Street, New York, NY 10003
tel 212-529-1790 *fax* 212-529-2716
Directors Robert Lescher, Susan Lescher

Full-length and short MSS (home 15%, overseas 25%). No unsolicited MSS; query first with sae. No reading fee. Founded 1966.

Ellen Levine Literary Agency Inc.*
Suite 1801, 15 East 26th Street, New York, NY 10010
tel 212-899-0620 *fax* 212-725-4501
Contacts Elizabeth Kaplan, Diana Finch, Louise Quayle, *UK Representative* A.M. Heath
Full-length MSS: biography, contemporary affairs, women's issues, history, science, literary and commercial fiction (home 15%, overseas 20%); in conjunction with co-agents, theatre, films, TV (15%). Will suggest revision. Works in conjunction with agents in Europe, Japan, Israel, Brazil, Argentina, Australia, Far East. No reading fee; preliminary letter and sae and US postage essential. Founded 1980.

Margret McBride Literary Agency*
7744 Fay Avenue, Suite 201, La Jolla, CA 92037
tel 619-454-1550 *fax* 619-454-2156
11684 Ventura Blvd., Suite 956, Studio City, CA 91604
tel 818-508-0031 *fax* 818-508-0039
President Margret McBride, *Vice-President, Associate Agent* Winifred Golden, *Associate Agent (LA office)* Kim Sauer, *Manager of Submissions* Mindy Riesenberg
Full-length and short MSS. Mainstream fiction and non-fiction; no poetry or children's books (home 15%, overseas 25%). No reading fee. Submit query letter with sae to Mindy Riesenberg. Founded 1981.

Gerard McCauley Agency Inc.*
PO Box 844, Katonah, NY 10536
tel 914-232-5700
Specialises in history, biography, science for general reader.

Anita D. McClellan Associates*
50 Stearns Street, Cambridge, MA 02138
tel 617-576-6950
Director Anita D. McClellan
General fiction and non-fiction. Full-length MSS (home 15%, overseas 20%). Will suggest revision for agency clients. No unsolicited MSS. Send preliminary letter and sae bearing US postage or IRC.

McIntosh & Otis Inc.*
310 Madison Avenue, New York, NY 10017
tel 212-687-7400 *fax* 212-687-6894
Adult Eugene H. Winick, Samuel L. Pinkus, *Adult, Subsidiary Rights* Whitney Calam, Sean

Ferrell, *Juvenile* Dorothy Markinko, Tracey Adams, *Film and TV* Evva Joan Pryor

Adult and juvenile literary fiction and non-fiction, film and TV rights. No unsolicited MSS; query first with outline, sample chapters and sae. No reading fee. Founded 1928.

Carol Mann Agency*
55 Fifth Avenue, New York, NY 10003
tel 212-206-5635 *fax* 212-675-4809
Associates Carol Mann, Gareth Esersky, Christy Fletcher

Psychology, popular history, biography, general non-fiction; fiction (home 15%, overseas 20%). Works in conjunction with foreign agents. No reading fee. Founded 1977.

Elaine Markson Literary Agency*
44 Greenwich Avenue, New York, NY 10011
tel 212-243-8480 *fax* 212-691-9014
Directors Elaine Markson, Geri Thoma, Sally Wofford-Girand

Full-length MSS. Literary and mainstream commercial fiction (no genre); biography, sociology, history, popular culture, feminism (home 15%, overseas 20%), performance rights (10%); will suggest revision. Works with overseas agents. No reading fee. Founded 1973.

Mildred Marmur Associates Ltd*
2005 Palmer Avenue, Suite 127, Larchmont, NY 10538-2469
tel 914-834-1170 *fax* 914-834-2840
e-mail marmur@westnet.com
President Mildred Marmur, *Associate* Jane Lebowitz

Serious non-fiction, literary fiction, juveniles, cookbooks. Full-length and short MSS (home licences 15%, overseas licences 20%), performance rights (15%). Works with co-agents in all major countries. No reading fee. Queries must include sae or International Reply Coupons. Founded 1987.

The Evan Marshall Agency*
6 Tristam Place, Pine Brook, NJ 07058-9445
tel 973-882-1122 *fax* 973-882-3099
e-mail esmarshall@juno.com
President Evan Marshall

General fiction and non-fiction (home 15%, overseas 20%). Works in conjunction with overseas agents. Will suggest revision; no reading fee. Founded 1987.

Elisabeth Marton Agency*
1 Union Square, Suite 612, New York, NY 10003-3303
tel 212-255-1908 *fax* 212-691-9061
Owner Tonda Marton

Stage plays only.

Harold Matson Company Inc.*
276 Fifth Avenue, New York, NY 10001
tel 212-679-4490 *fax* 212-545-1224

Full-length MSS (home 10%, UK 19%, translation 19%). No unsolicited MSS. No reading fee. Founded 1937.

Scott Meredith Literary Agency LP
845 Third Avenue, New York, NY 10022
tel 212-751-4545 *fax* 212-755-2972
web site http://www.writingtosell.com
President Arthur Klebanoff, *Vice-President* Lisa J. Edwards, *Director, Subsidiary Rights* Barry N. Malzberg
London office A.M. Heath & Co. Ltd

Full-length and short MSS. General fiction and non-fiction, books and magazines, juveniles, plays, TV scripts, motion picture rights and properties (home 10%, overseas 20%), performance rights (10%). Will read unsolicited MSS, queries, outlines. Single fee charged for readings, criticism and assistance in revision. Founded 1946.

Helen Merrill Ltd*
425 West 23rd Street, Suite 1F, New York, NY 10011
tel 212-691-5326 *fax* 212-727-0545

William Morris Agency Inc.*
1325 Avenue of the Americas, New York, NY 10019
tel 212-586-5100

Multimedia Product Development Inc.*
410 South Michigan Avenue, Suite 724, Chicago, IL 60605
tel 312-922-3063 *fax* 312-922-1905
Contact Jane Jordan Browne

General fiction and non-fiction (home 15%, overseas 20%), performance rights (15%). Works in conjunction with foreign agents. Will suggest revision; no reading fee. Founded 1971.

Jean V. Naggar Literary Agency*
216 East 75th Street, Suite 1E, New York, NY 10021
tel 212-794-1082
President Jean V. Naggar, *Agents* Anne Engel, Frances Kuffel, Alice Tasman

Mainstream commercial and literary fiction (no formula fiction); non-fiction: psychology, science, biography (home 15%, overseas 20%), performance rights (15%). Works in conjunction with foreign agents. No reading fee. Founded 1978.

Ruth Nathan Agency
53 East 34th Street, Suite 207, New York, NY 10016
tel/fax 212-481-1185
Director Ruth Nathan
Fine art, decorative arts, show biz, biographies pertaining to those areas; fiction (Middle Ages only). Home (15%), overseas (10-15%). No reading fee. Founded 1981.

New England Publishing Associates Inc.*
PO Box 5, Chester, CT 06412
tel 860-345-READ *fax* 860-345-3660
e-mail nepa@nepa.com
Directors Elizabeth Frost-Knappman, Edward W. Knappman
Serious non-fiction for the adult market (home 15%, overseas varies), performance rights (varies). Works in conjunction with foreign publishers. No reading fee; will suggest revision – if undertaken; 15% fee for placing MSS. London representative: Scott Ferris. Dramatic rights: **Renaissance**, Los Angeles. Founded 1982.

Harold Ober Associates Inc.*
425 Madison Avenue, New York, NY 10017
tel 212-759-8600 *fax* 212-759-9428
Directors Phyllis Westberg, Emma Sweeney, Wendy Schmalz
Full-length MSS (home 15%, British 20%, overseas 20%), performance rights (15%). Will suggest revision. No reading fee. Founded 1929.

Fifi Oscard Agency Inc.*
24 West 40th Street, New York, NY 10018
tel 212-764-1100 *fax* 212-840-5019
President Fifi Oscard, *Agents* Ivy Fischer Stone, Kevin McShane
Full-length MSS (home 15%, overseas 20%), performance rights (15%). Will suggest revision. Works in conjunction with many foreign agencies. No reading fee, but no unsolicited submissions.

James Peter Associates Inc.*
151 Sunset Lane, PO Box 772, Tenafly, NJ 07670
tel 201-568-0760 *fax* 201-568-2959
e-mail bertholtje@compuserve.com
Contact Bert Holtje

Non-fiction, especially history, politics, popular culture, health, psychology, reference, biography (home 15%, overseas 20%). Foreign rights handled by: Bobbe Siegel, 41 West 83rd Street, New York, NY 10024. Will suggest revision. No reading fee. Founded 1981.

The Pimlico Agency Inc.
Box 20447, Cherokee Station, New York, NY 10021
tel 212-628-9729 *fax* 212-535-7861
Contact Christopher Shepard, *Directors* Kay McCauley, Kirby McCauley
Specialise in general non-fiction and science fiction, horror and fantasy.

Pinder, Lane & Garon-Brooke Associates Ltd
159 West 53rd Street, Suite 14, New York, NY 10019
tel 212-489-0880 *fax* 212-586-9346
London Representative Abner Stein
Specialises in fiction. Writer must be referred by an editor or a client. Will not read unsolicited MSS

PMA Literary and Film Management Inc.
132 West 22nd Street – 12th Floor, New York, NY 10011
tel 212-929-1222 *fax* 212-206-0238
e-mail pmalitfilm@aol.com
President Peter Miller
Full-length MSS. Specialises in commercial fiction (especially thrillers), true crime, non-fiction (all types), and all books with global publishing and film/TV potential (home 15%, overseas 25%), films, TV (10-20%). Works in conjunction with agents worldwide. Preliminary enquiry with career goals, synopsis and resumé essential. Founded 1976.

Raines & Raines*
71 Park Avenue, New York, NY 10016
tel 212-684-5160
Directors Theron Raines, Joan Raines, Keith Korman
Full-length MSS (home 15%, overseas 20%). Works in conjunction with overseas agents. No unsolicited MSS. Founded 1961.

Renaissance – A Literary Talent Agency
9220 Sunset Boulevard, Los Angeles, CA 90069
tel 310-858-5365 *fax* 310-858-5389

e-mail renaissance@earthlink.net
Partners Joel Gotler, Alan Nevins, Irv Schwarz,
Agents Steve Fisher, Brian Lipson
Full-length MSS. Fiction and non-fiction,
plays (home 15%, overseas 20%), film
and TV rights (home 10%, overseas
20%), performance rights. No unsolicited
MSS; query first, submit outline. No
reading fee. Founded 1934.

Helen Rees Literary Agency*
308 Commonwealth Avenue, Boston,
MA 02115
tel 617-262-2401 *fax* 617-236-0133
Contact Joan Mazmanian
Business books, self-help, biography,
autobiography, political, literary fiction
(home 15%). Works with foreign agent.
No reading fee. Submit query letter with
sae. Founded 1982.

Rosenstone/Wender*
3 East 48th Street, New York, NY 10017
tel 212-832-8330 *fax* 212-759-4524
Contacts Phyllis Wender, Susan Perlman Cohen,
Sonia Pabley
Fiction, non-fiction, film and TV rights.
No unsolicited MSS; query first. No read-
ing fee.

Russell & Volkening Inc.*
50 West 29th Street, Suite 7E, New York,
NY 10001
tel 212-684-6050 *fax* 212-889-3206
Contacts Jennie Dunham, Timothy Seldes, Joseph
Regal
General fiction and non-fiction, film and
TV rights. No screenplays. No unsolicit-
ed MSS; query first with letter and sae.
No reading fee.

Susan Schulman Literary & Dramatic Agents Inc.*
454 West 44th Street, New York, NY 10036
tel 212-713-1633 *fax* 212-581-8830
e-mail schulman@aol.com
Agents for negotiation in all markets
(with co-agents) of fiction, general non-
fiction, children's books, academic and
professional works, and associated subsidiary rights including plays, film and
TV (home 15%, UK 7.5%, overseas
20%). Return postage required.

Charlotte Sheedy Literary Agency Inc.*
65 Bleecker Street, New York, NY 10012
tel 212-780-9800 *fax* 212-780-0308
Contact Charlotte Sheedy

Fiction and non-fiction, film and TV
rights. No unsolicited MSS; query first
with outline and sample chapters. No
reading fee.

The Shukat Company Ltd*
340 West 55th Street, Suite 1A, New York,
NY 10019
tel 212-582-7614 *fax* 212-315-3752
e-mail staff@shukat.com
President Scott Shukat, *Contact* Patricia
McLaughlin, Maribel Rivas
Theatre, films, novels, TV, radio (15%).
No reading fee. No unsolicited material
accepted.

Singer Media Corporation
Seaview Business Park, 1030 Calle Cordillera,
Unit 106, San Clemente, CA 92673
tel 714-498-7227
e-mail singer@deltanet.com
Vice-president Helen J. Lee
Interested in foreign language reprint
rights and syndication rights of published non-fiction and fiction.
Represented in most countries abroad
(home 15%, overseas 20%). Published
authors only. No unsolicited MSS; query
first with sae.

The Spieler Agency
154 West 57th Street, Room 135, New York,
NY 10019
tel 212-757-4439 *fax* 212-333-2019
Directors F. Joseph Spieler, Lisa M. Ross,
John F. Thornton
West Coast office 1328 6th Street, Berkeley,
CA 94710
tel 510-528-2616 *fax* 510-528-8117
Principal agent Victoria Shoemaker
Full- and short-length MSS. History, politics, ecology, business, consumer reference, some fiction (home 15%, overseas
20%). No reading fee. Query first with
sample and sae. Founded 1982.

Philip G. Spitzer Literary Agency*
50 Talmage Farm Lane, East Hampton,
NY 11937
tel 516-329-3650 *fax* 516-329-3651
General fiction and non-fiction; specialises in mystery/suspense, sports, politics,
biography, social issues.

Stepping Stone Literary Agency*
59 West 71st Street, Suite 9B, New York,
NY 10023
tel 212-362-9277 *fax* 212-501-8240
President Sarah Jane Freymann, *Associate*
Katharine Sands

Fiction and non-fiction, especially commercial and mainstream fiction (home/overseas 15%). Works in conjunction with Abner Stein and Marsh & Sheil in London. No reading fee. Founded 1974.

Sterling Lord Literistic Inc.
65 Bleecker Street, New York, NY 10012
tel 212-780-6050 *fax* 212-780-6095
Directors Peter Matson, Sterling Lord, Philippa Brophy, Jody Hotchkiss
Full-length and short MSS (home 15%, overseas 20%), performance rights (15%). Will suggest revision. No reading fee.

Gloria Stern Agency*
12535 Chandler Boulevard, Suite 3,
North Hollywood, CA 91607-1934
tel 818-508-6296 *fax* 818-508-6296
Director Gloria Stern
Fiction and films, electronics and multimedia (home 10%, overseas 15%). Reading fee; consultation fee for revisions; some author expenses for placing MSS. Founded 1984.

Roslyn Targ Literary Agency Inc.*
105 West 13th Street, New York, NY 10011
tel 212-206-9390 *fax* 212-989-6233
e-mail roslyntarg@aol.com
Non-fiction: query with outline, publication history and CV. Fiction: query with approx. 50 pages of MS, synopsis or outline, and CV. All submissions require sae. No phone or fax queries. Affiliates in most foreign countries. No reading fee.

Ralph M. Vicinanza Ltd*
111 8th Avenue, Suite 1501, New York, NY 10011
tel 212-924-7090
Contact Ralph Vicinanza, Christopher Lotts, Sharon Friedman, Christopher Schelling
Fiction: literary, women's, 'multicultural', popular (especially science fiction, fantasy, thrillers), children's. Non-fiction: history, business, science, biography, popular culture. Foreign rights specialists. No unsolicited MSS.

Austin Wahl Agency Inc.
1820 North 76th Court, Elmwood Park,
IL 60707-3631
tel 708-456-2301 *fax* 708-456-2031
President Thomas Wahl
Full-length and short MSS (home 15%, overseas 20%), theatre, films, TV (10%). No reading fee; professional writers only. Founded 1935.

Wallace Literary Agency Inc.*
177 East 70th Street, New York, NY 10021
tel 212-570-9090 *fax* 212-772-8979
Director Lois Wallace
Full-length MSS. No cookery, humour, how-to; film, TV, theatre for agency clients. Will suggest revision. No unsolicited MSS; no faxed queries. Will only answer queries with return postage. Founded 1988.

Watkins/Loomis Agency Inc.
133 East 35th Street, New York, NY 10016
tel 212-532-0080 *fax* 212-889-0506
e-mail watkloomis@aol.com
President Gloria Loomis, *Associate* Nicole Aragi, *Contact* Stacy Schwandt
Representatives Abner Stein (UK), The Marsh Agency (foreign)
Fiction and non-fiction, art, film and TV rights. No unsolicited MSS; query first with sae. No reading fee.

Sandra Watt and Associates
8033 Sunset Boulevard, Suite 4053, Hollywood, CA 90046
tel 213-653-2339
Owner Sandra Watt
Lead women's fiction, suspense, mysteries, New Age, cyber-punk; psychological self-help, gardening, single-volume reference works; screenplays (home 15%, overseas 25%), films (10%). Works in conjunction with foreign agents. Will suggest revision; no reading fee; $100 marketing fee for unpublished authors. Founded 1978.

Wecksler-Incomco
170 West End Avenue, New York,
NY 10023
tel 212-787-2239 *fax* 212-496-7035
President Sally Wecksler, *Associate* Joann Amparan
Illustrated books, non-fiction, some literary fiction, children's books (home 12-15%, overseas 20%); will suggest revision where appropriate. No reading fee. Founded 1971.

Rhoda Weyr Agency*
151 Bergen Street, Brooklyn, NY 11217
tel 718-522-0480 *fax* 718-522-0410
General non-fiction and fiction, particularly science, history, biography. Full-length MSS for fiction; proposal for non-fiction (home 15%, overseas 20%), performance rights (15%). Co-agents in all foreign markets. Sae required. Founded 1983.

Writers House Inc.*

21 West 26th Street, New York, NY 10010
tel 212-685-2400 *fax* 212-685-1781
President Albert Zuckerman, *Executive Vice-President* Amy Berkower
Fiction and non-fiction, including all rights; film and TV rights. No screenplays or software. Query first; no reading fee. Founded 1974.

The Wylie Agency Inc.

250 West 57th Street, New York, NY 10107
tel 212-246-0069 *fax* 212-586-8953
e-mail mail@wylieagency.com
Directors Andrew Wylie (president), Sarah Chalfant
Literary fiction/non-fiction. No unsolicited MSS accepted. London office: **The Wylie Agency UK Ltd.**

Mary Yost Associates Inc.*

59 East 54th Street, Suite 72, New York, NY 10022
tel 212-980-4988
Full-length and short MSS (home and overseas 10%). Works with individual agents in all foreign countries. Will suggest revision. No reading fee. Founded 1958.

Susan Zeckendorf Associates Inc.*

171 West 57th Street, New York, NY 10019
tel 212-245-2928
President Susan Zeckendorf
Literary fiction, women's commercial fiction, mysteries, thrillers, science, music (home 15%, overseas 20%), film, TV rights (15%). Works in conjunction with overseas agents. Will suggest revision. No reading fee. Founded 1978.

Overseas literary agents – other

Most of the agents listed here work in association with an agent in London. Before submitting a manuscript, writers are advised to send a preliminary letter and to ascertain terms.

Argentina

International Editors Co.

Avenida Cabildo 1156, 1426 Buenos Aires
tel 541-786-0888/788-2992
fax 541-786-0888/552-5832

The Nancy H. Smith Literary Agency

(formerly Lawrence Smith Agency)
Avenida de los Incas 3110, Buenos Aires 1426
tel/fax 552-5012
Founded 1938.

Australia

Curtis Brown (Australia) Pty Ltd

27 Union Street, Paddington, Sydney, NSW 2021
tel (02) 9331 5301/9361 6161 *fax* (02) 9360 3935
e-mail fiona@5056.aone.net.au

Literary Resources

6/88A Kurraba Road, Neutral Bay, NSW 2089
fax (02) 9909 3752
Principal Doug Nancarrow
Full-length and short MSS, adult fiction (home 10%, overseas 20%), performance rights (10%); will suggest revision. Works with overseas agents. Reading fee. Founded 1992.

Brazil

Agencia Literária Balcells Mello e Souza Riff

Rua Visconde de Pirajá, 414 s1 1108 Ipanema, 22410-002 Rio de Janeiro, RJ
tel (55-21) 287-6299 *fax* (55-21) 267-6393
e-mail lriff@mtec.com.br
Contact Lucia de Mello e Souza Riff

Karin Schindler, Rights Representative

(formerly Dr J.E. Bloch Literary Agency)
Caixa Postal 19051, 04505-970 São Paulo, SP
tel 241-9177 *fax* 241-9077

Canada

Acacia House Publishing Services Ltd

51 Acacia Road, Toronto, Ontario M4S 2K6
tel/fax 416-484-8356
Managing Director Mrs Frances A. Hanna
Literary fiction/non-fiction, quality commercial fiction, most non-fiction, except business books (15% English worldwide, 30% translation), performance rights (15-30%). No science fiction, horror or occult. Works with overseas agents. Reading fee on MS over 200pp, where an evaluation is also provided. Founded 1985.

Authors' Marketing Services Ltd

666 Spadina Avenue, Toronto, M5S 2H8
tel 416-920-1097 *fax* 416-920-5119
e-mail 102047.111@compuserve.com
Director Larry Hoffman
Adult fiction, biography and autobiography (home 15%, overseas 20%). Reading fee charged for unpublished writers; will suggest a revision. Founded 1978.

Anne McDermid & Associates

92 Willcocks Street, Toronto, Ontario M5S 1C8
tel 416-516-2667 *fax* 416-530-1773
e-mail amcdermid@sympatico.ca
Director Anne McDermid
Literary and commerial fiction, narrative non-fiction, film and TV writing (home 10%, overseas 20%). No reading fee. Founded 1996.

Eastern Europe

Artisjus

Mészáros u. 15-17, 1016 Budapest, Hungary
postal address H-1538 Budapest, Pf. 593, Hungary
tel 1-212-15-53 *fax* 1-212-15-52
e-mail artisjus@datanet.hu
Agency for Theatre and Literature of the Hungarian Bureau for the Protection of Authors' Rights.

Aura-Pont, Theatrical and Literary Agency Ltd

Radlická 99, Prague 5, Czech Republic
tel/fax (0422) 53 99 09, 53 63 51
Director Zuzana Jezková
Handles authors' rights in books, theatre, film, TV, radio, software – both Czech and foreign, literary scouting for Czech publishers (home 10%, overseas 15%). Founded 1990.

DILIA, Theatrical and Literary Agency

Krátkého 1, 190 03 Prague 9, Czech Republic
tel (02) 82 68 41-8 *fax* (02) 82 40 09
Theatrical and Literary Agency.

Lex Copyright

Szemere utca 21, 1054 Budapest, Hungary
tel (1) 332 9340 *fax* (1) 331 6181
e-mail lexcopy.bx@mail.datanet.hu
Director Dr Gyorgy Tibor Szanto
Specialises in representing American and British authors in Hungary. Founded 1991.

Lita

Partizánska 21, 815 30 Bratislava, Slovakia
tel/fax 42 7 313645
Slovak Literary Agency.

Andrew Nurnberg Associates Prague, s.r.o

Seifertova 81, Prague 3, Czech Republic
tel (42) 2278 2041 *fax* (42) 2278 2308
e-mail nurnprg@mbox.vol.cz
Contact Petra Tobisková

Prava i Prevodi

Koste Jovanovica 18, 11000 Belgrade, Yugoslavia
tel (11) 460 290 *fax* (11) 472 146
e-mail pipbelyu@eunet.yu
Director Ana Milenkovic
Specialises in representing American and British authors in former Eastern Europe (15 languages). Founded 1983.

France

Bureau Littéraire International Marguerite Scialtiel

14 rue Chanoinesse, 75004 Paris
tel (1) 43 54 71 16
Contact Geneviéve Ulmann

Agence Hoffman

77 Boulevard Saint-Michel, 75005 Paris
tel (1) 43 26 56 94 *fax* (1) 43 26 34 07
e-mail hoffman@starnet.fr

Mme Michelle Lapautre

6 rue Jean Carriès, 75007 Paris
tel (1) 47 34 82 41 *fax* (1) 47 34 00 90
e-mail lapautre@club-internet.fr

La Nouvelle Agence

7 rue Corneille, 75006 Paris
tel (1) 43 25 85 60 *fax* (1) 43 25 47 98
Contact Mary Kling

Germany (see also Switzerland)

Brigitte Axster
Dreieichstr. 43, D-60594 Frankfurt/Main
tel 069-629856 *fax* 069-623526
Full and short MSS: literary fiction and
non-fiction. Works in conjunction with
foreign agents. No reading fee. Queries
must include sae or IRC. Preliminary
enquiry with synopsis and resumé essential. Represents foreign language publishers in German-speaking countries only.

Agence Hoffman
Bechsteinstrasse 2, 80804 Munich
tel 089-308 48 07 *fax* 089-308 21 08

Michael Meller Literary Agency
PO Box 400323, 80703 Munich
tel (089) 366371 *fax* (089) 366372
Full-length MSS. Fiction and non-fiction,
screenplays for films and TV (home 15%,
overseas 20%). Own US office. No reading fee. Founded 1988.

Thomas Schlück GmbH
Literary Agency, Hinter der Worth 12, 30827
Garbsen
tel 05131-93053 *fax* 05131-93045
e-mail schlueckagent@compuserve.com

India

Ajanta Books International
1 U.B. Jawahar Nagar, Bungalow Road,
Delhi 110007
tel 7415016, 2926182, 7258630
fax 91-11-7415016/7132908/7213076
Proprietor S. Balwant
Full-length MSS in social sciences and
humanities (commission varies according
to market – Indian books in Indian and
foreign languages, foreign books into
Indian languages). Will suggest revision;
charges made if agency undertakes revision; reading fee. Founded 1975.

Israel

I. Pikarski Ltd Literary Agency
200 Hayarkon Street, PO Box 4006, Tel Aviv 61040
tel 03-5270159/5231880 *fax* 03-5270160
e-mail pikarski@netvision.net.il
Director Ilana Pikarski
General trade publishing and merchandising rights. Founded 1977.

Italy

Eulama SRL
Via Guido de Ruggiero 28, 00142 Rome
tel (06) 540 73 09 *fax* (06) 540 87 72
Directors Harald Kahnemann, Karin von
Prellwitz, Norbert von Prellwitz, Pina Ocello von
Prellwitz
Quality fiction and non-fiction; Latin
American literature; represents publish-
ers, authors and agencies in Europe and
the world. Founded 1962.

Grandi Associati SRL
Via Caradosso 12, 20123 Milan
tel (02) 469 55 41/481 89 62 *fax* (02) 481 95108
e-mail lgest@mbox.vol.it
Directors Laura Grandi, Stefano Tettamanti
Provides publicity and foreign rights
consultation for publishers and authors
as well as sub-agent services; will suggest revision where appropriate. Reading
fee. Founded 1988.

ILA – International Literary Agency
– USA
I-18010 Terzorio-IM
tel (0184) 48 40 48 *fax* (0184) 48 72 92
e-mail libri.gg@dmw.it
Publishers' and authors' agent, interested
only in series of best-selling and mass
market books by proven, published
authors with a track record. Also interested in published books on antiques
and collectibles. Founded 1969.

Agenzia Letteraria Internazionale
SRL
Via Fratelli Gabba 3, 20121 Milan
tel (02) 86 54 45/86 46 34 18/86 15 72
fax (02) 87 62 22

News Blitz International
c/o G/ Piccione, Via Tonezza 14, 00191 Rome, Italy
tel/fax 36 30 9179
Literary Department Giovanni A. Congiu

Japan

The English Agency (Japan) Ltd
Sakuragi Building 4F, 6-7-3 Minami Aoyama,
Minato-ku, Tokyo 107
tel 03-3406 5385 *fax* 03-3406 5387
Managing Director William Miller
Handles work by English-language writ-
ers living in Japan; arranges Japanese
translations for internationally estab-

lished publishers, agents and authors; arranges Japanese localisations for CD-Rom. Standard commission: 10%. Own representatives in New York and London. No reading fee. Founded 1979.

Orion Literary Agency
1-3-5-3F Kanda-Jimbocho, Chiyoda-ku, Tokyo 101
tel 03-3295-1405 *fax* 03-3295-4366

Netherlands

Auteursbureau Greta Baars-Jelgersma
Clingelbeeck, Utrechtseweg 131-6, NL-6812, AA Arnhem
tel (026) 446 24 31 *fax* (026) 446 21 97
Literature; illustrated co-productions, including children's, art, handicraft, hobby and nature (home/overseas 20%). Works with overseas agents. Occasionally charges a reading fee. Founded 1951.

Internationaal Literatuur Bureau B.V.
Postbus 10014, 1201 DA, Hilversum
tel (035) 621 35 00 *fax* (035) 621 57 71
e-mail mkohn@wxs.nl
Contact Menno Kohn

New Zealand

Glenys Bean Literary Agency
PO Box 47-098, Auckland 2
tel/fax (09) 378-6287
e-mail g.bean@clear.net.nz
Directors Glenys Bean, Fay Weldon
Adult and children's fiction, educational, non-fiction, film, TV, radio (home, UK 15%, foreign rights 20%). Represented by Sanford Greenburger (USA); translations – Sheil Land (UK). Preliminary letter, synopsis and sae required. Founded 1989.

Richards Literary Agency
3-49 Aberdeen Road, Castor Bay, Auckland 9
postal address PO Box 31240, Milford, Auckland 9
tel (09) 410-5681 *fax* (09) 410-6389
Partners Ray Richards, Nicki Richards Wallace
Full-length MSS, fiction, non-fiction, adult, juvenile, educational, academic books; films, TV, radio (home 10%, overseas 10-20%). Preliminary letter, synopsis with sae required. No reading fee. Founded 1977.

Nigeria

Joe-Tolalu & Associates (Nigeria) Ltd
Apt. 4, Tomoloju Estate, 4-6 Yaya Abatam Street, Ogba, PO Box 7031, Ikeja, Lagos
tel/fax 01-4922681
Directors Joseph Omosade Awolalu, Tosin Awolalu, Foluke Awolalu
Full-length MSS: fiction and non-fiction; Christian literature; short MSS: picture books only (home 10-15%, overseas 15-20%; translation 15%, performance/film/ TV 10%); will suggest revision. Works with overseas agents. Preliminary letter essential; no reading fee. Founded 1983.

Portugal

Ilidio da Fonseca Matos
Avenida Gomes Pereira, 105-3°-B, 1500 Lisbon
tel 716 29 88 *fax* 715 44 45

Russia

Prava I Perevody
(Permissions & Rights Ltd, Moscow)
Bolshaya Bronnaya Street 6A, Moscow 103670
tel (095) 203 5280 *fax* (095) 203 0229
e-mail prava@aha.ru
Director Konstantin Palchikov
Specialises in representing US and British authors in Russia, Latvia, Lithuania, Estonia and Ukraine. Founded 1993.

Scandinavia, including Finland and Iceland

A/S Bookman
Nørregade 45, DK-1165 Copenhagen K, Denmark
tel 33 14 57 20 *fax* 33 12 00 07
Handles rights in Denmark, Sweden, Norway, Finland and Iceland for foreign authors.

Gösta Dahl & Son, AB
Aladdinsvägan 14, S-167 61 Bromma, Sweden
tel 08 25 62 35 *fax* 08 25 11 18

Lennart Sane Agency AB
Holländareplan 9, S-374 34 Karlshamn, Sweden
tel 0454 123 56 *fax* 0454 149 20
Directors Lennart Sane, Elisabeth Sane, Ulf Töregård
Fiction, non-fiction, children's books. Founded 1969.

Leonhardt & Høier Literary Agency aps

Studiestraede 35, DK-1455 Copenhagen K, Denmark
tel 33 13 25 23 *fax* 33 13 49 92

Gustaf von Sydow

Lorensbergsvägen 76, S 136 69 Haninge, Sweden
tel/fax 08 776 10 54
Directors Gustaf von Sydow, Elizabeth von Sydow
Handles TV, film, celebrity and news features in Sweden, Norway, Denmark and Finland. Literary agent working in Sweden, Norway, Denmark and Finland. Founded 1988.

Sane Töregård Agency

Holländareplan 9, S-374 34 Karlshamn, Sweden
tel (46) 454 12356 *fax* (46) 454 14920
e-mail toregard@algonet.se
Directors Lennart Sane, Elisabeth Sane, Ulf Töregård
Represents authors, agents and publishers in Scandinavia and Holland for rights in fiction, non-fiction and children's books. Founded 1995.

Singapore

Susan Wakeford Literary Agency

11 Malcolm Road, Singapore 308254
tel/fax (65) 252-0391
Director Susan Wakeford
General fiction/non-fiction. Founded 1996.

South Africa

Frances Bond Literary Services

32B Stanley Teale Road, Westville North 3630, KwaZulu-Natal
postal address PO Box 223, Westville 3630
tel (031) 824532 *fax* (031) 822620
Managing Editor Frances Bond, *Chief Editor* Eileen Molver
Full length MSS. Fiction and non-fiction; juvenile and children's literature. Consultancy service on contracts and copyright. Preliminary phone call or letter and sae required. Founded 1985.

International Press Agency (Pty) Ltd

PO Box 67, Howard Place 7450
tel (021) 5311926 *fax* (021) 5318789
e-mail inpra@iafrica.com
Manager Terry Temple
UK office Ursula A. Barnett, 19 Avenue South, Surbiton, Surrey KT5 8PJ
tel/fax 0181- 390 4414

Literary Dynamics

PO Box 50971, Musgrave 4062
tel/fax (031) 3092913
e-mail literary@saol.com
Managing Editor Isabel Cooke
Full-length MSS, fiction and non-fiction, screenplays. Reading fee for in-depth evaluation. Public speaking consultant, company profiles, project reports, editorial services. Founded 1985.

Sandton Literary Agency

PO Box 785799, Sandton 2146
tel (011) 4428624
Directors J. Victoria Canning, M. Sutherland
Full-length MSS and screenplays; lecture agents. Professional editing. Write or phone first. Works in conjunction with Renaissance-Swan Film Agency Inc., Los Angeles, USA. Founded 1982.

Spain

ACER Literary Agency

Amor de Dios 1, 28014 Madrid
tel 1-369-2061 *fax* 1-369-2052
Directors Elizabeth Atkins, Laure Merle d'Aubigné
Represents UK, US, French and German publishers for Spanish and Portuguese translation rights; represents Spanish- and Portuguese-language authors (home/overseas 10%); will suggest revision where appropriate. £20 reading fee. Founded 1959.

Agencia Literaria Carmen Balcells S.A.

Diagonal 580, 08021 Barcelona
tel 200 89 33, 200 85 65
e-mail ag-balcells@mx2.redcstb.es
Contact Miss Carmen Balcells *fax* 414 23 76
Miss Gloria Gutiérrez *fax* 200 70 41

Mercedes Casanovas Literary Agency

Iradier 24, 08017 Barcelona
tel 212-47-91 *fax* 417-90-37
Literature, non-fiction, children's books (home 10%, overseas 20%). Works with overseas agents. No reading fee. Founded 1980.

Raquel de la Concha

Plaza de las Salesas 9, 1ºB-28004 Madrid
tel 308-55-85 *fax* 308-56-00
Director Raquel de la Concha

Representing foreign fiction, non-fiction, children's books and Spanish authors. No reading fee.

International Editors Co., S.A.
Rambla Cataluña 63, 3°-1ª, 08007 Barcelona
tel 215-88-12 fax 487-35-83
e-mail ieco@abafcrum.es

Lennart Sane Agency AB
Paseo de Mejico 65, Las Cumbres-Elviria,
E-29600 Marbella (Malaga)
tel (9) 52 83 41 80 fax (9) 52 83 31 96
Fiction, non-fiction, children's books, film and TV scripts. Founded 1965.

Julio F. Yañez
Agencia Literaria, Via Augusta 139, 6°-2ª,
08021 Barcelona
tel 200-71-07 fax 209-48-65

Switzerland

Paul & Peter Fritz AG Literary Agency
Jupiterstrasse 1, CH-8032 Zürich
postal address Postfach 1773, CH-8032 Zürich
tel (01) 388 41 40 fax (01) 388 41 30
e-mail info@fritzagency.ch
Represents authors, agents and publishers in German-language areas.

Liepman AG
Maienburgweg 23, CH-8044 Zürich

tel (01) 261 76 60 fax (01) 261 01 24
Contacts Eva Koralnik, Ruth Weibel
Represents authors, agents and publishers from all over the world for German translation rights, and selected authors for world rights.

Mohrbooks AG, Literary Agency
Klosbachstrasse 110, CH-8032 Zürich
tel (01) 251 16 10 fax (01) 262 52 13
Contact Sabine Ibach

Niedieck Linder AG
Zollikerstrasse 87, Postbox, CH-8034 Zürich
tel (01) 381 65 92 fax (01) 381 65 13
Represents German-language authors and Italian-language authors on the German market.

West Indies

CMS Literary Services
PO Box 993, Road Town, Tortola,
British Virgin Islands
tel 284-495-9202 fax 284-495-9043
e-mail maczero@caribsurf.com
Directors Allan McNaught, Ndigo Naka
Children's and adult fiction; Caribbean literature and poetry (10%). Will suggest revision; no reading fee. Willing to work with other agencies in publishing Caribbean writers. Founded 1994.

Literary agents for television, film, radio and theatre

Listings for these and other literary agents start on page 350.

US literary agents

A & B Personal Management Ltd
American Play Company Inc.*
Artellus Ltd
Yvonne Baker Associates
Berman, Boals & Flynn Inc.*
Blake Friedman Literary, TV &
  Film Agency Ltd
Alan Brodie Representation Ltd
Rosemary Bromley Literary
  Agency
Peter Bryant (Writers)

Casarotto Ramsay Ltd
Jonathan Clowes Ltd
Elspeth Cochrane Agency
Rosica Colin Ltd
Jane Conway-Gordon
Cruickshank Cazenove Ltd
Richard Curtis Associates Inc.*
Curtis Brown
Curtis Brown Ltd*
Judy Daish Associates Ltd
Felix De Wolfe

Eddison Pearson Literary Agents
Ann Elmo Agency Inc.*
Fact & Fiction Agency Ltd
Film Rights Ltd
Frieda Fishbein Ltd*
Laurence Fitch Ltd
Jill Foster Ltd
Robert A. Freedman Dramatic
  Agency Inc.*
Samuel French Inc.*
French's

Vernon Futerman Associates
Jüri Gabriel
Eric Glass Ltd
Richard Hatton Ltd
David Higham Associates Ltd
Valerie Hoskins Associates
ICM Ltd
International Copyright Bureau Ltd
Juvenilia
Ben F. Kamsler Ltd*
The Lazear Agency Inc.*
Ellen Levine Literary Agency Inc.*
Barbara Levy Literary Agency
Limelight Management
Christopher Little Literary Agency
Andrew Mann Ltd
Manuscript ReSearch
Martinez Literary Agency

Elisabeth Marton Agency*
Blanche Marvin
MBA Literary Agents Ltd
Scott Meredith Literary Agency LP*
Helen Merrill Ltd*
Richard Milne
William Morris Agency Inc.*
William Morris Agency (UK) Ltd
Multimedia Product Development Inc.*
Fifi Oscard Agency Inc.*
The Peters Fraser & Dunlop Group Ltd
PMA Literary and Film Management Inc.*
PVA Management Ltd
Radala & Associates
Renaissance – A Literary Talent Agency*

Rosenstone/Wender*
Tessa Sayle Agency
Susan Schulman Literary & Dramatic Agents Inc.*
The Sharland Organisation Ltd
Charlotte Sheedy Literary Agency Inc.*
Sheil Land Associates Ltd
The Shukat Company Ltd*
Simpson Fox Associates
Micheline Steinberg Playwrights' Agent
Sterling Lord Literistic Inc.*
Gloria Stern Agency*
Rochelle Stevens & Co.
J.M. Thurley Management
Austin Wahl Agency Inc.*
Warner/Chappell Plays Ltd
Watkins/Loomis Agency Inc.*
A.P. Watt Ltd
Sandra Watt and Associates*

Merchandising agents

A number of agents specialise in the exploitation of characters derived from books, films, television programmes, and so on. This can include selling properties to production companies as well as the handling and developing of any merchandise related to the characters concerned. What follows is a selective listing, both of agents and of properties handled.

BBC Licensing, BBC Worldwide Ltd

Woodlands, 80 Wood Lane,
London W12 0TT
tel 0181-576 2000 *fax* 0181-576 2228
Representing BBC TV and Radio and a selection of copyright owners. Properties: *Animal Hospital, Animals of Farthing Wood, Antiques Roadshow, The Archers, BBC News & Current Affairs, BBC Sport, Blue Peter, Doctor Who, EastEnders, Fawlty Towers, Fireman Sam, Gardeners' World, Grandstand, Keeping Up Appearances, Live & Kicking, Match of the Day, Masterchef, Mr Blobby, Oakie Doke, One Foot in the Grave, One Man & His Dog, Only Fools & Horses, Otis the Aardvark, Pingu, A Question of Sport, Radio 1, Radio 2, Radio 3, Radio 4, Radio 5 Live, Red Dwarf, Stressed Eric, Songs of Praise, Teletubbies, Top Gear, Top of the Pops, Wallace & Gromit.*

Copyright Promotions Ltd

12th Floor, Metropolis House, 22 Percy Street,
London W1P 0DN
tel 0171-580 7431 *fax* 0171-631 1147
Managing Director Richard Culley, *Public Relations Officer* Italo Cerullo
Properties: *Star Wars, Indiana Jones, Young Indiana Jones, Spider-Man, Fantastic Four, Ironman, The Incredible Hulk, Mask Animation, Sky Dancers, Dragon Flyz, Story Store, Judge Dredd, Judge Dredd the Movie, Mr Men and Little Miss, Pink Panther, Sonic the Hedgehog* (Sega); Kate Veal originals: *Oliver Otter & Friends, Cherished Teddies, Reboot, Wind in the Willows, Willows in Winter, Manga Video, Cosmopolitan* (Hearst Magazines), *Boyzone, Dennis the Menace, Desperate Dan, Minnie the Minx, Bash Street Kids, Zig and Zag, X Files, Tank Girl, Mighty Morphin Power Rangers Movie,* England and Wales Cricket Board, Rugby Football

Union, EURO 2000, National Federation of Anglers, Dennis Bergkamp. Founded 1974.

The Copyrights Company (UK) Ltd

Manor Barn, Milton, Nr Banbury,
Oxon OX15 4HH
tel (01295) 721188 *fax* (01295) 720145
London office 7 Square Rigger Row, Plantation Wharf, York Road, London SW11 3TZ
tel 0171-924 3292 *fax* 0171-924 3208
Directors Nicholas Durbridge (Managing), Linda Pooley, Mark Robinson, Julie Nellthorp, Karen Addison

Properties include *Beatrix Potter, Paddington Bear, Brambly Hedge, Postman Pat, Flower Fairies,* and other book-related properties for merchandise licensing.

Hawk Books

309 Canalot Studios, 222 Kensal Road,
London W10 5BN
tel 0181-969 8091 *fax* 0181-968 9012
Director Patrick Hawkey

Properties: *Billy Bunter, Dopey Dinosaur.*

Link Licensing Ltd

7 Baron's Gate, 33-35 Rothschild Road,
London W4 5HT
tel 0181-996 4800 *fax* 0181-747 9452
e-mail info@linklic.demon.co.uk
Directors Claire Derry, David Hamilton

Properties: *Asterix, Barbie, Bug Alert, Camberwick Green, Clatterhappy Ponies, Creature Comforts, The Forgotten Toys, Goosebumps,* Lord's, *The Magic Roundabout,* The Natural History Museum, *Noah's Island, Percy the Park Keeper, The Slow Norris, Teddybears, The Wind in the Willows.* Founded 1986.

Patrick, Sinfield (PSL)

95 White Lion Street, London N1 9PF
tel 0171-837 5440 *fax* 0171-837 5334
e-mail psluk@dircon.co.uk

Directors Christopher Patrick, John Sinfield
Represents properties of: *Rugrats; Clarissa Explains It All; The Ren & Stimpy Show; Rocko's Modern Life; Hey Arnold!; Aaahh!! Real Monsters; Fido Dido, Snoopy, Dilbert; World of Bears, Planet Happy; MTV logo; Beavis and Butt-Head; Garfield; Face Offs; The Mask of Zorro, Zorro – The animated TV series; Crayola; Love Letters, Due South; Are You Afraid of the Dark?; Lettuce the Rabbit.* Founded 1980.

WCA Licensing

18 Beckwith Road, London SE24 9LG
tel 0171-274 6263 *fax* 0171-274 1509
e-mail wca@pro-net.co.uk
Partners Elaine collins and Arabella Woods

Properties include *Coronation Street, Lexx, Tom & Vicky, The Grand, Cracker, Mrs Merton, This Morning* plus a range of celebrity chefs and comedians. Founded 1993.

Michael Woodward Creations

Parlington Hall, Aberford,
West Yorkshire LS25 3EG
tel 0113-281 3913 *fax* 0113-281 3911
e-mail art@mwc.uk.com
Contacts Michael Woodward, Janet Woodward (Licensing Director), Rebecca Sheavyn (Licensing Manager)

International licensing company with own US office and associated offices in Holland, Japan and Australia. Artist management, licensing of design and character merchandise worldwide. Current properties include: *Rambling Ted, Robots in Big Boots, Teddy Tum Tum,* Debbie Cook, Sarah Jane Szikora, Christine Jopling, James Hearne, Debbie Winger. New artists and concepts considered. Send sae with synopsis/illustrations; scripts only not accepted. Founded 1979.

Art and illustration

Freelancing for beginners

Full-time posts for illustrators are not only highly specialised but, sadly, very rare. Because the needs of those who commission illustration tend to change on a regular basis, most artists have little choice but to offer their skills to a variety of clients in order to make a living. **Fig Taylor** *describes the opportunities open to the freelance illustrator.*

As a freelance illustrator you will be entering a hugely competitive arena and a professional attitude towards targeting, presenting, promoting and delivering your work will be vital to your success. Equally crucial is a realistic understanding of how the illustration industry works and of your place within the scheme of things. Without adequate research into your chosen field of interest it is all too easy to approach inappropriate clients – a frustrating and disheartening experience for both parties, to say nothing of its being both expensive and time-consuming.

Who commissions illustration?

Magazines and newspapers

Whatever your eventual career goals, your first stop for research should be your largest local newsagent. Most illustrators receive their first commissions from editorial clients who, whilst offering comparatively modest fees, are actively keen to try out fresh talent. Briefs are by and large fairly loose, though deadlines can be short, particularly in the case of daily and weekly publications. However, fast turnover also ensures a swift appearance in print – positive proof of your professional status to clients in other, more lucrative, spheres. Given then that it is possible to use the editorial field as a springboard, it is essential to appreciate its breadth when seeking to identify your own individual market. Between them, magazines and newspapers accommodate an infinite variety of illustrative styles and techniques. Don't limit your horizons by approaching only the most obvious titles and/or those you would read yourself. Consider also trade and professional journals, free publications and those available on subscription from membership organisations or charities. Remember, the more potential clients you uncover, the brighter your future will be.

Greetings cards

Many decorative, humorous and fine art-biased illustrators are interested in providing designs for greetings cards and giftwrap, where there is a definite market for their skills. As with editorial, fees are unlikely to be high but many small card companies are keen to use new or lesser known artists. You may be expected to produce samples of artwork on a speculative basis prior to receiving a definite commission – therefore it makes sense to target those companies who are likely to be most responsive (see *Card sense*, page 395).

In addition to card shops and the gift departments of larger stores (many of whom employ commissioning buyers for their own ranges), you may find trade fairs such as London's bi-annual Top Drawer and Birmingham's International Spring and Autumn Shows yield the best results for your research. Geared primarily towards buyers, trade fairs offer you the opportunity to check out the forthcoming ranges of numerous card, stationery and giftware manufacturers as well as enabling you to make contacts.

Be warned, however, that most exhibitors will be far too busy selling to go through your work there and then. It is best to make a separate appointment to do this after the fair has ended. For further details, contact Top Drawer organisers, P&O Events, or Trade Promotion Services Ltd, which organise the International Shows.

Book publishing

With the exception of adult illustrated non-fiction, where the emphasis is on decorative, specialist and technical illustration, the majority of publishers are interested in full-colour figurative work for use on paperback and hardback book covers. Strong, realistic work which shows the figure in a narrative context is invaluable to those who commission massmarket fiction, which includes such genres as historical and contemporary romance, thrillers, family sagas, horror, science fiction and fantasy. On the whole, publishing deadlines are civilised and massmarket covers well paid. Illustrators whose work is more stylised or experimental would be better advised to approach those smaller imprints and independent publishing houses which deal with more literary, upmarket fiction. Although fees are significantly lower and commissions less frequent, briefs are less restrictive and a wider range of styles can be accommodated.

Children's publishers use a diversity of styles, covering the gamut from baby books, activity and early-learning through to full-colour picture books, older children's novels with black and white spot illustrations and teenage fiction and non-fiction. Author/illustrators are particularly welcomed by picture book publishers – though, whatever your style, you must be able to draw children well and to sustain a character throughout a narrative. See *Writing and illustrating children's books* on page 256.

Design

It is unnecessary for you to have design training in order to approach a design group for illustration work. However, it is advisable that you be in print. Both designers and their clients – who are largely uncreative and will ultimately be footing the bill – will be impressed and reassured by relevant, published work. Although fees are higher than those in editorial and publishing, this third-party involvement generally means a more restrictive brief. Deadlines may vary while styles favoured range from conceptual through to realistic, decorative, humorous and technical.

For research purposes, look at *Design Week* or the monthly *Creative Review* (both published by Centaur Communications), or the monthly *Graphics International* (published by Market Link Publishing). Design groups have different biases and specialities – for instance, some might concentrate on packaging while others may deal exclusively with corporate and financial literature.

The Creative Handbook (published by Variety Media Publications), available at some reference libraries, carries many listings. Individual contact names are also available at a price from File FX, which specialises in providing creative suppliers with up-to-date information on commissioning clients in all spheres.

Advertising

As with design, you should ideally be quite well established before seeking commissions in advertising. Fees can be high, deadlines short and clients extremely demanding. Advertising agencies currently use significantly less illustration than clients in other areas and have a tendency to 'play safe' stylistically. What little illustration they do commission might be incorporated into direct mail or press advertising, hoardings or, very occasionally, animated for television – fees will vary depending on whether a campaign is locally or nationally based.

Most agencies employ an art buyer to

look at portfolios. A good one will know what each creative team is working on at any given time and may refer you to specific art directors. Agency listings and client details may be found in the *BRAD Agencies & Advertisers* (published by Emap Media) and *ALF* (Account List File, published by Register Information Services), available at reference libraries. File FX can supply individual contact names. Magazines such as *Creative Review* and Haymarket's weekly, *Campaign*, also carry agency news.

Portfolio presentation

Obviously, the more outlets you can find for your talents the better. However, do not be tempted to develop a myriad of styles in an attempt to please every client you see. Firstly it's unlikely that you will and secondly, in the UK market, you'll stand a better chance of being remembered for one strong, consistent style. You'll also get far more commissions that way. Thus, when assembling your professional portfolio, try to exclude samples which are, in your own eyes, weak, irrelevant, uncharacteristic or simply unenjoyable to do – it is worth noting that even published work counts for little if the content is substandard. For maximum impact, aim to focus solely on your strengths. Should you be one of those rare, multi-talented individuals who find it hard to limit themselves stylistically, try splitting conflicting media or subject matter into separate portfolios geared towards different types of clients.

Having no formal illustrative training need not be a handicap providing your portfolio accurately reflects the needs of potential clients. With this is mind, some find it useful to assemble 'mock-ups' using existing magazine layouts. By responding to the copy, working in proportion to original images and replacing them with your own illustrations, both you and the client will be able to see how your work will look in context. Eventually, as you become more established, you'll be able to augment these with published pieces.

Ideally, your folder should be of the zip-up, ringbound variety and never any bigger than A2 as clients usually have very little desk space. Complexity of style and diversity of subject matter will be key elements in deciding how many pieces to include but all should be neatly, consistently mounted on lightweight paper or card and placed inside protective plastic leaves. Professional photographs of originals are acceptable to clients, as are good quality lasercopies or bubblejet prints. However, tacky, out-of-focus snapshots are not. Also avoid including too many sketchbooks and academic studies – particularly life drawings, which are anathema to clients. It will be taken for granted that you know how to draw from observation.

Interviews and beyond

Making appointments can be hard work but clients take a dim view of spontaneous visits from passing illustrators. Having identified the most relevant person to see (either from a written source or by asking the company directly), clients are best approached by letter or telephone call. Most magazines and publishing houses are happy to see freelances, though portfolio 'drop-offs' are becoming increasingly common within the industry. Some clients will automatically take photocopies of your work for their files. However, it is always advisable to have some form of self-promotional material to leave behind – for instance, a full-colour A6 postcard is ideal for this purpose. In the case of larger companies, it is also worth asking your contact if others might be interested in your work. An introduction by word of mouth has a distinct advantage over cold-calling.

Cleanliness, punctuality and enthusiasm are more important to clients than the kind of clothes you wear – as is a professional attitude towards taking and fulfilling a brief. A thorough understanding of what a job entails is paramount from the outset. You will need to know all your client's requirements regarding roughs; format, size and flexibility of artwork; preferred medium and whether the image is

Useful addresses

Centaur Communications
49-50 Poland Street, London W1V 4AX
tel 0171-439 4222
Publishes *Design Week* and *Creative Review.*

Emap Media
Emap Business Communications,
33-39 Bowling Green Lane, London EC1R 0DA
tel 0171-505 8000
Publishes *BRAD Agencies & Advertisers.*

File FX
Unit 14, 83-93 Shepperton Road,
London N1 3DF
tel 0171-226 6646
Specialises in providing creative suppliers with up-to-date information on commissioning clients in all spheres.

Association of Illustrators
1st Floor, 32-38 Saffron Hill, London EC1N 8FH
tel 0171-831 7377
Publishes *Survive – the Illustrators Guide to a Professional Career* and *Rights – the Illustrators Guide to Professional Practice.*

Market Link Publishing
The Mill, Bearwalden Business Park,
Wendens Ambo, Saffron Walden,
Essex CB11 4JX
tel (01799) 544200
Publishes *Graphics International.*

P&O Events Ltd
Earls Court Exhibition Centre, Warwick Road,
London SW5 9TA
tel 0171-370 8210
Top Drawer organisers.

Register Information Services
2 Holford Yard, Cruikshank Street,
London WC1X 9HF
tel 0171-833 3883
Publishes *ALF* (Account List File).

Trade Promotion Services Ltd
Exhibition House, 6 Warren Lane,
London SE18 6BW
tel 0181-855 9201

Variety Media Publications
34-35 Newman Street, London W1P 3RD
tel 0171-637 3663
Publishes *The Creative Handbook.*

to be executed in colour or black and white. You will also need to know when the deadline is. Never, under any circumstances, agree to undertake a commission unless you are certain you can deliver on time and always work within your limitations. Talent is nothing without reliability.

Be organised!

Once your career is off the ground it is imperative to keep organised records of all your commissions. Contracts can be verbal as well as written, though details – financial and otherwise – should always be confirmed in writing and duplicated for your files. Likewise, file away corresponding client faxes, letters and order forms. *Survive – the Illustrators Guide to a Professional Career* and *Rights – the Illustrators Guide to Professional Practice* (both published by the Association of Illustrators) offer artists a wealth of practical, legal and ethical information. Subjects covered include contracts, licences, royalties, copyright and ownership of artwork.

Money

Try not to undertake a commission before agreeing on a fee, although this may not always prove practicable in the case of rush jobs. Most publishing and editorial fees are fixed and, unfortunately, there are no hard and fast rules for negotiation where design and advertising are concerned. As a pointer, however, take into consideration the type of client involved and the distribution of the final printed product – obviously a national 48-sheet poster advertising a well-known supermarket chain is likely to pay better than a local press advertisement for a poodle parlour! Some illustrators find it helpful to work out a daily rate incorporating various overheads such as the cost of computer equipment, rent, heating, materials, travel and telephone charges – while others prefer to negotiate on a flat fee basis. Some clients will actually tell you if they have a specific figure in mind, though you may have to put them on the spot.

Certainly, as you become more established, you'll be able to use comparable jobs as benchmarks when negotiating a fee.

Basic book-keeping – making a simple, legible record of all your financial transactions, both incoming and outgoing – will be vital to your sanity once the tax inspector starts to loom. It will also make your accountant's job easier, thereby saving you money. If your annual turnover is less than £15,000, it is unnecessary to provide the Inland Revenue with detailed accounts of your earnings. Information regarding your turnover, allowable expenses and net profit may simply be entered on your tax return. Although an accountant is not integral to this process, many find it advantageous to employ one. The tax system is complicated and dealing with the Inland Revenue can be stressful, intimidating and time-consuming – not least since the changes regarding 'self-assessment', introduced in 1997. Accountants offer invaluable advice on tax allowances, National Insurance and tax assessments as well as dealing expertly with the Revenue on your behalf – thereby enabling you to attend to the business of illustrating. See *Income tax* on page 659, *Social security contributions* on page 669 and *Social security benefits* on page 677.

Fig Taylor began her career as an illustrators' agent in 1983. For 13 years she has been resident 'portfolio surgeon' at the Association of Illustrators and also operates as a private consultant to non-AOI member artists. In addition, she lectures extensively in Business Awareness to BA and HND illustration students.

Art agents and commercial art studios

Before submitting work, artists are advised to make preliminary enquiries and to ascertain terms of work. Commission varies but averages 25-30%. The Association of Illustrators (see page 479) provides a valuable service for illustrators, agents and clients.

*Member of The Society of Artists Agents

A.L.I. Press Agency Ltd
Boulevard Anspach 111-115, B9–1000 Brussels, Belgium
tel 02 512 73 94 *fax* 02 512 03 30
Director G. Lans
Cartoons, comics, strips, puzzles, entertainment features, illustrations for covers. All feature material for newspapers and magazines. Large choice of picture stories for children and adults. Market for transparencies: paintings, portraits, nudes, landscapes, handicrafts. Interest in video productions.

Allied Artists Ltd
31 Harcourt Street, London W1H 1DT
tel 0171-724 8809 *fax* 0171-262 8526
Director Gary Mills
Represents over 35 artists specialising in highly finished realistic figure illustration for magazines, books, video, plates, prints and advertising. Also offers extensive library of second rights illustrations for syndication.

Arena*
144 Royal College Street, London NW1 0TA
tel 0171-267 9661 *fax* 0171-284 0486
Contacts Tamlyn Francis, Valerie Paine, Alison Eldred
Represents 45 artists working mostly for book covers, children's books and design groups. Average commission 30%. Founded 1970.

Art Solutions
4 Granville Road, Sevenoaks, Kent TN13 1ER
tel/fax (01732) 458917
e-mail buky@centrenet.co.uk
Director Anne Buky

Unusually varied and versatile artwork suitable for reproduction on greetings cards, giftwrap, stationery, ceramics, gifts; children's and adult's publishing. Send sae with samples please. Commission: 30%. Founded 1992.

Associated Freelance Artists Ltd
124 Elm Park Mansions, Park Walk, London SW10 0AR
tel 0171-352 6890 *fax* 0171-352 8125
Directors Eva Morris, Doug FitzMaurice
Freelance illustrators mainly in children's and educational fields; and lots of greetings cards.

Beint & Beint*
3 Richborne Terrace, London SW8 1AR
tel 0171-793 7000 *fax* 0171-735 2565
Illustrations in a variety of styles for advertising, design groups and publishing. Founded 1976.

Sarah Brown Agency
10 The Avenue, London W13 8PH
tel 0181-998 0390 *fax* 0181-843 1175
e-mail sbagency@globalnet.com.uk
Contact Brian Fennelly
Illustrations for publishing and advertising. Sae essential for unsolicited material. Commission: 25% UK, 33.3% USA. Founded 1977.

Central Illustration Agency*
36 Wellington Street, London WC2E 7BD
tel 0171-240 8925/836 1106 *fax* 0171-836 1177
e-mail c.illustration.a@dial.pipex.comm.
Director Brian Grimwood
Illustrations for design, publishing and advertising. Commission: 30%. Founded 1983.

Barry Everitt Associates
23 Mill Road, Stock, Essex CM4 9LJ
tel (01277) 840639 *fax* (01277) 841223
Director Barry M. Everitt
UK/international representation for artists, illustrators and designers seeking high quality markets for their work. Greetings cards, fine art prints, calendars, collectors' ceramics, giftware, books, etc. Sae required for return of work. Member of the Association of Illustrators.

Jacqui Figgis*
Unit 4, Eel Brook Studios, 125 Moore Park Road, London SW6 4PS
tel 0171-610 9933 *fax* 0171-610 9944
Director Jacqui Figgis

Illustrations for advertising, design, publishing and editorial. Commission: 33%. Founded 1986.

Folio Illustrators' & Designers' Agents*
10 Gate Street, Lincoln's Inn Fields, London WC2A 3HP
tel 0171-242 9562 *fax* 0171-242 1816
All areas of illustration. Founded 1976.

Simon Girling & Associates
61B High Street, Hadleigh, Suffolk IP7 5DY
tel (01473) 824083 *fax* (01473) 827846
e-mail info@sga.keme.co.uk
Representing over 50 illustrators, accepting commissions for book publishing (children's and adult), encyclopaedias, magazines, dust jackets, as well as a portfolio of licensed characters. Commission: 30%. Founded 1985.

Graham-Cameron Illustration
The Studio, 23 Holt Road, Sheringham, Norfolk NR26 8NB
tel (01263) 821333 *fax* (01263) 821334
Partners Mike Graham-Cameron, Helen Graham-Cameron
All forms of illustration for publishing and communications. Specialises in educational and children's books. Founded 1988.

The Guild of Aviation Artists
Unit 410, Bondway Business Centre, 71 Bondway, London SW8 1SQ
tel/fax 0171-735 0634
President Michael Turner PGAVA, *Secretary* Hugo Trotter DFC
Professional body of 350 artists specialising in aviation art in all mediums. The Guild sells, commissions and exhibits members' work. Commission: 20%. Founded 1971.

Hambleside Ltd
Winton Road, Petersfield, Hants GU32 3HA
tel (01730) 231010 *fax* (01730) 231117
e-mail hambleside@btinternet.com
Directors D.R. Yellop, R.A. Jeffery, M.G.W. Goodman, W.J.Cumper, R.B. Gamble (USA)
Design studio specialising in all forms of promotional graphics, advertising and marketing. Enquiries from technical illustrators and special effect photographers welcome. Founded 1990.

John Hodgson Agency*
38 Westminster Palace Gardens, Artillery Row, London SW1P 1RR
tel 0171-580 3773 *fax* 0171-222 4468

Publishing (children's picture books) and advertising. Sae with samples please. Commission: 25%. Founded 1965.

Image by Design
First Floor Suite, 17 High Street, Keynsham, Bristol BS31 1DP
tel 0117-986 3066 *fax* 0117-986 3379
e-mail imagebydesign@compuserve.com
Partners John R. Brown, Burniece M. Brown

Artwork for prints, greetings cards, calendars, posters, stationery, book publishing, jigsaw puzzles, tableware, ceramics. Commission: negotiable. Founded 1987.

Kathy Jakeman Illustration*
20 Trefoil Road, London SW18 2EQ
tel 0181-875 9525 *fax* 0181-874 4874
e-mail kji@globalnet.co.uk
web site http://www.users.globalnet.co.uk/~kji

Illustration for publishing – especially children's; also design, editorial and advertising. Please send sae with samples. Commission: 25%.

Libba Jones Associates
Hopton Manor, Hopton, Nr Wirksworth, Derbyshire DE4 4DF
tel (01629) 540353 *fax* (01629) 540577
Contacts Libba Jones, Ieuan Jones

High quality artwork and design for china, greetings cards and giftwrap, jigsaw puzzles, calendars, prints, posters, stationery, book illustration, fabric design. Submission of samples required for consideration. Founded 1983.

Lavapepper Ltd
40 Weir Road, London SW12 0NA
tel (07050) 192354 *fax* 0181-673 4651
e-mail lavapepper@aol.com
web site http://members.aol.com/lavapepper
Directors Izabella Knights, James Muchmore

All styles of illustration considered, including computer-generated and collage. Please send sae with samples. Commission 25-30%. Founded 1998.

John Martin & Artists Ltd
26 Danbury Street, London N1 8JU
tel 0171-734 9000 *fax* 0171-226 6069
Directors W. Bowen-Davies, C.M. Bowen-Davies, B.L. Bowen-Davies, L.A. Bowen-Davies

Illustrations for children (educational and fictional), dust jackets, paperbacks, magazines, encyclopedias, advertising. Return postage with any artwork sent please. Founded 1956.

Meiklejohn Illustration*
28 Shelton Street, London WC2H 9HP
tel 0171-240 2077 *fax* 0171-836 0199
e-mail mjn@mjgrafix.demon.co.uk
web site http://www.demonweb.co.uk/eyesite/index/meikle/lainfo.htm
Contacts Paul Meiklejohn, Malcolm Sanders

All types of illustration.

N.E. Middleton
20 Trefoil Road, London SW18 2EQ
tel 0181-875 9525 *fax* 0181-874 4874

Designs for greetings cards, stationery, prints, calendars and china. Sae with samples, please.

Maggie Mundy Illustrators' Agency
14 Ravenscourt Park Mansions, Dalling Road, London W6 0HG
tel 0181-748 2029 *fax* 0181-748 0353
e-mail 106206.1417@compuserve.com

Represents 25 artists in varying styles of illustration for children's books. Return postage must be included with submissions.

The Organisation*
The Basement, 69 Caledonian Road, London N1 9BT
tel 0171-833 8268 *fax* 0171-833 8269
e-mail organise@easynet.co.uk
Partners Jane Buxton and Lorraine Owen

Various styles of illustration supplied for book work in adult, children's and educational markets. Also for print, advertising, packaging and editorial. Average commission: 30%. Sae essential for unsolicited samples. Founded 1986.

Oxford Illustrators Ltd
Aristotle Lane, Oxford OX2 6TR
tel (01865) 512331 *fax* (01865) 512408
e-mail richard@oxford-illustrators.co.uk
web site http://www.oxford-illustrators.co.uk
ISDN (01865) 310876

Studio of 25 full-time illustrators working for publishers, business and industry. All types of artwork including science, technical, airbrush, graphic, medical, biological, botanical, natural history, figure, cartoon, maps, diagrams, and charts. Artwork supplied as PMT, bromide, film, or on a Syquest, Zip optical disk or ISDN, Mac or PC, with both b&w and colour proofs. Not an agency. Founded 1968.

Pelham Fine Art

(formerly Aspect Art; incorporating Frame Up)
56 Redcliffe Square, London SW10 9HQ
tel/fax 0171-373 9250
e-mail pelham@aol.com
Contact Lady Vanessa Brown

Architectural art in any medium to sell commission or exhibit. Also publishes original limited edition prints. Commission: 35%. Founded 1994; renamed 1998.

Pennant Illustration*

Studio Crown Reach, 149A Grosvenor Road, London SW1V 3JY
tel 0171-630 8914 *fax* 0171-821 5350
Mobile (0850) 865591
e-mail pennant@online.rednet.co.uk
Director Matthew Doyle

Illustrations for publishing, design and advertising. Samples must be accompanied by an sae. Commission: 30%. Founded 1992.

Linda Rogers Associates

PO Box 330, 163 Half Moon Lane, London SE24 9WB
tel 0171-501 9106 *fax* 0171-501 9175
e-mail lr@lrassoc.force9.co.uk
web site http://www.lrassoc.force9.co.uk
Partners Linda Rogers and Peter Sims

Represents 65 illustrators and author/illustrators in all fields of illustration. Specialises in children's books, educational, information books; adult leisure books and magazines. Reply only with sae. Commission: 25%. Founded 1973.

Specs Art

93 London Road, Cheltenham, Glos. GL52 6HL
tel (01242) 515951 *fax* (01242) 518862
e-mail roland@specsart.co.uk
web site http://www.specsart.co.uk
Partners Roland Berry and Stephanie Prosser

High quality illustration work for advertisers, publishers and all other forms of visual communication.

Summer Lane Pictures Ltd

Lower Tower Street, Birmingham B19 3NE
tel 0121-359 6269 *fax* 0121-333 5366
Managing Director Malcolm McGivan

Design-led agency licensing artists' work to manufacturers and publishers in the gift industry; in-house reproduction facilities available. Freelance artists and surface pattern designers are invited to send samples; sae essential. Founded 1993.

Temple Rogers Artists' Agency

120 Crofton Road, Orpington, Kent BR6 8HZ
tel (01689) 826249 *fax* (01689) 896312
Contact Patrick Kelleher

Illustrations for children's educational books, picture strips and magazine illustrations. Commission: by arrangement.

Vicki Thomas Associates

195 Tollgate Road, London E6 4JY
tel 0171-511 5767 *fax* 0171-473 5177
Consultant Vicki Thomas

Considers the work of illustrators and designers working in greetings and gift industries, and promotes such work to gift, toy, publishing and related industries. Written application and b&w photocopies required. Commission: 30%. Founded 1985.

Wavecrest Studios Ltd

3 Grenville Place, London SW7 4RU
tel 0171-370 1209 *fax* 0171-373 8911
e-mail peter@wavcrest.demon.co.uk
web site http://web.ukonline.co.uk/Members/peter.baker/wavecrst/intro.htm
Directors Peter Baker, Keith West

Art and sculpture for collectibles and giftware, fine art prints and posters; licensed character publishing and animation; and for fine art galleries in the USA. Sources art for these markets from its database of over 1000 artists. Actively seeking good new artists for all these fields. Founded 1989.

Wildlife Art Agency

Studio 16 Muspole Workshops, 25-27 Muspole Street, Norwich, Norfolk NR3 1DJ
tel (01603) 617868 *fax* (01603) 219017
e-mail wildlife@paston.co.uk

Illustrations of all things natural, including gardening and food. Clients range from children's/adults' books to design and advertising agencies. Sae must be included with work submitted for consideration. Commission: 30%. Founded 1992.

Michael Woodward Creations

Parlington Hall, Aberford, West Yorkshire LS25 3EG
tel 0113-281 3913 *fax* 0113-281 3911
e-mail art@mwc.uk.com
Proprietor Michael R. Woodward

International art licensing agency with offices in the USA and subsidiary offices in Holland, Japan and Australia. Licenses artists' work for greetings cards, stationery, posters, fine art prints, gift products, etc. Specialist character merchandise division. Freelance artists please send samples with sae. Founded 1979.

Michael Woodward Fine Art
Parlington Hall, Aberford, West Yorkshire LS25 3EG
tel 0113-281 3913 *fax* 0113-281 3911

e-mail art@mwc.uk.com
Proprietor Michael R. Woodward
Artist management. Represents: Mackenzie Thorpe, Sarah Jane Szikora, John Holt. Artists wanting representation in the fine art field should send transparencies of work with biography, plus sae. Founded 1996.

Card sense

*Finding the right outlet for greetings card designs is easier once the market is explained. **William Shone** describes the differences between the two types of greetings card publishers and how to identify which to submit work to.*

The market

There are currently around 800 publishers of greetings cards, from multi-million pound organisations such as Hallmark to small-time sole traders operating at home. Publishers used to produce their own distinct ranges of cards with a common style or design theme but today intense competition has led to poaching of publishing territories in both the designs of cards and the retail outlets where they are sold. The market for artwork can usefully be divided between two broad categories of publisher – wholesale and direct-to-retail. Wholesale publishers produce the cards sold in corner shops, post offices and newsagents. Direct-to-retail publishers produce cards sold in specialist card shops.

The wholesale publisher

Wholesale cards are purchased by retailers from a warehouse or cash-and-carry shop. This type of card is for an occasion such as a birthday or Mother's Day, and carries a message or verse inside. The designs of wholesale cards fall into five main categories:
• 'traditional' – typically a vase of flowers or a country scene
• 'juvenile' – ponies and racing cars

• 'cute characters' – teddy bears
• 'whimsical' – boozy Christmas parties
• 'cute and whimsical' – boozy teddy bears.

Wholesale publishers have recently started to print commissioned contemporary art cards, i.e. cards that do not fit the above categories, but these are still comparatively scarce. Generally, wholesale cards need mass market – as opposed to so-called 'cutting edge' – appeal. Wholesale cards are cheaper to buy than direct-to-retail cards, so volume sales are critical. They have a short life expectancy and the subsequent high turnover of designs means established artists can expect a steady flow of new commissions.

Since wholesale sector cards are designed for a captioned occasion such as Mother's Day, the more occasions a design will fit the better its chances of being published. A teddy bear design for Father's Day might, if suitably executed, be republished at a later date with, say, a 'Happy Birthday Son' caption. Republishing the same design with a new caption will bring the artist a repeat fee.

When wholesale cards are displayed in shops, only the top third is visible because of the way they are stacked. The message and the most striking features of the artwork needs, therefore, to be in this part of the card and arranged in as eye-catching a way as possible – a card only has seconds to attract customers' attention.

Direct-to-retail publishers

Direct-to-retail publishers produce more innovative, some say more creative, ranges of cards than those from the wholesale sector. Each range is identified by a common design theme with a minimum of about eight designs per range. There may be some occasions cards but most of the ranges are blank. Categories of direct-to-retail cards include 'fine art', 'humour', 'children's', 'handmade,' 'contemporary' and 'photographic.' Specialist card shops buy the cards from publishers via agents or representatives.

The commissioned art cards found in the wholesale trade usually mimic trends created by direct-to-retail publishers. Cards produced by direct-to-retail publishers have a contemporary feel drawn from trends in illustration, design, photography and fashion. At the time of writing, bright colours are in as are square cards, hand-made cards, clean lines, alien motifs, smiley faces, floral prints and more besides. The most commercial card designs are original and exciting and ahead of their time, but only by about five minutes – anything too off-beat won't sell. There are some peculiar ranges of humour cards for the under 35's, but original cards that are successful tend also to be uncomplicated and warm.

Targeting

Too much good artwork boomerangs home because artists target unsuitable publishers. Before submitting work, look around card shops to see which card publishers might best suit your designs. The publisher's name, address and telephone number is printed on the back of every card. There is no standard procedure for presenting work so you will need to find out from publishers individually what they expect to see. First of all, telephone and ask if they will look at freelance work. Some of the larger wholesale pub-

Trade magazines

Progressive Greetings
Max Publishing Ltd, United House, North Road, London N7 9DP
tel 0171-700 6740 *fax* 0171-609 4222
Editor Jacqueline Brown
Monthly £30 p.a.
Includes names and addresses of publishers; the editor is keen to tailor the magazine more for artists. Also publishes a directory of services twice a year with some relevant information on agents and copyright consultants and a special supplement on art cards. The editor plans to organise seminars for artists who want to publish their work as greetings cards and she welcomes queries from artists about the greetings industry.

Greetings Magazine
Lema Publishing, Unit No. 1, Queen Mary's Avenue, Watford, Herts. WD1 7JR
tel (01923) 250909 *fax* (01923) 250995
10 p.a. £30 p.a.
Official journal of the Greeting Card Association. Articles, features and news related to the greetings card and giftwrap industry. A new artists' directory lists artists' names, contact details, medium and subject matter with up to 3 colour samples of work reproduced for each. It costs £120 p.a. to advertise in the directory.

lishers only employ in-house designers.

The wider your portfolio of styles the better, but ask whether the publisher prefers to see a range of finished work, some sketches or both. Remember that most designs will need to be in portrait because of the way cards are stacked in shops.

If you are sending work to a wholesale publisher, each design will need to be organised around a caption. It is usual to leave a blank space on the finished design for your suggested caption because, in the event of publication, the caption will be overprinted on the design. Check with the publisher for their requirements.

The majority of direct-to-retail cards are blank but there is a trend now toward captioning. Whereas a wholesale card caption is an overprinted and generally replaceable message, the caption of a direct-to-retail card is integral to the style and feel of that design – a part of the total artwork.

Always include a stamped addressed envelope with work. A colour laser copy, photograph or slide is perfectly adequate for assessment purposes – it is never a good idea to send originals.

The Greeting Card Association has a list of 45 of their members willing to receive freelance work (see also pages 398 and 449). A thoroughly concentrated search can be carried out at the various card and gift fairs which take place throughout the year. The major forthcoming shows are: the Spring Fair at the NEC, Birmingham, Top Drawer at Earls Court, London and the Harrogate Gift Trade Fair. The advantage of visiting trade fairs is that artists can meet the publishers face to face. It is useful to have a supply of business cards at hand. If publishers are too busy with buyers to see your portfolio, you can exchange cards and make an appointment after the fair has ended.

Copyright

Most publishers will pay freelance artists a one-off flat fee of between £175 and £300 per design. Royalties are generally only paid to artists with a long and successful track record in greetings card design. When you make an agreement with a publisher, it is important to have a signed written contract, a copy for each party. In all circumstances artists should retain the copyright of their designs and the ownership of the physical artwork. The licence agreement should specify this and other essential 'ground rules' concerning what a publishing company intends to use the design for (e.g. for only greetings cards or for other merchandise as well), where it will be used (in the UK, Europe, USA, or worldwide) and for how long it will be used. Defining the use and area leaves the artist free to exploit foreign rights without having to ask permission from the client (i.e. the card publisher). For further information on licensing

Further information

The Greeting Card Association
41 Links Drive, Elstree WD6 3PP
tel/fax 0181-236 0024
Contact Leslie Grace
Send an A5 sae for a list of members.

AN Publications
PO Box 23, Sunderland SR4 6DG
tel 0191-567 3589 *fax* 0191-564 1600
e-mail anpubs@anpubs.demon.co.uk
Publishes *Licensing Reproductions* and *Commissioning Contracts*. Price: £3.50 each.

Illustrators, The Association of
First Floor, 32-38 Saffron Hill,
London EC1N 8FN
tel 0171-831 7377 *fax* 0171-831 6277
Publishes *Rights* by Simon Stern, a comprehensive guide to commissioning. Price: £25 plus £1 p&p (non-members); £15 plus £1 p&p (members). (See also page 479.)

Trade fairs

The Spring Fair at the NEC
tel 0181-301 8663

Top Drawer at Earls Court 2, London
tel 0171-370 8210

Harrogate Home & Gift Fair
tel 0171-370 8360

agreements, see *British copyright law* on page 641.

In brief

Before submitting work, decide if you want to target the wholesale or direct-to-retail market, or both. Find out which publishers are suitable for your style(s)/designs and ask how they like work to be presented. If your artwork is accepted for publication or you are offered a commission, be clear about the terms of any proposed agreements.

William Shone has published a range of greetings cards and is now working on projects to develop links between artists and greetings card publishers.

Card and stationery publishers which accept illustrations and verses

Before submitting work, artists are advised to write giving details of the work they have to offer, and asking for requirements.

*Member of the Greeting Card Association

Abacus Cards Ltd*
Gazeley Road, Kentford, Newmarket,
Suffolk CB8 7QB
tel (01638) 552399 *fax* (01638) 552103
Partners Jeff Fothergill and Brian Carey, *Art Director* Bev Cunningham
Quality greetings cards and giftwrap. Most subjects considered; submit artwork or transparencies. Founded 1991.

The Andrew Brownsword Collection
– see Hallmark Cards UK – Bath*

Card Connection Ltd*
Park House, South Street, Farnham,
Surrey GU9 7QQ
tel (01252) 892300 *fax* (01252) 892338
e-mail ho@cardconnection.co.uk
Managing Director Adrian Atkinson, *Product Director* Jonathan Waterson
Cute, humour, traditional, floral, contemporary, sport. Submit artwork, colour copies or 5 x 4in transparencies of originals. No verses. Founded 1992.

Carlton Cards Ltd*
Mill Street East, Dewsbury,
West Yorkshire WF12 9AW
tel (01924) 465200
Marketing Director Keith Auty
Creative Director for Alternative Ranges Ged Backland
All types of artwork, any size; submit as colour roughs, colour copies or transparencies. Especially interested in humorous artwork and ideas.

Caspari Ltd*
9 Shire Hill, Saffron Walden,
Essex CB11 3AP
tel (01799) 513010 *fax* (01799) 513101
Managing Director Keith Entwisle

Traditional fine art/classic images; 5 x 4in transparencies. No verses. Founded 1990.

C.C.A. Art & Design Ltd*
Eastway, Fulwood, Preston PR2 9WS
tel (01772) 662967 *fax* (01772) 662987
Contact Design Department
Designers and manufacturers of greetings cards. Original design ideas including humour, verses for birthday and general occasions considered.

C.C.A. Stationery Ltd
Eastway, Fulwood, Preston PR2 9WS
tel (01772) 662800 *fax* (01772) 662900
Contact Design Department
Designers and manufacturers of personalised wedding stationery and Christmas cards. Pleased to consider original artwork, preferably of relevant subject matter; Christmas verses considered.

The Classic Card Company Ltd – see Hallmark Cards UK – Bath*

J. Arthur Dixon*
Forest Side, Newport, Isle of Wight PO30 5QW
tel (01983) 523381 *fax* (01983) 529719
Managing Director Andy McGarrick, *Head of Design* Carlton Knight
All subjects considered – artwork and photographs (transparencies 35mm or larger). Verses considered. Acquired by **Second Nature Ltd**. Founded 1930.

Gallery Five Ltd*
121 King Street, London W6 9JG
tel 0181-741 8394 *fax* 0181-741 4444
Contact F.C. Yates (art manager)
Send samples which give an idea of style; or phone for an appointment on

the day (i.e. no forward appointments). No verses. Founded 1960.

Gibson Greetings International Ltd*
Gibson House, Hortonwood 30, Telford, Shropshire TF1 4ET
tel (01952) 608333 *fax* (01952) 608363
Marketing Director Jan Taylor

All everyday and seasonal illustrations: cute, humorous, juvenile, traditional and contemporary designs, as well as surface pattern. Greeting card traditional and humorous verse. Founded 1991.

The Gordon Fraser Gallery* – see Hallmark Cards UK – Bath*

Graphic Humour Ltd
4 Britannia House, Point Pleasant, Wallsend, Tyne and Wear NE28 6HA
tel 0191-295 4200 *fax* 0191-295 3916

Risqué and everyday artwork ideas for greetings cards; short, humorous copy. Founded 1984.

Greetings Cards By Noel Tatt Ltd
t/a Noel Tatt Group, Appledown House, Barton Business Park, Appledown Way, New Dover Road, Canterbury, Kent CT1 3TE
tel (01227) 455540 *fax* (01227) 458976
Directors Jarle Tatt, Diane Tatt, Richard Parsons, Ian Hylands

Greetings cards, giftwrap and découpage. No verses. Founded 1988.

Hallmark Cards UK*
Henley office Hallmark House, Station Road, Henley-on-Thames, Oxon RG9 1LQ
tel (01494) 578383 *fax* (01494) 578817
Joint Managing Directors Ian Bant, Homer Kay, *Product and Marketing Director* By Arganbright

Humorous editorial ideas considered, including short jokes and punchlines. No traditional verse. Submit all ideas to the Editorial Department.
Bath office James Street West, Bath BA1 2BS
tel (01225) 444486 *fax* (01225) 444096
Senior Design Manager Nick Adsett

Contemporary, fine art, cute, humorous and traditional imagery reviewed for everyday, spring and Christmas seasons, for greetings cards and other associated products. Submit colour copies, transparencies or preferably original artwork. Please ensure all artwork is named and enclose a sae. No verses or traditional editorial but humorous ideas/jokes/visuals /copy/concepts welcomed. Publishing

Office for The Andrew Brownsword Collection, The Gordon Fraser Gallery and The Classic Card Company.

Hambledon Studios Ltd*
Metcalf Drive, Altham Industrial Estate, Altham, Accrington, Lancs. BB5 5SS
tel (01282) 687300 *fax* (01282) 687404
e-mail hambledon@aol.com
Studio Manager W. Hudson, *Art Managers* D. Jaundrell, K. Ellis, J. Ashton, *Trainee Art Manager* L. Thompson, *Marketing Manager* C. Holmes

Designs suitable for reproduction as greetings cards. *Brands* Arnold Barton, Donny Mac, Reflections, New Image.

Hammond Gower Publications*
14 Tideway Yard, Mortlake High Street, London SW14 8SN
tel 0181-878 5210 *fax* 0181-876 1487
Directors Alan Daly, Nicci Gower

Greetings cards and giftwrap: children's, contemporary, occasions, blank cards. All types of artwork considered: paintings, silk, line drawing, embroidery, etc. Founded 1985.

Hanson White
9th Floor, Wettern House, 56 Dingwall Road, Croydon, Surrey CR0 0XH
tel 0181-260 1200 *fax* 0181-260 1212
Product Development Manager Sarah Garratt

Artwork for greetings cards, giftwrap and related stationery items: humorous, contemporary, design-led. Humorous copy lines, including rude jokes, poems and punchlines; occasionally accept non-humorous verses. Founded 1958.

Images & Editions*
Bourne Road, Essendine, Nr Stamford, Lincs. PE9 4UW
tel (01780) 757118 *fax* (01780) 754629
Directors Lesley Forrow, Maurice Miller

Greetings card artwork: cute, floral, animals. Founded 1984.

Jodds
PO Box 353, Kidlington, Oxon OX5 2UU
tel (01865) 331437 *fax* (01865) 331007
Partners M. Payne and J.S. Payne

Bright contemporary art style greetings cards which include humour; must give out a warm feel. Submit colour photocopies with sae. No verses. Founded 1988.

Jooles Ltd*
Unit 5, St Margaret's Business Centre, Drummond Place, Moor Mead Road, Twickenham, Middlesex TW1 1JN

tel 0181-744 1333 *fax* 0181-891 4295
Product Manager Maggie Waller
Write with sae for submission of artwork.
Artwork for greetings cards: humorous,
traditional, cute. Founded 1988.

Ling Publishing Ltd*
14-20 Eldon Way, Paddock Wood, Kent TN12 6BE
tel (01892) 838574 *fax* (01892) 838676
Head of Publishing Veronica Ross
Artwork for greetings cards; no verses.

M.G. Media
22 Maze Street, Bolton, Lancs. BL3 1SB
tel (01204) 384768
Proprietor Marcia J. Galley
Freelance copywriter and consultant to
writers, publishers and artists in the
greetings card market. Researches publishers' requirements and helps find a
suitable outlet for creative work. All
styles and occasions represented.
Founded 1995.

Medici Society Ltd
34-42 Pentonville Road, London N1 9HG
tel 0171-837 7099 *fax* 0171-837 9152
Contact The Art Department
Requirements: full colour paintings suitable for reproduction as greetings cards.
Send preliminary letter with brief details
of work.

The Paper House Group plc*
Shepherd Road, Gloucester, Glos. GL2 6EL
tel (01452) 423451 *fax* (01452) 410312
Creative Director Chris Wilcox
Publishers of greetings cards depicting
old masters, the Impressionists, contemporary artists and humorous themed cartoon illustration.

Paperlink Ltd*
356 Kennington Road, London SE11 4LD
tel 0171-582 8244 *fax* 0171-587 5212
Directors Louise Tighe, Jo Townsend, Tim Porte,
Tim Purcell
Publishers of ranges of humorous and
contemporary art greetings cards,
giftwrap, calendars, notelets, mugs,
prints. Produce products under licence
for charities. Founded 1986.

Pepperpot
Godalming Business Centre, Woolsack Way,
Godalming, Surrey GU7 1XW
tel (01483) 426277 *fax* (01483) 426947
e-mail info@waverley.com
Publishing Controller Kate Gorman, *Design*

Manager Debborah Granger
Gift stationery (calendars, notecards, giftwrap). Colour illustrations; cute/tradi-
tional/floral. Submit original artwork or
5 x 4in transparencies. No verses.
Division of Quadrillion Publishing Ltd.

Pineapple Park Ltd
E1 Knowl Piece, Wilbury Way, Hitchin,
Herts. SG4 0TY
tel (01462) 442021 *fax* (01462) 440418
Directors Peter M. Cockerline, Sarah M. Parker
Illustrations and photographs for
publication as greetings cards (5 x 4in
and $6^1/_2$ x $6^1/_2$in). Contemporary, cute,
humour: submit artwork or laser copies
with sae. Transparencies of animals and
babies. No verses.

Pomegranate Europe Ltd
Fullbridge House, Fullbridge, Maldon,
Essex CM9 4LE
tel (01621) 851646 *fax* (01621) 852426
Sales Director Dave Harris
Contemporary art for cards, calendars
and gift stationery. Will consider original
artwork or transparencies of originals.
Founded 1993.

postLEEDS
4 Granby Road, Leeds LS6 3AS
tel/fax 0113-226 8726
e-mail leedspostcards@geo2.poptel.org.uk
web site http://www.poptel.org.uk/leedspostcards
Contact Christine Hankinson
Publisher and distributor of postcards.
Sold to individuals by mail order and to
overseas distributors. Artwork and
apherisms that challenge, subvert and
amuse. Must be politically aware (to the
Left). See web site. Founded 1979.

Nigel Quiney Publications Ltd*
Cloudesley House, Shire Hill, Saffron Walden,
Essex CB11 3FB
tel (01799) 520200 *fax* (01799) 520100
Contact Ms J. Arkinstall
Everyday and seasonal greetings cards
(sizes: 7 x 5in, 9 x 6in and 12 x 9in) and
giftwrap. Submit original artwork or
5 x 4in transparencies of originals.

Rainbow Cards Ltd*
Albrighton Business Park, Newport Road,
Albrighton, Wolverhampton,
West Midlands WV7 3ET
tel (01902) 374347
Directors M. Whitehouse, J. Whitehouse,
I. Mackintosh

Artwork for humorous greetings cards and verses. Founded 1977.

The Really Good Card Company Ltd*
Osney Mead, Oxford OX2 0ES
tel (01865) 246888 *fax* (01865) 246999
Director David Hicks
Do not send original artwork; send photocopies or snapshots with sae. No verses. Founded 1987.

Felix Rosenstiel's Widow & Son Ltd
Fine Art Publishers, 33-35 Markham Street, London SW3 3NR
tel 0171-352 3551
Invites offers of original oil paintings and strong watercolours of a professional standard for reproduction as picture prints for the picture framing trade. Any type of subject considered; send photographs of work.

Royle Publications Ltd – see The Paper House Group plc

Santoro Graphics Ltd
342-344 London Road, Cricket Green, Mitcham, Surrey CR4 3ND
tel 0181-640 9777 *fax* 0181-640 2888
Directors Lucio Santoro, Meera Santoro (art)
Publishers of innovative and award-winning designs for greetings cards, giftwrap and gift stationery. Bold contemporary images with an international appeal. Subjects covered: quirky and humorous, whimsical, 'Fifties, 'Seventies, futuristic! Submit photographs or colour photocopies. Founded 1985.

Scandecor Ltd*
3 The Ermine Centre, Hurricane Close, Huntingdon, Cambs. PE18 6XX
tel (01480) 456395 *fax* (01480) 456269
Director G. Huldtgren
Drawings all sizes. Founded 1967.

Second Nature Ltd*
10 Malton Road, London W10 5UP
tel 0181-960 0212 *fax* 0181-960 8700
Marketing/Publishing Director Rod Schragger
Contemporary artwork for greetings cards; jokes for humorous range; short modern sentiment; verses. Founded 1981.

W.N. Sharpe Ltd – see **Hallmark Cards UK***

Solomon & Whitehead Ltd
Lynn Lane, Shenstone, Staffs. WS14 0DX
tel (01543) 480696 *fax* (01543) 481619
Fine art prints and limited editions, framed and unframed.

Noel Tatt Appeals
57 Coombe Valley Road, Dover, Kent CT17 0EX
tel (01304) 213999 *fax* (01304) 240151
Directors B.W. Powell (chairman), T.J. Paulett (managing)
Greetings card publishers. Interested in Christmas designs for the charity card market. Division of Powell Print Ltd.

Valentines – see **Hallmark Cards UK***

Webb Ivory (Burton) Ltd
Queen Street, Burton-on-Trent, Staffs. DE14 3LP
tel (01283) 566311
High quality Christmas cards and paper products.

A serious look at marketing cartoons

There are many freelance opportunities for comic artists and illustrators. **John Byrne** *explores potential markets and offers guidance for success.*

Although in the business of being funny, cartoonists can be quite a morose bunch, bemoaning the passing of the original *Punch* and complaining that the market for general cartoons is growing smaller. Yet many of the most lucrative merchandising properties in recent years, from *Garfield* to *Judge Dredd*, started life as cartoons. Freelance cartooning has its share of ups and downs, but there are still many opportunities for comic artists and for illustrators and writers, too. Many cartoonists are certainly accomplished artists, but today funny ideas and sharp captions are just as important as the visuals. Writers with comic flair may consider collaborating with an artist or even trying their own simple drawings.

Research and presentation

See page 405 for *Newspapers and magazines which accept cartoons.*

Study the publication you are planning to submit to. What cartoon subjects feature most frequently, especially for joke or 'gag' cartoons (see 'Markets', below): married couples? children? animals? Are all the cartoons domestic or office based, or is there a mixture? Are the characters drawn in semi-realistic or more distorted styles? Are the jokes mainly in the captions or is the humour visual?

Be aware of changing fashions in humour. Thanks to Gary Larson's *The Far Side* the pun, formerly derided as a low form of wit, is currently very much in vogue. Consider technical details: Are the cartoons colour or black and white? What shape are they? It is pointless sending portrait-shaped cartoons to publications that only use landscape ones.

While most magazines still typeset cartoon captions, some now accept hand-drawn captions or balloons. Avoid spelling mistakes for which cartoonists are notorious and which often result in rejection of otherwise saleable drawings. This can also happen if a clever cartoon becomes illegible when reduced to printed size. Editors often squeeze cartoons into very small spaces – be sure your drawings are simple and bold enough to survive reduction.

It is useful to have a knowledge of copyright and libel. See *British copyright law* on page 641 and *Libel* on page 651.

Submitting cartoons

A preliminary letter saves wasted effort and can yield useful information. Busy editors find unsolicited phone calls very unamusing – but one call you will need to make is to check exactly who to address your letter to: full-time cartoon editors are rare and the person who chooses cartoons can be anyone from the art director to the person in charge of the puzzle page. Sending a number of cartoons together increases the chance of at least one being accepted, but quality is better than quantity. A few good jokes will get a better response when the editor doesn't have to extract them from a mountain of 'fillers'.

Rejections

While current fashions in cartoons encompass a wide range of styles, both

Useful organisations

For specialist advice, and to meet other members of what can be a solitary profession, make contact with:

Cartoon Art Trust
67-68 Hatton Gardens, London EC1N 8JY
tel 0171-405 4717

The Cartoonists' Guild and The Cartoonists' Club of Great Britain
46 Strawberry Vale,
Twickenham TW1 4SE
tel 0181-892 3621

Comics Creators Guild
48 Siddons Road, London SE23 2JQ
tel/fax 0181-699 4012

visual and in terms of being funny, humour is still very subjective. Rejections are a fact of life for even the most successful cartoonists, but one editor's rejected cartoon may be snapped up by another publication.

One way to lessen the sting is to have several submissions on the go at once. A strong pre-paid envelope will ensure that work comes back in one piece, ready for its next expedition. (Put your name and address on the back of each cartoon in case it gets detached from the main bundle.) If you are sending lots of cartoons back and forth to different publications it is wise to create a filing system. Otherwise you'll inevitably receive the dreaded response 'You've sent this one before ... and it wasn't funny the first time'.

Markets

General gag cartoons

The demise of the *Cartoonist, Squib* and other brave attempts to launch cartoon magazines in the wake of *Punch* may have suggested that the traditional gag cartoon is an endangered species. However, *Punch* has been resurrected and magazines like *Private Eye* and the *Spectator* still publish joke or gag cartoons alongside more topical items, and new cartoon magazines continue to appear.

Topical cartoons

Topical cartoons are a good market for the quick-witted artist. Remember that the cartoon must still be topical on the day it is published. This is (relatively) easy if the cartoon is for a newspaper coming out the next day, but a topical cartoon can become very outdated in the time it takes a weekly or fortnightly magazine to publish. Faxing roughs to the editor can save time. If accepted, you may need to produce finished artwork to very tight deadlines.

Try to get your cartoons back after publication – people featured in topical cartoons sometimes ask to buy the original artwork.

Specialist and trade publications

This is an under-exploited market for cartoonists who are able to tailor jokes to particular subjects – but remember you are dealing with an expert audience. A stereotypical cartoon chef may suffice for general cartoons, but you'd better get the terminology and different uniforms right for *Bakery World* or *Catering*.

Try creating your own markets. Think about jobs you've had, past or present, or your particular sports, hobbies and interests. No matter how obscure, there may be a related publication just waiting to be brightened up by your combination of cartoon skills and specialist knowledge.

Regular comic strips and syndication

For regular comic strips or cartoon features, editors need to see that you can produce not only funny material but that you can maintain a consistent output. Submit a good supply of roughs along with examples of finished cartoons to show that you can sustain the idea. The same applies when approaching a syndicate with your strip and feature ideas (see *Syndicates, news and press agencies* on page 149). Cartoons may be in syndication for a long time, and in different countries, so very topical humour and local references are best avoided. If cartoons are syndicated in other languages humour based on verbal puns may not translate very well.

Other

Card and stationery publishers which accept illustrations and verses on page 398 and *Merchandising agents* on page 385 should suggest other markets for cartoons. Cartoons are often used to illustrate books for both adults and children (listings of *Book publishers UK and Ireland* start on page 157 and *Book packagers* start on page 220). Some of the *Art agents and commercial art studios* listed on page 391 represent cartoonists.

Cartoon sites on the Internet are some of the most frequently visited and cartoonists selling their wares through this new medium have reported very good responses.

Finally ...

The life of a full-time funny person can be precarious, but properly researching and tailoring work to specific markets and adopting an organised approach to submissions should greatly reduce your rejection collection.

John Byrne combines his own writing and drawing career with internationally acclaimed training workshops on cartooning and comedy writing.

Further reading

John Byrne, *Drawing Cartoons that Sell*, HarperCollins, 1997

John Byrne, *Learn to Draw Cartoons*, HarperCollins, 1995

Hall, Robin, *The Cartoonist's Workbook*, A & C Black, 1995

Steve Whitaker, *The Encyclopaedia of Cartooning Techniques*, Headline, 1994

Newspapers and magazines which accept cartoons

Listed below are newspapers and magazines which take cartoons – either occasionally, or on a regular basis. Approach in writing in first instance (see listings starting on pages 3, 11 and 21 for addresses) to ascertain the editor's requirements.

Newspapers and colour supplements

Aberdeen Evening Express
Birmingham Evening Mail
Daily Mail
Daily Mirror
Daily Sport
Evening Echo
Evening Gazette
The Evening Press
Glasgow Evening Times
Grimsby Evening Telegraph
The Guardian Weekend
Hartlepool Mail
The Herald
The Independent Magazine
Independent on Sunday
The Journal
Lancashire Evening Post
Liverpool Echo
Mail on Sunday
The News, Portsmouth
Nottingham Evening Post
The Scotsman
South Wales Echo
The Star
The Sun
Sunday Mail
The Sunday Times
Telegraph Magazine
The Times
Western Daily Press
The Western Mail
Yorkshire Evening Post
Yorkshire Post
Young Telegraph

Consumer and special interest magazines

Aeroplane Monthly
Amateur Photographer
The Aquarist and Pondkeeper
Back Street Heroes
BBC Music Magazine
BBC Vegetarian GoodFood
Bella
Best
Big!
Bike
Boards
Bowls International
Bridge Magazine
British Chess Magazine
Bunty
Buster
Cage and Aviary Birds
Catholic Gazette
Catholic Pictorial
Cencrastus
Chapman
Church of England Newspaper
Classic Cars
Classic CD
Computer Weekly
Computing
The Countryman
Country-Side
Current Affairs Bulletin (Aus.)
The Dandy
Darts World
Dirt Bike Rider
Disability Now
Dogs Today
East Lothian Life
The Edge
The European
Everyday with Practical
   Electronics
Fishing World Magazine (Aus.)
Football Picture Story Library

Fore!
Fortean Times
Garden News
Gay Times
Golf Monthly
Golf World
Guiding
Health & Efficiency
   International
Herald of the South (Aus.)
Here's Health
Home and Country
Home Words
Horse & Pony
Index on Censorship
Ireland of the Welcomes
Jewish Telegraph
Kids Alive!
Life and Work
Live & Kicking Magazine
Making Music
Men Only
Modus
Motor Boat and Yachting
Motor Caravan Magazine
Musical Opinion
Musical Teacher
My Weekly Puzzle Time
(Napier) The Daily Telegraph
   (NZ)
New Christian Herald
New Internationalist
New Musical Express
New Statesman
The New Welsh Review
New World
New Zealand Farmer (NZ)
The Oldie
Opera Now
Organic Gardening
Overland (Aus.)
Park Home & Holiday Caravan
Performance Car
Picture Postcard Monthly
Planet

Poetry Review
Practical Photography
Pride
Priests & People
Private Eye
Punch
Red Pepper
Reform
Runner's World
Satellite Times
The Scots Magazine
Scottish Home and Country
Scouting
She
Sight and Sound
Smallholder
Snooker Scene
The Spectator
The Squash Player
Steam Classic
Sugar
The Tablet
Take a Break
Titbits
Today's Runner
Tribune
Trout and Salmon
Twinkle
The Universe
The Vegan
Viz
The Voice
Vox
War Cry

Waterways World
The Weekly Journal
The Weekly News
Weight Watchers Magazine
West Lothian Life
What's on TV
Woman
The Word (Ire.)
World Soccer
Yachting Monthly
Yachting World
Young People Now
Young Writer
Yours

Business and professional magazines

Accountancy
African Business
Air International
Army Quarterly & Defence
   Journal
Art Business Today
The Author
British Journal of General
   Practice
British Printer
Broadcast
Building Design
Carers World
Child Education
Control & Instrumentation

CTN
Drapers Record
The Economist
Education
Electrical Review
Electrical Times
Financial Adviser
Hospitality
HouseBuilder
International Construction
Irish Medical Times
Journalist
Justice of the Peace
Local Government Chronicle
Marketing Week
Mobile and Cellular Magazine
Nursing Times and Nursing
   Mirror
Office Secretary
PCS, The Magazine
Pig Farming
Pilot
Police Review
Post Magazine
Printing World
Publishing News
Solicitors Journal
Therapy Weekly
The Times Educational
   Supplement
Writers' Forum

Photography and picture research

The freelance photographer

*Many photographers make the mistake of thinking that technical perfection and creativity alone will take them to the top, but even the most well-known photographers continually have to sell themselves to maintain a strong foothold in this highly competitive profession. **Bruce Coleman** and **Ian Thraves** discuss possibilities for the freelance photographer.*

Becoming a successful freelance photographer is as much about marketing as photographic talent. Having an outstanding portfolio is one thing, but to receive regular commissions takes a good business head and sound market knowledge. Although working as a professional photographer can be tough, it is undoubtedly one of the most interesting and rewarding ways of earning a living.

Entering professional photography

A good starting point is to embark on one of the many college courses available, which range from GCSE to degree level, and higher. These form a good foundation, though most teach only the technical aspects of photography and very few cover the basics of running a business. But a good college course will provide students with the opportunity to become familiar with photographic equipment and develop skills without the restrictions and pressures found in the workplace.

In certain fields, such as commercial photography, it is possible to learn the trade as an assistant to an established photographer. A photographer's assistant will undertake many varied tasks, including preparing camera equipment and lighting, building sets, obtaining props and organising locations, as well as general mundane chores. It usually takes only a year or two for an assistant to become a fully competent photographer, having during that time learnt many technical aspects of a particular field of photography and the fundamentals of running a successful business. There is, however, the danger of a long-standing assistant becoming a clone of the photographer worked for, and it is for this reason that some assistants prefer to gain experience with other photographers rather than working for just one for a long period of time. The Association of Photographers can help place an assistant.

However, in other fields of photography, such as photojournalism or wildlife photography, an assistant is not generally required, and photographers in these fields have to learn for themselves as they work.

Identifying your market

From the outset, identify which markets are most suitable for the kind of subjects you photograph. Study each market carefully and only offer images which suit the client's in-house requirements.

Usually photographers who specialise in a particular field do better than those who generalise. By concentrating on one or two subject areas they become expert at what they do. Those who make a name for themselves are invariably specialists, and it is far easier for the images of, for example, an exceptional fashion photographer or an award-winning wildlife photographer to be remembered than the work of someone who covers a broad range of subjects.

In addition, photographers who produce work with individual style (e.g. by experimenting with camera angles or manipulating film to create unusual effects) are far more likely to make an impact. Alternative images which attract attention and can help sell a product are always sought after. This is especially true of advertising photography, but applies also to other markets such as book and magazine publishers, who are always seeking eye-catching images to use on front covers.

Promoting yourself

Effective self-promotion tells the market who you are and what service you offer. A first step should be to create an outstanding portfolio of images, tailored to appeal to the targeted market. Photographers targeting a few different markets should create an individual portfolio for each rather than presenting a single general one, including only a few relevant images. A portfolio containing between 10 and 20 images is enough for a potential client to judge a photographer's abilities.

Images should be presented in a format which the client is used to handling. Transparencies (perhaps duplicated to a larger size for easier viewing and general impact) are usually suitable for the editorial markets, but often more general companies prefer to view high-quality prints. Images can also be presented on CD-Rom. Any published material (often referred to as 'tear sheets') should also be added to a portfolio. Tear sheets are often presented mounted and laminated in plastic.

Business cards and letterheads should be designed to reflect style and professionalism. Consider using a good graphic designer to design a logo for use on cards, letterheads and any other promotional literature. Many photographers produce postcard-size business cards and include an image as well as their name and logo.

Other than word of mouth, advertising is probably the best way of making your services known to potential clients. For a local market, a business directory such as *Yellow Pages* is a good start. Specialist directories in which photographers can advertise include *The Creative Handbook* and *Contact Photographers*. Cold calling by telephone can also be a very productive way of making contacts, and these should be followed up by an appointment for a personal visit (if possible) in order to show a portfolio of images. This helps to ensure you will not be forgotten.

A well-organised exhibition of images is a very effective way of bringing your work to the attention of current and potential new clients. Throw a preview party with refreshments for friends, colleagues and specially invited guests from the industry. A show which is well reviewed by critics who write for newspapers and magazines can generate additional interest. Many photographic organisations have regular exhibitions. An excellent example is the Photographers Gallery in London, where work selected by the gallery board is exhibited free.

As a photographer's career develops, the budget for self-promotion should increase. Many established photographers will go as far as producing full-colour mailers, posters, and even calendars, which all contain examples of their work.

Digital photography

Digital photography and image-enhancement and manipulation using computer technology are now widely used in the photographic industry. Since the cost of digital cameras (which do not require film) and other hardware can be considerably cheaper than using large quantities of film, many studio photographers are now using this technology for large photographic shoots, such as product photography for catalogue companies. Image-enhancement and manipulation using a computer program such as Adobe Photoshop provides photographers with an on-screen darkroom where the possibilities for creating imaginative images are endless. As well as being useful for retouching purposes and creating photo compositions, it provides the photographer with an opportunity to create more unusual images. It is therefore especially useful for targeting the advertising market, where fantasy images are more important than reality.

Using a stock library

As well as undertaking commissions, photographers have the option of selling their images through a photographic stock library or agency. There are many stock libraries in the UK, some specialising in specific subject areas, such as wildlife photography, and others covering general subjects (see *Picture agencies and libraries*, page 412).

Stock libraries are fiercely competitive, all fighting for a share of the market, and it is therefore best to aim to place images with an established name, although competition amongst photographers will be strong. Each stock library has different specific requirements and established markets, so contact them first before making a submission. Some libraries will ask to see a few hundred images from a photographer in order to judge for consistency of quality and saleability. Stock libraries selling images through catalogues or over the Internet will often consider an initial submission of just a few images, knowing that it is possible to accumulate significant fees from a small number of outstanding individual images marketed this way.

Images placed with a library remain the property of the photographer and libraries do not normally sell images outright to clients, but lease them for a specific use for a fee, from which commission is deducted. This means that a single image can accumulate many sales over a period of time. The commission rate is usually about 50% of every sale generated by the library. This may sound high, but it should be borne in mind that the library takes on all overheads, marketing costs and other responsibilities involved in the smooth running of a business, allowing

Professional organisations

It may be worthwhile joining one of the reputable photographic organisations. For an annual fee, these offer services to photographers such as legal support, and also organise events where photographers can get together and share information.

Association of Photographers
Co-Secretary Gwen Thomas, 9-10 Domingo Street, London EC1Y 0TA
tel 0171-608 1441 *fax* 0171-253 3007
Protects and promotes the interests of fashion advertising and editorial photographers. Produces (amongst many other things) a prestigious annual photographic awards book, and can also help its members find anything from a model agency to an assistant. Annual subscription: £72-£355, depending on turnover.

BAPLA (British Association of Picture Libraries and Agencies)
See page 462.

British Institution of Professional Photography
Amwell End, Ware, Herts. SG12 9HN
tel (01920) 464011
See page 488.

Master Photographers Association
Hallmark House, 2 Beaumont Street, Darlington, Co. Durham DL1 5SZ
tel (01325) 356555 *fax* (01325) 357813
e-mail generalenquiries@mpauk.demon.co.uk
Promote and protects professional photographers. Members qualify for awards of Licentiate, Associate and Fellowship. Annual subscription: £99.

The Royal Photographic Society
The Octagon, Milsom Street, Bath BA1 1DN
tel (01225) 462841 *fax* (01225) 448688
e-mail rps@rps.org
web site http://www.rps.org
Open membership organisation which promotes the art and science of photography and electronic imagery; publishes *The Photographic Journal* (monthly) and the *Imaging Science Journal* (quarterly).

the photographer the freedom to spend more time taking pictures.

Photographers should realise, however, that stock photography is a long-term investment and it can take some time for sales to build up to a significant income. Clearly, photographers who supply the right images for the market, and are prolific, are those who do well, and there are a good number of photographers who make their entire living as full-time stock photographers, never having to undertake commissioned work.

Royalty-free CD companies

In recent years, a number of companies have started marketing royalty-free images on CD-Rom. These companies obtain images by purchasing them from photographers for a flat fee. Once a CD has been purchased by a client (usually at very low cost) they, in effect, own the images on the CD and are therefore able to reproduce them as many times as they wish, paying no further fees. Some royalty-fee companies, however, do pay to photographers royalties related to CD sales in addition to a flat fee for the images. A typical CD usually contains approximately one hundred high-resolution reproduction-quality images in a variety of subject areas, including most specialist subjects.

Although photographers may be tempted to sell images to these companies in order to gain an instant fee, they should be aware that placing images with a traditional stock library can be far more fruitful financially in the long term, since a good image can accumulate very high fees over a period of time and go on selling for many years to come. Furthermore, the photographer always retains the rights to his or her own images.

Running your own library

Photographers choosing to market their own images or start up their own library have the advantage of retaining a full fee for every picture sale they make. But it is unlikely that an individual photographer could ever match the rates of an estab-

Useful information

Bureau of Freelance Photographers
Focus House, 497 Green Lanes,
London N13 4BP
tel 0181-882 3315 *fax* 0181-886 5174
Chief Executive John Tracy
Helps the freelance photographer by providing information on markets and a free advisory service. Publishes *Market Newsletter* (monthly). Annual membership: £40.

Directories

Variety Media Publications
34-35 Newman Street, London W1P 3RD
tel 0171-637 3663
Publishes *The Creative Handbook*.

Elfande Ltd
Unit 39, Bookham Industrial Park, Church Road, Bookham, Surrey KT23 3EU
tel (01372) 459559 *fax* (01372) 459699
Publishes *Contact Photographers*.

lished library, or make the same volume of sales per image. However, the Internet has opened a new marketing avenue for photographers, who now have the opportunity to sell their images worldwide. Previously, only an established stock library would have been able to do this. Before embarking on establishing a home library, photographers should be aware that the business of marketing images is essentially a desk job which involves a considerable amount of paperwork, and time, which could be spent taking pictures.

When setting up a picture library, your first consideration should be whether to build up a library of your own images, or to take on other contributing photographers. Many photographers running their own libraries submit additional images to bigger libraries to increase the odds of making a good income. Often, a photographer's personal library is made up of work rejected by the larger libraries, which are usually only interested in images that will regularly sell and generate a high turnover. However, occasional sales can generate a significant amount of income for the individual. Furthermore, a photographer with a library of specialised subjects stands a good chance of gaining recognition with niche markets, which can be very lucrative if the competition for those particular subjects is low.

If you take on contributing photographers, the responsibility for another's work becomes yours, so it is important to draw up a contract with terms of business for both your contributing photographers and your clients. Loss or damage of images is the most important consideration when sending pictures to clients (most libraries will charge clients a fee of between £400-£600 per image for loss or damage of originals). It is often worth checking that a company wishing to receive transparencies does have adequate insurance to cover these fees, which can amount to a considerable figure if a large quantity of images is lost or damaged. On no account should images be sent to companies which refuse to take responsibility for loss or damage, nor to private individuals, unless they are working on a freelance basis for an established company. It should also be clearly stated in your terms that all pictures in the client's possession become the client's responsibility until they are returned and inspected for damage by the library.

Reproduction fees should also be established on a strict basis, bearing in mind that you owe it to your contributing photographers to command fees which are as high as possible when selling the rights to their images. It is also essential that you control how pictures will be used and the amount of exposure they will receive. The fees should be established according to the type of client using the image and how the image itself will be reproduced. Important factors to consider are where the image will appear, to what size it will be reproduced, the size of the print run, and the territorial rights required by the client. Many libraries also apply holding fees in cases where clients hold on to pictures for periods of time longer than a month.

Bruce Coleman is Managing Director of the Bruce Coleman Collection and past President of the British Association of Picture Libraries. **Ian Thraves** is a freelance photographer and former picture editor at the Bruce Coleman Collection.

Picture agencies and libraries

As well as supplying images to picture editors, picture researchers and others who use pictures, picture agencies and libraries provide a service to the free-lance photographer as one way of selling their work. Most of the picture agencies and libraries listed in this section take work from other photographers.

Before submitting examples of work, photographers should first telephone or write to ascertain the terms and conditions of a picture agency or library. Colour transparencies are most commonly required: medium and large format are preferred to 35mm. Only top quality transparencies are considered; inferior work is never accepted.

To find agencies and libraries which cover specific subjects, start by referring to the *Picture agencies and libraries by subject area* on page 442.

See also ...

- *Card and stationery publishers which accept photographs* on page 449
- *Syndicates, news and press agencies* on page 149
- *The freelance photographer* on page 407
- *Picture research* on page 450
- *National newspapers UK and Ireland* on page 3
- *Magazines by subject area* on page 126
- *Children's book publishers and packagers* on page 260.

*Member of the British Association of Picture Libraries and Agencies

A.A. & A. Ancient Art & Architecture Collection*

Suite 7, 2nd Floor, 410-420 Rayners Lane, Pinner, Middlesex HA5 5DY
tel 0181-429 3131 *fax* 0181-429 4646
e-mail ancienta@dircon.co.uk
Specialises in the history of civilisations of the Middle East, Mediterranean countries, Europe, Asia, Americas, from ancient times to recent past, their arts, architecture, beliefs and peoples.

A-Z Botanical Collection Ltd*

82-84 Clerkenwell Road,
London EC1M 5RJ
tel 0171-336 7942 *fax* 0171-336 7943
e-mail a-z@image-data.com
web site http://www.a-z.picture-library.com
Library Manager Alasdair McCombe
Colour transparencies of plant life world-wide, including named gardens, habitats, gardening, still life, romantic seasonal shots, fungi, pests and diseases, etc (6 x 6cm, 35mm, 5 x 4in).

Abode Interiors Photographic Library*

Albion Court, 1 Pierce Street, Macclesfield, Cheshire SK11 6ER
tel (01625) 500070 *fax* (01625) 500910
Contact Mary Jarvis or Judi Goodwin
Colour photo library specialising in English and Scottish house interiors of all styles, types and periods. High quality material only; terms by agreement. Please phone before sending material. Founded 1993.

Academic File News Photos

Eastern Art Publishing Group,
PO Box 13666, 27 Wallorton Gardens,
London SW14 8WF
tel 0181-392 1122 *fax* 0181-392 1422
e-mail easternart@compuserve.com
Director Sajid Rizvi
Daily news coverage in UK and general library of arts, cultures, people and places, with special reference to the Middle East, North Africa and Asia. New photographers welcomed to cover UK

and abroad. Pictures accepted in TIFF over e-mail. Founded 1985.

Ace Photo Agency*

Satellite House, 2 Salisbury Road,
London SW19 4EZ
tel 0181-944 9944 *fax* 0181-944 9940

General library: people, industry, business, travel, commerce, skies, sport, music and natural history. Worldwide syndication. Sae for enquiries. Very selective editing policy. Terms: 50%. Founded 1980.

Action Plus*

54-58 Tanner Street, London SE1 3PH
tel 0171-403 1558 *fax* 0171-403 1526

Specialist sports and action picture library. Comprehensive collection of creative images, including all aspects of professional and amateur sports worldwide. Covers all age groups, all ethnic groups and all levels of ability. 35mm colour stock and on-line digital archive accessible by ISDN or modem. Terms: 50%. Founded 1986.

Lesley and Roy Adkins Picture Library

Longstone Lodge, Aller, Langport,
Somerset TA10 0QT
tel (01458) 250075 *fax* (01458) 250858
web site http://ourworld.compuserve.com/homepages/adkins_archaeology

Colour library covering archaeology and heritage; prehistoric, Roman, Greek, Egyptian and medieval sites and monuments; landscape, countryside, architecture, towns, villages and religious monuments. Catalogue available. Founded 1989.

Aerofilms*

Aerofilms Ltd, Gate Studios, Station Road,
Borehamwood, Herts. WD6 1EJ
tel 0181-207 0666 *fax* 0181-207 5433
e-mail library@aerofilms.com

Comprehensive library – over 1.5 million photos going back to 1919 – of vertical and oblique aerial photographs of UK; large areas with complete cover. Founded 1919.

Air Photo Supply

42 Sunningvale Avenue, Biggin Hill,
Kent TN16 3BX
tel (01959) 574872

Aircraft and associated subjects, South-East England, colour and monochrome.

No other photographers' material required. Founded 1963.

AKG London*

(Arts and History Picture Library)
10 Plato Place, 72-74 St Dionis Road,
London SW6 4TU
tel 0171-610 6103 *fax* 0171-610 6125
e-mail enquiries@akg-london.co.uk
web site http://www.akg-london.co.uk

Principal subjects covered: art, archaeology and history. Exclusive UK and US representative for the Archiv für Kunst und Geschichte (AKG) with full access to the 10 million images held by AKG Berlin. Also exclusively represents the Erich Lessing Culture and Fine Art Archives in the UK. Founded 1994.

Bryan and Cherry Alexander Photography*

Higher Cottage, Manston, Sturminster Newton,
Dorset DT10 1EZ
tel (01258) 473006 *fax* (01258) 473333
e-mail arcticfoto@aol.com
web site http://members.aol.com/arcticfoto/

Polar regions with emphasis on Eskimos, Lapps and the modern Arctic, Siberia, Antarctica. Founded 1973.

Rev. J. Catling Allen

St Giles House, Little Torrington,
Devon EX38 8PS
tel (01805) 622497

Library of colour transparencies (35mm) and b&w photos of Bible Lands, including archaeological sites and the religions of Christianity, Islam and Judaism. Medieval abbeys and priories, cathedrals and churches in Britain. Also historic, rural and scenic Britain. (Not an agent or buyer.)

Allied Artists Ltd

31 Harcourt Street, London W1H 1DT
tel 0171-724 8809 *fax* 0171-262 8526
Contact Gary Mills

Agency for illustrators specialising in realistic figure illustration. Large colour library of illustrations for syndication. Founded 1983.

Allsport Photographic

3 Greenlea Park, Prince George's Road,
London SW19 2JD
tel 0181-685 1010 *fax* 0181-648 5240
web site http://www.allsport.com

International sport and leisure. Founded 1968.

American History Picture Library
3 Barton Buildings, Bath BA1 2JR
tel (01225) 334213 *fax* (01225) 480554
Photographs, engravings, colour transparencies covering the exploration and social, political and military history of North America from 15th to 20th century: conquistadors, civil war, railroads, the Great Depression, advertisements, Prohibition and gangsters, moon landings and space.

AMIS
(Atlas Mountains Information Services)
26 Kirkcaldy Road, Burntisland, Fife KY3 9HQ
tel (01592) 873546
Proprietor Hamish Brown
Picture library on Moroccan sites, topography, mountains, travel. Illustration service. Commissions undertaken. No pictures purchased.

Ancient Egypt Picture Library*
6 Branden Drive, Knutsford, Cheshire WA16 8EJ
e-mail AEgyptPL@aol.com
tel/fax (01565) 633106
Proprietor Bob Partridge
Images of Egypt, including most of the ancient sites and views of modern Egypt. All photographs (13,000 colour transparencies) taken by an Egyptologist, who can also provide full historical/archaeological information. Founded 1996.

Andalucía Slide Library
Apto 499, Estepona, Málaga 29680, Spain
tel/fax (34) 952-793647
e-mail library@andalucia.com
web site http://www.andalucia.com
Contact Chris Chaplow
Colour transparencies (35mm and medium format) covering all aspects of Andalucía and Spain, principally its geography and culture. Digitised images available by ISDN or modem. Commissions undertaken. Founded 1991.

Andes Press Agency*
26 Padbury Court, London E2 7EH
tel 0171-613 5417 *fax* 0171-739 3159
e-mail photos@andespress.demon.co.uk
Director Carlos Reyes
Social, political and economic aspects of Latin America, Africa, Asia, Middle East, Europe and Britain; specialises in Latin America and contemporary world religions. Founded 1983.

Heather Angel/Biofotos*
Highways, 6 Vicarage Hill, Farnham,
Surrey GU9 8HJ
tel (01252) 716700 *fax* (01252) 727464
Colour transparencies (35mm and 2¹/₄in square) with worldwide coverage of natural history and biological subjects including animals, plants, natural habitats (deserts, polar regions, rainforests, wetlands, etc), landscapes, gardens, close-ups and underwater images; also man's impact on the environment – pollution, acid rain, urban wildlife, etc. Large China file. Detailed catalogues on request by *bona fide* picture researchers.

Animal Photography*
4 Marylebone Mews, New Cavendish Street,
London W1M 7LF
tel 0171-935 0503 *fax* 0171-487 3038
e-mail thompson@animal-photography.co.uk
Horses, dogs, cats, small pets, East Africa, Galapagos. Founded 1955.

Aquarius Picture Library*
PO Box 5, Hastings,
East Sussex TN34 1HR
tel (01424) 721196 *fax* (01424) 717704
Contact David Corkill
Showbusiness specialist library with over one million colour and b&w images: film stills, classic portraiture, candids, archive material to present. New material added every week. Archival situation stills for advertising and magazine illustration use. Also television, vintage pop, opera, ballet and stage. Worldwide representation and direct sales. Collections considered, either outright purchase or 50%-50% marketing.

Aquila Wildlife Images
PO Box 1, Studley, Warks. B80 7JG
tel (01527) 852357 *fax* (01527) 857507
e-mail interbirdnet @dial.pipex.com
Specialists in ornithological subjects, but covering all aspects of natural history, also pets and landscapes, in both colour and b&w.

Arcaid Architectural Photography and Picture Library*
The Factory, 2 Acre Road, Kingston,
Surrey KT2 6EF
tel 0181-546 4352 *fax* 0181-541 5230
e-mail arcaid@arcaid.co.uk
web site http://www.arcaid.co.uk

'The built environment' – international collection: architecture, interior design details, gardens, travel, museums, historic and contemporary. Terms: 50%.

Archivio Veneziano – see Venice Picture Library*

Arctic Camera
66 Ashburnham Grove, London SE10 8UJ
tel/fax 0181-692 7651
Contact Derek Fordham
Colour transparencies of all aspects of Arctic life and environment. Founded 1978.

Ardea London Ltd*
35 Brodrick Road, London SW17 7DX
tel 0181-672 2067 *fax* 0181-672 8787
e-mail ardea@globalnet.co.uk
Contact Su Gooders
Specialist worldwide natural history photographic library of animals, birds, plants, fish, insects, reptiles, worldwide scenics and domestic pets.

Aspect Picture Library Ltd*
40 Rostrevor Road, London SW6 5AD
tel 0171-736 1998/731 7362 *fax* 0171-731 7362
General library including wildlife, tribes, cities, industry, science, Space. Founded 1971.

The Associated Press Ltd
News Photo Department,
The Associated Press House,
12 Norwich Street, London EC4A 1BP
tel 0171-427 4260/4266 (colour and b&w request), 0171-353 1515 ext 4264 (library manager) *fax* 0171-353 0836
News, features, sports.

Australia Pictures
28 Sheen Common Drive, Richmond, London TW10 5BN
tel/fax 0181-898 0150 *fax* 0181-876 3637
Contact John Miles
Comprehensive library covering Australia, Aboriginals and their art, indigenous peoples, underwater, Tibet, Peru, Bolivia, Iran, Irian Jaya, Pakistan, Yemen. Founded 1988.

Aviation Photographs International
15 Downs View Road, Swindon, Wilts. SN3 1NS
tel (01793) 497179 *fax* (01793) 434030
All types of aviation and military subjects. Assignments undertaken. Founded 1970.

Aviation Picture Library* (Austin J. Brown)
116 The Avenue, St Stephen's, London W13 8 JX
tel 0181-566 7712 *fax* 0181-566 7714
cellphone (01860) 670073
Worldwide aviation photographic library, including dynamic views of aircraft. Aerial and travel library including Europe, Caribbean, USA, and East and West Africa. Material taken since 1960. Specialising in air-to-air and air-to-ground commissions. Chief photographers for *Flyer* magazine. Founded 1970.

B. & B. Photographs
Prospect House, Clifford Chambers, Stratford upon Avon, Warks. CV37 8HX
tel (01789) 298106 *fax* (01789) 292450
35mm/medium format colour library of horticulture (especially pests and diseases) and biogeography (worldwide), natural history (especially Britain) and biological education. Other photographers' work not represented. Founded 1974.

Bandphoto Agency
(division of UPPA Ltd)
29-31 Saffron Hill, London EC1N 8FH
tel 0171-421 6000 *fax* 0171-421 6006
International news and feature picture service for British and overseas publishers.

Barnaby's Picture Library*
19 Rathbone Street, London W1P 1AF
tel 0171-636 6128/9 *fax* 0171-637 4317
e-mail barnabyspicturelibrary@ukbusinesss.com
General library of 4 million photos, colour and b&w, illustrating yesterday, today and tomorrow. Plus 500,000 engravings from 1500 to 1900.

Barnardo's Photographic Archive*
Tanners Lane, Barkingside, Ilford, Essex IG6 1QG
tel 0181-550 8822 *fax* 0181-550 0429
Extensive collection of b&w and colour images dating from 1874 to the present day covering social history with the emphasis on children and child care. Also 300 films dating from 1905. Founded 1874.

BBC Natural History Unit Picture Library*
BBC Broadcasting House, Whiteladies Road, Bristol BS8 2LR

tel 0117-9746720 *fax* 0117-9238166
e-mail nhu.picture.library@bbc.co.uk

Holds photographs relating to the Unit's film-making activities and represents the work of top wildlife photographers from around the world. Also has a unique collection of archive photographs relating to the history of film-making in the Unit. Founded 1995.

Dr Alan Beaumont
52 Squires Walk, Lowestoft, Suffolk NR32 4LA
tel (01502) 560126

Worldwide collection of monochrome prints and colour transparencies (35mm and 6 x 7cm) of natural history, countryside, windmills and aircraft. Subject lists available. No other photographers required.

Bee Photographs – see Heritage & Natural History Photography

Stephen Benson Slide Bureau
45 Sugden Road, London SW11 5EB
tel 0171-223 8635

World: agriculture, archaeology, architecture, commerce, everyday life, culture, environment, geography, science, tourism. Speciality: South America, the Caribbean, Australasia, Nepal, Turkey, Israel and Egypt. Assignments undertaken.

Bird Images
28 Carousel Walk, Sherburn in Elmet, North Yorkshire LS25 6LP
tel/fax (01977) 684666
Principal P. Doherty

Specialist in the birds of Britain and Europe. Expert captioning service available. Founded 1989.

John Birdsall Photography*
75 Raleigh Street, Nottingham NG7 4DL
tel 0115-978 2645 *fax* 0115-978 5546
e-mail birdsall@innotts.co.uk
web site http://www.johnbirdsall.co.uk
Contact Clare Marsh

Contemporary social documentary library covering children, youth, old age, health, disability, education, housing, work; also Nottingham and surrounding area; Spain – commissions and stock pictures. Founded 1980.

The Anthony Blake Photo Library*
54 Hill Rise, Richmond, Surrey TW10 6UB
tel 0181-940 7583 *fax* 0181-948 1224
e-mail anthonyblake.photo@virgin.net

Food and wine images from around the world, including raw ingredients, finished dishes, shops, restaurants, markets, agriculture and viticulture. Commissions undertaken. Contributors welcome. Brochure available.

John Blake Picture Library
74 South Ealing Road, London W5 4QB
tel 0181-840 4141 *fax* 0181-566 2568
Manager Alan Denny

General topography of England, Europe and the rest of the world. Landscapes, architecture, churches, gardens, countryside, towns and villages. Horse trials covered including Badminton and Gatcombe Park. Terms: 50%. Founded 1975.

Sarah Boait Photography and Picture Library
tel/fax (01458) 832600

Covers the British Isles, especially the West Country; also world travel, world religions. No contributors' work accepted.

Bodleian Library
Oxford OX1 3BG
tel (01865) 277214/277153 *fax* (01865) 277187
e-mail western.manuscripts@bodley.ox.ac.uk
web site http://www.bodley.ox.ac.uk/

Library of 32,000 35mm colour transparencies, of subjects mostly from medieval manuscripts with iconographical index to illuminations; 35mm filmstrips and selected slides available for immediate sale (not hire); other formats to order.

Bookart Architecture Picture Library
1 Woodcock Lodge, Epping Green, Hertford SG13 8ND
tel (01707) 875253 *fax* (01707) 875286
e-mail sharpd@globalnet.co.uk

Modern and historic buildings, landscapes, works of named architects in Great Britain, Europe, Scandinavia, North America, India, South-East Asia, Japan, North and East Africa; modern sculpture. Listed under style, place and personality. Founded 1991.

Boxing Picture Library
3 Barton Buildings, Bath BA1 2JR
tel (01225) 334213 *fax* (01225) 480554

Prints, engravings and photos of famous boxers, boxing personalities and famous fights from 18th century to recent years.

Bridgeman Art Library*
17-19 Garway Road, London W2 4PH
tel 0171-727 4065 *fax* 0171-792 8509
e-mail info@bridgeman.co.uk
web site http://www.bridgeman.co.uk
Comprehensive source of fine art images for publication, acting as an agent for over 750 museums, galleries and private collections around the world. Large format colour transparencies. Currently holds more than 100,000 different images and is growing by 500 every week. Fully computerised, the image database runs on a custom-written free text keyword search system. CD-Rom catalogues. Founded 1971.

Britain on View – see Stockwave

British Library Picture Library*
96 Euston Road, London NW1 2DB
tel 0171-412 7614 *fax* 0171-412 7771
e-mail bl-repro@bl.uk
web site http://portico.bl.uk/repro/
Illustrative and historical material from manuscripts, printed books, oriental and Indian items, maps, music and stamps. In addition to the stock collection, images from 15 million books can be sourced. Founded 1996.

David Broadbent/Peak District Pictures
66 Norfolk Street, Glossop, Derbyshire SK13 9RA
tel/fax (01457) 862997
The Peak District fully covered, landscape, natural history, birds a speciality; sports. Commissions undertaken. New material welcome. Terms: 50%. Founded 1989.

Hamish Brown, Scottish Photographic
26 Kirkcaldy Road, Burntisland, Fife KY3 9HQ
tel (01592) 873546
Picture library on Scottish sites, topography, mountains, travel. Book illustrations. Commissions undertaken. No pictures purchased.

Butterflies
27 Lucastes Lane, Haywards Heath, West Sussex RH16 1LE
tel (01444) 454254
Proprietors Dr J. Tampion, Mrs M.D. Tampion
Worldwide: butterflies, silkmoths, hawkmoths, adults, larvae, pupae, their foodplants, poisonous plants, wild, garden and greenhouse plants, botanical and gardening science, ecology, environment. Articles and line illustrations also available; commissions undertaken. Terms: 50%. Founded 1990.

Camera Press Ltd*
21 Queen Elizabeth Street, London SE1 2PD
tel 0171-378 1300 *fax* 0171-278 5126
B&w prints and colour transparencies including up-to-date coverage of British Royalty, portraits of world statesmen, politicians, entertainers, reportage, humour, nature, pop, features. Terms: 50%. Founded 1947.

Camerapix – see C.P.L. (Camerapix Picture Library)

J. Allan Cash Photolibrary (J. Allan Cash Ltd)*
74 South Ealing Road, London W5 4QB
tel 0181-840 4141 *fax* 0181-566 2568
Manager Alan Denny
Worldwide photographic library: travel, landscape, natural history, sport, industry, agriculture. Details available for photographers interested in contributing.

Cephas Picture Library*
Hurst House, 157 Walton Road, East Molesey, Surrey KT8 0DX
tel 0181-979 8647 or 07000 CEPHAS
fax 0181-224 8095
e-mail mickrock@cephas.co.uk
web site http://www.cephas.co.uk
Comprehensive library of food and drink photos: wine and vineyards, spirits, beer and cider, food and drink worldwide. Free catalogue available; specialist knowledge.

City Syndication Ltd* – see Monitor Syndication

COI Photo Library – see Stockwave

Michael Cole Camerawork*
The Coach House, 27 The Avenue, Beckenham, Kent BR3 2DP
tel/fax 0181-658 6120
Probably the largest and most comprehensive tennis library in the world comprising over half a million colour and b&w images. Includes over 50 years of the Wimbledon Championships. All grand slam and major events covered. Founded 1945.

Bruce Coleman Inc.
117 East 24th Street, New York, NY 10010-2919, USA

tel 212-979-6252 *fax* 212-979-5468
e-mail 72757,1343@compuserve.com,
norman@bciusa.com
President Norman Owen Tomalin
Specialising exclusively in colour transparencies. All formats from 35mm acceptable. All subjects required.

Bruce Coleman Collection*

16 Chiltern Business Village, Arundel Road,
Uxbridge, Middlesex UB8 2SN
tel (01895) 257094 *fax* (01895) 272357
e-mail alison@brucecoleman.co.uk
web site http://www.brucecoleman.co.uk
Colour transparencies on natural history, ecology, environment, geography, archaeology, anthropology, agriculture, science, scenics and travel.

Collections*

13 Woodberry Crescent, London N10 1PJ
tel 0181-883 0083 *fax* 0181-883 9215
The British Isles only: places, people, buildings, industry, leisure; specialist collections on customs, castles, bridges, London, emergency services; also family life from pregnancy through birth, childhood, education to being grown up. Founded 1990.

Colorific Photo Library*

The Innovation Centre, 225 Marsh Wall,
London E14 9FX
tel 0171-515 3000 *fax* 0171-538 3555
Handles the work of top international photographers, most subjects currently on file, upwards of 250,000 images. Represents the following agencies: Black Star (New York), Contact Press Images (New York/Paris), Visages (Los Angeles), Icone (Paris), Regards (Paris), ANA Press (Paris). Also represents *Sports Illustrated.*

Concannon Golf History Library*

2 Cairns Road, London SW11 1ES
tel 0171-801 7020 *fax* 0171-801 7070
e-mail congolflib.j15.co.uk
Contact Dale Concannon
Golfing images 1750-1950: famous players, courses, Ryder Cup, open championships, golf course architecture, memorabilia, US golf and artwork. Specialist advice available. Commissions undertaken. Founded 1997.

Sylvia Cordaiy Photo Library

72 East Ham Road, Littlehampton,
West Sussex BN17 7BQ
tel/fax (01903) 715297

e-mail 113023.2732@compuserve.com
web site http://www.photosource.co.uk/
photosource/sylvia-cordaiy.htm
Worldwide travel and architecture, global environmental topics, wildlife and domestic animals, veterinary, comprehensive UK files, ocean racing. Terms: 50%. Founded 1990.

C.P.L. (Camerapix Picture Library)

8 Ruston Mews, London W11 1RB
tel 0171-221 0077 *fax* 0171-792 8105
e-mail camerapixuk@btinternet.com
and PO Box 45048 Nairobi, Kenya
tel 448923 *fax* 448926
e-mail info@camerapix.com
Kenya, Tanzania, Pakistan, Jordan, Namibia, Nepal, Maldives, Mauritius, Seychelles, Zimbabwe; portraits, agriculture, industry, tribal cultures, landscapes; wildlife including rare species; extensive collection on Aldabra Island; Islamic portfolio: Mecca, Medina, Muslim pilgrimage. News material available and special assignments arranged. Further material available from collection held in Nairobi.

Crafts Council Picture Library

44A Pentonville Road, London N1 9BY
tel 0171-806 2503 or 0171-278 7700 ext. 503
fax 0171-837 6891
Large, medium and small format transparencies. Coverage includes ceramics, jewellery, textiles, metal and silver, furniture, wood, glass, knitting, weaving, bookbinding, fashion accessories, toys and musical instruments supplied by selected makers and from *Crafts* magazine. Founded 1973.

Peter Cumberlidge Photo Library

Sunways, Slapton, Kingsbridge, Devon TQ7 2PR
tel (01548) 580461 *fax* (01548) 580588
Contact Jane Cumberlidge
Nautical, travel and coastal colour transparencies 35mm and 6 x 6cm. Specialities: boats, harbours, marinas, inland waterways. Travel and holiday subjects in Northern Europe, the Mediterranean, and New England, USA. No other photographers' material required. Founded 1982.

Cumbria Picture Library*

PO Box 33, Kendal, Cumbria LA9 4SU
tel (015394) 48894 *fax* (015394) 48294
e-mail eelik@demon.co.uk

Contact Eric Whitehead
Specialist picture library with over 40,000 images covering every aspect of Cumbria and The Lake District. Subjects include: places, people, events, customs, outdoor pursuits and landscapes; snooker photos by Eric Whitehead. The library holds work from many photographers and commissions are accepted. Founded 1990.

Lupe Cunha
Photo-Arte Gallery, 19 Ashfield Parade, London N14 5EH
tel 0181-882 6441 *fax* 0181-882 6303
e-mail lupe.cunha@btinternet.com
Specialist library on all aspects of childhood from pregnancy to school age, also women's interest and health/medical with focus on the patient and nursing care. Commissioned photography undertaken. Also represents collection on Brazil for Brazil Photo Agency. Terms: 50%. Founded 1987.

Sue Cunningham Photographic*
56 Chatham Road, Kingston-upon-Thames, Surrey KT1 3AA
tel 0181-541 3024 *fax* 0181-541 5388
e-mail scphotographic@btinternet.com
International coverage on many subjects: Latin America, East Africa and Eastern Europe. Also Western Europe, London (including aerial) and Cornwall.

The Dance Library
12 Southwick Mews, London W2 1JG
tel 0171-262 6300 *fax* 0171-262 6400
Contemporary and historical dance: classical ballet, jazz, tap, disco, popping, ice dancing, musicals, variety, folk, tribal rites and rituals. Founded 1983.

Das Photo
Chalet le Pin, Domaine de Bellevue 181, 6940 Septon, Belgium
tel/fax (086) 322426
c/o Old School House, Llanfilo, Brecon, Powys LD3 0RH
tel (01874) 711953
Arab countries, Americas, Europe, SE Asia, Amazon, world festivals, archaeology, people, biblical, motor bikes, education, schools, modern languages. Founded 1975.

Barry Davies
Dyffryn, Bolahaul Road, Cwmffrwd, Carmarthen, Carmarthenshire SA31 2LP
tel/fax (01267) 233625

Natural history, landscape (especially waterfalls), Egypt, children, outdoor activities and general subjects. Formats 35mm, 6 x 6cm, 6 x 7cm, 5 x 4in. Other photographers' work not accepted. Founded 1983.

Dennis Davis Photography
9 Great Burrow Rise, Northam, Bideford, Devon EX39 1TB
tel (01237) 475165
Gardens, wild and garden flowers, domestic livestock including rare breeds and poultry, agricultural landscapes, architecture – interiors and exteriors, landscape, coastal, rural life. Commissions welcomed. No other photographers required. Founded 1984.

James Davis Travel Photography*
65 Brighton Road, Shoreham, West Sussex BN43 6RE
tel (01273) 452252 *fax* (01273) 440116
Proprietor Paul Seheult
Stock transparency library specialising in worldwide travel photos. Suppliers to publishers, advertising agents, etc.

Peter Dazeley*
The Studios, 5 Heathmans Road, London SW6 4TJ
tel 0171-736 3171 *fax* 0171-371 8876
Extensive golf library dating from 1970. Colour and b&w coverage of major tournaments. Constantly updated, with over 250,000 images of players (male and female), courses worldwide, action shots, portraits, trophies, including miscellaneous images: clubs, balls and teaching shots.

George A. Dey
'Drumcairn', Aberdeen Road, Laurencekirk, Kincardineshire AB30 1AJ
tel (01561 37) 8845
Scottish Highland landscapes, Highland Games, forestry, seabirds, castles of NE Scotland, gardens, spring, autumn, winter scenes, veteran cars, North Holland, New Zealand (North Island). Mostly 35mm, some 6 x 6cm. Founded 1986.

Douglas Dickins Photo Library
2 Wessex Gardens, London NW11 9RT
tel 0181-455 6221
Worldwide collection of colour transparencies (mostly 6 x 6cm, some 35mm) and b&w prints (10 x 8in originals), specialising in Asia, particularly India and Indonesia; also, USA, Canada, France,

Austria and Switzerland, Japan, China, Burma. Founded 1946.

Gordon Dickson
Flagstones, 72 Catisfield Lane, Fareham, Hants PO15 5NS
tel (01329) 842131
Colour transparencies of fungi, in natural habitat; also wildflowers, butterflies, moths, beetles. No other photographers required. Founded 1975.

C.M. Dixon*
The Orchard, Marley Lane, Kingston, Canterbury, Kent CT4 6JH
tel (01227) 830075 *fax* (01227) 831135
Europe and Ethiopia, Iceland, Jordan, Sri Lanka, Tunisia, Turkey, former USSR. Main subjects include agriculture, ancient art, archaeology, architecture, clouds, geography, geology, history, horses, industry, meteorology, mosaics, mountains, mythology, occupations, people.

Earth Images Picture Library
PO Box 43, Keynsham, Bristol BS18 2TH
tel/fax 0117-986 1144/(01275) 839643
Director Richard Arthur
Earth from Space (satellite remote sensing); earth science and art-in-science imagery – from cosmic to sub-atomic. Founded 1989.

Ecoscene*
The Oasts, Headley Lane, Passfield, Liphook, Hants GU30 7RX
tel (01428) 751056 *fax* (01428) 751057
e-mail ecoscene@photosource.co.uk
web site http://www.photosource.co.uk/ photosource/ecoscene.htm
Contact Sally Morgan
Specialists in environment and ecology. Subjects include agriculture, conservation, energy, industry, pollution, habitats and habitat loss, sustainability, wildlife; worldwide coverage. Terms: 55% to photographer. Founded 1987.

English Heritage Photographic Library*
23 Savile Row, London W1X 1AB
tel 0171-973 3338/3339 *fax* 0171-973 3027
Wide range of high quality, large format colour transparencies, ranging from ancient monuments to artefacts, legendary castles to stone circles, elegant interiors to industrial architecture and post-war listed buildings. Founded 1984.

Environmental Investigation Agency
15 Bowling Green Lane, London EC1R 0BD
tel 0171-490 7040 *fax* 0171-490 0436
e-mail eiauk@gn.apc.org
Photograph Co-ordinator Matthew Snead
Specialist library covering animal abuse, trade in endangered species, abuse of the environment; also animals in their natural environment. Founded 1985.

Greg Evans International Photo Library*
6 Station Parade, Sunningdale, Ascot, Berks. SL5 0EP
tel 0171-636 8238 *fax* 0171-637 1439
e-mail greg@geipl.demon.co.uk
web site http://www.geipl.demon.co.uk
Comprehensive, general colour library with over 300,000 transparencies. Subjects include: abstract, aircraft, arts, animals, beaches, business, children, computers, couples, families, food/restaurant, women, industry, skies, sports (action and leisure), UK scenics, worldwide travel. Visitors welcome; combined commissions undertaken; first search fee. Photographers' submissions welcome. Free brochure/CD-Rom. Founded 1979.

Mary Evans Picture Library*
59 Tranquil Vale, London SE3 0BS
tel 0181-318 0034 *fax* 0181-852 7211
e-mail lib@mepl.co.uk
Millions of historical illustrations documenting social, political, cultural, technical, geographical and biographical themes from ancient times to the mid 20th century. Photographs, original prints, and ephemera backed by a large international book and magazine collection. Special collections include Sigmund Freud, the Fawcett Library (women's rights), the Meledin Collection (20th-century Russian history) and individual photographers active from the 1930s to the 1970s. Colour brochure available. Compilers of the *Picture Researcher's Handbook*, published every 3 years by Pira International.

Eyeline Photography
259 London Road, Cheltenham, Glos. GL52 6YG
tel/fax (01242) 513567
Watersports, particularly sailing; windvanes; sheepdog trials. Founded 1979.

Chris Fairclough Colour Library
19 Radnor Road, Harrow,
Middlesex HA1 1RY
tel 0181-861 1122 *fax* 0181-861 4755
Modern religion, geography, people, travel, studio shots, education, places etc.

Famous*
Studio 4, Limehouse Cut, 46 Morris Road,
London E14 6NQ
tel 0171-510 2500 *fax* 0171-510 2510
e-mail famous@compuserve.com
web site http://www.famous.uk.com
Colour pictures and features library covering music, film and TV personalities.
Terms: 50%. Founded 1990.

Feature-Pix Colour Library – see World Pictures*

Financial Times Pictures*
Number One, Southwark Bridge,
London SE1 9HL
tel 0171-873 3671 *fax* 0171-873 4606
e-mail suzie.kew@ft.com
Colour and b&w library serving *The Financial Times*. Specialises in world business, industry and commerce; world politicians and statespeople; cities and countries; plus many other subjects. Also *FT* maps and graphics. All material available in colour and b&w, print and electronic formats. Library updated daily.

Fine Art Photographic Library*
Rawlings House, 2A Milner Street,
London SW3 2PU
tel 0171- 589 3127 *fax* 0171-584 1944
web site http://www.picture-library.com
Holds over 25,000 transparencies of paintings by British and European artists, from Old Masters to contemporary. Free brochure. Founded 1980.

FirePix International*
68 Arkles Lane, Anfield, Liverpool L4 2SP
tel/fax 0151-260 0111
e-mail tonymyers@firepixint.demon.co.uk
web site http://www.firepixint.demon.co.uk
Contact Tony Myers ARPS, GIFireE
Holds 15,000 images of fire and firefighters at work in the UK, USA, Japan and China. Also covers other emergency services. Established by photographer Tony Myers after 28 years in service with the British Fire Service. Many images are stored digitally; CD-Rom available. Founded 1993.

Fogden Natural History Photographs*
Basement, 10 Bellevue, Bristol BS8 1DA
tel 0117-923 8849 *fax* 0117-923 8543
Library Manager Susan Fogden
Wide natural history coverage, including camouflage, warning coloration, mimicry, breeding strategies, feeding, animal/plant relationships, environmental studies, especially in rain forests and deserts. Founded 1980.

Ron and Christine Foord
155B City Way, Rochester, Kent ME1 2BE
tel/fax (01634) 847348
Colour picture library of over 1000 species of wild flowers. Also British insects, garden flowers, pests and diseases, lichen, mosses and cacti.

Footprints Colour Picture Library
Goldfin Cottage, Maidlands Farm, Broad Oak,
Rye, East Sussex TN31 6BJ
tel (01424) 883076 *fax* (01424) 883078
Proprietor Paula Leaver
Specialises in underwater and above water coverage of holiday destinations in the tropics; also food and flowers by Debbie Patterson. Founded 1991.

Forest Life Picture Library*
Forestry Commission, 231 Corstorphine Road,
Edinburgh EH12 7AT
Picture Researcher Neill Campbell
tel 0131-314 6411
e-mail n.campbell@forestry.gov.uk
Business Manager Douglas Green
tel 0131-314 6200 *fax* 0131-314 6285
e-mail d.green@forestry.gov.uk
Tree species, forest and woodland management, employment, landscapes, wildlife, flora and fauna, conservation, sport and leisure. Founded 1983.

Werner Forman Archive*
36 Camden Square, London NW1 9XA
tel 0171-267 1034 *fax* 0171-267 6026
e-mail wfa@btinternet.com
Art, architecture, archaeology, history and peoples of ancient, oriental and primitive cultures. Founded 1975.

Format Photographers*
19 Arlington Way, London EC1R 1UY
tel 0171-833 0292 *fax* 0171-833 0381
e-mail format@formatphotogs.demon.co.uk
Contact Maggie Murray
A library and agency representing the work of 20 women documentary photog-

raphers. The images, mainly from the last 20 years, are constantly updated and offer a unique perspective of the world. Subjects covered: social and political life in Britain and abroad, health, education, women's issues, work, the elderly and the very young, disability, gay and lesbian, Black and Asian culture, the environment, housing and homelessness, transport and leisure. Countries from Albania to Zambia. Colour and b&w. Commission: 50%. Founded 1983.

Fortean Picture Library*

Henblas, Mwrog Street, Ruthin LL15 1LG
tel (01824) 707278 *fax* (01824) 705324
e-mail jbord@easynet.co.uk

Library of colour and b&w pictures covering all strange phenomena: UFOs, Loch Ness Monster, ghosts, Bigfoot, witchcraft, etc; also antiquities (especially in Britain – prehistoric and Roman sites, castles, churches).

Fotoccompli–The Picture Library

166 Boldmen Road, Sutton Coldfield B73 5UD
tel 0121-240 8950

Comprehensive library, ranging from abstracts to zoology, serving all of Britain, especially the Birmingham and West Midlands areas. Terms: 50%; minimum retention period – 3 years. Founded 1989.

Fotomas Index

12 Pickhurst Rise, West Wickham, Kent BR4 0AL
tel/fax 0181-776 2772

Specialises in supplying pre-20th century (mostly pre-Victorian) illustrative material to publishing and academic worlds, and for television and advertising. Complete production back-up for interior décor, exhibitions and locations.

Freelance Focus

7 King Edward Terrace, Brough,
East Yorkshire HU15 1EE
tel/fax (01482) 666036
Contact Gary Hicks

UK/international network of photographers. Over 2 million stock pictures available, covering all subjects, worldwide, at competitive rates. Assignments undertaken for all types of clients. Further details/subject list available on request. Also publishes directory of photographers and photo libraries/agencies. Founded 1988.

Frontline Photo Press Agency

18 Wall Street, Norwood, Australia 5067
postal address PO Box 162, Kent Town, Australia 5071
tel (08) 8333 2691 *fax* (08) 8364 0604
e-mail info@frontline.net.au
web site http://www.frontline.net.au
Photo Editor Carlo Irlitti

Stock photo agency, picture library and photographic press agency with 350,000 images. Covers sport, people, personalities, travel, scenics, environmental, agricultural, industrial, natural history, concepts, science, medicine, social documentary and press images. Seeking worldwide stock contributors. Assignments undertaken. Write, fax or e-mail for submission guidelines, photo requirements and other details. Terms: 60% to photographer (stock); assignment rates negotiable. Founded 1988.

Frost Historical Newspaper Collection

8 Monks Avenue, New Barnet, Herts. EN5 1DB
tel/fax 0181-440 3159

Headline stories from 60,000 British and overseas newspapers reporting major events since 1850.

Brian Gadsby Picture Library

17 route des Pyrénées, 65700 Labatut-Riviere, Hautes Pyrénées, France
tel (33) 05 62 96 38 44

Colour transparencies (6 x 4.5cm, 35mm) and b&w prints. Wide range of subjects but emphasis on travel and the environment: UK, Europe (particularly France), Ecuador and Galapagos Islands, Patagonia, Sri Lanka; Natural History: mainly birds and plant life (wild and garden). Large wildfowl file. Catalogue on request by picture researchers. No other photographers' material required.

Andrew N. Gagg's Photo Flora*

Fordbank Court, Henwick Road, Worcester WR2 5PF
tel/fax 01905 748515
e-mail gagg@mcmail.com
web site http://www.gagg.mcmail.com/photoflora.htm
Contact Andrew N. Gagg

Comprehensive collection of British and European wild plants. Travel: Egypt, India, Tibet, China, Nepal, Thailand, Mexico. Founded 1982.

Galaxy Picture Library*
1 Milverton Drive, Ickenham, Uxbridge,
Middlesex UB10 8PP
tel (01895) 637463 *fax* (01895) 623277
e-mail galaxypix@compuserve.com
web site http://ourworld.compuserve.com/
homepages/galaxypix
Contact Robin Scagell
Astronomy: specialities include the night
sky, amateur astronomy, astronomers and
observatories. Founded 1992.

Garden Matters Photographic Library*
Marlham, Henley's Down, Battle,
East Sussex TN33 9BN
tel (01424) 830566 *fax* (01424) 830224
e-mail gardens@ftech.co.uk, gardenpics@aol.com
web site http://web.ftech.net/~gardens
ISDN (01424) 830153
Contact Dr John Feltwell
Plant 6000 Over 6000 scientifically
named species and cultivars of garden
flowers, wild plants, trees (over 800
species), grasses, crops, herbs, spices,
houseplants, carnivorous plants,
climbers, roses and pests.
   General gardening How-to, gardening
techniques, garden design and embellish-
ments, cottage gardens, USA designer-
gardens, 200 garden portfolios from 16
states in the USA, 100 portfolios from 12
European countries. Several photographers now represented. Founded 1993.

Leslie Garland Picture Library
69 Fern Avenue, Jesmond,
Newcastle upon Tyne NE2 2QU
tel 0191-281 3442 *fax* 0191-209 1094
e-mail garland@cableinet.co.uk
All subjects in the geographic areas of:
Northumberland, Durham, Tyne & Wear,
Cumbria, Cleveland, Yorkshire,
Lancashire, Merseyside, Greater
Manchester, Derbyshire, Norway,
Sweden, Denmark, Finland, Iceland –
major cities, sites, scenes, heritage,
industry, etc.
   Applied science and engineering –
bridges, cranes, ship building, chemical
plants, all industrial processes, geography and geology, physics and chemistry.
Miscellaneous subjects such as: gal-
vanised crash barriers, household
objects, electric cars, etc. Colour transparencies only, medium format pre-

ferred; please send sae for guidelines.
Terms: 50%. Founded 1985.

Colin Garratt – see Railways – Milepost 92^1/$_2$*

Genesis Space Photo Library*
Greenbanks, Robins Hill, Raleigh, Bideford,
Devon EX39 3PA
tel (01237) 471960 *fax* (01237) 472060
e-mail tim@spaceport.co.uk
web site http://www.spaceport. co.uk
Contact Tim Furniss
Specialises in rockets, spacecraft, space-
men, Earth, Moon, planets. Founded 1990.

Geo Aerial Photography*
4 Christian Fields, London SW16 3JZ
tel/fax 0181-764 6292, 0115-981 5474 or
0115-981 9418
Director J.F.J. Douglas
Air-to-air and air-to-ground colour
library: natural and cultural/man-made
landscapes and individual features.
Commissions undertaken. Terms: 50%.
Founded 1992.

GeoScience Features*
(incorporates K.S.F. and RIDA photolibraries)
6 Orchard Drive, Wye,
Kent TN25 5AU
tel (01233) 812707 *fax* (01233) 812707
e-mail gsf@geoscience.demon.co.uk
web site http://www.geoscience.demon.co.uk
Director Dr Basil Booth
Colour library (35mm to 5 x 4in).
Animals, biology, birds, botany, chemistry, earth science, ecology, environment, geology, geography, habitats, landscapes, macro/micro, peoples, plants,
travel, sky, weather, wildlife and zoology; Americas, Africa, Australasia,
Europe, India, South-East Asia. Over one
third million colour images available as
film or high resolution digital images.
CD-Rom available to order.

Geoslides*
4 Christian Fields, London SW16 3JZ
tel/fax 0181-764 6292 or 0115-981 9418
Library Director John Douglas
Broadly based and substantial collections
from Africa, Asia, Antarctic, Arctic and
sub-Arctic areas, Australia (Blackwood
Collection). Worldwide commissions
undertaken. Photographs for all types of
publications, television, advertising.
Terms: 50% on UK sales. Founded 1968.

Mark Gerson Photography

3 Regal Lane, Regents Park Road,
London NW1 7TH
tel 0171-286 5894 *fax* 0171-267 9246

Portrait photographs of personalities, mainly literary, in colour and b&w from 1950 to the present. No other photographers' material required.

John Glover Photography

Fairfield, Hale House Lane, Churt, Farnham,
Surrey GU10 2NQ
tel (01428) 717196 *mobile* (0973) 307078
fax (01428) 717129
e-mail john@glovphot.demon.co.uk

Gardens and gardening, from overall views of gardens to plant portraits with Latin names; UK landscapes including ancient sites, Stonehenge, etc. Founded 1979.

Martin and Dorothy Grace*

40 Clipstone Avenue, Mapperley,
Nottingham NG3 5JZ
tel 0115-920 8248 *fax* 0115-962 6802
e-mail graces@lineone.net

General British natural history, specialising in native trees, shrubs, flowers, ferns, habitats and ecology. Founded 1984.

Tim Graham Picture Library

31 Ferncroft Avenue, London NW3 7PG
tel 0171-435 7693 *fax* 0171-431 4312

Royal Family in this country and on tours; background pictures on royal homes, staff, hobbies, sports, cars, etc; English and foreign country scenes; international heads of state, VIPs and celebrities. Founded 1978.

Greater London Record Office – see London Metropolitan Archives

Angela Hampton Family Life Picture Library

Holly Tree House, The Street, Walberton,
Arundel, West Sussex BN18 0PH
tel/fax (01243) 555952
Proprietor Angela Hampton

Images of contemporary lifestyle including pregnancy, childbirth, babies and children, parenting, behaviour, education, medical, holidays, pets, families, couples,teenagers, women's health, men's health, retirement. Also domestic and farm animals. Over 50,000 colour transparencies. Founded 1991.

Robert Harding Picture Library*

58-59 Great Marlborough Street, London W1V 1DD
tel 0171-287 5414 *fax* 0171-631 1070

Photographic library. Require photographs of outstanding quality for advertising and editorial use, all subjects considered particularly lifestyle.

Harper Horticultural Slide Library

219 Robanna Drive, Seaford, VA 23696, USA
tel 757-898-6453 *fax* 757-890-9378

160,000 35mm slides of plants, gardens and native habitats.

Heritage & Natural History Photography

37 Plainwood Close, Summersdale, Chichester,
West Sussex PO19 4YB
tel (01243) 533822 *fax* (01243) 533822
Contact Dr John B. Free

Archaeology, history, agriculture: Arabia, China, India, Iran, Ireland, Japan, Kenya, Mediterranean countries, Mexico, Nepal, North America, Oman, Russia, Thailand, UK. Bees and bee keeping, insects and small invertebrates, tropical crops and flowers.

Pat Hodgson Library & Picture Research Agency

Jasmine Cottage, Spring Grove Road, Richmond,
Surrey TW10 6EH
tel 0181-940 5986

Small collection of b&w historical engravings, book illustrations, ephemera, etc; some colour and modern photos. Subjects include history, Victoriana, ancient civilisations, occult, travel. Text written and research undertaken on any subject. Of special interest to educational publishers, film makers and exhibition designers.

Holt Studios International Ltd*

The Courtyard, 24 High Street, Hungerford,
Berks. RG17 0NF
tel (01488) 683523 *fax* (01488) 683511
e-mail library@holt-studios.co.uk
web site http://www.holt-studios.co.uk/library

80,000 pictures on worldwide agriculture, horticulture, crops and associated pests (and their predators), diseases and deficiencies, farming people and practices, livestock, machinery, landscapes, diverse environments, natural flora and fauna. Founded 1981.

Horizon International

Photographers' enquiries Horizon International Creative Images Ltd, PO Box 144, 3 St Anne's Walk, Alderney GY9 3HF, Channel Islands
tel (44) 1481 822587 *fax* (44) 1481 823880
e-mail horizon.int@virgin.net
Picture research and sales enquiries Horizon Stock Images (UK) Ltd, 212 Piccadilly, London W1V 9LD
tel 0171-917 2937 *fax* 0171-917 2938
web site http://www.hrzn.com
Specialist stock library for advertising covering leisure and lifestyle, business and industry, science and medicine, environment and nature, world travel. Founded 1978.

David Hosking FRPS*

Pages Green House, Wetheringsett, Stowmarket, Suffolk IP14 5QA
tel (01728) 861113 *fax* (01728) 860222
e-mail pictures@flpa-images.co.uk
web site http://www.flpa-images.co.uk
Natural history subjects, especially birds covering whole world. Also Dr D.P. Wilson's unique collection of marine photos.

Houses & Interiors Photographic Features Agency*

82-84 Clerkenwell Road, London EC1M 5RJ
tel 0171-336 7942 *fax* 0171-336 7943
e-mail vicky@image-data.com
web site http://www.a-z.picture-library.com
Contact Victoria Norman
Stylish house interiors and exteriors, people in their homes and gardens, home dossiers, renovations, architectural details, interior design, gardens and houseplants. Also step-by-step photographic sequences of DIY subjects, fresh and dried flower arrangements and gardening techniques. Food. Colour only. Commissions undertaken. Terms: 50%, negotiable. Founded 1985.

Hulton Getty Picture Collection*

101 Bayham Street, London NW1 0AG
tel 0171-544 3333 *fax* 0171-544 3334
web site http://www.hultongetty.com
One of the largest picture resources in Europe, with over 15 million b&w and colour images. Specialises in social history, Royalty, transport, war, fashion, sport, entertainment, people, places and early photography. Collections include *Picture Post, Express, Evening Standard*, Keystone, Fox and Topical Press.

Publisher of CD-Roms for creative image access.

Hutchison Picture Library*

118B Holland Park Avenue, London W11 4UA
tel 0171-229 2743 *fax* 0171-792 0259
e-mail katepink@hutchisonpic.demon.co.uk
General colour library; worldwide subjects: agriculture, environments, festivals, human relationships, industry, landscape, peoples, religion, towns, travel. Founded 1976.

The Illustrated London News Picture Library*

20 Upper Ground, London SE1 9PF
tel 0171-805 5585 *fax* 0171-805 5905
Engravings, photos, illustrations in b&w and colour from 1842 to present day, especially 19th and 20th century social history, wars, portraits, Royalty.

The Image Bank*

17 Conway Street, London W1P 6EE
tel 0171-312 0300 *fax* 0171-391 9111
web site http://www.imagebank.co.uk
Image Bank Dublin
11 Upper Mount Street, Dublin 2
tel (01) 676 0872 *fax* (01) 676 0873
Image Bank Manchester
4 Jordan Street, Manchester M15 4PY
tel 0161-236 9226 *fax* 0161-236 8723
Image Bank Scotland
14 Alva Street, Edinburgh EH2 4QG
tel 0131-225 1770 *fax* 0131-225 1660
General library of still and moving imagery from the world's top artists. Digital search facilities and CD catalogues. Founded 1979.

Image Diggers

618B Finchley Road, London NW11 7RR
tel/fax 0181-455 4564
Contact Neil Hornick
Stills archive covering performing arts, popular culture, human interest, natural history, architecture, nautical, children and people, strange phenomena, religions and other. Also audio and video for research purposes and ephemera including magazines, books, comic books, sheet music, postcards. Founded 1980.

Imagefinder Pte Ltd

228A South Bridge Road, Singapore 058777
tel (65) 324 3747 *fax* (65) 324 3748
e-mail imagef@mbox4.singnet.com.sg
web site http://www.profilephoto.com.hk
Director Neil Farrin

Thailand office
Room 406, 4th Floor Kitpanit Building,
18 Patpong Soi 1, Suriwonges Road, Bangrak,
Bangkok 10500
tel (662) 634 3065 *fax* (662) 634 3066
e-mail winyou@ksc9.th.com

General photo library. Film footage available. Terms: 50%. Founded 1982.

Images Colour Library Ltd*

Leeds Office Manager Jess Diebel
15-17 High Court Lane, The Calls,
Leeds LS2 7EU
tel 0113-243 3389 *fax* 0113-242 5605
London Office Manager Julie Chamberlain
Ramillies House, 1-2 Ramillies Street,
London W1V 1DF
tel 0171-734 7344 *fax* 0171-287 3933

General, contemporary stock library including people, business, UK and world travel, industry and sport. Founded 1983.

Images of Africa Photobank*

11 The Windings, Lichfield,
Staffs. WS13 7EX
tel (01543) 262898 *fax* (01543) 417154
Contact Jacquie Shipton, Library Manager
Proprietor David Keith Jones, ABIPP, FRPS

135,000 images covering 14 African countries: Botswana, Egypt, Ethiopia, Kenya, Malawi, Namibia, Rwanda, South Africa, Swaziland, Tanzania, Uganda, Zaire, Zambia and Zimbabwe. Specialities: wildlife, people, landscapes, tourism, hotels and lodges, National Parks and Reserves. Colour brochure available. Terms: 50%. Founded 1983.

Imperial War Museum*

Photograph Archive, Austral Street,
London SE11 4SL
tel 0171-416 5333/8 *fax* 0171-416 5355
e-mail photos@iwm.org.uk

National archive of over 5 million photos, dealing with war in the 20th century involving the armed forces of Britain and the Commonwealth countries. Open by appointment Mon-Fri. Enquiries should be as specific as possible; prints made to order. Founded 1917.

International Press Agency (Pty) Ltd

PO Box 67, Howard Place 7450,
South Africa
tel (021) 531 1926 *fax* (021) 531 8789
e-mail inpra@iafrica.com

Press photos for South African market. Founded 1934.

Isle of Wight Photo Library*

The Old Rectory, Calbourne,
Isle of Wight PO30 4JE
tel (01983) 531247 *fax* (01983) 531253

Specialist library of colour transparencies of the Isle of Wight: landscapes, seascapes, architecture, gardens, flora and boats. In association with **S. & O. Mathews**. Founded 1995.

Isle of Wight Pictures

60 York Street, Cowes, Isle of Wight PO31 7BS
tel/fax (01983) 290366 *mobile* (0468) 877914
Proprietor Patrick Eden

Covers all aspects of the Isle of Wight, including Cowes Week, sailing events, nautical aspects. Any picture not on file can be shot on request. Founded 1985.

Japan Archive

9 Victoria Drive, Horsforth, Leeds LS18 4PN
tel 0113-258 3244
e-mail stephen.turnbull@virgin.net
web site http://freespace.virgin.net/stephen.turnbull/japanarchive.htm
Contact S.R. Turnbull

Japan: modern, daily life, architecture, religion, history, personalities, gardens, natural world. Founded 1993.

Jazz Index*

26 Fosse Way, London W13 0BZ
tel/fax 0181-998 1232
e-mail 106400.1300@compuserve.com

Photo library of jazz, blues and contemporary musicians. Also photos of instruments, clubs, crowds at concerts. Photos sold on behalf of photographers. Terms: 50%. Founded 1979.

Joe Filmbase Photo Agency/Library

1 Town Mead Business Centre, William Morris Way, London SW6 2SZ
tel/fax 0171-371 9902
e-mail 113610.251@compuserve.com

General library: fashion, catwalk, people, ideas, art photos, business, traders, travel, dance, concerts, cars, boats, lifestyle, nature, worldwide. Transparencies only: 35mm, 6 x 7cm etc. Founded 1991.

JS Library International

101A Brondesbury Park, London NW2 5JL
tel 0181-451 2668 *fax* 0181-459 0223
e-mail jslibraryinternational@ukbusiness.com
web site http://www.ukbusiness.com/jslibraryinternational

The Royal Family, worldwide travel pictures, particularly the African continent, stage and screen celebrities, authors, worldwide general material. New material on any subject, in any quantity, always urgently required; features also required. Assignments undertaken. Founded 1979.

Just Europe
50 Basingfield Road, Thames Ditton,
Surrey KT7 0PD
tel/fax 0181-398 2468
Specialises in Europe – major cities, towns, people and customs. Assignments undertaken; background information available; advice/research service. Founded 1989.

Lakeland Life Picture Library
Langsett, Lyndene Drive, Grange-over-Sands,
Cumbria LA11 6QP
tel (015395) 33565 (answerphone)
English Lake District: industries, crafts, sports, shows, customs, architecture, people. Also provides colour and b&w, illustrated articles. Not an agency. Catalogue available on request. Founded 1979.

Frank Lane Picture Agency Ltd*
Pages Green House, Wetheringsett, Stowmarket,
Suffolk IP14 5QA
tel (01728) 860789 *fax* (01728) 860222
e-mail pictures@flpa-images.co.uk
web site http://www.flpa-images.co.uk
Natural history, ecology, environment, farming, geography, trees and weather.

Michael Leach
Brookside, Kinnerley, Oswestry SY10 8DB
tel/fax (01691) 682639
General worldwide wildlife and natural history subjects, with particular emphasis on mammals and urban wildlife. Comprehensive collection of owls from all over the world. No other photographers required.

Dave Lewis Nostalgia Collection
20 The Avenue, Starbeck, Harrogate,
North Yorkshire NG1 4QD
tel/fax (01423) 888642
e-mail davelewis@zoo.co.uk
web site http://www.zoo.co.uk/~davelewis
A collection of advertising, packaging and points of sale from 1800s to 1960s. Many images are on transparency and specific requests can be undertaken. Founded 1995.

Link Picture Library*
33 Greyhound Road, London W6 8NH
tel 0171-381 2261/2433 *fax* 0171-385 6244

e-mail lib@linkpics.demon.co.uk
Proprietor Orde Eliason
Specialist archives on Southern Africa, Asia, Southeast Asia, Israel and music. Electronic images on Photo CD Disc. Commissions accepted. Terms: 50%. Founded 1982.

London Metropolitan Archives
(formerly Greater London Record Office)
40 Northampton Road, London EC1R 0HB
tel 0171-332 3820 *fax* 0171-833 9136
minicom 0171-278 8703
e-mail lma@ms.corpoflondon.gov.uk
Over 350,000 photographic prints and 1,500,000 negatives of London and the London area from c.1860 to 1986. Especially strong on local authority projects, including schools, public housing and open spaces.

The Billie Love Historical Collection
Reflections, 3 Winton Street, Ryde,
Isle of Wight PO33 2BX
tel (01983) 812572 *fax* (01983) 811164
Proprietor Billie Love
Photos (late 19th century-1930s), engravings, coloured lithographs, covering subjects from earliest times, people, places and events up to the Second World War; also more recent material. Founded 1969.

Ludvigsen Library Ltd*
73 Collier Street, London N1 9BE
tel 0171-837 1700 *fax* 0171-837 1776
e-mail ludvigsen@mail.bogo.co.uk
Photographic resources Paul Parker
Specialist automotive and motor racing photo library. Includes much rare and unpublished material from John Dugdale, Edward Eves, Max le Grand, Karl Ludvigsen, Rodolfo Mailander, Ove Nielsen, Stanley Rosenthall and others. Founded 1984.

The MacQuitty International Collection*
7 Elm Lodge, River Gardens, Stevenage Road,
London SW6 6NZ
tel 0171-385 6031 *tel/fax* 0171-384 1781
300,000 photos covering aspects of life in 70 countries: archaeology, art, buildings, flora and fauna, gardens, museums, people and occupations, scenery, religions, methods of transport, surgery, acupuncture, funeral customs, fishing, farming, dancing, music, crafts, sports, weddings, carnivals,

food, drink, jewellery and oriental subjects. Period: 1920 to present day.

Mander & Mitchenson Theatre Collection*

The Mansion, Beckenham Place Park,
Beckenham, Kent BR3 2BP
tel 0181-658 7725 *fax* 0181-663 0313

Prints, drawings, photos, programmes, etc, theatre, opera, ballet, music hall, and other allied subjects including composers, playwrights, etc. All periods. Available for books, magazines, TV.

Mansell/Time Inc.

c/o Katz Pictures, Zetland House,
5-25 Scrutton Street, London EC2A 4LP
tel 0171-377 5888 *fax* 0171-377 5558

General historical material up to the 1920s, 1930s.

John Massey Stewart

20 Hillway, London N6 6QA
tel 0181-341 3544 *fax* 0181-341 5292

Large collection Russia/USSR, including topography, people, culture, Siberia, plus Russian and Soviet history, 3000 pre-revolutionary PCs, etc. Also Britain, Europe (including Bulgaria, Poland, Slovenia and Turkey), Alaska, USA, Israel, Sinai desert, etc.

S. & O. Mathews*

The Old Rectory, Calbourne,
Isle of Wight PO30 4JE
tel (01983) 531247 *fax* (01983) 531253

Gardens, flowers and landscapes.

Chris Mattison

138 Dalewood Road, Sheffield S8 0EF
tel/fax 0114-236 4433
e-mail chris.mattison@btinternet.com

Colour library specialising in reptiles and amphibians; other natural history subjects; habitats and landscapes in Africa, SE Asia, South America, USA, Mexico, Mediterranean. Captions or detailed copy supplied if required. No other photographers' material required.

Bill Meadows Picture Library

11 Tollhouse Drive, Oldbury Road, St Johns,
Worcester WR2 6AD
tel/fax (01905) 429254
Proprietor Bill Meadows

Aspects of Great Britain: general scenic including towns and villages; buildings and monuments; agricultural, industrial and building sites; urban scenes and services; misuse of the environment, vandalism, etc; recreational, 'people at play'; natural history subjects. 20,000 b&w photographs and 50,000 (6 x 6cm and 35mm) colour transparencies. Founded 1968.

Medimage

32 Brooklyn Road, Coventry CV1 4JT
tel/fax (01203) 668562
Contact Anthony King

Specialist library of 12,000 medium format transparencies of subjects in Mediterranean countries: agriculture, architecture, crafts, festivals, flora, industry, landscape, markets, portraits, recreation, seascapes, sport and transport. Commissions undertaken. Other photographers' work not accepted. Founded 1992.

Merseyside Photo Library

Suite 1, Egerton House, Tower Road, Birkenhead,
Wirral L41 1FN
tel 0151-650 6975 *fax* 0151-650 6976
e-mail ron@merseywide.demon.co.uk
Operated by Ron Jones Associates

Library specialising in images of Liverpool and Merseyside but includes other destinations. Founded 1989.

Microscopix

Middle Travelly, Beguildy, Nr Knighton,
Powys LD7 1UW
tel (01547) 510242 *fax* (01547) 510317
e-mail mik@micropix.demon.co.uk

Scientific photo library specialising in scanning electron micrographs and photomicrographs for technical and aesthetic purposes. Commissioned work, both biological and non-biological, undertaken offering a wide variety of applicable microscopical techniques. Founded 1986.

Military History Picture Library

3 Barton Buildings, Bath BA1 2JR
tel (01225) 334213 *fax* (01225) 480554

Prints, engravings, photos, colour transparencies covering all aspects of warfare and uniforms from ancient times to the present.

Mirror Syndication International*

One Canada Square, Canary Wharf,
London E14 5AP
tel 0171-293 3700 *fax* 0171-293 2712
e-mail desk@mirpix.com
web site http://www.mirpix.com

Specialises in current affairs, personalities, royalty, sport, cinema and travel. Agents for Mirror Group Newspapers.

Monitor Syndication
(incorporates the City Syndication library)
17 Old Street, London EC1V 9HL
tel 0171-253 7071 *fax* 0171-250 0966
Contact Joanna White
Specialists in portrait photos of leading national and international personalities from politics, trade unions, entertainment, sport, Royalty and well-known buildings in London. Plus editorial archive library dating back to the early days of photography. Founded 1960.

Motorcycles Unlimited
48 Lemsford Road, St Albans, Herts. AL1 3PR
tel (01727) 869001 *fax* (01727) 869014
e-mail rolandbrown@motobike.demon.co.uk
Owner Roland Brown
Bikes of all kinds, from latest roadsters to classics, racers to tourers. Detailed information available on all machines pictured. Founded 1993.

Mountain Dynamics
Heathcourt, Morven Way, Monaltrie,
Ballater AB35 5SF
tel (013397) 55081 *fax* (013397) 55526
e-mail gpa@globalnet.co.uk
Proprietor Graham P. Adams
Scottish and European mountains – from ground to summits – in panoramic (6 x 17cm), 5 x 4in and medium format. Commissions undertaken. Terms: 50%. Founded 1990.

Mountain Visions
25 The Mallards, Langstone, Havant,
Hants PO9 1SS
tel (01705) 478441
Contact Graham Elson and Roslyn Elson
Colour transparencies of mountaineering, skiing, and tourism in Europe, Africa, Himalayas, Arctic, Far East, South America and Australia. Does not act as agent for other photographers. Founded 1984.

The Mustograph Agency
19 Rathbone Street, London W1P 1AF
tel 0171-636 6128/9 *fax* 0171-637 4317
Britain only: b&w general subjects of countryside life, work, history and scenery.

National Maritime Museum Picture Library*
National Maritime Museum, Park Row,
London SE10 9NF
Contact David Taylor *tel* 0181-312 6631
Lindsey Macfarlane *tel* 0181-312 6704
Maritime, transport, time and space and historic photographs.

National Motor Museum, Beaulieu*
Motoring Picture Library, Beaulieu,
Hants SO42 7ZN
tel (01590) 612345 *fax* (01590) 612655
All aspects of motoring, cars, commercial vehicles, motor cycles, personalities, etc. Illustrations of period scenes and motor sport. Also large library of 5 x 4in and smaller colour transparencies of veteran, vintage and modern cars, commercial vehicles and motor cycles. Over 700,000 images in total.

Natural History Photographic Agency – see NHPA*

Natural Image
31 Shaftesbury Road, Poole,
Dorset BH15 2LT
tel (01202) 675916 *fax* (01202) 242944
e-mail bob.gibbons@which.net
Contact Dr Bob Gibbons
Colour library covering natural history, habitats, countryside and gardening (UK and worldwide); special emphasis on conservation. Commissions undertaken. Terms: 50%. Founded 1982.

The Nature and Landscape File
24 Southleigh Crescent, Leeds LS11 5TW
tel/fax 0113-2715535 *mobile* (0802) 540537
web site http://www.photosource.co.uk/photo-source/Nature&Landscape.htm
Proprietor Dr Mark Lucock
Natural history subjects and landscapes from around the world, especially the UK, southern Europe, North America. Specialises in photomacrographic images. Examples and subject list on web site. 30,000 large- and small-format colour transparencies. Founded 1997.

Peter Newark Pictures
3 Barton Buildings, Bath BA1 2JR
tel (01225) 334213 *fax* (01225) 480554
One million pictures: engravings, prints, paintings and photographs on all aspects of world history from ancient times to the present.

News Blitz International
Via Guido Banti 34, 00191 Rome, Italy
tel 333 26 41/333 02 52 *fax* 333 26 51
Contact Giovanni A. Congiu
News and general library.

NHPA*

(Natural History Photographic Agency)
57 High Street, Ardingly, West Sussex RH17 6TB
tel (01444) 892514 *fax* (01444) 892168
e-mail nhpa@nhpa.co.uk
web site http://www.nhpa.co.uk/nhpa
Represents more than 100 of the world's
leading natural history photographers
covering a wide range of wildlife, marine
life, domestic animals and pets, plants,
landscapes and environmental subjects.
Specialisations include the unique high-
speed photography of Stephen Dalton,
comprehensive coverage on North
America and Africa, and the ANT collection of Australasian material (for which
NHPA is UK agent). Recent additions to
the files include strong coverage on gardens, farm animals and big cats, plus
material from the Congo, Philippines and
New Caledonia. Pictures are generally
supplied to companies and institutions
only, and are sent to freelance writers
and artists by agreement with their publisher or commissioning company.

The Northern Picture Library*

Greenheys Business Centre, 10 Pencroft Way,
Manchester M15 6JJ
tel 0161-226 2007 *fax* 0161-226 2022
Proprietor Roy Conchie
General library covering Britain, the world,
industry, sport, leisure, etc. Submissions
considered from photographers.

Operation Raleigh – see Raleigh
International Picture Library

Orion Press

1-13 Kanda Jimbocho, Chiyodaku-ku,
Tokyo 101-0051, Japan
tel (03) 3295-1400 *fax* (03) 3295-0227
e-mail info@orionpress.co.jp
web site http://www.orionpress.co.jp
All subjects in all formats.

Christine Osborne/Middle East
Pictures Inc.*

53A Crimsworth Road, London SW8 4RJ
tel/fax 0171-720 6951
Specialises in the developing world,
notably Africa, Indian subcontinent,
Southeast Asia and Middle East/Arab
states (covers 30 Muslim countries).
Major files on Eastern cultures – religions (worship, rites of passage and festivals), geography, agriculture and food

production, architecture – rural and
urban environments, family life, education and social services, traditional
crafts, plus more than 50 travel destinations. Pictures updated by a small team
of contributors. Commissions undertak-
en. In-depth caption information provided. Fellow of the Royal Geographic
Society and the British Guild of Travel
Writers. French spoken. Founded 1984.

Oxford Scientific Films Ltd, Photo
Library*

(incorporating the Survival Anglia Photo Library)
Lower Road, Long Hanborough,
Oxon OX8 8LL
tel (01993) 881881 *fax* (01993) 882808
e-mail 101573.163@compuserve.com
300,000 colour transparencies of
wildlife, natural science, plants, gardens,
landscapes, habitats, agriculture, fossils,
minerals, rocks, domestic animals, tribal
people, weather, space and environmental images supplied by over 300 photographers worldwide. UK agents for
Animals Animals, New York; *Okapia*,
Frankfurt; *Dinodia*, India.

PA News Photo Library*

292 Vauxhall Bridge Road,
London SW1V 1AE
tel 0171-963 7032/34/35 *fax* 0171-963 7066
e-mail photo-sales@pa.press.net
web site http://www.pa.press.net
Over 5 million photos dating from the
turn of the century, covering news, sport,
royalty and showbiz. Library updated
daily. Searches undertaken, or customers
are welcome to visit. Founded 1902.

Panos Pictures*

1 Chapel Court, Borough High Street,
London SE1 1HH
tel 0171-234 0010 *fax* 0171-357 0094
e-mail panospics@corporate.nethead.co.uk
Third World and Eastern European documentary photos focusing on social, political and economic issues with a special
emphasis on environment and development. Files on agriculture, conflict, education, energy, environment, family life,
festivals, food, health, industry, landscape, people, politics, pollution,
refugees, religions, rural life, transport,
urban life, water, weather. Terms: 50%.
Founded 1986.

Papilio Natural History & Travel Library*
44 Palestine Grove, London SW19 2QN
tel/fax 0181-687 2202 *mobile* (0973) 310072
e-mail justine@papilio.demon.co.uk
Contacts Robert Pickett, Justine Bowler
Worldwide coverage of natural history and environmental subjects including travel section; commissions undertaken. Over 100,000 images held. Founded 1988.

Ann & Bury Peerless*
22 King's Avenue, Minnis Bay,
Birchington-on-Sea, Kent CT7 9QL
tel (01843) 841428 *fax* (01843) 848321
Art, craft (including textiles), archaeology, architecture, dance, iconography, miniature paintings, manuscripts, museum artefacts, social, cultural, agricultural, industrial, historical, political, educational, geographical subjects and travel in India, Pakistan, Bangladesh, Afghanistan, Burma, Cambodia, China, Egypt, Iran, Israel, Kenya, Libya, Malta, Malaysia, Morocco, Nepal, Russia (Moscow, St Petersburg, Samarkand and Bukhara, Uzbekistan), Sri Lanka, Spain, Sudan, Taiwan, Thailand, Tunisia, Uganda, Zambia and Zimbabwe. Specialist material on historical and world religions: Hinduism, Buddhism, Jainism, Judaism, Christianity, Confucianism, Islam, Sikhism, Taoism, Zoroastrianism (Parsees of India).

Chandra S. Perera Cinetra
437 Pethiyagoda, Kelaniya-11600, Sri Lanka
tel (94) 1-911885 *fax* (94) 1-541414/332867
B&w and colour library including news, wildlife, religious, social, political, sports, adventure, environmental, forestry, nature and tourism. Photographic and journalistic features on any subject. Founded 1958.

Performing Arts Library*
52 Agate Road, London W6 0AH
tel 0181-748 2002 *fax* 0181-563 0538
e-mail peformingartslibrary@compuserve.com
Specialist library with an international portfolio including: actors, singers, musicians, conductors, opera, composers, ballet, plays, musical instruments, venues and theatre ephemera. Originally based on the work of Clive Barda, the library now covers all aspects of the performing arts and holds over half a million images, including European and archival material dating from the early part of the century. Founded 1992.

Photo Link
126 Quarry Lane, Northfield, Birmingham B31 2QD
tel 0121-475 8712 *fax* 0121-604 0480
e-mail vines_photolink@compuserve.com
Contact Mike Vines
Colour and b&w aviation library, covering subjects from 1909 to the present day. Specialises in air-to-air photography. Assignments undertaken; can also research and write aviation press releases. Founded 1990.

Photo Resources*
The Orchard, Marley Lane, Kingston, Canterbury, Kent CT4 6JH
tel (01227) 830075 *fax* (01227) 831135
Ancient civilisations, art, archaeology, world religions, myth, and museum objects covering the period from 30,000 BC to AD 1900. European birds, butterflies, trees.

Photofusion*
17A Electric Lane, London SW9 8LA
tel 0171-738 5774 *fax* 0171-738 5509
web site http://www.photosource.co.uk/photosource/photofusion.htm
Covers all aspects of UK contemporary life with an emphasis on social issues. Catalogue available. Photographers available for commission.

The Photographers' Library*
81A Endell Street, London WC2H 9AJ
tel 0171-836 5591 *fax* 0171-379 4650
Requires transparency material on business, lifestyles, worldwide travel, industry, agriculture, sport, scenic. Colour only. Terms: 50%. Founded 1978.

Pictor International Ltd*
Lymehouse Studios, 30-31 Lyme Street, London NW1 0EE
tel 0171-482 0478 *fax* 0171-267 5759
e-mail postmaster@pictor.demon.co.uk
web site http://www.pictor.co.uk
Offices and agents in over 20 countries. All subjects. Terms: 50%.

The Picture Company
3 Barley Rise, Baldock, Herts. SG7 6RT
tel (01462) 894742 *Mobile* 0850-971491
fax (01438) 726969
Contact Chris Bonass

Colour transparencies ($2^{1}/4$ x $2^{1}/4$in and 35mm) of people and places worldwide. Taken by award-winning film and TV cameraman and largely unseen and unpublished. Also aviation pictures old and new, including air-to-air photography and a unique archive on 16mm film and broadcast videotape. Used by BBC, C4, etc. Assignments undertaken. Founded 1993.

Picture House

15A Oxton Road, Sandringham, Auckland, New Zealand
tel/fax (09) 846 6989 *Mobile* (025) 280 9735
UK tel (01274) 672 664
Director R.D. Langron

Creative travel in Europe, North and Central America, India, Nepal and New Zealand. Specialist subjects: Mayan civilisation in Mexico, Guatemala and Honduras; Himalayan life in Ladakh. Commission: 50%. Founded 1993.

Picture Research Service

Rich Research, One Bradby, 77 Carlton Hill, London NW8 9XE
tel/fax 0171-624 7755
Contact Diane Rich

Visuals found for all sectors of the media and publishing. Artwork and photography commissioned. Rights and permissions negotiated.

Picturepoint Ltd – see Topham Picturepoint*

Sylvia Pitcher Photo Library

75 Bristol Road, London E7 8HG
tel/fax 0181-552 8308

Musicians: blues, jazz, old-time country and bluegrass, cajun and zydeco plus related ephemera. Views and details of the USA: countryside, 'small-town America', shacks, railroads, rural Americana. Archival: early 20th century – mainly cottonfields, riverboats and various cities in the USA. 1960s-1970s: girls (both white and black) and couples. Founded 1968.

Pixfeatures

5 Latimer Road, Barnet, Herts. EN5 5NU
tel 0181-449 9946 *fax* 0181-441 2725
Contact Peter Wickman

Pictures and features covering big news events, royalty, showbiz and travel (all countries). National newspapers' extensive collection of people in the news to

1970. *Stern* magazine features (before 1985). Documentary and historical photos. Special collections: Dukes of Windsor and Kent, Kennedys, Beatles, Keeler/Levy, trainrobbers and Second World War. Terms: 50%.

Planet Earth Pictures*

The Innovation Centre, 225 Marsh Wall, London E14 9FX
tel 0171-293 2999 *fax* 0171-293 2998
e-mail planetearth@visualgroup.com
web site http://www.plant-earth-pictures.com

All aspects of natural history and the natural environment, farming, fishing, pollution and conservation. Founded 1969.

POPPERFOTO (Paul Popper Ltd)*

The Old Mill, Overstone Farm, Overstone, Northampton NN6 0AB
tel (01604) 670670 *fax* (01604) 670635

Over 13 million images, covering 150 years of photographic history. Unrivalled archival material, world-famous sports library and extensive stock photography. Credit line includes Reuters, Bob Thomas Sports Photography, UPI, AFP and EPA, Acme, INP, Planet, Paul Popper, Exclusive News Agency, Victory Archive, Odhams Periodicals Library, *Illustrated*, Harris Picture Agency, and H.G. Ponting which holds the Scott 1910-12 Antarctic expedition material.

Colour from 1940, b&w from 1870 to present. Major subjects covered worldwide include: events, personalities, wars, royalty, sport, politics, transport, crime, history and social conditions. POPPERFOTO policy is to make material available, same day, to clients throughout the world. Mac-desk accessible. Researchers welcome by appointment. Free catalogue available.

Power Pix International Picture Library – see S. & I. Williams, Power Pix International Picture Library

Premaphotos Wildlife

Amberstone, 1 Kirland Road, Bodmin, Cornwall PL30 5JQ
tel (01208) 78258 *fax* (01208) 72302
e-mail premaphotos@compuserve.com
Contact Dr Rod Preston-Mafham

Library of 35mm transparencies; wide range of natural history subjects from around the world, including camouflage, mimicry, warning coloration, parental care, courtship, mating, flowers, fruits, fungi, habitats (particularly rainforests and deserts), and many more. Specialists in invertebrate behaviour and cacti. Captions and copy can be provided. Founded 1978.

Press Association Photos – see PA News Photo Library*

Press Features Syndicate
9 Paradise Close, Eastbourne,
East Sussex BN20 8BT
tel (01323) 728760
For full details see page 153.

Public Record Office Image Library*
Public Record Office, Ruskin Avenue, Kew,
Surrey TW9 4DU
tel 0181-392 5225 *fax* 0181-392 5266
e-mail image-library@pro.gov.uk
web site http://www.pro.gov.uk/imagelibrary
Unique collection of millions of historical documents on a wide range of formats from 1066 to 1960s. Special collections include: Victorian and Edwardian advertisements and photographs, World War Two propaganda, military history, maps, decorative and technical designs and medieval illuminations. Founded 1995.

Punch Cartoon Library*
100 Brompton Road, London SW3 1ER
tel 0171-225 6711/6710 *fax* 0171-225 6712
e-mail edit@punch.co.uk
Comprehensive collection of cartoons and illustrations, indexed under subject categories: humour, historical events, politics, fashion, sport, personalities, etc. Founded 1841.

Railways – Milepost 92½*
Milepost 92½, Newton Harcourt,
Leics. LE8 9FH
tel 0116-259 2068 *fax* 0116-259 3001
e-mail michael@milepost.demon.co.uk
Comprehensive collection of all aspects of modern railway operations, and scenic pictures from the UK and abroad. Includes Colin Garratt's collection of world steam trains as well as archive b&w photos. Founded 1969.

Raleigh International Picture Library
Raleigh House, 27 Parson's Green Lane,
London SW6 4HS
tel 0171-371 8585 *fax* 0171-371 5116
e-mail Andrew@raleigh.org.uk
web site http://raleigh.org.uk
Contact Andrew Osborne
Source of stock colour images from locations around the world: the 100,000-plus images are updated 10 times a year. Open to researchers by appointment Mon and Tues, 9.30 a.m.-4.00 p.m.

Redferns Music Picture Library*
7 Bramley Road, London W10 6SZ
tel 0171-792 9914 *fax* 0171-792 0921
e-mail info@redferns.com
Contact Dede Millar
All styles of music, from 1920s jazz to current Top 10, plus instruments, crowds, festivals and atmospherics. Brochure available. Commission 50%. Founded 1963.

Retna Pictures Ltd*
1 Fitzroy Mews, Cleveland Street,
London W1P 5DQ
tel 0171-209 0200 *fax* 0171-383 7151
Library of colour transparencies and b&w prints of rock and pop performers, show business personalities, celebrities, actors and actresses. Also extensive lifestyle and stock library. Founded 1984.

Retrograph Nostalgia Archive Ltd
164 Kensington Park Road, London W11 2ER
tel 0171-727 9378 *answerphone* (outside office hours) 0171-727 9426 *fax* 0171-229 3395
e-mail mbreese999@aol.com
Worldwide advertising, packaging, posters, postcards, decorative and fine art illustrations from 1880-1970. Special collections include Victoriana illustrations and scraps (1860-1901), fashion and beauty (1880-1975), RetroTravel Archive: travel and tourism, RetroGourmet Archive: food and drink (1890-1950). Research service and Image Consultancy services; Retro-Montages: Victoriana montage design service. Free colour leaflets. Founded 1984.

Ann Ronan at Image Select*
19 Radnor Road, Harrow, Middlesex HA1 1RY
tel 0181-861 1122 *fax* 0181-861 4755
Woodcuts, engravings, etc, social and political history plus history of science and technology, including military and space, literature and music.

Roundhouse Ornithology Collection
c/o John Stewart-Smith, 24 Carneton Close,
Crantock, Newquay, Cornwall TR8 5RY
tel/fax (01637) 830546

Colour library specialising in birds of UK, Europe, Middle East (especially), North Africa, Far East and South America. Founded 1991.

Royal Geographical Society Picture Library*
1 Kensington Gore, London SW7 2AR
tel 0171-591 3060 *fax* 0171-591 3061
e-mail pictures@rgs.org
Contact Picture Library Manager
Worldwide coverage of geography, travel, exploration, expeditions and cultural environment from 1870s to the present. Founded 1830.

The Royal Photographic Society*
The Octagon, Milsom Street, Bath BA1 1DN
tel (01225) 462841 *fax* (01225) 448688
History of photography from 1827 to the present day. Founded 1853.

The Royal Society for Asian Affairs
2 Belgrave Square, London SW1X 8PJ
tel 0171-235 5122 *fax* 0171-259 6771
e-mail info@rsaa.org.uk
web site http://www.rsaa.org.uk
Archive library of original 19th and 20th century b&w photos, glass slides, etc, of Asia. Publishes *Asian Affairs* (3 p.a.).

Royal Society of Chemistry Library and Information Centre*
Burlington House, Piccadilly, London W1V 0BN
tel 0171-437 8656 *fax* 0171-287 9798
e-mail library@rsc.org
web site http://www.rsc.org
Covers all aspects of chemistry information. Images collection dating from 1538 includes prints and photographs of famous chemists, *Vanity Fair* cartoons, scenes, lantern slides of similar subjects and colour photomicrographs of crystal structures. Founded 1841.

RSPCA Photolibrary*
RSPCA Trading Ltd, Causeway, Horsham, West Sussex RH12 1HG
tel (01403) 223150 *fax* (01403) 241048
e-mail photolibrary@rspca.org.uk
Manager Andrew Forsyth
A comprehensive collection of natural history pictures representing the work of over 300 photographers, and a unique record of the work of the RSPCA. Its specialist collection covers: animal hospitals, veterinary treatment, wildlife rehabilitation work, cruelty to animals, animal welfare education, RSPCA inspectors at work and other animal welfare issues such as environmental problems and cruel sports. Founded 1993.

Dawn Runnals Photographic Library
5 St Marys Terrace, Kenwyn Road, Truro, Cornwall TR1 3SW
tel (01872) 279353
General library: land and seascapes, flora and fauna, sport, animals, people, buildings, boats, harbours, miscellaneous section and some specialised subjects – details on application. Other photographers' work not accepted. Sae appreciated with enquiries. Founded 1985.

Russia and Eastern Images*
Sonning, Cheapside Lane, Denham, Uxbridge, Middlesex UB9 5AE
tel (01895) 833508 *fax* (01895) 834028
Library Manager Mark Wadlow
Architecture, cities, landscapes, people and travel images covering Russia and the former Soviet Union. Excellent background knowledge available and Russian language spoken. Contributors welcome. Founded 1988.

Salamander Picture Library
8 Blenheim Court, Brewery Road, London N7 9NT
tel 0171-700 7799 *fax* 0171-700 3918
Picture Manager Terry Forshaw
General collection including American history, collectables, cookery, crafts, military, natural history, space and transport. Founded 1996.

Peter Sanders Photography*
24 Meades Lane, Chesham, Bucks. HP5 1ND
tel/fax (01494) 773674
e-mail petersanders.photography@btinternet.com
Specialises in Islamic world, but now expanding into other world religions, beliefs, cultures, architecture and industry. Founded 1987.

Steffi Schubert, Wildlife Conservation Collection Photographic Library
Bramble Cottage, Foxhill, St Cross, South Elmham, Harleston, Norfolk IP20 0NX
tel/fax (01986) 782279
All aspects of British wildlife and fauna. Founded 1990.

Science Photo Library*
112 Westbourne Grove, London W2 5RU
tel 0171-727 4712 *fax* 0171-727 6041
e-mail andy@sciencephoto.co.uk

web site http://www.sciencephoto.com
Scientific photography of all kinds –
medicine, technology, Space, nature.
110,000 different images. Founded 1979.

Science & Society Picture Library*
Science Museum, Exhibition Road,
London SW7 2DD
tel 0171-938 9750 *fax* 0171-938 9751
e-mail piclib@nmsi.ac.uk
web site http://www.nmsi.ac.uk/piclib/
Subjects include: science and technology,
medicine, industry, transport, social documentary and the media. Extensive collection; images drawn from the Science
Museum in London, the National
Railway Museum in York and the
National Museum of Photography, Film
and Television in Bradford. Free brochure
available on request. Founded 1993.

Scotland in Focus Picture Library
22 Fleming Place, Fountainhall, Galashiels,
Selkirkshire TD1 2TA
tel (01578) 760324 *fax* (01578) 760256
e-mail scotfocus@taynet.co.uk
web site http://www.scotland.net/postcards/
frameset_index.htm
Specialist library offering thousands of
stock images to illustrate every aspect of
Scottish life and work.
Scottish Wildlife Library
Environmental and natural history
subjects.
All Scottish material required on 35mm
and upwards, medium format preferred.
Photographers must enclose return
postage. Terms: 50%. Founded 1988.

SCR Photo Library
Society for Co-operation in Russian and Soviet
Studies, 320 Brixton Road, London SW9 6AB
tel 0171-274 2282 *fax* 0171-274 3230
Russian and Soviet life and history. Comprehensive coverage of cultural subjects:
art, theatre, folk art, costume, music;
agriculture and industry, architecture,
armed forces, education, history, places,
politics, science, sport. Also posters and
theatre props, artistic reference, advice.
Research by appointment only. Founded
1924.

Seaco Picture Library*
Sea Containers House, 20 Upper Ground,
London SE1 9PF
tel 0171-805 5831/5834 *fax* 0171-805 5807

Stills and video footage of: container
shipping; fast ferries and ports; produce
and fruit farming – India and Africa;
hotels and resorts in Botswana, South
Africa, Portugal, USA, Brazil, Italy and
Australia. Railways, including the
Venice-Simplon-Orient-Express and
Oriental Express luxury tourist train services and the recently launched Road to
Mandalay cruiseship in Burma. Founded
1995.

Sealand Aerial Photography Ltd*
Goodwood Airfield, Goodwood, Chichester,
West Sussex PO18 0PH
tel (01243) 781025 *fax* (01243) 531422
Aerial photo coverage of any subject that
can be photographed from the air in the
UK. Most stock on 2¼in format colour
negative/transparency. Subjects constantly
updated from new flying. Founded 1976.

S & G Press Agency Ltd*
63 Gee Street, London EC1V 3RS
tel 0171-336 0632 *fax* 0171-253 8419
Press photos and vast photo library. Send
photos, but negatives preferred.

Mick Sharp Photography
Eithinog, Waun, Penisarwaun, Caernarfon,
Gwynedd LL55 3PW
tel/fax (01286) 872425
Archaeology, ancient monuments, buildings, churches, countryside, environment, history, landscape, past cultures
and topography. Emphasis on British
Isles, but material also from other countries. Access to other specialist collections on related subjects. B&w prints
from 5 x 4in negatives, and 35mm and
6 x 4.5cm colour transparencies.
Founded 1981.

Shout Picture Library
Rowan House, Aston-le-Walls,
Northants. NN11 6UF
tel (01295) 660374 *fax* (01295) 660518
e-mail john@shout-pictures.demon.co.uk
web site http://www.shout-pictures.demon.co.uk
Contact John Callan
Specialises in the emergency services:
fires, road traffic accidents, surgery, various police and hospital units.
Commissions accepted; terms as recommended by BAPLA. Founded 1994.

Brian and Sal Shuel – see Collections*

Sites, Sights and Cities
2 Godsons Piece, High Street, Lower Brailes,
Banbury, Oxon OX15 5AQ
tel/fax (01608) 685119
e-mail devereuxp@aol.com
Director Paul Devereux

Ancient monuments, mainly in Britain, Egypt, Greece and USA; city features in UK, Europe and USA; general nature shots. Founded 1990.

Skishoot – Offshoot*
Hall Place, Upper Woodcott, Whitchurch,
Hants RG28 7PY
tel (01635) 255527 *fax* (01635) 255528
e-mail skishoot@surfersparadise.net
Librarian Fiona Foote

Library specialising in all aspects of skiing and snowboarding. Also France, all year round. Assignments undertaken. Terms: 50%. Founded 1986.

Skyscan Photolibrary*
Oak House, Toddington, Cheltenham,
Glos. GL54 5BY
tel (01242) 621357 *fax* (01242) 621343
e-mail info@skyscan.co.uk
web site http://www.skyscan.co.uk

Based on the unique Skyscan Balloon views of Britain, the library has expanded to include collections from across the aviation spectrum. Ballooning, paragliding and other aerial sports; aircraft both military and civil, air-to-air, RAF life; aviation; international air-to-ground images, etc. Terms: 50%. Founded 1984.

The Slide File*
79 Merrion Square South, Dublin 2,
Republic of Ireland
tel (01) 6766850 *fax* (01) 6624476

Specialises in Eire and Northern Ireland: landscapes, Irish natural history, agriculture and industry, Irish people and their traditions, Celtic heritage. Founded 1978.

Harry Smith Horticultural Photographic Collection
Mayfield Studio, South Hanningfield Road,
Wickford, Essex SS11 7PF
tel (01268) 710044 *fax* (01268) 710122
e-mail hsmithhortphoto@compuserve.com
Partners Françoise Davis and Barbara Elkington

All aspects of horticulture, including large and small gardens, specialist sections on all subjects including trees, fruit, vegetables, herbs, cacti, orchids, grasses, cultivated and wild flowers from all over the world, pests and diseases, action shots. Founded 1974.

Patrick Smith Associates
c/o Arioma, PO Box 53, Aberystwyth SY24 5WG
tel (01970) 871296 *fax* (01970) 871733

South London 1950-1977, mid-Wales, aviation; also The Patrick Smith Collection of London photos, now in The Museum of London. Founded 1964.

Society for Anglo-Chinese Understanding
Sally & Richard Greenhill Photo Library,
357A Liverpool Road, London N1 1NL
tel 0171-607 8549 *fax* 0171-607 7151

Colour and b&w prints of China, late 1960s-1989. Founded 1965.

Society for Co-operation in Russian and Soviet Studies – see SCR Photo Library

Source Photographic Archives
66 Claremont Road, Sandymount, Dublin 4,
Republic of Ireland
tel (01) 6607090
Director Thomas Kennedy

Mostly recent photos by living photographers on many different subjects. Founded 1974.

Spectrum Colour Library*
41-42 Berners Street, London W1P 3AA
tel 0171-637 1587 *fax* 0171-637 3681

Extensive general library of high-quality transparencies, for worldwide marketing, including electronically. Photographer's information pack available. Purchases photos and collections of photos.

Sporting Pictures (UK) Ltd*
7A Lambs Conduit Passage,
London WC1R 4RG
tel 0171-405 4500 *fax* 0171-831 7991
e-mail photos@sportingpictures.demon.co.uk
Director Crispin J. Thruston
Librarian Peter Collingwood

Specialises in sports, sporting events, sportsmen.

Peter Stiles Picture Library
49 Palmerston Avenue, Goring-by-Sea,
West Sussex BN12 4RN
tel/fax (01903) 503147 *mobile* (0976) 351369
e-mail p.stiles@btinternet.com
web site http://www.peterstiles.com

Specialises in horticulture, plus natural history, pictorial views. Sequences and illustrated features. Own pictures only. Commissions undertaken.

The Still Moving Picture Company*

67A Logie Green Road, Edinburgh EH7 4HF
tel 0131-557 9697 *fax* 0131-557 9699
e-mail StillmovingPictures@compuserve.com

250,000 pictures of Scotland and all things Scottish; sport (Allsport agent for Scotland). Founded 1991.

STILL Pictures Whole Earth Photo Library*

199 Shooters Hill Road, London SE3 8UL
tel 0181-858 8307 *fax* 0181-858 2049
e-mail stillpictures@stillpic.demon.co.uk
Proprietor Mark Edwards

Specialises in people and the environment; the Third World; wildlife and habitats. Includes industry, agriculture, indigenous peoples and cultures, nature and endangered species. Terms: 50%. Founded 1970.

Stockwave

43 Drury Lane, London WC2B 4RT
tel 0171-836 6608 *fax* 0181-836 6553
e-mail photos@stockwave.com
web site http://www.stockwave.com

Collections encompassing British culture, society, government, politics, royals, industry and tourism.

Britain on View

Photo library of the British Tourist Authority. British culture, society, events, landscapes, towns and villages, tourist attractions.

COI Photo Library

located at Stockwave's Aylesbury office
tel (01296) 747747 *fax* (01296) 748648
e-mail photos@stockwave.com
web site http://www.stockwave.com

The photo library of the Central Office of Information. The collection has many important and previously unseen images of Britain's political events, Government, British royals, science and technology, industry, agriculture, defence, Britain's overseas interests.

London Scene

A new library of contemporary, creative images being created by associate photographers and image makers using traditional and digital processes. Contributing artists need to be highly original and motivated. Founded 1998.

Tony Stone Images*

101 Bayham Street, London NW1 0AG
tel 0171-544 3333 *fax* 0171-544 3334
Contact Creative Dept

International photo library. Subjects required: travel, people, natural history, commerce, industry, technology, sport, etc. Terms: 50%.

Survival Anglia Photo Library – see Oxford Scientific Films Ltd*

Sutcliffe Gallery

1 Flowergate, Whitby, North Yorkshire YO21 3BA
tel (01947) 602239 *fax* (01947) 820287

Collection of 19th century photography, all by Frank M. Sutcliffe Hon. FRPS (1853-1941), especially inshore fishing boats and fishing community; also farming interests. Period covered 1872 to 1910.

Charles Tait Photo Library

Kelton, St Ola, Orkney KW15 1TR
tel (01856) 873738 *fax* (01856) 875313
e-mail charles.tait@zetnet.co.uk
web site http://www.velvia.demon.co.uk

Colour photo library specialising in islands: Orkney, Shetland and Western Isles (including St Kilda, North Rona, Sula Sgeir), as well as many parts of Scotland and France; also Venice. Subjects include archaeology, landscapes, transport, industry, seascapes, events, people and wildlife, especially seabirds and seals. Panoramic landscapes using Alpa Rotocam a speciality. Publisher of postcards, calendars, guidebooks. All transparencies with detailed captions and bar coded. See web site for more information and many photographs. Founded 1978.

The Tank Museum Photo Library & Archive

The Tank Museum, Bovington, Dorset BH20 6JG
tel (01929) 403463 *fax* (01929) 405360
e-mail admin@tankmuseum.demon.co.uk
web site http://www.tankmuseum.org.uk

International collection, from 1900 to present, of armoured fighting vehicles and military transport, including tanks, armoured cars, personnel carriers, self-propelled artillery carriers, missile launchers, cars, lorries and tractors. Founded c.1946.

Telegraph Colour Library*

The Innovation Centre, 225 Marsh Wall, London E14 9FX
tel 0171-987 1212 *fax* 0171-538 3309

Stock photography agency covering a wide subject range: business, sport, people, industry, animals, medical, nature, space, travel and graphics. Sameday service for all UK clients. Free catalogues available upon request.

Theatre Museum
National Museum of the Performing Arts,
1E Tavistock Street, London WC2E 7PA
tel 0171-836 7891 *fax* 0171-836 5148
In addition to extensive public displays on live entertainment and education programme, the Museum has an unrivalled collection of programmes, playbills, prints, photos, videos, texts and press cuttings relating to performers and productions from the 17th century onwards. Available by appointment, free of charge through the Study Room. Open Tues-Fri 10.30am-4.30pm. Reprographic services available.

3rd Millennium Music Ltd
22 Avon, Hockley, Tamworth, Staffs. B77 5QA
tel/fax (01827) 286086
e-mail Neil3MMLtd@aol.com
web site http://home.aol.com/Neil3MMLtd
Contact Neil Williams (Managing Director)
Specialises in classical music ephemera, including portraits of composers, musicians, conductors and opera singers. Old and sometimes rare photographs, postcards, antique prints, cigarette cards, stamps, concert programmes, Victorian newspapers, etc. Also modern photographs of composer references such as museums, statues, memorials etc.

Other subjects: music in art, ballet and dance, musical instruments, concert halls, opera houses and other music venues, manuscripts, church organs, ethnic music, jazz and other music groups. Founded 1996.

Tibet Pictures
38 Camac Road, Twickenham TW2 6NU
tel/fax 0181-898 0150 *tel* 0181-876 3637
Contact Jonathan Miller
Specialises in the people, architecture, history, religion and politics of Tibet. Also Yemen. Colour and b&w. Founded 1992.

Topham Picturepoint*
PO Box 33, Edenbridge, Kent TN8 5PB
tel (01342) 850313 *fax* (01342) 850244
e-mail pictures@topham.demon.co.uk

web site http://www.topham.co.uk/topham/
Contact Bernice Fairchild
Eight million contemporary and historical images, including the United Nations Environment Programme (UNEP) library. Delivery on-line if requested. New photographers – sample submission of 50 transparencies; 5-year contract, 50% commission.

B.M. Totterdell Photography*
Constable Cottage, Burlings Lane, Knockholt, Kent TN14 7PE
tel/fax (01959) 532001
Specialist volleyball library, covering all aspects of the sport. Founded 1989.

Transworld/Scope
26 St Cross Street, London EC1N 8UH
tel 0171-405 2997 *fax* 0171-831 4549
Contact Valerie Dobson
Colour: situations/beauty pictures.

Travel Images
Harpers Barn, Summerhill, Goudhurst, Kent TN17 1JU
tel (01580) 211132
Sales and Marketing Manager Frances Main Wilson
Comprehensive travel library, covering over 90 countries. Founded 1990.

Travel Ink Photo & Feature Library*
The Old Coach House, 14 High Street, Goring-on-Thames, Nr Reading, Berks. RG8 9AT
tel (01491) 873011 *fax* (01491) 875558
e-mail abbie@travink.demon.co.uk
web site http://www.photosource.co.uk/photosource/travink.htm
Travel, tourism and lifestyles covering around 150 countries – including the UK. Specialist sections include Hong Kong (including construction of the Tsing Ma Bridge), North Wales and Greece. Founded 1988.

Travel Photo International
8 Delph Common Road, Aughton, Ormskirk, Lancs. L39 5DW
tel/fax (01695) 423720
Touristic interest including scenery, towns, monuments, historic buildings, archaeological sites, local people. Specialises in travel brochures and books. Terms: 50%.

Tropix Photographic Library*
156 Meols Parade, Meols, Wirral, Merseyside L47 6AN
tel/fax 0151-632 1698

web site http://www.merseyworld.com/tropix/
All human and environmental aspects of tropics, sub-tropics and non-tropical developing countries. Environmental issues are accepted from locations worldwide. New collections welcome but preliminary enquiry in writing essential; send 4 first class stamps for details. Terms: 50%. Founded 1973.

True North Picture Source
5 Brunswick Street, Hebden Bridge,
West Yorkshire HX7 6AJ
tel/fax (01422) 845532
e-mail john@trunorth.demon.co.uk
web site http://www.trunorth.demon.co.uk
Proprietor John Morrison
The life and landscape of the North of England. No other photographers' work required. 30,000 transparencies (35mm and medium format). Commissions undertaken. Founded 1992.

Ulster Folk and Transport Museum
153 Bangor Road, Cultra, Holywood,
Co. Down BT18 0EU, Northern Ireland
tel (01232) 428428 *fax* (01232) 428728
Head of Dept of Photography T.K. Anderson
Photographs from 1850s to the present day, including the work of W.A. Green, Rose Shaw and R.J. Welsh while he was under contract to Harland and Wolf Ltd. Subjects include Belfast shipbuilding (80,000 photographs, including 70 original negatives of the *Titanic*), road and rail transport, folk life, agriculture and the linen industry. B&w and colour (35mm, medium and large format). Founded 1962.

Ulster Photographic Agency
22 Casaeldona Park, Belfast BT6 9RB
tel (01232) 795738
Motoring and motorsport. Terms: 50% or outright purchase. Founded 1985.

Universal Pictorial Press & Agency Ltd (UPPA)*
29-31 Saffron Hill,
London EC1N 8FH
tel 0171-421 6000 *fax* 0171-421 6006
Photo library containing notable Royal, political, company, academic, legal, diplomatic, church, military, pop, arts, entertainment and sports personalities and well-known views and buildings. Commercial, industrial, corporate and public relations photo assignments undertaken. Founded 1929.

Venice Picture Library*
(formerly Archivio Veneziano)
Rawlings House, 2A Milner Street,
London SW3 2PU
tel 0171-589 3127 *fax* 0171-584 1944
e-mail vpl@idsukltd.demon.co.uk
web site http://www.a-z.picture-library.com
Contact Michelle Wood
Specialises in Venice, covering most aspects of the city, islands and lagoon, especially architecture and the environment. Commissions undertaken; visitors welcome by appointment. Founded 1990.

John Vickers Theatre Collection
27 Shorrolds Road, London SW6 7TR
tel 0171-385 5774
Archives of British theatre and portraits of actors, writers and musicians by John Vickers from 1938-1974.

Vidocq Photo Library
162 Burwell Meadow, Witney, Oxon OX8 7GD
tel/fax (01993) 778518
Specialist in photographs for language and educational text books. Detailed coverage of France. Assignments undertaken. Founded 1983.

Visions in Golf
Noblethorpe Hall, Silkstone, Barnsley,
South Yorkshire S75 4NG
tel (01226) 791001 *fax* (01226) 791601
e-mail mnewco8420@aol.com
Proprietor Mark Newcombe
Every aspect of worldwide golf, including an archive dating back to the late 19th century and world-famous golf courses. Over 150,000 colour transparencies and 5000 b&w images. Commission: 50%. Founded 1984.

The Charles Walker Collection*
c/o Images Colour Library Ltd, Ramillies House,
1-2 Ramillies Street, London W1V 1DF
tel 0171-734 7344 *fax* 0171-287 3933
Contact Richard Heys
World's largest archive of colour pictures relating to the occult, magical, esoteric, mystical and mythological traditions. Founded 1983.

Simon Warner
Whitestone Farm, Stanbury, Keighley,
West Yorkshire BD22 0JW
tel/fax (01535) 644644
Landscape photographer with own stock pictures of northern England, North Wales and Northwest Scotland.

Waterways Photo Library*

39 Manor Court Road, London W7 3EJ
tel 0181-840 1659 *fax* 0181-567 0605
Contact Derek Pratt

British inland waterways; canals, rivers; bridges, aqueducts, locks and all waterside architectural features; watersports; waterway holidays, boats, fishing; town and countryside scenes. No other photographers' work required. Founded 1976.

Welfare History Picture Library

Heatherbank Museum of Social Work,
Caledonian University, Park Campus,
1 Park Drive, Glasgow G3 6LP
tel 0141-337 4402 *fax* 0141-337 4500
e-mail A.Ramage@gcal.ac.uk
web site http://jamba.gcal.ac.uk/hbank/home.htm

Social history and social work, especially child welfare, poorhouses, prisons, hospitals, slum clearance, women's movement, social reformers and their work. Catalogue on request. Founded 1975.

Wellcome Trust Medical Photographic Library

210 Euston Road, London NW1 2BE
tel 0171-611 8348 *fax* 0171-611 8577
e-mail photolib@wellcome.ac.uk
web site http://www.wellcome.ac.uk
Library Manager Catherine Draycott

Medical and social history; contemporary clinical and general medicine. Over 170,000 images. Founded 1936; renamed 1992.

Richard Welsby Photography

37 Grieveship Brae, Stromness,
Orkney Islands KW16 3BG
tel/fax (01856) 850910
e-mail richard.welsby@orkney.com
Contact Richard Welsby

Specialist library of the Orkney Islands: business and industry, scenics, geology, archaeology and historic; wide coverage of flowers, plants and other natural history subjects; aerials. Founded 1984.

Westcountry Pictures

PO Box 202, Exeter, Devon EX2 6YS
tel (01392) 426640 *fax* (01392) 271937
Contact Peter Cooper

All aspects of Devon and Cornwall – culture, places, industry and leisure. Founded 1989.

Western Americana Picture Library

3 Barton Buildings, Bath BA1 2JR
tel (01225) 334213 *fax* (01225) 480554

Prints, engravings, photos and colour transparencies on the American West, cowboys, gunfighters, Indians, including pictures by Frederic Remington and Charles Russell, etc.

Roy J. Westlake ARPS

West Country Photo Library, 31 Redwood Drive,
Plympton, Plymouth PL7 2FS
tel/fax (01752) 336444

Landscapes, seascapes, architecture, leisure activities, etc, for tourist brochures, advertising, books, magazines, calendars, etc. Also camping, caravanning and inland waterways subjects in Britain, including rivers and canals. Some world travel. Other photographers' work not accepted.

Eric Whitehead Picture Agency and Library – see Cumbria Picture Library*

Derek G. Widdicombe

Worldwide Photographic Library, 'Oldfield', High Street, Clayton West, Huddersfield HD8 9NS
tel/fax (01484) 862638 *pager* (0839) 764024

Landscapes, seascapes, architecture, human interest of Britain and abroad. Moods and seasons, buildings and natural features. Holds copyright of Noel Habgood FRPS Collection.

Wilderness Photographic Library*

Mill Barn, Broad Raine, Sedbergh,
Cumbria LA10 5ED
tel (015396) 20196 *fax* (015396) 21293
Director John Noble FRGS

Specialist library in mountain and wilderness regions, especially polar. Associated aspects of people, places, natural history, geographical features, exploration and mountaineering, adventure sports, travel.

Wildlife Matters Photographic Library*

Marlham, Henley's Down, Battle,
East Sussex TN33 9BN
tel (01424) 830566 *fax* (01424) 830224
e-mail gardens@ftech.co.uk, jfeltwell@aol.com
web site http://web.ftech.net/~gardens
ISDN (01424) 830153
Contact Dr John Feltwell

Ecology, conservation and environment; habitats and pollution; agriculture and horticulture; general natural history, entomology; Mediterranean wildlife; rainforests (Central America and

Indonesia); aerial pics of countryside UK, Europe, USA. Founded 1980.

David Williams Picture Library*
50 Burlington Avenue, Glasgow G12 0LH
tel 0141-339 7823 *fax* 0141-337 3031

Specialises in colour transparencies of Scotland and Iceland (2¹/₄in and 35mm). Subjects include landscapes, towns, villages, buildings, antiquities, geology and physical geography. Smaller collections include many European countries and Western USA. Catalogue available. Commissions undertaken. Founded 1989.

S. & I. Williams, Power Pix International Picture Library
Castle Lodge, Wenvoe, Cardiff CF5 6AD
tel (01222) 595163 *fax* (01222) 593905

Worldwide travel, people and views, girl and 'mood-pix', sub-aqua, aircraft, flora, fauna, agriculture, children. Agents worldwide. Founded 1968.

Windrush Photos*
99 Noah's Ark, Kemsing, Sevenoaks, Kent TN15 6PD
tel (01732) 763486 *fax* (01732) 763285
Owner David Tipling

Birds are a speciality. Strong coverage of British wildlife and landscapes. Ornothological consultancy. Photographic and features commissions undertaken. Terms: 50%. Founded 1991.

Timothy Woodcock
45 Lyewater, Crewkerne, Somerset TA18 8BB
tel (01460) 74488 *fax* (01460) 74988
e-mail timwoodc@aol.com

British and Eire landscape, seascape, architecture and heritage; children, parenthood, adults and education; gardens and containers; mountain biking. Location commissions undertaken. Terms: 50%. Founded 1983.

Woodmansterne Publications Ltd*
1 The Boulevard, Blackmoor Lane, Watford, Herts. WD1 8YW
tel (01923) 228236 *fax* (01923) 245788

Britain, Europe, Holy Land; architecture, cathedral and stately home interiors; general art subjects; museum collections; natural history, butterflies, geography, volcanoes, transport, Space; opera and ballet; major state occasions; British heritage.

World Pictures*
(formerly Feature-Pix Colour Library)
85A Great Portland Street, London W1N 5RA
tel 0171-437 2121/436 0440 *fax* 0171-439 1307
Directors Joan Brenes, David Brenes

Over 600,000 medium and large format colour transparencies aimed at travel and travel-related markets. Extensive coverage of cities, countries and specific resort areas, together with material of an emotive nature, i.e. children, couples and families on holiday, all types of winter and summer sporting activities, motoring abroad, etc. Terms: 50%; major contributing photographers 60%.

Murray Wren Picture Library
3 Hallgate, London SE3 9SG
tel 0181-852 7556

Outdoor nudes; nudist holiday resorts and activities in Europe and elsewhere; historic and erotic art of the nude through the ages. Media enquiries only; no new photographers required.

The Allan Wright Photo Library
t/a Cauldron Press Ltd, The Stables, Parton, Castle Douglas, Kirkcudbrightshire DG7 3NB
tel (016444) 70260 *fax* (016444) 70202

North Sea oil, offshore life 'on the rigs', Dumfries and Galloway, Argyll and Scottish highlands, scenic and environmental. Founded 1986.

Yemen Pictures
38 Camac Road, Twickenham TW2 6NU
tel/fax 0181-898 0150 or 0181-876 3637
Contact John Miles

Specialist colour library of Yemen, covering all aspects of culture, people, architecture, dance, qat and music. Also Africa, Australia, Middle East and Asia. Founded 1995.

York Archaeological Trust Picture Library
Cromwell House, 13 Ogleforth, York YO1 2JG
tel (01904) 663000 *fax* (01904) 640029
e-mail postmaster@yorkarch.demon.co.uk
web site http://www.yorkarch.demon.co.uk
Picture Librarian H. Dawson

York archaeology covering Romans, Dark Ages, Vikings and Middle Ages; traditional crafts; scenes of York and Yorkshire. Founded 1987.

Yorkshire in Focus
75A Selby Road, Garforth, Leeds LS25 1LR
tel 0113-286 3016
Transparencies, 35mm/6 x 9cm.
Landscapes, rivers, buildings, tourist
attractions in Yorkshire and the north.
Camping and caravanning subjects: sites,
caravans, motor caravans, tents and all
equipment. Large collection of touristy
stock subjects. Assignments undertaken.

Zoological Society of London
Regent's Park, London NW1 4RY
tel 0171-449 6293 *fax* 0171-586 5743
Librarian Ann Sylph
Archive collection of photographs, paintings and prints, from the 16th century
onwards, covering almost all vertebrate
animals, many now extinct or rare, plus
invertebrates. Founded 1826.

Picture agencies and libraries by subject area

This index gives the major subject area(s) only of each entry in the main list-
ing which begins on page 412, and should be used with discrimination.

Aerial photography

Aerofilms Ltd
Aviation Picture Library
Geo Aerial Photography
The Picture Company
Sealand Aerial Photography
Skyscan Photolibrary

Africa

Academic File News Agency
Ancient Egypt Picture Library
Animal Photography
Hamish Brown, Scottish
  Photographic
Sue Cunningham Photographic
  (East)
David Hosking (animals)
Images of Africa Photobank
Joe Filmbase Photo Agency/
  Library
Link Picture Library (Southern
  Africa)
Panos Pictures
Tibet Pictures (Yemen)
Tropix Photographic Library
Yemen Pictures

Agriculture and farming

The Anthony Blake Photo
  Library

Blitz International News &
  Photo Agency
Dennis Davis Photography
Frontline Photo Press Agency
Heritage & Natural History
  Photography
Frank Lane Picture Agency Ltd
Holt Studios International
Planet Earth Pictures
Sutcliffe Gallery

Aircraft and aviation

Air Photo Supply
Aviation Photographs
  International
Aviation Picture Library
Dr Alan Beaumont
Photo Link
The Picture Company
Patrick Smith Associates

Archaeology, antiquities, ancient monuments and heritage

A.A. and A. Ancient Art &
  Architecture Collection
Lesley and Roy Adkins Picture
  Library
AKG London

Rev. J. Catling Allen
Ancient Egypt Picture Library
C.M. Dixon
English Heritage Photo Library
Werner Forman Archive
Fortean Picture Library
Heritage & Natural History
  Photography
Pat Hodgson Library
Chandra S. Perera Cinetra
Mick Sharp Photography
Sites, Sights and Cities
Woodmansterne Publications Ltd
York Archaeological Trust
  Picture Library

Architecture, houses and interiors

A.A. & A. Ancient Art and
  Architecture Collection
Abode Interiors
ARCAID Architectural
  Photography and Picture
  Library
Bookart Architecture Picture
  Library
Dennis Davis Photography
English Heritage Photo Library
Houses & Interiors
  Photographic Features Agency
The Venice Picture Library
Woodmansterne Publications Ltd

Art, sculpture and crafts

A.A. & A. Ancient Art and Architecture Collection
Abode Interiors Photographic Library
Academic File News Agency
AKG London
Bodleian Library
Bookart Architecture Picture Library
Bridgeman Art Library
Crafts Council Picture Library
Fine Art Photographic Library
Werner Forman Archive
Photo Resources
Retrograph Nostalgia Archive Ltd
The Venice Picture Library

Asia

Academic File News Agency
Asian Affairs, The Royal Society for
Douglas Dickins Photo Library
Andrew N. Gagg's Photo Flora
Japan Archive
Link Picture Library
Ann & Bury Peerless
Picture House (Ladakh)
Society for Anglo-Chinese Understanding
Tibet Pictures
Travel Ink Photo & Feature Library (Hong Kong)
Yemen Pictures

Australia and New Zealand

Australia Pictures
George A. Dey
Yemen Pictures

Britain (see also Ireland, Scotland, Wales)

Rev. J. Catling Allen
John Blake Picture Library
Sarah Boait Photography and Picture Library
Britain on View Photographic Library
David Broadbent/Peak District Pictures
Collections
Cumbria Picture Library
English Heritage Photo Library
Fotoccompli – The Picture

Libraryy
Leslie Garland Picture Library (North England)
Isle of Wight Photo Library
Isle of Wight Pictures
Just Europe
Lakeland Life Picture Library (Lake District)
Bill Meadows Picture Library
Merseyside Photo Library
The Mustograph Agency
Spectrum Colour Library
True North Picture Source (North England)
Simon Warner (North England)
Westcountry Pictures (Devon, Cornwall)
Roy J. Westlake
Derek G. Widdicombe
Timothy Woodcock
Woodmansterne Publications Ltd
York Archaeological Trust Picture Library
Yorkshire in Focus

Business, industry and commerce

Financial Times Pictures
The Photographers' Library

Camping and caravanning

Roy J. Westlake
Yorkshire in Focus

Children and people (see also Social issues)

Barnardo's Photographic Archive
Collections
Lupe Cunha
Brian Gadsby Picture Library
Angela Hampton Family Life Picture Library
The Hutchinson Library
Photofusion
Telegraph Colour Library
Timothy Woodcock

Cities and towns (see also London)

Lesley and Roy Adkins Picture Library
Financial Times Pictures
Bill Meadows Picture Library
Sites, Sights and Cities
Skyscan Photolibrary
Waterways Photo Library

Civilisations, cultures and way of life

Bryan and Cherry Alexander Photography
Andalucía Slide Library (Spain)
Werner Forman Archive
Angela Hampton Family Life Picture Library
Medimage (Mediterranean)
Christine Osborne/Middle East Pictures Inc.
Photo Resources
Picture House (Mayan)
Peter Sanders Photography
Mick Sharp Photography
STILL Pictures Whole Earth Photo Library
Tibet Pictures (Yemen)

Countryside and rural life (see also Landscapes)

Andalucía Slide Library (Spain)
Dr Alan Beaumont
Ron and Christine Foord
Forest Life Picture Library
Tim Graham
Angela Hampton Family Life Picture Library
Isle of Wight Pictures
Lakeland Life Picture Library
Bill Meadows Picture Library
Sutcliffe Gallery
Ulster Folk and Transport Museum
Waterways Photo Library
Wildlife Matters Photographic Library

Developing countries

Geoslides
Christine Osborne/Middle East Pictures Inc.
Panos Pictures
STILL Pictures Whole Earth Photo Library
Tropix Photographic Library

Environment, conservation, ecology and habitats

Heather Angel
Aquila Wildlife Images
Ardea London Ltd
Dr Alan Beaumont
Butterflies
Bruce Coleman Ltd
George A. Dey (forestry, natural history)
Ecoscene
Environmental Investigation Agency
Fogden Natural History Photographs
Forest Life Picture Library
Martin and Dorothy Grace
Harper Horticultural Slide Library
Holt Studios International
Frank Lane Picture Agency Ltd
Chris Mattison
Natural Image
NHPA
Papilio Natural History & Travel Library
Planet Earth Pictures
Premaphotos Wildlife
STILL Pictures Whole Earth Photo Library
Tropix Photographic Library
Wildlife Matters Photographic Library
Windrush Photos

Europe and Eastern Europe (excluding UK/Ireland)

Andalucía Slide Library (Spain)
Sue Cunningham Photographic
Das Photo
James Davis Travel Photography
Douglas Dickins Photo Library
C.M. Dixon
Lesley Garland Picture Library (Norway)
Just Europe
John Massey Stewart
Medimage (Mediterranean)
Panos Pictures (Eastern Europe)
Russia & Eastern Images
The Venice Picture Library
Vidocq Photo Library (France)
David Williams Picture Library (Iceland)

Fashion and lifestyle

Joe Filmbase Photo Agency/ Library
The Photographers' Library

Food and drink

The Anthony Blake Photo Library
Cephas Picture Library
Footprints Colour Picture Library
Retrograph Nostalgia Archive

Gardens, gardening and horticulture (see also Plant life)

A-Z Botanical Collection
Ardea London Ltd
B. & B. Photographs
Butterflies
Collections
Dennis Davis Photography
Forest Life Picture Library
Garden Matters Photographic Library
John Glover Photography
Harper Horticultural Slide Library
Holt Studios International
Houses & Interiors Photographic Features Agency
S. & O. Mathews
Natural Image
Harry Smith Horticultural Photographic Collection
Peter Stiles Picture Library
Timothy Woodcock

General and stock libraries

Ace Photo Agency
Aspect Picture Library Ltd
Bandphoto Agency
Barnaby's Picture Library
Stephen Benson Slide Bureau
J. Allan Cash Photolibrary
Bruce Coleman Inc.
Bruce Coleman Ltd
Colorific Photo Library
Sylvia Cordaiy Photo Library
C.P.L. (Camerapix Picture Library)
Barry Davies
C.M. Dixon
Greg Evans International Photo Library

Fotoccompli – The Picture Libraryy
Freelance Focus
Frontline Photo Press Agency
Geo Aerial Photography
GeoScience Features
Geoslides
Robert Harding Picture Library
Horizon International
Hulton Getty Picture Collection
Hutchison Picture Library
The Image Bank
Images Colour Library
Joe Filmbase Photo Agency/ Library
Lears Magical Lanterns Museum
The MacQuitty International Collection
News Blitz International
The Northern Picture Library
Orion Press
Photofusion
The Photographers' Library
Pictor International Ltd
Picture Research Service
POPPERFOTO (Paul Popper Ltd)
Pro-file Photo Library
Raleigh International Picture Library
Retna Pictures Ltd
Royal Geographical Society Picture Library
The Royal Photographic Society
Dawn Runnals Photographic Library
S & G Press Agency Ltd
Source Photographic Archives
Spectrum Colour Library
Tony Stone Images
Telegraph Colour Library
Universal Pictorial Press & Agency Ltd (UPPA)
Vidocq Photo Library
Derek G. Widdicombe
S. & I. Williams, Power Pix International Picture Library
Yorkshire in Focus

Geography, biogeography and topography

Arctic Camera
B. & B. Photographs
John Blake Picture Library
Chris Fairclough Colour Library
Geoslides
John Massey Stewart

Glamour, moods and nudes

Transworld/Scope
S. & I. Williams, Power Pix
  International Picture Library
Murray Wren Picture Library

Health and medicine

Lupe Cunha
Wellcome Trust Medical
  Photographic Library
Science & Society Picture
  Library
Shout Picture Library

High-tech, high-speed, macro/micro, special effects and step-by-step

Earth Images Picture Library
  (high-tech)
GeoScience Features
Houses & Interiors Photographic
  Features Agency (step-by-step)
The Image Bank (high-tech,
  special effects)
Microscopix
NHPA (high-speed)
Oxford Scientific Films Ltd,
  Photo Library (special effects)

History

AKG London
Barnardo's Photographic Archive
Bodleian Library
British Library Picture Library
Mary Evans Picture Library
Frost Historical Newspaper
  Collection
Pat Hodgson Library
Dave Lewis Nostalgia Collection
The Billie Love Historical
  Collection
Mansell Collection Ltd
Peter Newark Pictures
Public Record Office Image
  Library
The Royal Photographic Society
Royal Society of Chemistry
  Library
Salamander Books Picture
  Archive
Science & Society Picture
  Library
Topham Picturepoint

Illustrations, prints, engravings, lithographs and cartoons

Allied Artists Ltd
Bodleian Library
British Library Picture Library
Mary Evans Picture Library
The Illustrated London News
  Picture Library
The Billie Love Historical
  Collection
Mansell/Time Inc.
Peter Newark Pictures
Public Record Office Image
  Library
Punch Cartoon Library
Royal Society of Chemistry
  Library
Zoological Society of London

Ireland

Picturepoint
The Slide File
Source Photographic Archives
Heritage & Natural History
  Photography

Landscapes and scenics

Bookart Architecture Picture
  Library
Cumbria Picture Library
Barry Davies
James Davis Travel Photography
George A. Dey (Scottish)
Eyeline Photography
Geo Aerial Photography
John Glover Photography
Isle of Wight Photo Library
Isle of Wight Pictures
S. & O. Mathews
Chris Mattison
Medimage (Mediterranean)
The Nature and Landscape File
The Picture Company
Scotland in Focus Picture
  Library
Mick Sharp Photography
Skyscan Photolibrary
Peter Stiles Picture Library
The Still Moving Picture Co.
Charles Tait Photo Library
Simon Warner
Richard Welsby Photography
  (Orkney Islands)
Roy J. Westlake
Derek G. Widdicombe
Windrush Photos
The Allan Wright Photo Library

Latin America

Andes Press Agency
Das Photo
Fogden Natural History
  Photographs

London

ARCAID Architectural
  Photographic and Picture
  Library
Greater London Record Office
The Illustrated London News
  Picture Library
Monitor Syndication
Skyscan Photolibrary
Patrick Smith Associates

Middle East

Academic File News Agency
Ancient Egypt Picture Library
Stephen Benson Slide Bureau
Das Photo
Christine Osborne/Middle East
  Pictures Inc.
Ann & Bury Peerless
Yemen Pictures

Military and armed forces

Air Photo Supply
Aviation Photographs
  International
Imperial War Museum
Military History Picture Library
Public Record Office Image
  Library
Salamander Books Picture
  Archive
The Tank Museum Photo
  Library & Archive

Mountains

AMIS
Hamish Brown, Scottish
  Photographic
Mountain Dynamics
Mountain Visions
Royal Geographical Society
  Picture Library
Wilderness Photographic
  Library

Natural history (see also Environment, Plant life)

A-Z Botanical Collection
Heather Angel
Animal Photography
Aquila Wildlife Images
Ardea London Ltd
B. & B. Photographs
BBC Natural History Unit
  Picture Library
Dr Alan Beaumont
Bird Images
David Broadbent/Peak District
  Pictures (birds)
Butterflies
Bruce Coleman Ltd
Sylvia Cordaiy Photo Library
Barry Davies
Gordon Dickson (fungi, insects)
Ecoscene
Environmental Investigation
  Agency
Fogden Natural History
  Photographs
Ron and Christine Foord
  (insects)
Footprints Colour Picture
  Library
Brian Gadsby Picture Library
Geoscience Features
Martin and Dorothy Grace
Heritage & Natural History
  Photography (insects, espe-
  cially bees)
David Hosking (birds)
Image Diggers
Michael Leach (owls)
Chris Mattison (reptiles,
  amphibians)
Natural Image
The Nature and Landscape File
NHPA
Oxford Scientific Films Ltd,
  Photo Library
Papilio Natural History &
  Travel Library
Planet Earth Pictures
Premaphotos Wildlife
Roundhouse Ornithology
  Collection
RSPCA Photolibrary
Salamander Books Picture
  Archive
Steffi Schubert, Wildlife
  Conservation Collection
  Photographic Library
Scotland in Focus Picture
  Library
Peter Stiles Picture Library
STILL Pictures Whole Earth
  Photo Library

Richard Welsby Photography
  (Orkney Islands)
Wildlife Matters Photographic
  Agency
Windrush Photos (birds)
Zoological Society of London

Nautical and maritime

Peter Cumberlidge Photo
  Library
National Maritime Museum
  Picture Library
Seaco Picture Library
Ulster Folk and Transport
  Museum

News, features and photo features

Academic File News Photos
The Associated Press Ltd
Bandphoto Agency
Press Features Syndicate
Financial Times Pictures
Frost Historical Newspaper
  Collection
International Press Agency
  (Pty) Ltd
News Blitz International
PA News Photo Library
Chandra S. Perera Cinetra
Pixfeatures
S & G Press Agency Ltd
Topham Picturepoint

North America

American History Picture
  Library
Douglas Dickins Photo Library
Western Americana Picture
  Library

Nostalgia, ephemera and advertising

Fotomas Index
Dave Lewis Nostalgia Collection
Retrograph Nostalgia Archive
  Ltd

Performing arts (theatre, dance, music)

Aquarius Picture Library
Camera Press Ltd
The Dance Library
Famous
Image Diggers
Jazz Index
Link Picture Library (music)
Mander & Mitchenson Theatre
  Collection
Performing Arts Library
Sylvia Pitcher
Redferns Music Picture Library
Theatre Museum
3rd Millennium Music Ltd
John Vickers Theatre Collection

Personalities and portraits (see also Royalty)

Aquarius Picture Library
Camera Press Ltd
Famous
Financial Times Pictures
Mark Gerson Photography
Tim Graham
Pat Hodgson Library (historical)
JS Library International
Mander & Mitchenson Theatre
  Collection
Monitor Syndication
Performing Arts Library
Pixfeatures
POPPERFOTO (Paul Popper
  Ltd)
Punch Cartoon Library
Retna Pictures Ltd
The Royal Photographic Society
Royal Society of Chemistry
  Library
Syndication International Ltd
Topham Picturepoint
Universal Pictorial Press &
  Agency Ltd (UPPA)
John Vickers Theatre Collection

Plant life (see also Gardens)

A-Z Botanical Collection Ltd
Heather Angel
Aquila Wildlife Images
Ron and Christine Foord
Andrew N. Gagg's Photo Flora
Garden Matters Photographic
  Library
John Glover Photography
Martin and Dorothy Grace
Harper Horiticultural Slide
  Library
Premaphotos Wildlife
Harry Smith Horticultural
  Photographic Collection
Source Photographic Archives
Richard Welsby Photography
  (Orkney Islands)

Polar and Arctic

Bryan and Cherry Alexander
  Photography
Arctic Camera
POPPERFOTO (Paul Popper Ltd)
Royal Geographical Society
  Picture Library
Wilderness Photographic Library

Religions and religious monuments

Lesley and Roy Adkins Picture
  Library
Rev. J. Catling Allen
Andes Press Agency
Sarah Boait Photography and
  Picture Library
Chris Fairclough Colour Library
Ann & Bury Peerless
Photo Resources
Peter Sanders Photography

Royalty

Camera Press Ltd
Tim Graham
JS Library International
Monitor Syndication
Pixfeatures
Syndication International Ltd

Russia

John Massey Stewart
Russia & Eastern Images
SCR Photo Library

Science, technology and meteorology

Ace Photo Agency
Earth Images Picture Library
Leslie Garland Picture Library
GeoScience Features
Frank Lane Picture Agency Ltd
Microscopix
Ann Ronan at Image Select
Royal Society of Chemistry
  Library
Science Photo Library
Science & Society Picture Library

Scotland

Hamish Brown, Scottish
  Photographic
George A. Dey (castles,
  Highland Games)
Scotland in Focus Picture
  Library
The Still Moving Picture
  Company
Charles Tait Photo Library
Simon Warner
David Williams Picture Library
The Allan Wright Photo Library

Social issues and social history

Andes Press Agency
Barnardo's Photographic Archive
John Birdsall Photography
Mary Evans Picture Library
FirePix
Greater London Record Office
Imperial War Museum
Photofusion
RSPCA Photolibrary
Ann Ronan at Image Select
Shout Picture Library
Welfare History Picture Library
Wellcome Trust Medical
  Photographic Library

South America

Animal Photography
  (Galapagos)
Australia Pictures
Stephen Benson Slide Bureau
Lupe Cunha (Brazil)
Sue Cunningham Photographic
David Hosking (Falklands)
Picture House (Mayan
  civilisation)

Space and astronomy

Aspect Picture Library
Earth Images Picture Library
Galaxy Picture Library
Genesis Space Photo Library
National Maritime Museum
  Picture Library
Salamander Books Picture
  Archive
Science Photo Library

Sport and leisure

Action Plus
Allsport Photographic
The Associated Press Ltd
John Blake Photo Library
  (equestrian)
Boxing Picture Library
Michael Cole Camerawork
Concannon Golf History Library
Cumbria Picture Library
  (snooker)
Peter Dazeley (golf)
Eyeline Photography (water-
  sports, sheepdog trials)
Frontline Photo Press Agency
Mountain Visions (moun-
  taineering, skiing)
POPPERFOTO (Paul Popper Ltd)
Skishoot – Offshoot
Sporting Pictures (UK) Ltd
The Still Moving Picture
  Company
B.M. Totterdell Photography
  (volleyball)
Ulster Photography Agency
  (motorsport)
Universal Pictorial Press &
  Agency Ltd (UPPA)
Visions in Golf
World Pictures

Strange phenomena, occult and mystical

Fortean Picture Library
Image Diggers
Sites, Sights and Cities
The Charles Walker Collection

Transport (cars and motoring, railways)

Ludvigsen Library
Motorcycles Unlimited
National Maritime Museum
  Picture Library

National Motor Museum,
 Beaulieu
Railways – Milepost 9¹/₂
Science & Society Picture
 Library
Seaco Picture Library
Ulster Folk and Transport
 Museum
Ulster Photographic Agency

Travel and tourism

Ace Photo Agency
Air Photo Supply
ARCAID Architectural
 Photography and Picture
 Library
Aspect Picture Library
Aviation Picture Library
Bandphoto Agency
The Anthony Blake Photo
 Library
Sarah Boait Photography and
 Picture Library
Britain on View Photographic
 Library
Sylvia Cordaiy Picture Library

Peter Cumberlidge Photo
 Library
James Davis Travel Photography
Ecoscene
Greg Evans International Photo
 Library
Chris Fairclough Colour Library
Footprints Colour Picture
 Library
Fotoccompli – The Picture
 Libraryy
Brian Gadsby Picture Library
Andrew N. Gagg's Photo Flora
The Hutchinson Library
The Illustrated London News
 Picture Library
JS Library International
Just Europe
Mountain Visions
Papilio Natural History &
 Travel Library
The Photographers' Library
The Picture Company
Picture House
Raleigh International Picture
 Library
Peter Sanders Photography
Seaco Picture Library

Spectrum Colour Library
Charles Tait Photo Library
Telegraph Colour Library
Travel Images
Travel Ink Photo & Feature
 Library
Travel Photo International
Wilderness Photographic
 Library
World Pictures

Wales

Patrick Smith Associates
Travel Ink Photo & Feature
 Library

Waterways

Peter Cumberlidge Photo
 Library
Waterways Photo Library
Roy J. Westlake

Card and stationery publishers which accept photographs

Before submitting work, photographers are advised to ascertain requirements, including terms and conditions. Only top quality material should be submitted; inferior work is never accepted. Postage for return of material should be enclosed.

*Member of the Greeting Card Association

Abacus Cards Ltd*

Gazeley Road, Kentford, Newmarket,
Suffolk CB8 7QB
tel (01638) 552399 *fax* (01638) 552103
Partners Jeff Fothergill and Brian Carey, *Art Director* Bev Cunningham

Quality greetings cards. Florals, garden scenes, still lifes etc.; submit 35mm transparencies or larger formats. Founded 1991.

Caspari Ltd*

9 Shire Hill, Saffron Walden, Essex CB11 3AP
tel (01799) 513010 *fax* (01799) 513101
Managing Director Keith Entwisle

Traditional fine art/classic images; 5 x 4in transparencies. No verses. Founded 1990.

Chapter and Verse*

Granta House, 96 High Street, Linton,
Cambs. CB1 6JT
tel (01223) 891951 *fax* (01223) 894137

Buildings, animals, flowers, scenic, or domestic subjects in series, suitable for greetings cards and postcards. All sizes of transparency. No verses. Founded 1981.

Dennis Print

Printing House Square, Melrose Street,
Scarborough, North Yorkshire YO12 7SJ
tel (01723) 500555 *fax* (01723) 501488/500545
e-mail dennis@etwltd.demon.co.uk
web site http://www.dennisprint.com

Interested in first-class transparencies for reproduction as local view postcards and calendars. 3^{1}/4 x 2^{1}/4in or 35mm transparencies ideal for postcard reproduction.

J. Arthur Dixon*

Forest Side, Newport,
Isle of Wight PO30 5QW
tel (01983) 523381 *fax* (01983) 529719
Managing Director Andy McGarrick, *Head of Design* Carlton Knight

All subjects considered; transparencies 35mm or larger. Verses considered. Acquired by **Second Nature Ltd.** Founded 1930.

Hambledon Studios Ltd*

Metcalf Drive, Altham Industrial Estate, Altham, Accrington, Lancs. BB5 5SS
tel (01282) 687300 *fax* (01282) 687404
Art Managers D. Jaundrell, J. Ashton, D. Fuller, N. Harrison, K. Ellis

Photos for reproduction as greetings cards. *Brands* Arnold Barton, Donny Mac, Reflections, New Image.

Images & Editions*

Bourne Road, Essendine, Nr Stamford,
Lincs. PE9 4UW
tel (01780) 757118 *fax* (01780) 754629
Directors Lesley Forrow, Maurice Miller

Greetings cards, giftwrap, gift products and social stationery: flowers, gardens and landscape, animals, especially cats and teddy bears. Any format accepted; transparencies preferred. Founded 1984.

Jane's Information Group

Sentinel House, 163 Brighton Road, Coulsdon,
Surrey CR5 2NH
tel 0181-700 3700 *fax* 0181-700 1006

Considers defence, aerospace, police and transportation transparencies.

Jarrold Publishing
Whitefriars, Norwich NR3 1TR
tel (01603) 763300 *fax* (01603) 662748
Managing Director Antony Jarrold, *Publishing Director* Caroline Jarrold
Photographic Librarian Vivienne Buckingham
tel (01603) 227325

Transparencies (35mm or larger) for calendars. Verses not required. Please telephone before submitting material. Founded 1770.

Pomegranate Europe Ltd
Fullbridge House, Fullbridge, Maldon, Essex CM9 4LE
tel (01621) 851646 *fax* (01621) 852426
Sales Director Dave Harris

Photographs or transparencies (any size) for cards, calendars, postcards and posters: art, architecture, the environment, Third World issues and art, history, politics and photography. Founded 1993.

J. Salmon Ltd
100 London Road, Sevenoaks, Kent TN13 1BB
tel (01732) 452381 *fax* (01732) 450951

Picture postcards, calendars and local view booklets.

Santoro Graphics Ltd
342-344 London Road, Cricket Green, Mitcham, Surrey CR4 3ND
tel 0181-640 9777 *fax* 0181-640 2888
Directors L. Santoro, M. Santoro

Publishers of innovative and award-winning designs for greetings cards, giftwrap and gift stationery. Bold contemporary images with an international appeal. Subjects covered: black and white, colour floral, quirky and humorous, whimsical, 'Fifties, 'Seventies, futuristic! All formats accepted in both b&w and colour; transparencies ideally 5 x 4in but will accept 35mm. Founded 1985.

Scandecor Ltd*
3 The Ermine Centre, Hurricane Close, Huntingdon, Cambs. PE18 6XX
tel (01480) 456395 *fax* (01480) 456269
Director G. Huldtgren

Transparencies all sizes. Founded 1967.

Picture research

A multitude of pictures are reproduced in the media and their images consumed by the viewer as part of daily life. The role of the picture researcher is to obtain these pictures and to be conversant with the legal implications concerning their reproduction. **Jennie Karrach** *explains.*

Picture research is the art of obtaining pictures – photos and illustrations – suitable for reproduction, which suit the project's brief, budget and deadline. It also includes the clearance of permissions, copyright, the negotiation of rights and fees, and the eventual return of pictures to their owners at the end of the project.

Picture researchers are responsible for supplying a vast range of clients: in the book and magazine industry – both publishers and packagers – advertising agencies, film, television and video companies, newspapers and exhibition organisers. Although the skills involved in picture research are relevant in all these contexts, the type of pictures required varies enormously. Consequently, researchers tend to specialise in the type of work they undertake, and they may well have a specialist knowledge of one particular area, such as science and technology.

Picture researchers are employed either as staff members or on a freelance basis, paid by the hour or day, or for the duration of a project, as appropriate. An employee working full time on a long-running project may have time to carry out extensive research, but freelance work is often constrained by the client's budget and schedule. It is here that experience counts. Knowing where to find material quickly to suit the brief saves time and therefore money.

The researcher's fees are often included in the total budget, so that although the final deadline for delivery of pictures to the client may be a month away, the total allowed for picture research amounts to three days' work. It may be that this is unrealistic, and that the job will require five days. These details all need to be clarified at the outset and some sort of agreement listing the picture brief, deadlines, budget and invoicing particulars needs to be drawn up. It is important to put everything in writing so that in the event of dispute both parties can refer back to the agreement. Pictures are often worth large amounts of money, and in the event of loss it will become difficult to agree who will pay compensation unless this has been pre-arranged. It can also prove difficult to collect payment for work completed, so it may be advisable to agree upon regular payments and an advance to cover expenses such as travel, postage and telephone, etc.

The brief

It is important to clarify the brief so that both parties, the picture researcher and the editor/design team, are agreed upon the image required. It may be that the picture requested needs no further description – a work of art, by a well-known artist, e.g. *The Mona Lisa* by Leonardo da Vinci, to be used in colour. Or it may be that the picture is to depict an historical event which occurred long before the advent of photography. What is required? A photo of a contemporary manuscript which describes the incident, or perhaps a contemporary illumination exists. Or does the client have in mind an illustration executed by a more recent artist, perhaps a nineteenth-century engraving? Or a photograph of the remains of an historic site? It may be that the client has no one image in mind, but rather needs to evoke a specific mood, or provoke a reaction. This is often the case in advertising campaigns. Pictures are highly subjective, and what is evocative to some will appear bleak to others. A good picture researcher is able to capture the image conjured up

in a picture meeting, responding to the ideas of an art director or editor.

It may be that the picture required must be a specific shape – portrait (upright) or landscape (horizontal), or it may need to have an area lacking in detail, such as sky, into which text can fit. Or a dark area suitable for text reversal. If there are too many design constraints it may be cost effective to commission a photographer, rather than to search for a non-existent 'existing' photo.

The budget, rights and deadline

Once the brief has been agreed, the budget, rights and deadline must be confirmed. These are interdependent. Picture fees increase according to the size and use made of the image; for instance, a picture used at quarter-page size in a school textbook will cost less than one used quarter-page size in a glossy, adult non-fiction book. Fees vary according to the media: books, magazines, television, video, CD-Rom, etc. The print run/circulation of a book/magazine also affects the price charged for use. Fees are calculated also according to the rights requested. The larger the territory, the larger the fee, although the percentage increase between the various categories will vary from agency to agency. The territories sold are usually:

- UK only
- UK and first foreign edition
- English language, world rights, excluding US
- English language, world rights, including US
- world rights, all languages.

It may well be that, as the European Union attempts to remove trade barriers, the rights available will change.

Other fees will need to be budgeted for. Many commercial picture agencies charge 'research' or 'service' fees. These may be linked to the amount of material they are loaning or there may be a fixed charge levied. In both cases the source should advise of this at the initial enquiry stage. Some will only charge if a personal visit is not possible and pictures are despatched by a member of their staff.

The levying of these fees can erode the total picture budget quickly. It is not unusual to receive a service fee of £30, which may be acceptable if this is the only source used, and the pictures obtained are accepted by the client. However, on projects where a selection of pictures to cover a wider range of topics is required, many sources will have to be approached. It is worth discussing service fees at the outset. It is not unknown for agencies to waive or reduce them if it increases the likelihood of a sale. Some only charge the service fee if all pictures are returned and none selected for use. Other sources do not loan out material but instead sell copy transparencies or prints. This is usually the case with museums who can supply a transparency of a particular object or manuscript, but are unable to respond to a vague request for a selection of pictures for possible use. Museums often charge a monthly hire fee as well as the final reproduction fee.

Most commercial picture libraries or agencies operate on a loan system. Pictures are selected and loaned for an agreed period, usually a month. After this time material not required should be returned and some indication given as to the fate of the pictures still held. Is a subsequent picture selection to be made, or are those retained going to be used? If material is kept longer than the agreed loan period, then holding fees may be charged. These should only be levied if a reminder sent fails to elicit news of the pictures or return. (Freelance picture researchers need to make sure that such reminders are forwarded to them either by the source or sent on by the client.) Holding fees are charged per picture, per week over the deadline, and are usually waived if a reasonable extension to the free loan period is requested.

Picture sources

Sources are many and various. They include government departments, institutions, companies, libraries, commercial picture libraries and agencies, individual collectors, and individual photographers.

Some of these sources supply pictures without charge, but that is not to say that they are necessarily easy to obtain, or that no copyright pertains. Many sources are not primarily concerned with the supply of pictures and give it low priority. Access to the collection may be limited to research students and those who hold a reader's card. Enquiries may have to be made in writing, and the idea of urgency is an alien one. Or lack of resources may prevent an efficient service.

There is no one source book which lists all picture sources and if one existed it would run to many volumes and be in need of constant updating. Commercial libraries and agencies maintain a high profile, advertising by mail shots to prospective clients. The larger ones produce glossy catalogues, usually free, which include a selection of their images, enough to give a flavour of the type of stock held.

New technology is affecting picture storage and use. Some large agencies produce CD-Roms which clients can purchase for future reference. These discs allow rapid viewing of thousands of images. On-line facilities at news agencies allow quick transmission of pictures to clients and use of the World Wide Web via the Internet enables subscribers to browse and download high resolution images for use. There are serious implications for copyright control resulting from electronic storage, e.g. unauthorised use or manipulation of photographs.

General stock libraries

'General stock libraries' hold pictures which fall into broad categories, namely: travel, architecture, food, business, science/medicine, people, sport, nature, animals, transport, etc. They would almost certainly hold pictures of famous foreign landmarks, e.g. the Eiffel Tower, photographed from the ground, the air, by night, by day, with lovers ... It is much more difficult to find pictures of less glamorous sites. Street furniture, cars and pedestrians date quickly, and some agencies, keen to keep pictures saleable for as

Useful directories

Picture Sources UK
by Rosemary Eakins, Macdonald, 1985
Now out of print but may be available through a library.

Picture Researcher's Handbook
by Hilary and Mary Evans, 6th edn, Blueprint Routledge, £50.00 (plus £3.00 p&p)
Available from bookshops and:
The Mary Evans Picture Library
59 Tranquil Vale, London SE3 0BS
tel 0181-318 0034 *fax* 0181-297 9819

BAPLA Directory
BAPLA, 18 Vine Hill, London EC1R 5DX
tel 0171-713 1780 *fax* 0171-713 1211
Lists all the current members of the British Association of Picture Libraries and Agencies (BAPLA), at present totalling around 300. Copies available (£10) from Linda Royles at BAPLA.

long as possible, will attempt to keep such features to a minimum. The result is strange; London, peopled only by bobbies and red buses, Venice reduced to St Mark's Square and gondoliers on the Grand Canal, Los Angeles depicted by traffic on freeways. This problem extends to the 'people' pictures, which tend to be stereotypes posed by models. It is not impossible to find pictures of 'real' people going about everyday activities, but it can be time-consuming. Directories cannot hope to express the nuances of photographic collections, and it is only over time, after visits to many sources, that an overview of the range available will emerge. Specialist picture libraries are usually one-subject libraries, and cover the whole range of picture needs. The level of captioning is usually higher in specialist sources as the photographer has expert knowledge. It can be the case that a good quality photograph badly captioned is rendered useless. A photo filed in the 'elderly people' category of a general stock agency showed a woman standing in a slight depression in the desert somewhere. The woman was actually a famous anthropologist, but her name meant nothing to the library so she had been miscaptioned and then wrongly filed. It may be that for certain purposes any train, boat, car, etc will be acceptable, but if the picture required is of a specific model then it is frustrating to find insubstantial captions and undated pictures.

Use of photos

Permission

Once pictures have been found which fit the brief, the next stage is clearance for use. Permission must be sought from the copyright holder for use of particular photos in set contexts. The supply of photos does not automatically guarantee permission to reproduce. It may be that the agency or picture source is not the copyright holder, and permission has to be sought elsewhere. This is often the case with photos of works of art still in copyright. The artist, or the artist's estate, may be represented by a copyright protection society such as DACS (Design and Artists Copyright Society – see page 473), which will approach the estate or artist on behalf of a picture researcher and, if permission is granted, often subject to conditions, issue a licence. Conditions could include the right to approve colour proofs. The production department or designer of the project would therefore need to be informed to allow time in the schedule. DACS has reciprocal representation agreements with similar copyright protection societies in some 26 countries. This simplifies a copyright enquiry considerably but sufficient time should be allowed for clearance. It may take a day or several weeks. If the copyright holder and the supplier of the photograph are not one and the same, then a fee may be due to both parties.

Context

It may be that the context in which the photo is to appear is a sensitive one, perhaps an article about child abuse, divorce, AIDS, or that the caption is to make some derogatory statement about the subject. If this is the case it is important to be honest about the context with the supplier of the photo. If the article is educational and positive in its approach, then the photo will play a different role from one appearing in an exposé of shameful goings on. It is prudent to enquire whether the photographer has obtained 'model release' from the subject in the photo. In return for a sum of money the model grants the photographer the right to sell the photos taken. This is standard procedure at photo sessions, where a particular shot has been commissioned by a client, or a personality has granted a shoot. The release may have certain riders attached as to use, precisely to avoid certain contexts.

An agency may grant permission to use the photo in a sensitive area, but insist on a declaration appearing with it or with the photo credits 'all photos posed by models'. Or it may be that the agency or photographer do not have model release for the photo. At present in the UK, if a person is photographed in public they cannot prevent that photo being published. Hence the breed of paparazzi photographers. There is as yet no law protecting against the invasion of privacy. (The situation is different in the USA.) As a result many British photo libraries hold photos of members of the public, taken 'in the public domain' for which they hold no model release. Most agencies reproduce the following or similar statement in their Terms & Conditions: 'although the agency takes all reasonable care, the agency shall not be liable for any loss or damage suffered by the client or by any third party arising from any defect in the picture or its caption, or in any way from its reproduction.' The onus is put onto the picture user. It is fair to say that if the context of the photo is an innocent one, most members of the public are pleased to be in the spotlight, and require no more than a complimentary copy of the book, magazine, or whatever.

Captions

It is important for picture researchers to make caption writers aware that litigation may result from derogatory or inappropriate captions. Staff researchers should attempt to prevent pictures which were obtained for one project, e.g. a book on health care, being transferred to another, such as a booklet on safe sex. Freelance researchers would be well advised to include a paragraph in the agreement mentioned above which would disclaim responsibility for use by the client of pictures supplied in any use other than that stated in the brief, and any subsequent copyright infringement by the client. It is not unknown for clients to withhold information or mislead picture researchers as to the length of the print run, or the production of foreign language editions.

Picture researchers do not generally write captions themselves but may be asked to provide information for captions. This can be very time-consuming if the pictures do not already have a reasonable amount of caption information attached, supplied by the source or photographer.

Credits and copyright

Once pictures have been selected, captioned, and sized for the project in hand, the credit or acknowledgement list will need to be drawn up. This usually includes a courtesy line thanking the various picture sources for permission to reproduce photographs. Sources are either listed alphabetically, with page numbers as to where their pictures appear, or the name of the source appears next to the picture.

Copyright

Under the provisions of the Copyright, Designs and Patents Act 1988, photographers have 'moral rights' which include the right to be identified as the author of a photograph (see *British copyright law*, page 641). Newspapers, magazines, encyclopedias, and other works of reference, are exempt from crediting contributors but most will include credits as a matter of course. Under the terms of the 1988 Act photography is copyright for the same duration and in the same way as other works of art. This was for 50 years after the death of the photographer until 1 January 1996, when 'the Term Directive' was implemented. The Term Directive harmonised copyright laws throughout the European Union and it extends the term of copyright in the UK to 70 years after the death of the photographer. Commissioned work, where previously the copyright belonged to the commissioner, is now the property of the photographer. This means that photos can only be kept for a limited period after a photo session, and rights must be agreed in the same way as for stock library images. All photos, used and unused, must be returned to the photographer. Staff photographers as employees do not own copyright on their photos.

A short booklet produced by the British Photographers Liaison Committee (BPLC), *The ABC Guide to UK Photographic Copyright*, summarises the changes in copyright relevant to photographers brought about by the 1988 Act. This is available from the Association of Photographers (£3.50 plus 50p p&p).

Last stages

When the pictures are ready to go off to the printer, a final check should be made to see that they have not been damaged by any of the people who have handled them – editors, designers, etc. If the printer returns photos damaged it will be easier to refute claims that pictures were already scratched if everything is checked as a matter of course. If prints or transparencies are damaged, a fee to compensate the agency or photographer is due. This will vary in amount according to whether the picture was an original or a duplicate. Some photographs are irreplaceable. The amount due for loss is stated in the Terms & Conditions listed on the reverse of most delivery notes. This may be in the region of £400 for an original. Sometimes pictures are not damaged irreparably but are returned by the printer with torn mounts, or still sticky from origination. It is best to return such pictures to the printer for cleaning, in case any damage occurs dur-

Useful organisations

BAPLA (British Association of Picture Libraries and Agencies)
18 Vine Hill, London EC1R 5DX
tel 0171-713 1780 *fax* 0171-713 1211
e-mail bapla@bapla.org.uk
web site http://www.bapla.org.uk
Chief Administrator Linda Royles
See page 462.

DACS (Design and Artists Copyright Society)
13 Northburgh Street, London EC1V 0AH
tel 0171-336 8811 *fax* 0171-336 8822
See page 473.

The Association of Photographers
9-10 Domingo Street, London EC1Y 01TA
tel 0171-608 1441 *fax* 0171-253 3007
e-mail aop@dircon.co.uk
web site http://www.aophoto.co.uk
Includes fashion and advertising photographers amongst its members.

The Picture Research Association
(formerly SPREd)
455 Finchley Road, London NW3 6HN
tel 0171-431 9886 *fax* 0171-431 9887
e-mail pra@pictures.demon.co.uk
web site http://www.pictures.demon.co.uk
Contact Emma Krikler (General Secretary)
A professional body for picture researchers, managers, picture editors and all those involved in the research, management and supply of visual material to all forms of the media.

The Association's main aims are to promote the interests and specific skills of its members internationally; to bring together those involved in the research and publication of visual material; to provide a forum for the exchange of information and to provide guidance to its members. It offers a free advisory service for members, regular meetings, a quarterly magazine, a monthly newsletter and Freelance Register. Founded in 1977 as the Society of Picture Researchers & Editors (SPREd).

ing a DIY cleaning session. Pictures should then be returned to their owners and one or two copies of the book or proofs supplied as evidence of use, as stated in the Terms & Conditions of the source.

Getting into picture research

This can be difficult as employers are loath to employ people without experience, and some picture sources are nervous about loaning pictures. A job with a picture library would give an insight into that particular source and might lead into a job as a picture researcher. Jobs in picture libraries, and picture research work, are advertised in the Creative, Media and Sales section of *The Guardian* on Saturdays and Mondays and in *The Independent* on Mondays. Sometimes such ads appear in *The Bookseller*, the weekly publishing journal, and *Campaign*, the weekly advertising magazine. These may all be available to read at your local library. Salaries tend to be low initially as one learns the skills involved. The idea of working freelance may appeal but it is difficult to obtain enough freelance work without the contacts amassed over a period of time.

Many picture researchers build up experience working for an employer full time, and then go freelance. This is not without risks. Getting enough work, being paid for work completed, sorting out tax and National Insurance to be paid, motivation, and loneliness are some of the problems which may arise.

Picture research courses

The Publishing Training Centre at Book House
45 East Hill, London SW18 2QZ
tel 0181-874 2718/4608 *fax* 0181-870 8985
Offers a 2-day course in picture research, designed for people working in book publishing. Its objectives are to give a professional approach to the search for and use of suitable sources; to make picture researchers aware of all the implications of their task: suitability for reproduction, legal and financial aspects, and efficient administration. Held in June and in December.

The London School of Publishing and PR
David Game House, 69 Notting Hill Gate, London W11 3JS
tel 0171-221 3399 *fax* 0171-243 1730
e-mail lsp@easynet.co.uk
Course Director John Dalton
Offers a 10-week course in picture research 4 times a year. Each course takes place between 6.30-8.30pm, one evening per week. On successful completion a certificate in picture research is awarded. NUJ approved.

Jennie Karrach is a freelance picture researcher and former chair of SPREd, who has worked with major national and international clients.

Societies, prizes and festivals

Societies, associations and clubs

The societies, associations and clubs listed here will be of interest to both writers and artists. They include appreciation societies devoted to specific authors, professional bodies and national institutions. Some also offer prizes and awards (see page 510); open exhibitions for artists are listed on page 543.

Yr Academi Gymreig (Welsh Academy)
3rd Floor, Mount Stuart House, Mount Stuart Square, The Docks, Cardiff CF1 6DQ
tel (01222) 472266
Chief Executive Peter Finch, *Administrator* Margaret Harlin
Founded to promote creative writing in the Welsh language. Existing members elect new members on the basis of their contribution to Welsh literature or criticism. Also provides a meeting point for writers in the English language who are of Welsh origin and/or take Wales as a main theme of their work. Publishes a literary magazine, *Taliesin*, books on Welsh literature and translations of modern European classics into Welsh; has recently published a new English/Welsh Dictionary. Founded 1959.

Acrylic Painters' Association, National (NAPA)
134 Rake Lane, Wallasey, Wirral, Merseyside L45 1JW
tel 0151-639 2980
web sites http://www.artarena force9.co.uk/napa
http://www.watercolour-online.com.napa
President Alwyn Crawshaw, *Vice-President* Prof Arthur Hughes, *Director/Founder* Kenneth J. Hodgson
Promotes interest in, and encourages excellence and innovation in, the work of painters in acrylic. Holds an annual open exhibition at the Royal Birmingham Society of Artists Gallery, and awards are made. Publishes an annual journal and a newsletter. Membership: £20 p.a. (full), £15 p.a. (associate). Founded 1985.

Agricultural Journalists, Guild of
President Lord Plumb, *Chairman* Arthur Anderson, *Hon. General Secretary* Don Gomery,

Charnwood, 47 Court Meadow, Rotherfield, East Sussex TN6 3LQ
tel (01892) 853187
Established to promote a high standard among journalists who specialise in agricultural matters and to assist them to increase their sources of information and technical knowledge.

Amateur Artists, Society of
PO Box 50, Newark, Notts. NG23 5GY
tel (01949) 844050 *fax* (01949) 844051
To inform, encourage and inspire everyone, whatever their ability, who wants to paint, and to promote friendship and companionship amongst fellow artists. Holds meetings and events at local level, organises painting holidays, workshops, local exhibitions and competitions, publishes newsletter *Paint* (quarterly). Initial membership fee: £17.50, overseas £27.50. Founded 1992.

American Correspondents, Association of
President Myron Belkind
Secretary Sandra Marshall, Associated Press, 12 Norwich Street, London EC4A 1BP
tel 0171-353 1515 ext 4202 *fax* 0171-936 2229

American Publishers, Association of Inc.
71 Fifth Avenue, New York, NY 10003, USA
tel 212-255-0200 *fax* 212-255-7007
President Patricia S. Schroeder, *Executive Vice-President* Thomas D. McKee
Founded 1970.

American Society of Composers, Authors and Publishers
One Lincoln Plaza, New York, NY 10023
tel 212-621-6000 *fax* 212-721-0955
President Marilyn Bergman
ASCAP is a membership association of over 50,000 writers and publishers,

which protects its members' rights and those of affiliated foreign societies. It licenses and collects royalties for public performance of copyrighted music. Annual membership: $10.00 (writers), $50.00 (publishers). Founded 1914.

American Society of Indexers
PO Box 48267, Seattle, WA 98148-0267, USA
tel 206-241-9196 *fax* 206-727-6430
e-mail asi@well.com
web site http://www.well.com/user/asi
Aims to improve the quality and standards of indexing and related areas of information science; acts as an advisory board on renumeration and qualifications of indexers and abstractors; defends and safeguards the professional interests of indexers. Holds meetings, seminars, workshops; provides *The Indexer* (bi-annual) and *Key Words* newsletter (6 p.a.). Annual membership: $65, $35 (student), $150 (corporate). Founded 1968.

Art and Design, National Society for Education in
The Gatehouse, Corsham Court, Corsham, Wilts. SN13 0BZ
tel (01249) 714825 *fax* (01249) 716138
General Secretary Dr John Steers NDD, ATC, DAE, PhD
Professional association of principals and lecturers in colleges and schools of art and of specialist art, craft and design teachers in other schools and colleges. Has representatives on National and Regional Committees concerned with Art and Design Education. Publication: *Journal of Art and Design Education* (3 p.a.), (Blackwells). Founded 1888.

Art Club, New English
17 Carlton House Terrace,
London SW1Y 5BD
tel 0171-930 6844 *fax* 0171-839 7830
Hon. Secretary William Bowyer RA, RWS, RP
For all those interested in the art of painting, and the promotion of fine arts. Open Annual Exhibition at the Mall Galleries, The Mall, London SW1.

Art Historians, Association of (AAH)
Cowcross Court, 77 Cowcross Street,
London EC1M 6BP
tel 0171-490 3211 *fax* 0171-490 3277
e-mail admin.aah@btinternet.com
web site http://www.gold.ac.uk/aah
Administrator Andrew Falconer
Hon. Secretary Dr Fintan Cullen, Dept. of Art

History, The Art Centre, University of Nottingham, University Park, Nottingham NG7 2RO
Formed to promote the study of art history, the AAH has become a large and lively organisation for professional art historians, researchers and teachers in the field. The history of art itself is a broad and constantly evolving subject enlivened by cross-fertilisation with many other disciplines. The association is keen not only to extend its promotion of all activities in the visual arts but to ensure a wider public recognition of the field's rich diversity. There are 3 options for personal membership, depending upon the choice of publications; special rates for students/unwaged; corporate membership available. Founded 1974.

Artists, Federation of British
17 Carlton House Terrace,
London SW1Y 5BD
tel 0171-930 6844 *fax* 0171-839 7830
Administers 9 major National Art Societies at The Mall Galleries, The Mall, London SW1.

Artists, The International Guild of
Briargate, 2 The Brambles, Ilkley,
West Yorkshire LS29 9DH
tel (01943) 609075
Director Leslie Simpson FRSA
Organises 4 seasonal exhibitions per year for three national societies: Society of Miniaturists, British Society of Painters in Oils, Pastels & Acrylics and British Watercolour Society. Promotes these 3 societies in countries outside the British Isles.

Artists Agents, Society of
144 Royal College Street, London NW1 0TA
tel 0171-267 9661
e-mail info@saa.co.uk
web site http://www.saa.co.uk
Contact Alison Eldred
Formed to promote professionalism in the illustration industry and to forge closer links between clients and artists through an agreed set of guidelines. The Society believes in an ethical approach through proper terms and conditions, thereby protecting the interests of the artists and clients. Founded 1992.

Artists in Ireland, Association of
Arthouse, Temple Bar, Dublin 2,
Republic of Ireland

tel (01) 8740529 fax (01) 6771585
e-mail artists_ireland@connect.ie
Director Stella Coffey
To support and advise professional visual artists in Ireland, to promote the visual arts, to develop international exchanges of artists. Publishes *Art Bulletin* (6 p.a.). Published (1994) *Irish Visual Artists' Handbook*, available by mail £14 (inc. p&p). Annual membership: £25. Founded 1981.

Artists, Royal Birmingham Society of

69A New Street, Birmingham B2 4DU
tel 0121-643 3768 fax 0121-644 5298
Society has its own galleries and rooms in the city centre. Members (RBSA) and Associates (ARBSA) are elected annually. Holds 3 Open Exhibitions: Oil & Sculpture (February), Watercolour & Crafts (May), Pastel & Drawing (December) – send sae for schedules, available 6 weeks prior to Exhibition. A further Open £1000 First Prize Exhibition is held (June/July) for works in any media. Other substantial money prizes can be won with no preference given to Members and Associates. Also an Exhibition of Printmakers (April), an Autumn Exhibition open to Members and Associates, and 2 Friends Exhibitions (February and August). Friends of the RBSA pay an annual subscription of £14, which entitles them to attend various functions and to submit work for the Annual Exhibitions.

Artists, Royal Society of British

17 Carlton House Terrace, London SW1Y 5BD
tel 0171-930 6844 fax 0171-839 7830
President Colin Hayes RA, Keeper Alfred Daniels
Incorporated by Royal Charter for the purpose of encouraging the study and practice of the arts of painting, sculpture and architectural designs. Annual Open Exhibition at the Mall Galleries, The Mall, London SW1.

Arts Boards – see Regional Arts Boards

Arts Club

40 Dover Street, London W1X 3RB
tel 0171-499 8581 fax 0171-409 0913
Secretary Mrs Jackie Downing
For all those connected with or interested in the arts, literature and science. Founded 1863.

The Arts Council/An Chomhairle Ealaíon

Literature Officer, 70 Merrion Square, Dublin 2, Republic of Ireland
tel (01) 6611840 fax (01) 6761302
Literature Officer Sinéad MacAodha, Visual Arts Officer Oliver Dowling
The national development agency for the arts in Ireland, including literature in English and Irish. Founded 1951.

Arts Council of England

14 Great Peter Street, London SW1P 3NQ
tel 0171-333 0100 fax 0171-973 6590
web site http://www.artscouncil.org.uk
Chairman Gerry Robinson, Secretary-General Peter Hewitt, Director of Literature Gary McKeone, Director of Visual Arts Marjorie Allthorpe-Guyton
To develop and improve the knowledge, understanding and practice of the arts, and to increase their accessibility to the public throughout England. The arts with which the Council is mainly concerned are dance, drama, mime, literature, music and opera, the visual arts, including photography and documentary films and videos on the arts.

Within literature, 15 annual writers' awards are awarded competitively (see also page 511). Subsidies are provided to literary organisations and magazines, and schemes include support for translation, writers' residencies in prisons, tours by authors and the promotion of literature in libraries and education.

The Visual Arts Department is committed to the long-term improvement of visual artists' economic standing and working conditions in England. In collaboration with the Regional Arts Boards it supports a number of national artists' agencies, provides grants for the benefit of individual practitioners and promotes artists' professional development initiatives.

Arts Council of Northern Ireland

MacNeice House, 77 Malone Road, Belfast BT9 6AQ
tel (01232) 385200 fax (01232) 661715
Chief Executive Brian Ferran, Literature Officer Ciaran Carson, Visual Arts Officer Paula Campbell
Promotes and encourages the arts throughout Northern Ireland. Artists in drama, dance, music and jazz, literature, the visual arts, traditional arts and com-

munity arts, can apply for support for specific schemes and projects. The value of the grant will be set according to the aims of the application. Applicants must have contributed regularly to the artistic activities of the community, with residency of at least one year in Northern Ireland.

Arts Council of Wales
9 Museum Place, Cardiff CF1 3NX
tel (01222) 394711 *fax* (01222) 221447
Chairman Sir Richard Lloyd Jones KCB, *Chief Executive* Joanna Weston, *Literature Director* Tony Bianchi, *Drama Director* Anna Holmes, *Visual Arts and Crafts Director* Isabel Hitchman
National organisation with specific responsibility for the funding and development of the arts in Wales. ACW receives grants from central and local government; also distributes the National Lottery funds in Wales. From these resources, ACW makes grants to support arts activity and facilities. Some of the funds are allocated in the form of annual revenue grants to full-time arts organisations; also operates schemes which provide financial and other forms of support for individual activities or projects. Undertakes this work in both the English and Welsh languages.

North Wales Regional Office
10 Wellfield House, Bangor, Gwynedd LL57 1ER
tel (01248) 353248 *fax* (01248) 351077

West Wales Regional Office
6 Gardd Llydaw, Carmarthen SA31 1QL
tel (01267) 234248 *fax* (01267) 233084

Arts, Manufactures and Commerce, Royal Society for the encouragement of (RSA)
8 John Adam Street, London WC2N 6EZ
tel 0171-930 5115 *fax* 0171-839 5805
e-mail rsa@rsa.ftech.co.uk
web site http://www.cs.mdx.ac.uk/rsa/
Chairman of Council Richard Onians
With 20,000 Fellows, the RSA sustains a forum for people from all walks of life to come together to address issues, shape new ideas and stimulate action. It works through projects, award schemes and its lecture programme, the proceedings of which are recorded in *RSA Journal*. Founded 1754.

Asian Affairs, The Royal Society for
2 Belgrave Square, London SW1X 8PJ
tel 0171-235 5122 *fax* 0171-259 6771
e-mail info@rsaa.org.uk
web site http://www.rsaa.org.uk
President The Lord Denman CBE, MC, TD, *Chairman of Council* Sir Donald Hawley KCMG, MBE, *Secretary* David Easton MA, FRSA, FRGS
For the study of all Asia past and present; fortnightly lectures, etc; library. Publishes *Asian Affairs* (3 p.a.), free to members. Subscription: £55 London, £45 more than 60 miles from London and overseas, Junior Members (to 25) £10. Founded 1901.

Aslib (The Association for Information Management)
Staple Hall, Stone House Court, London EC3A 7PB
tel 0171-903 0000 *fax* 0171-903 0011
e-mail aslib@aslib.co.uk
web site http://www.aslib.co.uk/
Membership Manager Helen Rebera
Actively promotes best practice in the management of information resources. It represents its members and lobbies on all aspects of the management of and legislation concerning information at local, national and international levels. Aslib provides consultancy and information services, professional development training, conferences, specialist recruitment, and publishes primary and secondary journals, conference proceedings, Directories and monographs. Founded 1924.

The Jane Austen Society
Secretary Mrs Susan McCartan, Carton House, Redwood Lane, Medstead, Alton, Hants GU34 5PE
tel (01705) 475855 *fax* (01705) 788842
e-mail rosemary@sndc.demon.co.uk
web site http://www.sndc.demon.co.uk/jas.htm
Founded in 1940 to promote interest in, and enjoyment of, Jane Austen's novels and letters. Eight branches in UK. Membership: UK £10, life £150; overseas £12, life £180.

Australia Council
PO Box 788, Strawberry Hills, NSW 2012, Australia
located at 181 Lawson Street, Redfern, NSW 2016
tel (02) 9950 9000 *fax* (02) 9950 9111
Chairperson Dr Margaret Seares
Provides a broad range of support for the arts in Australia, embracing music, theatre, literature, visual arts, crafts, Aboriginal arts, community and new media arts. It has 8 major Funds: Literature, Visual Arts/Craft, Music, Theatre, Dance, New Media, Community

Cultural Development, Major Organisations, as well as the Aboriginal and Torres Strait Islander Arts Board.

The Literature Fund
Australia Council, PO Box 788, Strawberry Hills, NSW 2012, Australia
tel (02) 9950 9000 *fax* (02) 9950 9111
Because of its size and isolation and the competition its literature meets from other English-speaking countries, Australia has always needed to subsidise writing of creative and cultural significance. The Fund's chief objective is the support of the writing of all forms of creative literature – novels, short stories, poetry, plays and literary non-fiction. It also assists with the publication of literary magazines, has a publishing subsidies programme, and initiates and supports projects of many kinds designed to promote Australian literature both within Australia and abroad.

Australian Library and Information Association
PO Box E441, Kingston, ACT 2604, Australia
tel (02) 6285 1877 *fax* (02) 6282 2249
e-mail enquiry@alia.org.au
web site http://www.alia.org.au/
Executive Director Virginia Walsh
Aims to promote and improve the services of libraries and other information agencies; to improve the standard of library and information personnel and foster their professional interests; to represent the interests of members to governments, other organisations and the community; and to encourage people to contribute to the improvement of library and information services by supporting the association.

Australian Publishers Association (APA)
89 Jones Street, Ultimo, NSW 2007, Australia
tel (02) 9281 9788 *fax* (02) 9281 1073
e-mail apa@magna.com.au
web site http://www.publishers.asn.au

The Australian Society of Authors
PO Box 1566, Strawberry Hills, NSW 2012, Australia
located at 98 Pitt Street, Redfern, NSW 2016, Australia
tel (02) 9318 0877 *fax* (02) 9318 0530
e-mail asauthors@peg.pegasus.oz.au
web site http://www.peg.apc.org/~asauthors
Executive Director José Borginho

Aims to represent and enhance author rights and interests, through providing information, contract advice, publications (newsletters and journals), representation in disputes. Also seminars, research and information on new issues and new directions in writing and publishing. Annual membership: $110 (full/associate), $70 (affiliate); joining fee: $20.

Australian Writers' Guild Ltd
60 Kellett Street, Kings Cross, NSW 2011, Australia
tel (02) 9357 7888 *fax* (02) 9357 7776
e-mail awgsyd@ozemail.com.au
Executive Officer Simon Lake
Professional association dedicated to promoting and protecting the professional interests of writers for stage, screen, TV and radio. Full membership: entrance fee $150, annual fee $165-$600 dependent on income from writing; associate membership: entrance fee $75, annual fee $95. Founded 1962.

Authors, The Society of
84 Drayton Gardens, London SW10 9SB
tel 0171-373 6642
e-mail authorsoc@writers.org.uk
web site http://www.writers.org.uk/society
Chairman Clare Francis, *General Secretary* Mark Le Fanu
Founded in 1884 by Sir Walter Besant with the object of representing, assisting and protecting authors. A limited company and independent trade union, the Society's scope has been continuously extended; specialist associations have been created for translators, broadcasters, educational, medical and children's writers and illustrators (details are elsewhere in this *Yearbook*). Members are entitled to legal as well as general advice in connection with their work, their contracts, their choice of a publisher, problems with publishers, broadcasting organisations, etc. Annual subscription: £70 (£65 by direct debit) with reductions available to authors under 35 or over 65. Full particulars of membership from the Society's offices (see also page 504).

Authors' Agents, The Association of
President Vivien Green, *Vice President* Jonathan Lloyd, *Treasurer* David Miller
Secretary Meg Davis, 62 Grafton Way, London W1P 5LD
tel 0171-387 2076 *fax* 0171-387 2042

Maintains a code of professional practice to which all members of the Association commit themselves; holds regular meetings to discuss matters of common professional interest; and provides a vehicle for representing the view of authors' agents in discussion of matters of common interest with other professional bodies. Founded 1974.

Authors' Club (at the Arts Club)
40 Dover Street, London W1X 3RB
tel 0171-499 8581 *fax* 0171-409 0913
Secretary Ann Carter
Founded by Sir Walter Besant, the Authors' Club welcomes as members writers, publishers, critics, journalists, academics and anyone involved with literature. Administers the Authors' Club Best First Novel Award, Sir Banister Fletcher Award, Marsh Biography Award and the Marsh Award for Children's Literature in Translation. Membership: apply to Secretary. Founded 1891.

The Authors League of America Inc.
330 West 42nd Street, New York, NY 10036, USA
tel 212-564-8350 *fax* 212-564-8363
National membership organisation to promote the professional interest of authors and dramatists, procure satisfactory copyright legislation and treaties, guard freedom of expression and support fair tax treatment for writers. Founded 1912.

Authors' Licensing and Collecting Society Ltd (ALCS)
Marlborough Court, 14-18 Holborn, London EC1N 2LE
tel 0171-395 0600 *fax* 0171-395 0660
e-mail alcs@alcs.co.uk
web site http://www.alcs.co.uk
ALCS is the British collecting society for all writers and their heirs. Its principle purpose is to ensure that hard-to-collect revenues due to authors are efficiently collected and speedily distributed. ALCS is not a union but it does aim to protect and promote the rights of authors, maintaining a watching brief on copyright matters and fostering awareness of the rights of all authors. ALCS is a non-profit making organisation owned by writers and financed primarily by a commission levied on distributions. See page 630 for more information about the Society's work and for membership details.

Authors' Representatives Inc., Association of
Ten Astor Place, 3rd Floor, New York, NY 10003, USA
tel 212-353-3709
Founded 1991.

Aviation Artists, The Guild of
(incorporating the Society of Aviation Artists)
The Bondway Business Centre, 71 Bondway, Vauxhall Cross, London SW8 1SQ
tel/fax 0171-735 0634
President Michael Turner PGAvA, *Secretary* Hugo Trotter DFC
Formed in 1971 to promote aviation art through the organisation of exhibitions and meetings. Holds annual open exhibition in July in London; £1000 for 'Aviation Painting of the Year'. quarterly members' journal. Associates £40, Members £55 (by invitation), non-exhibiting artists and friends £15.

AXIS
Visual Arts Information Service, Room H201, Leeds Metropolitan University, Calverley Street, Leeds LS1 3HE
tel 0113-283 3125 *fax* 0113-283 5938
e-mail axis@gn.apc.org
web site http://www.lmu.ac.uk/ces/axis/
A unique arts information service which promotes the work of contemporary visual artists through the AXIS Database, a sophisticated multimedia database which records and displays comprehensive information about each artist, including a full CV and high quality colour images. Over 2000 practising artists are represented on the Database, which is used by commissions agents, curators, journalists, researchers, architects and other interested parties. AXIS offers a telephone and written enquiry service, providing information on artists. It also operates a public access point network where visitors can personally use the Database, currently located in Leeds, Newcastle, Glasgow and Inverness. Founded 1991.

BAPLA (British Association of Picture Libraries and Agencies)
18 Vine Hill, London EC1R 5DX
tel 0171-713 1780 *fax* 0171-713 1211
e-mail bapla@bapla.demon.co.uk
web site http://www.bapla.org.uk
Chief Administrator Linda Royles
BAPLA is the trade organisation representing the British picture library and

agency industry, offering an impressive 300 million pictures. With 340 members, it is the largest organisation of its kind in the world, and offers a unique pool of material and expertise. The Association promotes the highest standards of professionalism and service in the loan and reproduction of pictures. No library or agency is admitted to membership unless it undertakes to abide by the code of practice. BAPLA is active in lobbying to protect intellectual property rights both in the UK and internationally. Founded 1975.

BASCA (British Academy of Songwriters, Composers and Authors)
The Penthouse, 4 Brook Street, London W1Y 1AA
tel 0171-629 0992 *fax* 0171-629 0993
e-mail basca@basca.org.uk
Contact Guy Fletcher (Chairman)
Europe's largest composer body. Represented on PRS and MCPS boards. Competitions. Quarterly magazine. Song for Europe. Presents Ivor Novello Awards. Founded 1947.

The Beckford Society
Secretary Sidney Blackmore, 15 Healey Street, London NW1 8SR
tel 0171-267 7750 *fax* (01985) 213195
Aims to promote an interest in the life and works of William Beckford of Fonthill (1760-1844) and his circle. Encourages Beckford studies and scholarship through exhibitions, lectures and publications, including *The Beckford Journal* (annual) and occasional newsletters. Annual subscription: £10 minimum. Founded 1995.

Thomas Lovell Beddoes Society
11 Laund Nook, Belper, Derbyshire DE56 1GY
tel (01773) 828066
Aims to promote an interest in the life and works of Thomas Lovell Beddoes (1803-1849). The Society promotes and undertakes Beddoes studies, and disseminates and publishes useful research. Founded 1994.

The E.F. Benson Society
The Old Coach House, High Street, Rye, East Sussex TN31 7JF
tel (01797) 223114
Secretary Allan Downend
To promote interest in the author E.F.

Benson and the Benson family. Arranges annual literary evening, annual outing to Rye (July), talks on the Bensons and exhibitions. Archive includes the Austin Seckersen Collection, transcriptions of the Benson diaries and letters. Publishes postcards, anthologies of Benson's works and an annual journal, *The Dodo*. Annual subscription: £7.50 single, £8.50 2 people at same address, £12.50 overseas. Founded 1984.

E.F. Benson: The Tilling Society
5 Friars Bank, Pett Road, Guestling, East Sussex TN35 4ET
Secretaries Cynthia and Tony Reavell
To bring together enthusiasts for E.F. Benson and his Mapp & Lucia novels; annual gathering in Rye. Publishes 2 lengthy newsletters p.a. Annual subscription: £8, overseas £10; full starters membership (including all back newsletters) £22, overseas £26. Founded 1982.

Bibliographical Society
c/o Wellcome Institute, 183 Euston Road, London NW1 2BE
tel 0171-611 7244 *fax* 0171-611 8703
e-mail jm93@dial.pipex.com
President R. Myers, *Hon. Secretary* D. Pearson
Acquisition and dissemination of information upon subjects connected with historical bibliography. Founded 1892.

The Blackpool Art Society
The Studio, Wilkinson Avenue, Blackpool FY3 9HB
President Jim Collins
Hon. Secretary Denise Fergyson, 29 Stafford Avenue, Poulton-le-Fylde, Lancs. FY6 8BJ
tel (01253) 884645
Summer and autumn exhibition (members' work only). Studio meetings, practicals, lectures, etc, out-of-door sketching workshops. Founded 1884.

Book Packagers Association
93A Blenheim Crescent, London W11 2EQ
tel 0171-221 9089
e-mail rosemarypettit@msn.com
Secretary Rosemary Pettit
Aims to represent the interests of book packagers; to exchange information at meetings and seminars; to provide services such as standard contracts and display/ meeting facilities at book fairs. Annual subscription: £75-£150. Founded 1985.

Book Trust

Book House, 45 East Hill, London SW18 2QZ
tel 0181-516 2977 *fax* 0181-516 2978
Patron HRH Prince Philip, Duke of Edinburgh,
Chairman Prof Eric Bolton, *Director* Brian
Perman

Book Trust exists to open up the world of books and reading to people of all ages and cultures. Its services include the Book Information Service, a unique, specialist information and research service for all queries on books and reading (business callers are charged via a premium rate telephone service and should phone 0897-161193; calls are charged at £1.50 per minute). Book Trust administers a number of literary prizes, including the Booker Prize and produces a wide range of books, pamphlets and leaflets designed to make books more easily accessible to the public. Founded 1925 as the National Book Council.

Young Book Trust

The arm of Book Trust concerned with children's literature, YBT provides practical help and advice on all aspects of children's books and reading. An on-site library houses a unique collection of every children's title published in the UK during the last 2 years. On joining, subscribers receive a welcome pack containing free copies of all Young Book Trust publications, information, posters, etc, plus author information, Book Week material and book lists. YBT produces a termly children's book magazine, ideal for schools, libraries, booksellers and publishers. Annual YBT subscription: £30 plus VAT.

Book Trust Scotland

The Scottish Book Centre, 137 Dundee Street, Edinburgh EH11 1BG
tel 0131-229 3663 *fax* 0131-228 4293

With a particular responsibility towards Scottish writing, the Trust exists to promote literature and reading, and aims to reach (and create) a wider reading public than has existed before. It also organises exhibitions, readings and storytellings, operates an extensive children's reference library available to everyone and administers literary prizes, including the Stakis Prize for the Scottish Writer of the Year. The Trust also publishes posters, literary guides and Directories and advises other relevant art organisations.

In addition, the Trust administers the Writers in Scotland scheme which supports writers' visits throughout Scotland. Readiscovery Touring, the Trust's touring arm, runs the Readiscovery Book Bus and publishes the literary *Touring Co-ordination Newsletter* (quarterly). Founded 1960.

Books Across the Sea

The English-Speaking Union of the Commonwealth, Dartmouth House,
37 Charles Street, London W1X 8AB
tel 0171-493 3328 *fax* 0171-495 6108
e-mail esu@mailbox.ulcc.ac.uk
web site http://www.esu.org
The English Speaking Union of the United States,
16 East 69th Street, New York, NY 10021, USA
tel 212-879-6800 *fax* 212-772-2886

World voluntary organisation devoted to the promotion of international understanding and friendship. Exchanges books with its corresponding BAS Committees in New York, Russia and Australia. The books are selected to reflect the life and culture of each country and the best of its recent publishing and writing. New selections are announced by bulletin, *The Ambassador Booklist*.

Booksellers Association of Great Britain and Ireland

272 Vauxhall Bridge Road, London SW1V 1BA
tel 0171-834 5477 *fax* 0171-834 8812
e-mail 100437.2261@compuserve.com
Chief Executive T.E. Godfray
Founded 1895.

The George Borrow Society

Hon. Secretary Dr James H. Reading, The Gables, 112 Irchester Road, Rushden, Northants. NN10 9XQ
tel/fax (01933) 312965

Promotes knowledge of the life and works of George Borrow (1803-81), traveller and author. Publishes *Bulletin* (bi-annual). Annual membership: £10. Founded 1991.

Botanical Artists, Society of

Founder President Suzanne Lucas FLS, PRMS, FPSBA, *Hon. Treasurer* Pamela Davis, *Executive Vice President* Margaret Stevens
Executive Secretary Mrs Pam Henderson, 1 Knapp Cottages, Wyke, Gillingham, Dorset SP8 4NQ
tel (01747) 825718, 0171-222 2723 (during exhibitions)

Aims to encourage the art of botanical

painting. Membership through selection. Annual Open Exhibition held, around Easter time, at The Westminster Gallery, Westminster Central Hall, Storey's Gate, London SW1H 9NH; hand in end February. Information and entrance forms available from the Executive Secretary from October, on receipt of sae. Membership: £90; lay members £20. Founded 1985.

British Academy

10 Carlton House Terrace, London SW1Y 5AH
tel 0171-969 5200 *fax* 0171-969 5300
e-mail secretary@britac.ac.uk
web site http://britac3.britac.ac.uk
President Sir Tony Wrigley, *Vice-Presidents* Prof M.M. McGowan, Prof R.J.P. Kain *Treasurer* Mr J.S. Flemming, *Foreign Secretary* Prof B.E. Supple, *Publications Secretary* Prof F.G.B. Millar, *Secretary* P.W.H. Brown CBE

The British Academy is the national Academy for the humanities and social sciences. It is an independent and self-governing fellowship of scholars, elected for distinction and achievement in one or more branches of the academic disciplines that make up the humanities and social sciences. In the absence of a research council with responsibility for the humanities, the British Academy is now the principal channel outside the universities for the Government's support of advanced research in the humanities, and it receives a Parliamentary grant-in-aid to support its activities. These include a wide range of grant schemes for research at postdoctoral level, and the organisation of the national scheme for postgraduate awards in the humanities. Founded 1901.

British Amateur Press Association (BAPA)

Secretary Mr L.E. Linford, Flat 36, Priory Park, Botanical Way, St Osyth, Essex CO16 8TE

A non-profit making, non-sectarian hobby organisation to 'promote the fellowship of amateur writers, artists, editors, printers, publishers and others, and to encourage them to edit, print and publish, *as a hobby*, magazines and newsletters, etc' by letterpress and other processes, including photocopiers and DTP/word-processors. Not an outlet for placing work commercially, only with other members in their private publications circulated within the association and friends. A fraternity providing contacts between amateur writers, poets, editors, artists, etc. Postal enquiries only, please send first class stamp. Founded 1890.

British American Arts Association (BAAA)

118 Commercial Street, London E1 6NF
tel 0171-247 5385 *fax* 0171-247 5256
e-mail baaa@easynet.co.uk
Director Jennifer Williams

A non-profit-making organisation working in the field of arts and education. BAAA conducts research, organises conferences, produces a quarterly newsletter and is part of an international network of arts and education organisations. As well as a specialised arts and education library, BAAA has a more general library holding information on opportunities for artists and performers both in the UK and abroad. BAAA is not a grant-giving organisation.

The British Council

10 Spring Gardens, London SW1A 2BN
tel 0171-930 8466 *fax* 0171-839 6347
web site http://www.britcoun.org/
Chairman Sir Martin Jacomb, *Director-General* Dr David Drewry, *Director of Literature* Alastair Niven, *Director, Arts Group* John Tod OBE

The British Council promotes Britain abroad, by providing access to British ideas, talent and experience in education and training, books and the English language, information, the arts, the sciences and technology. The Council is an authority on teaching English as a second or foreign language and gives advice and information on curriculum, methodology, materials and testing. It also promotes British literature overseas through writers' tours, academic visits, seminars and exhibitions. The Council works in 109 countries where it runs over 200 libraries and resource centres and 118 teaching centres.

The Council's lending and reference libraries throughout the world stock material appropriate to the Council's priorities in individual countries. Where appropriate the libraries act as showcases for the latest British publications. They vary in size from small reference collections and information centres to comprehensive libraries equipped with reference works, CD-Rom, on-line facilities and a selection of British periodicals. Bibliographies of British books on special subjects are prepared on request.

The Council organises book and electronic publishing exhibitions for showing overseas, ranging from small specialist displays to larger exhibitions at major international book fairs such as Frankfurt.

The Council publishes *New Writing*, an annual anthology; a series of literary bibliographies, including *The Novel in Britain since 1970*; *Contemporary Writers*, a series of over 30 pamphlets on modern British writers; and exhibitions on literary topics such as *Writers Abroad British Travel Writing*. A catalogue is available on request, as is a catalogue of other publications, covering the arts, books, libraries and publishing, education and training, English language teaching and information for and about overseas students.

The Visual Arts Department, part of the Council's Arts Division, develops and enlarges overseas knowledge and appreciation of British achievement in the fields of painting, sculpture, printmaking, design, photography, the crafts and architecture, working closely with the Council's overseas offices and with professional colleagues in Britain and abroad.

The Council acts as an agent of the Department for International Development for book aid projects for developing countries. In 1997/98 the Council also supported over 2000 events in the visual arts, film and TV, drama, literature, dance and music, ranging from the classical to the contemporary.

Further information about the work of the British Council is available from the Press and Public Relations Department at the headquarters in London or from British Council offices and libraries overseas.

British Film Institute (BFI)

21 Stephen Street, London W1P 2LN
tel 0171-255 1444 *fax* 0171-436 7950
Director John Woodward, *Head of Press and Corporate Affairs* Tony Slaughter

Set up in 1933 and now established by Royal Charter, the BFI is the UK national agency with responsibility for encouraging the arts of film and TV and conserv-

ing them in the national interest. The BFI's aim is to ensure that the many audiences in the UK are offered access to the widest possible choice of cinema and TV, so that their enjoyment is enhanced through a deeper understanding of the history and potential of these vital and popular art forms. The BFI's National Library contains the world's largest collection of published and unpublished material relating to film and TV. Annual membership: £11.95; includes NFT monthly programmes. Library passes: £17.50 (members); £30 (non-members). Concessionary rates are available.

British Interactive Multimedia Association (BIMA)

5-6 Clipstone Street, London W1P 7EB
tel 0171-436 8250 *fax* 0171-436 8251
e-mail enquiries@bima.co.uk
web site http://www.bima.co.uk
Secretary Norma Hughes

BIMA was established to promote a wider understanding of the benefits of interactive multimedia to industry, government and education and to provide a regular forum for the exchange of views amongst members. Members come from the fields of application development, computer manufacturing, publishing, disk pressing, hardware distribution, programming and consultancy. Membership is open to any organisation or individual with an interest in multimedia. As well as regular monthly meetings, BIMA publishes a quarterly newsletter. Membership: commercial £650; institutional £300; individual £150. Founded 1984.

Broadcasting Entertainment Cinematograph and Theatre Union (BECTU), Writers Section

111 Wardour Street, London W1V 4AY
tel 0171-437 8506 *fax* 0171-437 8268
Supervisory Official Marilyn Goodman, *General Secretary* R. Bolton

To defend the interests of writers in film, TV and radio. By virtue of its industrial strength, the Union is able to help its writer members to secure favourable terms and conditions. In cases of disputes with employers, the Union can intervene in order to ensure an equitable settlement. Its production agreement with PACT lays down minimum terms for writers working in the documentary area. Founded 1946.

Broadcasting Group
84 Drayton Gardens, London SW10 9SB
tel 0171-373 6642

Specialist group within the Society of Authors (see page 504) for radio and TV writers and others involved in broadcasting.

The Brontë Society
Membership Secretary, The Brontë Parsonage Museum, Haworth, Keighley,
West Yorkshire BD22 8DR
tel (01535) 642323 *fax* (01535) 647131
web site http://www.virtual-pc.com/bpmweb

Examination, preservation, illustration of the memoirs and literary remains of the Brontë family; exhibitions of MSS and other subjects. Publishes *The Transactions of the Brontë Society* (annual) and *The Brontë Gazette* (bi-annual).

The Browning Society
Secretary Ralph Ensz, 163 Wembley Hill Road, Wembley Park, Middlesex HA9 8EL
tel 0181-904 8401

Aims to widen the appreciation and understanding of the lives and poetry of Robert Browning and Elizabeth Barrett Browning, and other Victorian writers and poets. Membership: £15. Founded 1881; refounded 1969.

The John Buchan Society
Hon. Secretary Russell Paterson, Limpsfield, 16 Ranfurly Road, Bridge of Weir, Renfrewshire PA11 3EL
tel (01505) 613116

Promotes a wider understanding and appreciation of the life and works of John Buchan. Encourages publication of a complete annotated edition of Buchan's works, and supports the John Buchan Centre and Museum at Broughton, Borders. Holds regular meetings and social gatherings; produces a Newsletter and a Journal. Annual subscription: £10.00 full/overseas; other rates on application. Founded 1979.

Byron Society (International)
Byron House, 6 Gertrude Street,
London SW10 0JN
tel 0171-352 5112 *fax* 0171-352 1226
Hon. Director Mrs Elma Dangerfield OBE

To promote research into the life and works of Lord Byron by seminars, discussions, lectures and readings. Publishes *The Byron Journal* (annual, £5 plus postage). Annual subscription: £18. Founded 1971.

The Cable Communications Association
Fifth Floor, Artillery House, Artillery Row, London SW1P 1RT
tel 0171-222 2900 *fax* 0171-799 1471
Founded 1934.

Randolph Caldecott Society
Secretary Kenn Oultram, Clatterwick Hall, Little Leigh, Northwich, Cheshire CW8 4RJ
tel (01606) 891303 (office hours)

To encourage an interest in the life and works of Randolph Caldecott, the Victorian artist, illustrator and sculptor. Meetings held in Chester and London. Annual subscription: £7-£10. Founded 1983.

Canada, Periodical Writers Association of
54 Wolseley Street, Toronto, Ontario M5T 1A5, Canada
tel 416-504-1645 *fax* 416-703-0059
e-mail pwac@web.net
web site http://www.web.net/~pwac
Executive Director Ruth Biderman.
Founded 1976.

Canada, Writers Guild of
123 Edward Street, Suite 1225, Toronto, Ontario MSG 1E2, Canada
tel 416-979-7907 *toll free* 1-800-567-9974
fax 416-979-9273
Executive Director Maureen Parker

To further the professional, creative and economic rights and interests of writers in radio, TV, film, video and all recorded media; to promote full freedom of expression and communication, and to oppose censorship unequivocally. Annual membership: $150, plus 2% of fees earned in the Guild's jurisdiction.

Canada, The Writers' Union of
24 Ryerson Avenue, Toronto, Ontario M5T 2P3, Canada
tel 416-703-8982 *fax* 416-703-0826
e-mail twuc@the-wire.com
web site http://www.swifty.com/twuc

Canadian Authors Association
PO Box 419, Campbellford, Ontario K0L 1L0, Canada
tel 705-653-0323 *fax* 705-653-0593
e-mail canauth@redden.on.ca
web site http://www.CanAuthors.org/national.html
President Murphy Shewchuk, *Administrator* Alec McEachern

Canadian Magazine Publishers Association
130 Spadina Avenue, Suite 202, Toronto, Ontario M5V 2L4, Canada
tel 416-504-0274 *fax* 416-504-0437
General Manager Cindy Goldrick
Founded 1989.

Canadian Poets, League of
54 Wolseley Street, 3rd Floor, Toronto, Ontario M5T 1A5, Canada
tel 416-504-1657 *fax* 416-703-0059
e-mail league@ican.net
web site http://www.swifty.com/lc/
Executive Director Edita Petrauskaite
To promote the interests of poets and to advance Canadian poetry in Canada and abroad. Administers 2 annual awards; runs an annual poetry competition, a Canadian chapbook manuscript competition, and a youth poetry competition; publishes a newsletter and *Poetry Markets for Canadians, Who's Who in The League of Canadian Poets, Poets in the Classroom* (teaching guide), *Vintage* (contest anthology). Promotes and sells members' poetry books. Founded 1966.

Canadian Publishers, Association of
110 Eglinton Avenue West, Suite 401, Toronto, Ontario M4Y 1A3, Canada
tel 416-487-6116 *fax* 416-487-8815
e-mail info@canbook.org
web site http://www.publishers.ca
Director Paul Davidson
Founded 1976; formerly Independent Publishers Association, 1971.

Canadian Publishers' Council
250 Merton Street, Suite 203, Toronto, Ontario M4S 1B1, Canada
tel 416-322-7011 *fax* 416-322-6999
e-mail pubadmin@pubcouncil.ca
web site http://www.pubcouncil.ca
Executive Director Jacqueline Hushion

Career Development Group
(formerly Association of Assistant Librarians)
c/o The Library Association, 7 Ridgmount Street, London WC1E 7AE
President Andrew Fripp BA, MA, ALA,
Hon. Secretary Anne Partridge BSc, MSc
Publishes bibliographical aids, the journal *Impact*, works on librarianship; and runs educational courses. Founded 1895.

Careers Writers' Association
Membership Secretary Barbara Buffton, 71 Wimborne Road, Colehill, Wimborne, Doreset BH21 2RP
tel/fax (01202) 880320)
Society for established writers on the inter-related topics of education, training and careers. Holds occasional meetings on subjects of interest to members, and circulates details of members to information providers. Annual membership: £15. Founded 1980.

(Daresbury) Lewis Carroll Society
Secretary Kenn Oultram, Clatterwick Hall, Little Leigh, Northwich, Cheshire CW8 4RJ
tel (01606) 891303 (office hours)
To encourage an interest in the life and works of Lewis Carroll, author of *Alice's Adventures*. Meetings at Carroll's birth village (Daresbury, Cheshire). Elects an annual 'Alice'. Annual subscription: £5. Founded 1970.

The Lewis Carroll Society
Secretary Sarah Stanfield, Acorns, Dargate, Nr Faversham, Kent ME13 9HG
To promote interest in the life and works of Lewis Carroll (Revd Charles Lutwidge Dodgson) and to encourage research. Activities include regular meetings and publication of *The Carrollian* (2 p.a.) and newsletter *Bandersnatch* (quarterly). Annual subscription: £13 (UK), £15 (Europe), £17 (elsewhere); apply for special rates for retired and institutions. Founded 1969.

Cartoonists Club of Great Britain
Secretary Terry Christien, 46 Strawberry Vale, Twickenham TW1 4SE
tel 0181-892 3621 *fax* 0181-891 5946
Aims to encourage social contact between members and endeavours to promote the professional standing and prestige of cartoonists. Fee on joining: full, provisional, or associate £35; thereafter annual fee £25.

Centerprise Literature Development Project
Centerprise Trust, 136-138 Kingsland High Street, London E8 2NS
tel 0171-254 9632 ext. 211, 214
fax 0171-923 1951
e-mail cldd@cnpr.demon.co.uk
New Writing Eva Lewin, *Black Literature* Kadija George
An advice and resource centre for writers of fiction and poetry, servicing Central, East and North London. Runs courses and workshops in creative writing,

organises poetry and book readings, discussions and debates on literary and relevant issues. Funded by London Arts Board and London Borough of Hackney. Founded 1995.

The Chesterton Society
Hon. Secretary Robert Hughes, 11 Lawrence Leys, Bloxham, Nr Banbury, Oxon OX15 4NU
tel (01295) 720869
To promote interest in the life and work of G.K. Chesterton and those associated with him or influenced by his writings. Annual subscription: £12.50. Founded 1974.

Children's Book Circle
c/o Naomi Cooper, Transworld Children's Books, 61-63 Uxbridge Road, London W5 5SA
tel 0181-231 6648 *fax* 0181-231 6727
e-mail n.cooper@transworld-publishers.co.uk
Membership Secretary Gaby Morgan
tel 0171-881 8199
Provides a discussion forum for anybody involved with children's books. Monthly meetings are addressed by a panel of invited speakers and topics focus on current and controversial issues. Holds the annual Patrick Hardy lecture and administers the Eleanor Farjeon Award. Annual membership: £15 if working inside M25; outside £12. Founded 1962.

Children's Book Foundation – now Young Book Trust; see Book Trust

Children's Books History Society
Secretary Mrs Pat Garrett, 25 Field Way, Hoddesdon, Herts. EN11 0QN
tel/fax (01992) 464885
e-mail cbhs@abcgarrett.demon.co.uk
Aims 'to promote an appreciation of children's books, and to study their history, bibliography and literary content'. Holds approx. 6 meetings and produces 3 *Newsletters* and an occasional paper per year. The Harvey Darton Award is given biennially for a book that extends knowledge of British children's literature of the past. Subscription: £10.00 p.a.; overseas rates on application. Founded 1969.

Children's Writers and Illustrators Group
84 Drayton Gardens, London SW10 9SB
tel 0171-373 6642
Subsidiary group for writers and illustrators of children's books, who are members of the Society of Authors (see page 504).

Christian Literature, United Society for
Albany House, 67 Sydenham Road, Guildford, Surrey GU1 3RY
tel (01483) 888580 *fax* (01483) 888581
e-mail feedtheminds@gn.apc.org
Chairman John Clark, *General Secretary* Dr Alwyn Marriage
To aid Christian literature principally in the world's poorest countries. Founded 1799.

Christian Writers, Association of
Chairman Juliet Hughes, 74 Longleaze, Wootton Bassett, Swindon, Wilts. SN4 8AS
tel (01793) 852296
Aims to see the quality of writing in every area of the media, either overtly Christian or shaped by a Christian perspective, reaching the widest range of people across the UK and beyond. To inspire and equip people to use their talents and skills with integrity to devise, write and market excellent material which comes from a Christian world view. Annual membership: individual £10; couples/overseas £12.50. Founded 1971.

Agatha Christie Society
PO Box 985, London SW1X 9XA
e-mail agathachristie@dial.pipex.com
Secretary Elaine Z. Wiltshire
To promote communication between the fans of Agatha Christie and the various media who bring her works to the public. Publishes newsletters (4 p.a.). Annual subscription: £12.50 (UK), £15 (Europe), $24 (USA), £15 (rest of world). Founded 1993.

Circle of Wine Writers
Secretary Stephen Skelton, 21 Golden Square, Tenterden, Kent TN30 6RN
tel (01580) 765242 *fax* (01580) 765224
e-mail spskelton@btinternet.co
An association for those engaged in communicating about wines and spirits. Produces *Circle Update* newsletter (5 p.a.), organises tasting sessions as well as a programme of meetings and talks. Membership is by election (£35 p.a.). Founded 1960.

Civil Service Authors, Society of
Secretary Mrs J.M. Hykin, 4 Top Street, Wing, Nr Oakham, Rutland LE15 8SE
Aims to encourage authorship by present and past members of the Civil Service (and some other public service bodies). Holds annual competitions for poetry,

short stories, etc, open to members only, and annual 'Writer of the Year' award. Publishes *The Civil Service Author* magazine, free to members; subscription £15 p.a. Poetry Workshop offers newsletter, weekend, anthology; subscription additional £3.

The John Clare Society
The Stables, 1A West Street, Helpston, Peterborough PE6 7DU
tel (01733) 252678
web site http://human.ntu.ac.uk/foh/cms/clare.html
Promotes a wider appreciation of the life and works of the poet John Clare. Annual subscription: £9.50 (UK individual); other rates (including overseas) on application. Founded 1981.

Classical Association
Secretary (Council) Dr M. Schofield, St John's College, Cambridge CB2 1TP
Publicity Officer Dr J. March, PO Box 38, Alresford, Hants SO24 0ZQ
To promote and sustain interest in classical studies, to maintain their rightful position in universities and schools, and to give scholars and teachers opportunities for meeting and discussing their problems. Benefits include the journal *CA News* (2 p.a.) and the handsomely printed annual Presidential Address. Organises an annual conference lasting 4 days, in a university centre, and sponsors over 20 branches, which arrange programmes, lectures and discussions. Annual subscription: £5; life membership £105 (individuals only).

Clé: The Irish Book Publishers' Association
34 North Frederick Street, Dublin 1, Republic of Ireland
tel (01) 8729090 *fax* (01) 8722035
President John Murphy, *Administrator* Orla Martin

The William Cobbett Society
Chairman Molly Townsend, Johnsons Farm, Sheet, Petersfield, Hants GU32 2BY
tel (01730) 262060
To make the life and work of William Cobbett better known. Annual subscription: £8. Founded 1976.

The Wilkie Collins Society
Membership Secretary Paul Lewis, 47 Hereford Road, London W3 9JW
Chairman Andrew Gasson

To promote interest in the life and works of Wilkie Collins. Publishes a newsletter, an occasional scholarly journal and reprints of Collins's lesser known works. Annual subscription: £8.50, £12.50 (USA). Founded 1981.

Comedy Writers Association of Great Britain
61 Parry Road, Wolverhampton WV11 2PS
tel/fax (01902) 722729
Contact Ken Rock
Aims to develop and promote comedy writing in a professional and friendly way. Annual membership: £40. Founded 1981.

Comhairle nan Leabhraichean/The Gaelic Books Council
22 Mansfield Street, Glasgow G11 5QP
tel 0141-337 6211 *fax* 0141-353 0515
Chairman Boyd Robertson
Stimulates Scottish Gaelic publishing by awarding publication grants for new books, commissioning authors and providing editorial services and general assistance to writers and readers. Founded 1968.

Comics Creators Guild
(formerly Society for Strip Illustration)
48 Siddons Road, London SE23 2JQ
tel/fax 0181-699 4012
Open to all those concerned with, or interested in, professional comics creation. Holds monthly meetings and publishes a newsletter (monthly), a Directory of Members' Work, Submission Guidelines for the major comics publishers, sample scripts for artists, a 'Guide to Contracts' and 'Getting Started in Comics', a beginners' guide to working in the industry, and *Comics Forum* (quarterly), a magazine of art and criticism.

The Commonwealth Institute
Kensington High Street, London W8 6NQ
tel 0171-603 4535 *fax* 0171-602 7374
e-mail info@commonwealth.org.uk
web site http://www.commonwealth.org.uk/
Director General David French
Promotes Commonwealth education and culture in Britain. The Resource Centre offers services to teachers and school groups, and includes a specialist Literature Library. Open to the public Mon-Sat 10am-4pm. Founded 1893.

Communicators in Business, The British Association of

42 Borough High Street, London SE1 1XW
tel 0171-378 7139 *fax* 0171-378 7140
e-mail bacb@globalnet.co.uk
web site http://www.bacb.org.uk

Aims to be the market leader for those involved in corporate media management and practice by providing professional, authoritative, dynamic, supportive and innovative services. Founded 1949.

Composers, The Association of Professional

The Penthouse, 4 Brook Street,
London W1Y 1AA
tel 0171-629 4828 *fax* 0171-629 0993
e-mail a.p.c@dial.pipex.com
Administrator Rosemary Dixson

Furthers the collective interest of its members and informs and advises them on professional and artistic matters. Holds 4 general meetings p.a., and arranges a number of seminars and workshops. Publishes *The Composer's Guide to Music Publishing*, *Professional Composing* and a Newsletter (3 p.a.). Annual subscription: £50, plus 2% levy on PRS royalties. Founded 1980.

The Composers' Guild of Great Britain

The Penthouse, 4 Brook Street, London W1Y 1AA
tel 0171-629 0886 *fax* 0171-629 0993

Aims to represent and protect the professional interests of composers and to nurture the art of composition. It provides copyright and commissioning advice. Publications include *Composer News* and *First Performances*. Annual membership: £45 (full), £35 (associate), £10 (student). Further particulars obtainable from the General Secretary.

The Joseph Conrad Society (UK)

Chairman Keith Carabine, *President* Philip Conrad, *Secretary* Hugh Epstein
The Conradian, Dept. of English,
St Mary's University College, Twickenham,
Middlesex TW1 4SX
Editor Allan Simmons

Maintains close and friendly links with the Conrad family. Activities include an annual international conference; publication of *The Conradian* and a series of pamphlets; and maintenance of a study centre at the Polish Cultural Centre, 238-246 King Street, London W6 0RF.

Administers the Juliet McLauchlan Prize: £100 annual award for the winner of an essay competition. Founded 1973.

Contemporary Art Society (CAS)

17 Bloomsbury Square,
London WC1A 1LP
tel 0171-831 7311 *fax* 0171-831 7345

Aims to increase the support and appreciation of contemporary art. As a charity, the CAS acquires paintings, sculpture, photographs, videos, installation work and applied art and crafts by contemporary artists to give to public museums. Annual membership: single £30.00; 2 people at same address £35.00; students £22.50. Founded 1910.

Contemporary Arts, Institute of

The Mall, London SW1Y 5AH
tel 0171-930 0493 *fax* 0171-873 0051
web site http://www.illumin.co.uk/ica

Encourages collaboration between artforms, promotes experimental work and the mutual interchange of ideas and cultural practice at a national and international level. Produces diverse monthly programme of exhibitions, theatre, dance, music, literature, cinema, video, lectures, conferences, discussions. Open 1200-0100 Mon-Sat, 1200-2300 Sun. Various levels of membership available; open to the public with daypass £1.50.

Copyright Clearance Center Inc.

222 Rosewood Drive, Danvers,
MA 01923, USA
tel 978-750-8400 *fax* 978-750-4470
web site http://www.copyright.com

Operates a centralised permissions system for photocopying, republication services, reproduction authorisations, and royalty distributions for copyrighted materials throughout the world. Licensing services aid users in efforts to comply with US copyright law, and copyright owners in efforts to protect their printed works. Registration is free of charge to all rightsholders. 9600 publishers, and hundreds of thousands of authors and creators work with CCC directly or through their representatives. Founded 1978.

Copyright Council, The British

Copyright House, 29-33 Berners Street,
London W1P 4AA

President Denis de Freitas OBE, *Vice-President* Geoffrey Adams, *Chairman* Maureen Duffy, *Vice Chairmen* Rachel Duffield, Mark Le Fanu, Robert Montgomery, *Secretary* Janet Ibbotson, *Treasurer* Lord Brain

Aims to defend and foster the true principles of creators' copyright and their acceptance throughout the world, to bring together bodies representing all who are interested in the protection of such copyright, and to keep watch on any legal or other changes which may require an amendment of the law.

The Copyright Licensing Agency Ltd (CLA)

90 Tottenham Court Road, London W1P 0LP
tel 0171-436 5931 *fax* 0171-436 3986
e-mail cla@cla.co.uk
web site http://www.cla.co.uk
Chief Executive Peter Shepherd

The CLA administers collectively photocopying and other copying rights that it is uneconomic for writers and publishers to administer for themselves. The Agency issues collective and transactional licences, and the fees it collects, after the deduction of its operating costs, are distributed at regular intervals to authors and publishers via their respective societies. See also page 632. Founded 1983.

Crime Writers' Association

60 Drayton Road, Kings Heath,
Brimingham B14 7LR
Secretary Judith Cutler

For professional writers of crime novels, short stories, plays for stage, TV and sound radio, or of serious works on crime. Associate membership open to publishers, journalists, booksellers specialising in crime literature. Publishes *Red Herrings* (monthly), available to members only. Founded 1953.

The Critics' Circle

President Allen Robertson, *Hon. General Secretary* Charles Hedges
Contact Catherine Cooper, Administrator, c/o The Stage Newspaper, 47 Bermondsey Street, London SE1 3XT
tel 0171-403 1818 Ext. 106

Aims to promote the art of criticism, to uphold its integrity in practice, to foster and safeguard the professional interests of its members, to provide opportunities for social intercourse among them, and to support the advancement of the arts. Membership is by invitation of the Council. Such invitations are issued only to persons engaged professionally, regularly and substantially in the writing or broadcasting of criticism of drama, music, films, dance and the visual arts. Founded 1913.

The Cromwell Association

Press Liaison Officer B. Denton, 10 Melrose Avenue, off Bants Lane, Northampton NN5 5PB
tel/fax (01604) 582516 (office hours)

Encourages the study of Oliver Cromwell and his times. Holds academic lectures and meetings, publishes annual journal *Cromwelliana*. Annual subscription: £15. Founded 1935.

Cultural Desk, International

6 Belmont Crescent, Glasgow G12 8ES
tel 0141-339 0090 *fax* 0141-337 2271
e-mail icd@dial.pipex.com
web site http://dspace.dial.pipex.com/icd/
Development Manager Hilde Bollen, *Information Officer* Anne Robb

Aims to assist Scottish artists and arts organisations to take up international opportunities by providing timely and targeted information and advice. The Desk provides information and advice on funding sources, European cultural policy development, international cultural networks, basic data on international opportunities, and contact and partner finding as a starting point for international collaborations. Publishes *Communication* (bimonthly) and *InFocus*, a new series of specialised guides with an international focus. Founded 1994.

Cyngor Llyfrau Cymru – see Welsh Books Council

The De Vere Society

8 Western Road, Henley-on-Thames, Oxon RG9 1JL
tel (01491) 576662 *fax* (01491) 579111
e-mail 100644.3717@compuserve.com
web site http://www.shakespeare-oxford.com
Secretary Christopher H. Dams

Aims to seek, and if possible to establish, the truth concerning the authorship of the Shakespeare plays and poems and, in addition, to promote research into the life of Edward de Vere, 17th Earl of Oxford. Founded 1986.

Deaf Broadcasting Council

70 Blacketts Wood Drive, Chorleywood,
Rickmansworth, Herts. WD3 5QQ
tel/fax (01923) 283127 (text phone only)
e-mail dmyers@cix.co.uk
web site http://www.waterlow.com.dbc
Secretary Ruth Myers
Aims to ensure that TV and radio are
accessible to deaf, deafened and hard of
hearing people and that access is of suitable quality. Annual membership: £3.
Founded 1980.

Design and Artists Copyright Society Ltd (DACS)

Parchment House, 13 Northburgh Street,
London EC1V 0AH
tel 0171-336 8811 *fax* 0171-336 8822
e-mail info@dacs.co.uk
Chief Executive Rachel Duffield, *Deputy Chief
Executive* Mary Hildyard, *Administrator* Janet
Tod
DACS is the British copyright and collecting society for the visual arts. It aims
to protect and administer visual artists'
copyright both nationally and internationally. DACS provides individual and
blanket licences to users of artistic works
in the UK. The Society also advises
about copyright for visual creators, and
pursues infringements where appropriate. Life membership: £25 (inc. VAT).
Founded 1983.

Designers, The Chartered Society of

First Floor, 32-38 Saffron Hill, London EC1N 8FH
tel 0171-831 9777 *fax* 0171-831 6277
e-mail csd@csd.org.uk
web site http://www.designweb.co.uk/csd
Director Brian Lymbery
Works to promote and regulate standards
of competence, professional conduct and
integrity, including representation on
government and official bodies, design
education and competitions. The services
to members include general information,
publications, guidance on copyright and
other professional issues, access to professional indemnity insurance and a cred-
it-checking/debt collection service.
Activities in the regions are included in
an extensive annual programme of events
and training courses. The Society publishes a Code of Conduct, and has developed a Business and Design Programme
to strengthen the links between designers
and clients in business and industry.

Designers in Ireland, Institute of

8 Merrion Square, Dublin 2, Republic of Ireland
tel/fax (01) 4962806
Irish design profession's representative
body, covering every field of design.
Details from the honorary secretary.
Annual membership: £130 (full), £45
(licentiate). Founded 1972.

Dickens Fellowship

The Dickens House, 48 Doughty Street,
London WC1N 2LF
tel 0171-405 2127 *fax* 0171-831 5175
Hon. Secretary Edward G. Preston
Based in house occupied by Dickens
1837-9; publishes *The Dickensian* (3
p.a.). Membership rates and particulars
on application. Founded 1902.

Directory & Database Publishers Association

Secretary Rosemary Pettit, 93A Blenheim
Crescent, London W11 2EQ
tel 0171-221 9089
Maintains a code of professional practice; aims to raise the standard and professional status of UK directory and database publishing and to protect (and promote) the legal, statutory and common
interests of directory publishers; provides for the exchange of technical, commercial and management information
between members. Annual subscription:
£115-£11400. Founded 1970.

'Sean Dorman' Manuscript Society

Cherry Trees, Crosemere Road, Cockshutt,
Ellesmere, Shropshire SY12 0JP
tel (01939) 270293
Director Mary Driver
Provides mutual help among writers and
aspiring writers in the UK. By means of
circulating MSS parcels, members receive
constructive criticism of their own work
and read and comment on the work of others. Each 'Circulator' has up to 9 participants and members' contributions may be
in any medium: short stories, chapters of a
novel, poetry, magazine articles etc. Send
sae for full details and application form.
Founded 1957.

The Arthur Conan Doyle Society

Organisers Christopher and Barbara Roden,
PO Box 1360, Ashcroft, B.C., Canada V0K 1A0
tel 250-453-2045 *fax* 250-453-2075
e-mail ashtree@mail.netshop.net
Promotes the study of the life and works

of Sir Arthur Conan Doyle. Publishes *ACD* journal (annual), *The Parish Magazine* newsletter (bi-annual) and occasional reprints of Conan Doyle material. Major annual convention. Annual subscription: £15, overseas £16 (airmail extra). Founded 1989.

Early English Text Society
Christ Church, Oxford OX1 1DP
Hon. Director Prof John Burrow
Executive Secretary R.F.S. Hamer
To bring unprinted early English literature within the reach of students in sound texts. Annual subscription: £15. Founded 1864.

The Eckhart Society
Summa, 22 Tippings Lane, Woodley, Reading, Berks. RG5 4RX
tel/fax 0118-9690118
web site http://www.op.org/eckhart
Secretary Ashley Young
Aims to promote the understanding and appreciation of Eckhart's writings and their importance for Christian thought and practice; to facilitate scholarly research into Eckhart's life and works; and to promote the study of Eckhart's teaching as a contribution to inter-religious dialogue. Membership: £14 p.a.; £7.50 p.a. OAPs/students. Founded 1987.

Edinburgh Bibliographical Society
c/o Dept. of Special Collections, Edinburgh University Library, George Square, Edinburgh EH8 9LJ
tel 0131-650 3412 *fax* 0131-650 6863
Secretary M.C.T. Simpson, *Treasurer* K. Thomson
Encourages bibliographical activity through organising talks for members, particularly on bibliographical topics relating to Scotland, and visits to libraries. Also publishes *Transactions* (bi-annual, free to members) and other occasional publications. Membership: £10 p.a. (£15 p.a. institutions; £5 full-time students). Founded 1890.

Editors, Association of British
Executive Director Jock Gallagher, Broadvision, 49 Frederick Road, Edgbaston, Birmingham B15 1HN
tel 0121-455 7949 *fax* 0121-454 6187
Independent organisation set up to study and enhance the practice of journalism in all media; to protect and promote the freedom of the media, in the UK and throughout the world; to consider com-

mon problems independent of any individual, group or interest. Publishes *British Editor* journal (quarterly). Annual subscription: £50. Founded 1985.

Educational Writers Group
84 Drayton Gardens, London SW10 9SB
tel 0171-373 6642
Specialist group within the membership of the Society of Authors (see page 504).

The Eighteen Nineties Society
Patron HRH Princess Michael of Kent, *President* Countess of Longford CBE, *Chairman* Martyn Goff OBE
Hon. Membership Secretary Steven Halliwell, Rivendale, Constables Croft, Nr Bicester, Oxon OX6 0PG
tel (01869) 248340
e-mail steve@ft-1980s-society.demon.co.uk
web site http://www.1980s.org
The Society celebrates and investigates the entire artistic and literary scene of the 1890s. Holds lectures, readings, exhibitions; publishes a quarterly newsletter, *Keynotes*, and an annual scholarly *Journal*; also an 'Occasional Series' of monographs: biographies of neglected authors/artists, bibliographies, etc. Founded 1963.

The George Eliot Fellowship
President Jonathan G. Ouvry
Secretary Mrs K.M. Adams, 71 Stepping Stones Road, Coventry CV5 8JT
tel (01203) 592231
Promotes an interest in the life and work of George Eliot (1819-80) and helps to extend her influence; arranges meetings; produces an annual journal and a quarterly newsletter. Awards the annual George Eliot Fellowship Prize (£100) for an essay on Eliot's life or work, which must be previously unpublished and not exceed 2500 words. Annual subscription: £10. Founded 1930.

English Association
University of Leicester, University Road, Leicester LE1 7RH
tel 0116-252 3982 *fax* 0116-252 2301
e-mail engassoc@le.ac.uk
web site http://www.le.ac.uk/engassoc
Chairman Roger Knight, *Chief Executive* Helen Lucas
Aims to further knowledge, understanding and enjoyment of English literature and the English language, by working towards a fuller recognition of English

as an essential element in education and in the community at large; by encouraging the study of English literature and language by means of conferences, lectures and publications; by fostering the discussion of methods of teaching English of all kinds; and by the establishment of local groups for the exchange of views and to work to further the status of English literature and language in the community.

English Regional Arts Boards – see Regional Arts Boards

English Speaking Board (International) Ltd
26A Princes Street, Southport PR8 1EQ
tel (01704) 501730 *fax* (01704) 539637
e-mail admin@esbuk.demon.co.uk
web site http://www.esbuk.demon.co.uk
President Christabel Burniston MBE, *Chairman* Richard Ellis

Aims to foster all activities concerned with oral communication. The Board conducts examinations and training courses for teachers and students in schools and colleges where stress is on individual oral expression; also for those engaged in technical or industrial concerns, and for those using English as an acquired language. Members receive *Spoken English* (Mar/Sept); articles are invited on any special aspect of spoken English. Members can purchase other ESB publications at reduced rates. Conference and AGM in the spring. Membership: individuals, £20 p.a., corporate £35 p.a.

The English-Speaking Union
Dartmouth House, 37 Charles Street, London W1X 8AB
tel 0171-493 3328 *fax* 0171-495 6108
e-mail esu@esu.org
web site http://www.esu.org
Director-General Mrs Valerie Mitchell

Aims to promote international understanding and human achievement through the widening use of the English language throughout the world. The ESU is an educational charity which sponsors scholarships and exchanges, educational programmes promoting the effective use of English, and a wide range of international and cultural events. Members contribute to our work across the world. Annual

membership: various categories. See also Books Across the Sea. Founded 1918.

European Broadcasting Union
Ancienne Route 17, CH-1218 Grand Saconnex (Geneva), Switzerland
tel (22) 7172111 *fax* (22) 7172481
e-mail ebu@ebu.ch
Secretary-General Dr Jean-Bernard Münch

Supports and promotes co-operation between its members and broadcasting organisations worldwide; represents the interests of its members in programme, legal, technical and other fields. Founded 1950.

European Publishers, Federation of
President Ulrico C. Hoepli
Secretary Mechthild von Alemann, 204 avenue de Tervuren, 1150 Brussels, Belgium
tel (2) 770 11 10 *fax* (2) 771 20 71
e-mail fep.vonalemann@linkline.be

Represents the interests of European publishers on EU affairs; informs members on the development of EU policies which could affect the publishing industry. Founded 1967.

Fabian Society
11 Dartmouth Street, London SW1H 9BN
tel 0171-222 8877 *fax* 0171-976 7153

Membership organisation which serves as a forum for the discussion on the Centre-Left. Holds conferences and publishes pamphlets and *Fabian Review* journal (quarterly). Individual membership: £27 (£13 reduced rate), library subscription: £65.

Fantasy Society, The British
2 Harwood Street, Heaton Norris, Stockport SK4 1JJ
tel 0161-476 5368 (after 6pm)
e-mail syrinx.2112@btinternet.com
web site http://www.geocities.com/soho/6859
President Ramsey Campbell, *Secretary* Robert Parkinson

For devotees of fantasy, horror and related fields, in literature, art and the cinema. Publications include *British Fantasy Newsletter* (bi-monthly) featuring news and reviews and several annual booklets, including: *Dark Horizons*; *Masters of Fantasy* on individual authors. There is a small-press library and an annual convention and fantasy awards sponsored by the Society. Annual membership: £17. Founded 1971.

Federation Against Copyright Theft Ltd (FACT)

7 Victory Business Centre, Worton Road, Isleworth, Middlesex TW7 6DB
tel 0181-568 6646 *fax* 0181-560 6364
Director General Reg Dixon, *Company Secretary* David Lowe

FACT aims to protect the interests of its members and others against infringement in the UK of copyright in cinematograph films, TV programmes and all forms of audio-visual recording. Founded 1982.

The Fine Art Trade Guild

16-18 Empress Place, London SW6 1TT
tel 0171-381 6616 *fax* 0171-381 2596
e-mail information@fineart.co.uk
web site http://www.fineart.co.uk
Managing Director Rosie Sumner

Promotes the sale of fine art prints and picture framing in the UK and overseas markets; establishes and raises standards amongst members and communicates these to the buying public. The Guild publishes *The Directory* and *Art Business Today*, the trade's longest established magazine and various specialist books. Founded 1910.

FOCAL (Federation of Commercial AudioVisual Libraries Ltd)

PO Box 422, Harrow, Middlesex HA1 3YN
tel/fax 0181-423 5853
e-mail anne@focalltd.demon.co.uk
web site http://www.focalltd.demon.co.uk
Administrator/Secretariat Anne Johnson
Founded 1985.

The Folklore Society

University College, Gower Street, London WC1E 6BT
tel 0171-387 5894
Hon. Secretary Dr Jacqueline Simpson
Collection, recording and study of folklore. Founded 1878.

Food Writers, Guild of

Administrator Christina Thomas, 48 Crabtree Lane, London SW6 6LW
tel 0171-610 1180 *fax* 0171-610 0299
e-mail ckthomas@compuserve.com

Aims to bring together professional food writers including journalists, broadcasters and authors, to print and issue an annual list of members, to extend the range of members' knowledge and experience by arranging discussions, tastings and visits, and to encourage the development of new writers by every means including competitions and awards. Membership: £45.00 p.a. Founded 1984.

Foreign Press Association in London

Registered Office 11 Carlton House Terrace, London SW1Y 5AJ
tel 0171-930 0445 *fax* 0171-925 0469
President Barbara Kollmeyer, *Secretaries* Davina Crole and Catherine Flury

Aims to promote the professional interests of its members. Full Membership open to overseas professional journalists residing in the UK; Associate Membership available for British press and freelance journalists. Entrance fee: £139.23; annual subscription: £117.50. Founded 1888.

Free Painters & Sculptors

Loggia Gallery and Sculpture Garden, 15 Buckingham Gate, London SW1E 6LB
tel 0171-828 5963

Exhibits progressive work of all artistic allegiances and provides opportunities for FPS members to meet and discuss their work in either one-person or group shows. Gallery hours: Mon-Fri 6-8pm, Sat 11am-5pm Sun 1-5pm.

Freelance Editors and Proofreaders, Society of (SFEP)

Office Mermaid House, 1 Mermaid Court, London SE1 1HR
tel 0171-403 5141
web site http://www.sfep.demon.co.uk

Aims to promote high editorial standards and achieve recognition of its members' professional status, through local and national meetings, an annual conference, a monthly newsletter and a programme of reasonably priced workshops/training sessions. These sessions help newcomers to acquire basic skills, enable experienced editors to update their skills or broaden their competence, and also cover aspects of professional practice or business for the self-employed. An annual Directory of members' services is available to publishers. The Society supports moves towards recognised standards of training and accreditation for editors and proofreaders; its own system of accreditation came into operation in 1996. It has close links with the Publishing Training Centre and the Society of Indexers, is represented on the BSI Technical Committee dealing with copy preparation and proof correction (BS 5261), and works to foster good relations with all relevant bodies and organisations in the UK and worldwide. Founded 1988.

Freelance Photographers, Bureau of
Focus House, 497 Green Lanes, London N13 4BP
tel 0181-882 3315 *fax* 0181-886 5174
Chief Executive John Tracy
To help the freelance photographer by providing information on markets, and free advisory service. Publishes *Market Newsletter* (monthly). Annual membership: £40. Founded 1965.

French Publishers' Association
(Syndicat National de l'Edition)
115 Blvd St Germain, 75006 Paris, France
tel (1) 44 41 40 50 *fax* (1) 44 41 40 77

The Gaelic Books Council – see Comhairle nan Leabhraichean

The Gaskell Society
Far Yew Tree House, Over Tabley, Knutsford, Cheshire WA16 0HN
tel (01565) 634668
e-mail JoanLeach@aol.com
web site http://www.lang.nagoya-ac.jp/~matsuoka/gaskell.html
Hon. Secretary Mrs Joan Leach
Promotes and encourages the study and appreciation of the work and life of Elizabeth Cleghorn Gaskell. Holds regular meetings in Knutsford, London and Manchester, visits and residential conferences; produces an annual Journal and bi-annual Newsletters. Annual subscription: £8, corporate and overseas £12. Founded 1985.

Gay Authors Workshop
Kathryn Byrd, BM Box 5700, London WC1N 3XX
tel 0181-520 5223
To encourage writers who are lesbian, gay or bisexual. Quarterly newsletter. Membership: £5.00; unwaged £2.00. Founded 1978.

General Practitioners Writers Association
President Dr Robin Hull, West Carnliath, Strathtay, Pitlochry, Perthshire PH9 0PG
tel (01887) 840380
Aims to improve the writing by, for, from or about general medical practice. Publishes *The GP Writer* (2 p.a.); register of members' writing interests is sent to medical editors and publishers. Founded 1985.

German Publishers' and Booksellers' Association
(Börsenverein des Deutschen Buchhandels e.V.)
Postfach 100442, 60004 Frankfurt am Main, Germany
tel (069) 13060 *fax* (069) 1306201
web site http://www.buchhandel.de
General Manager Dr Hans-Karl von Kupsch

Graphic Fine Art, Society of
15 Willow Way, Hatfield, Herts AL10 9QD
President Jean Canter
A fine art society holding an annual open exhibition. Membership by election, requires work of high quality with an emphasis on good drawing, whether by pen, pencil (with our without wash), watercolour, pastel or any of the forms of print making. Founded 1919.

Graphical, Paper & Media Union
Keys House, 63-67 Bromham Road, Bedford MK40 2AG
tel (01234) 351521 *fax* (01234) 270580
e-mail gpmu@geo2.poptel.org.uk
web site http://www.gpmu.org.uk
General Secretary Tony Dubbins
Trade union representing the interests of employees in the printing, paper, publishing and allied industries.

The Greeting Card Association
41 Links Drive, Elstree, Herts. WD6 3PP
tel/fax 0181-236 0024
web site http://greeting-card.assoc.co.uk
Publishes *Greetings* (10 p.a.).

Guernsey Arts Council
St James Concert and Assembly Hall, St Peter Port, Guernsey, CI
tel (01481) 721902
Secretary Angela Simon
Co-ordinates the organisations under the council's umbrella, presents artistic events, sponsors reports, aims to bring about the creation of an arts centre in Guernsey and to encourage all the arts in Guernsey, Alderney and Sark. Membership: £5, under 18 £2. Founded 1981.

The Neil Gunn Society
Secretary Mrs J. Campbell, 25 Newton Avenue, Wick, Caithness KW1 5LJ
tel (01955) 602607
To promote the works of the Scottish novelist, Neil Gunn; to research into the background of, and to encourage discussion on and evaluation of, Gunn's work; to collect material related to his life and

work; to provide a focal point for and help with any Gunn-related activity. Annual membership: £5.00, students £2.00. Founded 1985.

Hakluyt Society
c/o The Map Library, The British Library, Great Russell Street, London WC1B 3DG
tel (01986) 788359 fax (01986) 788181
e-mail haksoc@paston.co.uk
web site http://www.sas.ac.uk/warburg/hakuyt.htm
President Sarah Tyacke, Hon. Secretary Anthony P. Payne

Publication of original narratives of voyages, travels, naval expeditions, and other geographical records. Founded 1846.

The Thomas Hardy Society Ltd
PO Box 1438, Dorchester,
Dorset DT1 1YH
tel (01305) 251501

Publishes *The Thomas Hardy Journal* (3 p.a.). Biennial conference in Dorchester, 1998. Annual subscription: £12.00 (£15.00 overseas). Founded 1967.

Harleian Society
College of Arms, Queen Victoria Street, London EC4V 4BT
Chairman J. Brooke-Little CVO, MA, FSA, Hon. Secretary T.H.S. Duke, Chester Herald of Arms

Instituted for transcribing, printing and publishing the heraldic visitations of Counties, Parish Registers and any manuscripts relating to genealogy, family history and heraldry. Founded 1869.

Heraldic Arts, Society of
46 Reigate Road, Reigate, Surrey RH2 0QN
tel (01737) 242945
Secretary John Ferguson ARCA, SHA, DFACH, FRSA

Aims to serve the interests of heraldic artists, craftsmen, designers and writers, to provide a 'shop window' for their work, to obtain commissions on their behalf and to act as a forum for the exchange of information and ideas. Also offers an information service to the public. Candidates for admission as craft members should be artists or craftsmen whose work comprises a substantial element of heraldry and is of a sufficiently high standard to satisfy the requirements of the society's advisory council.Annual membership: £12 (associate); £17 (craft). Founded 1987.

Historical Novel Society
Secretary Richard Lee, Marine Cottage, The Strand, Starcross, Devon EX6 8NY

tel (01626) 891962 fax (01392) 438714
e-mail h.j.lee@exeter.ac.uk
web site http://www.ex.ac.uk/histnov/

To promote the historical novel via short story competitions, a society magazine *Solander* (2 p.a.), an annual bibliography of historical novels in print (*Browser*), and reviews (*Historical Novels Review*, quarterly). Annual membership: £12.00. Founded 1997.

The Sherlock Holmes Society of London
President A.D. Howlett MA, LLB, Chairman Richard Lancelyn-Green
General enquiries Heather Owen, 64 Graham Road, London SW19 3SS
tel/fax 0181-540 7657
e-mail abcc@msn.com
Membership R.J. Ellis, 13 Crofton Avenue, Orpington, Kent BA6 8DU
tel/fax (01689) 811314

Aims to bring together those who have a common interest as readers and students of the literature of Sherlock Holmes, and to encourage the pursuit of knowledge of the public and private lives of Sherlock Holmes and Dr Watson. Annual subscription: £14.00 (UK/Europe), £18.00 (Far East), US$30.50 (USA), including *The Sherlock Holmes Journal* (2 p.a.). Founded 1951.

Hopkins Society
Secretary 36 Prince's Drive, Colwyn Bay LL29 8LA

To promote and celebrate the work of the poet, Gerard Manley Hopkins, to inform members about the latest publications about Hopkins and to support educational projects concerning his work. Annual lecture held in North Wales in the spring; publishes Newsletter (2 p.a.) Annual subscription: £5. Founded 1990.

Housman Society
80 New Road, Bromsgrove, Worcs. B60 2LA
tel (01527) 874136 fax (01527) 837274
Chairman Jim Page

Aims to foster interest in and promote knowledge of A.E. Housman, his sister Clemence and their brother Laurence. Membership: £7.50 p.a. Founded 1973.

Hesketh Hubbard Art Society
17 Carlton House Terrace, London SW1Y 5BD
tel 0171-930 6844 fax 0171-839 7830
President Simon Whittle

Weekly drawing workshops open to all.

Illustration, Society of Architectural
PO Box 22, Stroud, Glos. GL5 3DH
tel/fax (01453) 882563
e-mail info@sai-uk.demon.co.uk
web site http://www.sai-uk.demon.co.uk
Administrator Eric Monk
Professional body to represent all who
practise architectural illustration, including the related fields of model making
and photography. Founded 1975.

Illustrators, The Association of
First Floor, 32-38 Saffron Hill,
London EC1N 8FN
tel 0171-831 7377 *fax* 0171-831 6277
Contact Stephanie Smith
To support illustrators, promote illustration and encourage professional standards in the industry. Publishes monthly
magazine; presents an annual programme
of events; annual competition, Images –
the Best of British Illustration: call for
entries March/April. Founded 1973.

**Independent Programme Producers
Association – see PACT**

Indexers, Society of
Secretary Mrs C. Shuttleworth, Mermaid House,
1 Mermaid Court, London SE1 1HR
tel 0171-403 4947
Aims to improve the standard of indexing, and to raise the status of indexers
and to safeguard their interests.
Maintains a Register of Indexers; acts as
an advisory body on the qualifications
and remuneration of indexers; publishes
or communicates books, papers and
notes on the subject of indexing; publishes and runs an open-learning indexing
course, 'Training in Indexing'. The
Society's journal, *The Indexer*, is sent
free to members. Annual subscription:
£40 UK/Europe (£52 overseas), corporate
£60 (£80 overseas).

Indian Publishers, The Federation of
18/1-C Institutional Area, Aruna Asaf Ali Marg
(near JNU), New Delhi 110067, India
tel 6964847, 6852263 *fax* 91-11-6864054

The Irish Copyright Licensing Agency
19 Parnell Square, Dublin 1, Republic of Ireland
tel (01) 8729202 *fax* (01) 8722035
Administrator Orla O'Sullivan
Licences schools and other users of
copyright material to photocopy extracts
of such material, and distributes the

monies collected to the authors and publishers whose works have been copied.
Founded 1992.

Irish Playwrights, Society of
(Cumann Drámadóirí na hÉireann)
Irish Writers' Centre, 19 Parnell Square, Dublin 1,
Republic of Ireland
tel (01) 8721302 *fax* (01) 8726282
Secretary Sean Moffatt
To safeguard the rights of Irish play-
wrights and to foster and promote Irish
playwriting. Annual subscription: IR£25.
Founded 1969.

Irish Translators' Association
Irish Writers' Centre, 19 Parnell Square, Dublin 1,
Republic of Ireland
tel (01) 8721302 *fax* (01) 8726282
e-mail translation@tinet.ie
web site http://homepage.tinet.ie/~translation
Secretary Miriam Lee
Promotes translation in Ireland, the
translation of Irish authors abroad and
the practical training of translators, and
promotes the interests of translators.
Catalogues the works of translators in
areas of Irish interest; secures the awarding of prizes and bursaries for translators; and maintains a detailed register of
translators. Annual membership: £15
(member), £30 (professional member).
Founded 1986.

**Irish Writers' Union/Comhar na
Scríbhneoirí**
Irish Writers' Centre, 19 Parnell Square, Dublin 1,
Republic of Ireland
tel (01) 8721302 *fax* (01) 8726282
e-mail iwc@iol.ie
Secretary Mara Rainwater
The Union aims to advance the cause of
writing as a profession, to achieve better
remuneration and more favourable conditions for writers and to provide a
means for the expression of the collective opinion of writers on matters affecting their profession. Founded 1986.

The Richard Jefferies Society
President Richard Mabey
Hon. Secretary Phyllis Treitel, Eidsvoll,
Bedwells Heath, Boars Hill, Oxford OX1 5JE
tel (01865) 735678
Worldwide membership. Promotes inter-
est in the life, works and associations of
the naturalist and novelist, Richard
Jefferies; helps to preserve buildings and

memorials, and co-operates in the development of a Museum in his birthplace. Arranges regular meetings in Swindon, and occasionally elsewhere; organises outings and displays; publishes a Journal and Newsletter in spring and an Annual Report in September. Annual subscription: £7. Founded 1950.

The Johnson Society

Johnson Birthplace Museum, Breadmarket Street, Lichfield, Staffs. WS13 6LG
tel (01543) 264972
Hon. General Secretary Norma Hooper

To encourage the study of the life and works of Dr Samuel Johnson; to preserve the memorials, associations, books, manuscripts, letters of Dr Johnson and his contemporaries; preservation of his birthplace.

Johnson Society of London

President The Revd Dr E.F. Carpenter KCVO
Secretary Mrs Zandra O'Donnell MA,
255 Baring Road, London SE12 0BQ
tel 0181-851 0173

To study the life and works of Dr Johnson, and to perpetuate his memory in the city of his adoption. Founded 1928.

Journalists, The Chartered Institute of

General Secretary Christopher Underwood FCIJ,
2 Dock Offices, Surrey Quays Road,
London SE16 2XU
tel 0171-252 1187 *fax* 0171-232 2302
e-mail cioj@dircon.co.uk

The senior organisation of the profession, founded in 1884 and incorporated by Royal Charter in 1890. The Chartered Institute maintains an employment register and has accumulated funds for the assistance of members. A Freelance Division links editors and publishers with freelances and a Directory is published of freelance writers, with their specialisations. There are special sections for broadcasters, motoring correspondents and public relations practitioners. Occasional contributors to the media may qualify for election as Affiliates. Annual subscription: related to earnings – maximum £155, minimum £75; affiliate £105.

Journalists, National Council for the Training of

Latton Bush Centre, Southern Way, Harlow, Essex CM18 7BL
tel (01279) 430009 *fax* (01279) 438008
e-mail nctj@itecharlow.co.uk
web site http://www.itecharlow.co.uk.nctj/
Chief Executive Rob Selwood

A registered charity which aims to advance the education and training of trainee journalists, including press photographers. Founded 1952.

The Sheila Kaye-Smith Society

Secretary Grace Chatfield, 5 Leeds Close, Ore, Hastings, East Sussex TN35 5BX
tel (01424) 437413

Aims to stimulate and widen interest in the work of the Sussex writer and novelist, Sheila Kaye-Smith (1887-1956). Produces *The Gleam* (annual) and occasional papers, and organises talks. Annual membership: £6 single, £9 joint. Founded 1987.

Keats-Shelley Memorial Association

Hon. Treasurer R.E. Cavaliero, 10 Lansdowne Road, Tunbridge Wells, Kent TN1 2NJ
tel (01892) 533452 *fax* (01892) 519142
Patron HM Queen Elizabeth the Queen Mother, *Chairman* Hon. Mrs H. Cullen, *Hon. Secretary* D.R. Leigh-Hunt

Owns and supports house in Rome where John Keats died, and celebrates the poets Keats, Shelley and Leigh Hunt. Occasional meetings; poetry competitions; annual *Review* and progress reports. Subscription to 'Friends of the Keats-Shelley Memorial', minimum £10 p.a. Founded 1903.

Kent and Sussex Poetry Society

President Laurence Lerner, *Chairman* Clive Eastwood
Hon. Secretary Mrs Doriel Hulse, Costens, Carpenters Lane, Hadlow, Kent TN11 0EY
tel (01732) 851404

Based in Tunbridge Wells, the society was formed in 1946 to create a greater interest in Poetry. Well-known poets address the Society, a Folio of members' work is produced and a full programme of recitals, discussions, competitions and readings is provided. See page 523 for details of Open Poetry Competition. Annual subscription: attending members £6, country members £3, students £1.

Kinematograph, Sound and Television Society, British

63-71 Victoria House, Vernon Place,
London WC1B 4DB
tel 0171-242 8400 *fax* 0171-405 3560
Executive Director Anne Fenton, *Hon. Secretary* Wendy Laybourn

Aims to encourage technical and scientific progress in the industries of its title. Publishes technical information, arranges international conferences and exhibitions, lectures and demonstrations, and encourages the exchange of ideas. Journals: *Image Technology* (monthly), *Images* (monthly), *Cinema Technology* (quarterly). Founded 1931, incorporated 1946.

The Kipling Society

Hon. Secretary J.W. Michael Smith, 2 Brownleaf Road, Brighton, East Sussex BN2 6LB
tel (01273) 303719
e-mail info@dex.co.uk
web site http://www.kipling.org.uk

Aims to honour and extend the influence of Rudyard Kipling (1865-1936), to assist in the study of his writings, to hold discussion meetings, to publish a quarterly journal, and to maintain a Kipling Library in London and a Kipling Room in The Grange, Rottingdean, near Brighton. Membership details on application.

The Lancashire Authors' Association

President Frank Sunderland
General Secretary Eric Holt, 5 Quakerfields, Westhoughton, Bolton BL5 2BJ
tel (01942) 791390

'For writers and lovers of Lancashire literature and history.' Publishes *The Record* (quarterly). Annual subscription: £9.00. Founded 1909.

The T.E. Lawrence Society

PO Box 728, Oxford OX2 6YP

Promotes the memory of T.E. Lawrence and furthers knowledge by research into his life; publishes *Journal* (bi-annual) and *Newsletter* (quarterly). Annual subscription: £15, overseas £20. Founded 1985.

Learned and Professional Society Publishers, The Association of

Secretary-General Prof B.T. Donovan, 48 Kelsey Lane, Beckenham, Kent BR3 3NE
tel 0181-658 0459
web site http://www.alpsp.org

Aims to promote and develop the publishing activities of learned and professional organisations. Membership is open to professional and learned societies and allied organisations. Founded 1972.

Librarians, Association of Assistant – see Career Development Group

The Library Association

7 Ridgmount Street, London WC1E 7AE
tel 0171-636 7543 *fax* 0171-436 7218
e-mail info@la-hq.org.uk
web site http://www.la-hq.org.uk
Chief Executive R. Shimmon FLA

For over a century, the Library Association has promoted and defended the interests of the Library and Information Service profession, those working within it and the people who use the services. The journal *The Library Association Record* (monthly), is distributed free to all members. Subscription: varies according to income. Founded 1877.

Limners, The Society of

Founder/President Elizabeth Davys Wood PSLM, SWA
Executive Secretary Mrs C. Melmore, 104 Poverest Road, Orpington, Kent BR5 2DQ

Aims to promote an interest in miniature painting (in any medium), calligraphy and heraldry and encourage their development to a high standard. New members are elected after the submission of 4 works of acceptable standard and guidelines are provided for new artists. Members receive up to 4 newsletters a year and 2 annual exhibitions are arranged. Annual membership: £20; Friends (£12). Friends membership is open to non-exhibitors and includes newsletters and invitations to exhibitions and seminar. Founded 1986.

Linguists, Institute of

Saxon House, 48 Southwark Street, London SE1 1UN
tel 0171-940 3100 *fax* 0171-940 3101
e-mail info@iol.org.uk
web site http://www.iol.org.uk

To provide language qualifications; to encourage Government and industry to develop the use of modern languages and encourage recognition of the status of professional linguists in all occupations; to promote the exchange and dissemination of information on matters of concern to linguists.

Literacy Trust, National

Swire House, 59 Buckingham Gate, London SW1E 6AJ
tel 0171-828 2435 *fax* 0171-931 9986
e-mail contact@literacytrust.org.uk
web site http://www.literacytrust.org.uk
Director Neil McClelland, *Secretary* Jacky Taylor

Aims are to work with others to enhance literacy standards in the UK, to encourage more reading and writing for pleasure by children, young people and adults, and to raise the profile of the importance of literacy in the context of social and technological change. Runs Reading Is Fundamental, UK, an extension of the US-based organisation, set up to promote reading and books amongst children and parents. It also works closely with DfEE to launch the government's National Year of Reading campaign which will run for 12 months from September 1998. Founded 1993.

Literary Societies, Alliance of
Secretary Bill Adams, 71 Stepping Stones Road, Coventry CV5 8JT
tel (01203) 592231
e-mail www.sndc.demon.co.uk
Chapter One, Clatterwick Hall, Little Leigh, Northwich, Cheshire CW8 4RJ
tel (01606) 891303 (office hours)
Editor Kenn Oultram
Any literary society may affiliate and may attend the annual convention and receive an allocation of the official publication *Chapter One*. Some financial assistance may be granted to small societies. Subscription: graded dependent upon size of society.

Literature, Royal Society of
1 Hyde Park Gardens, London W2 2LT
tel 0171-723 5104 *fax* 0171-402 0199
Chairman of Council Michael Holroyd CBE, FRSL, FRHistS, *Secretary* Maggie Fergusson
For the advancement of literature by the holding of lectures, discussions, readings, and by publications. Administers the Royal Society of Literature Award under the W.H. Heinemann Bequest and the Winifred Holtby Memorial Prize. Annual subscription: £30. Founded 1823.

Little Presses, Association of (ALP)
Chairperson Lawrence Upton,
32 Downside Road, Sutton, Surrey SM2 5HP
web site http://www.melloworld.com/alp
Loosely-knit association of individuals running little presses who have grouped together for mutual self-help, while retaining their right to operate autonomously. Publications include: Newsletter, *Poetry and Little Press Information*, *Catalogue of Little Press*

Books in Print, *Getting Your Poetry Published*, *Publishing Yourself*. It does not publish any creative writing. Annual membership: £12.50. Founded 1966.

Little Theatre Guild of Great Britain
Public Relations Officer Marjorie Havard, 19 Abbey Park Road, Great Grimsby DN32 0HJ
tel (01472) 343424
Aims to promote closer co-operation amongst the little theatres constituting its membership; to act as co-ordinating and representative body on behalf of the little theatres; to maintain and advance the highest standards in the art of theatre; and to assist in encouraging the establishment of other little theatres. Yearbook available to non-members £5.00.

Arthur Machen, The Friends of
Secretary Ray Russell, 5 Birch Terrace, Hangingbirch Lane, Horam, East Sussex TN21 0PA
tel (01435) 813224
Provides a forum for the exchange of ideas and information about Arthur Machen, novelist, and aims to bring his work before a new generation of readers. Publishes *Faunus*, a 64-page hardback journal (bi-annual) and a newsletter (bi-annual). Relevant second-hand and small press booklist available. Annual subscription: £15 (UK), £18 (overseas and libraries), US$ account.

Marine Artists, Royal Society of
17 Carlton House Terrace, London SW1Y 5BD
tel 0171-930 6844 *fax* 0171-839 7830
President Mark Myers
To promote and encourage marine painting. Open Annual Exhibition at the Mall Galleries, London.

The Marlowe Society
Secretary Miss C.M. Barford, c/o Alleyn's School, Dulwich, London SE22 8SU
tel 0181-693 3422
To extend appreciation and widen recognition of Christopher Marlowe (1564-93) as the foremost poet and dramatist preceding Shakespeare, whose development he influenced. Holds meetings and cultural visits, and issues a quarterly magazine. Annual subscription: £12, concessions £7, overseas £15/$26. Founded 1955.

The John Masefield Society
Chairman Peter J.R. Carter, The Frith, Ledbury, Herefordshire HR8 1LW

tel (01531) 633800
web site http://www.ucl.ac.uk/~uczzpwe/jms1.htm
To stimulate interest in and public awareness and enjoyment of the life and works of the poet John Masefield. Holds an annual lecture and other, less formal, readings and gatherings; publishes an annual journal and frequent newsletters. Annual membership: £5, overseas £10, family/institutions £8. Founded 1992.

Mechanical-Copyright Protection Society Ltd (MCPS)
Elgar House, 41 Streatham High Road, London SW16 1ER
tel 0181-664 4400 *fax* 0181-769 8792
e-mail corpcomms@mcps.co.uk
Chief Executive John Hutchinson, *Contact* Corporate Communications Department
Grants licences for the use of copyright material by mechanical reproduction, be it sound, film, radio and TV recordings, magnetic tape or videocassettes. Protection is worldwide, by virtue of its affiliations with other similar organisations and agencies. Membership of the Society is open to all music copyright owners, composers, lyric writers and publishers. No entrance fee or subscription. Founded in 1910.

The Media Society
Secretary Peter Dannheisser, 56 Roseneath Road, London SW11 6AQ
tel/fax 0171-223 5631
To promote and encourage collective and independent research into the standards, performance, organisation and economics of the media and hold regular discussions, debates, etc. on subjects of topical or special interest and concern to print and broadcast journalists and others working in or with the media. Annual subscription: £25. Founded 1973.

Medical Journalists Association
Hon. Secretary Jenny Sims, 2 St George's Road, Kingston-upon-Thames, Surrey KT2 6DN
tel 0181-549 1019 *fax* 0181-255 4964
e-mail jennysims@compuserve.com
Chairman John Illman, Gwen Yates
Aims to improve the quality and practice of health and medical journalism. Administers major awards for health and medical journalism and broadcasting. Publishes The *MJA Directory* and *MJA News* newsletter. Annual membership: £30. Founded 1966.

Medical Writers Group
84 Drayton Gardens, London SW10 9SB
tel 0171-373 6642
Specialist group within the membership of the Society of Authors (see page 504) giving contractual and legal advice. Also organises talks, day seminars covering many aspects of medical writing, and administers the medical prizes sponsored by the Medical Society of London.

Miniature Painters, Sculptors and Gravers, Royal Society of
Executive Secretary Mrs Pam Henderson, 1 Knapp Cottages, Wyke, Gillingham, Dorset SP8 4NQ
tel (01747) 825718; 0171-222 2723 (during exhibitions)
President Suzanne Lucas FLS, PRMS, FPSBA, *Treasurer* Alastair MacDonald, *Hon. Secretary* Pauline Gyles
Membership is by selection and standard of work over a period of years (ARMS associate, RMS full member). Annual Open Exhibition in November at the Westminster Gallery in London. Hand in Sept/Oct; schedules available in July (send sae). Applications and enquiries to the Executive Secretary. Founded 1895.

Miniaturists, British Society of
Director Leslie Simpson FRSA, Briargate, 2 The Brambles, Ilkley, West Yorkshire LS29 9DH
tel (01943) 609075
'The world's oldest miniature society.' Holds 2 open exhibitions p.a. Membership by selection. Founded 1895.

Miniaturists, The Hilliard Society of
The Executive Officer Mrs S.M. Burton, 15 Union Street, Wells, Somerset BA5 2PU
tel (01749) 674472 *fax* (01749) 672918
President Com. G.W.G. Hunt, RMS, HS, MASF, RN
International society with approx. 300 members. Founded to increase knowledge and promote the art of miniature painting. Annual Exhibition held in May/June at Wells; seminars; Young People's Awards (11-19 years). Encourages Patron membership to keep collectors in touch with artists. Informative Newsletter includes technical section and news from miniature societies around the world. Membership: from £25. Founded 1982.

William Morris Society
Kelmscott House, 26 Upper Mall, London W6 9TA
tel 0181-741 3735

Secretary Peter Faulkner

To spread knowledge of the life, work and ideas of William Morris; publishes *Newsletter* (quarterly) and *Journal* (2 p.a.). Library and collections open to the public Thu and Sat, 2-5pm. Founded 1955.

Motoring Artists, The Guild of
Administrator David Purvis, 71 Brook Court, Watling Street, Radlett, Herts. WD7 7JA
tel (01923) 853803

To promote, publicise and develop motoring fine art; to build a recognised group of artists interested in motoring art, holding events and exchanging ideas and support; to hold motoring art exhibitions. Annual membership: £27.50, associate £22.50, friend £18. Founded 1986.

Motoring Writers, The Guild of
Contact General Secretary, 30 The Cravens, Smallfield, Surrey RH6 9QS
tel (01342) 843294 *fax* (01342) 844093

To raise the standard of motoring journalism. For writers, broadcasters, photographers on matters of motoring, but who are not connected with the motor industry.

Music Publishers Association Ltd
3rd Floor, Strandgate, 18-20 York Buildings, London WC2N 6JU
tel 0171-839 7779 *fax* 0171-839 7776
e-mail mpa@mcps.co.uk
Chief Executive Sarah Faulder

The only trade organisation representing the UK music publishing industry; protects and promotes its members' interests in copyright, trade and related matters. A number of sub-committees and groups deal with particular interests. Details of subscriptions available on written request. Founded 1881.

Musical Association, The Royal
Contact Dr Jonathan King, The New Grove Dictionary of Music and Musicians, 25 Eccleston Place, London SW1W 9NF
fax 0171-881 8496
e-mail j.king@newgrove.co.uk
web site http://www.soton.ac.uk/~stilwell/rma.html

Musicians, Incorporated Society of
10 Stratford Place, London W1N 9AE
tel 0171-629 4413 *fax* 0171-408 1538
e-mail membership@ism.org
web site http://www.ism.org
President 1998-9: John Hosier CBE, *Chief Executive* Neil Hoyle

Professional body for musicians. Aims to promote the art of music; protect the interests and raise the standards of the musical profession; provide services, support and advice for its members. Publishes *Music Journal* (12 p.a.); Yearbook and 3 Registers of Specialists annually. Annual subscription: £87.

Musicians, The Worshipful Company of
1st Floor, 74-75 Watling Street, London EC4M 9BJ
tel 0171-489 8888 *fax* 0171-489 1614
Clerk S.F.N. Waley

Founded 1500.

Name Studies in Britain and Ireland, Society for
Hon. Secretary Miss Jennifer Scherr, c/o Queen's Building Library, University of Bristol, University Walk, Bristol BS8 1TR
Membership Secretary Dr M. Higham, 22 Peel Park Avenue, Clitheroe, Lancs. BB7 1ET

Aims to advance, promote and support research into the place-names and personal names of Britain and Ireland and related regions by the collection, documentation and interpretation of such names; the publication of the material and the results of such research; the exchange of information between the various regions. Acts as a consultative body on Name Studies; holds annual conferences; publishes an annual journal, *Nomina*, and an occasional newsletter. Annual subscription: £15.

National Campaign for the Arts (NCA)
Francis House, Francis Street, London SW1P 1DE
tel 0171-828 4448 *fax* 0171-931 9959
e-mail newmail@artscampaign.org
web site http://www.artscampaign.org
Secretary Jennifer Edwards

Aims to be a strong advocate for all art forms on the national stage; to fight government funding cuts; to seek recognition for the value of the arts in a civilised society; to represent the diverse views and wishes of its members. Membership: £21.50; unwaged £15; special rates for organisations. Founded 1985.

The National Small Press Centre
BM BOZO, London WC1N 3XX
Director John Nicholson, *Press Officer* Cecilia Boggis, *Liaison Officer* John Dench, *Treasurer* Andy Hopton

Provides a focus for small presses and

independent self-publishers and actively promotes them by collecting and disseminating information in the form of exhibitions, talks, courses, workshops, conferences and fairs. Publishes *News from the Centre* (bi-monthly) and *Small Press Listings* (quarterly) – joint subscription: £12 p.a.; *Handbook* £12 plus £1.50 p&p.

Small Press Fairs are held annually in the Royal Festival Hall, London. The Centre is twinned with the Mainz Mini-Press Archive in Mainz, Germany and the New York Small Press Center. Founded 1992.

National Union of Journalists
Head Office Acorn House, 314-320 Gray's Inn Road, London WC1X 8DP
tel 0171-278 7916 *fax* 0171-837 8143
e-mail nuj@mcr1.poptel.org.uk
Trade union for working journalists with 28,000 members and 147 branches throughout the UK and the Republic of Ireland, and in Paris, Brussels, Geneva and the Netherlands. It covers the newspaper press, news agencies and broadcasting, the major part of periodical and book publishing, and a number of public relations departments and consultancies, information services and Prestel-Viewdata services. Administers disputes, unemployment, benevolent and provident benefits. Official publications: *The Journalist, Freelance Directory, Freelance Fees Guide* and policy pamphlets.

National Year of Reading – see Literacy Trust, National

The Edith Nesbit Society
73 Brookehowse Road, London SE6 3TH
tel 0181-698 8907
Aims to promote an interest in the life and works of Edith Nesbit (1858-1924) by means of talks, a regular newsletter and and other publications, and visits to relevant places. Annual membership: £5; organisations/overseas £10. Founded 1996.

New Science Fiction Alliance (NSFA)
Chris Reed, BBR, PO Box 625, Sheffield S1 3GY
web site http://www.syspace.co.uk/bbr/nsfa-cat.html
Publicity Officer Chris Reed
The NSFA is committed to supporting the work of new writers and artists by promoting independent and small press

publications worldwide. It was founded by a group of independent publishers to give writers the opportunity to explore the small press and find the right market for their material. It offers a mail order service for magazines. Founded 1989.

New Writing North
7-8 Trinity Chare, Quayside, Newcastle upon Tyne NE1 3DF
tel 0191-232 9991 *fax* 0191-230 1883
e-mail clarie.malcolm@virgin.net
Director Claire Malcolm, *Administrator* Anna Barker
Aims to encourage and develop new writers and writing, in all genres, across the Northern Arts region. Offers training and advice through workshops and surgeries and unbiased feedback on work through its critical reading service. Founded 1996.

New Zealand, Book Publishers Association of Inc.
Box 36477, Northcote, Auckland, New Zealand
tel (09) 480-2711 *fax* (09) 480-1130
President Wendy Harrex

New Zealand Copyright Council Inc.
PO Box 5028, Wellington, New Zealand
tel (04) 472-4430 *fax* (04) 471-0765
Chairman Bernard Darby, *Secretary* Tony Chance

Newspaper Press Fund
Dickens House, 35 Wathen Road, Dorking, Surrey RH4 1JY
tel (01306) 887511 *fax* (01306) 876104
web site http://www.foundation.reuters.com/npf
Secretary P.W. Evans
For the relief of hardship amongst member journalists, their widows and dependants. Financial assistance and retirement housing are provided. Limited help is available for non-member journalists and their dependants. Further information can be found via the Reuter Foundation web site (above).

The Newspaper Publishers Association Ltd
34 Southwark Bridge Road, London SE1 9EU
tel 0171-207 2200 *fax* 0171-928 2067

Newspaper Society
Bloomsbury House, 74-77 Great Russell Street, London WC1B 3DA
tel 0171-636 7014 *fax* 0171-631 5119
AdDoc DX35701 Bloomsbury
e-mail ns@newspapersoc.org.uk
Director David Newell

Oil Painters, Royal Institute of

17 Carlton House Terrace, London SW1Y 5BD
tel 0171-930 6844 *fax* 0171-839 7830
President Frederick Beckett Hon. RI

Promotes and encourages the art of painting in oils. Open Annual Exhibition at the Mall Galleries, London.

Oils, Pastels and Acrylics, British Society of Painters in

Briargate, 2 The Brambles, Ilkley,
West Yorkshire LS29 9DH
tel (01943) 609075
Director Leslie Simpson FRSA

Promotes interest and encourages high quality in the work of painters in these media. Holds 2 open exhibitions p.a. Membership by selection. Founded 1988.

The Orton Society

21 Brockenhurst Road, Croydon,
Surrey CR0 7DR
President Sue Townsend, *Chairman* Bill Kelly

Aims to promote the life and work of Joe Orton and to draw him to the attention of future generations. Membership: £5.00 p.a. Founded 1994.

Outdoor Writers' Guild

Secretary Terry Marsh, PO Box 520,
Bamber Bridge, Preston, Lancs. PR5 8LF
tel/fax (01772) 696732
e-mail 101551.2323@compuserve.com

Aims to promote and maintain a high professional standard among writers and photographers who specialise in outdoor activities; represents members' interests to representative bodies in the outdoor leisure industry; circulates members with news of media opportunities; provides a forum for members to meet colleagues and others in the outdoor leisure industry. Presents annual literary and photographic awards. Annual membership: £35 plus £10 joining fee. Founded 1980.

Wilfred Owen Association

17 Belmont, Shrewsbury SY1 1TE
tel/fax (01743) 235904

To commemorate the life and work of Wilfred Owen, and to encourage and enhance appreciation of his work through visits, public events and a newsletter. Annual subscription: £4 (£6 overseas), groups/institutions £10, senior citizens/students/unemployed £2. Founded 1989.

PACT (Producers Alliance for Cinema and Television)

45 Mortimer Street, London W1N 7TD
tel 0171-331 6000 *fax* 0171-331 6700
Chief Executive Shaun Williams
Membership Officer David Alan Mills

PACT serves the feature film and independent TV production sector and is the UK contact point for co-production, co-finance partners and distributors.

Painter-Printmakers, Royal Society of

Bankside Gallery, 48 Hopton Street,
London SE1 9JH
tel 0171-928 7521
e-mail re&rws@bankside-gallery.demon.co.uk
President Prof David L. Carpanini Hon. RWS, RBA,
RWA, NEAC

Membership (RE) open to British and overseas artists. An election of Associates is held annually, and applications for the necesssary forms and particulars should be addressed to the Secretary. The Society organises workshops and lectures on original printmaking; holds one members' exhibition per year. Friends of the RE open to all those interested in artists' original printmaking. Founded 1880.

Painters, Sculptors and Printmakers, National Society of

President Denis Baxter PNS, UA, FRSA
Hon. Secretary Gwen Spencer, 122 Copse Hill,
London SW20 0NL
tel 0181-946 7878

An annual exhibition in London representing all aspects of art for artists of every creed and outlook. Newsletter (2 p.a.) for members. Founded 1930

The Pastel Society

17 Carlton House Terrace, London SW1Y 5BD
tel 0171-930 6844 *fax* 0171-839 7830
President Thomas Coates

Pastel and drawings in pencil or chalk. Annual Exhibition open to all artists working in dry media held at the Mall Galleries, London. Members elected from approved candidates' list. Founded 1899.

The Mervyn Peake Society

Hon. President Sebastian Peake, *Chairman* Brian Sibley
Secretary Frank Surry, 2 Mount Park Road,
London W5 2RP

Devoted to recording the life and works of Mervyn Peake; publishes a journal and newsletter. Annual subscription: £12 (UK and Europe), £5 (students), £14 (all other countries). Founded 1975.

PEN, International
International President Homero Aridjis
International Secretary Alexandre Blokh,
9-10 Charterhouse Buildings, Goswell Road, London EC1M 7AT
tel 0171-253 4308 *fax* 0171-253 5711

English PEN Centre
President Rachel Billington
General Secretary Gillian Vincent, 7 Dilke Street, London SW3 4JE
tel 0171-352 6303 *fax* 0171-351 0220

Scottish PEN Centre
President Robin Lloyd-Jones
Secretary Chris Dolan, 6 Turnberry Road, Glasgow G11 5AE
tel/fax 0141-3570145

Welsh PEN Centre
President Ned Thomas, University of Wales Press, Gwynneth Street, Cathays, Cardiff CF2 4YD
tel (01222) 231919

A world association of writers. PEN was founded in 1921 by C.A. Dawson Scott under the presidency of John Galsworthy, to promote friendship and understanding between writers and to defend freedom of expression within and between all nations. The initials PEN stand for Poets, Playwrights, Editors, Essayists, Novelists – but membership is open to all writers of standing (including translators), whether men or women, without distinction of creed or race, who subscribe to these fundamental principles. PEN takes no part in state or party politics. The International PEN Writers in Prison Committee works on behalf of writers imprisoned for exercising their right to freedom of expression, a right implicit in the PEN Charter to which all members subscribe. The International PEN Translations and Linguistic Rights Committee strives to promote the translations of works by writers in the lesser-known languages and to defend those languages. The Writers for Peace Committee exists to find ways in which writers can work for peaceful co-existence in the world. The Women Writers' Committee works to promote women's

writing and publishing in developing countries. International Congresses are held most years. The 65th Congress was held in Helsinki in 1998; the 66th Congress will be held in Warsaw in 1999.

Membership of any one Centre implies membership of all Centres; at present 131 autonomous Centres exist throughout the world. Membership of the English Centre is £30 p.a. for country and overseas members, £35 for London members. Associate membership is available for writers not yet eligible for full membership and for persons connected with literature. The English Centre has a programme of literary lectures, discussion, dinners and parties. A yearly Writers' Day is open to the public as are some literary lectures.

Please apply to the Scottish and Welsh Centres for information about their membership fees and activities.

Performing Right Society Ltd
29-33 Berners Street, London W1P 4AA
tel 0171-580 5544 *fax* 0171-306 4050
Contact Corporate Communications

An association of composers, authors and publishers of copyright musical works, established in 1914, to grant licences and collect royalties for the public performance, broadcasting and diffusion by cable of such works; also to restrain unauthorised use thereof. The Society is affiliated to the national societies of more than 30 other countries. All composers of musical works and authors of lyrics or poems which have been set to music are eligible for membership. An initial admission fee only is payable. Founded 1914.

Periodical Publishers Association
Queens House, 28 Kingsway, London WC2B 6JR
tel 0171-404 4166 *fax* 0171-404 4167
e-mail info1@ppa.co.uk
web site http://www.ppa.co.uk
Chief Executive Ian Locks

The Personal Managers' Association Ltd
Liaison Secretary Angela Adler, 1 Summer Road, East Molesey, Surrey KT8 9LX
tel/fax 0181-398 9796

Association of theatrical agents in the theatre, film and entertainment world generally.

Photographers, The Association of

Co-Secretary Gwen Thomas, 9-10 Domingo Street, London EC1Y 0TA
tel 0171-608 1441 *fax* 0171-253 3007
e-mail aop@dircon.co.uk
web site http://www.aophoto.co.uk

To protect and promote the interests of fashion advertising and editorial photographers. Annual subscription: £72-£355, depending on turnover. Founded 1969.

Photographers Association, Master

Hallmark House, 2 Beaumont Street, Darlington, Co. Durham DL1 5SZ
tel (01325) 356555 *fax* (01325) 357813
e-mail generalenquiries@mpauk.demon.co.uk

To promote and protect professional photographers. Members qualify for awards of Licentiate, Associate and Fellowship. Annual subscription: £99.

Photographic Society, The Royal

The Octagon, Milsom Street, Bath BA1 1DN
tel (01225) 462841 *fax* (01225) 448688
e-mail rps@rps.org
web site http://www.rps.org

Open membership organisation which promotes the art and science of photography and electronic imagery; publishes *The Photographic Journal* (monthly) and the *Imaging Science Journal* (quarterly). Founded 1853.

Photography, British Institute of Professional

Amwell End, Ware, Herts. SG12 9HN
tel (01920) 464011

To represent all who practise photography as a profession in any field; to improve the quality of photography; establish recognised examination qualifications and a high standard of conduct; to safeguard the interests of the public and the profession. Admission can be obtained either via examinations, or by submission of work and other information to the appropriate examining board. Fellows, Associates and Licentiates are entitled to the designation Incorporated Photographer or Incorporated Photographic Technician. Organises numerous meetings and conferences in various parts of the country throughout the year; publishes *The Photographer* journal (monthly), and an annual Register of Members and *Guide to Buyers of Photography*, plus various pamphlets and leaflets on professional photography. Founded 1901, incorporated 1921.

Picture Libraries and Agencies, British Association of – see BAPLA

The Picture Research Association

(formerly SPREd)
455 Finchley Road, London NW3 6HN
tel 0171-431 9886 *fax* 0171-431 9887
e-mail pra@pictures.demon.co.uk
Chair Emma Krikler

Professional organisation of picture researchers and picture editors. See page 455.

Player-Playwrights

Secretary Peter Thompson, 9 Hillfield Park, London N10 3QT
tel 0181-883 0371

Meets on Monday evenings at St Augustine's Church Hall, Queen's Gate, London SW1. The society reads, performs and discusses plays and scripts submitted by members, with a view to assisting the writers in improving and marketing their work. Newcomers and new acting members are always welcome. Membership fees: £10 in the first year and £6 thereafter (and £1 per attendance). Founded 1948.

Playwrights Trust, New

Interchange Studios, Dalby Street, London NW5 3NQ
tel 0171-284 2818 *fax* 0171-482 5292
e-mail npt@easynet.co.uk
Executive Director Jonathan Meth

Research and development organisation for writers and aspiring writers for all forms of live and recorded performance, and those interested in developing and producing new work. Services include script-reading; information guides; writer/company Link Service; 6-weekly *Newsletter*. Subscription: rates on application.

Poetry Book Society

Book House, 45 East Hill, London SW18 2QZ
tel 0181-870 8403 *fax* 0181-877 1615
Chairman Martyn Goff, *Director* Clare Brown

Foremost in getting books of new poetry to readers through quarterly selections, special offers, and 300-strong backlist which it sells at favourable rates to members. Publishes *Bulletin* (quarterly) and holds quarterly readings at the Royal Festival Hall. Runs the annual T.S. Eliot Prize for the best collection of new poetry. Operates as a charitable Book Club with annual membership (£10, £30, £120) open to all. Education resources for secondary schools.

Poetry Foundation, National

27 Mill Road, Fareham, Hants PO16 0TH
tel (01329) 822218

Aims to provide a truly national poetry organisation which in turn provides free advice on publishing, information and a magazine, all for a single low-cost fee, and to help poets have a book of their own poetry published at no additional cost, once they have sufficient poetry of a high enough standard. The Foundation also gives grants to deserving causes directly related to poetry and gives free advice on problems relating to book publication. Founded 1981.

The Poetry Society

22 Betterton Street, London WC2H 9BU
tel 0171-420 9880 *fax* 0171-240 4818
e-mail poetrysoc@dial.pipex.com
web site http://www.poetrysoc.com
Chairman Mary Enright, *Director* Chris Meade

National membership body, open to all, to help poets and poetry thrive in Britain today. Publishes *Poetry Review* (quarterly) and *Poetry News* (quarterly), has an information and imagination service, runs promotions and educational projects, helps co-ordinate National Poetry Day, and administers the annual National Poetry Competition and the biennial European Poetry Translation Prize. Runs the Poetry Place and Poetry Café at its premises in Covent Garden, and the Poetry Places scheme of residencies and placements for poets. Founded 1909.

The John Polidori Literary Society

Contact The Secretary, Ebenezer House,
31 Ebenezer Street, Langley Mill, Notts. NG16 4DA
tel 0181-994 5902 *fax* 0181-995 3275
Founder/President Franklin Charles Bishop
London Area President Kathy McGrath
tel 0181-560 9916

Promotes and encourages the appreciation of the life and works of John William Polidori MD (1795-1821) – novelist, poet, tragedian, philosopher, diarist, essayist, reviewer, traveller and one of the youngest ever students to obtain a medical degree at the age of 19. He introduced into English literature the icon of the vampire portrayed as an aristocratic, handsome seducer both cynical and amoral with his seminal work

The Vampyre – A Tale (1819). The Society houses a collection of rare letters and memorabilia connected with Polidori. Members receive newsletters, invitations to social events and publication offers. Subscription: £15 p.a. Founded 1990.

Portrait Painters, Royal Society of

17 Carlton House Terrace, London SW1Y 5BD
tel 0171-930 6844 *fax* 0171-839 7830
President Daphne Todd

Annual Exhibition at the Mall Galleries, London, when work may be submitted by non-members with a view to exhibition. Also commissions consultancy service. Founded 1891.

Portuguese Association of Publishers and Booksellers

(Associação Portuguesa de Editores e Livreiros)
Av. Estados Unidos da América, 97-6° Esq.,
Lisboa 1700, Portugal (1)
tel 8489136 *fax* (1) 8489377

Beatrix Potter Society

Chairman Mike Hemming
Secretary Marian Werner, 32 Etchingham Park Road, London N3 2DT

Promotes the study and appreciation of the life and works of Beatrix Potter as author, artist, diarist, farmer and conservationist. Annual subscription: UK £10, overseas US$25/Can$30/Aus$30. Founded 1980.

The Powys Society

Hon. Secretary Chris Gostick, Old School House, George Green Road, George Green, Wexham, Bucks. SL3 6BJ
tel (01753) 578632
e-mail gostick@altavista.net
web site http://www.iaehv.nl/users/tklijn/pws/powys.htm

Aims to promote the greater public recognition and enjoyment of the writings, thought and contribution to the arts of the Powys family, particularly John Cowper (1872-1963), Theodore (1875-1953) and Llewelyn (1884-1939) Powys, and the many other family members and their close friends. Publishes an annual scholarly journal (*The Powys Journal*) and 3 newsletters per year, and holds an annual weekend conference in August, as well as other activities. Founded 1967.

Press Agencies, National Association of

The Administrator, 41 Lansdowne Crescent, Leamington Spa, Warks. CV32 4PR
tel (01926) 424181 *fax* (01926) 424760

Trade association representing the interests of the leading national news and photographic agencies. Annual subscription: £250. Founded 1983.

The Press Complaints Commission
Chairman The Rt Hon Lord Wakeham
Director Guy Black, 1 Salisbury Square, London EC4Y 8AE
tel 0171-353 1248 *Helpline tel* 0171-353 3732
fax 0171-353 8355
e-mail pcc@pcc.org.uk
web site http://www.pcc.org.uk
Independent body founded to oversee self-regulation of the Press. Deals with complaints by the public about the contents and conduct of British newspapers and magazines and advises editors on journalistic ethics. Complaints must be about the failure of newspapers or magazines to follow the letter or spirit of a Code of Practice, drafted by newspaper and magazine editors, adopted by the industry and supervised by the Commission. Founded 1991.

Printmakers Council
Clerkenwell Workshops, 31 Clerkenwell Close, London EC1R 0AT
tel 0171-250 1927 *fax* 0171-608 3848
President Stanley Jones, *Chair* Sheila Sloss
Artist-led group which aims 'to promote the use of both traditional and innovative printmaking techniques by:
• holding exhibitions of prints;
• providing information on prints and printmaking to both its membership and the public;
• encouraging co-operation and exchanges between members, other associations and interested individuals.'
Annual membership: £45; students £22.50. Founded 1965.

Private Libraries Association
Ravelston, South View Road, Pinner, Middlesex HA5 3YD
President Robin de Beaumont, *Hon. Editors* David Chambers and Paul W. Nash, *Hon. Secretary* Frank Broomhead
International society of book collectors and private libraries. Publications include *Private Library* (quarterly), annual *Private Press Books*, and other books on book collecting. Annual subscription: £25. Founded 1956.

The Producers Association – see PACT

Public Art Commissions Agency
Studio 6, Victoria Works, Vittoria Street, Birmingham B1 3PE
tel 0121-212 4454 *fax* 0121-212 4426
and 118 Commercial Street, London E1 6NF
tel/fax 0171-247 2484
Director Vivien Lovell
Commissions Managers Rachel Bradley (Birmingham), Stephen Beddoe (London)
A charity and non-profit consultancy for public art commissions throughout the UK and Europe. Advice is given to developers, government departments, local authorities, transport and health authorities, private sector clients, artists, architects, landscape architects, etc. Holds lectures and workshops, and has a commissioning service. Founded 1987.

The Publishers Association
1 Kingsway, London WC2B 6XF
tel 0171-565 7474 *fax* 0171-836 4543
e-mail mail@publishers.org.uk
Chief Executive Ronnie Williams OBE, *Director of International and Trade Divisions (BDC)* Ian Taylor, *Director of Educational and Academic and Professional Publishing* John Davies
Founded 1896.

Publishers Association, International
3 avenue de Miremont, CH-1206 Geneva, Switzerland
tel (022) 346-30-18 *fax* (022) 347-57-17
President Alain Gründ, *Secretary-General* J. Alexis Koutchoumow
Founded 1896.

Publishers Guild, Independent
25 Cambridge Road, Hampton, Middlesex TW12 2JL
tel 0181-979 0250 *fax* 0181-979 6393
Full membership is open to new and established publishers and book packagers; supplier membership is available to specialists in fields allied to publishing (but not printers and binders). The Guild offers a forum for the exchange of ideas and information and represents the interests of its members. Annual membership: £75 (plus VAT). Founded 1962.

Publishers Licensing Society Limited
5 Dryden Street, London WC2E 9NW
tel 0171-829 8486 *fax* 0171-829 8488
Chairman Maurice Long, *Manager* Caroline Elmslie
Aims to exercise and enforce on behalf of publishers the rights of copyright and

other rights of a similar nature; to authorise the granting of licences for the making of reprographic copies of copyright works; and to receive and distribute to publisher copyright owners the sums received from licensed use. PLS intends to increase the range and repertoire of those mandated publishers including, specifically, seeking their authorisation for electro-storage of information and digital copying. Founded 1981.

Publishers Publicity Circle
Secretary Christina Thomas, 48 Crabtree Lane, London SW6 6LW
e-mail ppc-@lineone.net
tel/fax 0171-385 3708
Enables all book publicists to meet and share information regularly. Monthly meetings provide a forum for press journalists, TV and radio researchers and producers to meet publicists collectively. Awards are presented for the best PR campaigns. Monthly newsletter includes recruitment advertising. Founded 1955.

Puzzle Writers, International Association of
Secretary Dr Jeremy Sims, 42 Brigstocke Terrace, Ryde, Isle of Wight PO33 2PD
e-mail jeremy@global-net-trade.com
tel (01983) 811688
Aims to bring puzzle writers and games designers worldwide, both amateur and professional, closer together and to provide support and information. Promotes the art of puzzle writing and games design to publishers, games manufacturers and the general public. Membership is free but send 6 stamps or IRCs to cover postage of bi-monthly newsletter. Founded 1996.

The Radclyffe International Philosophical Association
BM-RIPhA, Old Gloucester Street, London WC1N 3XX
President William Mann FRIPhA, *Secretary General* John Khasseyan FRIPhA
Aims to dignify those achievements which might otherwise escape formal recognition; to promote the interests and talent of its members; to encourage their good fellowship; and to form a medium for the exchange of ideas between members. Annual subscription: £25.00 (Fellows, Members and

Associates). Published authors and artists usually enter at Fellowship level. Founded 1955.

RADIO
(formerly Independent Association of Radio Producers – IARP)
PO Box 14880, London NW1 9ZD
tel 0171-485 0873 *fax* 0171-428 0541
Chair Ian Willox
The trade association for independent producers in radio and audio. Annual membership: student £30, full £50. Founded 1993.

The Radio Academy
PO Box 4SZ, London W1A 4SZ
tel 0171-255 2010 *fax* 0171-255 2029
e-mail info@radacad.demon.co.uk
Director John Bradford
The Radio Academy is the professional association for those engaged in the UK radio industry with over 1800 individual members and 30 corporate patrons. It organises conferences, seminars, debates, the annual UK Radio Festival and social events for members; publishes newsletter *Off Air* (monthly), and an annual *Yearbook*. The Academy also has a number of Collegiate members and offers some practical training opportunities for students of radio.

Railway Artists, Guild of
Chief Executive Officer F.P. Hodges, 45 Dickins Road, Warwick CV34 5NS
tel (01926) 499246
Aims to forge a link between artists depicting railway subjects and to give members a corporate identity; also stages railway art exhibitions and members' meetings. Founded 1979.

Regional Arts Boards (RABs)
web site http://www.arts.org.uk
Following a process of restructuring in 1990/91, a network of 10 Regional Arts Boards now covers England. The RABs are autonomous, strategic bodies which work in partnership with local authorities and a wide variety of other sectors and organisations and are policy led. Legally, they are limited companies with charitable status. They are concerned with all the arts and crafts – visual, performing, media, published – and work at regional level as partners of the 3 nation-

al agencies which provide most of their funds: the Arts Council, the British Film Institute, the Crafts Council.

The Arts Council retains the national responsibility for funding and assessing the 'national companies', the symphony orchestras and a handful of other high profile clients. The building-based drama companies are mostly funded by the RABs. The overall planning system is becoming more 'integrated' with the principle of subsidiarity being increasingly applied. The resources available to the RABs during 1998/99 total over £70 million.

The Welsh Regional Arts Associations have been integrated with the Arts Council of Wales (see page 460). There are no regional arts boards in Scotland and all enquiries should be addressed to the Scottish Arts Council (see page 494).

English Regional Arts Boards
5 City Road, Winchester, Hants SO23 8SD
tel (01962) 851063 *fax* (01962) 842033
e-mail info.erab@artsfb.org.uk
Chief Executive Christopher Gordon, *Assistant* Carolyn Nixson

The representative body for the 10 Regional Arts Boards in England. Its secretariat provides project management, services and information for the members and acts on their behalf in appropriate circumstances.

Eastern Arts Board
Cherry Hinton Hall, Cherry Hinton Road, Cambridge CB1 4DW
tel (01223) 215355 *fax* (01223) 248075
Chief Executive Lou Stein, *Literature Officer* Emma Drew, *Visual Arts Officer* Niki Braithwaite

Bedfordshire, Cambridgeshire, Essex, Hertfordshire, Lincolnshire, Norfolk and Suffolk; unitary authority of Luton. Founded 1971.

East Midlands Arts Board
Mountfields House, Epinal Way, Loughborough, Leics. LE11 0QE
tel (01509) 218292 *fax* (01509) 262214
Chief Executive John Buston, *Literature Officer* Sue Stewart, *Visual Arts Officer* Janet Currie

Derbyshire (excluding High Peak District), Leicestershire, Northamptonshire and Nottinghamshire; unitary authorities of Derby, Leicester and Rutland. Founded 1969.

London Arts Board
Elme House, 133 Long Acre, London WC2E 9AF
Helpline 0171-240 4578
tel 0171-240 1313 *fax* 0171-240 4580
Principal Literature Officer John Hampson, *Principal Visual Arts and Crafts Officer* Holly Tebbutt

The area of the 32 London Boroughs and the City of London. Founded 1991.

North West Arts Board
Manchester House, 22 Bridge Street, Manchester M3 3AB
tel 0161-834 6644 *fax* 0161-834 6969
Chief Executive Sue Harrison, *Director Visual Arts & Media* Aileen McEvoy, *Media Officer, Literature* Bronwen Williams

Greater Manchester, Merseyside, High Peak District of Derbyshire, Lancashire and Cheshire. Founded 1966.

Northern Arts
9-10 Osborne Terrace, Newcastle upon Tyne NE2 1NZ
tel 0191-281 6334 *fax* 0191-281 3276
Chief Executive Andrew Dixon, *Head of Published and Broadcast Arts* Janice Campbell, *Visual Arts Officer* James Bustard

Cumbria, Durham, Northumberland, metropolitan districts of Newcastle, Gateshead, Sunderland, North Tyneside and South Tyneside; unitary authorities of Darlington, Hartlepool, Middlesbrough, Redcar and Cleveland, and Stockton. Founded 1961.

South East Arts Board
10 Mount Ephraim, Tunbridge Wells, Kent TN4 8AS
tel (01892) 515210 *Information Dept. ext.* 205/206 *fax* (01892) 549383
Chief Executive Felicity Harvest, *Literature Officer* Anne Downes (*ext.* 210/211), *Visual Arts Officer* Jim Shea (*ext.* 213)

Kent, Surrey, East Sussex and West Sussex; unitary authority of Brighton and Hove. Information and publications list available. Founded 1973.

South West Arts
Bradninch Place, Gandy Street, Exeter, Devon EX4 3LS
tel (01392) 218188 *fax* (01392) 413554
Chief Executive Graham Long, *Director, Visual Arts & Crafts* Val Millington, *Director, Media & Published Arts* David Drake

Cornwall, Devon, Dorset (except Districts of Bournemouth, Christchurch and Poole), Gloucestershire, Somerset; unitary authorities of Bristol, Bath and North-East

Somerset, South Gloucestershire, North Somerset. Founded 1956.

Southern Arts Board
13 St Clement Street, Winchester, Hants SO23 9DQ
tel (01962) 855099 *fax* (01962) 861186
e-mail sarts-info@geo2.poptel.org.uk
Chief Executive Robert Hutchison, *Literature Officer* Keiran Phelan, *Visual Arts Officer* Philip Smith

Berkshire, Buckinghamshire, Hampshire, Isle of Wight, Oxfordshire, Wiltshire and South East Dorset; unitary authorities of Bournemouth, Milton Keynes, Poole, Portsmouth, Southampton and Swindon. Founded 1968.

West Midlands Arts Board
82 Granville Street, Birmingham B1 2LH
tel 0121-631 3121 *fax* 0121-643 7239
Chief Executive Sally Luton, *Director, Visual Arts, Crafts & Media* Caroline Foxhall

County of Hereford and Worcester, Shropshire, Staffordshire, Warwickshire and the metropolitan districts of Birmingham, Coventry, Dudley, Sandwell, Solihull, Walsall and Wolverhampton; unitary authority of Stoke on Trent. Founded 1971.

Yorkshire and Humberside Arts
21 Bond Street, Dewsbury,
West Yorkshire WF13 1AX
tel (01924) 455555 *fax* (01924) 466522
e-mail yharts-info@geo2.poptel.org.uk
Chief Executive Roger Lancaster, *Director of Visual and Media Arts* Nima Poovaya-Smith, *Literature Officer* Steve Dearden

Metropolitan districts of Barnsley, Bradford, Calderdale, Doncaster, Kirklees, Leeds, Rotherham, Sheffield, Wakefield, North Yorkshire; unitary authorities of York, Hull, East Riding, North Lincolnshire and North-East Lincolnshire. Funds schemes and projects for the promotion of contemporary literature and writing activities. Provides grants for festivals, events, courses, residencies, publishing. Offers advice and information on various aspects of literature. Preliminary enquiry advised. Founded 1991.

Ridley Art Society
50 Crowborough Road, London SW17 9QQ
tel 0181-682 1212
President Ken Howard RA, *Chairman* dickon

Represents a wide variety of attitudes towards the making of art. In recent years has sought to encourage young artists. At least one central London exhibition annually. Founded 1889.

The Romantic Novelists' Association
Chairman Angela Arney, 43 Wilton Gardens, Shirley, Southampton SO15 2QS
tel/fax (01703) 774538
Hon. Secretary Norma Curtis, 38 Makepeace Avenue, London N6 6EL
tel/fax 0181-341 6275

To raise the prestige of Romantic Authorship. Open to romantic and historical novelists. See also under Literary Awards.

Royal Academy of Arts
Piccadilly, London W1V 0DS
tel 0171-300 8001 *fax* 0171-300 8000
web site http://www.royalacademy.org.uk
President Sir Philip Dowson CBE, *Keeper* Leonard McComb RA, *Treasurer* Michael Kenny RA, *Secretary* David Gordon

Academicians (RA) are elected from the most distinguished artists in the UK. Major loan exhibitions throughout the year with the Annual Summer Exhibition, June to August. Also runs art schools for 60 post-graduate students in painting and sculpture.

The Royal Literary Fund
144 Temple Chambers, Temple Avenue, London EC4Y 0DA
tel 0171-353 7150
President His Honour Sir Stephen Tumim, *Secretary* Fiona Clark

Founded in 1790, the Fund is the oldest and largest charity serving literature, set up to help writers and their families who face hardship. It does not offer grants to writers who can earn their living in other ways, nor does it provide financial support for writing projects. But it sustains authors who have for one reason or another fallen on hard times – illness, family misfortune, or sheer loss of writing form. Applicants must have published work of approved literary merit, which may include important contributions to periodicals. The literary claim of every new applicant must be accepted by the General Committee before the question of need can be considered.

The Royal Society
6 Carlton House Terrace, London SW1Y 5AG
tel 0171-839 5561 *fax* 0171-930 2170

President Sir Aaron Klug OM, FRS, *Treasurer* Sir Eric Ash CBE, FRS, *Biological Secretary* Prof P. Lachmann FRS, *Physical Secretary* Prof J.S. Rowlinson F.Eng, FRS, *Foreign Secretary* Prof B. Heap CBE, FRS, *Executive Secretary* Mr S. Cox CVO Promotion of the natural sciences (pure and applied). Founded 1660.

The Ruskin Society of London

Hon. Secretary Miss O.E. Forbes-Madden, 351 Woodstock Road, Oxford OX2 7NX
tel (01865) 310987/515962
To promote literary and biographical interest in John Ruskin and his contemporaries. The Society issues an annual *Ruskin Gazette* free to members. Annual subscription: £10. Founded 1985.

The Dorothy L. Sayers Society

Chairman Christopher J. Dean, Rose Cottage, Malthouse Lane, Hurstpierpoint, West Sussex BN6 9JY
tel (01273) 833444 *fax* (01273) 835988
web site http://www.sayers.org.uk/
Secretaries Lenelle Davis, Jasmine Simeone
To promote and encourage the study of the works of Dorothy L. Sayers; to collect relics and reminiscences about her and make them available to students and biographers; to hold an annual seminar and other meetings; to publish proceedings, pamphlets and a bi-monthly bulletin. Annual subscription: £12. Founded 1976.

Science Fiction Association Ltd, The British

President Arthur C. Clarke
Membership Secretary Paul Billinger, 1 Long Row Close, Everdon, Daventry, Northants. NN11 3BE
e-mail bsfa@enterprise.net
For authors, publishers, booksellers and readers of science fiction, fantasy and allied genres. Publishes *Matrix*, an informal magazine of news and information; *Focus*, an amateur writers' magazine; *Vector*, a critical magazine and The Orbiter Service, a network of postal writers workshops. Founded 1958.

Science Writers, Association of British

c/o British Association for the Advancement of Science, 23 Savile Row, London W1X 2NB
tel 0171-439 1205 *fax* 0171-973 3051
e-mail absw@absw-demon.co.uk
Chairman Richard Stevenson, *Administrator* Barbara Drillsma
Association of science writers, editors, and radio, film and TV producers concerned

with the presentation and communication of science, technology and medicine. Aims to improve the standard of science writing and to assist its members in their work.

Scientific and Technical Communicators, The Institute of

Blackhorse Road, Letchworth, Herts SG6 1YY
tel (01462) 486825 *fax* (01462) 483480
e-mail istc@istc.org.uk
web site http://www.istc.org.uk
President Gerry Gentle, *Secretary* Peter Lightfoot
Professional body for those engaged in the communication of scientific and technical information. Aims to establish and maintain professional standards, to encourage and co-operate in professional training and to provide a source of information on, and to encourage research and development in, all aspects of scientific and technical communication. Publishes *The Communicator* (4 p.a.), the official journal of the Institute. Founded 1972.

Scottish Academy, Royal

The Mound, Edinburgh EH2 2EL
tel 0131-225 6671 *fax* 0131-225 2349
President William J.L. Baillie CBE, PRSA, *Secretary* Ian McKenzie Smith OBE, RSA, *Treasurer* James Morris RSA
Academicians (RSA) and Associates (ARSA) and non-members may exhibit in the Annual Exhibition of Painting, Sculpture and Architecture, held approximately mid April to July; Festival Exhibition August/October. Other artists' societies' annual exhibitions, normally between October and January. Royal Scottish Academy Student Competition held in March. Founded 1826.

Scottish Arts

24 Rutland Square, Edinburgh EH1 2BW
tel 0131-229 1076
Hon. Secretary Colin J.M. Sutherland
tel 0131-229 8157
Art, literature, music. Annual subscription: £275 (full); reductions available.

Scottish Arts Council

12 Manor Place, Edinburgh EH3 7DD
tel 0131-226 6051
Chairman Magnus Linklater, *Director* Seona Reid, *Literature Director* Jenny Brown, *Visual Arts Director* Susan Daniel-McElroy
Principal channel for government funding of the arts in Scotland, the Scottish

Arts Council is funded by the Scottish Office. It aims to develop and improve the knowledge, understanding and practice of the arts, and to increase their accessibility throughout Scotland. It offers about 1300 grants a year to artists and arts organisations concerned with the visual arts, drama, dance and mime, literature, music, festivals, and traditional, ethnic and community arts. It is also the distributor of National Lottery funds to the arts in Scotland.

Scottish Book Marketing Group

Scottish Book Centre, 137 Dundee Street, Edinburgh EH11 1BG
tel 0131-228 6866 *fax* 0131-228 3220
e-mail enquiries@scottishbooks.org
Co-ordinator Allan Shanks

Co-operative venture set up by the Scottish Publishers Association and the Booksellers Association (Scottish Branch) which aims to promote Scottish books through member booksellers. Founded 1986.

Scottish Daily Newspaper Society

48 Palmerston Place, Edinburgh EH12 5DE
tel 0131-220 4353 *fax* 0131-220 4344
Director J.B. Raeburn FCIS

Scottish History Society

Dept of Scottish History, University of Edinburgh, 17 Buccleuch Place, Edinburgh EH8 9LN
tel 0131-650 4035
Hon. Secretary Steve Boardman PhD

The Society exists to publish documents illustrating the history of Scotland. Founded 1886.

Scottish Literary Studies, Association for (ASLS)

c/o Dept of Scottish History, 9 University Gardens, University of Glasgow G12 8QH
tel 0141-330 5309
e-mail cmc@arts.gla.ac.uk
Hon. President Dorothy McMillan, *Hon. Secretary* Jim Alison, *Hon. Treasurer* Dr Elaine Petrie, *Publishing Manager* Catherine McInerney

Promotes the study, teaching and writing of Scottish literature and furthers the study of the languages of Scotland. Publishes annually an edited text of Scottish literature, an anthology of new Scottish writing and a series of academic journals, and a twice-yearly Newsletter and a schools supplement. Also publishes *Scotnotes* – comprehensive study guides to major Scottish writers, and literary texts and commentary cassettes designed to assist the classroom teacher, and a series of occasional papers. The ASLS organises 3 conferences a year. Annual membership: individuals/schools £33, UK students £19, corporate £61. Founded 1970.

Scottish Newspaper Publishers' Association

48 Palmerston Place, Edinburgh EH12 5DE
tel 0131-220 4353 *fax* 0131-220 4344
President A. Lumsden
Director J.B. Raeburn FCIS

Scottish Publishers Association

Scottish Book Centre, 137 Dundee Street, Edinburgh EH11 1BG
tel 0131-228 6866 *fax* 0131-228 3220
e-mail enquiries@scottishbooks.org
web site http://www.scottishbooks.org
Director Lorraine Fannin, *Administrator* Davinder Bedi, *Marketing Manager* Alison Rae, *Scottish Book Marketing Group/Training* Allan Shanks

Founded 1973.

Screenwriters' Workshop, London

114 Whitfield Street, London W1P 5RW
tel 0171-387 5511
web site http://www.lsw.org.uk
Contact Alan Denman, Paul Gallagher

Forum for contact, information and tuition, the LSW helps new and established writers work successfully in the film and TV industry, and organises a continuous programme of activities, events, courses and seminars, many of which are free/reduced to members and open to non-members at reasonable rates. LSW is the largest screenwriting group in Europe and supports Euroscript, a Media II-funded organisation developing scripts for film and TV throughout the EU. Annual subscription: £30. Founded 1983.

SCRIBO

Contact K. & P. Sylvester, Flat 1, 31 Hamilton Road, Bournemouth BH1 4EQ

A postal forum for novelists (published and unpublished), SCRIBO aims to give friendly, informed encouragement and help, to discuss all matters of interest to novelists and to offer criticism via MSS folios: crime/thrillers, fantasy/sci-fi, mainstream, aga-saga/popular women's fiction, 2 literary folios (mostly graduates writing serious fiction). Porn is not accepted. No subscription but a £5 joining fee is required. Founded 1971.

Sculptors, Royal Society of British (RBS)
108 Old Brompton Road, London SW7 3RA
tel 0171-373 8615 or 0171-244 8431
fax 0171-370 3721
President John W. Mills

Established to promote and advance the art and practice of sculpture,the RBS is now assisted in its endeavours by The Sculpture Company, its commissioning and event management arm. The Sculpture Company has a resource centre to assist corporate, municipal or private patrons to commission or purchase sculpture. The Sculpture Company also organises exhibitions, lectures and awards on behalf of the RBS and supports the RBS education policy and *Sculpture*, the RBS publication. Founded 1904.

The Shaw Society
Secretary Barbara Smoker, 51 Farmfield Road, Downham, Bromley, Kent BR1 4NF
tel 0181-697 3619

Improvement and diffusion of knowledge of the life and works of Bernard Shaw and his circle. Meetings in London; annual festival at Ayot St Lawrence in July; publishes *The Shavian*. Annual membership: £10/$20.

Society of Authors – see Authors, The Society of, and page 504

Songwriters & Composers, The Guild of International
Sovereign House, 12 Trewartha Road, Praa Sands, Penzance, Cornwall TR20 9ST
tel (01736) 762826 *fax* (01736) 763328
e-mail songmag@aol.com
web site http://www.icn.co.uk/gisc.html
Secretary Carole Ann Jones

Gives advice to members on contractual and copyright matters; assists with protection of members rights; assists with analysis of members' works; international collaboration register free to members; outlines requirements to record companies, publishers, artists. Publishes *Songwriting & Composing* (quarterly). Annual subscription: £38 (UK), £50 (EU/overseas).

Songwriters, Composers and Authors, British Academy of – see BASCA

South Africa, Publishers' Association of (PASA)
PO Box 116, St James, 7946 Cape Town, South Africa
tel (021) 788-6470 *fax* (021) 788-6469
e-mail pasa@icon.co.za

South African Writers' Circle
Secretary Pat Lister, PO Box 10558, Marine Parade, Durban 4056, South Africa
tel (031) 251-769

Aims to help and encourage all writers, new and experienced, in the art of writing. Publishes a monthly *Newsletter*, and runs competitions with prizes for the winners. Annual subscription: R60 (local), R90 (overseas). Founded 1960.

Southwest Scriptwriters
149 St Andrew's Road, Montpelier, Bristol BS6 5EL
tel 0117-944 5424 *fax* 0117-944 5413
e-mail 100621.2037@compuserve.com
Secretary John Colborn

Aims to promote the work of people writing for the stage, screen, radio and TV in the region. The group focuses on script development through workshop sessions and rehearsed readings, supported by talks on scriptwriting technique and visits from established writers. Provides a friendly, informal forum where dramatists can meet and discuss their work. Newsletter subscription £5 p.a. Founded 1994.

Spanish Publishers' Association, Federation of
(Federación de Gremios de Editores de España)
Juan Ramón Jiménez 45 9° Izda., 28036 Madrid, Spain
tel 350 91 05/03 *fax* 345 43 51
President Juan Isasa, *Secretary* Ana Moltó Blasco

SPREd (Society of Picture Researchers and Editors) – see The Picture Research Association

Stationers and Newspaper Makers, Worshipful Company of
Stationers' Hall, London EC4M 7DD
tel 0171-248 2934 *fax* 0171-489 1975
Master Vernon F. Sullivan, *Clerk* Brig. Denzil Sharp, AFC

One of the Livery Companies of the City of London. Connected with the printing, publishing, bookselling, newspaper and allied trades. Operates a Registry for those requiring proof of ownership of copyright. Written works or those on tape, record, video or computer disk can be registered. Founded 1557.

Strip Illustration, Society for – now Comics Creators Guild

Sussex Authors, The Society of
Secretary Michael Legat, Bookends, Lewes Road, Horsted Keynes, Haywards Heath, West Sussex RH17 7DP
tel/fax (01825) 790755

Aims to encourage social contact between members, and to promote interest in literature and authors. Membership open to writers living in Sussex who have had at least one book commercially published or who have worked extensively in journalism, radio, TV or the theatre. Annual subscription: £10. Founded 1969.

Sussex Playwrights' Club
Hon. Secretary, Sussex Playwrights' Club, 2 Princes Avenue, Hove, East Sussex BN3 4GD

Members' plays are read by local actors before an audience of Club members. The Club from time to time sponsors productions of members' plays by local drama companies. Non-writing members welcome. Founded 1935.

Swedish Publishers' Association
(Svenska Förläggareföreningen)
Drottninggatan 97, 2 tr., 113 60 Stockholm, Sweden
tel 08-736 19 40 *fax* 08-736 19 44
Director Kristina Ahlinder
Founded 1843.

Television Society, Royal
Holborn Hall, 100 Gray's Inn Road, London WC1X 8AL
tel 0171-430 1000 *fax* 0171-430 0924
Executive Director Michael Bunce, *Membership Secretary* Bonnie Gray

The Society is a unique, central, independent forum to debate the art, science and politics of TV. Holds awards, conferences, dinners, lectures and workshops. Annual membership: £57. Founded 1927.

The Tennyson Society
Secretary Kathleen Jefferson, Brayford House, Lucy Tower Street, Lincoln LN1 1XN
tel (01522) 552851 *fax* (01522) 552858
e-mail lincs.lib@dial.pipex.com

Promotes the study and understanding of the life and work of the poet Alfred, Lord Tennyson and supports the Tennyson Research Centre in Lincoln; holds lectures, visits and seminars; publishes the *Tennyson Research Bulletin* (annual), Monographs and Occasional Papers; tapes/recordings available. Annual membership: £8, family £10, institutions £15. Founded 1960.

Theatre Exchange, International
Secretariat 19 Abbey Park Road, Grimsby DN32 0HJ
tel (01472) 343424

To encourage, foster and promote exchanges of theatre; student, educational, adult, puppet theatre activities at international level. To organise international seminars, workshops, courses and conferences, and to collect and collate information of all types for national and international dissemination.

Theatre Research, The Society for
c/o The Theatre Museum, 1E Tavistock Street, London WC2E 7PA
Hon. Secretaries Eileen Cottis and Frances Dann

Publishes annual volumes and journal, *Theatre Notebook*, holds lectures, runs enquiry service and makes annual research grants (current total sum approx. £4000). Starting in 1998, the Society's 50th anniversary, it will award an annual prize, initially £400, for the best book published in English on the historical or current practice of the British theatre.

Theatre Writers' Union – incorporated into The Writers' Guild of Great Britain

Angela Thirkell Society
Chairman Mrs J.E. Self, Mayfair, Hamstreet Road, Shadoxhurst, Ashford, Kent TN26 1NL
tel (01233) 733445
Secretary Mrs I.J. Cox, 32 Murvagh Close, Cheltenham, Glos. GL53 7QY
tel (01242) 251604

Aims 'to honour the memory of Angela Thirkell (1890-1960) as a writer, and to make her works available to new generations'. Publishes an *Annual Journal*, and encourages Thirkell studies. Annual membership: £5. Founded 1980.

The Edward Thomas Fellowship
Butler's Cottage, Halswell House, Goathurst, Nr Bridgwater, Somerset TA5 2DH

tel (01278) 662856
Hon. Secretary Richard N. Emeny

To perpetuate the memory of Edward Thomas, poet and writer, foster an interest in his life and work, to assist in the preservation of places associated with him and to arrange events which extend fellowship amongst his admirers. Annual subscription: £5. Founded 1980.

The Tolkien Society
Secretary Sally Kennett, 210 Prestbury Road, Cheltenham, Glos. GL52 3ER
Membership Secretary Trevor Reynolds, Caer Las, 16 Gibsons Green, Heelands, Milton Keynes MK13 7NH
e-mail trevor@caerlas.demon.co.uk
web site http://www.tolkiensociety.org

Dedicated to promoting research into and educating the public in the life and works of Prof J.R.R. Tolkien. Annual subscription: UK £15; overseas rates on application. Founded 1969.

Translation & Interpreting, The Institute of (ITI)
Contact The Secretary, 377 City Road, London EC1V 1NA
tel 0171-713 7600 *fax* 0171-713 7650
e-mail iti@compuserve.com
web site http://www.iti.org.uk

The ITI is a professional association of translators and interpreters which aims to promote the highest standards in translating and interpreting. It has a strong corporate membership and runs professional development courses and conferences, sometimes in conjunction with its language, regional and subject networks. Membership is open to those with a genuine and proven involvement in translation and interpreting. As a full and active member of the International Federation of Translators, it maintains good contacts with translators and interpreters worldwide. ITI's directory of members and its bi-monthly bulletin are available from the Secretariat.

The Translators Association
84 Drayton Gardens, London SW10 9SB
tel 0171-373 6642

Specialist unit within the membership of the Society of Authors (see page 504), exclusively concerned with the interests and special problems of translators into English whose work is published or per-

formed commercially in Great Britain and English-speaking countries overseas. Members (and Associate Members who have received an offer for publication) are entitled to general and legal advice on all questions connected with their work, including remuneration and contractual arrangements with publishers, editors, broadcasting organisations. Administers a range of translation prizes (see page 536). Annual subscription: £65 by direct debit, £70 by cheque – includes membership of the Society of Authors. Founded 1958.

Travel Writers, The British Guild of
Hon. Secretary Brenda Birmingham, 45 Priory Avenue, London W4 1TZ

Arranges meetings, discussions and visits for its 170 members (who are all professional travel journalists) to help them encourage the public's interest in travel. Publishes a monthly newsletter (for members only) and an annual *Yearbook*, which contains details of members and lists travel industry PRs and contacts.

The Trollope Society
9A North Street, London SW4 0HN
tel 0171-720 6789
e-mail hvn@cix.compulink.co.uk
Chairman John Letts

Aims to produce the first ever complete edition of the novels of Anthony Trollope (36 vols now available). Membership: £24 p.a., £240 (life). Founded 1987.

The Turner Society
BCM Box Turner, London WC1N 3XX
Chairman Evelyn Joll

To foster a wider appreciation of all facets of Turner's work; to encourage exhibitions of his paintings, drawings and engravings. Publishes *Turner Society News* (3 p.a.). Annual subscription: £10; other rates on application. Founded 1975.

Typographic Designers, Society of
President John Harrison FSTD, *Chair* David Quay FSTD/Freda Sack FSTD
Hon. Secretary Helen Cornish, Chapelfield Cottage, Randwick, Stroud, Glos. GL6 6HS
tel (01453) 759311 *fax* (01453) 759311

Advises and acts on matters of professional practice, provides a better understanding of the typographic craft and the rapidly changing technology in the graphic industries by lectures, discussions and through the journal *Typographic* and the Newsletter. Typographic students are encouraged to gain Licentiate membership of the Society, by entering the annual student assessment project. Founded 1928.

Undeb Awduron Cymru
(Union of Welsh Writers)
Cil-y-waun, Salem, Llandeilo, Caerfyrddin
tel (01558) 822718

Aims to provide practical and inspirational help to writers in the Welsh language. Produces a newsletter/magazine (3 p.a.); meets at Aberystwyth (2 or 3 p.a.) and annually at the National Eisteddfod. Annual subscription: £10. Founded 1975.

Ver Poets
Organiser/Editor May Badman, Haycroft,
61-63 Chiswell Green Lane, St Albans,
Herts. AL2 3AL
tel (01727) 867005

Encourages the writing and study of poetry as a part of our culture. Help and advice, assessment and comment on work are available on request. Holds meetings (fortnightly) in St Albans; organises workshops and competitions for members, and produces anthologies of members' work. The annual Open Competition is also open to non-members. Annual membership: £10 UK, £12.50 ($25) overseas. Founded 1966.

Visiting Arts
11 Portland Place, London W1N 4EJ
tel 0171-389 3019 *fax* 0171-389 3016
e-mail office@visitingarts.demon.co.uk
web site http://www.britcoun.org/visitingarts/
Director Terry Sandell OBE

A joint venture of the 4 UK arts councils, the Crafts Council, the Foreign Office and the British Council. It promotes and facilitates the flow of foreign arts into the UK in the context of the contribution they can make to cultural relations, cultural awareness, and fostering mutually beneficial international arts contacts and activities at national, regional, local and institutional levels. Founded 1977.

Visual Communication Association, International (IVCA)
Bolsover House, 5-6 Clipstone Street,
London W1P 8LD
tel 0171-580 0962 *fax* 0171-436 2606
e-mail info@ivca.org

web site http://www.ivca.org
Membership Secretary Nick Gardiner

For those who use or supply visual communication. Aims to promote the industry and provide a collective voice; provides a range of services, publications and events to help existing and potential users to make the most of what video, film, multimedia and live events can offer their business. Annual membership: from £165. Founded 1987.

Voice of the Listener & Viewer (VLV)
101 King's Drive, Gravesend, Kent DA12 5BQ
tel (01474) 352835
Chairman Jocelyn Hay, *Administrative Secretary* Linda Forbes

Independent association representing the citizen's voice in broadcasting and the interests of listeners and viewers on all broadcasting issues. Concerned to maintain the principle of public service plus independence, quality and diversity in British broadcasting. Has over 2000 individual members, 20 charities as corporate members and more than 50 colleges in academic membership. Holds frequent public conferences. Publishes a quarterly newsletter and briefings on broadcasting developments. Founded 1983.

Wales, Arts Council of – see Arts Council of Wales

Edgar Wallace Society
Kohlbergsgracht 40, NL-6462 CD Kerkrade,
The Netherlands
tel (045) 5670070 *fax* (045) 5670060
Organiser Kai Jörg Hinz

To promote an interest in the life and work of Edgar Wallace through the *Crimson Circle* magazine (quarterly). Annual subscription: Europe £15 (students/senior citizens £10), rest of world £20 (students/senior citizens £15). Founded 1969.

The Walmsley Society
Secretary Fred Lane, April Cottage,
1 Brand Road, Hampden Park, Eastbourne,
East Sussex BN22 9PX
Membership Secretary Mrs Elizabeth Buckley,
21 The Crescent, Hipperholm, Halifax,
West Yorkshire HX3 8NQ

Aims to promote and encourage an appreciation of the literary and artistic heritage left to us by Leo and J. Ulric Walmsley. Founded 1985.

Water Colours, Royal Institute of Painters in

17 Carlton House Terrace, London SW1Y 5BD
tel 0171-930 6844 *fax* 0171-839 7830
President Ronald Maddox Hon. RWS

The Institute promotes the appreciation of watercolour painting in its traditional and contemporary forms, primarily by means of an annual exhibition at the Mall Galleries, London SW1 of members' and non-members' work and also by members' exhibitions at selected venues in Britain and abroad. Members elected from approved candidates' list. Founded 1831.

Watercolour Society, British

Director Leslie Simpson, Briargate,
2 The Brambles, Ilkley,
West Yorkshire LS29 9DH
tel (01943) 609075

Promotes the best in traditional watercolour painting. Holds 2 open exhibitions p.a. Membership by selection. Founded 1830.

Watercolour Society, Royal

Bankside Gallery, 48 Hopton Street,
London SE1 9JH
tel 0171-928 7521
e-mail re&rws@bankside-gallery.demon.co.uk
President John Doyle MBE

Membership (RWS) open to British and overseas artists. An election of Associates is held annually, and applications for the necessary forms and particulars should be addressed to the Secretary. The Society gives lectures on watercolour paintings; organises residential/non-residential course; holds open exhibition in summer. Exhibitions: spring and autumn. Friends of the RWS open to all those interested in watercolour painting. Founded 1804.

Mary Webb Society

Secretary Mary Palmer, 15 Melbourne Rise,
Gains Park, Shrewsbury SY3 5DA
tel (01743) 271278

For devotees of the literature and works of Mary Webb and of the beautiful countryside of her novels. Publishes annual journal in September, organises summer schools in various locations related to Webb's life and works. Archives, lectures; tours arranged for individuals and groups. Founded 1972.

The H.G. Wells Society

Hon. General Secretary J.R. Hammond,
49 Beckingthorpe Drive, Bottesford,
Nottingham NG13 0DN

Promotes an active interest in and an appreciation of the life, work and thought of H.G. Wells. Publishes *The Wellsian* (annual) and *The Newsletter* (bi-annual). Annual subscription £14, corporate £20. Founded 1960.

Welsh Books Council/Cyngor Llyfrau Cymru

Castell Brychan, Aberystwyth, Ceredigion SY23 2JB
tel (01970) 624151 *fax* (01970) 625385
e-mail castellbrychan@cllc.org.uk
Director Gwerfyl Pierce Jones

Founded in 1961 to promote Welsh-language and English-language books of Welsh interest. Editorial, design, marketing, distribution and children's books promotion services provided for publishers.

Welsh Union of Writers

Secretary John Harrison, 4 Teilo Street,
Pontcanna, Cardiff CF1 9JN
tel (01222) 640041
e-mail wuw@btinternet.com
web site http://info.cf.ac.uk/ccin/wuw/wuw
home.html

Independent union open to persons born or working in Wales with at least one publication in a quality outlet, fiction, non-fiction or poetry. Lobbies for writing in Wales; represents members in disputes; annual conference; occasional events and publications. Annual subscription: £10 plus £5 joining fee. Associate membership now available for others with a committed interest in writing: £5 plus £5 joining fee. Founded 1982.

Welsh Writers, Union of – see Undeb Awduron Cymru

The West Country Writers' Association

President Christopher Fry FRSL, DLitt, *Chair* Frances Brown
Hon. Secretary Anne Double, Malvern View,
Garway Hill, Orcop, Hereford HR2 8EZ
tel/fax (01981) 580495

To foster love of literature in the West Country and to give authors an opportunity of meeting to exchange news and views. Holds Annual Weekend Congress and Regional Meetings. Newsletter (2 p.a.). Membership open to published authors. Annual subscription: £10.

West of England Academy, Royal

Queens Road, Clifton, Bristol BS8 1PX
tel 0117-973 5129 *fax* 0117-923 7874
President Peter Thursby PRWA, FRBS, *Academy Secretary* Rachel Fear

Aims to further the interests of practising painters and sculptors. Holds art exhibitions and is a meeting place for artists and their work. Founded 1844.

The Oscar Wilde Society

154 Derwent Road, Leighton Buzzard,
Beds. LU7 7XT
tel (01525) 851481
Secretary Rosemary McGlashon

To promote knowledge, appreciation and study of the life, personality and works of the writer and wit Oscar Wilde. Activities include exhibitions, readings, meetings and lectures. Members receive *The Wildean* journal (bi-annual), and a Newsletter (6 p.a.). Annual membership: £13 (UK), £15 (Europe), £20 (elsewhere); student/unwaged £11; household £18. Founded 1990.

Wildlife Artists, Society of

17 Carlton House Terrace,
London SW1Y 5BD
tel 0171-930 6844 *fax* 0171-839 7830
President Bruce Pearson

To promote and encourage the art of wildlife painting and sculpture. Open Annual Exhibition at the Mall Galleries, The Mall, London SW1.

Charles Williams Society

26 Village Road, London N3 1TL
Secretary Gillian Lunn

To promote interest in the life and work of Charles Walter Stansby Williams (1886-1945) and to make his writings more easily available. Founded 1975.

The Henry Williamson Society

Chairman Will Harris
General Secretary/Membership Secretary
Mrs Margaret Murphy, 16 Doran Drive, Redhill, Surrey RH1 6AX
tel (01737) 763228

Aims to encourage a wider readership and greater understanding of the literary heritage left by Henry Williamson. Two meetings annually; also weekend activities. Publishes an annual journal. Annual subscription: £8.00; family, student and overseas rates available. Founded 1980.

Women Artists, The Society of

Executive Secretary 1 Knapp Cottages, Wyke, Gillingham, Dorset SP8 4NQ
tel (01747) 825718 *fax* (01747) 826835
web site http://www.nal.vam.ac.uk/
President Prof Barbara Tate

Annual exhibition for painting and sculpture, open to all women, held just before Easter at the Westminster Gallery, Westminster Central Hall, London SW1H 9NU. Founded 1855.

Women in Publishing

c/o The Publishers Association, 1 Kingsway, London WC2B 6XF
web site http://www.cyberiacafe.net/wip/

Promotes the status of women within publishing; encourages networking and mutual support among women; provides a forum for the discussion of ideas, trends and subjects to women in the trade; offers practical training for career and personal development; supports and publicises women's achievements and successes. Annual subscription: £20. Founded 1977.

Women Writers and Journalists, Society of

Secretary Jean Hawkes, 110 Whitehall Road, London E4 6DW
tel 0181-529 0886

For women writers: lectures, monthly lunchtime meetings; free literary advice for members. *The Woman Journalist* (3 p.a.). Annual subscription: town £25, country £21, overseas £15; joining fee £10. Founded 1894.

Women Writers Network

Membership Secretary Cathy Smith,
23 Prospect Road, London NW2 2JU
tel 0171-794 5861

London-based network serving both salaried and independent women writers from all disciplines, and providing a forum for the exchange of information, support and networking opportunities. Holds monthly meetings, workshops and publishes a newsletter and members' Directory. Send A5 or A4 sae for information. Annual membership: £30. Meetings only: £5 at door. Founded 1985.

Worker Writers and Community Publishers, The Federation of

Box 540, Burslem, Stoke-on-Tent ST6 6DR
tel/fax (01782) 822327
e-mail fwwcp@mcmail.com

web site http://www.fwwcp.mcmail.com
A network of writers groups and community publishers which promotes working-
class writing and publishing. Annual
membership: funded groups £40;
unfunded £20. Founded 1976.

Writers' Circles

Contact Jill Dick, Oldacre, Horderns Park Road,
Chapel-en-le-Frith, High Peak SK23 9SY
tel (01298) 812305
e-mail jillie@cix.compulink.co.uk
web site http://www.cix.co.uk/~oldacre
The *Directory of Writers' Circles*, containing addresses of over 600 writers' circles,
guilds, workshops, literary clubs, societies and organisations, is published regularly. Copies of the 8th edition (£5 post
free) are available from the compiler/edi-
tor, Jill Dick.

Writers' Groups, National Association of

The Arts Centre, Biddick Lane, Washington,
Tyne and Wear NE38 8AB
tel 0191-416 9751 *fax* 0191-431 1263
Secretary Brian Lister
Aims 'to advance the education of the
general public throughout the UK,
including the Channel Islands, by promoting the study and art of writing in all
its aspects.' Annual membership: £16 per
group. Founded 1995.

Writers Guild of America, East Inc. (WGAE)

Executive Director Mona Mangan,
555 West 57 Street, Suite 1230, New York,
NY 10019, USA
tel 212-767-7800
Represents writers in screen and TV for
collective bargaining. It oversees member
services (pension and health) as well as
educational and professional activities.
Annual membership: 1.5% of covered
earnings. Founded 1954.

Writers Guild of America, West Inc. (WGA)

Executive Director Brian Walton,
7000 West 3rd Street, Los Angeles, CA 90048,
USA
tel 213-951-4000 *fax* 213-782-4800
web site http://www.@wga.org
Union representing and servicing 9000
writers in film, broadcast, cable and multimedia industries for purposes of collective bargaining, contract administration
and other services, and functions to pro-

tect and advance the economic, professional and creative interests of writers.
Monthly publication, *Written by*, available by subscription. Membership: initia-
tion $2500, quarterly $25, annually 1.5%
of income. Founded 1933.

The Writers' Guild of Great Britain

(incorporating the Theatre Writers' Union)
430 Edgware Road, London W2 1EH
tel 0171-723 8074 *fax* 0171-706 2413
e-mail postie@wggb.demon.co.uk
web site http://www.writers.org.uk/guild
General Secretary Alison V. Gray
Founded in 1959 as the Screenwriters'
Guild, now a trade union affiliated to the
TUC, representing writers' interests in
film, radio, TV, theatre and publishing. Its
scope extends into all areas of freelance
writing and copyright protection and,
where necessary, discusses at Government
level policies on legislative matters affecting writers. The Guild's basic function is
to negotiate minimum terms in those
areas in which its members work. The
Guild, by constitution non-political,
employs a permanent secretariat and staff
and is administered by an Executive
Council of 26 members. There are also
Regional/Branch Committees representing
Scotland, Wales, and all the English
regions. See also page 506.

Writers in Oxford

41 Kingston Road, Oxford OX2 6RH
tel (01865) 513844 *fax* (01865) 510017
Membership Secretary Elizabeth Newbery,
3 North Street, Oxford OX2 0AY
To promote valuable discussion and
social meetings among all kinds of professional writers in and around
Oxfordshire. Activities include: topical
lunches and dinners, where subjects
important to the writer are discussed;
showcase evenings; parties. Quarterly
newsletter, *The Oxford Writer*. Annual
subscription: £15. Founded 1992.

Writers' Postal Workshops and Folios

Compiler Catherine M. Gill, Drakemyre Croft,
Cairnorrie, Methlick, Ellon,
Aberdeenshire AB41 7JN
Writers' postal workshops and folios provide criticism, guidance, encouragement
and support to both published and
unpublished writers and enable regular
contact to be made by post with others of

similar interests. *The Cottage Guide to Writers' Postal Workshops* contains full details of postal workshops, folios and similar organisations and is published and updated regularly by Croftspun Publications. Price £2 post free from the compiler.

Yachting Journalists' Association
3 Friars Lane, Maldon, Essex CM9 6AG
tel (01621) 855943 *fax* (01621) 852212
Secretary Peter Cook
Aims to further the interests of yachting, sail and power, and yachting journalism. Organises the annual Yachtsman of the Year Awards, currently sponsored by BT. Membership: £30 p.a. Founded 1969.

The Yorkshire Dialect Society
Hon. Secretary Michael Park, 51 Stepney Avenue, Scarborough YO12 5BW
Aims to encourage interest in: dialect speech, the writing of dialect verse, prose and drama; the publication and circulation of dialect literature; the study of the origins and the history of dialect and kindred subjects. Organises meetings; publishes *Transactions* (annual) and *The Summer Bulletin* free to members; list of other publications on

request. Annual subscription: £6. Founded 1897.

Young Book Trust – see Book Trust

Young Publishers, Society of
Contact The Secretary, c/o 12 Dyott Street, London WC1A 1DF
Provides a lively forum for discussion on subjects relevant to its members in publishing. Membership open to anyone employed in publishing, printing, bookselling or allied trades with associate membership available to those over 35. Meetings held at the Publishers Association, usually on the last Wednesday of the month at 6.30pm The SYP also organises social and other events. Please enclose an sae when writing. Founded 1949.

Francis Brett Young Society
Secretary Mrs J. Willcox, 48 Meadow Croft, Hagley, Stourbridge, West Midlands DY9 0LJ
tel (01562) 887255
To provide opportunities for members to meet, correspond, and to share the enjoyment of the author's works. Journal published 2 p.a. Annual subscription: £7 (individual), life membership £70 (other rates on application). Founded 1979.

The Society of Authors

The Society of Authors is an independent trade union, representing writers' interests in all aspects of the writing profession, including publishing, broadcasting, television and films, theatre and translation.

Founded over 100 years ago by Walter Besant, the Society now has more than 6000 members. It has a professional staff, responsible to a Management Committee of 12 authors, and a Council (an advisory body meeting twice a year) consisting of 60 eminent writers. There are specialist groups within the Society to serve the particular needs of broadcasters, literary translators, educational writers, medical writers and children's writers and illustrators. There are also regional groups representing Scotland, the North of England and the Isle of Man.

'When we begin working, we are so poor and so busy that we have neither the time nor the means to defend ourselves against the commercial organisations which exploit us. When we become famous, we become famous suddenly, passing at one bound from the state in which we are, as I have said, too poor to fight our own battles, to a state in which our time is so valuable that it is not worth our while wasting any of it on lawsuits and bad debts. We all, eminent and obscure alike, need the Authors' Society. We all owe it a share of our time, our means, our influence'
– Bernard Shaw

What the Society does for members

Through its permanent staff (including a solicitor), the Society is able to give its members a comprehensive personal and professional service covering the business aspects of authorship, including:
• providing information about agents, publishers, and others concerned with the book trade, journalism, broadcasting and the performing arts;
• advising on negotiations, including the individual vetting of contracts, clause by clause, and assessing their terms both financial and otherwise;
• taking up complaints on behalf of members on any issue concerned with the business of authorship;
• pursuing legal actions for breach of contract, copyright infringement, and the non-payment of royalties and fees, when the risk and cost preclude individual action by a member and issues of general concern to the profession are at stake;

• holding conferences, seminars, meetings and social occasions;
• producing a comprehensive range of publications, free of charge to members, including the Society's quarterly journal, *The Author. Quick Guides* cover many aspects of the profession such as: copyright, publishing contracts, libel, income tax, VAT, authors' agents, permissions, indexing, and the protection of titles. The Society also publishes occasional papers on subjects such as film agreements, packaged books, revised editions, multimedia, and vanity publishing.

Membership benefits

Members have access to:
• the Retirement Benefit Scheme;
• a group Medical Insurance Scheme with BUPA;
• the Pension Fund (which offers discretionary pensions to a number of members);
• the Contingency Fund (which provides

financial relief for authors or their dependents in sudden financial difficulties);
- automatic free membership of the Authors' Licensing and Collecting Society (ALCS);
- books at special rates;
- membership of the Royal Over-Seas League at a discount;
- use of the Society's photocopying machine at special rates.

The Society frequently secures improved conditions and better returns for members. It is common for members to report that, through the help and facilities offered, they have saved more, and sometimes substantially more, than their annual subscriptions (which are an allowable expense against income tax).

What the Society does for authors

The Society lobbies Members of Parliament, Ministers and Government Departments on all issues of concern to writers. Recent issues have included the operation and funding of Public Lending Right, the threat of VAT on books, copyright legislation and European Community initiatives. Concessions have also been obtained under various Finance Acts.

The Society litigates in matters of importance to authors. For example, the Society backed Andrew Boyle when he won his appeal against the Inland Revenue's attempt to tax the Whitbread Award.

The Society campaigns for better terms for writers. With the Writers' Guild, it has negotiated agreements with BBC Publications, Bloomsbury, Bodley Head, Jonathan Cape, Century, André Deutsch, Faber & Faber, Hamish Hamilton, HarperCollins, Hodder Headline, Hutchinson, Michael Joseph, Methuen, Penguin Books, Sinclair-Stevenson, Transworld and Viking. Other publishers are now being approached, and the campaign is active. The translators' section of the Society has also drawn up a minimum terms agreement for translators which has been adopted by Faber & Faber, and has been used on an individual basis by a number of other publishers.

The Society is recognised by the BBC for the purpose of negotiating rates for writers' contributions to radio drama, as well as for the broadcasting of published material. It was instrumental in setting up the Authors' Licensing and Collecting Society (ALCS), which collects and distributes fees from reprography and other methods whereby copyright material is exploited without direct payment to the originators.

The Society keeps in close touch with the Arts Councils, the Association of Authors' Agents, the British Council, the

---

Membership

The Society of Authors

84 Drayton Gardens, London SW10 9SB
tel 0171-373 6642

There are two categories of membership (admission to each being at the discretion of the Committee of Management):

Full Membership – those authors who have had a full-length work published, broadcast or performed commercially in the UK or have an established reputation in another medium.

Associate Membership – those authors who have had a full-length work accepted for publication, but not yet published; and those authors who have had occasional items broadcast or performed, or translations, articles, illustra-tions or short stories published.

Associate members pay the same annual subscription and are entitled to the same benefits as full members. The owner or administrator of a deceased author's copyrights can become a member on behalf of the author's estate.

The annual subscription (which is tax deductible under Schedule D) for full or associate membership of the Society is £70 (£65 by direct debit after the first year), and there are special joint membership terms for husband and wife. Authors under 35, who are not yet earning a significant income from their writing, may apply for membership at a lower subscription of £52. Authors over 65 may apply to pay at the reduced rate after their first year of membership.

Broadcasting Entertainment Cinematograph and Theatre Union, the Institute of Translation and Interpreting, the Secretary of State for National Heritage, the National Union of Journalists, the Publishers Association and the Writers' Guild of Great Britain.

The Society is a member of the European Writers Congress, the British Copyright Council, the National Book Committee and the International Confederation of Societies of Authors and Composers (CISAC).

Awards

The Society of Authors administers:
• two travel awards: the Somerset Maugham Awards and the Travelling Scholarships;
• four prizes for novels: the Betty Trask Awards, the Encore Award, the McKitterick Prize and the Sagittarius Prize;
• two poetry awards: the Eric Gregory Awards and the Cholmondeley Awards;
• the Tom-Gallon Award for short story writers;
• the Authors' Foundation and Kathleen Blundell Trust, which are endowed with wide powers to support work in progress;
• the Margaret Rhondda Award for women journalists;
• awards for translations from French, German, Italian, Dutch, Portuguese, Spanish, Swedish and Japanese into English;
• the Francis Head Bequest for assisting authors who, through physical mishap, are temporarily unable to maintain themselves or their families.

The Writers' Guild of Great Britain

The Writers' Guild of Great Britain is the writers' trade union, affiliated to the TUC, and represents writers' interests in film, radio, television, theatre and publishing.

The Writers' Guild of Great Britain, incorporating the Theatre Writers' Union, is the writers' trade union, affiliated to the TUC, and represents writers' interests in film, radio, television, theatre and publishing. Formed in 1959 as the Screenwriters' Guild, the union gradually extended into all areas of freelance writing activity and copyright protection. In 1974, when book authors and stage dramatists became eligible for membership substantial numbers joined. In June 1997 the Theatre Writers' Union membership unified with that of the Writers' Guild to create a larger, more powerful writers' union. Each branch of writing is represented on the Executive Council of the Guild.

Apart from necessary dealings with Government and policies on legislative matters affecting writers, the Guild is, by constitution, non-political, has no involvement with any political party, and pays no political levy.

The Guild employs a permanent secretary and staff and is administered by an Executive Council of 31 members. The Guild has a national and regional/branch structure with committees representing Scotland, Wales, London and the South East, the North West, the North East, the Midlands and the South West of England.

The Guild comprises practising professional writers in all media, united in common concern for one another and regulating the conditions under which they work.

The Writers' Guild and agreements

The Guild's basic function is to negotiate minimum terms in those areas in which its members work. Those agreements form the basis of the individual contracts signed by members. Further details are given below. The Guild also gives individual advice to its members on contracts.

Television

The Guild has national agreements with the BBC and the ITV companies which regulate minimum fees and going rates, copyright licence, credit terms and conditions for television plays, series and serials, dramatisations and adaptations. One of the most important achievements in recent years has been the establishment of pension rights for Guild members. The BBC pay an additional 7.5% of the going rate on the understanding that the Guild member pays 5% of their fee. ITV companies now pay an additional 8% and the writer 5%. The Guild Pension Fund amounts to well over £3 million at present.

The advent of digital and cable television channels and the creation of the BBC's commercial arm has seen the Guild in constant negotiation. At the time of writing, negotiations were close to being finalised with the BBC over use of material on the Flextech and the Australian Entertainment Channel, as well as for the BBC's own digital and cable channels. In addition, the Guild was close to concluding an agreement with the BBC for use of programme clips on the Internet.

In 1997, the Guild negotiated substantial revised terms and conditions for writers who are commissioned by the ITV companies. The new agreement includes a provision for the non-arms length sale of material to digital and cable channels, thus ensuring that writers receive market prices for the use of their material on these new channels.

Film

On 11 March 1985, an important agreement was signed with the two producer organisations: The British Film and Television Producers' Association and The Independent Programme Producers Association (now known as PACT, the Producers' Alliance for Cinema and Television). For the first time, there exists an industrial agreement which covers both independent television productions and independent film productions. Pension fund contributions have been negotiated for Guild members in the same way as for the BBC and ITV. The Agreement was comprehensively renegotiated and concluded in February 1992. The areas of participation have been improved and the money paid upfront is considerably more than it was in the past.

The Guild is involved in constant negotiations in this important field. At the time of writing, negotiations were well under way for a new PACT agreement. The Guild is also involved in ensuring that its members receive proper screenwriting and is often involved in credit arbitrations where disputes arise.

Radio

The Guild has fought for and obtained a standard agreement with the BBC, establishing a fee structure which is annually reviewed. The current agreement includes a Code of Practice which is important for establishing good working conditions for the writer working for the BBC. In December 1985 the BBC agreed to extend the pension scheme already established for television writers to include radio writers. In 1994 a comprehensive revision of the Agreement was undertaken, and 1997 saw the Guild negotiate special agreements for the new daily Serial on Radio 4 and the new World Service soap *West Way*. In 1997 the Guild also came to an agreement with the BBC for a year's trial simultaneous broadcast of the World Service over the Internet.

Books

The Guild fought long, hard and successfully for the loans-based Public Lending Right to reimburse authors for books lent in libraries. This is now law and the Guild is constantly in touch with the Registrar of the scheme, which is administered from offices in Darlington.

The Guild, together with the Society of Authors, has drawn up a draft Minimum

Terms Book Agreement which has been widely circulated amongst publishers. In 1984, the unions achieved a significant breakthrough by signing agreements with two major publishers; negotiations were also opened with other publishers. The publishing agreements will, it is hoped, improve the relationship between the writer and publisher and help to clarify what writers might reasonably expect from the exploitation of copyright in works written by them.

Agreements have now been signed with W.H. Allen, BBC Publications, Bloomsbury, Chapmans, André Deutsch, Faber & Faber, Hamish Hamilton, HarperCollins, Hodder Headline, Methuen, Random House, Penguin Books, Sinclair-Stevenson, Transworld and Viking. Negotiations are currently taking place with Macmillan.

Theatre

In 1979, the Guild, together with the Theatre Writers' Union, negotiated the first ever industrial agreement for theatre writers and in April 1993 a new Agreement was concluded. The Theatre National Committee Agreement covers the Royal Shakespeare Company, the National Theatre Company and the English Stage Company.

A new Agreement was signed in 1986 with the Theatrical Management Association, which covers some 95 provincial theatres. In 1993, this agreement was comprehensively revised and included a provision for a year-on-year increase in fees in line with the Retail Price Index.

After many years of negotiation, an Agreement was concluded in 1991 between the Guild and Theatre Writers' Union, and the Independent Theatre Council, which represents some 200 of the smaller and fringe theatres as well as educational, touring companies. This Agreement was substantially renegotiated in 1997, and now includes a significant increase in fees and for the first time establishes the principle of royalty payments for writers in these smaller theatres.

Only the West End is not covered by a union agreement.

Membership

The Writers' Guild of Great Britain
(incorporating the Theatre Writers' Union)
430 Edgware Road, London W2 1EH
tel 0171-723 8074 *fax* 0171-706 2413
e-mail postie@wggb.demon.co.uk
web site http://www.writers.org.uk/guild

Membership of the Writers' Guild is open to all writers who are entitled to claim a single piece of written work of any length for which payment has been received under written contract in terms not less favourable than those existing in current minimum term agreements negotiated by the Guild.

Previously unpublished, broadcast or performed writers can apply for membership when they receive their first contract. The Guild's advice before signature can be vital. Candidate membership (£35) is open to all those who are taking their first steps into writing but who have not yet received a contract. Affiliate membership is enjoyed by agents.

The minimum subscription is £80 plus 1% of that part of an author's income over £8000 earned from professional writing sources in the previous calendar year with a cap of £930.

All Full members are automatically members of the Authors Licensing and Collecting Society (ALCS) – see page 630. The Guild is a corporate member of the ALCS and maintains its links through representation on its board.

Members receive two types of newsletters. *The Writers' Newsletter* (6 p.a.), the official publication of the Guild, carries articles, letters and reports written by members. *The Guild Network* (10 p.a.) includes market information and opportunities for writers.

Members are entitled to various other benefits, such as free entry to the British Library reading rooms, and reduced entry to the National Film Theatre and the Museum of the Moving Image.

Copies of all the above agreements are available to members and non-members. There is a charge to non-members.

Other activities

The Guild is in constant touch with Government and national institutions wherever and whenever the interests of writers are in question or are being discussed. The Guild has been holding cross-party Parliamentary lobbies every 18 months since 1989 with Equity and the Musicians Union to ensure that the various art forms they represent are properly cared for.

Working with the Federation of Entertainment Unions, the Guild makes its views known to Government bodies on a broader basis. It keeps in touch with the Arts Council, the Independent Television Commission and other national bodies.

The Guild has close working relationships with Equity and the Musicians Union, all three having agreed to work closely together where they share a common interest. Representatives of the three governing bodies meet on a regular basis.

Internationally, the Guild plays a leading role in the International Affiliation of Writers' Guilds, which includes the American Guilds East and West, the Canadian Guilds (French and English), and the Australian and New Zealand Guilds. When it is possible to make common cause, the Guilds act accordingly.

The Guild takes a leading role in the European Writers' Congress, which is becoming increasingly important and successful. An initiative from the Guild saw the setting up of a Copyright Committee to protect writers' interests within the EU

in particular and throughout Europe in general. The Guild is becoming more and more involved with matters at European level where the harmonisation of copyright law and the regulation of a converged audiovisual/telecommunications are of immediate interest. The Guild is also very involved in the campaign to maintain the Television Without Frontiers Directive and secure a commitment to Public Service Broadcasting in the European Treatise.

Membership activities

The Guild in its day-to-day work takes up problems on behalf of individual members, gives advice on contracts, and helps with any problems which affect the lives of its members as professional writers. It now has a legal hotline so that members can quickly and easily seek legal advice.

Regular Craft Meetings are held by all the Guild's specialist committees. This gives Guild members the opportunity of meeting those who control, work within, or affect the sphere of writing within which they work.

In conclusion

The writer is an isolated individual in a world in which individual voices are not always heard. The Guild brings together those writers in order to make common cause in respect of the many vitally important matters which are susceptible to influence only from the position of the collective strength which the Guild enjoys. The writer properly cherishes his or her individuality; it will not be lost within a union run by other writers.

Prizes and awards

This list provides details of many British prizes, competitions and awards for writers and artists, including grants, bursaries and fellowships, as well as details of major international prizes. On page 540 is a quick reference to its contents. Listings of Open art exhibitions for artists start on page 543.

J.R. Ackerley Prize for Autobiography
Information PEN, 7 Dilke Street, London SW3 4JE
tel 0171-352 6303 *fax* 0171-351 0220
An annual prize given for an outstanding work of literary autobiography written in English and published during the previous year by an author of British nationality or an author who has been a long-term resident in the UK. No submissions please – books are nominated by the judges only. First awarded in 1982.

The Alexander Prize
Literary Director, Royal Historical Society, University College London, Gower Street, London WC1E 6BT
tel/fax 0171-387 7532
An annual award of £250. Candidates must either be under the age of 35 or be registered for a higher degree now or within the last 3 years. They may choose their own subject for a paper, but they must submit their choice for approval to the Literary Director. Closing date 1 November.

The Hans Christian Andersen Medals
Details International Board on Books for Young People, Nonnenweg 12, Postfach, CH-4003 Basel, Switzerland
tel (61) 272 29 17 *fax* (61) 272 27 57
e-mail ibby@eye.ch
The Medals are awarded every 2 years to a living author and an illustrator who by the outstanding value of their work are judged to have made a lasting contribution to literature for children and young people.

Arc Short Story Competition
Application form Rosemary Jones, Short Story Competition, Arc Publications, Nanholme Mill, Shaw Wood Road, Todmorden, Lancs. OL14 6DY
tel (01706) 812338 *fax* (01706) 818948

Further information

In the UK, details of awards for novels, short stories and works of non-fiction, as they are offered, will be found in such journals as the *Author*.

Book Trust
Book House, 45 East Hill, London SW18 2QZ
tel 0181-870 9055
Publishes a list of prizes, *Guide to Literary Prizes 1997* (£3.99) and a free leaflet on grants and awards.

This competition (total prize money £500) is open to residents of the area covered by Northern Arts, North West Arts and Yorkshire and Humberside Arts Boards (see page 491), as well as Derbyshire and Lincolnshire. Stories may be on any subject, of no more than 3000 words. Closing date: 30 June each year; entry forms available from beginning of March. Founded 1988.

Rosemary Arthur Award
Details National Poetry Foundation, 27 Mill Road, Fareham, Hants PO16 0TH
tel (01329) 822218
An annual award for a book of poetry. The prize consists of the full cost of publishing the winner's book, £100 and an engraved clock. Closing date: 31 December 1998. The 1998 award will be the last. Founded in 1989.

The Arts Council/An Chomhairle Ealaíon, Ireland
Details The Arts Council (An Chomhairle Ealaíon), 70 Merrion Square, Dublin 2, Republic of Ireland

tel (01) 6180200 *fax* (01) 6761302
These literary awards are available only to Irish citizens, or to those who have been resident in Ireland for the previous 5 years.

Bursaries for Creative Writers
In 1997 awards totalling IR£97,000 were offered to creative writers of poetry, fiction and drama to enable them to concentrate on or complete writing projects. In excess of IR£100,00 will be distributed in 1998. A limited number of literary non-fiction projects are also eligible.

Denis Devlin Memorial Award
This award, value IR£3000, is made triennially for the best book of poetry in the English language by an Irish citizen published in the preceding 3 years. The next award will be made in 1999.

Macaulay Fellowship
Fellowships, value IR£3500, are awarded once every 3 years to writers under 30 years of age (or in exceptional circumstances under 35 years) in order to help them to further their liberal education and careers. The cycle of awards is: Visual Arts (1997), Music (1998), Literature (1999).

The Marten Toonder Award
This award is given to an artist of recognised and established achievement on a rotating cycle as follows: Music (1997), Literature (1998), Visual Arts (1999). Candidates must be Irish-born (Northern Ireland is included). Value IR£4500.

An Duais don bhFilíocht i nGaeilge
This is Ireland's major award to Irish-language poetry; it is given triennially for the best book of Irish-language poetry published in the preceding 3 years. The next award will be made in 1999. Value IR£3000.

Travel Grants
Creative artists (including writers) may apply for assistance with travel grants to attend seminars, workshops and to carry out background research to their works in progress. Applications are assessed twice a year.

Arts Council of England
Details Arts Council of England, 14 Great Peter Street, London SW1P 3NQ
tel 0171-333 0100

Writers' Awards
The Arts Council gives annual awards to writers whose work is of outstanding quality. In 1998-99 there will be 15 such awards. They will be offered only to previously published authors who are writing works of poetry, fiction, autobiography, biography and literature for young people. At least one award will be reserved specifically for the Literature for Young People category. The value of each bursary is £7000. Closing date for applications: 30 September each year. Details are available from July onwards from the Literature Department.

Translation Fund
This fund supports the publication of translated work. Any text suggested for support should already have secured a publisher by whom nominations should be made. Grants may be given for specimen chapters of a work in progress. Grants are occasionally given to initiatives outside publishing which support an appreciation of translation. The budget for 1998-99 is just over £100,000 and there are 3 deadline dates each year. Further information from Jilly Paver, Literature Officer.

The Arts Council of Wales Awards to Writers
Literature Department, The Arts Council of Wales, Museum Place, Cardiff CF1 3NX
tel (01222) 394711 *fax* (01222) 221447

Book of the Year Award
A £3000 prize is awarded to winners, in Welsh and English, and £1000 to 4 other short-listed authors for works of exceptional merit by Welsh authors (by birth or residence) published during the previous calendar year in the categories of poetry, fiction and creative non-fiction.

Bursaries
Bursaries totalling about £75,000 are awarded annually to authors writing in both Welsh and English. Write for further details of the Arts Council of Wales' policies.

Arvon Foundation International Poetry Competition
Details Arvon Foundation Poetry Competition, Lumb Bank, Heptonstall, Hebden Bridge, West Yorkshire HX7 6DF
tel (01422) 843714

e-mail l-bank@arvonfoundation.org
A biennial competition for previously unpublished poems written in English. First prize £5000, plus at least £5000 in other cash prizes. Founded in 1980.

Authors' Club Awards
Details Ann Carter, Secretary, Authors' Club, 40 Dover Street, London W1X 3RB
tel 0171-499 8581 *fax* 0171-409 0913

Best First Novel Award
An award of £750 is presented at a dinner held in the Club, to the author of the most promising first novel published in the UK during each year. Entries (one from each publisher's imprint) are accepted during October and November and must be full-length novels – short stories are not eligible. Instituted by Lawrence Meynell in 1954.

Sir Banister Fletcher Award for Authors' Club
The late Sir Banister Fletcher, a former President of both the Authors' Club and the Royal Institute of British Architects instituted an annual prize 'for the book on architecture or the arts most deserving'. The award is made on the recommendation of the Professional Literature Committee of RIBA, to whom nominations for eligible titles (i.e. those written by British authors or those resident in the UK and published under a British imprint) should be submitted by the end of May of the year after publication. The prize of £750 is awarded by the Authors' Club during September. First awarded in 1954.

Marsh Award for Children's Literature in Translation
This biennial award of £750 is given to a British translator of a book for children (aged 4-16) from a foreign language into English and published in the UK by a British publisher. Electronic books, and encyclopedias and other reference books, are not eligible. Next award: October 1998. Founded in 1995.

Marsh Biography Award
This major national biography prize of £3500 plus a trophy is presented every 2 years. Entries must be serious biographies written by British authors and pub-

lished in the UK. Next award: October 1997 (and then October 1999). Founded 1985-86.

The Authors' Foundation
Society of Authors, 84 Drayton Gardens, London SW10 9SB
Grants are available to novelists, poets and writers of non-fiction who are published authors working on their next book. The aim is to provide funding (in addition to a proper advance) for research, travel or other necessary expenditure. Closing date: 30 April. Write for an information sheet. Founded in 1984 to mark the centenary of the Society of Authors.

BA/Bookseller Author of the Year
Details The Booksellers Association of Great Britain and Ireland, 272 Vauxhall Bridge Road, London SW1V 1BA
tel 0171-834 5477 *fax* 0171-834 8812
This annual award of £1000 is judged by members of the Booksellers Association of Great Britain and Ireland (4000 bookshops) in a postal ballot. Any living, British or Irish published writer is eligible and the award is given to the author judged to have had the most impact in the year. Founded in 1993.

Verity Bargate Award
Details Verity Bargate Award, The Soho Theatre Company, 21 Dean Street, London W1V 6NE
This bi-annual award is made to the writer of a new and previously unperformed full-length play. In addition to the cash prize of £1500, the winning play usually goes on to a full production by the Soho Theatre Company. Accordingly, the chosen playwright is required to offer first option to produce the winning play to the Soho Theatre Company. It is also intended that emerging writers of interest – such as those whose plays are shortlisted – will be provided with workshop facilities to assist in their further development. Created as a memorial to the founder of the Soho Theatre Company. Send an sae for details.

Northampton Borough Council Writers' Competition Award for the H.E. Bates Short Story
Details Events Team Office, Directorate of Environment Services, Cliftonville House, Bedford Road, Northampton NN4 7NR
tel (01604) 233500 ext 4243

This annual prize is awarded for a short story – maximum length 2000 words – to anyone resident in Great Britain. The first prize is for £200, other prizes to a total value of £150. Further details on receipt of sae from the Events Team.

BBC Wildlife Magazine Awards for Nature Writing

Details BBC Wildlife Magazine, Broadcasting House, Whiteladies Road, Bristol BS8 2LR
tel 0117-9738402 *fax* 0117-9467075
e-mail wildlifemag@gn.apc.org

BBC Wildlife Magazine awards prizes annually with the aim of reviving the art of nature writing, discovering and encouraging new essayists and focusing attention on those writers whose skills might otherwise be neglected. Entries are accepted from professional or amateur writers, and from young writers aged 17 and under. Send an sae for further information or see *BBC Wildlife Magazine*.

The BBC Wildlife Magazine Poet of the Year Contest

Details BBC Wildlife Magazine, Broadcasting House, Whiteladies Road, Bristol BS8 2LR
tel 0117-973 8402 *fax* 0117-946 7075
e-mail wildlifemag@gn.apc.org

An annual competition for poems (up to 50 lines) that express thoughts and feelings about the natural world. Prizes: winner £500, runners-up £75, winners of young poet categories £50. Closing date: varies from year to year. Founded 1991.

The Samuel Beckett Award

Details Editorial Department, Faber and Faber, 3 Queen Square, London WC1N 3AU

This award is open to residents of the UK and the Republic of Ireland for new dramatic writing, professionally performed. The provisions of the award are currently under review. Founded in 1983.

The David Berry Prize

Council of the Royal Historical Society, University College London, Gower Street, London WC1E 6BT
tel/fax 0171-387 7532

Candidates may select any subject dealing with Scottish history, provided such subject has been previously submitted to and approved by the Council. Closing date: 31 October each year. Value of prize: £250.

The BFC Mother Goose Award

Books for Children, 4 Furzeground Way, Stockley Park, Middlesex UB11 1DP

Open to artists having published a first major book for children during the previous year, only books first published in Britain will be considered, including co-productions where the illustration originated in Britain. The award, presented annually in May, is a bronze egg together with a cheque for £1000. Recommendations for the award are invited from publishers and should be sent to each panel member, whose names and addresses are available from the address above. Sponsored by Books for Children.

The Bisto Book of the Year Awards

Details The Coordinator, The Bisto Book of the Year Awards, Children's Books Ireland, 19 Parnell Square, Dublin 1, Republic of Ireland
tel/fax (01) 872 5854

Annual awards open to authors and/or illustrators who were born in Ireland, or who were living in Ireland at the time of a book's publication.

The Bisto Book of the Year Award
An award of £1500 and a bronze trophy is presented to the overall winner (text and/or illustration).

Bisto Merit Awards
Awards of £500 each are awarded to 3 authors or illustrators.

Bisto Ellís Dillon Award
An award of £500 and a glass trophy is presented to an author for a first children's book (text only).

Closing date: 31 January 1999 for work published during 1 January-31 December 1998. Submission forms are available from September. Founded in 1990.

The James Tait Black Memorial Prizes

Submissions Department of English Literature, David Hume Tower, George Square, Edinburgh EH8 9JX
tel 0131-650 3619 *fax* 0131-650 6898

Two prizes of £3000 are awarded annually: one for the best biography or work of that nature, the other for the best novel, published during the calendar year. The adjudicator is the Professor of English Literature in the University of Edinburgh. Eligible novels and biographies are those written in English, originating with a British publisher, and usually first published in Britain in the year of the award. Both prizes may go to the same author, but neither to the same author a second time. Publishers should submit a copy of any appropriate biography, or work of fiction, as early as possible with a note of the date of publication, marked 'James Tait Black Prize'. Closing date for submissions: 30 September. Founded in memory of a partner in the publishing house of A. & C. Black, these prizes were instituted in 1918.

The Kathleen Blundell Trust

Kathleen Blundell Trust, Society of Authors, 84 Drayton Gardens, London SW10 9SB

Awards are given to published writers under the age of 40 to assist them with their next book. Applications should be in the form of a letter giving reasons for the application, and must be accompanied by a copy of the author's latest book. The author's work must 'contribute to the greater understanding of existing social and economic organisation', but fiction is not excluded. Closing date: 30 April. Send sae for an information sheet.

The Boardman Tasker Prize

Details Mrs Dorothy Boardman, 14 Pine Lodge, Dairyground Road, Bramhall, Stockport, Cheshire SK7 2HS

This annual prize of £2000 is given for a work of fiction, non-fiction or poetry, the central theme of which is concerned with the mountain environment. Authors of any nationality are eligible but the work must be published or distributed in the UK. Entries from publishers only. Founded in 1983.

The Book Art Prize

Details Sophie Birula, Studio Administrator, Design Dept., Transworld Publishers Ltd., 61-63 Uxbridge Road, London W5 5SA *tel* 0181-579 2652 *fax* 0181-231 6639

An annual prize (£1000) to promote excellence in book cover design and to build awareness of the art of illustration. Illustrators and photographers are both eligible. Founded 1997.

The Booker Prize

Book Trust, Book House, 45 East Hill, London SW18 2QZ *tel* 0181-516 2972/2973

This annual prize for fiction of £26,000, including £1000 to each of 6 shortlisted authors, is awarded to the best novel published each year. It is open to novels written in English by citizens of the British Commonwealth and Republic of Ireland and published for the first time in the UK by a British publisher, although previous publication of a book outside the UK does not disqualify it. Entries only from UK publishers who may each submit not more than 2 novels with scheduled publication dates between 1 October of the previous year and 30 September of the current year, but the judges may also ask for other eligible novels to be submitted to them. In addition, publishers may submit one eligible title by authors who have been shortlisted or won the Booker Prize previously. Sponsored by Booker plc.

BP Natural World Book Prize

(in partnership with The Wildlife Trusts) *Details/entry form Book* Trust, Book House, 45 East Hill, London SW18 2QZ *tel* 0181-516 2973

Awards of £5000 to the winner and £1000 to the runner up for an adult book which most imaginatively promotes the conservation of the natural environment and all its animals and plants. Books must have been published in the UK between 1 October of the previous year and 31 October of the year of the award. An amalgamation of the BP Conservation Book Prize and the Natural World Book of the Year Award.

BP Portrait Award

Details National Portrait Gallery, St Martin's Place, London WC2H 0HE *tel* 0171-306 0055 *fax* 0171-306 0056 *web site* http://www.npg.org.uk

An annual award to encourage young artists (EC citizens aged 18-41) to focus upon and develop the theme of portraiture within their work. 1st prize: £10,000 plus at the judges' discretion a commission worth £3000 to be agreed between the NPG and the artist; 2nd prize £5000; 3rd prize: £3000; commendation: up to 5 entrants may be awarded £1000 each. Closing date: April. A selection of entrants' work is exhibited at the National Portrait Gallery between June and September. Founded 1978.

Alfred Bradley Bursary Award

Details BBC Radio Drama Department,
BBC North, New Broadcasting House, Oxford
Road, Manchester M60 1SJ
tel 0161-244 4254

This biennial bursary of £6000 (spread
over 2 years, plus a full commission for a
radio play) is awarded to a writer resident or born in the North of England
who has had a small amount of work
published or produced. The scheme also
allows for a group of finalists to receive
small bursaries and participate in workshops. Founded in 1992.

The Bridport Prize

Details Competition Secretary, Arts Centre,
South Street, Bridport, Dorset DT6 3NR
tel (01308) 427183 *fax* (01308) 424204

Annual prizes are awarded for poetry and
short stories – 1st £2500, 2nd £1000, 3rd
£500 in both categories. Entries should be
in English, original work, typed or clearly
written, and never published, read on
radio/television/stage or entered for any
other current competition. Closing date: 30
June each year. Winning stories are read
by leading London literary agent, without
obligation, and an anthology of winning
entries is published each autumn.
Founded as the Bridport Arts Centre
Creative Writing Competition in 1980.

Katharine Briggs Folklore Award

Details The Convenor, The Folklore Society,
University College London, Gower Street,
London WC1E 6BT
tel 0171-387 5894

An award of £50 and an engraved goblet
is given annually for a book in English
having its first, original and initial publication in the UK, which has made the
most distinguished contribution to folklore studies. The term folklore studies is
interpreted broadly to include all aspects
of traditional and popular culture, narrative, belief, customs and folk arts.

British Academy Medals and Prizes

The British Academy, 10 Carlton House Terrace,
London SW1Y 5AH
tel 0171-969 5200 *fax* 0171-969 5300
e-mail secretary@britac.ac.uk

A number of medals and prizes are
awarded for outstanding work in various
fields of the humanities on the recommendation of specialist committees: Burkitt

Medal for Biblical Studies; Derek Allen
Prize (made annually in turn in musicolo-
gy, numismatics and Celtic studies); Sir
Israel Gollancz Prize (in English studies);
Grahame Clark Medal for Prehistory;
Kenyon Medal for Classical Studies; Rose
Mary Crawshay Prize (for English litera-
ture); Serena Medal for Italian Studies.

The British Academy Research Awards

Details/application form The British Academy,
10 Carlton House Terrace, London SW1Y 5AH
tel 0171-969 5200 *fax* 0171-969 5300
e-mail secretary@britac.ac.uk

These awards are made quarterly to
scholars conducting advanced academic
research in the humanities and social
sciences, and normally resident in the
UK. Applications are accepted for travel
and maintenance expenses in connection
with an approved programme of
research, and costs of preparation of
research for publication.

British Book Awards

Details Merric Davidson, 12 Priors Heath,
Goudhurst, Cranbrook, Kent TN17 2RE
tel/fax (01580) 212041

Presented annually, major categories
include: Author of the Year, Publisher of
the Year, Bookseller of the Year, and
Children's Book of the Year. Founded in
1989.

British Fantasy Awards

Details Robert Parkinson, Secretary,
The British Fantasy Society, 2 Harwood Street,
Stockport SK4 1JJ

Members of the British Fantasy Society
vote annually for the best novel, short
fiction, artist, small press and anthology
of the preceding year. A further award,
the Committee Award, is decided separately. The awards take the form of a statuette. Closing date for nominations: end
August each year. Founded in 1972.

Cardiff International Poetry Competition

Details/entry form Cardiff International Poetry
Competition, PO Box 438, Cardiff CF1 6YA

Fourteen annual prizes totalling £5000
are awarded for unpublished poetry, written in English (1st prize £1000; 2nd £750;
3rd £500; 11 prizes of £250 each). Next
closing date: 11 December 1998.

Carnegie Medal – see The Library Association Carnegie and Kate Greenaway Awards

Children's Book Award

Details Marianne Adey, The Old Malt House, Aldbourne, Marlborough, Wilts. SN8 2DW
tel (01672) 540629 *fax* (01672) 541280

This award is given annually to authors of works of fiction for children published in the UK. Children participate in the judging of the award. 'Pick of the Year' booklist is published in conjunction with the award. Founded in 1980 by the Federation of Children's Book Groups.

Cholmondeley Awards

Administered by The Society of Authors, 84 Drayton Gardens, London SW10 9SB

These non-competitive awards are for the benefit and encouragement of poets of any age, sex or nationality. Submissions are not required. Total value of awards about £8000. Established by the then Dowager Marchioness of Cholmondeley in 1965.

Arthur C. Clarke Award

Details Paul Kincaid, 60 Bournemouth Road, Folkestone, Kent CT19 5AZ
e-mail mks_pk@cix.co.uk

An annual award of £1000 plus engraved bookend is given for the best science fiction novel with first UK publication during the previous calendar year. Titles are submitted by publishers. Founded 1985.

The David Cohen British Literature Prize

Details The Literature Department, Arts Council of England, 14 Great Peter Street, London SW1P 3NQ
tel 0171-333 0100

This prize of £30,000, currently the largest in the UK, will be awarded every 2 years to a living writer, novelist, short story writer, poet, essayist or dramatist in recognition of a lifetime's substantial body of achievement. Work must be written primarily in English and the writer must be a British citizen. In addition, the Arts Council will make available an extra £10,000 to enable the winner to encourage reading or writing among younger people. No application needed; the choice of the winner is made by a distinguished jury on the basis of its collective reading.

Commonwealth Writers Prize

Details/entry form Book Trust, Book House, 45 East Hill, London SW18 2QZ
tel 0181-516 2973 *fax* 0181-516 2978

This annual award is for the best work of fiction in English by a citizen of the Commonwealth published in the year prior to the award. A prize of £10,000 is awarded for best entry and a prize of £3000 for best first published book, selected from 8 regional winners who each receive prizes of £1000. Sponsored by the Commonwealth Foundation.

The Duff Cooper Prize

Details Artemis Cooper, 54 St Maur Road, London SW6 4DP
tel 0171-736 3729 *fax* 0171-731 7638

An annual prize for a literary work in the field of biography, history, politics or poetry published in English or French and submitted by a recognised publisher during the previous 12 months. The prize of £2500 comes from a Trust Fund established by the friends and admirers of Duff Cooper, 1st Viscount Norwich (1890-1954) after his death.

The Rose Mary Crawshay Prizes

The British Academy, 10 Carlton House Terrace, London SW1Y 5AH
tel 0171-969 5200 *fax* 0171-969 5300
e-mail secretary@britac.ac.uk

One or more prizes are awarded each year to women of any nationality who, in the judgement of the Council of the British Academy, have written or published within the 3 calendar years immediately preceding the date of the award an historical or critical work of sufficient value on any subject connected with English literature, preference being given to a work regarding Byron, Shelley or Keats. Founded in 1888.

CWA awards

Crime Writers' Association, 60 Drayton Road, Kings Heath, Brimingham B14 7LR
web site http://www.twbooks.co.uk/cwa/cwa.html

CWA Cartier Diamond Dagger

This award is for an outstanding contribution to the genre. Nominations are not required. Sponsored by Cartier in conjunction with the CWA. First awarded 1986.

CWA John Creasey Memorial Dagger

An award given annually for the best crime novel by an author who has not previously published a full-length work of fiction. Nominations by publishers only. Sponsored by Chivers Press. Founded in 1973 following the death of John Creasey, to commemorate his foundation of the CWA.

CWA Macallan Gold Dagger and Silver Dagger
An annual award for a crime novel published in the UK. Nominations by publishers only. Sponsored by The Macallan in conjunction with the CWA. Founded in 1955.

CWA Macallan Gold Dagger for Non-Fiction
An annual award for a non-fiction crime book to an author published in the UK. Chosen by 4 judges of different professions. Nominations by publishers only. Sponsored by The Macallan in conjunction with the CWA. Founded in 1977.

CWA Macallan Short Story Dagger
An award for the best published short story of the year, to be submitted by publishers. Panels of judges vary from year to year. The winner receives a cheque and a Dagger lapel pin. Sponsored by The Macallan. Instituted in 1993.

The Rhys Davies Trust
Details Mr Meic Stephens, The Secretary, The Rhys Davies Trust, 10 Heol Don, Whitchurch, Cardiff CF4 2AU
tel(01222) 623359 *fax* (01222) 529202
The Trust aims to foster Welsh writing in English and offers financial assistance to English-language literary projects in Wales, directly or in association with other bodies. It also supports the annual Rhys Davies Lecture at the University of Glamorgan.

DT Charitable Trust Awards

David Thomas Self-Publishing Awards
Details/entry form Self-Publishing Awards, DT Charitable Trust, Writers News Ltd, PO Box 6055, Nairn IV12 4YB
tel (01667) 454441
These awards are given annually to anyone resident in the UK who has self-published a book during the calendar year preceding the award. The awards are in 4 categories – fiction, non-fiction, poetry, children – with a prize of £250 in each category. Closing date: 15 January each year. (In addition, the Trust sponsors other writing competitions; details available from Lorna Edwardson.) Established in 1993.

DT Charitable Trust Open Poetry Competition
Details/entry form Lorna Edwardson, Writing Magazine, PO Box 6055, Nairn IV12 4YB
tel (01667) 454441
This annual award is open to anyone aged over 16 and writing in the English language. Poems can be up to 36 lines; there are no restrictions on form but send for subject details, which vary annually. The total prize money is £1200 and the overall winner holds the Silver Cup for one year. Established in 1994.

DT Charitable Trust Annual Ghost Story Competition
Details/entry form Lorna Edwardson, Writing Magazine (as above)
Open to anyone aged over 16, this competition is for a ghost story in 1600-1800 words. First prize is £1000 plus publication in *Writing Magazine*; 2 runners up of £100. The winner holds the Ghost Story Silver Cup for one year. Closing date: 15 January each year.

DT Charitable Trust Annual Love Story Competition
Details/entry form Lorna Edwardson, Writing Magazine (as above)
Open to anyone aged over 16, this competition is for a love story in 1600-1800 words. First prize is £1000 plus publication in *Writing Magazine*; 2 runners up of £100. The winner holds the Love Story Silver Cup for one year. Closing date: 15 January each year.

The Dundee Book Prize
Details Niall Scott, Beattie Communications, 4 Prospect House, Dundee Technology Park, Dundee DD2 1TY
tel (01382) 598408 *fax* (01382) 598442
e-mail beattiemedia-d@sol.co.uk
web sites http://www.dundee.ac.uk/pressreleases/dunpri.htm *and* http://dundeecity.gov.uk/dcchtml/cofd/bookprize.html
A biennial prize (£6000 and the chance of publication by Polygon) awarded for an unpublished novel set in Dundee in the past or present. Founded 1996.

The T.S. Eliot Prize
Applications Poetry Book Society, Book House, 45 East Hill, London SW18 2QZ
tel 0181-516 2973

An annual prize of £5000 is awarded to the best collection of new poetry published in the UK or the Republic of Ireland during the year. Submissions are invited from publishers in the autumn. Founded in 1993.

Encore Award
Details The Society of Authors, 84 Drayton Gardens, London SW10 9SB
tel 0171-373 6642
This annual award of £7500 is for the best second novel of the year. The work submitted must be:
• a novel by one author who has had one (and only one) novel published previously, and
• in the English language, first published in the UK.
Closing date: 30 November.

European Jewish Publication Society Grants
Details Dr Colin Shindler, Coordinator, European Jewish Publication Society, 37-43 Sackville Street, London W1X 2DL
tel 0171-333 8111 *fax* 0171-333 0660
Awards of up to £3000 are given to publishers to assist in the publication of books of Jewish interest. Translations from other languages are considered eligible. Founded 1995.

The European Poetry Translation Prize
Administered by The Poetry Society, 22 Betterton Street, London WC2H 9BU
A prize of £1500 is given every 2 years for a published volume of poetry which has been translated into English from a European language. Next award 1999. Funded by the Arts Council of England. Founded in 1983.

Christopher Ewart-Biggs Memorial Prize
Details The Secretary, Memorial Prize, Flat 3, 149 Hamilton Terrace, London NW8 9QS
fax 0171-328 0699
This prize of £4000 is awarded once every 2 years to the writer, of any nationality, whose work is judged to contribute most to:
• peace and understanding in Ireland;
• to closer ties between the peoples of Britain and Ireland;
• or to co-operation between the partners of the European Union.

Eligible works must be published during the 2 years to 31 December 1998.

The Geoffrey Faber Memorial Prize
An annual prize of £1000 is awarded in alternate years for a volume of verse and for a volume of prose fiction, first published originally in the UK during the 2 years preceding the year in which the award is given which is, in the opinion of the judges, of the greatest literary merit. Eligible writers must be not more than 40 years old at the date of publication of the book and a citizen of the UK and Colonies, of any other Commonwealth state or of the Republic of Ireland. The 3 judges are reviewers of poetry or fiction who are nominated each year by the literary editors of newspapers and magazines which regularly publish such reviews. Faber and Faber invite nominations from reviewers and literary editors. No submissions for the prize are to be made. Established in 1963 by Faber and Faber Ltd, as a memorial to the founder and first Chairman of the firm.

The Eleanor Farjeon Award
An annual prize of (minimum) £750 may be given to a librarian, teacher, author, artist, publisher, reviewer, TV producer or any other person working with or for children through books. Sponsored by Scholastic Ltd. Instituted in 1965 by the Children's Book Circle for distinguished services to children's books and named after the much-loved children's writer.

The Fidler Award
Administered by Book Trust Scotland, The Scottish Book Centre, 137 Dundee Street, Edinburgh EH11 1BG
An annual award for an unpublished novel for children aged 8-12 years, to encourage authors new to writing for this age group. The work should be the author's first attempt to write for this age range. The winner will receive £1000 and the work will be published by Hodder Children's Books, the new sponsors of the award. Send sae for details.

E.M. Forster Award
The distinguished English author, E.M. Forster, bequeathed the American publication rights and royalties of his posthu-

mous novel *Maurice* to Christopher Isherwood, who transferred them to the American Academy of Arts and Letters (633 West 155th Street, New York, NY 10032, USA), for the establishment of an E.M. Forster Award, currently $15,000, to be given annually to an English writer for a stay in the United States. Applications for this award are not accepted.

Forward Poetry Prizes
Details Forward Poetry Prize Administrator, Colman Getty PR, Carrington House, 126-130 Regent Street, London W1R 5FE
tel 0171-439 1783 *fax* 0171-439 1784

Three prizes are awarded annually:
• best collection of poetry published between 1 October and 30 September (£10,000);
• best first collection of poetry published between 1 October and 30 September (£5000); and
• best individual poem, published but not as part of a collection between 1 May 1998 and 30 April 1999 (£1000).
All poems entered are also considered for inclusion in the *Forward Book of Poetry*, an annual anthology. Entries must be submitted by book publishers and editors of newspapers, periodicals and magazines in the UK and Eire. Individual entries from poets will not be accepted. Established in 1992.

Miles Franklin Literary Award
Details Arts Management Pty Ltd,
Station House, Rawson Place, 790 George Street, Sydney, NSW 2000, Australia
tel (02) 9212 5066
e-mail vbraden@ozemail.com.au

This annual award of $27,000 is for a novel or play first published in the preceding year, which presents Australian life in any of its phases. More than one entry may be submitted by each author, and collaborations between 2 or more authors are eligible. Biographies, collections of short stories or children's books are not eligible. Closing date: approx. 31 January each year. Founded in 1957.

Freedom Award
Details The Hon. Secretary, London Press Club, c/o Freedom Forum, Stanhope House, Stanhope Place, London W2 2HH
tel 0171-402 2566 *fax* 0171-262 4631

An annual award of a crystal globe for the individual and/or organisation doing most to promote the freedom of the press. Founded 1998.

The Fulbright Commission Awards
Fulbright House, 62 Doughty Street, London WC1N 2LS
tel 0171-404 6880 *fax* 0171-404 6834
web site http://www.fulbright.co.uk

Application forms are available on the web site or on receipt of sae (39p).

Fulbright Postgraduate Student Awards
Awards are made to outstanding graduate students who are able to demonstrate leadership qualities. There are about 20 annual awards to cover travel and maintenance costs. Closing date: usually end October/beginning November of the preceding academic year of study.

Fulbright Scholarship Grants
Awards are made to potential or established leaders of professional, academic and artistic excellence. Subjects which provide an opportunity for collaborative innovation of international significance or a focus on Anglo-American relations are of particular interest. Awards are for £1750 and applicants must have an invitation to lecture or research at an approved US institution. Closing date: early Spring.

The Lionel Gelber Prize
Details Prize Manager, The Lionel Gelber Prize, c/o Meisner Publicity, 112 Braemore Gardens, Toronto, Ontario M6G 2C8, Canada
tel 416-652-1947 *fax* 416-658-5205
e-mail meisner@interlog.com

This international prize of $50,000 is awarded annually in Canada to the author of the year's most outstanding work of non-fiction in the field of international relations. Submissions must be published in English or in English translation between 1 September and 31 August of the following year. Submissions deadline: 31 May, i.e. 3 months before the end of the period in question. Established in 1989.

The Alasdair Gilchrist-Fisher Memorial Award
Cadogan Contemporary, 108 Draycott Avenue, London SW3 3AE
tel 0171-581 5451 *fax* 0171-589 9120
e-mail artcad@dircon.co.uk

Biennial prize (approx. £3500) awarded to a young artist (aged under 30) for a landscape painting. Founded 1987.

Gladstone History Book Prize
Submissions Executive Secretary, Royal Historical Society, University College London, Gower Street, London WC1E 6BT

An annual award (value £1000) for a history book. The book must:
• be on any historical subject which is not primarily related to British history;
• be its author's first solely written history book;
• have been published in English during the calendar year of 1998 by a scholar normally resident in the UK;
• be an original and scholarly work of historical research.

Three non-returnable copies of an eligible book should be submitted before 31 December 1998.

Glaxo ABSW Wellcome Science Writers Awards
Details Claire Jowett, Glaxo Wellcome plc, Glaxo Wellcome House, Berkeley Avenue, Greenford, Middlesex UB6 0NN
tel 0171-493 4060 *fax* 0181-966 8827

Awards are given to the writers who, in the opinion of the judges, have done most to enhance the quality of science journalism. Entries will be accepted from specialist writers, newspaper reporters and freelances. There are 6 categories, each worth £2500. Organised in conjunction in the Association of British Science Writers. Closing date: 31 January. Founded 1966.

The Glenfiddich Awards
Details The Glenfiddich Awards, 27 Fitzroy Square, London W1P 5HH
tel 0171-383 3024 *fax* 0171-383 4593

Awards are given annually to recognise excellence in writing, publishing and broadcasting relating to the subjects of food and drink. £800 is given to each of 12 categories, together with a case of Glenfiddich Single Malt Scotch Whisky and an engraved quaich. The overall winner receives The Glenfiddich Trophy and an additional £3000. Founded in 1970.

Juliet Gomperts Memorial Scholarship
Enquiries B.D. Gomperts, 31 Addison Avenue, London W11 4QS

e-mail rmka101@ucl.ac.uk

Established in honour of Juliet Gomperts who was tragically killed when she was an art student in Pakistan. The 5 annual scholarships (value £600) provide tuition, board and lodging for 2 weeks in the summer at the Verrocchio Arts Centre in Italy. Open to artists aged 18-40. Closing date: end of February. Send sae for details. Founded 1990.

Kate Greenaway Medal – see The Library Association Carnegie and Kate Greenaway Awards

E.C. Gregory Trust Fund
Details Society of Authors, 84 Drayton Gardens, London SW10 9SB

A number of substantial awards are made annually for the encouragement of young poets who can show that they are likely to benefit from an opportunity to give more time to writing. An eligible candidate must:
• be a British subject by birth but not a national of Eire or any of the British dominions or colonies and be ordinarily resident in the UK or Northern Ireland;
• be under the age of 30 on 31 March in the year of the Award (i.e. the year following submission);
• submit for consideration a published or unpublished work of belles-lettres, poetry or drama poems (not more than 30 poems). Entries: no later than 31 October.

The Guardian Children's Fiction Prize
tel 0171-239 9694

The *Guardian's* annual prize of £1500 is for a work of children's fiction (for children over 8) published by a British or Commonwealth writer. The winning book is chosen by the Children's Book Editor together with a team of 3 or 4 other authors of children's books.

The Guardian Fiction Prize
tel 0171-239 9694

The *Guardian's* annual prize of £5000 is for a work of fiction showing originality and promise published by a British or Commonwealth writer. The winning book will be chosen by the Literary Editor in conjunction with the *Guardian's* regular reviewers of new fiction.

The Hawthornden Prize
Details The Administrator, 42A Hays Mews, Berkeley Square, London W1X 7RU
This prize is awarded annually to the author of what, in the opinion of the Committee, is the best work of imaginative literature published during the preceding calendar year by a British author. Books do not have to be specially submitted.

Hawthornden Writers' Fellowships
Details The Administrator, Hawthornden Castle International Retreat for Writers, Hawthornden Castle, Lasswade, Midlothian EH18 1EG
tel 0131-440 2180
Applications are invited from novelists, poets, dramatists and other creative writers whose work has already been published. Four-week fellowships are offered to those working on a current project.

The Martin Healy Short Story Award
Details The Martin Healy Short Story Award, Model Arts Centre, The Mall, Sligo, Republic of Ireland
tel (71) 41405 *fax* (71) 43694
e-mail modelart@iol.ie
A competition for short stories of 3000 words or less open to Irish writers or writers resident in Ireland. Prizes £1000 (1st), £200 (2nd), £100 (3rd). Entry fees: £5 for first entry, £3 for subsequent entries. Closing date: 20 July 1999. Founded 1997.

The Felicia Hemans Prize for Lyrical Poetry
Submissions The Registrar, The University of Liverpool, PO Box 147, Liverpool L69 3BX
tel 0151-794 2458 *fax* 0151-794 3765
e-mail wilderc@liv.ac.uk
This annual prize of books or money, open to past and present members and students of the University of Liverpool only, is awarded for a lyrical poem, the subject of which may be chosen by the competitor. Only one poem, either published or unpublished, may be submitted. The prize shall not be awarded more than once to the same competitor. Poems, endorsed 'Hemans Prize', must be sent on or before 1 May.

Heywood Hill Literary Prize
Administration Heywood Hill Booksellers, 10 Curzon Street, London W1Y 7FJ
An award of £10,000 is given annually to a person chosen for their lifetime's contribution to the enjoyment of books. No applications. Established in 1995.

David Higham Prize for Fiction
Entry form Book Trust, Book House, 45 East Hill, London SW18 2QZ
tel 0181-516 2973
This prize of £1000 is awarded annually to a citizen of the British Commonwealth or Republic of Ireland for a first novel or book of short stories written in English and published during the current year. Publishers only may submit books. Founded in 1975.

William Hill Sports Book of the Year Award
Details Graham Sharpe, William Hill Organisation, Greenside House, 50 Station Road, London N22 4TP
tel 0181-918 3731
This award is given annually in November for a book with a sporting theme (record books and listings excluded). The title must be in the English language, and published for the first time in the UK during the relevant calendar year. Total value of prize is £10,000, including 7000 guineas in cash. An award for the best cover design has total value of £1000. Founded in 1989.

The Calvin and Rose G. Hoffman Memorial Prize for Distinguished Publication on Christopher Marlowe
Applications The Headmaster, The King's School, Canterbury, Kent CT1 2ES
tel (01227) 595501 *fax* (01227) 595595
This annual prize of between £5000 and £6000 is awarded to the best unpublished work that examines the life and works of Christopher Marlowe and the relationship between the works of Marlowe and Shakespeare. Closing date: 1 September.

The Winifred Holtby Memorial Prize
Submissions The Royal Society of Literature, 1 Hyde Park Gardens, London W2 2LT
This prize (value £800) is awarded for the best regional novel of the year written in the English language. The writer must be of British or Irish nationality, or a citizen of the Commonwealth. Translations, unless made by the author of the work, are not eligible for consideration. If in any year it is considered that

no regional novel is of sufficient merit the prize may be awarded to an author, qualified as aforesaid, of a literary work of non-fiction or poetry, concerning a regional subject. Novels published during the current year should be submitted by 31 October.

L. Ron Hubbard's Writers and Illustrators of the Future Contests

Administrator Andrea Grant-Webb, PO Box 218, East Grinstead, West Sussex RH19 4GH

Aims to encourage new and aspiring writers and illustrators of science fiction, fantasy and horror. In addition to the quarterly prizes there is an annual prize of £2500 for each contest. All 24 winners are invited to the annual L. Ron Hubbard Achievement Awards, which include a series of writers' and illustrators' workshops, and their work is published in an anthology. Write for an entry form.

Writers of the Future Contest

Entrants should submit a short story of up to 10,000 words or a novelette of less than 17,000 words. Prizes of £640 (1st), £480 (2nd) and £320 (3rd) are awarded each quarter. Founded 1984.

Illustrators of the Future Contest

Entrants should submit three black and white illustrations on different themes. Three prizes of £320 are awarded each quarter. Founded 1988.

Hunting Art Prizes

Details Parker Harris & Co., PO Box 279, Esher, Surrey KT10 8YZ
tel (01372) 462190 *fax* (01372) 460032
Contact Jane Sowerby

An annual national art competition open to all artists resident in the UK. Total prize monies: £20,500. Entry fee is £10 (£4 students) per work and artists may submit up to 3 works. Closing date: mid November. 1998 winning entries will be exhibited at the Royal College of Art 4-14 February 1999 and at the Victoria Art Gallery, Bath mid March to early April 1999. Established 1980.

Images – The Best of British Illustration

Details Association of Illustrators, 1st Floor, 32-38 Saffron Hill, London EC1N 8FH
tel 0171-831 7977 *fax* 0171-831 6277
e-mail sb@a-o-illustrators.demon.co.uk
web site http://www.aoi.co.uk

Illustrators are invited to submit work for possible inclusion in the *Images Annual*, a jury-selected showcase of the best of contemporary British illustration. Selected work forms the Images exhibition, which tours the UK. The competition is open to all types of illustration, from children's books to architecture. Prizes include the AOI/Kall Kwik Illustrator Award (£1000), the Client Award (£400) and the Print and Design Award (£500). UK illustrators or illustrators working for UK clients are all eligible. Entry forms available mid April. Closing date: beginning of June each year. Founded 1976.

The Richard Imison Memorial Award

Details/entry form The Secretary, The Broadcasting Committee, The Society of Authors, 84 Drayton Gardens, London SW10 9SB
tel 0171-373 6642

This annual prize of £1000 is awarded to any new writer of radio drama first transmitted within the UK during the period 1 January-31 December 1998 by a writer new to radio. Founded in 1993.

The Independent/Scholastic Story of the Year Competition

Prizes are awarded annually for the best short stories (1500-2500 words) for 6-9-year-old children. Prizes: £2000 winner, £500 each to runners up, £200 each to up to 7 finalists, whose entries are included in an anthology which is published each autumn. Full entry details are advertised in the *Independent* each spring (February). Founded in 1993.

International IMPAC Dublin Literary Award

Details The International IMPAC Dublin Literary Award Office, Dublin City Public Libraries, Administrative Headquarters, Cumberland House, Fenian Street, Dublin 2, Republic of Ireland
tel (01) 6619000 *fax* (01) 6761628
e-mail dublin.city.libs@iol.ie
web site http://www.iol.ie/~dubcilib

An annual award of IR£100,000 is presented to the author of a work of fiction, written and published in the English language or written in a language other than English and published in English translation, which in the opinion of the judges is of high literary merit and constitutes a lasting contribution to world literature. Nominations accepted from library systems of major cities from all over the world, regardless of national origin of the author or the place of publication. Founded in 1995.

International Playwriting Festival
Details/entry form Festival Administrator, Warehouse Theatre, Dingwall Road, Croydon CR0 2NF
tel 0181-681 1257 *fax* 0181-688 6699
An annual competition for full-length unperformed plays, judged by a panel of theatre professionals. Finalists are given rehearsed readings during the festival week in November. Entries are welcome from all parts of the world. For further details and entry forms send an sae. Deadline for entries: usually by the first week of July. Founded 1985.

Irish Times Literary Prizes
Details Gerard Cavanagh (administrator)
tel (3531) 6792022 *fax* (3531) 6709383
These biennial prizes are awarded from nominations submitted by literary editors and critics. The 1997 Irish Literature Prizes were IR£5000 for each of 3 categories:
• fiction (novel, novella or collection of short stories);
• non-fictional prose (history, biography, autobiography, criticism, politics, sociological interest, travel, current affairs and belles-lettres);
• poetry (collection of works or long poem or sequence of poems or revised/updated edition of previously published selection or collection of a poet's work). The work must be published in English or Irish. Launched in 1989.

International Fiction Prize
A biennial prize of IR£7500 is awarded for a work of fiction written in the English language and published in Ireland, the UK or the USA.

Japan Festival Awards
Details The Japan Festival Fund, Swire House, 59 Buckingham Gate, London SW1E 6AJ
tel 0171-630 5552 *fax* 0171-931 8453
Prizes are awarded annually for recent outstanding achievements in furthering the understanding of Japanese culture in the UK. A literary prize (£1000) is given to this end for a new work of fiction or non-fiction. Closing date: 31 March each year. Founded 1993.

Jewish Quarterly Literary Prizes
Details The Administrator, Jewish Quarterly, PO Box 2078, London W1A 1JR
tel 0171-629 5004 *fax* 0171-629 5110
Prizes are awarded annually for a work of fiction (£4000) and non-fiction (£4000) which best stimulate an interest in and awareness of themes of Jewish concern among a wider reading public. Founded in 1977.

The Petra Kenney Poetry Competition
Details Writers' Forum, 21 Belle Vue Street, Filey, North Yorkshire YO14 9HU
tel/fax (01723) 513729
This annual competition is for unpublished poems on any theme and in any style, and is open to everyone. Poems should be no more than 80 lines. Prizes: £1000 (1st), £500 (2nd), £250 (3rd); all the winning entries will be published in *Writers' Forum* magazine. Entry fee: £3 per poem. Closing date: 1 December each year. Founded 1995.

Kent and Sussex Poetry Society Open Poetry Competition
Submissions The Organiser, 8 Edward Street, Southborough, Kent TN4 0HP
This competition is open to all unpublished poems, no longer than 40 lines in length. Prizes: 1st £500, 2nd £200, 3rd £100, 4th 4 at £50. Closing date: 31 January. Entries should include an entry fee of £3 per poem, the author's name and address and a list of poems submitted. Founded in 1985.

The John Kobal Photographic Portrait Award
The John Kobal Foundation, PO Box 3838, London NW1 3JF
tel 0171-383 2979 *fax* 0171-383 0044
Portrait photography is defined here as 'photography concerned with portraying people with the emphasis on their identity as individuals' and the award is open to anyone over the age of 18. Total prize monies: £5500. Deadline for entries: 5 June. Established 1992.

Kraszna-Krausz Awards
Details Andrea Livingstone, Administrator, Kraszna-Krausz Foundation, 122 Fawnbrake Avenue, London SE24 0BZ

tel/fax 0171-738 6701

Awards totalling over £10,000 are made each year, alternating annually between the best books on:

- still photography: art, culture and history; craft, technology and scientific (1998); and
- moving image (film, TV and video): culture and history, business, techniques and technology (1999).

The prize in each category will be awarded to the best book published in the preceding 2 years. Closing date: 1 July. Instituted in 1985. The Foundation is also open to applications for grants concerned with the literature of photography and the moving image.

LAB/LBC London Radio Playwrights' Festival

Details London Radio Playwrights' Festival, IRDP, PO Box 518, Manningtree, Essex CO11 1XD

Organised by Independent Radio Drama Productions and LBC Radio, the festival falls into 2 parts: a workshop programme and a script competition. It is hoped that writers attending the workshops will enter the competition but this is not a condition. Two commissions are offered, one for an established writer and the other for a writer who has previously completed one play for radio. Three other plays will be chosen by open competition. Entrants must live, work or study in London. Send sae for details. Founded 1987.

The Lady Short Story Competition

The Lady, 39-40 Bedford Street, London WC2E 9ER

This competition is open to anyone possessing a coupon from the first October issue of the *Lady*. First prize is £1000. Subjects for short stories change each year. Further information in the relevant issue – please do not contact the magazine office directly in connection with the competition. Founded in 1993.

The Laing Art Competition

Details Mrs J. Donlevy, John Laing plc (Art Competition), Maxted House, 13 Maxted Road, Hemel Hempstead, Herts HP2 7DX
tel (01442) 286752

An annual national open art competition (seascapes and landscapes) open to all artists resident in the UK and held at regional venues. 1st prize: £5000; 5 highly commended prizes: £1000; regional 1st prizes: £1000. Winning entries will be exhibited in the spring regionally and at the Mall Galleries, London. Founded 1972.

Langhe Ceretto Prize for Food and Wine Culture, The International

Details Segreteria del Premio, Biblioteca Civica 'G. Ferrero', Via Paruzza 1, 12051 Alba, Italy
tel (0) 173 290092 *fax* (0) 173 362075

The Langhe Ceretto Prize is awarded for the work judged best at dealing with a topic relating to a historic, scientific, dietological, gastronomic or sociological aspect of food and wine (It.L 15,000,000). Publishers should send 13 copies to the Prize Secretariat, usually by mid March each year. Founded 1991.

Leverhulme Research Fellowships and Grants

The Leverhulme Trust, 1 Pemberton Row, London EC4A 3BA
tel 0171-822 6964 *fax* 0171-822 5084
e-mail jcater@leverhulme.org.uk
web site http://www.leverhulme.org.uk

The Leverhulme Trustees offer annually approx. 120 Fellowships and Grants to individuals in aid of original research. These awards are not available as replacement for past support from other sources. Applications will be considered in all subject areas. The maximum total of a Fellowship or Grant is £16,440. Completed application forms must be received by 12 November 1998. Founded 1933.

The Library Association Carnegie and Kate Greenaway Awards

e-mail info@la-hq.org.uk
web site http://www.la-hq.org.uk/

Recommendations for the following 2 awards are invited from members of the Library Association, who are asked to submit a preliminary list of not more than 2 titles for each award, accompanied by a 50-word appraisal justifying the recommendation of each book. The awards are selected by the Youth Libraries Group of the Library Association.

Carnegie Medal

Awarded annually for an outstanding book for children (fiction or non-fiction) written in English and first published in the UK during the preceding year or co-published elsewhere within a 3-month time lapse.

Kate Greenaway Medal
Awarded annually for an outstanding illustrated book for children first published in the UK during the preceding year or co-published elsewhere within a 3-month time lapse. Books intended for older as well as younger children are included, and reproduction will be taken into account.

The Library Association Reference Awards
e-mail info@la-hq.org.uk
web site http://www.la-hq.org.uk/

The Besterman Medal
Awarded annually for an outstanding bibliography or guide to the literature first published in the UK during the preceding year either in print or in electronic form. Recommendations for the award are invited from members of the Library Association, who are asked to submit a preliminary list of not more than 3 titles, and submissions from publishers are welcome.

The McColvin Medal
Awarded annually for an outstanding reference work either in print or in electronic form first published in the UK during the preceding year. Works eligible for consideration are encyclopedias, general and special; dictionaries, general and special; biographical dictionaries; annuals, yearbooks and directories; handbooks and compendia of data; atlases. Recommendations for the award are invited from members of the Library Association, who are asked to submit a preliminary list of not more than 3 titles, and submissions from publishers are welcome.

The Walford Award
Awarded annually to an individual who has made a sustained and continued contribution to the science and art of British bibliography over a period of years. The bibliographer's work can encompass effort in the history, classification and description of printed, written, audiovisual and machine-readable materials.

Recommendations may be made for the work of a living person or persons, or for an organisation. The award can be made to a British bibliographer or to a person or organisation working in the UK.

The Wheatley Medal
Awarded annually for an outstanding index published during the preceding 3 years. Printed indexes to any type of publication may be submitted for consideration, providing that the whole work, including the index, or the index alone has originated in the UK. Recommendations for the award are invited from members of the Library Association and the Society of Indexers, publishers and others. The final selection is made by a committee consisting of representatives of the Library Association Cataloguing and Indexing Group and the Society of Indexers.

The Lichfield Prize
Details Tourist Information Centre, Donegal House, Bore Street, Lichfield, Staffs. WS13 6NE
tel (01543) 252109 *fax* (01543) 417308
Lichfield District Council's biennial prize of £5000 and the chance of publication, is for the best novel based recognisably on the geographical area of Lichfield District, Staffordshire. Next closing date expected to be 30 April 1999. Instituted in 1988.

The Livingstone Award for Travel
Details The Livingstone Award for Travel, PO Box 3821, London NW2 3DQ
This award is open to any writer of a travel guide printed in the English language and published in the 12 months prior to closing date (31 August). The prize is £1000 plus an engraved goblet. Founded in 1990.

The London New Writing Competition
Entry form London Arts Board, Elme House, 133 Long Acre, London WC2E 9AF
tel 0171-240 1313 *fax* 0171-240 4580
e-mail jhn@lonab.demon.co.uk
Open to adults resident in Greater London, this biennial competition offers awards of £200 each (plus publication in an anthology) for the best creative pieces about London. Next closing date: late 1998. Founded in 1992.

The Sir William Lyons Award
Details General Secretary, 30 The Cravens, Smallfield, Surrey RH6 9QS

tel (01342) 843294 *fax* (01342) 844093

This annual award (trophy, £1000 and 2 years' probationary membership of The Guild of Motoring Writers) was set up to encourage young people in automotive journalism, including broadcasting, and to foster interest in motoring and the motor industry through these media. Open to any person of British nationality resident in the UK under the age of 23, it consists of writing 2 essays and an interview with the Award Committee.

The Macallan/Scotland on Sunday Short Story Competition
Details The Administrator, The Macallan/Scotland on Sunday Short Story Competition, 20 North Bridge, Edinburgh EH1 1YT

These annual prizes (1st £6000; 2nd £600; 4 runners up £100 each; publication of winning entries in *Scotland on Sunday*) are awarded for the best short story of less than 3000 words written by a person born in Scotland, now living in Scotland or by a Scot living abroad. The best 20 stories will be published in a special collection by Polygon. Instituted in 1990.

The McKitterick Prize
Details The Society of Authors, 84 Drayton Gardens, London SW10 9SB

This annual award of £4000 is open to first published novels and unpublished typescripts by authors over the age of 40. Closing date: 16 December. Endowed by the late Tom McKitterick.

The Enid McLeod Literary Prize
Details Executive Secretary, Franco-British Society, Room 623, Linen Hall, 162-168 Regent Street, London W1R 5TB
tel/fax 0171-734 0815

This annual prize of £250 is given for a full-length work of literature which contributes most to Franco-British understanding. It must be written in English by a citizen of the UK, British Commonwealth, the Republic of Ireland, Pakistan, Bangladesh or South Africa, and first published in the UK.

The Macmillan Prize for a Children's Picture Book
Applications Marketing Director, Macmillan Children's Books, 25 Eccleston Place, London SW1W 9NF

Three prizes are awarded annually for unpublished children's book illustrations by art students in higher education establishments in the UK. Prizes: £1000 (1st), £500 (2nd) and £250 (3rd).

Macmillan Silver Pen Award for Fiction
Details PEN, 7 Dilke Street, London SW3 4JE
tel 0171-352 6303 *fax* 0171-351 0220

This award of £500 is given annually for an outstanding collection of short stories written in English and published during the previous year by an author of British nationality or an author who has been a long-term resident in the UK. No submissions please – books are nominated by members of the PEN Executive Committee. Sponsored by Macmillan since 1986. Founded in 1969.

The Mail on Sunday/John Llewellyn Rhys Prize
Entry form The Mail on Sunday/John Llewellyn Rhys Prize, c/o Book Trust, Book House, 45 East Hill, London SW18 2QZ
tel 0181-516 2973

This annual prize of £5000 (plus £500 to each shortlisted author) is offered to the author of the most promising literary work of any kind published for the first time during the current year. The author must be a citizen of this country or the Commonwealth, and not have passed his or her 35th birthday by the date of publication of the work submitted. Publishers only may submit books. Inaugurated in memory of the writer John Llewellyn Rhys.

The Kurt Maschler Award
Details Book Trust, Book House, 45 East Hill, London SW18 2QZ
tel 0181-516 2973

This annual prize of £1000 is awarded to a British author/artist or an author/artist who has been resident in Britain for more than 10 years for a children's book in which text and illustrations are of excellence and enhance and balance each other. Founded in 1982.

The Somerset Maugham Awards
Details The Society of Authors, 84 Drayton Gardens, London SW10 9SB

These annual awards, totalling about £15,000, are for young writers. Mr Maugham urged that originality and promise should be the touchstones: he did not wish the judges to 'play for safety' in their choice. A candidate must be a British subject by birth and ordinarily resident in the UK or Northern Ireland, must be under 35 and must submit a published literary work in the English language, of which the candidate is the sole author. Poetry, fiction, non-fiction, belles-lettres or philosophy, but not dramatic works, are eligible. Four, non-returnable copies of one published work should be submitted, and must be accompanied by a statement of the author's date and place of birth, and other published works. Closing date: 31 December.

MCA Book Prize
Details Andrea Livingstone, Administrator, MCA Book Prize, 122 Fawnbrake Avenue, London SE24 0BZ
tel/fax 0171-738 6701
An annual main prize of £5000, and a Young Writers Award (under 40 years old) of up to £2000, are given to books which contribute stimulating, original and progressive ideas on management issues. Authors must be British subjects domiciled in the UK. Next closing date: 16 November 1998. Founded in 1993.

The Medical Society of London Prizes
Details The Secretary, MWG, Society of Authors, 84 Drayton Gardens, London SW10 9SB
Closing date for submissions of medical basic books; advanced authored books; advanced multi-contributor books; medical history: 30 June 1999. The Medical Writers Group of the Society of Authors administers the prizes sponsored by The Medical Society of London.

Meyer-Whitworth Award
Details Theatre Writing Section, Drama Department, Arts Council of England, 14 Great Peter Street, London SW1P 3NQ
tel 0171-333 0100 ext 431
e-mail info.drama.ace@artsfb.org.uk
Set up to help further the careers of UK contemporary playwrights who are not yet established, this award of up to £8000 is given annually for an English-language play which shows writing of individual quality and the promise of a developing new talent. Candidates will have had no more than 2 of their plays professionally produced. Nominated plays must have

been produced professionally in the UK for the first time between 1 August and 31 July; closing date: last Friday in August.

Millennial Science Essay Competition
Details The Wellcome Trust, 210 Euston Road, London NW1 2BE
tel 0171-611 7221/8264 *fax* 0171-611 8269
e-mail comm+ed@wellcome.ac.uk
web site http://www.wellcome.ac.uk
Postgraduate students (in science, engineering or technology) currently writing up their theses are invited to write an entertaining essay of no more than 700 words on their research. The aim is to make the research topic interesting and accessible to a wider non-specialist audience. Applicants must be registered at an internationally recognised institution. The competition is a collaboration between The Wellcome Trust and *New Scientist* magazine and prizes are: £1,500 and publication in *New Scientist* (1st), £750 (2nd), two 3rd prizes of £375 each. All winners, including the next 10 best essays, receive a one-year subscription to *New Scientist.* Founded 1993.

Millfield Arts Projects
Atkinson Gallery, Millfield, Butleigh Road, Street, Somerset BA16 0YD
tel (01458) 442291 *fax* (01458) 447276
Director of Art Len Green
'The mandate of the Millfield Arts Project programme is to search for, promote and support, primarily but not exclusively, young aspiring artists at local, regional, national and international levels.' In a professional art context MAP offers:
• Sculpture Commission. Artists work on campus for 8 weeks (£7500). Deadline for entries: mid January.
• Summer Show. An open exhibition. Application forms available: March.
• Six Gallery exhibitions selected by the Director of Art. Interested artists should send slides and CV to the Director of Art.
• Sculpture Summer Show. Campus sculpture exhibition in July/August/September.

Mind Book of the Year/Allen Lane Award
Details Anny Brackx, Corporate Promotion Department, Granta House, 15-19 Broadway, London E15 4BQ
tel 0181-519 2122 *fax* 0181-522 1725

This £1000 award is given to the author of any book (fiction or non-fiction) published in the UK in the current year which outstandingly furthers public understanding of the prevention, causes, treatment or experience of mental health problems. Entries by 31 December. Administered by Mind, the National Association for Mental Health. Inaugurated in memory of Sir Allen Lane in 1981.

The Oscar Moore Screenwriting Prize

Details The Oscar Moore Foundation, 33-39 Bowling Green Lane, London EC1R 0DA *tel* 0171-505 8112 *fax* 0171-505 8116 *e-mail* moyral@media.emap.co.uk

The Foundation works to build for a Europe-wide culture of screenwriting excellence and to this end makes this annual award (£10,000) to finance the second draft of a promising screenplay. A different genre is chosen for each year: 1998 – comedy, 1999 – to be announced at prizegiving of 1998 prize in January 1999. Closing date: 1 September 1998. Founded 1997.

John Moores Liverpool Exhibition

Walker Art Gallery, William Brown Street, Liverpool L3 8EL *tel* 0151-478 4199 *fax* 0151-478 4190 *Contact* Stephen Guy

Biennial painting exhibition open to any artist living or working in the UK. Cash prize of £20,000 plus acquisition (by gift) of prize-winning painting by the Walker Art Gallery. Hand in August 1999. Exhibition October 1999-February 2000. Founded 1957.

Shiva Naipaul Memorial Prize

Details The Spectator, 56 Doughty Street, London WC1N 2LL

This annual prize of £3000 is given to an English language writer of any nationality under the age of 35 for an essay of not more than 4000 words describing a visit to a foreign place or people. Founded 1985.

The National Art Library Illustration Awards

Enquiries The National Art Library, Victoria and Albert Museum, South Kensington, London SW7 2RL *tel* 0171-938 8313 *web site* http://www.nal/vam.ac.uk *Contact* Dr Leo De Freitas *tel/fax* (01295) 256110

These annual awards are given to practising book and magazine illustrators, for work first published in Great Britain in the 12 months preceding the judging of the awards. Book covers, illustrations of a purely technical nature and photographs together with works produced as limited editions are excluded. Cover illustrations to magazines are eligible. Sponsored by The Enid Linder Foundation.

National Poetry Competition

Competition Organiser, The Poetry Society, 22 Betterton Street, London WC2H 9BU *tel* 0171-240 4810 *fax* 0171-240 4818 *e-mail* poetrysoc@dial.pipex.com *web site* http://www.poetrysoc.com

One of Britain's major annual open poetry competitions. Prizes: 1st £5000, 2nd £1000, 3rd £500, 10 runners up of £50 plus a Montblanc pen. Maximum length 40 lines. Closing date: 31 October each year. Send an sae for rules and entry form.

National Poetry Competition (Ireland)

Poetry Ireland, National Poetry Competition, Bermingham Tower, Upper Yard, Dublin Castle, Dublin 2, Republic of Ireland *tel* (01) 6714632 *fax* (01) 6714634 *e-mail* poetry@iol.ie

An annual poetry competition with a prizes of Ir£1000 for the best poem and Ir£250 for the best poem by a poet who has never been published in any form. Poems can be on any subject in either English or Irish. All poems should be previously unpublished and no longer than 40 lines. Entry fees: £3 for the first poem, £2 for each subsequent poem, and £1 for all entries from under 18-year-olds. Closing date: 28 November 1997. Founded 1992.

The New Writer Poetry Prizes

Details The New Writer Poetry Prizes 1998, PO Box 60, Cranbrook, Kent TN17 2ZR *tel* (01580) 212626 *fax* (01580) 212041

Poets may submit either one or a collection of 6-10 previously unpublished poems. Up to 25 prizes (total prize money £2500) will be presented as well as publication for the prize-winning poets in an anthology, plus the chance for a further 10 shortlisted poets to have their work published in the *New Writer* magazine. Entry fees: £3 per poem; £10 for a collection of 6-10 poems. Closing date: 20 November 1998. Founded 1997.

The Nobel Prize in Literature

Awarding authority Swedish Academy, Box 2118,
S-10313 Stockholm, Sweden
tel (08) 10-65-24 *fax* (08) 24-42-25
e-mail sekretariat@svenskaakademien.se
web site http://svenska.gu.se/academy.html

This is one of the awards stipulated in
the will of the late Alfred Nobel, the
Swedish scientist who invented dyna-
mite. No direct application for a prize
will be taken into consideration. For
authors writing in English it was
bestowed upon Rudyard Kipling in 1907,
W.B. Yeats in 1923, George Bernard Shaw
in 1925, Sinclair Lewis in 1930, John
Galsworthy in 1932, Eugene O'Neill in
1936, Pearl Buck in 1938, T.S. Eliot in
1948, William Faulkner in 1949, Bertrand
Russell in 1950, Sir Winston Churchill in
1953, Ernest Hemingway in 1954, John
Steinbeck in 1962, Samuel Beckett in
1969, Patrick White in 1973, Saul Bellow
in 1976, William Golding in 1983, Wole
Soyinka in 1986, Joseph Brodsky in 1987,
Nadine Gordimer in 1991, Derek Walcott
in 1992, Toni Morrison in 1993 and
Seamus Heaney in 1995.

Northern Arts Writers' Awards

Details Chrissie Glazebrook, Published &
Broadcast Arts Department, Northern Arts,
9-10 Osborne Terrace, Jesmond,
Newcastle upon Tyne NE2 1NZ
tel 0191-281 6334
e-mail cgk@norab.demon.co.uk

Up to £3000 is available annually to support previously published novelists,
short story writers, poets and literary
critics living in the Northern Arts region
of Teesside, Cumbria, Co Durham, Tyne
& Wear and Northumberland.

The Observer Hodge Award/Exhibition

The Observer Hodge Award, The Observer,
119 Farringdon Road, London EC1R 3ER
tel 0171-278 2332 *fax* 0171-713 4368
e-mail sara@guardian.co.uk, rachel@guardian.co.uk
Contact Sara Rhodes or Rachel Cave

Set up in memory of photographer David
Hodge who died aged 30, the award is
given to student and professional photographers under 30. First prize: £3000 plus
a photographic assignment for the
Observer. Best student prize: £1000.
Other prizes: 2nd, 3rd and highly commended. The exhibition will be at The
Photographers' Gallery in autumn/win-
ter. Deadline for entries: early spring.
Founded 1986.

P.J. O'Connor Awards

P.J. O'Connor Awards, RTE Radio Drama,
Donnybrook, Dublin 4, Republic of Ireland
fax (01) 2083304
Producer in Charge Michael Campion

An annual competition for a 30-minute
original radio play, open to unproduced
writers born in or living in Ireland. 1st
prize: £1000, 2nd prize: £750, £3rd prize:
£500. Closing date: 8 November 1997.

One Voice

Details One Voice, c/o Theatr Cwmtawe, Parc
Ynysderw, Pontardawe, W. Glamorgan SA8 4EG
tel (01792) 830111 *fax* (01792) 862020

This competition is open to all writers.
Finalists' work will be performed and
published. The Catrin Collier Random
House Prize enables a writer in the Short
Story section to spend a day with Catrin
Collier and an editor from Random
House and to attend a professional per-
formance of the winning entries. There
are 2 categories: Story and Monologue.
Workshops and surgeries are available to
all entrants. Founded in 1992.

Orange Prize for Fiction

Orange Prize for Fiction, Book Trust,
Book House, 45 East Hill, London SW18 2QZ
tel 0181-516 2973 *fax* 0181-516 2978

This award of £30,000 is for a full length
novel written in English by a woman of
any nationality and first published in the
UK between 1 April 1997 and 31 March
1998.

George Orwell Memorial Prize

Details The Literary Editor, The Political Quarterly,
8A Bellevue Terrace, Edinburgh EH7 4DT
e-mail brc@tattoo.ed.ac.uk

Two prizes of £1000 each are awarded in
March each year – one for the best political book, and one for best political journalism – of the previous year, giving
equal merit to content and good style
accessible to the general public. Next
closing date: 20 January 1999 for work
published in 1998. Founded in 1993.

Catherine Pakenham Memorial Award

Entry form Lucy Goodwin, Public Relations Dept,
The Sunday Telegraph, 1 Canada Square,
Canary Wharf, London E14 5DT
tel 0171-538 6259 *fax* 0171-513 2512

This award is open to young women journalists aged 18-25 who have had at least one piece of work published. Entrants are asked to submit a non-fiction 750-2000-word article by the first week of March. The winner will receive £1000 and the chance to write for a *Telegraph* publication. Three runners-up each receive £200. Entry forms are available after 1 September. Founded in 1970 in memory of Catherine Pakenham, who died in a car crash while working for the *Telegraph Magazine*.

Peterloo Poets Open Poetry Competition

Details Peterloo Poets, 2 Kelly Gardens, Calstock, Cornwall PL18 9SA

This annual competition offers for 1999 a first prize of £4000 and 5 other prizes totalling £2100. Closing date: 2 March 1999. Founded in 1986.

'Poem of the Month' Competition

Erix Publications, 27 Old Gloucester Street, London WC1N 3XX

e-mail editor@writing.co.uk

web site http://www.writing.co.uk

An ongoing monthly competition with a prize of £100 plus publication on the Internet. Entry fee: £3 per poem. Closing date: last day of each month. Write for details. Founded 1996.

Poetry Life Open Poetry Competition

14 Pennington Oval, Lymington, Hants SO41 8BQ

tel (01590) 679269

A competition held 3 times a year with a first prize of £500. Any style is acceptable with an 80-line limit on each poem. Poems entered must be previously unpublished (in book form) and must have not won a competition or prize on any other occasion. Winning entries will be published in *Poetry Life*. Entry fee: £3 per poem. Send sae for further details. Founded 1994.

The Portico Prize

Details Miss Emma Marigliano, Librarian, Portico Library, 57 Mosley Street, Manchester M2 3HY

tel 0161-236 6785 *fax* 0161-236 6803

This biennial prize of £2500 (next prize 1999) is awarded for a published work of fiction or non-fiction, of general interest and literary merit set wholly or mainly in the North-West of England (Lancashire, Manchester, Liverpool, High Peak of Derbyshire, Cheshire and Cumbria). Founded in 1985.

Dennis Potter Play of the Year Award

Details Tessa Ross, Head of Independent Commissioning, Room 6021, c/o BBC Television Centre, London W12 7RJ

Information about this award is obtainable from the above office after October 1998. Founded in 1994.

The Mathew Prichard Award for Short Story Writing

Details The Competition Secretary, The Mathew Prichard Award, 95 Celyn Avenue, Lakeside, Cardiff CF2 6EL

Prizes (1st £1000, 2 runner-up prizes of £250) are awarded annually in this open competition for original short stories in English of not more than 2500 words. Adjudication is organised in May each year by the South and Mid Wales Association of Writers. Next closing date: 1 March 1999.

The Questors National Student Playwriting Competition

The Questors Theatre, 12 Mattock Lane, London W5 5BQ

tel 0181-567 0011 *fax* 0181-567 8736

An annual playwriting competition (funds permitting) open to full-time writing students for a play which has not been performed before. £1000 is awarded plus a full production of the play for one week. Founded 1986.

Trevor Reese Memorial Prize

Details The Seminar & Conference Secretary, Institute of Commonwealth Studies, 28 Russell Square, London WC1B 5DS

tel 0171-580 5876 *fax* 0171-255 2160

This prize of £1000 is awarded biennially, usually for a scholarly work by a single author in the field of Imperial and Commonwealth history. The next award (for a book published in 1998 or 1999) will be given in 2000.

The Margaret Rhondda Award

Details The Society of Authors, 84 Drayton Gardens, London SW10 9SB

This award, is given every 3 years to a woman writer as a grant-in-aid towards the expenses of a research project in journalism, in recognition of the service which women journalists give to the public through journalism. Closing date for next award: 31 December 2001. First awarded in July 1968 on the tenth anniversary of Lady Rhondda's death.

The Rhône-Poulenc Prizes for Science Books

Details COPUS, c/o The Royal Society, 6 Carlton House Terrace, London SW1Y 5AG
tel 0171-839 5561 *fax* 0171-451 2693
e-mail caroline.bay@royalsoc.ac.uk
web site http://www.royalsoc.ac.uk/rs/

These prizes, established in 1988 by COPUS and the Science Museum and sponsored by Rhône-Poulenc, are awarded annually for the best popular science books for the non-specialist reader. Eligible books must be written in English and published for the first time in the UK in the year preceding the prize. The Rhône-Poulenc prize (£10,000) is for a book with a general readership; the Junior Prize (£10,000), is for a book written specifically for young people (under 14): publishers may enter any number of books for each prize. Entries may cover any aspect of science and technology, including biography and history, but books published as educational textbooks or for professional or specialist audiences are not eligible. A prize-winning author will be ineligible for another Rhône-Poulenc Prize for 2 years.

Rhyme International Annual Poetry Competition

Details/entry form Orbis Literary Magazine, 27 Valley View, Primrose, Jarrow, Tyne & Wear NE32 5QT
tel 0191-4897055

The only annual international competition exclusively devoted to rhymed poetry. Total annual prizes average around £1000, divided into 2 classes, 'formal' and 'open'. Entry fee: £2.50 per poem, minimum £5. Closing date: 30 September each year. Adjudicated by a different leading poet each year. Founded as Rhyme Revival in collaboration with Coventry Chamber of Commerce in 1981.

The Rio Tinto David Watt Memorial Prize

Details/entry form The Administrator, The Rio Tinto David Watt Memorial Prize, Rio Tinto plc, 6 St James's Square, London SW1Y 4LD

This £5000 prize is awarded for outstanding written contributions towards the greater understanding of international and political issues. Those eligible for the prize are writers actively engaged in writing for newspapers and journals in the English language. Entries should comprise a published article in English of not more than 5000 words. Closing date for entries and nominations: end March. Funded and administered by Rio Tinto plc. Founded in 1988.

Romantic Novelists' Association Award

Details Audrey Willsher, 11 Cranborne Gardens, Manor Road, Oadby, Leics LE2 4EZ
tel 0116-2715695

This annual award for the best romantic novel of the year is open to both members and non-members of the Romantic Novelists' Association, provided they are domiciled in the UK. Novels must be published between the previous 1 December and 30 November of the year of entry. Three copies of the novel are required. Entry forms and details are available from July onwards.

New Writers' Award
Details Marina Oliver, Half Hidden, West Lane, Bledlow, Princes Risborough, Bucks. HP27 9PF
tel (01844) 345973 *fax* (01844) 274661
e-mail marina.oliver@virgin.net
web site http://freespace.virgin.net/marina.oliver/

This award is for writers previously unpublished in the romantic novel field and who are probationary members of the Association. MSS are submitted each September under the New Writers' Scheme. All receive a critique. Any MSS which have passed through the Scheme and which are subsequently accepted for publication become eligible for the Award.

The Rooney Prize for Irish Literature

Details J.A. Sherwin, Strathin, Templecarrig, Delgany, Co. Wicklow, Republic of Ireland
tel (01) 287 4769 *fax* (01) 287 2595
e-mail jsherwin@iol.ie

This prize is to encourage young Irish writing talent. IR£5000 is awarded annually to a different individual, who must be Irish, published in either Irish or English and under 40 years of age. The prize is non-competitive and there is no application procedure or entry form. Founded in 1976.

The Royal Society of Literature Award under the W.H. Heinemann Bequest

Submissions Royal Society of Literature, 1 Hyde Park Gardens, London W2 2LT

tel 0171-723 5104

Set up to encourage the production of literary works of real worth, works in any branch of literature, originally written in the English language, may be submitted by their publishers for this annual award of £5000. Prose fiction is not excluded, but the Testator's intention was primarily to reward less remunerative classes of literature: poetry, criticism, biography, history, etc. The recipient of a Prize shall not be eligible again for 5 years. Closing date for entries: 31 October.

Runciman Award

Details The Administrator, Anglo-Hellenic League, Flat 4, 68 Elm Park Gardens, London SW10 9PB
tel 0171-352 2676 *fax* 0171-351 5657

Annual prizes of up to £9000 for books wholly or mainly about Greece or the Hellenic scene from antiquity to the present – history, archaeology, biography, the arts, fiction, poetry, etc. Funded by the Onassis Foundation and administered by the Anglo-Hellenic League. Established in 1985.

The Ian St James Awards

Details/entry form The New Writers' Club, PO Box 60, Cranbrook, Kent TN17 2ZR
tel (01580) 212626

These annual awards are for writers of short stories: top prize £2000 and runner-up prizes of £200 each, plus publication in annual collection. The remaining 40 shortlisted writers are published throughout the year in the *New Writer* magazine. Eligible writers must be 18 or over and not have had a novel or novella previously published. Entries must be in English but can come from anywhere in the world. Closing date: 30 April. Founded in 1989.

Alastair Salvesen Art Scholarship

The Royal Scottish Academy, The Mound, Edinburgh EH2 2EL
tel 0131-225 6671 *fax* 0131-225 2349

The Scholarship consists of 2 parts:
• A 3-6 months travel scholarship of up to £8000 depending on the plan submitted; and
• An exhibition lasting about 3 weeks (November/December) in the lower gallery of the Royal Scottish Academy.

Applicants must be painters aged 25-35 who have been trained at one of the 4 Scottish colleges of art; are currently living and working in Scotland; have worked for a minimum of 3 years outside a college or student environment; and have during 1997 had work accepted for an exhibition in the Annual Exhibition organised by certain Scottish institutes or, in a recognised gallery, have held a one-artist exhibition or participated in a group exhibition. Founded 1989.

Scoop of the Year Award

Details The Hon. Secretary, London Press Club, Freedom Forum, Stanhope House, Stanhope Place, London W2 2HH
tel 0171-402 2566 *fax* 0171-262 4631
e-mail 101455.3575@compuserve.com

Chosen by a panel of senior editors, this annual award of a bronze statuette is given for the reporting scoop of the year, appearing in either a newspaper or electronic media. Founded in 1990.

The Scottish Arts Council

Writers' Bursaries
Contact Jenny Brown, Literature Director, The Scottish Arts Council, 12 Manor Place, Edinburgh EH3 7DD
tel 0131-226 6051
e-mail jenny.brown.sac@arts.fb.org

A limited number of bursaries – of between £3000 and £8000 each – are offered to enable professional writers to devote more time to writing. Priority is given to writers of fiction and verse, but writers of literary non-fiction are also considered. Application normally open only to writers who have been living and working in Scotland for at least 2 years. Applications may be discussed with Jenny Brown.

Book Awards
Details Gavin Wallace, Literature Officer, The Scottish Arts Council, 12 Manor Place, Edinburgh EH3 7DD
tel 0131-226 6051
e-mail gavin.wallace.sac@arts.fb.org

Five awards of £1000 each are made in both spring and autumn. Preference is given to literary fiction and verse, but literary non-fiction is also considered. Authors should be Scottish or resident in Scotland, but books of Scottish interest by other authors are eligible for consideration. Books by Scottish writers for children are eligible for a new annual award. Publishers should apply for further information.

The Scottish Book of the Year and Scottish First Book

Details The Saltire Society, 9 Fountain Close, 22 High Street, Edinburgh EH1 1TF *tel* 0131-556 1836 *fax* 0131-557 1675 *e-mail* saltire@saltire.org.uk

These 2 annual awards (£5000 and £1500) are open to any author of Scottish descent or living in Scotland, or for a book by anyone which deals with the work or life of a Scot or with a Scottish problem, event or situation. Nominations are made by literary editors of Scottish newspapers and periodicals. Supported by the *Scotsman* and the Post Office. Established in 1982 and 1988 respectively.

The Scottish International Open Poetry Competition

Details The Secretary, Ayrshire Writers' and Artists' Society, 42 Tollerton Drive, Irvine, Ayrshire KA12 0QE

An annual competition open to all poets over the age of 16 with no restriction on style or length. 1st prize UK section: £100 plus The MacDiarmid Trophy; 1st prize Scots section: The Clement Wilson Trophy; 1st prize international section: The International Trophy. Entry fee: none. Closing date 31 December 1997. Founded 1972.

The Seebohm Trophy – Age Concern Book of the Year

Application form Age Concern England, Astral House, 1268 London Road, London SW16 4ER *tel* 0181-679 8000 ext. 7456 *e-mail* marshav@ace.org.uk

An annual award is made to the author and publisher of a non-fiction title (published in the previous calendar year) which, in the opinion of the judges, is most successful in promoting the wellbeing and understanding of older people. The author receives £1000, the publisher the silver Seebohm Trophy. Nominations must be received before the end of April each year. Founded in 1995 in memory of Frederic, Lord Seebohm, President of Age Concern, 1971-89.

The Signal Poetry for Children Award

Details The Thimble Press, Lockwood, Station Road, South Woodchester, Stroud, Glos. GL5 5EQ

A prize of £100 is given annually for an outstanding book of poetry published for children in Britain and the Commonwealth during the previous year, whether single poem or anthology and regardless of country of original publication. Articles about the winning book are published in *Signal* each May. Not open to unpublished work.

The André Simon Memorial Fund Book Awards

Details Tessa Hayward, 5 Sion Hill Place, Bath BA1 5SJ *tel* (01225) 336305 *fax* (01225) 421862

Two awards (£2000 each) are given annually, one each for the best new book on food and on drink, plus one Special Commendation of £1000 in either category. Closing date: November each year. Founded in 1978.

Singer & Friedlander/Sunday Times Watercolour Competition

Details Parker Harris & Co., PO Box 279, Esher, Surrey KT10 8YZ *tel* (01372) 462190 *fax* (01372) 460032

An annual competition 'to promote the continuance of the British tradition of fine watercolour painting'. Total prize money: £25,000. Open to artists born or resident in the UK. Closing date: May 1998. Winning entries will be exhibited in London, Manchester, Leeds and Birmingham. Launched 1987.

Smarties Book Prize

Details Book Trust, Book House, 45 East Hill, London SW18 2QZ *tel* 0181-516 2973

A prize (Gold Award) of £2500 is awarded to each of the 3 age category winners (0-5, 6-8 and 9-11 years). Runners-up (Silver Award) receive £1500 each, and third prize (Bronze Award) winners receive £500 each. Eligible books must be published in the UK in the 12 months ending 30 September of the year of presentation and be a work of fiction or poetry for children written in English by a citizen or resident of the UK. Closing date for entries: 31 July of the year of presentation. Sponsored by Nestlé Smarties. Established in 1985.

The W.H. Smith Annual Literary Award

Details W.H. Smith Group, Audrey House,
Ely Place, London EC1N 6SN
tel 0171-404 4242

A prize of £10,000 is awarded annually
to a Commonwealth author (including a
citizen of the UK) whose book is judged
to make the most outstanding contribution to literature. Books must be written
in English and published in the UK within 12 months ending on 31 December
preceding the date of the Award.
Submissions are not accepted; the judges
make their decision independently.

W.H. Smith Thumping Good Read Award

An annual award of £5000 is presented
to the best new fiction author of the year.
The award is judged by a panel of WHS
customers. Founded in 1992.

The Jill Smythies Award

The Linnean Society of London, Burlington
House, Piccadilly, London W1V 0LQ
tel 0171-434 4479 *fax* 0171-287 9364
e-mail john@linnean.demon.co.uk
web site http://www.linnean.org.uk

Established in honour of Jill Smythies
whose career as a botanical artist was cut
short by an accident to her right hand.
The rubic states that 'the Award, to be
made by Council usually annually consisting of a silver medal and a purse (currently £1000) … is for published illustrations, such as drawings and paintings, in
aid of plant identification, with the
emphasis on botanical accuracy and the
accurate portrayal of diagnostic charac-
teristics. Illustrations of cultivars of garden origin are not eligible.' Closing date
for nominations: 30 September. Founded
1988.

Southern Arts Literature Prize

Details The Literature Department,
Southern Arts, 13 St Clement Street, Winchester,
Hants SO23 9DQ
tel (01962) 855099 *fax* (01962) 861186

This prize is awarded annually on a
rotating basis for a published novel,
poetry collection, or work of literary
non-fiction to writers living within the
Southern Arts region. Prize: £1000 plus a
craft commission to the value of £600.
The 1999 award is for fiction. Closing
date: 30 June 1998.

The Stakis Prize for the Scottish Writer of the Year

Details The Stakis Prize, Book Trust Scotland,
Scottish Book Centre, 137 Dundee Street,
Edinburgh EH11 1BG
tel 0131-229 3663 *fax* 0131-228 4293

An annual prize of £1000 is awarded to
each of 5 shortlisted writers, plus a further £9000 to the winner. Submissions
include novels, volumes of short stories,
poetry, biography, autobiography, journalism, science fiction and children's
books as well as theatre, cinema, radio
and television scripts. Open to writers
who were born or have been resident in
Scotland, who have Scottish parents, or
who take Scotland as their inspiration.
Closing date: 31 July for work first made
public during the previous 12 months.

Stand Magazine Awards

Details Stand Magazine, 179 Wingrove Road,
Newcastle upon Tyne NE4 9DA
tel/fax 0191-273 3280

Stand Magazine Short Story Competition

This biennial short story competition –
with prizes to the value of £2500 – is open
to any writer for an original, untranslated
story in English, not longer than 8000
words, not previously published, broadcast or under consideration elsewhere.
Next competition opens January 1999 and
closes June 1999. Entry forms available
from November 1998 on receipt of a UK
sae or 2 IRCs. Founded in 1980.

Stand Poetry Competition

A new international biennial competition with prizes to the value of £2500.
Entrants may submit as many poems as
they wish but each poem must be accompanied by a donation of at least £3.50/
$7.50 for the first, and £3.00/$7.00 for
each subsequent poem. Competition
opens 1 January 1998 and closes 30 June
1998. For further details and entry form
on receipt of a UK sae or 2 IRCs.

The Steinbeck Award

Details William Heinemann, Michelin House,
81 Fulham Road, London SW3 6RB
tel 0171-581 9393 *fax* 0171-225 9095

This bi-annual award is given to a writer
under the age of 40 for a new work of fiction in English, written in the spirit of
Steinbeck, e.g. a work dedicated to issues

of poverty, race or political injustice. The award is £10,000, half of which goes to a charity of the winner's choice. Closing date: 1 March. Founded in 1994.

The Stern Silver Pen Award for Non-Fiction
Details PEN, 7 Dilke Street, London SW3 4JE
tel 0171-352 6303 *fax* 0171-351 0220
This award of £1000 is given annually for an outstanding work of non-fiction written in English and published during the previous year by an author of British nationality or an author who has been a long-term resident in the UK. No submissions please – books are nominated by members of the PEN Executive Committee. Sponsored by the Stern family since 1996. Founded in 1969.

The Suspended Sentence Award
Details The James Joyce Foundation, PO Box 104, Kings Cross, NSW 2011, Australia
tel (02) 9332 3649 *fax* (02) 9363 0507
An award for accomplishment in writing. James Joyce believed that it wasn't simply a matter of getting the right words but of getting those words in the right order. The Award will be given to that piece of writing which in the opinion of the judges most closely approximates to Joyce's standard of musical precision and significant content. It may be in prose or verse and can be in the form of fiction or non-fiction. Applicants must be residents of Australia and have had work previously published in book form or had 60 minutes of material produced (radio, TV, film or theatre), or must be recommended by a literary agent, publisher, producer or director. Entry fee: $20. Closing date: May 1998. Send sae for details.

Reginald Taylor and Lord Fletcher Essay Competition
Submissions Hon. Editor, Dr Martin Henig, British Archaeological Association, Institute of Archaeology, 36 Beaumont Street, Oxford OX1 2PG
A prize of a medal and £300 is awarded biennially for the best unpublished essay, not exceeding 7500 words, which shows original research on a subject of archaeological, art-historical or antiquarian interest within the period from the Roman era to ad 1830. The successful competitor may be invited to read the essay before the Association and the essay may be published in the Association's *Journal*. Competitors should notify the Hon. Editor in advance of the intended subject of their work. Next award: November 2000 (to be presented as one of the British Archaeological Awards), and the essay should be submitted not later than 1 June 1998, enclosing an sae. Founded in memory of E. Reginald Taylor FSA and Lord Fletcher FSA.

Society for Theatre Research Book Prize
Details The Society for Theatre Research, c/o The Theatre Museum, 1E Tavistock Street, London WC2E 7PA
An annual award (£400) is given to the author whose book, in the opinion of the judges, is the best original research into any aspect of the history and technique of the British theatre. Books must have been published in English in the preceding calendar year. Founded 1997.

The Thomas Cook Travel Book Award
Details Travel Book Award, Thomas Cook Publishing, PO Box 227, Thorpe Wood, Peterborough PE3 6PU
tel (01733) 503566
This annual award is given to encourage the art of travel writing. Travel narrative books (150pp minimum) written in English and published between 1 January and 31 December of the preceding year are eligible. Established in 1980.

Northampton Borough Council Anne Tibble Poetry Competition
Details Events Team Office, Directorate of Environment Services, Cliftonville House, Bedford Road, Northampton NN4 7NR
tel (01604) 233500 ext 4243
This annual prize is awarded for a poem, maximum length 20 lines, to anyone resident in Great Britain. The first prize is £200; other prizes to a total value of £200.

The Times Educational Supplement Book Awards
Details TES Book Awards, The Times Educational Supplement, Admiral House, 66-68 East Smithfield, London E1 9XY
tel 0171-782 3000 *fax* 0171-782 3200
The Times Educational Supplement Information Book Awards
There are 2 annual awards for the best information books for children. The

Junior Award is for books for 5-10 year-olds, and the Senior Award is for books for 11-16 year-olds.

The Times Educational Supplement Schoolbook Awards
There are 2 annual awards for the best primary and secondary school textbooks. The subject varies each year.

Tir Na N-og Awards
Details Welsh Books Council, Castell Brychan, Aberystwyth, Ceredigion SY23 2JB
tel (01970) 624151 *fax* (01970) 625385
There are 3 annual awards to children's authors and illustrators:
• best original Welsh fiction, including short stories and picture books;
• best original Welsh non-fiction book of the year;
• best English book with an authentic Welsh background.
Total prize value is £3000. Founded 1976.

The Tom-Gallon Trust
Submissions The Secretary, The Society of Authors, 84 Drayton Gardens, SW10 9SB
A biennial award is made to fiction writers of limited means who have had at least one short story accepted for publication. An award of £600 was made in 1997. Authors wishing to enter should send to the Secretary:
• a list of their already published fiction, giving the name of the publisher or periodical in each case and the approximate date of publication;
• one published or unpublished short story;
• a brief statement of their financial position;
• an undertaking that they intend to devote a substantial amount of time to the writing of fiction as soon as they are financially able to do so;
• an sae for the return of the work submitted.
Next closing date: 20 September 2000.

The Translators Association Awards
Details Kate Pool, The Translators Association, 84 Drayton Gardens, London SW10 9SB
The Translators Association of the Society of Authors administers a number of prizes for translations into English. They include prizes for translations of Dutch and Flemish, French, German, Italian, Japanese, Portuguese, Spanish and Swedish works.

The Betty Trask Awards
Details The Society of Authors, 84 Drayton Gardens, London SW10 9SB
These awards are for the benefit of young authors under the age of 35 and are given on the strength of a first novel (published or unpublished) of a romantic or traditional nature. It is expected that prizes totalling at least £25,000 will be presented each year. The winners are required to use the money for a period or periods of foreign travel. Closing date: 31 January. Made possible through a generous bequest from Miss Betty Trask.

The Travelling Scholarships
These are non-competitive awards administered by the Society of Authors. Submissions are not required.

The Trewithen Poetry Prize
Details The Competition Secretary, Treskewes Cottage, Trewithen Moor, Stithians, Truro, Cornwall TR3 7DU
An annual prize to promote poetry with a rural theme. Poems can reflect contemporary rural living, environmental concerns, or any other aspect of nature or rural life in any country. Total prize money: £600. In addition, prize-winners will have their poems published in the *Trewithen Chapbook*, a biennial limited edition publication. Entry fee: £2.50. Send sae for entry form. Closing date: 31 October 1998.

T.E. Utley Memorial Fund Award
Details Virginia Utley, 111 Sugden Road, London SW11 5ED
tel 0171-228 3900
Prizes of £2500 and 2 of £1500 are awarded annually for an essay on a given subject.

'Charles Veillon' European Essay Prize
Details The Secretary, Charles Veillon Foundation, CH 1017 Lausanne, Switzerland
tel (021) 701 4147
A prize of 25,000 Swiss francs is awarded annually to a European writer or essayist for essays offering a critical look at modern society's way of life and ideology. Founded in 1975.

Ver Poets Open Competition

Organiser May Badman, Ver Poets,
61-63 Chiswell Green Lane, St Albans,
Herts. AL2 3AL
tel (01727) 867005

A competition open to anyone for poems
of up to 30 lines of any genre or subject
matter, which must be unpublished work
in English. Prizes: £500 (1st), £300 (2nd),
£100 (2 x 3rd). Entry fee: £2.50 per poem
(each year a gift to charity is made).
Closing date 30 April 1998.

Edgar Wallace Award

Details The Hon. Secretary, London Press Club,
Freedom Forum, Stanhope House, Stanhope
Place, London W2 2HH
tel 0171-402 2566 *fax* 0171-262 4631
e-mail 101455.3575@compuserve.com

Chosen by a panel of senior editors, this
annual award of a silver inkstand is
given for outstanding writing or reporting by a journalist. Founded in 1990.

Wandsworth London Writers Competition

Details Assistant Director of Leisure and Amenity
Services (Community Services), Wandsworth
Town Hall, High Street, London SW18 2PU
tel 0181-871 7037 *fax* 0181-871 7630

Open to writers of 16 years and over who
live, work or study in the Greater
London Area. Awards are made annually
in 2 classes, Poetry and Short Story, the
prizes totalling £1000 in each class.
Entries must be previously unpublished
work. Judging is under the chairmanship
of Martyn Goff, Chairman of the Poetry
Book Society.

Wellcome Trust Prize

Details The Wellcome Trust, 210 Euston Road,
London NW1 2BE
tel 0171-611 7221/8264 *fax* 0171-611 8269
e-mail comm+ed@wellcome.ac.uk
web site http://www.wellcome.ac.uk

A prize of £25,000 (paid quarterly over
one year) gives the opportunity for a
professional life scientist to take a break
from their normal routine to write a
popular book about their work which
will educate, captivate and inspire the
non-specialist lay reader. The winning
work will be published by HarperCollins.
Applicants must be resident in the UK
and have not previously published a
popular science book. Founded 1997.

Whitbread Book Awards

Details Denise Bayat, The Booksellers
Association, Minster House,
272 Vauxhall Bridge Road, London SW1V 1BA
tel 0171-834 5477 *fax* 0171-834 8812
e-mail 100437.2261@compuserve.com

The awards celebrate the best contemporary British writing of the year. Judged in
2 stages and offering a total of £39,000
prize money, the awards are open to 4
categories: Novel, First Novel,
Biography/Autobiography, Poetry. The
winner in each category receives a
Whitbread Award of £2000. These 4 nominations are judged for the Whitbread
Book of the Year, the overall winner
receiving an additional £21,000. Writers
must have lived in Great Britain and
Ireland for 3 or more years. Submissions
only from publishers. Closing date: early
July.

Whitbread Children's Book of the Year
Run in parallel to the Book of the Year
Award, the overall winner receives
£10,000. Sponsored by Whitbread plc.

The Whitfield Prize

Submissions Executive Secretary, Royal
Historical Society, University College London,
Gower Street, London WC1E 6BT
tel/fax 0171-387 7532

The Prize (value £1000) is announced in
July each year for the best work on a subject within a field of British history. It
must be its author's first solely written
history book, an original and scholarly
work of historical research and have
been published in the UK in the preceding calendar year. Three non-returnable
copies of an eligible book should be submitted before 31 December to the
Executive Secretary.

John Whiting Award

Details Drama Dept, Arts Council of England,
14 Great Peter Street, London SW1P 3NQ
tel 0171-333 0100 ext 431
e-mail info.drama.ace@artsfb.org.uk

This prize of £6000 is given annually.
Eligible to apply are any writers who have
received during the previous 2 calendar
years an award through the Arts Council
new theatre writing schemes, or who have
had a commission or premier production
by a theatre company in receipt of an
annual subsidy. Founded 1965.

Wildlife Photographer of the Year

Details Wildlife Photographer of the Year,
The Natural History Museum, Cromwell Road,
London SW7 5BD
tel 0171-938 8714 *fax* 0171-938 8788
e-mail wildphoto@nhm.ac.uk
web site http://www.nhm.ac.uk
An annual award given to the photographer whose individual image is judged to be the most striking and memorable. The winner receives a bronze trophy and £2000. Open to anyone aged 18 and over. Closing date for entries: mid May 1999. Sponsored by BG plc. Founded 1983.

The Raymond Williams Community Publishing Prizes

Details The Secretary, Literature Department, The Arts Council of England, 14 Great Peter Street, London SW1P 3NQ
tel 0171-973 6442
These annual prizes are awarded to non-profit making publishers for works of outstanding imaginative and creative quality which reflect the voices and experiences of the people of particular communities. First prize: £2000 to publisher, £1000 to writer/group, runner-up: £1500 to publisher, £500 to writer/group. Founded in 1990.

David T.K. Wong Fellowship

Details David T.K. Wong Fellowship, School of English & American Studies, University of East Anglia, Norwich NR4 7TJ
tel (01603) 592810 *fax* (01603) 507728
Founded by David Wong, retired senior civil servant, journalist and businessman, the annual Fellowship (worth £25,000) at the University of East Anglia will give writers of exceptional talent the chance to produce a work of fiction in English which deals seriously with some aspect of life in the Far East. Write for further details. Closing date: 31 October each year. Founded 1997.

The Woolwich Young Radio Playwrights' Competition

Details The Woolwich Young Radio Playwrights' Competition, IRDP, PO Box 518, Manningtree, Essex CO11 1XD
Writers aged 25 or under are invited to create half-hour radio plays. The 10 winning plays will be professionally produced and broadcast on the radio. Send sae for details. Founded 1990.

World Review Award

Details World Review, 14-16 Carroun Road, London SW8 1JT
tel/fax 0171-582 3996
For each issue of *World Review* (quarterly) the authors of 12 books on subjects of worldwide importance are invited to write about the themes of their books. An award of £1000 is given annually to the author whose book is judged to deserve to be the most influential. Founded 1996.

Write A Story for Children Competition

Entry forms The Academy of Children's Writers, PO Box 95, Huntingdon, Cambs. PE17 5RL
tel (01487) 832752
Three prizes are awarded annually (1st £1000, 2nd £200, 3rd £100) for a short story for children, maximum 1000 words, by an unpublished writer of children's fiction. Founded in 1984.

Writers' Forum Short Story Competition

Details Writers' Forum, 21 Belle Vue Street, Filey, North Yorkshire YO14 9HU
tel/fax (01723) 513279
An annual competition open to unpublished short stories of up to 2000 words. Prizes are £300 (1st), £100 (2nd), £50 (3rd); all the winning entries will be published in *Writers' Forum* magazine. Entry fee: £4. Closing date: 16 March 1999. Founded 1991.

The Writers' Guild Awards

Details 430 Edgware Road, London W2 1EH
tel 0171-732 8074 *fax* 0171-706 2413
There are 5 categories of awards:
• radio – original drama, comedy/light entertainment, dramatisations, children's;
• theatre – West End, fringe, regional, children's;
• books – non-fiction, fiction, children's;
• film – best screenplay;
• television – original play/film, original drama series, original drama serial, dramatisation/adaptation, situation comedy, light entertainment, children's.
There are also awards for Non-English Language, New Writer of the Year, and Lifetime Achievement. The various shortlists are prepared by a different jury in each category and presented to the Guild Membership for its final vote.
Nominations are made from works which have been published, performed

or broadcast during the period 1 January-31 December each year. No nominations are required from the public. Established 1961; relaunched 1991.

Xenos Annual Short Story Competition
22 Poplar Street, Haslingden,
Rossendale BB4 5LY
tel (01706) 211590
e-mail xenos@xenos.demon.co.uk
web site http://www.xenos.demon.co.uk
Short stories of 2000-10,000 words of all genres are considered, except graphic horror/blood and gore or anything with an explicit sexual content. Cash prizes and/or publication in *Xenos* magazine, a bi-monthly platform for both new and established writers. Write for details. Founded 1990.

Yorkshire Children's Book Cover Award
Details Steve Hird, Schools Library Service, Maltby Library Headquarters, High Street, Maltby, Rotherham, South Yorkshire S66 8LA
tel (01709) 813034 *fax* (01709) 798269
An annual award for the best jacket on a children's book published in the relevant year. Established 1995 by Yorkshire Libraries for Children.

Yorkshire Post Literary Awards
Submissions Margaret Brown,
Yorkshire Post Literary Awards,
Yorkshire Post Newspapers Ltd, PO Box 168,
Wellington Street, Leeds LS1 1RF
Submissions are accepted only from publishers. For the first 2 awards, authors should be British or resident in the UK; for the third, authors need not be British, nor residents.

Yorkshire Post Book of the Year
A prize of £1200 annually for the Best Book, either fiction or non-fiction. Next closing date: 31 December.

Yorkshire Post Best First Work Award
A prize of £1000 is awarded for the Best First Work by a new author, either fiction or non-fiction. Next closing date: 31 December.

Yorkshire Post Art and Music Book Award
Prizes of £1000 each are given to authors whose books are judged to have contributed most to the understanding and appreciation of Art and of Music. Next closing date: 31 January.

Young Wildlife Photographer of the Year
Details Young Wildlife Photographer of the Year, The Natural History Museum, London SW7 5BD
tel 0171-938 8714 *fax* 0171-938 8788
e-mail wildphoto@nhm.ac.uk
web site http://www.nhm.ac.uk
An annual competition open to photographers aged 17 or under for pictures showing wild animals or plants, or wild landscapes. The award will be given to the photographer whose image is judged to be the most striking and memorable. The winner receives a bronze trophy of an ibis and £500, plus a day out with photographer Heather Angel. Sponsored by BG plc. Closing date for entries: mid May 1999. Founded 1984.

Young Writers' Festival: Write Your Play
Details Young Writers' Festival, Royal Court Young People's Theatre, 309 Portobello Road, London W10 5TD
tel 0181-960 4641 *fax* 0181-960 1434
Anyone aged 25 or under can submit a play on any subject. A selection of plays is professionally presented by the Royal Court Theatre with the writers fully involved in rehearsal and production. Workshops are run by professional theatre practitioners and designed to help everyone attending to write a play.

Prizes and awards by subject area

This list provides a quick reference to the main listings of prizes, competitions and awards which starts on page 510.

Biography

J.R. Ackerley Prize
Authors' Club Marsh Biography Award
James Tait Black Memorial Prize
The Duff Cooper Prize
The Royal Society of Literature Award under the W.H. Heinemann Bequest
The Runciman Award
The Stakis Prize for the Scottish Writer of the Year
Whitbread Book Awards

Children

Hans Christian Andersen Medal
The Bisto Book of the Year Award
Children's Book Award
The Eleanor Farjeon Award
The Fidler Award
The Guardian Children's Fiction Prize
The Independent/Scholastic Story of the Year Competition
The Library Association Carnegie and Kate Greenaway Awards
The Macmillan Prize for a Children's Picture Book
Kurt Maschler Award
The BFC/Mother Goose Award
The Signal Poetry for Children Award
Smarties Book Prize
The Times Educational Supplement Book Awards
Tir Na N-og Awards
Write a Story for Children Competition
Writers' Guild Awards
Yorkshire Children's Book Cover Award

Drama – theatre, TV and radio

The David Cohen British Literature Prize
Verity Bargate Award
Samuel Beckett Award
Miles Franklin Literary Award
The Richard Imison Memorial Award
LAB/LBC London Radio Playwrights' Festival
Meyer-Whitworth Award
P.J. O'Connor Awards
Dennis Potter Play of the Year Award
Questors National Student Playwriting Competition
John Whiting Award
The Woolwich Young Radio Playwrights' Competition
Writers' Guild Awards
Young Writers' Festival: Write Your Play

Essays

The David Cohen British Literature Prize
Millennial Science Essay Competition
Shiva Naipaul Award
Reginald Taylor and Lord Fletcher Essay Competition
T.E. Utley Memorial Fund Award
Charles Veillon European Essay Prize

Fiction

Authors' Club Best First Novel Award
James Tait Black Memorial Prize
The Booker Prize
Arthur C. Clarke Award
The David Cohen British Literature Prize
Commonwealth Writers Prize
CWA Awards
The Dundee Book Prize
Encore Award
Christopher Ewart-Biggs Memorial Prize
The Geoffrey Faber Memorial Prize
Miles Franklin Literary Award
Mind Book of the Year/Allen Lane Award
The Guardian Fiction Prize
The Hawthornden Prize
David Higham Prize for Fiction
The Winifred Holtby Memorial Prize
International IMPAC Dublin Literary Award
Irish Times Literary Prizes
Japan Festival Awards
Jewish Quarterly Literary Prizes
The Lichfield Prize
The McKitterick Prize (published/unpublished)
The Enid McLeod Literary Prize
Macmillan Silver Pen Award for Fiction
The Mail on Sunday-John Llewellyn Rhys Prize
The Somerset Maugham Awards
Mind Book of the Year/Allen Lane Award
Orange Prize for Fiction
The Portico Prize
Romantic Novelists' Association Awards
The Runciman Award
Scottish Arts Council Book Awards
W.H. Smith Annual Literary Award
W.H. Smith Thumping Good Read Award
Southern Arts Literature Prize
The Stakis Prize for the Scottish Writer of the Year
The Steinbeck Award

The Suspended Sentence Award
The Betty Trask Awards
Whitbread Book Awards
David T.K. Wong Fellowship
Writers' Guild Awards
Yorkshire Post Literary Awards

Fine art – see Visual art

Grants, bursaries and fellowships

Arts Council of England
The Arts Council of Ireland
Arts Council of Wales
Authors' Foundation
Kathleen Blundell Trust
Alfred Bradley Bursary
British Academy Research
  Awards
The Rhys Davies Trust
European Jewish Publication
  Society Grants
E.M. Forster Award
The Fulbright Commission
  Awards
E.C. Gregory Trust Fund
Hawthornden Writers'
  Fellowships
Leverhulme Research
  Fellowships and Grants
Northern Arts Writers' Awards
The Margaret Rhondda Award
Scottish Arts Council
The Travelling Scholarships
Wellcome Trust Prize
David T.K. Wong Fellowship

Illustration

Hans Christian Andersen Medal
Bisto Book of the Year Award
The Book Art Prize
British Fantasy Awards
The Eleanor Farjeon Award
L. Ron Hubbard's Illustrators of
  the Future Contest
Images – The Best of
  Illustration
The Macmillan Prize for a
  Children's Picture Book
Kurt Maschler Award
The BFC/Mother Goose Award
The National Art Library
  Illustration Awards
The Jill Smythies Award
Tir Na N-og Awards
Yorkshire Children's Book
  Cover Award

Journalism

Freedom Award
Glaxo Wellcome ABSW Science
  Writers Awards
George Orwell Memorial Prize
Catherine Pakenham Memorial
  Award
Margaret Rhondda Award
Scoop of the Year Award
The Stakis Prize for the
  Scottish Writer of the Year
Edgar Wallace Award

Non-fiction

Alexander Prize (History)
Authors' Club Sir Banister
  Fletcher Award (Architecture)
BBC Wildlife Magazine Awards
  for Nature Writing
David Berry Prize (History)
BP Natural World Book Prize
Katharine Briggs Folklore Award
British Academy Medals and
  Prizes
The Duff Cooper Prize
The Rose Mary Crawshay Prizes
CWA Awards
Christopher Ewart-Biggs
  Memorial Prize
Gladstone History Book Prize
Glenfiddich Awards (Food and
  Drink)
The Calvin and Rose G.
  Hoffman Memorial Prize
Irish Times Literary Prizes
Jewish Quarterly Literary Prizes
Kraszna-Krausz Awards
The International Langhe
  Ceretto Prize for Food and
  Wine Culture
Japan Festival Awards
The Library Association
  Reference Awards
The Livingstone Award for
  Travel
The Mail on Sunday-John
  Llewellyn Rhys Prize
The Somerset Maugham
  Awards
MCA Book Prize (Management)
Enid McLeod Prize
Mind Book of the Year/Allen
  Lane Award
The Portico Prize
Trevor Reese Memorial Prize
The Rhône-Poulenc Prizes for
  Science Books
The Royal Society of Literature
  Award under the W.H.
  Heinemann Bequest

The Medical Society of London
  Prizes
The Rio Tinto David Watt
  Memorial Prize
Runciman Award
Scottish Arts Council Book
  Awards
The André Simon Memorial
  Fund Book Awards (Food and
  Drink)
W.H. Smith Annual Literary
  Award
The Society for Theatre
  Research Book Prize
Southern Arts Literature Prize
The Stern Silver Pen Award for
  Non-Fiction
The Suspended Sentence Award
The Thomas Cook Travel Book
  Award (Travel writing)
The Times Educational
  Supplement Book Awards
The Whitfield Prize (History)
Writers' Guild Awards
Yorkshire Post Literary Awards

Photography – see Visual art

Poetry

Rosemary Arthur Award
Arvon Foundation
BBC Wildlife Magazine Poet of
  the Year Contest
The David Cohen British
  Literature Prize
Denis Devlin Memorial Award
Arts Council of Ireland
Arts Council of Wales
The Bridport Prize
Cholmondeley Award
Cardiff International Poetry
  Competition
DT Charitable Trust Open
  Poetry Competition
The T.S. Eliot Prize
Geoffrey Faber Memorial Prize
Forward Poetry Prizes
The Felicia Hemans Prize for
  Lyrical Poetry
Irish Times Literary Prizes
Kent & Sussex Poetry Society
  Open Poetry Competition
The Somerset Maugham
  Awards
National Poetry Competition
National Poetry Competition
  (Ireland)
The New Writer Poetry Prizes

Peterloo Poets Open Poetry Competition
'Poem of the Month' Competition
Poetry Life Open Poetry Competition
Rhyme International Annual Poetry Competition
The Royal Society of Literature Award under the W.H. Heinemann Bequest
The Runciman Award
Scottish Arts Council Book Awards
The Scottish International Open Poetry Competition
The Signal Poetry for Children Award
Smarties Book Prize
Southern Arts Literature Prize
The Stakis Prize for the Scottish Writer of the Year
Stand Poetry Competition
Northampton Borough Council Anne Tibble Poetry Competition
The Trewithen Poetry Prize
Ver Poets Open Competition
Wandsworth London Writers Competition
Whitbread Book Awards

Short stories

Arc Story Competition
Northampton Borough Council Writers' Competition Award for the H.E. Bates Short Story
The Bridport Prize
The David Cohen British Literature Prize
CWA/The Macallan Short Story Dagger
DT Charitable Trust Annual Ghost Story Competition
DT Charitable Trust Annual Love Story Competition
The Martin Healy Short Story Award
David Higham Prize for Fiction
L. Ron Hubbard's Writers of the Future Contest
The Lady Short Story Competition

Macallan/Scotland on Sunday Short Story Competition
Macmillan Silver Pen Award for Fiction
One Voice
The Matthew Prichard Award for Short Story Writing
The Ian St James Awards
The Stakis Prize for the Scottish Writer of the Year
Stand Magazine Short Story Competition
The Tom-Gallon Trust Award
Wandsworth London Writers Competition
Write A Story for Children Competition
Writers' Forum Short Story Competition
Xenos Annual Short Story Competition

Translation

European Translation Prize Arts Council of England
Authors' Club Marsh Award
The European Poetry Translation Prize
The Translators Association Awards

Specialist

BA/Bookseller Author of the Year Award
European Literary Prize (Literature)
The Boardman Tasker Prize (Mountain Literature)
British Academy Medals and Prizes
British Book Awards
British Fantasy Awards
DT Charitable Trust Awards – Self-Publishing Award
The Lionel Gelber Prize (International Relations)
The Writers' Guild Awards
Heywood Hill Literary Prize
William Hill Sports Book of the Year Award
The Library Association Wheatley Medal (Indexing)

The London New Writing Competition
The Enid McLeod Literary Prize
The Somerset Maugham Awards
The Nobel Prize in Literature
One Voice
The Portico Prize
The Rooney Prize for Irish Literature
The Runciman Award (Greece)
Scottish Arts Council Book Awards
Scottish Book of the Year and Scottish First Book
The Seebohm Trophy – Age Concern Book of the Year
The W.H. Smith Annual Literary Award
Times Educational Supplement Book Awards
The Raymond Williams Community Publishing Prizes
World Review Award

Visual art

The Book Art Prize
BP Portrait Award
The Alasdair Gilchrist Memorial Award
Juliet Gomperts Memorial Scholarship
Hunting Art Prizes
Images – The Best of British Illustration
The John Kobal Photographic Portrait Award
Laing Art Prize
Millfield Arts Projects
John Moores Liverpool Exhibition
The Observer Hodge Award/Exhibition
Alastair Salvesen Art Scholarship
Singer & Friedlander/Sunday Times Watercolour Competition
Young Wildlife Photographer of the Year

Open art exhibitions

This list should be used as a guide only. Many handing-in and exhibition dates had not been finalised as the Yearbook went to press. Send an sae to the relevant address for further information and entry forms. A handling fee is normally charged for each work entered. See Societies, associations and clubs section on page 457 for general information on the societies listed here.

Artists, Royal Birmingham Society of
69A New Street, Birmingham B2 4DU
tel 0121-643 3768 *fax* 0121-644 5298
Oil and Sculpture (February); Watercolour and Craftwork (May); RBSA Prize Competition (June); Pastel and Drawing (December).

Artists, Royal Society of British
17 Carlton House Terrace, London SW1Y 5BD
tel 0171-930 6844 *fax* 0171-839 7830
Held annually at the Mall Galleries, London SW1. Hand in August for exhibition in September. Prizes and awards.

Botantical Artists, Society of
1 Knapp Cottages, Wyke, Gillingham, Dorset SP8 4NQ
tel (01747) 825718; 0171-222 2723 (during exhibitions)
Held annually (Easter) at the Westminster Gallery, Westminster Central Hall, London SW1. Hand in on 1 March 1999 for 16-24 April exhibition.

BP Portrait Award – see Prizes and awards, page 510

The Discerning Eye
17 Carlton House Terrace, London SW1Y 5BD
tel 0171-930 6844 *fax* 0171-839 7830
Held annually at the Mall Galleries, London SW1. Work selected by a panel of 2 critics, 2 collectors, and 2 artists. Prizes. Hand in 4-5 September for 20 November-6 December 1998 exhibition.

Graphic Fine Art, Society of
15 Willow Way, Hatfield, Herts. AL10 9QD
Held annually at the Art Connoisseur Gallery. Hand in mid August for mid September exhibition.

Hunting Art Prizes – see Prizes and awards, page 510

Illustrators, The Association of – see Prizes and awards, page 510

Laing Art Prize – see Prizes and awards, page 510

Marine Artists, Royal Society of
17 Carlton House Terrace, London SW1Y 5BD
tel 0171-930 6844 *fax* 0171-839 7830
Held annually at the Mall Galleries, London SW1. Hand in September for exhibition in October. Prizes and awards.

Millfield Summer Show – see Prizes and awards, page 510

Miniature Painters, Sculptors and Gravers, Royal Society of
1 Knapp Cottages, Wyke, Gillingham, Dorset SP8 4NQ
tel (01747) 825718; 0171-222 2723 (during exhibitions)
Held annually (November) at the Westminster Gallery, Westminster Central Hall, London SW1. Hand in on 20 September 1999 for 12-20 November exhibition.

Miniaturists, British Society of
Briargate, 2 The Brambles, Ilkley, West Yorkshire LS29 9DH
tel (01943) 609075
Two per year: summer (5-13 June 1999) and Christmas (27 November-5 December 1999).

John Moores Liverpool Exhibition – see Prizes and awards, page 510

New English Art Club

17 Carlton House Terrace, London SW1Y 5BD
tel 0171-930 6844 *fax* 0171-839 7830

Held annually at the Mall Galleries, London SW1. Hand in October for exhibition in November. Prizes and awards.

Oil Painters, Royal Institute of

17 Carlton House Terrace, London SW1Y 5BD
tel 0171-930 6844 *fax* 0171-839 7830

Held annually at the Mall Galleries, London SW1. Hand in October for exhibition in December. Prizes and awards.

Oils, Pastels and Acrylics, British Society of Painters in

Briargate, 2 The Brambles, Ilkley, West Yorkshire LS29 9DH
tel (01943) 609075

Two per year: spring (13-21 March 1999) and autumn (18-26 September 1999).

Oriel Mostyn Open

12 Vaughan Street, Llandudno LL30 1AB
tel (01492) 879201/870875 *fax* (01492) 878869

Held annually (December-February). Total prizes: £6000. For entry forms, send sae in August.

Painters in Water Colours, Royal Institute of

17 Carlton House Terrace, London SW1Y 5BD
tel 0171-930 6844 *fax* 0171-839 7830

Held annually at the Mall Galleries, London SW1. Hand in end of February for exhibition in April.

The Pastel Society

17 Carlton House Terrace, London SW1Y 5BD
tel 0171-930 6844 *fax* 0171-839 7830

Held annually at the Mall Galleries, London SW1. Hand in January for exhibition in March.

Portrait Painters, Royal Society of

17 Carlton House Terrace, London SW1Y 5BD
tel 0171-930 6844 *fax* 0171-839 7830

Held annually at the Mall Galleries, London SW1. Hand in March for exhibition in May.

Ridley Art Society

50 Crowborough Road, London SW17 9QQ
tel 0181-682 1212

Held annually in Central London.

Royal Academy of Arts

Piccadilly, London W1V 0DS
tel 0171-300 5680

Summer Exhibition held annually. Closing date for entry forms: 14 April. Hand in during April for June-August exhibition.

Royal Over-Seas League

Park Place, St James's Street, London SW1A 1LR
tel 0171-408 0214 ext. 219 *fax* 0171-499 6738

Open to artists aged up to and including 35 years who are UK and Commonwealth citizens. Awards total more than £7000. Exhibition held annually September-November. Submissions: July.

Scottish Academy, Royal

The Mound, Edinburgh EH2 2EL
tel 0131-225 6671 *fax* 0131-225 2349

Exhibition held annually (April-July) for painting, sculpture and architecture.

Singer & Friedlander/Sunday Times Watercolour Competition – see Prizes and awards, page 510

Stockport Art Gallery

Wellington Road South, Stockport SK3 8AB
tel 0161-474 4453 *fax* 0161-480 4960

Held annually (summer); open to artists in the northwest. Four merit award prizes.

Watercolour Society, British

Briargate, 2 The Brambles, Ilkley, West Yorkshire LS29 9DH
tel (01943) 609075

Two per year: summer (5-13 June 1999) and Christmas (27 November-5 December 1999).

West of England Academy, Royal

Queens Road, Clifton, Bristol BS8 1PX
tel 0117-973 5129 *fax* 0117-923 7874

Held annually. Hand in 24-25 September 1998 for 25 October-12 December exhibition.

Wildlife Artists, Society of

17 Carlton House Terrace, London SW1Y 5BD
tel 0171-930 6844 *fax* 0171-839 7830

Held annually at the Mall Galleries, SW1. Hand in June for July exhibition.

Women Artists, The Society of

Executive Secretary 1 Knapp Cottages, Wyke, Gillingham, Dorset SP8 4NQ
tel (01747) 825718 *fax* (01747) 826835

Held annually for painting and sculpture, open to all women. Hand in 2 February 1999 for 12-27 March exhibition at Westminster Gallery, Westminster Central Hall, London SW1H 9NU.

Literature festivals

There are hundreds of arts festivals held in the UK each year – too many to mention in this Yearbook and many of which are not applicable specifically to writers. We give here a selection of literature festivals and general arts festivals which include literature events. Space constraints and the nature of an annual publication together determine that only brief details are given; contact festival organisers for a full programme of events.

Aldeburgh Poetry Festival
Aldeburgh Poetry Trust, Goldings, Goldings Lane, Leiston, Suffolk IP16 4EB
tel (01728) 830631 *fax* (01728) 832029
Festival Co-ordinator Michael Laskey
Takes place 6-8 Nov 1998
An annual international festival of contemporary poetry. A celebratory weekend including readings, workshops, a public masterclass, a lecture and a children's event. Twenty different poets as well as fringe events. Preceded by an extended residency for one of the invited poets. Festival prize for the year's best first collection.

Aspects Festival
North Down Heritage Centre, The Castle, Bangor, Co. Down BT20 4BT
tel (01247) 271200 *fax* (01247) 271370
Festival Director Kenneth Irvine
Contact Paula Clamp (Arts Officer)
Takes place 23-27 Sept 1998
An annual celebration of contemporary Irish writing with novelists, poets, playwrights and non-fiction writers. Includes readings, discussions, workshops and a children's day.

Ballymena Arts Festival
Ballymena Borough Council, Ardeevin, 80 Galgorm Road, Ballymena, Co. Antrim BT42 1AB
tel (01266) 660300 *fax* (01266) 660400
Takes place 30 Sept-17 Oct 1998
A general arts festival which includes literature events.

Bath Literature Festival
Bath Festivals Trust, 2 Midland Bridge Road, Bath BA2 3EQ
tel (01225) 462231 *fax* (01225) 445551
Programme Director Laurence Staig
Takes place 27 Feb-7 March 1999
An annual 9-day festival with leading guest writers. Includes readings, debates, discussions and workshops, and children's activities. Education & Community Programme includes author visits to schools and a children's writing competition. Each year has a chosen theme.

Belfast Festival at Queen's
Festival House, 25 College Gardens, Belfast BT9 6BS
tel (01232) 667687 *fax* (01232) 663733
Assistant Director Rosie Turner
Takes place November
The largest annual arts event in Ireland. Includes literature events. Programme available mid-September.

Birmingham Readers & Writers Festival
Festival Office, Central Library, Chamberlain Square, Birmingham B3 3HQ
tel 0121-303 4244 *fax* 0121-233 9702
e-mail readers.writers@dial.pipex.com
Festival Director Helen Cross
Takes place October/November
An annual 9-day festival which aims to promote the best in contemporary literature, both from within the city and internationally. Over 100 events are on offer: workshops, performances, talks, discussions, plus a special day of events for children. Leading guest writers and poets; poet in residence; BBC tie-ins. The festival runs the *Midlands Poetry Competition* and organises the *Birmingham Cable Children's Book Awards*.

Book Now!

Leisure Service Department,
London Borough of Richmond upon Thames,
Langholm Lodge, 146 Petersham Road,
Richmond, Surrey TW10 6UX
tel 0181-332 0534 *fax* 0181-940 7568
Principal Arts Officer Nigel Cutting
Takes place throughout November

An annual literature festival covering a broad range of subjects. Leading British guest writers and poets hold discussions, talks, debates and workshops and give readings. There are also exhibitions, storytelling sessions and a schools programme.

Brighton Festival

Brighton Festival Society Ltd, 21-22 Old Steine, Brighton BN1 1EL
tel (01273) 292950 *fax* (01273) 622453
e-mail info@brighton-festival.org.uk
web site http://www.brighton-festival.org.uk
Takes place May

An annual general arts festival with a large literature programme. Leading guest writers cover a broad range of subjects in a diverse programme of events. Programme published end of February.

Broadstairs Dickens Festival

c/o Rooftops, 58 High Street, Broadstairs, Kent CT10 1JT
tel (01843) 863453
Contact Honorary Festival Organiser
Takes place June

An annual festival held annually since 1937 with a variety of events inspired by Dickens. Includes walks, talks, dramatic readings, and a festival play of a Dickens work.

Cambridge Conference of Contemporary Poetry

c/o Ian Patterson, King's College, Cambridge CB2 1ST
tel (01223) 327455
e-mail ikp1000@cam.ac.uk
Takes place April

An annual weekend of poetry readings, discussion and performance of international poetry in the modernist tradition.

Canterbury Festival

Festival Office, Christ Church Gate,
The Precincts, Canterbury, Kent CT1 2EE
tel (01227) 472820 *fax* (01227) 781830
Takes place 10-24 Oct 1998

An annual general arts festival with a literature programme. Programme published in July.

Chaucer Festival

Chaucer Heritage Trust, 22 St Peter's Street, Canterbury, Kent CT1 2BQ
tel (01227) 470379 *fax* (01227) 761416 or
tel/fax 0171-229 0635
Manager and Events Organiser Philippe Wibrotte
Takes place Spring and Summer

An annual festival which includes commemoration services, theatre productions, exhibitions, readings, recitals, Chaucer site visits, medieval fairs, costumed cavalcades, educational programmes for schools. Takes place in London, Canterbury and the County of Kent in the Spring (Easter Chaucer Pilgrimage) and Summer (June-July).

Cheltenham Festival of Literature

Town Hall, Imperial Square, Cheltenham, Glos. GL50 1QA
tel (01242) 521621 *fax* (01242) 256457
web site http://www.cheltenham.gov.uk
Festival Organiser Sarah Smyth
Takes place 9-18 Oct 1998, 8-17 Oct 1999

This annual festival is the largest of its kind in Europe and celebrates its 50th year in 1999. A wide range of events include talks and lectures, poetry readings, novelists in conversation, exhibitions, discussions, workshops and a large bookshop. *Book It!* is a festival for children within the main festival with an extensive programme of events and a multimedia room. Brochures are available in August.

Chichester Festivities

Canon Gate House, South Street, Chichester, West Sussex PO19 1PU
tel (01243) 785718 *fax* (01243) 528356
Takes place June/July

An annual general arts festival with a programme of literature events. Programme published in April.

City of London Festival

City Arts Trust, Bishopsgate Hall,
230 Bishopsgate, London EC2M 4QD
tel 0171-377 0540 *fax* 0171-377 1972
e-mail cityfest@dircon.co.uk
web site http://www.city-of-london-festival.org.uk
Takes place 22 June-15 July 1999

An annual general arts festival with a programme of literature events, including leading guest writers. Programme published in April.

Durham Literature Festival

c/o Durham City Arts Ltd, Byland Lodge,
Hawthorn Terrace, Durham DH1 4TD

tel 0191-386 6111 ext.338 fax 0191-386 0625
Takes place Telephone for information about the
1999 festival

Edinburgh Book Festival
Scottish Book Centre, 137 Dundee Street,
Fountainbridge, Edinburgh EH11 1BG
tel 0131-228 5444 fax 0131-228 4333
e-mail edadmin@edbookfest.co.uk
Director Faith Liddell
Takes place 15-31 Aug 1998, 14-30 Aug 1999
Now regarded as Europe's largest book
event for the public. In addition to the
displays of books, over 250 international
writers contribute to the programme of
events. Programme details available in
June. Runs concurrently with Edinburgh
International Festival.

Edinburgh International Festival
21 Market Street, Edinburgh EH1 1BW
tel 0131-473 2001 fax 0131-473 2002
Takes place 16 Aug-5 Sept 1998, 15 Aug-4 Sept 1999
An annual international arts festival
including world class theatre, dance,
opera and music. Programme published
late March.

Elsteddfod Genedlaethol Frenhinol Cymru
(Royal National Eisteddfod of Wales)
40 Parc Ty Glas, Llanishen, Cardiff CF4 5WU
tel (01222) 763777 fax (01222) 763737
web site http://eisteddfod.org.uk
Marketing Officer Eleri Twynog Davies
Takes place 31 July-7 Aug 1999
An annual festival promoting the Welsh
language and the culture of Wales. Over
200 competitions in all artistic fields are
held each year. A contemporary art exhibition is one of the highlights with over
4000 submissions each year. Eisteddfod
dates back to 1176; founded as annual
arts festival 1880.

Exeter Festival
Festival Office, Civic Centre, Exeter EX1 1JJ
tel (01392) 265200 fax (01392) 265265
web site http://www.exeter.gov
City Marketing Officer Gerri Bennett
Takes place July
An annual general arts festival which
includes a programme of literary evenings.
Programme of events available in April.

Federation of Worker Writers and Community Publishers Festival of Writing
PO Box 540, Burslem, Stoke-on-Trent ST6 6DR
tel/fax (01782) 822327
web site http://www.fwwcp.mcmail.com
Takes place April
The Federation was formed in 1976 to promote working-class writing as an alternative to establishment literature. An annual
weekend festival of readings, workshops,
discussions and an opportunity to meet
writers from different communities.

Female Eye National Festival of Women's Writing
Female Eye, Watersmead, Norwood Green Hill,
Halifax, West Yorkshire HX3 8QX
tel/fax (01274) 670181
Takes place June
Female Eye is a non-profit-making organisation set up to encourage and promote
writing by women. Each year has a chosen
theme and the festival comprises performance, writing workshops and discussion.
Female Eye also runs collaborative events
with other festivals and provides a networking base.

Festival at the Edge
c/o 3 Highpoint, Little Wenlock, Telford,
Shrops. TF6 5BT
tel (01952) 504929
Contact Jackie Douglas
Takes place second full weekend of July
'Tales at the Edge' story club hosts an
annual weekend of storytelling, music
and song.

Guildford Book Festival
c/o Arts Office, University of Surrey,
Guildford GU2 5XH
tel (01483) 259167
e-mail v.smith@surrey.ac.uk
web site http://www.surreyweb.org.uk/
Festival Organiser Joan König tel (01273) 478943
Takes place 23 Oct-1 Nov 1998
An annual festival on a chosen theme,
with a programme of over 40 events at 12
different venues. Includes readings, literary lunches and dinners, discussions,
performance poetry, writing competitions, a writer in residence, the annual
University of Surrey Poetry Lecture and
children's events.

Harrogate International Festival
The Festival Office, Royal Baths, Harrogate,
North Yorkshire HG1 2RR
tel (01423) 562303 fax (01423) 521264
e-mail info@harrogate-festival.org.uk
web site http://www.harrogate-festival.org.uk
Takes place July/Aug

An annual international general arts festival which includes a programme of literary events. Programme available in May.

Hastings Poetry Festival

c/o Burdett Cottage, 4 Burdett Place,
George Street, Hastings, East Sussex TN34 3ED
tel (01424) 428855 *fax* (01424) 428855
Organiser and Editor of First Time Josephine Austin
Takes place 7-8 Nov 1998

Started in 1968, this national festival is now held in the Marina Pavilion, St Leonards-on-Sea. Includes the prize-giving of the *Hastings National Poetry Competition*. Poems are invited for consideration for the bi-annual *First Time* poetry magazine. Please include sae.

The Hay Festival

Festival Office, Hay-on-Wye HR3 5BX
tel (01497) 821217 *fax* (01497) 821066
Takes place May/June

This annual festival aims to celebrate the best in writing and performance from around the world, to commission new work, and to promote and encourage young writers of excellence and potential. Over 100 events in 10 days with leading guest writers. Programme published mid-March.

Huddersfield Poetry Festival

The Word Hoard Ltd, 46-47 Byram Arcade,
Westgate, Huddersfield HD1 1ND
tel (01484) 452070
Contact Dianne Darby
Takes place Spring and Autumn

This annual festival consists of a Spring season (April) and an Autumn season (October). Both seasons include multi art form performances, participatory projects, and workshops.

Ilkley Literature Festival

Manor House, Ilkley, West Yorkshire LS29 9DT
tel (01943) 601210 *fax* (01943) 817079
e-mail ilf@dial.pipex.com
Director David Porter
Takes place throughout the year

Celebrating its 25th season, this festival takes place in various venues in and around Ilkley, Leeds and Bradford, with events throughout the year. Events include: readings, talks, lectures, writing and performance workshops, discussions and an open poetry competition. There is also an extensive programme of work to encourage young people's participation in literature-based activities. It aims to bring to West Yorkshire the best new and established writers from Britain and abroad.

International Playwriting Festival

Warehouse Theatre, Dingwall Road,
Croydon CR0 2NF
tel 0181-681 1257 *fax* 0181-688 6699
Contact Rose Marie Vernon

Takes place in 2 parts. The competition has a script submission deadline in July (see page 523). The November festival includes performed excerpts from the shortlisted plays, workshops and discussions, a performance from our partner's festival in Italy, the Premio Candoni Arta Terme, and a staged reading of the winning play.

King's Lynn Festival

27-29 King Street, King's Lynn,
Norfolk PE30 1ET
tel (01553) 767557 *fax* (01553) 767688
Press and Marketing Officer tba
Takes place 23-31 July 1999

An annual general arts festival with literature events featuring leading guest writers.

Lancaster LitFest

Sun Street Studios, 23-29 Sun Street,
Lancaster LA1 1EW
tel (01524) 62166 *fax* (01524) 841216
Contact Andrew Darby
Takes place end of October

Annual festival featuring readings, performances and workshops by contemporary writers for adults, young people and children. The LitFest also acts as a year-round literature development agency, organising readings and workshops, and offering advice and information to writers and readers in Lancashire.

Leicestershire Literature Festival

Leicestershire Libraries and Information Service,
County Hall, Glenfield, Leicester LE3 8SS
tel 0116-265 7386 *fax* 0116-265 7370
Contact Bob Parsons
Takes place to be confirmed

A biennial festival with a set theme each year. Includes readings, discussions, exhibitions, workshops and competitions, with contributions from leading guest writers.

Lincolnshire Literature Festival

Education and Cultural Services Directorate,
Lincolnshire County Council, County Offices,
Lincoln LN1 1YL

tel (01522) 552831 *fax* (01522) 552811
e-mail david.lambert@lincolnshire.gov.uk
County Arts Development Officer David Lambert
Takes place throughout the year
A monthly series of literary events throughout Lincoln. Occasional festivals throughout the county.

Lit Up!
The Beaford Arts Centre, Beaford, Winkleigh, Devon EX19 8LU
tel (01805) 603201 *fax* (01805) 603202
e-mail beaford@globalnet.co.uk
Contact Catriona Rose
Takes place 1-4 Oct 1997
An all-year-round literature programme including workshops, readings, performances and exhibitions.

The London Festival of Literature: The Word
245 St John Street, London EC1V 4NB
tel 0171-837 2555 *fax* 0171-278 0480
e-mail the.word@virgin.net
Festival Director Peter Florence, *Development Manager* Louise Ansari
Takes place 19-28 March 1999
A carnival celebration of The Word from the first steps of literacy to the greatest poets of the age. It will give the people of London access to the best contemporary writing in every media in a programme of events, performances and conversations featuring the world's largest gathering of writers, musicians and artists.

Norfolk and Norwich Festival
42-58 St George's Street, Norwich NR3 1AB
tel (01603) 614921 *fax* (01603) 632303
e-mail info@nnfest.eastern-arts.co.uk
web site http://www.eab.org.uk/festivals
Festival Director Marcus Davey
Takes place 7-18 Oct 1998
A general arts festival with some literary events. Programme published in June.

North East Lincolnshire Annual Literature Festival
Arts Development Unit, North East Lincolnshire Council, Knoll Street, Cleethorpes DN35 8LN
tel (01472) 323350
Festival Programmer Donna Fox
Takes place February/March
Reflecting the heritage and culture of the area, this annual festival aims to make literature accessible to all ages and abilities through a varied and unusual programme. Write or telephone for details.

Off the Shelf Festival of Reading and Writing
c/o Sheffield Libraries and Information Services, Central Library, Surrey Street, Sheffield S1 1XZ
tel 0114-273 6645 *fax* 0114-273 5009
Contact Judith Adam
Takes place 17-31 Oct 1998
The festival comprises a wide range of events for adults and children, including writing workshops, talks, storytelling, drama sessions, illustration workshops and exhibitions. Programme available in September.

Poetry International
Literature Department, Royal Festival Hall, London SE1 8XX
tel 0171-921 0906 *fax* 0171-928 2049
web site http://www.sbc.org.uk
Takes place 10 days in Oct/Nov 2000
The biggest poetry festival in the British Isles, bringing together a wide range of poets from around the world. Includes readings, workshops, discussions and events for children. Poetry International is a biennial festival.

Royal Court Young Writers' Festival
The Royal Court Young People's Theatre, 309 Portobello Road, London W10 5TD
tel 0181-960 4641
Contact Aoife Mannix
Takes place varies
Each festival targets a different area of the UK. Anyone up to the age of 25 can enter. Promising plays which arise from the workshops are then developed and performed at the Royal Court's Theatre Upstairs and at venues in the participating area (see page 539).

Salisbury Festival
75 New Street, Salisbury, Wilts. SP1 2PH
tel (01722) 323883 *fax* (01722) 410552
Director Helen Marriage
Takes place May/June
An annual general arts festival with a literature programme of events. Each year has a chosen theme. Programme published in March.

Warwick & Leamington Festival
Warwick Arts Society, Northgate, Warwick CV34 4JL
tel (01926) 410747 *fax* (01926) 407606
Festival Director Richard Phillips, *Literary Consultant* Barbara Jagger
Takes place first half of July

A music festival which includes some literature and poetry events: readings, performances and workshops.

Ways With Words Literature Festival

Droridge Farm, Dartington, Totnes, Devon TQ9 6JQ
tel (01803) 867311 *fax* (01803) 863688
Contact Kay Dunbar
Takes place middle of July each year

The festival includes readings, talks, interviews, discussions, seminars, workshops with leading guest writers. Literary weekends and writing courses also organised.

Wells Festival of Literature

Tower House, St Andrew Street, Wells, Somerset BA5 2UN
tel (01749) 673385
Takes place late October

This annual festival features leading guest writers and poets; includes writing workshops and competitions.

Writearound: Cleveland's Annual Festival for Writers and Readers

c/o Cleveland Arts, Gurney House, Gurney Street, Middlesbrough, Cleveland TS1 1JL
tel (01642) 262424 *fax* (01642) 262429
Contact Bob Beagrie, Andy Croft
Takes place 9-18 Oct 1998

Writearound is an independent non-profit-making organisation dedicated to encouraging, promoting and developing literary activity on Teesside and surrounding areas, through an annual literary festival. A programme of events is offered throughout Middlesbrough, including workshops, performances, poetry, open readings and children's events.

Preparing for publication

Preparing and submitting a manuscript

A well-presented manuscript will make a good impression on the publisher's reader. Guidelines on how best to present your manuscript are given here.

Even though the majority of material for potential publication is originated on disk, the text is still referred to as a manuscript – after all, it is the printout which is read. A well-presented manuscript will make a good impression on the publisher's reader. Many publishers refuse even to consider handwritten manuscripts; and no publisher will accept them as final copy.

Typing

A neatly typed manuscript (or typescript – the words are interchangeable in present usage) is essential not only to make a good impression on a publisher, but also for the publisher's copy editor to work on. The typesetter must be able to read the manuscript with any amendments quickly and accurately, plus interpret the code of marks made by the copy editor or designer. Wide margins are therefore essential to accommodate all these additions. The left-hand margin should be a minimum of 3cm, and the right-hand, top and bottom margins should all be generous. Use the same margins throughout, so that the type on each page is of the same width and, except at the beginning and end of each chapter, there will be the same number of lines on each page. If you use a word processor, do not use its facility for 'justifying' the type on the right-hand side.

Lay out the text in double spacing, i.e. a full line of space between two lines of copy – not half a line of space. This will allow space for any last minute changes you wish to make and for the copy editor's amendments. Indent the first line of each paragraph a few spaces and do not leave a blank line between paragraphs unless you want to indicate a change of subject, scene, time or viewpoint.

Be as consistent as possible in your choice of variant spellings, use of sub-headings, etc. For example, use either -ise or -ize suffixes consistently throughout.

Number the pages (or 'folios' as publishers prefer to call them to distinguish them from the pages of the final book) straight through from beginning to end – don't start each chapter at folio 1. If you need to include an extra folio after, say, folio 27, call it 27a and write at the foot of folio 27: 'Folio 27a follows'. Then write at the foot of 27a: 'Folio 28 follows'. Don't do this too often or you will confuse and irritate your readers.

Create a front page (unnumbered) for your manuscript. Type the title about halfway down the page, with your name (or pen name) immediately beneath. In the bottom left-hand corner, type your name and address, plus the word count (see below). It is worth including your name and address on the last page as well, in case the first folio becomes detached.

Most authors use a word processor for writing and/or for presenting the finished material (see *Word processing* on page 555). Use standard A4 paper, rather than

---

Manuscript checklist

- Allow generous margins
- Use double spacing
- Number each folio
- Include a front page
- Keep a duplicate of the manuscript

continuous listing paper, for your print-out and use one side only. This printout is referred to as 'hard copy', or more traditionally, the 'manuscript'. Work prepared on a typewriter should also be on A4 paper, using only one side of each sheet.

Corrections to your manuscript

Keep your corrections to the final printout to a minimum. Often the publisher's editor will suggest a few additional changes, and once these are included, the manuscript may have become very messy. If the publisher then feels it is not in a fit state for the typesetter to work from they may well ask you incorporate the changes and make a new printout.

Presentation

Publishers prefer to handle each folio separately, so do not use a binder which will make this impossible; ring binders are acceptable. It is best to place the separate sheets in a cardboard envelope folder, obviating the need for pins (which scratch), paperclips (which pick up other papers from an editor's desk), or staples (which make it awkward to read the typescript). The typescript can be protected by placing a piece of stiff card at front and back. Do not use a plastic folder as they tend to slip when placed in a pile, and both publishers and literary agents keep manuscripts piled on their desks.

Word count

The length of a book is referred to by publishers as the 'extent'. It is usual to give an approximation of the number of words

contained in a typescript. You do not have to count every word yourself. Use the word count facility on your word processor, or make a rough calculation, counting the number of words on a few pages to get an average and multiplying that figure by the number of pages in the typescript.

Submitting your manuscript

Choosing the right publisher

You will save time and postage if you check first that you are sending your manuscript to a publisher that will consider it. Publishers specialise – it is no use sending a work of romantic fiction to a firm that specialises in high-brow novels translated from obscure languages. It is still less use to send it to a firm which publishes no fiction at all. (For an index of *Publishers of fiction* see page 226.) By studying the entries in the *Yearbook*, examining publishers' lists of publications, or by looking for the names of suitable publishers in the relevant sections in libraries and bookshops, you will find the names of several publishers which might be interested in seeing your material. (Remember, though, that paperbacks are often editions of books published first in hardback editions.)

It is important how you approach a publisher. Many publishers will not accept unsolicited material – you must enquire first if they would be willing to read the whole manuscript. A few publishers are prepared to speak on the telephone, allowing you to describe, briefly, the work on offer. Most prefer a preliminary letter; and many publishers, particularly of fiction, will only see material submitted through a literary agent (listings of literary agents start on page 350). It has to be said that some publishing houses, the larger ones in particular, may well employ all three methods!

There is no point whatsoever in asking for an interview: the publisher will prefer to consider the manuscript on its own merits. In the event of a manuscript being rejected, the publisher will not be willing to discuss the reasons in person.

Treatment for plays

For plays, use capitals for character names and underline stage directions in red by hand. If a traditional typewriter is employed, use red for names of characters, stage directions, etc, and black for dialogue. See also *Presenting scripts for television and film* on page 305.

Preliminary letter

This will save you time, money and probably frustration. Most publishers prefer to see a brief preliminary letter together with a synopsis of the book and the first couple of chapters (enclose postage for their return). From this material the publisher can judge whether the book will fit the list, in which case you will be asked to send the complete manuscript. This is especially advisable in the case of non-fiction – most non-fiction books are commissioned as the result of an initial submission in the form of a synopsis and specimen chapters. Writers have been known to send out such letters in duplicated form, an approach unlikely to stimulate a publisher's interest. However, simultaneous submission to more than one publisher is permissible, provided that you inform each publisher that the book is being considered elsewhere at the same time. Always enclose return postage, even for a letter, when approaching a publisher. Remember, also, that whilst every reasonable care will be taken of material in the publishers' possession, responsibility cannot be accepted if material is lost or damaged. At all costs, keep a copy of your manuscript with all the most recent changes to the text included on it.

In the hands of the publisher

There is usually a considerable interval between submission and the publisher's decision. Most publishers acknowledge receipt of manuscripts; if you do not receive one it is advisable to check that your manuscript has arrived. Apart from that, it is not worth chasing the publisher for a quick decision: if pressed, the publisher will probably reject, purely because this is the safer decision.

You should hear from the publisher within about two months. During this time the manuscript will either have been read in-house or it will have been sent to one or more advisers whose opinions the publisher respects. Favourable readers' reports may mean that the publisher will immediately accept the manuscript, particularly if it fits easily into the current publishing programme.

On the other hand, a reader's report may be glowing, but the publisher may still hesitate. Publishers want to be sure they will be able to sell a book profitably, so may obtain further opinions, and/or explore the financial viability, before making a final decision.

If you have not had a decision after two months, write either a tactful letter saying 'I don't want to rush you, but ...' or, alternatively, request an immediate decision and be prepared to start again with another publisher. If your book is topical you have a right to a speedy decision, but it is as well to establish this early on.

Illustrations

If illustrations form a large part of your proposed book and you expect to provide them yourself, then they should be included with the manuscript. If you are sending specimen pages you should include also some sample illustrations: this applies largely to children's picture books and to travel and technical books. Do not send the originals – send duplicate photographs, photocopies of line drawings and so on so that little harm is done if illustrations go astray.

In the case of a children's book, if you intend to illustrate it yourself, obviously one finished piece of artwork is essential, plus photocopies of roughs for the rest (the final artwork may have to be drawn to a particular size and the number of illustrations fixed according to the format chosen by the publisher). If you have written a children's story, or the text for a picture book, do not ask a friend to provide the illustrations; the publisher who likes your story may well not like your friend's artwork. Of course this does not apply when an artist and author work closely together to develop an idea, but in that case it is best to start by finding a publisher who likes the artist's work before submitting the story. See *Writing and illustrating children's books* on page 256 and *Children's book publishers and packagers* on page 260.

Travel manuscripts should be accompanied by a sketch map to show the area you are writing about, so the publisher has sufficient detail with which to follow your manuscript.

Many illustrated books these days have illustrations collected by the publishers. It is best to establish early on who is responsible for the illustration costs: a seemingly generous royalty offer might be less attractive if you have to gather the pictures, obtain permission for use, and foot the bills.

Quotations

It is normally the author's responsibility to obtain (and pay for) permission to quote written material which is still in copyright. Permission should always be sought from the publisher of the quoted work, not from the author. Fees for quotation vary enormously: for fashionable modern writers permission may be costly, but in other cases only a nominal fee is charged. There is no standard scale of fees. It is permissible to quote up to about 200 words for the purpose of criticism or review, but this does not apply to use in anthologies, nor does it apply to poetry. And it is a concession, not a right. Even though this is your area of responsibility, your publisher will be able to give you some advice.

Proofs for the author

When the publisher accepts your manuscript, if you have typed it on a word processor they may well ask you to supply the text on disk. The files containing your manuscript should be unformatted plain text – doing a fancy layout is a waste of time as it will be unformatted by the publisher or typesetter. Having the material on disk will save time and money in production costs, as well as cut down the margin for errors creeping in. Today, it is unusual for large publishing houses to take text which is not on disk.

As author you will see either one or two stages of proofs. Sometimes you will be shown the finalised copy of the manuscript immediately before it goes to the typesetter. If so, this is really your last chance to make changes which will not tend to sour relations with your publisher! Take the opportunity to comb through the manuscript, and if there are changes which you suspect you will want to make in proof, make them now. There was a time when authors could virtually rewrite their books in galley proof, and revise them again at page, but those days are long gone! (See *Correcting proofs* on page 563 for the conventional proof-correcting marks.)

Making corrections at proof stage is time-consuming and costly. You will probably have signed a contract undertaking to pay the cost of corrections (other than typesetter's errors) over say 10-15% of the cost of composition. This does not mean that you can change 10 or 15 lines in every 100.

Increasingly often only one stage of proofs is used in book production, and there is rarely any need for the author to see more than one stage. The proofs may be in several forms. You may only see a computer printout which has had all the amendments incorporated; this will bear no resemblance to the finished book but will contain everything that will appear in that book. Galley proofs are produced by the typesetter and are columns of continuous text. Page proofs have been made up into pages, including page numbers, headlines, illustrations, and so on. It is prohibitively expensive to make corrections at this stage, except to the printer's own errors.

The production of highly illustrated books, such as children's or 'coffee table' books, is dealt with differently. The fitting together of the pictures and text on each page is an important stage when the designer and the editor work together, modifying the text to make the final result come together happily.

Word processing

*There is little need to explain the basic ideas and advantages of moving words about on a screen before we print them. In this article, **Randall McMullan** considers how to write more effectively and more professionally while using a word processor.*

Methods of writing are very personal but they all involve a comfortable interaction between yourself and something mechanical, even if the equipment has to be a pad and pencil on your knee in front of the fire. But before you become set in the way you use the keyboard and screen of your word processor, do consider the information in the following sections. They contain techniques used by authors which may improve your efficiency, your income, your sanity – and even your writing.

Creating

If your creative habit depends upon letting the words flow, like Enid Blyton in her hidey-hole, then the word processor is an ideal companion. You can be a 'sprinter' or a 'fingertip' writer and rapidly get your narrative or ideas onto the screen. There is no need to stop; the layout and the order doesn't matter, you can work on those later.

Ordering your thoughts

More reflective methods of creation involve the use of reference materials, notes, outlines, ordering and assembly of portions of text. Any word processor allows you to develop personalised routines for these actions but you can also try some of the software packages which support these operations.

For example, many word processors have an 'outliner' which helps you to order your thoughts by using hierarchies of headings or 'layers' of text. If such ordered working is too much of a straight-jacket then you may like the type of writing tool which searches your notes and offers links between sections containing similar words and ideas.

Writers' tools

A thesaurus can lead you through pleasant webs of cross-references. Other programs will analyse your writing and give a report on content and style. The grammatical comments are often debatable and a report on your sexism or pomposity may irritate you, but a correct analysis of the reading age of your text may surprise you.

A sample of writers' tools which have been on the market have names which give a clue to their purpose: Storyspace, Plot unlimited, Poetry Processor, WordPerfect Rhymer, Idea Fisher, IdeaList, Quotemaster, Lexica, StyleWriter, Readability Plus, Concise Oxford Dictionary, Oxford Concordance, Oxford Science Shelf.

Now that CD-Roms are standard in modern computers, the size, speed and utility of these reference works have increased dramatically. Available, for example, is a single CD-Rom which contains complete texts of out-of-copyright classics from Aristotle through Shakespeare to Wilde. The texts can be quickly searched for key words, displayed in a window on screen, and pasted into your own work as desired.

The Internet has various web sites devoted to the cares and concerns of authors. For example, if you enter a 'forum' and ask advice about general or particular software tools for writers, you will be guaranteed many direct and personal responses. There are also sites where you can download freeware packages or demonstration versions of commercial software packages for authors.

The well-known word processing programs include an indexing tool which may sound more useful than it may prove to be. You will still have to provide the thought, make the decisions, flag words or insert flagged phrases in the text. The indexer will then automatically sort and merge all your references with correct page numbers and update this index if you change the text.

Inputting text

You should abandon two habits from typewriter days: correcting errors as you enter, and typing 'over' existing text. You can't truly 'process' the words until all the words are there on the screen. Correcting, polishing and rearranging text are more efficient when done later as separate editing operations.

Don't stop for a typing mistake, even when you know you have just made one. Errors can be fixed automatically by the spell checker at an editing stage. On some word processors, typos can be automatically corrected as you write. The software can be set by you to change 'hte', for example, into 'the' – as you type.

Save, save, save your work as you write. It costs nothing and secures everything. Your creation on screen is transient until it is magnetically saved onto the hard disk or onto a floppy disk. A save command is usually a simple keystroke which should be given at the end of every page, every ten minutes, when the phone rings, and when the cat approaches the keyboard.

The physical aspects of putting text into the word processor should also be considered. You can learn or improve your typing skills from the various cheap and popular programs which use your screen and keyboard to train the eyes and fingers. If you intend to remain a two-finger typist, then at least keep each hand on its correct side of the keyboard.

Editing

Copy your work before making changes. Duplicate your work before and after making changes as you may be glad to go back to yesterday's version. Let the spell checker run through your entire text to correct the typos and the misspelt words. Remember that this tool can't correct for sense and that a correctly spelt word may still be the wrong word. Some of these wrong words can only be detected when your brain is in a different mode. The best editing is often done by reading and marking up a printout while away from your work area, preferably the next day.

As you make changes to text you need not 'overwrite' old text, as in typewriter days. Keep the word processor in normal 'insert' mode and let any text in front of your screen cursor be 'pushed along' in front of your new writing. The two versions can then be compared on the screen before deleting the unwanted text. A modern word processor also allows you to control revisions using coloured underlining and strike-through lines.

Become fluent in the commands of your word processor which allow you to mark 'blocks' of text and then copy or move them to new locations. A block of text can also be copied into a separate file docu-

---

RSI

The pain and disability of repetitive strain injury (RSI) has always been a risk for non-stop keyboardists, quill pen clerks and other repetitive workers such as chicken pluckers. Take heed of the following points to help minimise the risk of RSI to the hands and arms:

- ensure that your chair and your posture are comfortable and correct;
- locate the phone and the files away from the computer – moving and stretching is good for you;
- take regular breaks from working at the keyboard;
- do stretching exercises.

ment for use in future documents or for repeated insertion into your current document. Any stored text can be 'inserted' into the current text at the place where you have left the screen cursor. You can therefore open a new blank document and 'boilerplate' a new assembly of text out of existing saved text.

Formatting

The final layout and the style of print on the page should be thought of as a separate process carried out after the creation and the editing of text. A publishing house will prefer to receive your work as totally unformatted plain text, as do desktop publishing programs described in *Desktop publishing* (see page 559).

Ideally, your plain text should contain:
- no indents
- no padded word spaces
- no alignments
- no centring
- no line spaces
- no carriage returns except to start new paragraphs.

Save to 'text only' or 'plain text' – the save command of your word processor should have this type of option. Seek the agreement of the final publisher before using underlining, emboldening, large font and other effects.

Plain text looks cramped and uninspiring so you may, for creative reasons, wish to work with a copy of your text laid out in a form which resembles the final page. After inputting your text unformatted you can keep a copy of the plain text version before doing your fancy version. To control some writing projects you may need to set up your page to a certain width of line and length. Word processors can save these personal formats as blank templates.

Many word processing programs have desktop publishing features which allow you to do final page layout on the word processor screen if you wish. These activities, which require the skills and knowledge described in the desktop publishing article, are inspiring to some writers and of little interest to others.

Housekeeping

Authors can never be too rich, too thin, or have too many computer copies of their work. Each electronic document is stored as an electronic file or folder on the magnetic disk with a file or folder name chosen by yourself. Use a document or file 'copy' command to make a clone copy of your work but with a different filename.

If your work is being stored on the hard disk fitted inside your computer, then make a copy onto a portable floppy disk at daily intervals. Keep several floppy disk copies, some of them in a different room or building. If the computer fails, or is stolen, then you will be glad to go back to last week's version of your work.

Word processing files take up relatively little disk space compared to other computer files such as graphics. You can probably fit your entire year's writing onto one floppy disk but please don't do so as the disk may develop a fault and trap your masterpiece in a magnetic limbo. Floppy disks are so cheap that they are given away on magazine covers.

Training

Please *read* about your word processor; other writers have written to you! If you don't have a manual or a book then display the screen help items, print them out, and read them in bed. You don't need to spend money on a training course as you can't damage your word processor by experimenting. But you can remain ignorant of a feature which is just what you have been wanting to know about.

All modern word processors offer high level features such as automated routines (macros), printing envelopes and labels, and mail shots. If you want to use these features you should learn about them and try them.

Equipment

The simple broad aim is to use the same hardware as those people with whom you work or from whom you can obtain support. It is a fact that around 90% of the market for business PCs belongs to the IBM PC/Intel families of machines made by a wide variety of manufacturers, not usually IBM.

The ability to gain information, swap disks, share equipment is often more important than other considerations. For most people that choice will be an IBM-compatible PC. For some it will be an Apple. The Apple Macintosh range has always used a 'graphical interface' which executes commands by moving a pointer on screen and 'clicking' the mouse. PC-compatible machines are now supplied with Microsoft Windows which provides a graphical interface similar to that of the Macintosh.

The PC and the Apple 'platforms' are slowly converging and the leading word processing packages work on both types of machine with minimal differences. The most common word processor package being bought for modern offices is Microsoft Word for Windows.

However, there are several dozen other word processing packages which have been in use over the years and they all do everything that most writers require. Conversion software allows you to convert text in one major format to another major format, although fancy layouts may become mangled. Most word processors should also be able to exchange information via the plain text or ASCII format.

The purchase of computer goods often relates to how you personally buy an item like a washing machine or television. You may purchase at a John Lewis department store and arrange for full delivery and installation, or you might bring the equipment home from a discount warehouse in an unopened box and set it up yourself.

It is common to buy computer equipment by mail order and credit card from reputable discount warehouses, so you should use the Internet or buy a magazine like *MicroMart* (Micromart UK Ltd) or *Personal Computer World* (VNU Business Publications) to get an idea of prices. Otherwise choose a dealer in a convenient location and use your magazine prices to negotiate a suitable package of price and help.

Randall McMullan is a writer and educational adviser who has been using word processors for over 20 years. He is the author of various works in the fields of fiction, busines computing, environmental science and construction.

Desktop publishing

Ten years ago, preparing the words to be printed on the pages of a publication was the domain of the typesetter. Since then, the use of desktop publishing has become widespread and has opened up a whole range of opportunities for producing publications. However, no matter how sophisticated the program may be, it cannot plan and design a publication. **Richard Williams** *introduces design considerations and describes how to prepare for publication using desktop publishing.*

Essential equipment

Because of the rapid pace of change, this article gives only general guidance on buying desktop publishing (DTP) equipment and software. For more detailed and up-to-date information, read the specialist computer magazines.

When buying a new computer, choose a machine which more than meets your current needs, and preferably one that can be upgraded since each release of a program is likely to require more power, machine memory and hard disk capacity than the last. Also take into account all the other things you may want to use a computer for: video editing, playing games, running CD-Roms, e-mailing, surfing the Internet, etc.

Because graphics and DTP professionals favour the Macintosh, programs used by them have tended in the past to appear first on that machine, and only later (if at all) on IBM-compatibles. Nowadays there is little difference between the two types of machine, though IBM-compatibles probably still offer the widest choice of programs overall. Whichever machine you choose, make sure it has a decent sized monitor screen. These are classified by the screen diagonal measurement; the smallest useful size is 15in, but a 17in monitor, the minimum size for sustained work, can now be bought for a modest extra cost. Recently, the substantial size and price gap between these and the 21in monitors used by professionals has been bridged by 19in monitors, at a similarly modest differential over 17in monitors.

A mouse is essential for DTP work. These have always been provided with Macs, and nowadays IBM-compatible machines usually include one. If not, resist the temptation to buy a cheap model.

A printer is essential for proofing your work and can also be used to produce camera-ready copy (CRC). With the virtual disappearance of dot matrix printers, the choice now lies between inkjet and laser printers. Each has its advantages: inkjets are cheaper and quieter but laser printers give the best quality and a lower consumables cost per page. If you are using a printer to proof work for commercial printing, it is probably worth paying the extra cost for PostScript. This is almost universally used to produce the final bromide or film and gives a much better match between proof and final output. If you want to produce CRC, a 1200 dots per inch laser printer is the ideal, but PostScript is not essential.

Proofing full-colour printing still needs a costly printer for real accuracy, but the standard of colour now achieved by inexpensive inkjets makes these a practical proposition, either for preliminary layouts, or to produce prints from a digital camera.

Optional extras

A CD-Rom drive gives you access to illustrations in electronic form, ready to drop into the page. These can be either your own photos transferred to Photo CDs, or commercial collections of stock photos and drawn 'clip art'. You can also use the huge range of fonts now available in this format. CD-Rom drives are now relatively inexpensive to buy, and are generally provided as part of a new computer. If not, one can be easily added. If you also want to use it for multimedia and games, make sure that it is at least an eight speed drive and buy a sound card as well (these often come bundled with drives).

A scanner, to convert existing paper illustrations or photographs into electronic form, is another useful extra. Now that flatbed scanners are more affordable, the choice between these and compact scanners depends more on convenience and type of media than on price. Compact scanners save space, and often come with sophisticated document management software, but flatbeds are better for scanning in colour and can cope not only with loose sheets but with transparencies, books and even objects.

Optical character reading (OCR) software can convert scans of existing typed or printed text directly into electronic format, avoiding the need to retype it.

A digital camera cuts out the scanning stage by producing images in electronic form, ready for immediate use. Affordable models are still restricted to relatively low definition (equivalent to a standard computer screen) but are useful if you need a lot of small-scale pictures quickly.

Software

Desktop publishing programs have tended to polarise between the inexpensive but competent, and the expensive and fully professional. For anyone doing a significant amount of DTP work the extra cost of the high end programs will be worthwhile, just for their power and ease of use (though not necessarily ease of learning). If you are not sure, start with one of the low end programs which will give you a clearer idea of your requirements if, or when, you come to buy a more powerful program.

Most high-end DTP programs now enable you to publish on the Internet, as well as in more conventional form. This is particularly useful if you want to convert existing documents for Web use; for creating a Web site from scratch, the specialist authoring programs offer more flexibility and power.

Designing the publication

Planning is the most important first step in creating a document or publication. Before starting work you need to be clear what kind of document it is, and who it is aimed at. At the practical level you should decide, roughly at least, how many pages there will be, what size, and how they are to be printed and bound. Obviously, these decisions are often interlinked – your choice of page size will be limited if it is to be produced by laser printer, photocopier or quick printer, but much wider if it is to be commercially printed. Before you set up the page layout, spend as much time as you can looking critically at other publications. See what works, and what doesn't, and don't be afraid to copy a design that pleases you.

Try to avoid over-elaborate page designs. Use elements such as lines and boxes with a purpose, to clarify rather than ornament, and remember that white space has a vital role to play. Most programs allow you to set up a grid of guidelines, so use these to give pages a structure, particularly important in illustrated works.

When you start, work on just a few pages at first, the minimum needed to show all the possibilities in the document as a whole. For something simple, like a novel, you only need a double page spread of ordinary text, another spread for chapter start and finish, and possibly a single page for the table of contents. Non-fiction is usually more complex, and may require extra pages to show the treatment of headings and illustrations plus an index, if present. Work on these pages until you are happy with the result, then try a sample chapter as a check before laying out the rest of the book. In this way, problems can be solved at an early stage, and changes made, with a minimum impact on the work already done.

Using typefaces sensibly

Because DTP programs allow access to lots of typefaces, beginners tend to use too many. The basic rule is to use no more than two individual typefaces on a page, and get the necessary variety with different sizes and weights. One popular scheme is to combine a sans-serif face for headings with a serif face for text. This gives both variety and readability (serif faces are generally reckoned to be more legible for large amounts of text, except at very small sizes).

Beginners also err by carrying over the conventions of the typewriter, with plentiful use of capitals and underlining. In print this is unnecessary – use upper case (capital letters) sparingly, and don't use underlines at all. Instead use either bold or italics for emphasis: bold for an isolated word or phrase but italics for a longer passage, which would otherwise be over-emphatic.

Other common mistakes are using two spaces after a full stop, two hyphens for a dash, and the normal typewriter single and double quotation marks. For professional looking results, make sure there is only a single space, use proper dashes and opening and closing quotation marks, and avoid indents in the first paragraph after a heading.

The right spacing

The correct balance of spacing between letters, words and lines is crucial for legibility. Here the basic rule is that spacing between letters should be less than between words, and that between words less than between lines. Provided the relationship between these elements is correct, the actual amount of spacing is a matter of taste.

The ideal page should have an even texture, avoiding obvious variations in spacing from line to line. Letter spacing should normally be fixed, and word spacing should not be less than two thirds, or more than one and a half times the average setting. This may cause problems with shorter lines, but the solution here is intelligent use of hyphenation (avoiding more than two successive hyphens) and the use of unjustified text for short lines. The ideal line length is generally reckoned to be about 60 to 70 characters – much less gives problems with spacing, whilst longer lines are more difficult to read.

Space should be used to differentiate headings from body text; there should be at least as much space below a heading as between paragraphs, and more above, so that it clearly relates to the following text.

To ensure that text in adjoining columns lines up across the page, the total space occupied by a heading (the type itself, plus space above and below) must always be a multiple of the point size of the body text. Resist the temptation to use too many different levels of heading – three should be enough for almost any purpose.

Even with these rules to guide you, experimentation will be necessary to get a satisfactory combination of typefaces and spacing. Don't skimp this, but persevere until you are really happy with the result – if it doesn't look right, then it probably isn't. If you are not sure, put the sample page on one side for a day or more, so that you come back to it with a fresh eye.

Adding text and illustrations

Once you are happy with the layout and typography of your sample pages, you are ready to apply these to the whole text. You should be able to do this by creating 'styles' which format a paragraph in a single operation by 'tagging' it. The foolproof method is to prepare text in the word processor without any formatting at all, then use the appropriate style to format it in the DTP program. Text can also be tagged in a word processor, but this requires more expert knowledge.

Although simple graphics can be created in many DTP programs, it is better to use a separate program to create illustrations – a drawing program for diagrams and charts, a spreadsheet for graphs. Avoid the so-called paint programs if possible – these can give a jagged look to the finished result. If you must use one of these, make sure you create the illustration at least the size of the printed version and preferably larger.

Photographs can liven up a text page, but only if properly handled. Two common faults are to include too much detail for the size of the picture, and to print it too dark. Cropping can get rid of extraneous detail, and most DTP or graphics programs can do this.

Dot gain (the tendency of half-tone dots to be larger on paper than on the printing plate) causes photos to print darker than the original. This can be compensated for either in scanning or in the DTP program itself. Conventionally screened photos should take this into account, and pasting these into a bromide rather than scanning them may be the simplest solution.

Final stages

Make sure that you check the final proofs carefully – any mistakes not found at this stage will be expensive to correct later. Spell checkers need to be used intelligently – they are great for catching obvious errors but are no substitute for careful conventional proofreading.

One task that normally has to wait for this stage is the preparation of an index. Although DTP programs can help in this, the process still requires human intervention, and for anything more than a simple index a professional indexer will give a much better result.

Final output

Conventional printing is expensive for short runs, so consider using either a high quality copier in a quick printer, or one of the new machines which are a hybrid of copier and printer. For longer runs it is better to use a commercial printer. The first time you do so, get some sample pages (the ones you produced for deciding on layout and typography) run off by the printer or service bureau. Any sensible firm will be happy to do this, knowing that snags found at this stage will avoid much worse problems later.

Although some service bureaux will accept files in the format of the DTP program, PostScript files are easier for them to handle and the final output is more likely to match your proofs. If you are using a Windows-based program, make sure that the bureau can handle output in this format and has the appropriate fonts (Mac fonts may not be compatible.)

When you send a job to a service bureau or printer, list the files that you want to be output, and enclose proofs with the disks so that they can see how the finished job should look. For anything more than a short document, break it up into separate files of a few pages each, which makes it easier to recover from any problems. Doing this and getting sample pages printed beforehand should cope with most potential problems, but make sure they have a telephone number to contact you if necessary.

Richard Williams is the author of several books on desktop publishing and other computer applications and works as a consultant.

Correcting proofs

The following notes and table are extracted from BS 5261: Part 2: 1976 (1995) and are reproduced by permission of the British Standards Institution. Copies of the complete Standard are available from the British Standards Institution, 2 Park Street, London W1A 2BS.

The marks to be used for marking up copy for composition and for the correction of printers' proofs shall be as shown in table 1.

The marks in table 1 are classified in three groups as follows.

(a) Group A: general.

(b) Group B: deletion, insertion and substitution.

(c) Group C: positioning and spacing.

Each item in table 1 is given a simple alpha-numeric serial number denoting the classification group to which it belongs and its position within the group.

The marks have been drawn keeping the shapes as simple as possible and using sizes which relate to normal practice. The shapes of the marks should be followed exactly by all who make use of them.

For each marking-up or proof correction instruction a distinct mark is to be made:

(a) in the text: to indicate the exact place to which the instruction refers;

(b) in the margin: to signify or amplify the meaning of the instruction.

It should be noted that some instructions have a combined textual and marginal mark.

Where a number of instructions occur in one line, the marginal marks are to be divided between the left and right margins where possible, the order being from left to right in both margins.

Specification details, comments and instructions may be written on the copy or proof to complement the textual and marginal marks. Such written matter is to be clearly distinguishable from the copy and from any corrections made to the proof. Normally this is done by encircling the matter and/or by the appropriate use of colour (see below).

Proof corrections shall be made in coloured ink thus:

(a) printer's literal errors marked by the printer for correction: green;

(b) printer's literal errors marked by the customer and his agents for correction: red;

(c) alterations and instructions made by the customer and his agents: black or dark blue.

564 Preparing for publication

Table 1. Classified list of marks

NOTE. The letters M and P in the notes column indicate marks for
marking-up copy and for correcting proofs respectively.

Group A   General

Number	Instruction	Textual mark	Marginal mark	Notes
A1	Correction is concluded	None	/	P Make after each correction
A2	Leave unchanged	_ _ _ _ _ _ under characters to remain	(✓)	M P
A3	Remove extraneous marks	Encircle marks to be removed	✕	P e.g. film or paper edges visible between lines on bromide or diazo proofs
A3.1	Push down risen spacing material	Encircle blemish	⊥	P
A4	Refer to appropriate authority anything of doubtful accuracy	Encircle word(s) affected	(?)	P

Group B   Deletion, insertion and substitution

Number	Instruction	Textual mark	Marginal mark	Notes
B1	Insert in text the matter indicated in the margin	⋏	New matter followed by ⋏	M P Indentical to B2
B2	Insert additional matter identified by a letter in a diamond	⋏	⋏ Followed by for example ⟨A⟩	M P The relevant section of the copy should be supplied with the corresponding letter marked on it in a diamond e.g. ⟨A⟩
B3	Delete	/ through character(s) or ⊢——⊣ through words to be deleted	♂	M P
B4	Delete and close up	⌒/⌣ through character or ⊢——⊣ through characters e.g. chara͡cter charac͡ter	♂⌣	M P

Table 1 *(continued)*

Number	Instruction	Textual mark	Marginal mark	Notes
B5	Substitute character or substitute part of one or more word(s)	/ through character or ⊢————⊣ through word(s)	New character or new word(s)	M P
B6	Wrong fount. Replace by character(s) of correct fount	Encircle character(s) to be changed	⊗	P
B6.1	Change damaged character(s)	Encircle character(s) to be changed	✕	P This mark is identical to A3
B7	Set in or change to italic	———— under character(s) to be set or changed	⊔	M P Where space does not permit textual marks encircle the affected area instead
B8	Set in or change to capital letters	≡≡≡ under character(s) to be set or changed	≡	
B9	Set in or change to small capital letters	≡≡ under character(s) to be set or changed	=	
B9.1	Set in or change to capital letters for initial letters and small capital letters for the rest of the words	≡ under initial letters and ≡≡ under rest of the word(s)	≡	
B10	Set in or change to bold type	∿∿∿ under character(s) to be set or changed	∿	
B11	Set in or change to bold italic type	∿∿∿ under character(s) to be set or changed	⊔∿	
B12	Change capital letters to lower case letters	Encircle character(s) to be changed	⧥	P For use when B5 is inappropriate

Table 1 *(continued)*

Number	Instruction	Textual mark	Marginal mark	Notes
B12.1	Change small capital letters to lower case letters	Encircle character(s) to be changed		P For use when B5 is inappropriate
B13	Change italic to upright type	Encircle character(s) to be changed		P
B14	Invert type	Encircle character to be inverted		P
B15	Substitute or insert character in 'superior' position	/ through character or ʎ where required	under character e.g.	P
B16	Substitute or insert character in 'inferior' position	/ through character or ʎ where required	over character e.g.	P
B17	Substitute ligature e.g. ffi for separate letters	through characters affected	e.g. ffi	P
B17.1	Substitute separate letters for ligature		Write out separate letters	P
B18	Substitute or insert full stop or decimal point	/ through character or ʎ where required		M P
B18.1	Substitute or insert colon	/ through character or ʎ where required		M P
B18.2	Substitute or insert semi-colon	/ through character or ʎ where required	;	M P

Table 1 *(continued)*

Number	Instruction	Textual mark	Marginal mark	Notes
B18.3	Substitute or insert comma	/ through character or ⋀ where required	,	M P
B18.4	Substitute or insert apostrophe	/ through character or ⋀ where required	⁹⁷	M P
B18.5	Substitute or insert single quotation marks	/ through character or ⋀ where required	⁶⁷ and/or ⁹⁷	M P
B18.6	Substitute or insert double quotation marks	/ through character or ⋀ where required	⁶⁶⁷ and/or ⁹⁹⁷	M P
B19	Substitute or insert ellipsis	/ through character or ⋀ where required	• • •	M P
B20	Substitute or insert leader dots	/ through character or ⋀ where required	⊙(•••)	M P Give the measure of the leader when necessary
B21	Substitute or insert hyphen	/ through character or ⋀ where required	⊢⁻⊣	M P
B22	Substitute or insert rule	/ through character ⋀ where required	⊢⊣	M P Give the size of the rule in the marginal mark e.g. ⊢1 em⊣ ⊢4 mm⊣

Table 1 *(continued)*

Number	Instruction	Textual mark	Marginal mark	Notes
B23	Substitute or insert oblique	/ through character or ⋀ where required	⊘	M P

Group C Positioning and spacing

Number	Instruction	Textual mark	Marginal mark	Notes
C1	Start new paragraph			M P
C2	Run on (no new paragraph)			M P
C3	Transpose characters or words	between characters or words, numbered when necessary		M P
C4	Transpose a number of characters or words	3 2 1	1 2 3	M P To be used when the sequence cannot be clearly indicated by the use of C3. The vertical strokes are made through the characters or words to be transposed and numbered in the correct sequence
C5	Transpose lines			M P
C6	Transpose a number of lines		———— 3 ———— 2 ———— 1	P To be used when the sequence cannot be clearly indicated by C5. Rules extend from the margin into the text with each line to be transposed numbered in the correct sequence
C7	Centre	enclosing matter to be centred	[ ]	M P
C8	Indent			P Give the amount of the indent in the marginal mark

.Table 1 *(continued)*

Number	Instruction	Textual mark	Marginal mark	Notes
C9	Cancel indent			P
C10	Set line justified to specified measure	and/or		P Give the exact dimensions when necessary
C11	Set column justified to specified measure			M P Give the exact dimensions when necessary
C12	Move matter specified distance to the right	enclosing matter to be moved to the right		P Give the exact dimensions when necessary
C13	Move matter specified distance to the left	enclosing matter to be moved to the left		P Give the exact dimensions when necessary
C14	Take over character(s), word(s) or line to next line, column or page			P The textual mark surrounds the matter to be taken over and extends into the margin
C15	Take back character(s), word(s), or line to previous line, column or page			P The textual mark surrounds the matter to be taken back and extends into the margin
C16	Raise matter	over matter to be raised / under matter to be raised		P Give the exact dimensions when necessary. (Use C28 for insertion of space between lines or paragraphs in text)
C17	Lower matter	over matter to be lowered / under matter to be lowered		P Give the exact dimensions when necessary. (Use C29 for reduction of space between lines or paragraphs in text)
C18	Move matter to position indicated	Enclose matter to be moved and indicate new position		P Give the exact dimensions when necessary

Marked galley proof of text

(B9.1) =/

At the sign of the red pale Y/ (C22)

(B13) 4/

The Life and Work of William Caxton, by H W Larken

(C7) [ ]/

[An Extract] w/ (B10)

(C9) ⊐/

Few people, even in the field of printing, have any clear =/ (B9)
conception of what William Caxton did or, indeed, of
what he was. Much of this lack of knowledge is due to the
absence of information that can be counted as factual
and the consequent tendency to vague generalization. i/ (B1)

(B12) ≠/

Though it is well known that Caxton was born in the
county of Kent, there is no information as to the precise
place. In his prologue to the *History of Troy*, William Caxton ⊘/ (A2)

(B18.5) 4/

wrote 'for in France I was never and was born and .../ (B19)
learned my English in Kent in the Weald where I doubt
not is spoken as broad and rude English as in any place Y/ (C23)

(B18.5) 4/

of England.' During the fifteenth century there were a ⌐/ (C1)
great number of Flemish cloth weavers in Kent; most

(B6) ⊗/

of them had come to England at the instigation of
Edward III with the object of teaching their craft to the
English. So successful was this venture that the English t/ (B5)

(B17) ƒ/

cloth trade flourished and the agents who sold the cloth
(the mercers) became very wealthy people. There have b ♂/ (B3)

(C8) ⊐/

There have been many speculations concerning the origin
of the Caxton family and much research has been carried

(B14) ∩/

out. It is assumed often that Caxton's family must have ⌐/ (C3)
been connected with the wool trade in order to have
secured his apprenticeship to an influential merchant.

(A4) ℗/
(B7) ⊔/

W. Blyth Crotch (*Prologues and Epilogues of William
Caxton*) suggests that the origin of the name Caxton (of ⊔/ (B7)
which there are several variations in spelling) may be
traced to Cambridgeshire but notes that many writers
have suggested that Caxton was connected with a family

(A3.1) ⊥/
(B18.1) ⊙/

at Hadlow or alternatively a family in Canterbury. ==/ (C20)
Of the Canterbury connection a William Caxton
became freeman of the City in 1431 and William Pratt,

(B15) 4/

a mercer who was the printer's friend, was there too.
H. R. Plomer suggests that Pratt and Caxton might possibly
have been schoolboys together, perhaps at the school St. ⟨A⟩/ (B2)

(C26) ⅄/

Alphege. In this parish there lived a John Caxton who
used as his mark three cakes over a barrel (or tun) and
who is mentioned in an inscription on a monument in
the church of St. Alphege.

In 1941, Alan Keen (an authority on manuscripts) ×/ (A3)
secured some documents concerning Caxton; these are

(B8) =/
(B6) ⊗/

now in the BRITISH MUSEUM. Discovered in the library of ≠/ (B12.1)
Earl Winterton at Shillinglee Park by Richard Holworthy,
the documents cover the period 1420 to 1467. One of

(C27)

Winterton's ancestors purchased the manor of West
Wratting from a family named Caxton, the property
being situated in the Weald of Kent.

There is also record of a property mentioning Philip ⊃/ (C2)

(B18) ⊙/

Caxton and his wife Dennis who had two sons, Philip ♂/ (B4)
(born in 1413) and William.

Particularly interesting in these documents is one

(C27)

recording that Philip Caxton junior sold the manor of
Little Wratting to John Christemasse of London in 1436 1e
the deed having been witnessed by two aldermen, one of H/ (B22)
whom was Robert Large, the printer's employer. (C14)

(B18.3) '/

Further, in 1439 the other son, William Caxton, con H/ (B21)
Wratting to John Christemasse, and an indenture of 1457 2/
concerning this property mentions one William Caxton 3/ (C6)
veyed his rights in the manor Bluntes Hall at Little 1
alias Causton. It is an interesting coincidence to note that
the lord of the manor of Little Wratting was the father of

(C21) ⊂/

Margaret, Duchess of Burgundy. ↑/ (C25)
In 1420, a Thomas Caxton of Tenterden witnessed the

(C19) |||/

will of a fellow townsman; he owned property in Kent and ⟨+1pt (C28)
appears to have been a person of some importance.

¹ See 'William Caxton'. ⟩−1pt (C29)

Ⓐ *attached to Christchurch Monastery in the parish of*

Revised galley proof of text incorporating corrections

AT THE SIGN OF THE RED PALE

The Life and Work of William Caxton, *by H W Larken*

An Extract

FEW PEOPLE, even in the field of printing, have any clear conception of what William Caxton did or, indeed, of what he was. Much of this lack of knowledge is due to the absence of information that can be counted as factual and the consequent tendency to vague generalisation.

Though it is well known that Caxton was born in the county of Kent, there is no information as to the precise place. In his prologue to the *History of Troy*, William Caxton wrote '. . . for in France I was never and was born and learned my English in Kent in the Weald where I doubt not is spoken as broad and rude English as in any place of England.'

During the fifteenth century there were a great number of Flemish cloth weavers in Kent; most of them had come to England at the instigation of Edward III with the object of teaching their craft to the English. So successful was this venture that the English cloth trade flourished and the agents who sold the cloth (the mercers) became very wealthy people.

There have been many speculations concerning the origin of the Caxton family and much research has been carried out. It is often assumed that Caxton's family must have been connected with the wool trade in order to have secured his apprenticeship to an influential merchant.

W. Blyth Crotch (*Prologues and Epilogues of William Caxton*) suggests that the origin of the name Caxton (of which there are several variations in spelling) may be traced to Cambridgeshire but notes that many writers have suggested that Caxton was connected with a family at Hadlow or alternatively a family in Canterbury.

Of the Canterbury connection: a William Caxton became freeman of the City in 1431 and William Pratt, a mercer who was the printer's friend, was born there. H. R. Plomer[1] suggests that Pratt and Caxton might possibly have been schoolboys together, perhaps at the school attached to Christchurch Monastery in the parish of St. Alphege. In this parish there lived a John Caxton who used as his mark three cakes over a barrel (or tun) and who is mentioned in an inscription on a monument in the church of St. Alphege.

In 1941, Alan Keen (an authority on manuscripts) secured some documents concerning Caxton; these are now in the British Museum. Discovered in the library of Earl Winterton at Shillinglee Park by Richard Holworthy, the documents cover the period 1420 to 1467. One of Winterton's ancestors purchased the manor of West Wratting from a family named Caxton, the property being situated in the Weald of Kent. There is also record of a property mentioning Philip Caxton and his wife Dennis who had two sons, Philip (born in 1413) and William.

Particularly interesting in these documents is one recording that Philip Caxton junior sold the manor of Little Wratting to John Christemasse of London in 1436—the deed having been witnessed by two aldermen, one of whom was Robert Large, the printer's employer. Further, in 1439, the other son, William Caxton, conveyed his rights in the manor Bluntes Hall at Little Wratting to John Christemasse, and an indenture of 1457 concerning this property mentions one William Caxton alias Causton. It is an interesting coincidence to note that the lord of the manor of Little Wratting was the father of Margaret, Duchess of Burgundy.

In 1420, a Thomas Caxton of Tenterden witnessed the will of a fellow townsman; he owned property in Kent and appears to have been a person of some importance.

[1] See 'William Caxton'.

Table 1 *(continued)*

Number	Instruction	Textual mark	Marginal mark	Notes
C19	Correct vertical alignment						P
C20	Correct horizontal alignment	Single line above and below misaligned matter e.g. mi_saligned		P The marginal mark is placed level with the head and foot of the relevant line
C21	Close up. Delete space between characters or words	linking ⌒ characters	⌒	M P
C22	Insert space between characters	| between characters affected	Y	M P Give the size of the space to be inserted when necessary
C23	Insert space between words	Y between words affected	Y	M P Give the size of the space to be inserted when necessary
C24	Reduce space between characters	| between characters affected	⋀	M P Give the amount by which the space is to be reduced when necessary
C25	Reduce space between words	⋀ between words affected	⋀	M P Give amount by which the space is to be reduced when necessary
C26	Make space appear equal between characters or words	| between characters or words affected	Ⴝ	M P
C27	Close up to normal interline spacing	(each side of column linking lines)		M P The textual marks extend into the margin

Table 1 *(continued)*

Number	Instruction	Textual mark	Marginal mark	Notes
C28	Insert space between lines or paragraphs			M P The marginal mark extends between the lines of text. Give the size of the space to be inserted when necessary
C29	Reduce space between lines or paragraphs			M P The marginal mark extends between the lines of text. Give the amount by which the space is to be reduced when necessary

Editorial, literary and production services

The following specialists offer a wide variety of services to writers (both new and established), to publishers, journalists and others. Services include advice on manuscripts, editing and book production, indexing, translation, research and writing. For an index of the services offered here, see page 589.

'A Feature Factory' Editorial Services
(incorporating Academic Projects)
4 St Andrews Court, 53 Yarmouth Road,
Norwich NR7 0EW
tel (01603) 435229
Editors Dr Dennis Chaplin, Hazel Cripps
Produces company magazines, brochures, company histories, press releases/features (including sameday turnaround), advertisement features, ghostwriting, research briefs for press/broadcasting, backgrounders, writing and research tuition, DTP. Extra researchers often needed for projects.

Abbey Writing Services
Portsmouth Cottage, St Mary Bourne, Andover,
Hants SP11 6BP
tel/fax (01264) 738556
Director John McIlwain
Educational consultants. Lexicography. Comprehensive non-fiction writing, project management and editorial service. Founded 1989.

Academic File
(in association with The Centre for Near East Afro-Asia Research – NEAR)
27 Wallorton Gardens, PO Box 13666,
London SW14 8WF
tel 0181-392 1122 *fax* 0181-392 1422
Director Sajid Rizvi
Research, advisory and consultancy services related to politics, economics and societies of the Near and Middle East, Asia and North Africa and related issues in Europe. Risk analysis, editorial assessment, editing and publishing design and production. Founded 1985.

Adkins Archaeology
Longstone Lodge, Aller, Langport,
Somerset TA10 0QT
tel (01458) 250075 *fax* (01458) 250858
web site http://ourworld.compuserve.com/homepages/adkins_archaeology
Contact Lesley and Roy Adkins
Work with an archaeological, historical and heritage theme undertaken, including all types of research, critical assessment of MSS, contract writing for publishers, project management, copy-editing, indexing, some illustration, and picture research.

Advice and Criticism Service
1 Beechwood Court, The Street, Syderstone,
King's Lynn, Norfolk PE31 8TR
tel (01485) 578594 *fax* (01485) 578138
Contact Hilary Johnson
Authors' consultant: detailed and constructive assessment of typescripts/practical advice regarding publication. Recent organiser of Romantic Novelists' Association's New Writers' Scheme and publishers' reader. Specialities: crime/thrillers/popular women's fiction.

Alpha Word Power
3 Bluecoat Buildings, Claypath, Durham DH1 1RF
tel 0191-384 7219 *fax* 0191-384 3767
e-mail p.g.h@btinternet.com
web site http://www.btinternet.com/~p.g.h/awp.htm
Publishing services: camera-ready copy, word processing, text from and/or to disk, desk editing, proofreading, liaison with printers/binders/graphic design; full secretarial services; business services. Specialise in versatility and speed of turnaround. Founded 1985.

Lucia Alvarez de Toledo MITI, MTG
138B Melrose Avenue, London NW2 4JX
tel 0181-450 5344 *fax* 0181-452 9005
Research, interpreting, translation, subtitles, voice overs, proofreading, editing,

copy-writing, into/from English, Spanish, French, Italian. Founded 1979.

Anvil Editorial Associates
Lleifior, Malltraeth, Bodorgan,
Anglesey LL62 5AF
tel/fax (01407) 840688
Director Dr H. Bernard-Smith

Comprehensive editorial service, including editing, copy-editing, and proofreading. Planning, preparation, writing and editing of books, house journals, company histories, reports, brochures, promotional literature, pamphlets, and scripts. In-house photography. Full MS service. Founded 1966.

Arioma Editorial Services
1 St Albans, Clarach Road, Borth SY24 5LN
tel (01970) 871296 *fax* (01970) 871733
Proprietor Moira W. Smith

Research, co-writing, ghost-writing, DTP, complete book production service. Specialities: military, naval, aviation history and autobiography.

Arkst Publishing
1 Lindsey House, Lloyds's Place, London SE3 0QF
tel 0181-297 9997 *fax* 0181-318 4359
Director James H. Willis MA, FRCP (Edin.)

General editing of MSS; advice on rewrites. Independent appraisal of MSS – fiction and non-fiction. Founded 1995.

Linda Auld Associates
Ashley House, Mill Road, Peasenhall,
Saxmundham, Suffolk IP17 2LW
tel/fax (01728) 660550
Proprietor Linda Auld

Project management, managing editing, rewriting, copy-editing, proofreading, indexing, on-screen editing. All subjects. Member of Society of Freelance Editors and Proofreaders. Founded 1981.

Authors' Advisory Service
Halfway House, 24A Lyndale Avenue, Childs Hill,
London NW2 2QA
tel 0171-794 3285

All typescripts professionally evaluated in depth and edited by long-established publishers' reader specialising in constructive advice to new writers and with wide experience of current literary requirements. Critic and reader for literary awards. Lecture service on the craft and technique of writing for publication. Founded 1972.

Authors' Aid
46 Cartier Close, Westbrook, Warrington,
Cheshire WA5 5TD
tel (01925) 445196 and 838431
Partners Mrs C.A. Sawyer and Miss D.E. Ramage

Provides an honest critical appraisal of MSS and offers advice and guidance on such topics as style, presentation, characterisation, plot and marketability. A personalised service by an established writer with the aim of getting the work published. Other services: word processing, editing, reappraisal. Established 1991.

Authors Appraisal Service
12 Hadleigh Gardens, Boyatt Wood, Eastleigh,
Hants SO5 4NP
Literary consultant J. Evans

Professional writer offers critical appraisal of MSS – fiction only. Specialises in romantic and historical fiction. Competitive rates. Preliminary letter essential. Founded 1988.

Authors' Research Services
32 Oak Village, London NW5 4QN
tel 0171-284 4316
Contact Richard Wright

Offers comprehensive research service to writers, academics and business people worldwide, including fact checking, bibliographical references and document supply. Specialises in English history, social sciences, business. Founded 1966.

Ayrshire Business Services
48 Main Street, Loans, Ayrshire KA10 7EX
tel/fax (01292) 319006
Owner/Manager Janet Spufford

Full manuscript service – word processing or desktop publishing; assists new authors with placement of book and liaises with agent/publisher on behalf of author. Founded 1989.

Richard A. Beck
49 Curzon Avenue, Stanmore,
Middlesex HA7 2AL
tel 0181-933 9787 *fax* 0181-904 5182

Editing, proofreading, indexing, research, writing and rewriting. Reduced rates for new authors, senior citizens, the unemployed, etc. Founded 1991.

Beswick Writing Services
19 Haig Road, Stretford M32 0DS
tel 0161-865 1259
Contact Francis Beswick

Editing, research, information books. Special interests: religious, ecology, outdoor activities, philosophical and educational. Expertise in correspondence courses and Open Learning materials. Founded 1988.

Black Ace Book Production

PO Box 6557, Forfar DD8 2YS
tel (01307) 465096 *fax* (01307) 465494
Directors Hunter Steele, Boo Wood

Book production and text processing, including text capture (or scanning), editing, proofing to camera-ready/film, printing and binding, jacket artwork and design. Delivery of finished books; can sometimes help with distribution. Founded 1990.

Blair Services

Blair Cottage, Aultgrishan, Melvaig, Gairloch, Wester Ross IV21 2DG
tel/fax (01445) 771228
Director Ian Mertling-Blake MA, DPhil

Editing and revision: fiction and non-fiction (such as prospectus for schools and other educational purposes). Also specialist academic revision for books/articles on archaeology and associated subjects. Founded 1992.

Book Production Consultants

25-27 High Street, Chesterton, Cambridge CB4 1ND
tel (01223) 352790 *fax* (01223) 460718
e-mail apl@bpccam.demon.co.uk
Directors A.P. Littlechild, C.S. Walsh

Complete publishing service: writing, editing, designing, illustrating, translating, indexing, artwork; production management of printing and binding; specialised sales and distribution; advertising sales. For books, journals, manuals, reports, magazines, catalogues, electronic media. Founded 1973.

Book-in-Hand Ltd

20 Shepherds Hill, London N6 5AH
tel/fax 0181-341 7650
Contact Ann Kritzinger

Production of cost-effective short-run books for small and self-publishers, from typescript (or disk) to bound copies (hardbacks or paperbacks, sewn or unsewn).

Bookwatch Ltd

15-up, East Street, Lewin's Yard, Chesham, Bucks. HP5 1HQ
tel (01494) 792269 *fax* (01494) 784850
e-mail 100615.1643@compuserve.com

Directors Peter Harland, Jennifer Harland
Market research, bestseller lists, syndicated reviews, features. Publishers of *Books in the Media*, weekly for booksellers and librarians. Founded 1982.

David Bradley Science Writer

67 Vicarage Close, Waterbeach, Cambridge CB5 9QG
tel/fax (01223) 440834
e-mail bradley@enterprise.net
web site http://homepages.enterprise.net/bradley/bradhome.html
Partners David Bradley BSc (Hons) CChem MRSC and Patricia Bradley BSc (Hons), GIPD, Dip RSA

General and specialist articles and scripts on scientific, technology and medical subjects. Editing and rewriting of articles, newsletters, scripts, brochures and technical MSS. Member of ABSW and recipient of several writing awards. Most word processing and picture formats handled; HTML aware. Established 1989.

Brittan Design Partnership

Clarence House, 35 Clarence Street, Market Harborough, Leics. LE16 7NE
tel (01858) 466950 *fax* (01858) 434632
e-mail b.d.p@virgin.net
web site http://www.freespace.virgin.net/b.d.p
Partners Derek W. Brittan MCSD, Nick J. Brittan

Complete editorial design and publishing service; in-house typesetting; high end computer graphics and pre-press; film production. Founded 1978.

Brooke Projects

21 Barnfield, Urmston, Manchester M41 9EW
tel 0161-746 8140 *fax* 0161-746 8132
e-mail urmston@brooke.u-net.com

Research, editing and contract writing. Specialises in business, management, tourism, history, biography and social science.

Mrs D. Buckmaster

51 Chatsworth Road, Torquay, Devon TQ1 3BJ
tel/fax (01803) 294663

General editing of MSS, specialising in traditional themes in religious, metaphysical and esoteric subjects; also success and inspirational books or articles. Founded 1966.

John Button

14 Manor House Way, Brightlingsea, Colchester, Essex CO7 0QN
tel/fax (01206) 302769
Ewer House, 44-46 Crouch Street, Colchester, Essex CO3 3HH

tel (01206) 548452

Copy-editing and proofreading, specialising in legal, financial, taxation, business education and corporate identity publications; Legal Reference Library series. Founded 1991.

Calderbridge Associates
3 Lion Chambers, Huddersfield,
West Yorkshire HD1 1ES
tel/fax (01484) 512817
Directors R. Sharp, B. Bedar

MSS criticism and advice; editing; proofreading; word processing; multimedia/internet services. Founded 1995.

Causeway Resources
8 The Causeway, Teddington,
Middlesex TW11 0HE
tel/fax 0181-977 8797
Director Keith Skinner

Genealogical, biographical and historical research, specialising in police history and true crime research. Founded 1989.

Vanessa Charles
38 Ham Common, Richmond, Surrey TW10 7JG
tel/fax 0181-940 9225
e-mail 101361,1176@compuserve.com

Design and book production services. Founded 1975.

Karyn Claridge Book Production
244 Bromham Road, Biddenham,
Bedford MK40 4AA
tel (01234) 347909

Complete book production management service offered from MS to bound copies; graphic services available; sourcing service for interactive book projects. Founded 1989.

Johnathon Clifford
27 Mill Road, Fareham, Hants PO16 0TH
tel/fax (01329) 822218

Offers a free, unbiased advice service for anyone looking for a publisher or who has experienced difficulties with a publishing house. Has extensive knowledge of vanity publishing and acted as adviser to the Advertising Standards Authority regarding the wording of the 'Advice Note Vanity Publishing July 1997'. Established 1994.

Combrógos
Mr Meic Stephens, 10 Heol Don, Whitchurch,
Cardiff CF4 2AU
tel (01222) 623359 *fax* (01222) 529202

Specialises in books (including fiction and poetry) about Wales or by Welsh authors, providing a full editorial service and undertaking arts and media research. Founded 1990.

Copywriting One-to-One
Cowieslinn, Eddleston, Peeblesshire EH45 8QZ
tel/fax (01721) 730 350
Director Patrick Quinn

Correspondence course in copywriting with telephone helpline. Founded 1994.

Ingrid Cranfield
16 Myddelton Gardens, London N21 2PA
tel/fax 0181-360 2433

Advisory and editorial services for authors and media, including critical assessment, rewriting, proofreading, copy-editing, writing of marketing copy, indexing, research, interviews, transcripts. Special interests: geography, travel, exploration, adventure (own archives), language, education, youth training, art and architecture (notably Japanese). Translations from German and French. Founded 1972.

Clarissa Cridland
4 Rock Terrace, Coleford, Bath,
Somerset BA3 5NF
tel (01373) 812705 *fax* (01373) 813517
e-mail cridland@telecall.co.uk

Full service on all aspects of author and publisher contracts, including but not limited to reading, typing and negotiating contracts. Established 1994.

David A. Cross
75 Croslands Park, Barrow-in-Furness,
Cumbria LA13 9LB
tel (01229) 822694

Research and information service; editing texts, specialising in art history, English literature, biography and genealogy; creative writing tutorials; lectures on artists and writers of the Lake District.

D & N Publishing
Membury Business Park, Lambourn Woodlands,
Hungerford, Berks. RG17 7TJ
tel (01488) 71210 *fax* (01488) 71220
e-mail DandNPub@aol.com
Partners David and Namrita Price-Goodfellow

Complete project management including commissioning, editing, picture research, illustration and design, page layout, indexing, printing and repro. All stages managed in-house and produced on Apple Macs running Quark XPress, FreeHand and Photoshop. Founded 1991.

Meg and Stephen Davies
31 Egerton Road, Ashton, Preston, Lancs. PR2 1AJ
tel (01772) 725120 *fax* (01772) 723853

Indexing at general and post-graduate level in the arts and humanities. Can offer indexes on PC disk. Also proofreading and copy-editing. Registered indexer with Society of Indexers since 1971.

Editorial/Visual Research
21 Leamington Road Villas, London W11 1HS
tel 0171-727 4920 *mobile* (0973) 820020
Contact Angela Murphy

Comprehensive research service including historical, literary, film and picture research for writers, publishers, film and TV companies. Services also include copy-writing, editing, and travel and feature writing. Founded 1973.

Dr Martin Edwards
66 Cooden Drive, Bexhill-on-Sea,
East Sussex TN39 3AX
tel/fax (01424) 224273

Specialist editorial and research service in the medico-scientific field: copy-editing, co-editorial/-authorship, proofreading, abstracting and conference productions. Special interest in the improvement of foreign texts. Founded 1985.

Lewis Esson Publishing
45 Brewster Gardens, London W10 6AQ
tel 0181-969 0951 *fax* 0181-968 1623
e-mail 101465.2252@compuserve.com

Project management of illustrated books in areas of food, art and interior design; editing and writing of food books. Founded 1989.

etr (Edward Twentyman Resources)
4 Little Green, Cheveley, Newmarket CB8 9RG
tel (01638) 731332 *fax* (01638) 731152
e-mail freelance@etr.co.uk
web site http://www.etr.co.uk
Proprietor Edward Twentyman

Employment agency specialising solely in freelance people in publishing. Founded 1992.

First Edition Translations Ltd
6 Wellington Court, Wellington Street,
Cambridge CB1 1HZ
tel (01223) 356733 *fax* (01223) 321488
e-mail info@firstedit.co.uk

web site http://www.firstedit.co.uk
Directors Sheila Waller, Jeremy Waller

Translation, interpreting, voice recording, editing, proofreading, indexing, DTP; books, manuals, reports, journals and promotional material. Founded 1981.

FJN Associates
Little Theobald, Sandy Cross, Heathfield,
East Sussex TN21 8BT
tel (01435) 866653 *fax* (01435) 868998
Partners Frederick J. Nixon, Brenda Mellen Nixon

Comprehensive DTP and editorial service including magazine and newsletter design and production; advice to authors, editing and preparation of manuscripts for submission to publishers/editors; proofreading. Founded 1990.

James Wilson Flegg
via Paolini 11, 10138 Turin, Italy
tel/fax (011) 4331192

Language consultant; writing, ghosting, copy-editing, translation, abstracting; projects and commissions undertaken. Founded 1970.

Christine Foley Secretarial Services
Glyndedwydd, Login, Whitland,
Carmarthenshire SA34 0TN
tel/fax (01994) 448414
Partners Christine Foley, Michael Foley

Word processing service: preparation of MSS from handwritten/typed notes and audio-transcription. Complete secretarial support. Founded 1991.

Brian J. Ford
Rothay House, 6 Mayfield Road, Eastrea,
Cambs. PE7 2AY
tel/fax (01733) 350888
e-mail bjford@sciences.demon.co.uk
web site http://www.sciences.demon.co.uk

Scientist and adviser on scientific matters; author, producer/director scientific films and programmes in addition to editor/contributor to many leading books and journals. Has hosted many leading BBC TV and radio programmes, and overseas documentaries.

Freelance Editorial Services
45 Bridge Street, Musselburgh,
Midlothian EH21 6AA
tel 0131-665 7825
Contact Bill Houston BSc, DipLib, MPhil

Editing, proofreading, indexing, abstracting, translations, bibliographies; particularly scientific and medical. Founded 1975.

Freelance Market News

Sevendale House, 7 Dale Street,
Manchester M1 1JB
tel 0161-228 2362 *fax* 0161-228 3533

Market Research Department for freelance
writers issues a monthly Market News
service the *Freelance Market News*; £29
p.a. A good rate of pay made for news of
editorial requirements. Information on
UK and overseas publications with editorial content, submission requirements
and contact details. Founded 1968.

Freelance Services, Joan Shannon

41A Newal Road, Ballymoney, Co. Antrim,
Northern Ireland BT53 6HB
tel (012656) 62953 *fax* (012656) 65019

Writing and editorial service. Production
and desktop design. Photography: commercial, scenic, architecture, etc.
Founded 1991.

Shelagh Furness

Hallgarth Farmhouse, The Hallgarth, Durham,
Co. Durham DH1 3BJ
tel 0191-384 3840

Research and information service, specialising in environmental, scientific and
geographical topics, also North East
England; word processing service.
Founded 1992.

Roy Gaylor

4 Spring Shaw Road, Orpington, Kent BR5 2RH
tel 0181-300 0139

Copy-editing, proofreading, writing and
rewriting. Special interests: sport, social
history, history, travel. Established 1991.

Geo Group & Associates

4 Christian Fields, London SW16 3JZ
tel/fax 0181-764 6292

Publishing services. From copy-editing
and proofreading to complete package.
Research and publishing consultancy.
Two photo libraries (including aerial);
photography commissioned. Special
rates to author-publishers. Established
1968.

C.N. Gilmore

27 Salisbury Street, Bedford MK41 7RE
tel (01234) 346142

Sub-editing, copy-editing, slush-pile
reading, reviewing. Will also collaborate.
Undertakes work in all scholarly and
academic fields as well as fiction and
practical writing. Founded 1987.

Graham-Cameron Publishing

The Studio, 23 Holt Road, Sheringham,
Norfolk NR26 8NB
tel (01263) 821333 *fax* (01263) 821334
Partners Helen Graham-Cameron, Mike
Graham-Cameron

Complete editorial, including writing,
illustration and production services.
Founded 1984.

Guildford Reading Services

17 Burwood Gardens, Ash Vale, Aldershot,
Hants GU12 5HN
tel (01252) 317950
Director B.V. Varney

proofreading, press revision, copy preparation, sub-editing. Founded 1978.

John Hall

20 Drury Avenue, Horsforth,
Leeds LS18 4BR
tel 0113-258 4902

Writing, editing, proofreading.
Specialises in crime fiction but all subjects covered. Established 1990.

Bernard Hawton

6 Merdon Court, Merdon Avenue,
Chandler's Ford, Hants SO53 1FP
tel (01703) 267400

Proofreading, copy-editing.

Heath Associates

Garden Flat, 15 South Hill Park Gardens,
London NW3 2TD
tel/fax 0171-435 4059
e-mail 74101.624@compuserve.com
Proprietor Richard Williams

Consultancy on desktop publishing,
word processing and graphics programs
for IBM PC; design and illustration specialising in academic and technical
works; writing and editing for computing
and related topics. Founded 1988.

Antony Hemans

Maranatha, 1 Nettles Terrace, Guildford,
Surrey GU1 4PA
tel (01483) 574511

Biographical and historical research, specialising in industrial archaeology – railways, canals and shipping, air, military
and naval operations – genealogy and
family history. Founded 1981.

Mark P. Hempshell

9 Heath Drive, Boston Spa,
West Yorkshire LS23 6PB
tel/fax (01937) 845585
e-mail markhempshell@compuserve.com

Freelance writer specialising in careers/ employment, business, live and work abroad, and how-to books and articles. Also research and all kinds of advertising copywriting, especially direct mail. Established 1986.

Holland-Ford's Associates
103 Lydyett Lane, Barnton, Northwich, Cheshire CW8 4JT
tel (01606) 76960
Director Robert Holland-Ford
Impresarios, concert/lecture agents.

Rosemary Horstmann
122 Mayfield Court, 27 West Savile Terrace, Edinburgh EH9 3DR
tel 0131-667 1377
Broadcasting scripts evaluated; general consultancy on editorial and marketing matters.

E.J. Hunter
6 Dorset Road, London N22 4SL
tel 0181-889 0370
Editing, copy-editing, proofreading; appraisal of MSS. Special interests: novels, short stories, drama, children's stories; primary education, alternative medicine, New Age.

Hurst Village Publishing
Henry and Elizabeth Farrar, High Chimneys, Davis Street, Hurst, Reading RG10 0TH
tel 0118-9345211 *fax* 0118-9342073
Offers design, photography, typesetting, printing and binding services, using the latest desktop publishing programs, photographic equipment and high resolution colour and laser printers. Founded 1989.

Indexers, Society of
Mermaid House, 1 Mermaid Court, London SE1 1HR
tel 0171-403 4947
See pages 479 and 591 for further details.

Indexing Specialists
202 Church Road, Hove, East Sussex BN3 2DJ
tel (01273) 738299 *fax* (01273) 323309
e-mail indspec@pavilion.co.uk
web site http://www.pavilion.co.uk/indspec
Director Richard Raper BSc, DTA
Indexes for all types of books, journals and reference publications on professional, scientific and general subjects; copy-editing, proofreading services; consultancy on indexing and training projects. Founded 1965.

The Information Bureau
(formerly Daily Telegraph Information Bureau)
51 The Business Centre, 103 Lavender Hill, London SW11 5QL
tel 0171-924 4414 *fax* 0171-924 4456
Contact Jane Hall
Offers an on-demand research service on a variety of subjects including current affairs, business, marketing, history, the arts, media and politics. Resources include range of cuttings amassed by the bureau since 1948.

Ken Jackson
30 The Boundary, Langton Green, Tunbridge Wells, Kent TN3 0YB
tel (01892) 545198
Copy-editing, proofreading, indexing, particularly of technical, historical or religious MSS. Founded 1985.

JG Editorial
54 Mount Street, Lincoln LN1 3JG
tel (01522) 821246 *fax* (01522) 821247
e-mail jennigoss@compuserve.com
Directors Janet Goss, Jenni Goss, John Goss
Independent critique service for fiction, general non-fiction (no poetry), academic/ business/professional books; rewriting/ ghosting; word processing/presentation/ keying (MSS/audio); project management; editorial reports; copy and disk editing (PC/Mac); proofreading. Design/ indexing/ PR by arrangement. Founded 1988.

Library Research Agency
Burberry, Devon Road, Salcombe, Devon TQ8 8HJ
tel (01548 84) 2769
Directors D.J. Langford MA, B. Langford
Research and information service for writers, journalists, artists, businessmen from libraries, archives, museums, record offices and newspapers in UK, USA and Europe. Sources may be in English, French, German, Russian, Serbo-Croat, Bulgarian, and translations made if required. Founded 1974.

The Literary Consultancy (TLC)
PO Box 12939, London N8 9WA
tel/fax 0181-372 3922, 0181-374 2812
e-mail tlc@hannahg.dircon.co.uk
Directors Hannah Griffiths, Rebecca Swift
Offers a detailed assessment of fiction, non-fiction and poetry from a team of editors and writers, all of whom have experience of publishing. Fees based on

length. Quick turnaround. Personal links with agents and publishers. Established 1996.

Miles Litvinoff
104 Doyle Gardens, London NW10 3SR
tel 0181-965 3427
Writer and editor on environment, human rights and development. Writing, editing, commissioning, co-authorship, project management, editorial advice; especially environment, Third World, human rights, and development, including books for young people. Founded 1984.

Dr Kenneth Lysons
Lathom, Scotchbarn Lane, Whiston, Nr Prescot, Merseyside L35 7JB
tel 0151-426 5513
Contact Dr Kenneth Lysons MA, MEd, DPA, DMS, FCIS, FInstPS, FBIM
Company and institutional histories, support material for organisational management and supervisory training, house journals, research and reports service. Full secretarial support. Founded 1986.

Duncan McAra
28 Beresford Gardens, Edinburgh EH5 3ES
tel/fax 0131-552 1558
Consultancy on all aspects of general trade publishing; editing; proof correction. Main subjects include art, architecture, archaeology, biography, military, Scottish and travel. See also Literary agents. Founded 1988.

McText
Denmill, Tough, By Alford, Aberdeenshire AB33 8EP
tel/fax (019755) 62582
e-mail mctext@highland-pony.demon.co.uk
web site http://www.highland-pony.demon.co.uk/mctext.htm
Partners K. and Duncan McArdle
Editing, copy-editing, proofreading, web site authoring. Specialist interests: archaeology, equestrian. Founded 1986.

Manuscript Appraisals
Quill Cottage, Penffordd, Narberth, Pembs SA66 7HU
tel (01437) 563822
Proprietor Raymond J. Price
Consultants N.L. Price MBIM, Mary Hunt
Independent appraisal of authors' MSS (fiction and non-fiction, but no poetry) with full editorial guidance and advice. In-house editing, copy-editing, rewriting and proofreading if required. Interested in the work of new writers. Founded 1984.

Marlinoak
22 Eve's Croft, Birmingham B32 3QL
tel/fax 0121-475 6139
Proprietor Hazel J. Billing JP, BA, DipEd
Preparation of scripts, plays, books, MSS service, ghostwriting, proof reading, research; also audio-transcription, word processing and full secretarial facilities. Founded 1984.

M.C. Martinez
60 Oakwood Avenue, London N14 6QL
tel 0181-886 5829
Partners Mary Martinez, Françoise Budd
Advice and evaluation of MSS; critical assessment of MSS specialising in fiction and children's books; full desktop publishing service; translation in French and Spanish. Possible change of address; please telephone first. Founded 1988.

Susan Moore Editorial Services
65 Albion Road, London N16 9PP
tel/fax 0171-923 2480
Troubleshooting service for publishers, packagers and agents: co-authorship with specialists, ghostwriting, rewiting, translation fine tuning, re-drafting. Founded 1994.

Morley Adams
20 Spectrum House, 32-34 Gordon House Road, London NW5 1LP
tel 0171-284 1433 *fax* 0171-284 4494
Editor Mike Hutchinson
Specialists in the production of cross-words and other puzzles, quizzes, etc. Founded 1917.

MS-S
Julia MacRae, 13 Pattison Road, London NW2 2HL
tel/fax 0171-435 7882 and
Christopher Sinclair-Stevenson, 3 South Terrace, London SW7 2TB
tel/fax 0171-581 2550
Full editorial/advisory service. Fees negotiable. Founded 1996.

Murder Files
Marienau, Brimley Road, Bovey Tracey, Devon TQ13 9DH
tel (01626) 833487 *fax* (01626) 835797
Director Paul Williams
Crime writer and researcher specialising in UK murders. Holds information on

thousands of well-known and less well-known murders dating from 1400 to the present day. Copies of press cuttings on murder cases available from 1920 to date. Research also undertaken for general enquirers, writers, TV, radio, video, etc. Founded 1994.

Elizabeth Murray
3 Gower Mews Mansions, Gower Mews, London WC1E 6HR
tel/fax 0171-636 3761
Literary, biographical, historical, crime, military, cinema, genealogy research for authors, journalists, radio and TV from UK, European and USA sources. Founded 1975.

My Word!
138 Railway Terrace, Rugby, Warks. CV21 3HN
tel (01788) 571294 *fax* (01788) 550957
e-mail roddie@compuserve.com
Partners Roddie Grant, Janet Grant
Complete DTP service; word processing service either to hard copy or disk; editing, copy-editing and proofreading. Work done includes books, magazines, theses and CVs. Founded 1994.

Paul Nash
Munday House, Aberdalgie, Perth PH2 0QB
tel/fax (01738) 621584
e-mail paulnash@zetnet.co.uk
Indexer specialising in sciences, technology, environmental science. Winner of Library Association Wheatley Medal (1992) for outstanding index. Founded 1979.

Peter Nickol
6 High Street, Ringstead, Kettering NN14 4DA
tel/fax (01933) 625349
Editing and page layout; typesetting and music engraving; copyright licensing; project management including mixed media coordination, CD recording and production. Specialises in music and music education. Established 1987.

Nidaba Publishing Services
19 Khartoum Road, London SW17 0JA
tel 0181-767 8470
Contact Allie Glenny PhD Eng. Lit.
Copy-editing, text keying (Word, Quark), proofreading. Computer translation and zip disk facilities. All work carried out by published writer with extensive publishing experience. Established 1997.

Paul H. Niekirk
40 Rectory Avenue, High Wycombe, Bucks. HP13 6HW
tel (01494) 527200
Text editing for works of reference and professional and management publications, particularly texts on law; freelance writing. Founded 1976.

Northern Writers Advisory Services
77 Marford Crescent, Sale, Cheshire M33 4DN
tel 0161-969 1573
Proprietor Jill Groves
Offers copy-editing, proofreading and typesetting to small publishers, societies and authors. Founded 1986.

Northgate Training
Scarborough House, 29 James Street West, Bath BA1 2BT
tel (01225) 339733 *fax* (01225) 429151
Directors M.R. Lynch, J.M. Bayley
Writing and design of management games and training exercises. Specialists in distance and open learning training packages. Founded 1978.

Oakleaf Systems Ltd
64 Baldock Street, Ware, Herts. SG12 9DT
tel/fax (01920) 486526
e-mail sue@oakleaf.demon.co.uk
Managing director Paul Procter BA
Suppliers to publishers, societies and other organisations of customised database management systems, with advanced retrieval mechanisms, and electronic publishing systems for the preparation of dictionaries, reference books, encyclopedias, catalogues, journals, archives. PC (Windows) based.

Oriental Languages Bureau
Lakshmi Building, Sir P. Mehta Road, Fort, Bombay 400001, India
tel 2661258/2665640 *fax* 2664598
Proprietor Rajan K. Shah
Undertakes translations and printing in all Indian languages and a few foreign languages.

Ormrod Research Services
Weeping Birch, Burwash, East Sussex TN19 7HG
tel (01435) 882541
and at 4 Croftleigh Gardens, Solihull B91 1TG
tel 0121-711 7200
Comprehensive research service; literary, historical, academic, biographical, commercial. Critical reading with report,

editing, indexing, proofreading, ghosting. Founded 1982.

Oxprint Design

Aristotle House, Aristotle Lane, Oxford OX2 6TR
tel (01865) 512331 *fax* (01865) 316763
e-mail name@oxprint.co.uk
Directors Per Saugman, John Webb (managing), Peter Lawrence BA (Hons), Andrew King (company secretary)

Design, typesetting, editorial, illustrating scientific, educational and general books. Specialists in project management. Macintosh desktop and bureau facilities, computer aided design and illustration. Founded 1974.

Pageant Publishing

1 Weir Gardens, Pershore, Worcs. WR10 1DX
tel (01386) 561125 *fax* (01386) 561119
Director Gillian Page

Consultancy on all aspects of academic publishing: publication of academic journals. Founded 1978.

Pages Editorial & Publishing Services

Ballencrieff Cottage, Ballencrieff Toll, Bathgate, West Lothian EH48 4LD
tel (01506) 632728 *fax* (01506) 635444
e-mail suse@pages.clara.net
Director Susan Coon

Editorial and production service of magazines/newspapers for companies or for commercial distribution; promotional literature; publishing service for authors wishing to self-publish. Founded 1995.

Geoffrey D. Palmer

47 Burton Fields Road, Stamford Bridge, York YO4 1JJ
tel/fax (01759) 372874
e-mail gdp@msn.com

Editorial and production services, including STM and general copy-editing, on-screen editing, artwork editing, proofreading and indexing. Pre-press project management. Founded 1987.

Roger Palmer Ltd

23C Tavistock Place, London WC1H 9SE
tel 0171-383 5454 *fax* 0171-383 3234
e-mail contracts@rogerpalmerltd.co.uk
Directors Roger Palmer, Stephen Aucutt
Consultant Angela Elkins

Drafts, advises on and negotiates all media contracts for publishers, agents, packagers, authors and others; operates outsourced contracts department functions; undertakes contractual audits and devises contracts and permissions systems; provides advice on copyright and related issues; provides training and seminars. Special terms for members of the Society of Authors. Founded 1993.

Penman Literary Service

Mark Sorrell, 185 Daws Heath Road, Benfleet, Essex SS7 2TF
tel (01702) 557431

Advisory, editorial and typing service for authors. Rewriting, re-drafting, ghostwriting, proofreading; critical assessment of MSS.

Phoenix 2

Lantern House, Lodge Drove, Woodfalls, Salisbury, Wilts SP5 2NH
tel (01725) 512200 *fax* (01725) 511819
Partners Bryan Walker, Amanda Walker

Writing, editing, sub-editing, typesetting and design of magazines, newsletters, journals, brochures and promotional literature. Specialist areas are business, tourism, social affairs and education. Founded 1994.

Christopher Pick

41 Chestnut Road, London SE27 9EZ
tel 0181-761 2585 *fax* 0181-761 6388

Publications consultancy, project management, writing and editing for companies and private-sector, public-sector and voluntary-sector organisations: e.g. brochures and booklets, information materials and training manuals, multimedia, strategy documents, research reports, company histories. Special expertise in technology, health and social policy, government affairs, education.

Picture Research Agency

Jasmine Cottage, Spring Grove Road, Richmond, Surrey TW10 6EH
tel 0181-940 5986
Contact Pat Hodgson

Illustrations found for books, films and TV. Written research also undertaken particularly on historical subjects, including photographic and film history. Small picture library.

Picture Research Service – see Rich Research

Reginald Piggott

Decoy Lodge, Decoy Road, Potter Heigham, Norfolk NR29 5LX

tel (01692) 670384
Cartographer to the University Presses and academic publishers in Britain and overseas. Maps and diagrams for academic and educational books. Founded 1962.

Keith Povey Editorial Services

Stoneleigh House, South Brentor, Tavistock, Devon PL19 0NW
tel (01822) 810190 *fax* (01822) 810191
e-mail Povedservs@aol.com

Copy-editing, indexing, proofreading, publisher/author liaison. Partnership with:

T & A Typesetting Services

189 Drake Street, Rochdale, Lancs. OL11 1EF
tel (01706) 861662 *fax* (01706) 861673
e-mail a.edmondson@zen.co.uk

Specialist book-typesetting to CRC and negs, graphic design.

Victoria Ramsay

Abbots Rest, Chilbolton, Stockbridge, Hants SO20 6BE
tel (01264) 860251 *fax* (01264) 860026

Freelance editing, copy-editing and proofreading; non-fiction research and writing of promotional literature and pamphlets. Any non-scientific subject undertaken. Special interests: education, cookery, travel, Africa and Caribbean and works in translation. Established 1981.

Reading and Righting (Robert Lambolle Services)

618B Finchley Road, London NW11 7RR
tel/fax 0181-455 4564

MSS/script analysis and evaluation service: fiction, non-fiction, stage plays and screenplays; editorial services; one-to-one tutorials, creative writing courses, lectures and research. Send sae for leaflet. Founded 1987.

S. Ribeiro Literary Services

42 West Heath Court, North End Road, London NW11 7RG
tel 0181-458 9082
Contact S. Ribeiro BA

From preparation to publication: MSS appraisal, rewriting, ghosting, sensitive editing, and submission to publishers. Analysis of structure and style, with close attention to detail. Can edit author's disk (all systems) with laser reprint, to publication standard. Creative writing tuition. New writers welcome. Also book reviews and copywriting.

Special interests: fiction; general non-fiction; memoirs and poetry. Telephone or send sae for further information. Founded 1986.

Rich Research

One Bradby, 77 Carlton Hill, London NW8 9XE
tel/fax 0171-624 7755
Contact Diane Rich

Picture research service. Visuals found for all sectors of the media and publishing. Artwork and photography commissioned. Rights and permissions negotiated. Founded 1978.

Anton Rippon Press Services

20 Chain Lane, Mickleover, Derby DE3 5AJ
tel (01332) 512379/384235 *fax* (01332) 292755

Writer and researcher on historical, sociological and sporting topics. Features, programmes, brochures produced; ghost writing. Radio and film documentary scripts. Complete book production service available.

Vernon Robinson Editorial Services

22 Granhams Close, Great Shelford, Cambridge CB2 5LG
tel (01223) 840391

Copy-editing and proofreading of all educational books, specialising in science, maths, engineering, economics, computer science, biology, etc. Also English correction of technical MSS translated into English for European publishers. Founded 1973.

David Sanders

4 Cliasmol, Harris, Isle of Harris HS3 3AR
tel/fax (01859) 560250
e-mail davidsanders@compuserve.com

Copy-editing and proofreading, hard copy or disk. Core subjects: religion and theology, especially Roman Catholicism, spirituality. Established 1994.

Sandhurst Editorial Consultants

36 Albion Road, Sandhurst, Berks. GU47 9BP
tel (01252) 877645 *fax* (01252) 890508
e-mail mail@sand-con.demon.co.uk
web site http://www.sand-con.demon.co.uk
Partners Lionel Browne, Janet Browne

Specialists in technical, professional and reference work. Project management, editorial development, writing, ghosting, text processing, Americanisation, and general editorial consultancy. Founded 1991.

Sandton Literary Agency
PO Box 785799, Sandton 2146, South Africa
tel (011) 442-8624
Directors J. Victoria Canning, M. Sutherland
Evaluating, editing and/or indexing book MSS. Preparing reports, company histories, house journals, etc. Ghost writing and ghost painting. Critical but constructive advice to writers. Lecture agents. Please write or phone first. Founded 1982.

Science Unit
Rothay House, 6 Mayfield Road, Eastrea, Cambs. PE7 2AY
tel/fax (01733) 350888
e-mail unit@sciences.demon.co.uk
web site http://www.sciences.demon.co.uk
Independent scientific consultancy specialising in microscopical matters and new directions in science. Advises on programmes and publications in general scientific field. Activities are worldwide, with publications in many overseas and foreign-language editions.

SciText
18 Barton Close, Landrake, Saltash, Cornwall PL12 5BA
tel/fax (01752) 851451
e-mail bg22@open.ac.uk
Dr Brian Gee. proofreading and editing in science, engineering and the history of science and technology; IBM compatible PC. Founded 1988.

Scriptmate
20 Shepherd's Hill, London N6 5AH
tel/fax 0181-341 7650
Contact Ann Kritzinger
An editing service in conjunction with **Book-in-Hand Ltd** for selected work in fiction and non-fiction. Founded 1985.

Mrs Ellen Seager
3 Hereford Court, Hereford Road, Harrogate, North Yorkshire HG1 2PX
tel (01423) 509770
Critical assessment of fiction and non-fiction work with helpful direction, tuition and advice; creative writing tutor; ghost writing; publishing and market information.

SeaStar Editorial Services
9A Londsdale Road, Southend-on-Sea, Essex SS2 4LZ
tel (01702) 601800
Proprietor Terry E. Scott

MSS revision and rewriting; compilation, layout, keying-in for floppy disk, disk conversion; photography; desktop publishing services; printer liaison.

Serpentine Editorial
50 Quaker's Hall Lane, Sevenoaks, Kent TN13 3TU
tel/fax (01732) 457360
e-mail john.rowe@virgin.net
Partners Molly Perham, Julian Rowe
Publishing service for children's books: editing, writing and rewiting, planning and management of complete projects to CRC; DTP on PC or Apple Mac. All subjects, but science a speciality. Founded 1991.

SFEP (Society of Freelance Editors and Proofreaders) – see page 476

Gill Shepherd
87 Elm Park Mansions, Park Walk, London SW10 0AP
tel 0171-352 1770
Research, fact checking, rewriting for authors. Specialises in history, politics, biography and genealogy. Established 1985.

I.R. Sinclair
Saltire, Livermere Road, Gt Barton, Bury St Edmunds, Suffolk IP31 2RZ
tel (01284) 788312
e-mail iansin@globalnet.co.uk
Technical writing (electronics and computing). Typesetting to CRC, particularly mathematical setting. Founded 1984.

Small Print
The Old School House, 74 High Street, Swavesey, Cambridge CB4 5QU
tel (01954) 231713 *fax* (01954) 232777
e-mail info @smallprt.demon.co.uk
Proprietor Naomi Laredo
Editorial, DTP, project management, and audio production services, specialising in ELT and foreign language courses for secondary schools and home study; also phrase books, travel guides, general humanities. Translation from/to and editing in many European and Asian languages. Photography and picture research. Founded 1986.

Robert and Jane Songhurst
3 Yew Tree Cottages, Grange Lane, Sandling, Nr Maidstone, Kent ME14 3BY
tel (01622) 757635

Literary consultants, authors' works advised upon (fees by agreement), literary and historical research, feature writing, reviewing, editing, proofreading. Founded 1976.

Special Edition Pre-press Services
Partners Romilly Hambling, 17 Almorah Road, London N1 3ER
tel/fax 0171-226 5339 and
Corinne Orde, 2 Caledonian Wharf, London E14 3EW
tel/fax 0171-987 9600
Integrated Mac-based editing and page make-up for publishers of general and STM titles. Linguistics and music a speciality. Design and project management undertaken. Established 1993.

Mrs Gene M. Spencer
63 Castle Street, Melbourne, Derbyshire DE73 1DY
tel (01332) 862133
Editing, copy-editing and proofreading; feature writing; theatrical profiles; book reviews; freelance writing. Founded 1970.

SPREd (Society of Picture Researchers and Editors) – now The Picture Research Association – see page 455

Stationers' Hall Registry Ltd
Stationers' Hall, Ave Maria Lane, London EC4M 7DD
tel 0171-248 2934 fax 0171-489 1975
The Registry exists for those requiring proof of existence of their material for ownership of copyright purposes. Written works or those on tape, record, video or computer disk can be registered. Established 16th century.

Strand Editorial Services
16 Mitchley View, South Croydon, Surrey CR2 9HQ
tel/fax 0181-657 1247
Joint Principals Derek and Irene Bradley
Provides a comprehensive service to publishers, editorial departments, and public relations and advertising agencies. Proofreading and copy-editing a speciality. Founded 1974.

Streetwise Town Plans Ltd
3 Rayleigh Road, Basingstoke, Hants RG21 7TJ
tel (01256) 328186
Contacts P.J. Corcoran, Rosemary Corcoran

Top quality computer-generated maps of almost every town in Europe, plus major towns and cities throughout the world. All maps personalised to order.

Hans Tasiemka Archives
80 Temple Fortune Lane, London NW11 7TU
tel 0181-455 2485 fax 0181-455 0231
Proprietor Mrs Edda Tasiemka
Comprehensive newspaper cuttings library from 1850s to the present day on all subjects for writers, publishers, picture researchers, film and TV companies. Founded 1950.

Lyn M. Taylor (UK)
(Eve-Line Proofs)
1 Eglinton Crescent, Edinburgh EH12 5DH
tel 0131-225 6152 fax 0131-467 6260
e-mail 106253.3476@compuserve.com
National comprehensive editorial service for publishers and printers: copy-editing and proofreading in all subjects. Specialises in complex scientific and medical. Hard copy or disk.

Teamwork
Unit 5, Spurlings Yard, Spurlings Road, Fareham PO17 6AB
tel (01329) 827672, (0421) 417499
fax (01329) 829136
Proprietors Mrs D. Emmerson, N. Emmerson
Typesetting, paste-up, camera-ready artwork, design and preparation of books to print stage, illustration, proofreading, indexing, general editing and research services. Founded 1973.

Tecmedia Ltd
Bruce House, 258 Bromham Road, Biddenham, Beds. MK40 4AA
tel (01234) 325223 fax (01234) 353524
e-mail jojobaxter@compuserve.com
Managing Director J.D. Baxter
Specialists in the design, development and production of training and information packages, newsletters and promotional material. Founded 1972.

Teral Research Services
111 The Avenue, Bournemouth, Dorset BH9 2UX
tel (01202) 519220
Contact Alan C. Wood
and 45 Forest View Road, Bournemouth, Dorset BH9 3BH
tel/fax (01202) 516834
Contact Terry C. Treadwell
Research and consultancy on military aviation, army, navy, defence, space,

weapons (new and antique), police, intelligence, medals, uniforms and armour. Founded 1980.

3 & 5 Promotion
Crag House, Witherslack, Grange-over-Sands, Cumbria LA11 6RW
tel (015395) 52286 *fax* (015395) 52013
e-mail musicbks @rdooley.demon.co.uk
Proprietor Rosemary Dooley

Collaborative publishers' exhibitions: music books. Founded 1985.

Felicity Trotman
Downside, Chicklade, Salisbury, Wilts. SP3 5SU
tel/fax (01747) 820503

Editing, copy-editing, proofreading, writing, rewriting, assessment of MSS. Specialises in children's books, fiction and non-fiction, all ages. Established 1982.

John Vickers
27 Shorrolds Road, London SW6 7TR
tel 0171-385 5774

Archives of British Theatre photographs by John Vickers, from 1938-1974.

Valerie Vogel Picture Research
141 Chestnut Street, Montclair, NJ 07042, USA
tel 201-746-8560 *fax* 201-746-8471
e-mail vvpics@adsight.com
web site http://adsight.com/vvpics

Freelance picture researcher/photo editor. Diverse experience in wide range of subjects for books, magazines, advertising, corporate and film. Uses traditional and online sources. Established 1980.

Gordon R. Wainwright
22 Hawes Court, Sunderland SR6 8NU
tel/fax 0191-548 9342

Criticism, advice and revision for publishers. Articles on education and training matters supplied to newspapers, journals and magazines. Training in report writing, rapid reading, effective meetings, etc. Lecture service. Consultancy service in all aspects of communication. Travel writing assignments undertaken. Established 1961.

Caroline White
78 Howard Road, London E17 4SQ
tel/fax 0181-521 5791
e-mail 101317.3643@compuserve.com

Research and writing of features for newspapers, magazines and radio, specialising in health and social issues. Corporate literature and reports. Press and public rela-

tions. Written and spoken Italian, Spanish and French. Founded 1985.

David L. Williams
7 Buckbury Heights, Newport,
Isle of Wight PO30 2LX
tel (01983) 528729 *fax* (01983) 822116

Picture and text research. Specialises in transport, particularly maritime and aviation; military and naval, particularly the World Wars. Also indexing and proofreading. Established 1982.

David Winpenny
17 Newlands Drive, York YO2 5PQ
tel/fax (01904) 784616
e-mail WinpennyD@aol.com
web site http://bounce.to/dw

Writer and editor, including research and writing of features, news stories, brochures, speeches, advertising copy. Special interest in architectural history, the arts, music, landscape, heritage, business and the North. Founded 1991.

Rita Winter Editorial Services
'Kilrubie', Eddleston, Peeblesshire, EH45 8QP
tel/fax (01721) 730353
e-mail rita@ednet.co.uk

On-screen editing, copy-editing and proofreading (English and Dutch). Academic and general material, books, dictionaries, company literature. Special interests: art, art history, exhibition catalogues.

Witan Publishing Services
Cherry Tree House, 8 Nelson Crescent, Cotes Heath, via Stafford ST21 6ST
tel (01782) 791673
Director Jeff Kent

Editing, proofreading, typesetting, publishing advice, design and artwork, printing, marketing, publicity, repping, distribution advice. Established 1980.

The Word Service
Bob Gallagher, 143 Sirdar Road, London N22 6QS
tel 0181-888 6962

Radio drama script analysis, evaluation and polishing; copy-editing and proofreading; research, specialising in Irish history, literary lives and the history of psychiatry. Founded 1994.

Wordwise
37 Elmthorpe Road, Wolvercote, Oxford OX2 8PA
tel (01865) 510098 *fax* (01865) 310556
e-mail wordwise@mendes.demon.co.uk
Director Valerie Mendes

Provides a range of publishing services, including creative writing (particularly for children); editing; educational, arts and humanities and English Language Teaching publishing; report analysis and full project management. Founded 1990.

WordWise Editorial Services
66 Russell Road, Lee-on-the-Solent, Hants PO13 9HP
tel (01705) 359960 *fax* (01705) 552950
e-mail wordwise@cix.co.uk
web site http://www.citsoft.co.uk/wordwise
Contact Martyn Yeo

Copy-editing, rewriting, proofreading, indexing, on-screen editing, project management, database publishing. Typesetting service for printed publications; HTML coding for electronic publishing and web sites. Copy typing service. Member of Corel Ventura Users and the SFEP. Established 1984.

Richard M. Wright
32 Oak Village, London NW5 4QN
tel 0171-284 4316

Indexing, copy-editing, specialising in politics, history, business, social sciences. Founded 1977.

Write on …
62 Kiln Lane, Oxford OX3 8EY
tel (01865) 761169
Contact Yvonne Newman

Writing seminars and holiday workshops. Writing as a therapy. Non-fiction writing courses. Founded 1989.

The Writers Advice Centre for Children's Books
Palace Wharf, Rainville Road, London W6 9HN
tel/fax 0181-874 7347

Directors Louise Jordan, Nancy Smith, Jane Baker
Editorial and marketing advice to children's writers; training; mail order books; agency service.Founded 1994.

The Writers' Exchange
14 Yewdale, Clifton Green, Swinton, Manchester M27 8GN
tel (01706) 877480
Secretary Mike Wright

Copywriting, ghostwriting and editorial services, including appraisal service for amateur writers preparing to submit material to literary agents/publishers. Offers 'constructive, objective evaluation service, particularly for those who cannot get past the standard rejection slip barrier, or who have had work rejected by publishers and need an impartial view of why it did not sell'; fee £5 per 1000 words. Novels, short stories, film, TV, radio and stage plays. Send sae for details. Founded 1977.

Hans Zell, Publishing Consultant
11 Richmond Road, PO Box 56, Oxford OX1 2SJ
tel (01865) 511428 *fax* (01865) 311534
e-mail hzell@dial.pipex.com
web site http://www.hanszell.co.uk

Consultancies, project evaluations, market assessments, feasibility studies, research and surveys, funding proposals, freelance editorial work, commissioning, journals management, exhibition services. Specialises in services to publishers and the book community in Third World countries and provides specific expertise in these areas. Also mailing list services. Founded 1987.

Editorial, literary and production services by specialisation

Addresses for editorial, literary and production services start on page 574.

Complete editorial, literary and book production services

'A Feature Factory' Editorial Services
Academic File
Linda Auld Associates
Book Production Consultants
Brittan Design Partnership
Karyn Claridge Book Production
D & N Publishing
Geo Group & Associates
Graham-Cameron Publishing
Northern Writers Advisory Services
Oxprint Design
Christopher Pick
Keith Povey Editorial Services
Anton Rippon Press Services
Small Print
Teamwork
Rita Winter Editorial Services
Wordwise

Advisory and consultancy services, critical assessments, reports

Academic File
Adkins Archaeology
Advice and Criticism Service
Arkst Publishing
Authors' Aid
Authors Appraisal Service
Authors' Advisory Service
Blair Services
Bookwatch
Calderbridge Associates
Jonathon Clifford
Ingrid Cranfield
Clarissa Cridland
Lewis Esson Publishing
FJN Associates

James Wilson Flegg
Geo Group & Associates
C.N. Gilmore
Heath Associates
Rosemary Horstmann
E.J. Hunter
Indexing Specialists
JG Editorial
The Literary Consultancy (TLC)
Miles Litvinoff
Duncan McAra
Manuscript Appraisals
M.C. Martinez
Susan Moore Editorial Services
MS-S
Pageant Publishing
Penman Literary Service
Christopher Pick
Reading and Righting
S. Ribeiro Literary Services
Sandhurst Editorial Consultants
Sandton Literary Agency
Science Unit
Scriptmate
Mrs Ellen Seager
Robert and Jane Songhurst
Teral Research Services
Felicity Trotman
Gordon R. Wainwright
Caroline White
Joan Wilkins Associates
Witan Publishing Services
The Word Service
Wordwise
The Writers Advice Centre for Children's Books
The Writers' Exchange
Hans Zell, Publishing Consultant

Editing, copy-editing, proofreading

Abbey Writing Services
Alpha Word Power
Lucia Alvarez de Toledo
Anvil Editorial Associates
Arkst Publishing

Linda Auld Associates
Authors' Advisory Service
Authors' Aid
Richard A. Beck
Beswick Writing Services
Black Ace Book Production
Blair Services
David Bradley Science Writer
Brooke Publications
Mrs D. Buckmaster
John Button
Calderbridge Associates
Combrógos
Ingrid Cranfield
David A. Cross
Meg and Stephen Davies
Editorial/Visual Research
Dr Martin Edwards
Lewis Esson Publishing
First Edition Translations
FJN Associates
James Wilson Flegg
Freelance Editorial Services
Freelance Services, Joan Shannon
Roy Gaylor
C.N. Gilmore
Guildford Reading Services
John Hall
Bernard Hawton
Heath Associates
E.J. Hunter
Indexing Specialists
Ken Jackson
JG Editorial
Miles Litvinoff
Duncan McAra
McText
Manuscript Appraisals
Marlinoak
My Word!
Peter Nickol
Nidaba Publishing Services
Paul H. Niekirk
Geoffrey D. Palmer
Penman Literary Service
Phoenix 2
Christopher Pick

Victoria Ramsay
Reading and Righting
S. Ribeiro Literary Services
Vernon Robinson Editorial
  Services
David Sanders
Sandhurst Editorial Consultants
Sandton Literary Agency
SciText
SeaStar Editorial Services
Serpentine Editorial
Small Print
Robert and Jane Songhurst
Mrs Gene M. Spencer
Strand Editorial Services
Lyn M. Taylor (UK)
Felicity Trotman
Gordon R. Wainwright
Caroline White
David L. Williams
David Winpenny
Rita Winter Editorial Services
Witan Publishing Services
The Word Service
Wordwise
WordWise Editorial Services
Richard M. Wright
The Writers' Exchange
Hans Zell, Publishing Consultant

Design, typing, word processing, DTP, book production

'A Feature Factory' Editorial
  Services
Alpha Word Power
Arioma Editorial Services
Authors' Aid
Ayrshire Business Services
Black Ace Book Production
Book-in-Hand
Calderbridge Associates
Vanessa Charles
First Edition Translations
FJN Associates
Christine Foley Secretarial
  Services
Freelance Services, Joan
  Shannon
Shelagh Furness
Heath Associates
Hurst Village Publishing
JG Editorial
Marlinoak
M.C. Martinez
My Word!
Peter Nickol
Nidaba Publishing Services
Oriental Languages Bureau
Pageant Publishing

Pages Editorial & Publishing
  Services
Penman Literary Service
Phoenix 2
Sandhurst Editorial Consultants
SeaStar Editorial Services
Serpentine Editorial
I.R. Sinclair
Small Print
Special Edition Pre-press
  Services
Tecmedia
Witan Publishing Services
WordWise Editorial Services

Research and/or writing, rewriting, picture research

'A Feature Factory' Editorial
  Services
Abbey Writing Services
Adkins Archaeology
Lucia Alvarez de Toledo
Anvil Editorial Associates
Arioma Editorial Services
Arkst Publishing
Linda Auld Associates
Authors' Research Services
Beswick Writing Services
Blair Services
Bookwatch
David Bradley Science Writer
Brooke Publications
Causeway Resources
Combrógos
Ingrid Cranfield
David A. Cross
Editorial/Visual Research
Dr Martin Edwards
Lewis Esson Publishing
First Edition Translations
James Wilson Flegg
Freelance Services, Joan
  Shannon
Shelagh Furness
Roy Gaylor
Geo Group & Associates
John Hall
Heath Associates
Antony Hemans
Mark Hempshall
The Information Bureau
Library Research Agency
Miles Litvinoff
Kenneth Lysons
Manuscript Appraisals
Marlinoak
Susan Moore Editorial Services
Murder Files
Elizabeth Murray

Paul H. Niekirk
Ormrod Research Services
Penman Literary Service
Phoenix 2
Christopher Pick
Picture Research Agency
Victoria Ramsay
S. Ribeiro Literary Services
Rich Research
Anton Rippon Press Services
Sandhurst Editorial Consultants
Sandton Literary Agency
SeaStar Editorial Services
Serpentine Editorial
Gill Shepherd
I.R. Sinclair
Small Print
Robert and Jane Songhurst
Mrs Gene M. Spencer
Teral Research Services
Valerie Vogel Picture Research
Caroline White
David L. Williams
David Winpenny
The Word Service
The Writers' Exchange
Hans Zell, Publishing Consultant

Indexing

Adkins Archaeology
Linda Auld Associates
Richard A. Beck
Ingrid Cranfield
Meg and Stephen Davies
First Edition Translations
Freelance Editorial Services
Society of Indexers
Indexing Specialists
Ken Jackson
Paul Nash
Geoffrey D. Palmer
Sandton Literary Agency
David L. Williams
WordWise Editorial Services
Richard M. Wright
The Writers' Exchange

Translations

Lucia Alvarez de Toledo
Ingrid Cranfield
First Edition Translations
James Wilson Flegg
Freelance Editorial Services
Library Research Agency
M.C. Martinez
Oriental Languages Bureau
Small Print
Caroline White

Specialist services

Archives

Murder Files
Hans Tasiemka Archives
John Vickers

Cartography, artwork, cartoons, puzzles

Morley Adams
Reginald Piggott
Streetwise Town Plans

Cassettes, visual aids

Small Print

Contracts and copyright services

Clarissa Cridland
Peter Nickol

Roger Palmer
Stationers' Hall Registry

Database services

WordWise Editorial Services

Freelance agency

etr

Interpreting

First Edition Translations

Lecture agents

Holland-Ford's Associates
Sandton Literary Agency

Media and publicity services

Freelance Market News
3 & 5 Promotion

Tuition, lectures, conference services

Authors' Advisory Service
Copywriting One-to-One
David A. Cross
Northgate Training
Reading and Righting
S. Ribeiro Literary Services
Mrs Ellen Seager
Gordon R. Wainwright
Joan Wilkins Associates
Write on...
The Writers Advice Centre for
   Children's Books

Voice overs, subtitles

Lucia Alvarez de Toledo
First Edition Translations

Indexing

A good index is a joy to the user of a non-fiction book; a bad index will down-grade an otherwise good book. The function of indexes, together with the skills needed to compile them, are examined here.

An index is a detailed key to the contents of a document, in contrast to a contents list, which gives only the titles of the parts into which the document is divided (chapters, for example). Precisely, an index is 'A systematic arrangement of entries designed to enable users to locate information in a document'. The document may be a book, a series of books, an issue of a periodical, a run of several volumes of a periodical, an audiotape, a map, a film, a picture, a computer disk, an object, or any other information-carrying artefact in print or non-print form.

The objective of an index is to guide enquirers to information on given subjects in a document by providing the terms of their choice (single words, phrases, abbreviations, acronyms, dates, names, and so on) in an appropriately organised list which refers them to specific locations using page, column, section, frame, figure, table, paragraph, line or other appropriate numbers.

An index differs from a catalogue, which is a record of the documents held in a particular collection, such as a library; though a catalogue may require an index, for example to guide searchers from subject words to class numbers.

A document may have separate indexes for different classes of heading, so that personal names are distinguished from subjects, for example, or a single index in which all classes of heading are interfiled.

The Society of Indexers

The Society of Indexers is a non-profit organisation founded in 1957 and is the

---

What makes a good indexer?

An index compiler needs:
- the ability to analyse the text on behalf of a wide range of users who may want to locate information on a particular topic;
- the ability to scan the index to assess the scope of the book;
- the ability to find out how particular themes or ideas are developed;
- the ability to return to passages they remember reading;
- a good knowledge of the subject matter;
- the ability to devise suitable terms expressing the concepts in the text concisely and precisely;
- the ability to organise the entries in the index in the most appropriate and retrievable fashion;
- a passion for accuracy.

---

only autonomous professional body for indexers in the UK. It is affiliated with the American Society of Indexers, the Australian Society of Indexers, the Indexing and Abstracting Society of Canada, and the Association of South African Indexers and Bibliographers, and has close ties with the Library Association and the Society of Freelance Editors and Proofreaders.

The main objectives of the Society are to promote all types of indexing standards and techniques and the role of indexers in the organisation of knowledge; to provide, promote and recognise facilities for both the initial and the further training of indexers; to establish criteria for assessing indexing standards; and to conduct research and publish guidance, ideas and information about indexing. It seeks to establish good relationships between indexers, librarians, publishers and authors both to advance good indexing and to improve the role and well-being of indexers.

Services to indexers

The Society publishes a learned journal *The Indexer*, a newsletter and *Occasional Papers in Indexing*. Meetings are held regularly on a wide range of subjects while local and special interest groups provide the chance for members to meet to discuss common interests. A weekend conference is held every year. All levels of training are supported by regular workshops held at venues throughout the country.

Professional competence is recognised in two stages by the Society. Accredited Indexers who have completed the open-learning course qualification (see 'Training in indexing' below) have shown theoretical competence in indexing while Registered Indexers have proved their experience and competence in practical indexing through an assessment procedure and admission to the Register of Indexers. The services of Registered Indexers are actively promoted by the Society while all trained and experienced members have the opportunity of an annual entry in *Indexers Available*, a directory published by the Society and distributed without charge to over 1000 publishers to help them find an indexer.

The Society sets annually a minimum recommended indexing rate (£13.00 per hour in 1998) and provides advice on the business side of indexing to its members.

Services to publishers and authors

Anyone who commissions indexes needs to be certain of engaging a professional indexer working to the highest standards and able to meet deadlines.

Indexers Available lists only members of the Society and gives basic contact details (name, address, etc), subject specialisms and indexing experience. Those accepted for listing need to fall into the following categories:
- Registered Indexers who have had their competence in practical indexing recognised by the Society;
- Accredited Indexers who have passed the Society's tests of technical competence; and
- others who have successfully completed other recognised training courses.

Advice on the selection of indexers is available from the Registrar, who may also be able to suggest names of professionals able to undertake related tasks such as thesaurus construction, terminology control or database indexing. The Registrar will also advise on relations with indexers.

The Society co-operates with The Library Association in the award of the Wheatley Medal for an outstanding index.

Training in indexing

The Society's course is based on the principle of open learning with Units, tutorial support and formal tests all available separately so that individuals can learn in their own way and at their own pace. The Units cover five core subjects and contain practical exercises and self-administered tests. Members of the Society receive a substantial discount on the cost although anyone can purchase the Units. Only members of the Society can apply for the formal tests or for tutorial support.

Further information

Society of Indexers, Mermaid House, 1 Mermaid Court, London SE1 1HR
tel 0171-403 4947
Secretary Mrs C. Shuttleworth
Write to The Secretary for further information. Enquiries from publishers and authors seeking to commission an indexer should be made to The Registrar.

Further reading

British Standards Institution, *British Standard recommendations for examining documents, determining their subjects and selecting indexing terms,* BSI, 1984 (BS6529:1984)

Information and documentation – guidelines for the content, organization and presentation of indexes (ISO 999:1996)

Translation

The role of the translator in enabling written work to pass beyond national frontiers is receiving growing recognition. In view of the general increase of activity in this field, it is not surprising that many people with writing ability and a knowledge of languages should think of adopting freelance translating as a full- or part-time occupation. This article is for such would-be translators.

The first difficulty the beginner will encounter is the unwillingness of publishers to entrust a translation to anyone who has not already established a reputation for sound work. The least the publisher will demand before commissioning a translation is a fairly lengthy specimen of the applicant's work, even if unpublished. The publisher cannot be expected to pay for a specimen sent in by a translator seeking work. If, on the other hand, a publisher specifically asks for a lengthy specimen of a commissioned book the firm will usually pay for this specimen at the current rate.

Perhaps the best way would-be translators can begin is to select some book of the type which they feel competent and anxious to translate, ascertain from the foreign author or publisher that the English-language rights are still free, translate a substantial section of the book and then submit the book and their specimen translation to an appropriate publisher. If they are extremely lucky, this may result in a commission to translate the book. More likely, however – since publishers are generally very well informed about foreign books likely to interest them and are rarely open to a chance introduction – the publisher will reject the book as such. But publishers who are favourably impressed may commission a translation of some other book of a similar nature which they already have in mind.

In this connection it is important to stress that translators should confine themselves to subjects of which they possess an expert knowledge. In the case of non-fiction, they may have to cope with technical expressions not to be found in the dictionary and disaster may ensue if they are not fully conversant with the subject. The translation of fiction, on the other hand, demands different skills (e.g. in the writing of dialogue) and translators should be confident that they possess these skills before taking steps to secure work of this nature.

Having obtained a commission to translate a book, the translator will be faced with negotiating terms. These vary considerably from publisher to publisher but are usually based on a rate per 1000 words. Translators should be able to arrange that the advance is on account of a royalty of 2.5% and a small share of the proceeds from secondary uses such as paperback reprint and American rights. However, some publishers avoid paying royalties to the translator even after reducing the royalties they pay to the original author. In the past it was common practice for translators to assign their copyright to the publisher outright, but this is no longer the rule. Most reputable publishers will now sign agreements specifying the rights they require in the translation and leaving the copyright in the translator's hands.

A Quick Guide to Literary Translation (£2.00) and advice regarding contracts for full-length works, copyright, Public Lending Right and other matters may be obtained from the Translators Association of the Society of Authors (see page 504). The Institute of Translation and Interpreting (see page 498) offers membership to all categories of qualified translators, in particular technical and commercial translators.

Annual or biennial prizes are awarded by the Translators Association for translations from German, Italian, French and other languages.

Resources for writers

Research and the Internet

The Internet is an almost infinite library that is constantly being updated. Users can often find the facts they seek in a few minutes, without leaving their desk, and at relatively low cost. **David Couchman** *introduces the Internet as a research tool for writers.*

Recently, I was trying to locate a vaguely remembered quotation from a 19th-century American poet. My wife wanted to find out about Chronic Fatigue Syndrome; and my daughter needed to discover large prime numbers for her maths homework. A few years ago we would have gone to the library. It might not have had the information we were seeking, and whatever it did have would probably have been out of date. Today we use the Internet.

The Internet is a worldwide network of computers. It began in the USA as a military communication system designed to keep going in the event of a nuclear war. It expanded significantly as universities and commercial organisations joined. Today it is growing explosively: well in excess of 50 million people already have access to it and another 90,000 gain access every day.

Getting on-line

There are more and more opportunities to explore the Internet through library, 'Cyber-Café' and university or college sites. These allow you to dip your toe in the water, but if you decide to go further you will need your own Internet access. This requires:

• A computer – if you have a PC which can use Microsoft Windows, or an Apple 'Mac', you are already well on the way.
• A modem – this device makes it possible for one computer to communicate with another over an ordinary telephone line.
• An 'Internet access provider' – this enables a computer to be connected to the Internet, just as a telephone company connects telephone users to the worldwide phone network.
• Special computer programs – these will be supplied by the access provider.

Once the modem has been linked up, the programs installed, and a connection established to an access provider, the computer is 'on-line'.

Choosing an access provider

The choice of access provider is the most important single decision that will affect your use of the Internet. Some of the best-known access providers include Demon, Global Internet, Pipex, and Virgin. Telephone companies such as BT and Cable & Wireless are also access providers. In addition, there are many smaller access providers which are local to specific areas. These are worth investigating as they can provide good value for money. There are also major on-line services such as the Microsoft Network (MSN), America Online (AOL), and Compuserve (AOL bought out Compuserve at the end of 1997 but at the time of writing the two services are still being run separately). As well as giving access to the Internet, these provide information and discussion groups (see below) within their service, and are usually easier to use than 'raw' Internet access. However, as you gain in experience they may seem restrictive.

Some access providers charge a flat rate monthly fee regardless of how long you spend on-line. Others charge a lower monthly fee but make an additional charge for time over and above the first few hours on-line. The cost can escalate rapidly if you are on-line for more than a few hours a month.

Quality of service is important: How quickly can you get a connection? How fast does the data you need reach you? (Remember that the whole time you spend on-line is being charged to your telephone bill. It may only be a local call but charges mount up.) Some access providers offer a much better service than others. It can be helpful to consult friends and colleagues who are already using the Internet to find out what they think of their access providers. Internet magazines such as *.net*, *Wired* and *Internet Business* carry advertisements for different access providers and up-to-date comparative reviews – essential reading in a sphere that is changing so rapidly. If the service of your access provider proves unsatisfactory it is easy to change to another.

Research using the World Wide Web

The most important part of the Internet for research is the 'World Wide Web', often abbreviated to WWW, or just 'the web'. The web is a vast collection of linked pages of information about every imaginable subject. In order to read these pages a special computer program called a 'web browser' is required, the two most widely used of which are Netscape Navigator and Microsoft Internet Explorer.

Each page of information on the web has its own unique address – usually beginning http://www. To access a page, have the web browser program running and type in the address. The browser will fetch the appropriate page from the computer where it is stored and display it on the screen. That computer could be anywhere in the world – you may not even know where it is – but it does not matter. Distance is not an issue as your computer is connected by phone to your access provider, and the cost is usually that of a local phone call.

A web page displayed on the screen incorporates 'hyperlinks' to other pages.

Some major search engines
Altavista
http://www.altavista.digital.com/
Lycos
http://www.uk.lycos.de/
Infoseek
http://www.infoseek.com/
Yahoo
http://www.yahoo.com/

A hyperlink may be a key word in the text (usually underlined), a small graphic, or part of a larger graphic. It is a 'link' because it points the computer towards the address of another web page. Hyperlinks are a powerful cross-referencing system: by clicking the mouse on a hyperlink the web browser automatically fetches the new page to which the link points. (The on-screen help files in 'Windows' are similar to a hyperlink.) Some useful web site addresses are listed in the box on page 597.

Finding information

How do you know where to find the key facts you need among all the millions of pages of information? If the Internet is like a vast library, beautifully cross-referenced, it is unfortunately also the worst indexed library in the world. To help with the task there are a number of 'search engines', which are themselves sites on the Internet.

One of the most widely used search engines is the Altavista web site. By typing in a key word or phrase Altavista gives you a list of all the sites it can find which contain that word or phrase. The list will contain hyperlinks to these sites, so you can simply click the mouse on the links to access them. For example, when we were trying to find out more about Chronic Fatigue Syndrome, we typed this name into the Altavista search engine. One of the first sites it found was the CFS home page of the American Centers for Disease Control and Prevention – a goldmine of information (http://www.cdc.gov/ncidod/diseases/cfs/).

Some of the other major search engines are listed in the box on page 596. Each search engine uses a different approach. For example, while Altavista searches for key words, 'Yahoo' is based on a directory or 'tree' structure, organised into major search areas including Arts and Humanities, Business and Economy, Education, Health, News and Media, and Society and Culture.

Newsgroups

In addition to the World Wide Web, there are other sources of information on the Internet. Most important among these are the discussion groups or newsgroups which go under the collective name of 'Usenet'. Discussion groups are just that – groups where anyone can send a message and everyone else in the group receives it. There are more than 20,000 such groups covering every interest under the sun – including some specifically for writers, for example:

    alt.publish.books
    alt.writing
    misc.writing
    rec.arts.prose

The Deja News web site is dedicated to helping find newsgroup postings on particular subjects (http://www.dejanews.com/). The quality of newsgroups is variable; however a question to an appropriate group can often elicit information that cannot be found elsewhere. Your access provider can give you a list of the discussion groups that it carries.

Join only a few carefully chosen groups that cover your key interests. If you join too many you will be inundated by the number of messages and will soon reach the point where you do not read any of them.

Sending a message to a group is called 'posting'. When you first join a group it is a good idea to 'lurk' for a while – to read the messages posted by existing members before you start to post your own. This helps you to get a feel for the 'style' of the group and thus avoid blunders.

As in any sphere, beginners often ask the same questions over and over again.

Useful web addresses

In addition to the addresses given below, many of the newspapers, magazines, book publishers, picture libraries and other organisations listed in this *Yearbook* include a web site address.

Amazon Bookshop
http://www.amazon.com/

Associated Press
http://wire.ap.org/

BAISE
http://portico.bl.uk/
The British Library's automated information service.

The BBC
http://www.beeb.com/

Channel 4
http://www.channel4.com/

The CIA
http://www.odci.gov/cia/

Financial Times
http://www.ft.com/

The Internet Bookshop
http://www.bookshop.co.uk/

Meridian TV
http://www.meridian.tv.co.uk/

New Scientist
http://www.newscientist.com/

New WWW sites
http://www.whatsnew.com/

Reuters
http://www.reuters.com/

Sky TV
http://www.sky.co.uk/

The Times
http://www.the-times.co.uk/

The White House
http://www.whitehouse.gov/

The Writers Site
http://www.writers.org.uk/
http://www.writers.org.uk/society/
http://www.writers.org.uk/guild/
Contains both the Society of Authors and the Writers Guild of Great Britain.

The Internet has evolved its own particular solution to this problem – the FAQ, an information 'sheet' containing the answers to Frequently Asked Questions. The FAQ may be posted to the group on a regular basis. FAQs on particular subjects are often made available on the World Wide Web too and can be a goldmine of useful information, so are well worth reading.

Premium services

Discussion groups are free. So is the World Wide Web – mostly. However, more and more commercial services are being launched that provide quality information not available elsewhere, but at a cost. For example, the Electronic Share Information site (http://www.esi.co.uk/) provides several grades of share price information. The lowest grades are free, but if you need the most current prices you have to pay to access them. These services are usually too expensive for an individual subscriber, but they may be worth investigating if you need a specific kind of information. Open web sites of commercial organisations often give information about related premium services (e.g. the Reuters' site).

Where next?

An article as brief as this can only begin to introduce the power of the Internet as a research tool. So where do you go to find out more? The Internet is changing so fast that books current today could be completely out of date in a few months' time. However, a few suggestions for further reading are given below. The Internet itself is the most useful tool to find out more. For example, Charlie Harris has written an essential guide for writers wanting to use the Internet for research (http://www.pure-fiction.com/pages/res1. htm).

No turning back

Today I can usually research the information I need without leaving my desk and my findings are more comprehensive and more up to date than ever before. I cannot imagine going back to a pre-Internet world any more than I can imagine throwing away my word processor and taking up a quill.

David Couchman is a project manager at Focus Radio, where he previously worked as a scriptwriter and producer. He is a former lecturer in computing and has set up a public web site as a research tool for businessmen and academics working in part of the former Soviet Union. He uses the Internet regularly for his own research.

Further reading

Gilster, Paul, *Finding it on the Internet*, John Wiley & Sons Inc., 1996. More technical, but worth consulting as your interest grows.

Sue, Schofield, *The UK Internet Handbook*, Addison-Wesley, 1995. Also more technical, but worth consulting as your interest grows.

Wentk, Richard, *The Which? Guide to the Internet*, Which? Books, 1997. An excellent introduction, and reasonably non-technical.

Books, research and reference

Almost every writing project will involve the use of books or research at some stage. Some references are quickly found; other projects require numerous books or information files on a specific topic, visits to specialist libraries and to other relevant places or people. **Margaret Payne** ALA *gives an introduction to printed sources.*

Although research can be an interest or pleasure in itself, it can also be time-consuming, cutting into writing or earning time. Even checking a single fact can take hours or days if you ask the wrong question or check the wrong source first. No article or book can hope to solve all problems – sometimes there are no answers, or the lack of information is itself the answer – but a few guidelines as to routines and sources may save much time and money.

Many reference books are now on CD-Rom and the Internet is increasingly being used for research (see *Research and the Internet*, page 595), but this article is an introduction to printed sources. For a more detailed approach, Ann Hoffmann's *Research for Writers* (A & C Black, 5th edn 1996, £11.99) includes guides to original and unpublished material, and covers methods, sources, specific organisations and specialist libraries.

Suggestions for a core collection of reference books to own are given under 'A writer's reference bookshelf' on page 602. The final choice of title often depends on personal preference and interests, space, the frequency with which it needs to be consulted, its cost and the proximity of your nearest public reference library. Anyone living in or near a large city has an advantage over the country dweller, with a choice of major reference libraries; a variety of specialist sources such as headquarters of various societies, companies and organisations; academic and other specialist libraries and the govern-

ment. Often a question can be answered much nearer home, but you may find the further back in time you go, or the more detailed your research, the further afield you need to travel.

Checking a fact

What do you really want to know?

Clarifying your question in advance can save much work for you or your researcher. If you want to check someone's date of birth and know the person is alive or very recently dead and in *Who's Who*, then ask for that book, or phrase your telephone request so that the librarian goes straight to that source. Do not start with general questions such as 'Where are the biographies?' In a branch library you may be shown sections of individual lives; on the telephone you are adding unnecessarily to your telephone bill, as well as wasting time. If the person is dead, did he or she die recently enough to have a newspaper obituary – it often mentions the date of birth – or long enough ago to be in a volume of *Who Was Who* or the *Dictionary of National Biography*? Never assume that information that you know is necessarily common knowledge; it needs to be specified.

Go straight to the index

Most reference books are arranged in alphabetical order but, if not, they should have an index. Some indexes may seem inadequate, but have you used the right key word? A good index should refer you from the one not used. For example, some will use carpentry and ignore woodwork as an entry. Others will ignore both and go straight to the object to be made or repaired. If there is no index, turn first to the contents page, as in some books the index is at the front rather than the back.

Is it important to be up to date?

Most books have the date of publication on the back of the title page. Is the answer given in the book one which may be surpassed or superseded? Despite some instant publishing, when dealing with statistics most books have a built-in obsolescence. There is a cut-off date when the text goes to the printer and the updating must wait for the next edition. Some current events are too recent to be found in books at all, although well documented at the time in newspapers and magazines (see below).

If in doubt, re-check your answer

If the answer is of importance, try not to depend on one source. Mistakes can occur in print or in transcribing. Sometimes it is necessary to check another source for verification or to obtain another point of view. In all cases you should ...

Note your source

Even if you think you will remember, always note where you find your information, preferably next to the answer, or in a card file or book where it can be easily found. Note the title, author, publisher and date of publication as well as the page number. Nothing is more annoying than having to undertake the same search twice.

Researching a subject

Reference has already been made to Ann Hoffmann's book for detail, but Kipling's six honest serving men can still be the

---

Sources of information

Reference libraries. Use the largest one in your vicinity for encylopedias, specialised reference books, annuals and for back numbers of newspapers and periodicals. Ask for *Walford's Guide to Reference Material*: three volumes list the standard reference works of subjects, most of which should be available for consultation.

Lending libraries. Find the class number of the books you want, and see what is available.

Special libraries. *The Aslib Directory of Information Sources in the United Kingdom* should be available in your reference library. It gives details of special libraries of industries, organisations and societies.

Catalogues, bibliographies and subject guides. Most library catalogues are now on-line, with author, title or key word access. There is a series of subject catalogues to the British Library up to 1975 and the *British National Bibliography* updates this (see 'Compiling a bibliography' on page 601).

Newspapers and bibliographies. There is a monthly index to *The Times*, cumulated annually, which often provides the date of an event. The index also includes the *The Times Supplements*. For periodical articles, begin with the *British Humanities Index*, and, if necessary, check also the specialist indexes and abstracting journals such as *Current Technology Index*. Your public library can often locate runs of periodicals and magazines, and the interloan service can obtain specific periodical articles if you have the details. *Profile*, an on-line index to quality newspapers, is the most up to date available, but retrospective only to 1985. *Clover* is a printed index to the same broadsheet press.

---

basis for any subject: What? Why? When? How? Where? Who? cover aspects of most enquiries. The starting point depends on the writer's personal knowledge of the subject. Where it is unfamiliar always start from the general and go on to the particular. An article in an encyclopedia can fill in the background and often recommend bibliographies or other references. If an article in the *Encyclopaedia Britannica* is too detailed or too complex, try *The World Book* which can be found in the children's library. Because *The World Book* has to appeal to a wider readership, the text and illustrations are clearer. Avoid a detailed book on the subject until you need it; it may tell you more than you want to know.

Compiling a bibliography

Checking what books are already available may reveal both the range of titles already in print and the potential market for your work. If yours is to be the tenth book on the subject published in the last two years, saturation point may be near. On the other hand, if you know the books and believe you can do better, or have evolved a different approach, you can mention this in a covering letter to a potential publisher. A quick way to evaluate what is available is by checking the shelves of a public library or bookshop, but it should be remembered that in a library, many of the best books will be on loan. This practice also makes one aware of publishers' interests.

A more comprehensive and systematic list of recent books can be compiled by consulting the *British National Bibliography*, a cumulating list based on the copyright books in the British Library, with advance notice (up to three months) of new books through the Cataloguing in Publication scheme. The arrangement is by the Dewey Decimal Classification used in all public libraries. Other subject lists are less satisfactory to consult. The British Museum (now British Library) has a series of subject indexes up to 1975, and many British books are included in the American *Cumulative Book Index* (1928 on). *Whitaker's Books in Print* is predominantly an author-title list, but does index some books under the key word of a subtitle; as its name implies, out-of-print books are excluded.

Facilities now exist to obtain a bibliography on any subject by using one of the computer data banks based on the British Library, the Library of Congress or commercial firms. The difficulties are expense and finding local access points.

Obtaining books

Books in print

In 1997 100,029 different books were published in the United Kingdom alone, joining the many thousands of other titles still in print from previous years. The number of books available means that the chances of finding a copy of what you want on your bookseller's shelf, when you want it, may be slim. But if it is in print it can be ordered for you, although delivery times vary with each publisher. Most large bookshops and libraries now have the monthly microfiche or CD-Rom editions of *Whitaker's Books in Print* giving details of author, publisher, price, number of pages and ISBN. Supplying the ISBN number is often useful for speeding the order.

Out of print books

Out of print books present more difficulty. Generally the older the book, the more difficult it may be to obtain. Such books are no longer available from the publishers, who retain only a file copy, all other stocks having been sold. Therefore you are lucky enough to find an unsold copy on a bookseller's shelves, it must be sought in the second-hand market or through a library loan. There are many specialist second-hand and antiquarian booksellers, and a number of directories listing them and their interests. The most well known are *Sheppard's Book Dealers in the British Isles*, now published by R. Joseph. Copies of these should be in your local reference library. Many advertise in *Book and Magazine Collector*, a monthly magazine, which has extensive 'wants' and 'for sale' columns.

Public libraries

Public libraries should be able to obtain books for you, whether or not they are in print, either from their own stock, from other libraries in the system or through the interloan scheme. This operates through the British Lending

Library, but all requests must go through your library as you cannot apply direct. Your local library tickets may sometimes be used in other libraries, but different issuing systems have discouraged this in recent years. Most library systems now have a data-based catalogue of all branch stock.

A writer's reference bookshelf

The increasing use of personal computers and the Internet is extending the sources of information from print to multimedia. Many reference books are available on CD-Rom and much knowledge can be accessed through web sites. But as yet few libraries in the UK have the funds, expertise or space to make such sources available, and in the meantime there is a growing division between individuals who prefer or only have access to print and those who are computer literate and can afford and have the time to explore what knowledge is available electronically, as well as what is not.

However good and accessible a public library may be, there are some books required for constant or instant consultation, which should be within easy reach of your work area. The choice of title may vary, but the following list is offered as suggestions for a core collection.

Dictionaries

With the use of word processor packages, a dictionary is no longer quite so essential for spelling checks, although still needed to clarify definitions and meanings. A book is often easier to consult, and portable. The complete *Oxford English Dictionary* is not, and although the definitive work, neither the full nor the compact edition with its magnifying glass, nor the two volume *Shorter Oxford Dictionary* is easy to handle for quick reference, so a one volume dictionary is more practical. The number of new words and meanings coming into vogue suggests a replacement every five years or so, or supplementing your choice by a good paperback edition. If you use an old copy, you will be surprised by the improved format and readability of the new editions.

The most popular one volume dictionaries are the *Concise Oxford Dictionary* (8th edn 1991, £16.99 – 80,000 definitions), *Chambers' English Dictionary* (7th edn 1997, £30.00 – 150,000 entries, appealing to crossword addicts), *The Collins English Dictionary* (Harper-Collins, 4th edn 1994, £25.00 – 110,000 entries). A recommended paperback dictionary is the *Oxford Paperback Dictionary and Thesaurus* (1997, £5.99 – 50,000 entries). If you write for the American market, it is advisable also to have an American dictionary to check variant spellings and meanings. The equivalent of the Oxford family of dictionaries is Webster's, the most popular one volume edition being Webster's *New World Dictionary* (Random House, 4th edn 1994, £17.95).

Roget's Thesaurus

When the exact word or meaning eludes you, a thesaurus may help clear a mental block. There are many versions of Roget available, both in hardback and paperback, including a revision by E.M. Kirkpatrick (Houghton-Mifflin, 1987, £16.99) and a paperback edition from Penguin (1984, £5.99). *The Bloomsbury Thesaurus* (Bloomsbury, 1993, £15.99) is a new compilation which includes 1000 knowledge categories and 1500 quotations.

Grammar and English usage

A wide choice is available but *New Fowler's Modern English Usage* remains a standard work (3rd edn 1996, revised R.W. Burchfield, Oxford UP, £16.99). Many prefer Sir Ernest Gowers' *Complete Plain Words* (4th edn 1994, rev. Sidney Greenbaum and Jane Whitcut, Penguin, £7.99). More recent works are *The Oxford Guide to English Usage* (Oxford UP, 2nd edn 1994, £4.99), and Michael Legat's *The Nuts and Bolts of Writing* (Hale, 1989, £9.95 and £5.99).

Encyclopedias and annuals

Multi-volume encyclopedias are both expensive and space consuming. They are best left for consultation at the nearest reference library, where the most up-to-date versions should be available, unless your need justifies ownership or you prefer the CD-Rom version. Of the single volumes, *Pears Cyclopaedia* contains a surprising amount of general information and a new edition is issued annually (Pelham Books, 1998-9, £15.99). For those concerned with current affairs, the complete edition of *Whitaker's Almanack* has valuable statistics and information on government and countries, as well as many miscellaneous facts not found elsewhere. For annual replacement if constantly used.

Atlases, gazetteers and road maps

These also need replacing with updated editions from time to time. An old edition can be misleading with recent changes of place names and metrication. The *The Times Atlas of the World* is the definitive work, but it is expensive and bulky for quick reference. The *The Times Concise Atlas of the World* (HarperCollins, 7th edn 1995, £45.00) has the most comprehensive gazetteer-index. It is a little more manageable but still requires special shelving.

With the building of the M25 and other motorways, many existing road atlases of Britain may be out of date and need replacing. There are many paperback editions at 3 miles to 1 inch (1:190,080) for less than £5.00, but most detailed is *A-Z Great Britain Road Atlas* (Geographers A-Z, 1997, £7.95; 1:250,000) with 31,000 place names and 56 town maps. For London and environs *Greater London Street Atlas* (Nicholson, rev. edn 1997, £26.99 and £14.99) is a detailed 3.17 miles to 1 inch, 1:20,000 street map for the whole M25 area.

Literary companions and dictionaries

There are many to choose from, and frequency of consultation will determine whether all or some of the following are desirable. *Brewer's Dictionary of Phrase and Fable* (Cassell, 15th edn 1994, £25.00 and £16.99) and its companion volume *Brewer's Twentieth Century Dictionary of Phrase and Fable* (Cassell, 1996, £25.00 and £10.99) avoid many distractions by settling queries, as does *The Oxford Companion to English Literature* (6th edn edited by Margaret Drabble, Oxford UP, 1995, £25.00). This new edition complements rather than replaces Sir Paul Harvey's earlier editions. Either can be used for checking an author's work, but the definitive and exhaustive lists are to be found in the *New Cambridge Bibliography of English Literature*. The four volumes and the index volume can be found in major reference libraries.

Books of quotations

Once divorced from their text and unattributed, quotations are not easy to trace. This should be a warning to any writer or researcher to note author, title and page number to any item copied. Tracing quotations often needs resort to more than one collection, but the most popular anthologies are *The Oxford Dictionary of Quotations* (Oxford UP, 4th edn 1992, £25.00) and the *Bloomsbury Dictionary of Quotations* (Bloomsbury, 2nd edn 1991, paperback, £14.95) and *The New Penguin Dictionary of Quotations* (Penguin, 1993, £7.99).

Biographical dictionaries

Pears Cyclopaedia contains a brief but useful section, but for a fuller working tool the standard works are *Chambers' Biographical Dictionary* (Chambers, 6th edn 1997, £40.00 – 15,000 entries) or the American-biased Webster's *New Biographical Dictionary* (Merriam-Webster Inc., 1996, £17.95 – 150,000 entries). Frequency of consultation will determine whether you need a personal copy of *Who's Who* or the *Concise Dictionary of National Biography*, which are available in most libraries.

Dates, anniversaries and names

A brief guide to current anniversaries is included in the *Journalists' calendar* (see below). *Dent's Everyman's Dictionary of Dates* (Weidenfeld, 8th edn 1995, £20.00) and *The Independent Book of Anniversaries* (Headline, 1993, o.p.) are useful. For historical facts *The Companion to British History* by Charles Arnold-Baker (Longcross Press, 1997, £48.00) is a comprehensive dictionary of events and people. Leslie Dunkling's *Guinness Book of Names* (Guinness, 7th edn 1995, £11.99) is an encyclopedic source on its subject from first names to places and pubs, with a comprehensive index.

Working directories for writers

A current copy of *Writers' & Artists' Yearbook* is essential, as recent moves and mergers have made so many publishers' details out of date. It is useful for very much more information besides that found in the first section. Browse through, or use the index, in spare moments to familiarise yourself with its contents for future reference.

Frequency of consultation will determine whether you also need *Willings Press Guide* (Hollis Directories Ltd, annual) or *Benn's Media Directory* (2 vols. annual, Benn). Both are expensive but very comprehensive in their coverage of British and overseas newspapers, magazines and other media information. *Cassell's Directory of Publishing* complements all the above, but gives more information about publishing personnel not found elsewhere.

Margaret Payne ALA has worked in public and academic libraries in the UK and Canada and also as a librarian in a book trade library, in which subject she retains a special interest.

Journalists' calendar 1999

This Journalists' calendar has been compiled by the Information Bureau from a variety of sources and is designed as a guideline only. As some anniversary dates are disputed in different sources, all dates should be checked further before embarking on any major project involving any of these dates.

January

1 The North American Free Trade Agreement (NAFTA) between Canada, the US and Mexico came into force, 1994

The European Monetary Institute, based in Frankfurt, came into operation, 1994

2 Rt Rev Kenneth Woollcombe, Canon of St Paul's Cathedral, born 1924

Ranasinghe Premadasa sworn in as President of Sri Lanka (following his election victory in December 1988), 1989

4 Mick Mills, Southampton and England footballer, born 1949

US naval fighter planes shot down two Libyan air force aeroplanes over the Mediterranean, claiming self-defence, 1989

5 Tim Yeo resigned his post as Minister of State at the Department of Environment, 1994

6 Government of Iraq resigned and new Cabinet formed by General Nuri Pasha, 1949

The first church service in Britain broadcast from St Martin-in-the-Fields, 1924

Sir Robert Clark, chairman of Hill Samuel, born 1924

Satwat Singh and a fellow conspirator executed for murdering Prime Minister Indira Gandhi (1988), 1989

USSR announced mass rehabilitation of citizens who were victims of Stalin purges (1930-50), 1989

7 Francis Poulenc, composer, born 1899

Emperor Hirohito of Japan died after a 62-year reign; he was succeeded by his son Crown Prince Akihito, 1989

8 Ron Moody, actor, born 1924

Wilkie Collins, originator of the English detective story, born 1824

British Midland Boeing 737 crashed on M1 motorway near East Midlands Airport, killing 46 people, 1989

9 Income tax introduced in Britain by William Pitt the Younger as a war measure, 1799

Sydney was cut off from the rest of Australia by bush fires which burned for several days; suburbs north and south of Sydney were devastated, 1994

10 Cuban troops began withdrawal from Angola following signing of tripartite agreement in December 1988 providing for Namibian independence in 1990, 1989

The Eagle comic ceased publication, 1994

11 Mrs Sue Rosenkowitz in Cape Town gave birth to the first sextuplets (three boys and three girls) to survive, 1974

14 The Duchess of Kent received into the Roman Catholic Church, 1994

15 Ian Stewart, Olympic bronze medallist at 5000 metres (Munich, 1972), born 1949

16 Robert Service, Canadian author whose works include ballads and novels based on his years in the Oxen, born 1874

17 Al Capone, legendary Chicago gangster and Mafia leader, born 1899

The first TV situation comedy, *The Goldbergs*, was screened on CBS, 1949

20 Edmund Blunden, British poet and author, died 1974

George Bush inaugurated as 41st President of USA, 1989

The Department of Transport's investigation into the wreck of the oil tanker *Braer* off Shetland in January 1993 was published; it accused the tanker's captain of serious dereliction of duty, 1994

21 Telly Savalas, actor (Kojak), born 1924

Vladimir Ilyich Ulyanov, better known as Lenin, founder of the Russian Communist Party, died 1924

Stonewall Jackson, Confederate General in the American Civil War, born 1824

Lorena Bobbitt was cleared of maliciously wounding her husband when she cut off his penis in June 1993 after he had allegedly raped her, 1994

22 August Strindberg, Swedish playwright, novelist and short-story writer, born 1849

The first Labour Government was formed: King George V sent for James Ramsay MacDonald, 1924

Baroness Lockwood, chairman of the Equal Opportunities Commission, born 1924

23 The first woman doctor, Elizabeth Blackwell, graduated MD, 1849

Lord Denning, the longest serving and most controversial judge who was Master of the Rolls for 20 years (1962-82), born 1899

Sir James Lighthill, Provost of University College, London, born 1924

The first woman Minister of State was Miss Margaret Bondfield, appointed Under-Secretary of State to the Minister of Labour, 1924

24 Earl Spencer, father of Diana, Princess of Wales, born 1924

Charles James Fox, Whig politician, born 1749

International Cricket Conference agreed to ban cricketers who played in South Africa from Test Matches for five years, 1989

25 W. Somerset Maugham, short story writer, born 1874

Paul-Henri Spaak, one-time Prime Minister of Belgium, later Secretary-General of NATO and one of the founding fathers of the Common Market, born 1899

The first radio manufacturer, Wireless Telegraph & Signal Co., opened factory in Chelmsford, 1924

The first Winter Olympics held at Chamonix (to 4 February), 1924

Michael Jackson reached an out-of-court settlement with a 14 year-old boy who had accused him of sexual abuse, 1994

26 The report of an independent inquiry cleared Thames TV of most criticisms of its documentary *Death on the Rock*, but the British government disagreed with findings, 1989

27 Brian Rix, Secretary-General of Mencap and past master of farce, born 1924

The worst floods since 1893 in Brisbane and surrounding areas of Queensland: 8000 people abandoned their homes, 1974

28 Terry Venables appointed coach of the England football team, 1994

29 Alfred Sisley, Impressionist painter, died 1899

De facto recognition of Israel by the British government, 1949

30 Lord Bernstein, founder and architect of the Granada Group, born 1899

Derek Ricketts, international show jumper, born 1949

Charles I beheaded at Whitehall, 1649

Gerry Adams granted a US visa to attend a conference on Northern Ireland in New York, 1994

31 Carol Hawkins, actress, born 1949

Samuel Goldwyn, US film magnate, died 1974

The last British-owned major car manufacturer, Rover, sold to the German firm BMW for £800 million, 1994

February

1 Great Train Robber Ronald Biggs recaptured in Rio de Janeiro, nine years after escaping from Wandsworth Prison, 1974; later that year the birth of a child to his Brazilian girlfriend meant that, under Brazilian law, Biggs could not be extradited to Britain

2 President Pik Botha, who had suffered a stroke, resigned as leader of ruling National Party and was succeeded by F.W. de Klerk, 1989

3 John of Gaunt, Duke of Lancaster, third son of Edward III, died 1399

Gertrude Stein, avant-garde writer and critic, born 1874

Woodrow Wilson, former US President, died 1924

President Clinton lifted the US trade embargo against Vietnam, 1994

4 John Lowein, former chairman and chief executive of Mobil Oil, born 1924

Patricia Hearst, granddaughter of late W.R. Hearst, kidnapped by Symbionese Liberation Army, 1974

5 The GMT time signal and its preceding 'pips' first broadcast regularly by the BBC, 1924

Launch of Sky TV, Britain's first satellite station, 1989

6 Manuel Orantes, Spanish tennis player, born 1949

Billy Wright, former England soccer captain, born 1924

Ramon Novarro, film actor who starred in the original 1925 version of *Ben Hur*, born 1899

7 Dora Bryan, actress-comedienne, born 1924

Alan Lancaster, of rock group Status Quo, born 1949

9 David Basnett, former General Secretary of the General and Municipal Workers' Union, born 1924

10 Samuel Plimsoll, social reformer who gave his name to the 'Plimsoll Line', which governs the loading of ships, born 1824

11 Architect John Poulson and civil servant W.R. Pottinger received five-year jail sentences for corruption; Poulson later received a further seven years to run concurrently, 1974

12 Rubber galoshes first advertised by J.W. Goodrich of Boston, Massachusetts, 1824

General Sir John Archer, chief executive of the Royal Hong Kong Jockey Club, born 1924

John Burke, deputy chairman of the Royal Bank of Scotland, born 1924

13 Ted Croker, Secretary and Chief Executive of the Football Association, born 1924

Jean-Jacques Servan-Schreiber, radical French politician, author and journalist, born 1924

Alexander Solzhenitsyn, Nobel prize-running author, deported from USSR to West Germany and deprived of Soviet citizenship, 1974

14 Countess Mountbatten of Burma, daughter of the late Earl Mountbatten and married to Lord Brabourne, born 1924

Iranian leader Ayatollah Khomeini called on Muslims to kill Salman Rushdie and his publishers because of alleged blasphemy against Islam in his book, *The Satanic Verses*, 1989

15 Sir Ernest Shackleton, Antarctic explorer, born 1874

Soviet troops completed their withdrawal after nine years of occupation of Afghanistan as rebels massed around Kabul; 15,000 soldiers had died in conflict, 1989

16 Sir James Swaffield, Director-General and Clerk to the ILEA (1983-4), born 1924

Sir Peter Webster, High Court judge, born 1924

The Europol Drugs Agency established in the Hague, 1994

19 Lee Marvin, US actor, born 1924

20 UK announced immediate withdrawal of its diplomats from Tehran in response to threats against British author Salman Rushdie: other EC countries agreed to withdraw their ambassadors in support, 1989

21 Robert Gabriel Mugabe, President of Zimbabwe, born 1924

In Czechoslovakia, eminent dissident playwright Vaclav Havel goaled for inciting public disorder in Prague in January 1989

Woodrow Wilson, 28th President of USA, died 1924

MPs defeated a motion to lower the age of consent for homosexuals to 16 but agreed to lower it to 18, 1994

22 Benjamin Disraeli became leader of the Conservative Party, 1849

Niki Lauda, Austrian Grand Prix driver and former world champion, born 1949

24 John Lever, former cricketer, born 1949

The Guitar Player by Vermeer, valued at £1 million, stolen from Kenwood House in London; recovered undamaged on 8 May, 1974

Publication of official inquiry's report of the murder of Jonathan Zito in 1992 by Christopher Clunis, a paranoid schizophrenic, 1994

25 Baron Von Reuter, founder of Reuters press agency, died 1899

Malaysia imposed a trade embargo on Britain in response to allegations in the British press of corruption among Malaysian politicians after £234 million of British aid to the Pergau dam project in the 1980s was linked to a £1 billion arms deal, 1994

Granada took over London Weekend Television with a £765 million hostile bid, 1994

26 The remains of 16 year-old Heather West and two other young women found buried in the garden of 25 Cromwell Street, Gloucester. The remains of six more young women subsequently found under the cellar and bathroom of the house. Frederick and Rosemary West, Heather West's parents, were later charged with the murders, 1994

28 Harold Wilson took office as Prime Minister of a minority Labour Government following the General Election which produced no overall majority for any one party, 1974

29 Sir David Beattie, Governor-General of New Zealand, born 1924

March

2 Dame Naomi James, single-handed round-the-world yachtswoman (1977-8), born 1949

John Peter Rhys Williams, former Welsh full-back, born 1949

The first TV schools service inaugurated by the Philadelphia Board of Education, 1949

4 The Royal National Lifeboat Institution founded, 1824

7 Eduardo Paolozzi, sculptor and tutor in ceramics at Royal College of Art, born 1924

Iran formally broke diplomatic relations with UK over Rushdie affair; on 8 March Britain expelled 20 Iranians on security grounds, 1989

China imposed martial law in Lhasa, Tibet, following three days of violent anti-Chinese protests which had left 40-60 people dead; more than 1000 were later reported arrested as Chinese authorities sought to suppress unrest, 1989

8 John Ericsson, engineer and inventor of the screw propeller for steamships, born 1803, died 1889

9 Neil Hamilton, former Tory MP for Tatton, born 1949

Four IRA mortar bombs were fired at Heathrow Airport; two landed on the north runway but none exploded. Four more were fired on 10 March, 1994

11 The State of Emergency in the UK, declared 13 November 1973, ended; coalminers returned to work following acceptance of pay deal, 1974

13 Sir Peter Harding resigned as chief of the defence staff after newspaper reports of an extra-marital affair, 1994

15 Admiral Sir Raymond Lygo, former managing director of British Aerospace, born 1924.

17 The first radio distress signal was transmitted from the East Goodwin Lightship when it ran aground on the Goodwin Sands, 1899

Patrick Duffy, US actor, born 1949

18 Alex (Hurricane) Higgins, world professional snooker champion (1982), born 1949

A consortium led by Mirror Group newspapers took control of the *Independent* and the *Independent on Sunday*, 1994

20 Princess Anne and Capt. Mark Phillips escaped unhurt when gunman Ian Ball attacked their car in a kidnap attempt in the Mall, 1974

21 Alvin Kallicharran, cricketer who played in the historic 1983 tour of South Africa, born 1949

24 *Exxon Valdez* tanker ran aground in Prince William Sound, Alaska, spilling an estimated 11 million gallons of oil, the largest spillage in US history, 1989

27 The first international radio transmission made across the English Channel by Guglielmo Marconi, 1899

Sarah Vaughan, jazz singer, born 1924

29 Britain annexed the Punjab by treaty with Maharajah of Lahore, 1849

30 Alan Davidson, author, seafood expert and former diplomat, born 1924

Red Rum won the Grand National for the second year running, 1974

April

1 The first Anglo-American military alliance; combined land operation by RN and USN forces at Apia during the Samoan campaign, 1899

Linda Goodwill became the first woman jockey to win a mixed race at Nottingham, 1974

2 Paul Gambaccini, disc jockey, born 1949

Georges Pompidou, former Prime Minister and President of France, died 1974

3 Marlon Brando, US actor and minority ethnic champion, born 1924

Doris Day, US actress and singer, born 1924

4 The first all-England badminton championship held at London Scottish Drill Hall, 1899

5 Rt Hon. Richard Crossman, former MP, Leader of the House of Commons and Lord President of the Council, died 1974

President Gorbachev paid a three-day visit to Britain: he made a speech at the Guildhall and lunched with The Queen at Windsor, 1989

6 Harry Houdini, magician and escapologist, born 1874

Richard I (Coeur de Lion), reigned 1189-99, died 1199

8 General Sir Anthony Farrar-Hockley, military historian; Commander-in-Chief, Allied Forces Northern Europe (1979-82), born 1924

Kurt Cobain, lead singer of Nirvana, found dead at his home in Seattle, USA, 1994

9 James Scott, Duke of Monmouth, illegitimate son of Charles II and Lucy Walter, who led an unsuccessful rebellion against James II, born 1649

10 The first safety-pin patented by Walter Hunt in New York, 1849

The first crossword-puzzle book published by Simon & Schuster in New York, 1924

12 Raymond Barre, French MP, economist and former premier (1976-81), born 1924

14 Dame Mary Warnock, Oxford philosopher, Mistress of Girton, Cambridge, born 1924

15 John Grigg, commentator and biographer, once much buffeted for his strictures on the Queen, born 1924

Neville Marriner, conductor, founder and director of the Academy of St Martin-in-the-Fields, born 1924

Britain's worst sports disaster: 95 died in a crush as fans swarmed into Hillsborough football ground: a judicial inquiry was ordered by Home Secretary, 1989

16 John Harvey-Jones, chairman of ICI, born 1924

Patricia Hearst, kidnapped on 4 February, believed to have joined terrorists and taken part in San Francisco bank robbery, 1974

17 The first Unitarian chapel in Britain, Essex Street Chapel in the Strand registered, 1774

18 Marcel Pagnol, French playwright and film-maker, died 1974

19 George Gordon, 6th Lord Byron, poet, died 1824

20 Leslie Phillips, British actor, born 1924

The first Badminton Horse Trials won by Capt. John Shedden on *Golden Willow*, 1949

21 Eleanora Duse, actress who achieved worldwide fame as a tragedienne, died 1924

22 Immanuel Kant, critical philosopher, born 1724

23 Malcolm Anson, chairman of the Imperial Group (1980-1), born 1924

The first pictorial postage stamp in Britain issued: the 'Wembley Commemorative', 1924

24 The first aeroplane flight round the world Seattle-Seattle by Lt L.H. Smith in Douglas *Chicago* and Lt Erik Nelson in Douglas *New Orleans*, 1924

Budd Abbot, died 1974.

25 Guglielmo Marconi, inventor of a successful system of radio telegraphy, born 1874

Regime of Dr Caetano in Portugal overthrown by military coup, 1974

27 In China 100,000 pro-democracy students and workers held a peaceful protest in Tiananmen Square, Beijing; by early May, demonstrations had intensified and spread to other cities, 1989

28 Kenneth Kaunda, former President of Zambia, born 1924

In Belgium, 14 Liverpool supporters sentenced for three years for manslaughter during the 1985 Heysel stadium riot, 1989

In USA, Aldrich Ames, former head of the Soviet branch of the CIA counter intelligence, sentenced to life imprisonment for selling secrets to the Soviet Union, 1994

The Italian President asked Silvio Berlusconi, leader of the right-wing Freedom Alliance, to form a government; the Freedom Alliance had won the Italian general election with a clear majority, 1994

29 Zizi Jeanmaire, French dancer and cabaret star, born 1924

Duke Ellington, US jazz composer and bandleader, born 1899

May

1 Ayrton Senna killed in the San Marino Grand Prix at Imola, 1994

2 Sir Hugh Cortazzi, British ambassador to Japan (1980-4), born 1924

4 Mrs Thatcher celebrated 10 years as Prime Minister: she was longest continuously serving British Prime Minister since Lord Liverpool, who took office in 1812, 1989

6 The Queen and President Mitterrand opened the Channel Tunnel, 1994

Paula Jones, a former Arkansas state employee, launched a legal action against President Clinton for allegedly making sexual propositions to her while he was Governor of Arkansas, 1994

7 Conservative MP Michael Brown resigned as junior government whip following a newspaper allegation that he had had a homosexual relationship with a 20 year-old student, 1994

9 Billy Joel, singer, born 1949

Lilian Baylis, theatrical manager of the Old Vic and Sadler's Wells, born 1874

The first self-service launderette opened by Bendix Home Appliances Ltd at Queensway, London, 1949

10 Fred Astaire, Hollywood dancing star, born 1899

Inauguration in Pretoria of Nelson Mandela as president of South Africa, 1994

12 John Smith, leader of the Labour Party, died 1994

13 Jane Glover, conductor and musical director of Glyndebourne Touring Opera, born 1949

Zoë Wanamaker, actress, born 1949

Test flight of the first British-designed jet bomber, the English Electric Canberra B Mk 1, 1949

In UK, the Social Democrat Party announced that it would cease fighting all-out as a national party but would not be wound up, 1989

14 In the presidential election in Argentina, Carlos Menem (Peronist) defeated Eduardo Angeloz of ruling Radical Party; he was sworn in on 8 July, 1989

15 General Antonio de Spinola sworn in as President of Portugal and a civilian Provisional Government installed, led by Senhor Adelino da Palma Carlos, 1974

President Gorbachev began three-day visit to China: the first Sino-Soviet summit for 30 years. His schedule in both Beijing and Shanghai disrupted by pro-democracy demonstrators, 1989

17 Vice-Admiral Sir Thomas Baird, Flag Officer, Scotland and Northern Ireland 1979-82, born 1924

Edward Jenner, physician who discovered vaccination, born 1749

18 Pierre-Augustin Beaumarchais, comic dramatist, died 1799

19 Sandy Wilson, composer, lyric writer and playwright, born 1924

20 Honoré de Balzac, novelist, born 1799

Chinese Government imposed martial law for first time in 40 years in attempt to quell demonstrations which had brought Beijing to a standstill, 1989

In Spain, 13 convicted, 25 acquitted, over their part in distribution of contaminated cooking oil in 1981 which killed more than 600 people, 1989

22 Maria Edeworth, novelist, died 1849

23 Thomas Hood, poet and humorist, born 1799

At least 250 Muslim pilgrims crushed to death during a ceremony near Mecca, 1994

24 Duke Ellington, US jazz composer and bandleader, died 1974

25 The Camelot consortium awarded the contract to run the National Lottery, 1994

27 Inauguration of President Giscard d'Estaing, 1974

29 G.K. Chesterton, journalist and writer, born 1874

Francis Rossi, lead singer of rock group Status Quo, born 1949

30 Bob Willis, cricketer, born 1949

Armstrong Whitworth pilot J.O. Lancaster was the first British pilot to use an ejection seat in an emergency: he made a successful escape from the experimental AWA 52 delta-wing jet when it went out of control above Coventry, 1949

June

1 The first Pullman cars introduced in Britain by the Midland Railway, 1874

The Nypro chemical plant at Flixborough destroyed by explosion and fire: 29 people died, 1974

2 Transjordan renamed the Hashemite Kingdom of Jordan, 1949

Sir Arnold Lunn, pioneer skier and inventor of the slalom race, born 1888, died 1974

Chinook helicopter crashed in thick fog on the Mull of Kintyre killing 19 senior intelligence and security officers from the army and RUC, six civil servants from the Northern Ireland Office and four crew members, 1994

3 Franz Kafka, Czech novelist, died 1924

Johann Strauss The Younger, composer, died 1899

In China, troops, tanks and heavy artillery moved into Beijing's Tiananmen Square, which had been occupied by protesting students for seven weeks; several thousand were believed killed during the military crackdown, 1989

Brian Lara set a new world record of seven centuries in eight innings when he scored 101 not out for Warwickshire at Edgbaston, 1994

John Major announced the UK's ratification of the 1992 Rio summit's biodiversity convention, 1994

4 Marguerite, Countess of Blessington, novelist, died 1849

50th anniversary of D Day. Memorial service at the US military cemetery at Madingley, Cambs.; the Prime Minister and President Clinton attended. The Queen attended commemoration banquet for heads of state at Portsmouth Guildhall, 1994

5 President Bush suspended all arms sales to China as Western leaders condemned massacre of students in Beijing on 3-4 June, 1989

Drumhead thanksgiving and remembrance service held on Southsea Common, Portsmouth to mark the 50th anniversary of D Day, 1994

6 Alexander Pushkin, the national poet of Russia, born 1799

The Queen, Duke of Edinburgh, Prime Minister and President Mitterrand attended commemorative service at the Bayeux war cemetery, 1994

Brian Lara set a new world record for an individual first class score with 501 not out, and a new world record of 390 runs scored by an individual in one day, 1994

7 Augustin Daly, playwright and theatre manager who founded the New York theatre that bore his name, died 1899

The Crusaders arrived in front of Jerusalem, 1099

9 The Book of Common Prayer adopted throughout England, 1549

The first moving staircase brought into operation at the Otis Elevator Co. factory in New York, 1899

Tony Britton, British actor, born 1924

12 George Bush, former President of the US (1989-93), born 1924

17 IRA bomb exploded in Houses of Parliament: 11 people injured, 1974

18 O.J. Simpson, actor and former US football player, arrested and charged with murdering his former wife and a male friend of hers, 1994

19 Sir Edward Youde, former Governor of Hong Kong, born 1924

21 Wally Fawkes, cartoonist, born 1924

In China, three pro-democracy demonstrators publicly executed in Shanghai; seven others were executed in Beijing on 22 June; many other executions are believed to have taken place, 1989

22 The first osteopath, Dr Andrew Taylor Still, commenced practice, 1874

Alan Osmond, of the pop group the Osmonds, born 1949

Meryl Streep, US actress, born 1949

23 Ranasinghe Premadasa, former Prime Minister and President of Sri Lanka who was assassinated by a suicide bomber (1 May 1993), born 1924

Chief Moshood Abiola arrested in Lagos after proclaiming himself President of Nigeria, 1994

25 Sidney Lumet, film director, born 1924

Patrick Tambay, French Grand Prix driver, born 1949

27 Most Revd Dermot Ryan, Roman Catholic Archbishop of Dublin and Primate of Ireland, born 1924

29 Maria Estela Perón became the first woman president; sworn in as President of Argentina, 1974

30 Alberta King, mother of the late Martin Luther-King, assassinated during a church service, 1974

July

1 The first child kidnapped for ransom: Charley Ross kidnapped at Philadelphia, 1874

Charles Laughton, US actor, born 1899

The first woman motor racing driver on record, Mme Labrousse of Paris, competed in the Paris-Spa Race, 1899

Juan Perón, former President of Argentina, died 1974

2 Martina Navratilova played her last match at Wimbledon in the Ladies Singles Final, 1994

5 In USA, Lt Col. Oliver North received three-year suspended sentence and $150,000 fine for his part in the Iran-Contra affair, 1989

8 Kim Il-Sung, premier and president of North Korea, died 1994

9 For first time in Wimbledon tennis tournament both singles championships at were won by West Germans (Boris Becker and Steffi Graff), 1989

10 Conservative MPs David Tredinnick and Graham Riddick were suspended after the Sunday Times alleged that they had each accepted £1000 to table a parliamentary question on behalf of a reporter posing as a businessman, 1994

11 Robert The Bruce, King of Scotland, born 1274

The first film drama made for TV shot at Marylebone Studios by Vizio Films Ltd: A Dinner Date with Death (also the first British TV drama to be televised on US networks), 1949

12 John Ehrlichman and three co-defendants found guilty of conspiracy to violate the constitutional rights of Dr Daniel Ellsberg's psychiatrist, 1974

13 Sir James Craig, British ambassador to Saudi Arabia (1979-84), born 1924

Kim Jong-Il, son of President Kim Il-Sung was appointed President, party chief and military commander of North Korea, 1994

14 Gerald Ford inaugurated as 38th President of the USA, 1974

Lady Sarah Armstrong-Jones married Daniel Chatto, 1994

15 President Makarios of Cyprus overthrown in coup led by Greek-officered National Guard, 1974

16 Sir Richard Stratton, former High Commissioner to New Zealand, born 1924

Former EOKA leader Nicos Sampson appointed President of Cyprus by insurgents, 1974

17 James Cagney, actor, born 1899

Isaac Watts, nonconformist hymn writer, born 1674

IRA bomb explosion at the Tower of London killed one woman and injured 37 people, 1974

In USA, revolutionary B2 'Stealth' bomber plane made its maiden flight in California, 1989

18 Dennis Lillee, cricketer, born 1949

The Rwandan Patriotic Front announced a cease-fire, declared victory in the civil war and appointed a government of national unity led by Hutu moderates, 1994

20 Turkish forces invaded Cyprus at dawn and after shelling Kyrenia thrust inland towards Nicosia, 1974

21 Ernest Hemingway, Nobel Prize-winning author, born 1899

Tony Blair elected leader of the Labour Party and John Prescott elected deputy leader, 1994

The South African cricket team played its first Test in England in 24 years, 1994

24 The first public opinion poll conducted at Wilmington, Delaware to determine voters' intentions in the US Presidential election, 1824

Vice-Admiral Sir David Loram, Deputy Supreme Allied Commander Atlantic (1977-80), born 1924

Sir James Chadwick, Nobel Prizewinner for Physics for discovery of the neutron, died 1974

In UK Government shuffle John Major succeeded Sir Geoffrey Howe as Foreign Secretary; Sir Geoffrey became Deputy Prime Minister and Leader of the House of Commons; Kenneth Baker was named chairman of the Conservative Party, 1989

25 London dock strike ended, 1949

27 The first jet airliner flight in Britain: the de Havilland Comet, 1949

28 Sir Peter Green, chairman of Lloyds (1980-3), born 1924

Chief Moshood Abiola went on trial for treason in Nigeria, 1994

29 The first televised weather forecasts introduced in Britain by the BBC, 1949

Former Italian Prime Minister Bettino Craxi sentenced to eight and a half years in jail for fraud, 1994

31 Ralph Koltai, stage designer, born 1924

August

1 The discovery of DDT first reported by Othmar Zeidler in Strasbourg, 1874

Lisa Marie Presley confirmed that in May 1994 she had married pop star Michael Jackson, 1994

2 James Baldwin, US novelist and playwright, born 1924

Jacques-Étienne Montgolfier, pioneer balloonist, died en route to Annonay, 1799

Dr Jacob Bronowski, scientist and humanist, died 1974

3 Sir Jock Taylor, British ambassador in Bonn (1981-4), born 1924

Joseph Conrad, writer, died 1924

5 President Nixon admitted that he withheld information on Watergate and that he was involved in the cover-up after the break-in, 1974

7 Kenneth Kendall, BBC TV newsreader (1955-81) and founder of the Queen's English Society, born 1924

8 In a nationwide TV broadcast President Nixon announced his resignation as President of the USA, 1974

9 Gerald Ford sworn in as 38th President of the USA, 1974

10 Herbert Hoover, former US President, born 1874

12 Mark Knopfler, lead guitarist with Dire Straits, born 1949

Robert Southey, Poet Laureate and historian, born 1774

14 In South Africa, President Botha resigned office; F.W. de Klerk sworn in as acting President pending elections on 6 September 1989

Illich Ramirez Sanchez, known as Carlos the Jackal, who was wanted in connection with over 80 terrorist murders since 1972, arrested in Sudan and extradited to France, 1994

15 Robert Bolt, playwright, born 1924

19 Margaret Mitchell, author, died 1949

20 Pleasureboat *Marchioness* rammed by a dredger on the River Thames: 51 people died, 1989

22 US Spacecraft *Voyager 2* began transmission of live pictures of planet Neptune (the spacecraft had left Earth in 1977 and flown 4500 million miles), 1989

23 Geoff Capes, former British shot putt champion, born 1949

William Henley, poet, critic and editor, born 1849

More than two million people in Baltic republics formed human chain in nationalist demonstration to mark 50th anniversary of non-aggression pact between Soviet Union and Nazi Germany, 1989

24 Jorge Luis Borges, Argentinian anglophile novelist and short-story writer, born 1899

George Stubbs, portrait and animal painter, born 1724

25 Martin Amis, novelist, born 1949.

26 Charles Lindbergh, the first man to fly solo across the Atlantic, died 1974

A 62 year-old man received a permanent artificial heart in pioneering operation at Papworth Hospital, 1994

28 Johann von Goethe, poet, playwright and scientist, born 1749

31 Norman Eric Kirk, former New Zealand Prime Minister, died 1974

The IRA announced a complete cessation of military operations from midnight, 1994

September

2 Ros Hepplewhite resigned as chief executive of the Child Support Agency, 1994

3 Edward Heath's yacht *Morning Cloud* wrecked off Shoreham: two people died, 1974

4 Joan Aiken, children's author and playwright, born 1924

Tom Watson, golfer, born 1949

Anton Bruckner, composer, born 1824

6 The first motorcycle despatch riders: four motor tricyclists of the French army took part in the army manoeuvres in the Verdun-Sainte-Menehould region, 1899

7 Dianne Hayter, General Secretary of the Fabian Society (1976-82), born 1949

8 Alexandra Kollantai became the first woman ambassador, 1924

Richard Strauss, light opera composer, died 1949

9 At a retrial, Alfred Dreyfus is condemned with extenuating circumstances, 1899

John Curry, former British European, World and Olympic figure skating champion, born 1949

The USA and Cuba reached an agreement to end the seaborne flight of thousands of Cubans to Florida, 1994

10 Attempted escape of five IRA prisoners from Whitemoor prison: a prison guard was shot and injured, 1994

11 Roger Uttley, former England and British Lions rugby footballer, born 1949

13 Arnold Schoenberg, composer, born 1874

The first regular newspaper motoring feature 'Motoring Notes' appeared in the *Daily Mail*, 1899

14 Two giant pandas, Ching-Ching and Chia-Chia, presented by China to commemorate Edward Heath's visit, arrived in London Zoo, 1974

16 Lauren Bacall, actress, born 1924

The ban on broadcasting the voices of members of Sinn Fein (imposed 1988) lifted, 1994

18 A US negotiating team reached agreement with the Haitian military junta for their resignation, the return of President Aristide and the deployment of a US and later UN peace-keeping force, 1994

19 Alfred Dreyfus pardoned by presidential decree, 1899

Twiggy (Lesley Hornby), model-turned-actress/singer, born 1949

The European Commission of Human Rights ruled that Ernest Saunders, former chief executive of Guinness, convicted in 1990 of theft and

conspiracy to defraud, had not received a fair trial, 1994

21 Gustav Holst, composer, born 1874

The first inter-urban motorway, the Milano-Varese Autostrada opened by the King of Italy, 1924

The first comprehensive school in Britain opened; Holyhead County Secondary, 1949

22 IRA bomb explosion at Royal Marines School of Music, Deal, Kent: 10 killed (another marine died on 19 October), 1989

Lord Moran, British High Commissioner in Canada (1981-4), born 1924

23 Bruce Springsteen, singer/songwriter, born 1949

Ceefax, the first teletext service, inaugurated, 1974

24 Johann Strauss the Elder, composer, died 1849

25 Nikolai Poliakov, circus clown known as Coco, died 1974

Norman Ayrton, theatre and opera director, born 1924

26 Vietnamese troops withdrew from Kampuchea, marking the end of their involvement in 10-year civil war, 1989

27 The ferry *Estonia* sank in the Baltic Sea: at least 909 people drowned, 1994

28 Ferdinand Marcos, former ruler of the Philippines, died in exile in Hawaii; President Aquino refused to allow his body to be returned for burial, 1989

Francis Turner Palgrave, poet and compiler of *The Golden Treasury*, born 1824

29 Richard II became the first English monarch to abdicate, 1399

30 Truman Capote, US author, born 1924

October

1 Watergate cover-up trial opened in Washington, 1974

Jimmy Carter, former US President, born 1924

4 Charlton Heston, US actor, born 1924

Lloyd's Names won damages estimated at £504 million after alleging that negligence on the part of underwriters had led to losses of £629 million on the insurance market, 1994

5 IRA bomb explosions in two public houses in Guildford: five people killed and 65 injured, 1974

Barbara Kelly, Canadian-born actress and TV personality, born 1924

6 UN weapons inspection team began monitoring Iraq's weapons manufacturing plants to ensure that weapons of mass destruction are not built, 1994

7 Edgar Allan Poe, poet, critic and writer, died 1849

9 The first full-size petrol bus in Britain introduced by the Motor Traction Co. on a route from Kennington to Victoria Station, 1899

11 The Boer War began, 1899

12 The first safety-pin in Britain patented by Charles Rowley, 1849

13 Anatole France, (pseudonym of J. Thibault), French writer, died 1924

The first election address broadcast on radio, made on behalf of the Labour Party by Rt Hon J. Ramsay MacDonald, 1924

Dow Jones industrial index fell nearly 200 points, its second ever biggest fall; 16 September world stock markets fell sharply but recovered much of their losses following a rally on Wall Street, 1989

The Combined Loyalist Military Command announced a cease-fire from midnight, 1994

14 Lillian Gish, actress, born 1899

Françoise Pascal, actress, born 1949

Ffyona Campbell became the first woman to walk around the world, 1994

17 Frédéric Chopin, composer, born 1849

Major earthquake in Northern California: 67 people killed; extensive damage in and around San Francisco, 1989

18 Jeanne Geneviève Garnerin became the first woman parachutist, 1799

19 In the House of Commons Labour MP Stuart Bell accused Tim Smith and Neil Hamilton of accepting payment to ask parliamentary questions on behalf of Westminster lobbying company, 1994

20 Eddie Macken, Irish international show jumper, born 1949

21 Portland cement patented by Joseph Aspdin, 1824

24 Earl of Ulster, son of the Duke and Duchess of Gloucester, born 1974

26 Nigel Lawson resigned as Chancellor of the Exchequer and replaced by John Major; Douglas Hurd appointed Foreign Secretary and succeeded at the Home Office by David Waddington, 1989

28 Ottmar Mergenthaler, inventor of the Linotype machine, died 1899

30 Muhammad Ali defeated George Foreman to regain world heavyweight boxing championship in Zaire, 1974

November

2 Ladysmith besieged in the Boer War, 1899

The first crossword puzzle published in Britain, 1924

3 Larry Holmes, world heavyweight boxing champion, born 1949

4 Judith Ward jailed for 30 years for causing the M62 coach explosion and blast at National Defence College, Latimer, 1974

Gabriel Fauré, composer, died 1924

6 The first woman Conservative Minister in Britain, Duchess of Atholl, became Parliamentary Under-Secretary, Board of Education, 1924

7 Eric Linklater, Scottish author, died 1974

Wolf Mankowitz, author and authority on porcelain, born 1924

8 London's Covent Garden market closed, 1974

John Milton, poet, died 1674

Allegations published in the *Sun* that Bruce Grobbelaar had taken bribes to fix Premier League match results; he denied the allegations and issued libel writs, 1994

9 Lord Brabourne, film and TV producer, born 1924

10 East German authorities began demolition of sections of Berlin Wall; it was reported on 13 November that some two million East Germans had visited the West during the weekend, 1989

11 London's new Covent Garden market opened at Nine Elms, Battersea, 1974

12 The first war (British) scenes filmed: 5th Northumberland Fusiliers at Orange River, South Africa, by John Bennett Stanford, 1899

13 William Etty, artist, died 1849

14 Vittorio de Sica, Italian film director, died 1974

Eurostar passenger service between London and Paris launched, 1994

The National Lottery was launched, 1994

15 Polish Solidarity leader, Lech Walesa, became first private citizen in 175 years to address joint session of US Congress, 1989

Martina Navratilova played the last singles match of her career in New York, 1994

18 Eugene Ormandy, former conductor and musical director of the Philadelphia Orchestra, born 1899

19 The first draw of the National Lottery, 1994

22 Lord (Robert) Clive, founder of the British Empire in India, died 1774

23 Norman Hunter, author and creator of Professor Branestaum, born 1899

Perkin Warbeck, who impersonated Richard, Duke of York, the younger of the Princes in the Tower, hanged at Tyburn, 1499

24 Frances Hodgson Burnett, author, born 1849

26 Pat Phoenix, actress, born 1924

In first national referendum in Hungary for 40 years, voters approved proposal that President of the Republic should be elected by a multi-party parliament, 1989

Videotape first used as evidence in Britain, 1974

27 Czechoslovakian workers staged general strike demanding end to Communist rule, 1989

Chaim Weizmann, Zionist who became first President of Israel in 1948, born 1874

28 Geoffrey Clarke, artist and sculptor, born 1924

The Norwegian electorate voted against membership of the European Union in a referendum, 1994

29 Giacomo Puccini, Italian composer, died 1924

President Yeltsin warned warring factions in Chechenia to stop fighting or a state of emergency would be declared within 48 hours; Russian warplanes bombed Grozny Airport, 1994

30 Sir Winston Churchill, British statesman, born 1874

December

1 Radio first used in warfare, 1899

Romanian Olympic gymnast, Nadia Comaneci, sought political asylum in USA, 1989

2 General Alexander Haig, US Secretary of State (1981-2) and former Supreme Allied Commander, Europe (1974-9), born 1924

4 William Drummond of Hawthornden, poet and songwriter, died 1649

5 Margaret Thatcher defeated Sir Anthony Meyer in ballot for leadership of Conservative Party, 1989

6 Sir Henry Tate, sugar refiner and art collector, died 1899

The first national state education system implemented in Austria under Johann von Felbiger's Educational Statute, 1774

7 President Makarios returned to Cyprus to a hero's welcome after four and a half months in exile, 1974

10 Michael Manley, Prime Minister of Jamaica (1972-80), born 1924

11 Forcible repatriation of Vietnamese boat people from Hong Kong began; the first were flown to Hanoi amid widespread criticism in UK and USA, 1989

Russian armoured columns entered Chechenia and moved towards Grozny in an attempt to overthrow the regime of President Dudayev, 1994

13 The first Smithfield Show was held at Wootton's Dolphin Yard, London by Smithfield Cattle and Sheep Society, 1799

Sir George Bellew, Garter Principal King of Arms (1950-61), born 1899

Launch of the first motor trade association in Britain, Motor Trades Association, 1899

14 George Washington, first President of USA, died 1799

Walter Lippmann, newspaper columnist, died 1974

Diane Modahl, former 800-metre Commonwealth champion, banned for four years after testing positive to drugs in June, 1994

16 Sir Noël Coward, playwright, actor, composer and wit, born 1899

17 The first bowler hat first tried on by customer William Coke of Norfolk, 1849

19 US troops invaded Panama to overthrow the regime of General Noriega; fighting continued for several days, 1989

Edmund Purdom, British-born Hollywood actor, born 1924

22 Dwight Moody, US evangelist who, together with Ira Sankey, organised revival campaigns in USA and England, died 1899

Romanian government of Nicolae Ceausescu overthrown when the army joined forces with anti-government demonstrators, 1989

Silvio Berlusconi resigned after his coalition government collapsed over a corruption investigation into his Finnivest business, 1994

24 Vasco da Gama, navigator, died 1524

25 Nicolae Ceausescu and his wife executed, 1989

Sissy Spacek, US actress, born 1949

Humphrey Bogart, film actor, born 1899

26 Jack Benny, US comedian, died 1974

28 Alexander Dubcek, 1968 Communist reform leader, elected chairman of Czechoslovak Parliament, 1989

29 Vaclav Havel, playwright and former dissident, unanimously elected Czechoslovakia's first non-communist president for 41 years, 1989

31 Donna Summer, singer, born 1949

Government offices and public services

Enquiries, accompanied by a sae, should be sent to the Public Relations Officer. The names and addresses of many other public bodies can be found in Whitaker's Almanack.

Advertising Standards Authority
2 Torrington Place, London WC1E 7HW
tel 0171-580 5555 *fax* 0171-631 3051

AEA Technology
Harwell, Didcot, Oxon OX11 0RA
tel (01235) 821111 *fax* (01235) 432916

Agriculture, Fisheries and Food, Ministry of
3-8 Whitehall Place, London SW1A 2HH
Helpline (0645) 335577
tel 0171-270 3000 *fax* 0171-270 8419

Arts Council of England
14 Great Peter Street, London SW1P 3NQ
tel 0171-333 0100
Library/enquiry line 0171-973 6517
fax 0171-973 6590
e-mail information.ace@artscouncil.org.uk
web site http://www.artscouncil.org.uk
For full details, see page 459.

Arts Council of Northern Ireland
185 Stranmillis Road, Belfast BT9 5DU
tel (01232) 381591 *fax* (01232) 661715

Arts Council of Wales
9 Museum Place, Cardiff CF1 3NX
tel (01222) 394711 *fax* (01222) 221447

Australian High Commission
Australia House, Strand, London WC2B 4LA
tel 0171-379 4334 *fax* 0171-240 5333

Austrian Embassy
18 Belgrave Mews West, London SW1X 8HU
tel 0171-235 3731 *fax* 0171-344 0292
e-mail embassy@austria.org.uk

Bahamas High Commission
Bahamas House, 10 Chesterfield Street,
London W1X 8AH
tel 0171-408 4488 *fax* 0171-499 9937
e-mail bahamas.hicom.lon@cableinet.co.uk

Bangladesh High Commission
28 Queen's Gate, London SW7 5JA
tel 0171-584 0081-4 *fax* 0171-225 2130
e-mail bdesh-Lon@dial.pipex.com

The Bank of England
Threadneedle Street, London EC2R 8AH
tel 0171-601 4444 *fax* 0171-601 4771
web site http://www.bankofengland.co.uk

Barbados High Commission
1 Great Russell Street, London WC1B 3JY
tel 0171-631 4975 *fax* 0171-323 6872

Belgian Embassy
103 Eaton Square, London SW1W 9AB
tel 0171-470 3700 *fax* 0171-259 6213
e-mail info@belgium-embassy.co.uk
web site http://www.belgium-embassy.co.uk

Benefits Agency, Pensions and Overseas Benefits Directorate (POD) – see Social Security, Department of

Bodleian Library
Oxford OX1 3BG
tel (01865) 277000 *fax* (01865) 277182

Bosnia-Herzegovina, Embassy of
320 Regent Street, London W1R 5AB
tel 0171-255 3758 *fax* 0171-255 3760

Botswana High Commission
6 Stratford Place, London W1N 9AE
tel 0171-499 0031

British Broadcasting Corporation
Broadcasting House, London W1A 1AA
tel 0171-580 4468
web site http://www.bbc.co.uk

British Coal – see The Coal Authority

The British Council
10 Spring Gardens, London SW1A 2BN
tel 0171-930 8466 *fax* 0171-839 6347

British Film Commission
70 Baker Street, London W1M 1DJ
tel 0171-224 5000 *fax* 0171-224 1013
e-mail info@britfilmcom.co.uk
web site http://www.britfilmcom.co.uk

British Film Institute
21 Stephen Street, London W1P 2LN
tel 0171-255 1444 *fax* 0171-436 7950
web site http://www.bfi.org.uk

The British Library
96 Euston Road, London NW1 2DB
tel 0171-412 7111 *fax* 0171-412 7168

British Library Document Supply Centre
Boston Spa, Wetherby, West Yorkshire LS23 7BQ
tel (01937) 546060 *fax* (01937) 546333
e-mail dsc-customer-services@bl.uk
web site http://opac97.bl.uk

Offers remote supply of photocopies and loans either direct to registered customers or through a national network of local and academic libraries. Free access to material (preferably with advance notice), including recordings from the National Sound Archive, in the Reading Room. Many catalogues are available on the web site, which also offers a document ordering link for registered and non-registered customers.

British Library Newspaper Library
Colindale Avenue, London NW9 5HE
tel 0171-412 7353 *fax* 0171-412 7379
e-mail newspaper@bl.uk
web site http://portico.bl.uk/newspaper

British Museum
Great Russell Street, London WC1B 3DG
tel 0171-636 1555 *fax* 0171-323 8118
e-mail pr-bm@mailbox.ulcc.ac.uk
web site http://www.britishmuseum.ac.uk

British Railways Board
Whittles House, 14 Pentonville Road, London N1 9HF
tel 0171-904 5000 *fax* 0171-904 5040

British Standards Institution
Information Centre, 389 Chiswick High Road, London W4 4AL
tel 0181-996 7111 *fax* 0181-996 7048
e-mail standards_enquiries@bs.org.uk
web site http://www.bs.org.uk/

British Tourist Authority/English Tourist Board
Thames Tower, Black's Road, London W6 9EL
tel 0181-846 9000 *fax* 0181-563 0302
web site http://www.bta.org.uk

The Broadcasting Complaints Commission – see Broadcasting Standards Commission

Broadcasting Standards Commission
7 The Sanctuary, London SW1P 3JS
tel 0171-233 0544 *fax* 0171-222 3172

Bulgaria, Embassy of the Republic of
186-188 Queen's Gate, London SW7 5HL
tel 0171-584 9400/9433, 0171-581 3144 (5 lines)
fax 0171-584 4948

The Cabinet Office
70 Whitehall, London SW1A 2AS
tel 0171-270 1234

Cadw: Welsh Historic Monuments
Crown Building, Cathays Park, Cardiff CF1 3NQ
tel (01222) 500200 *fax* (01222) 826375

Canadian High Commission
Cultural Affairs Section, Canada House, Trafalgar Square, London W1X 0AB
tel 0171-258 6366 *fax* 0171-258 6322

Central Office of Information
Hercules Road, London SE1 7DU
tel 0171-928 2345

In the UK conducts press, television, radio and poster advertising; produces booklets, leaflets, films, radio and television material, exhibitions and other visual material on behalf of other government organisations.

Central Statistical Office – now part of National Statistics, Office for

Centre for Information on Language Teaching and Research (CILT)
20 Bedfordbury, London WC2N 4LB
tel 0171-379 5101 *fax* 0171-379 5082
e-mail library@cilt.org.uk
web site http://www.cilt.uk

Supports the work of all professionals concerned with modern language teaching and learning throughout the UK, across every sector and stage of education. Offers a full conference programme, plus free on-site INSET for teachers, a complete range of publications and the CILT Teaching Resources Library with extensive IT and AV facilities. CILT also provides a comprehensive information service and knowledge of research and developmental activity.

Charity Commission
St Alban's House, 57-60 Haymarket,
London SW1Y 4QX
tel 0171-210 4556 *fax* 0171-210 4545
2nd Floor, 20 King's Parade, Queen's Dock,
Liverpool L3 4DQ
tel 0151-703 1500 *fax* 0151-703 1555
Woodfield House, Tangier, Taunton,
Somerset TA1 4B1
tel (01823) 345000 *fax* (01823) 345003

The Coal Authority
200 Lichfield Lane, Mansfield, Notts. NG18 4RG
tel (01623) 427162 *fax* (01623) 622072

College of Arms (or Heralds' College)
Queen Victoria Street, London EC4V 4BT
tel 0171-248 2762 *fax* 0171-248 6448

The Commonwealth Institute
Kensington High Street, London W8 6NQ
tel 0171-603 4535 *fax* 0171-602 7374
e-mail info@commonwealth.org.uk
web site http://www.commonwealth.org.uk
For full details, see page 470.

Contributions Agency, International Services (InS) – see Social Security, Department of

Copyright Tribunal
Room 148, 25 Southampton Buildings,
London WC2A 1AY
tel 0171-438 4776 *fax* 0171-438 4780
Minicom (0645) 222250
e-mail copyright.tribunal@patent.gov.uk

Countryside Commission
John Dower House, Crescent Place, Cheltenham,
Glos. GL50 3RA
tel (01242) 521381 *fax* (01242) 584270

Court of the Lord Lyon
HM New Register House, Edinburgh EH1 3YT
tel 0131-556 7255 *fax* 0131-557 2148

Crafts Council
44A Pentonville Road, London N1 9BY
tel 0171-278 7700 *fax* 0171-837 6891
web site http://www.craftscouncil.org.uk
Exhibition gallery, picture library, reference library, reference service, shop, education workshop, café.

Croatia, Embassy of the Republic of
21 Conway Street, London W1P 5HL
tel 0171-387 1790 *fax* 0171-387 3289

Culture, Media and Sport, Department for
2-4 Cockspur Street, London SW1V 5DH
tel 0171-211 6000

Responsible for government policy relating to the arts, broadcasting, the press, museums and galleries, libraries, sport and recreation, historic buildings and ancient monuments, tourism and the music industry. It funds the Arts Councils and other arts bodies, is responsible for policy on the National Lottery and the Millenium, and sponsors the Millennium Commission. Established in July 1997 from the former Department of National Heritage.

Cyprus High Commission
93 Park Street, London W1Y 4ET
tel 0171-499 8272 *fax* 0171-491 0691

Czech Republic, Embassy of the
26 Kensington Palace Gardens,
London W8 4QY
tel 0171-243 1115 *fax* 0171-727 9654
e-mail london@embassy.mzv.cz

Royal Danish Embassy
55 Sloane Street, London SW1X 9SR
tel 0171-333 0200 *fax* 0171-333 0270
web site http://www.denmark.co.uk

Data Protection Registrar, Office of the
Wycliffe House, Water Lane, Wilmslow,
Cheshire SK9 5AF
tel (01625) 545745(enquiries) (01625) 545700
(switchboard) *fax* (01625) 524510
e-mail data@wycliffe.demon.co.uk
web site http://www.open.gov.uk/dpr/dprhome.htm

Defence, Ministry of
Main Building, Whitehall, London SW1A 2HB
tel 0171-218 9000
web site http://www.mod.uk/

The Design Council
34 Bow Street, London WC2E 7DL
tel 0171-420 5200 *fax* 0171-420 5300
web site http://www.design-council.org.uk

DFID: Department for International Development
94 Victoria Street, London SW1E 5JL
tel 0171-917 7000
web site http://www.dfid.gov.uk
Abercrombie House, Eaglesham Road,
East Kilbride, Glasgow G75 8EA
tel (01355) 844000
Established in May 1997 from the former Overseas Development Administration of the Foreign and Commonwealth Office. It deals with British development assistance to overseas countries and global environmental assistance.

DTI: Department of Trade and Industry

1 Victoria Street, London SW1H 0ET
tel 0171-215 5000 (general enquiries)
fax 0171-222 2629
Minicom/text phone 0171-215 6740
Business in Europe 0117-944 4888

Economic and Social Research Council

Polaris House, North Star Avenue, Swindon,
Wilts. SN2 1UJ
tel (01793) 413000 *fax* (01793) 413001
web site www.esrc.ac.uk

Education and Employment, Department for

Sanctuary Buildings, Great Smith Street,
London SW1P 3BT
tel (0870) 0012345 (switchboard) 0171-925 5555
(public enquiries)

Electricity & Gas Regulation Northern Ireland, Office of (OFREG)

Brookmount Buildings, 42 Fountain Street,
Belfast BT1 5EE
tel (01232) 311575 *fax* (01232) 311740
e-mail ofreg@nics.gov.uk
web site http://ofreg.nics.gov.uk/

Electricity Regulation, Office of

Hagley House, Hagley Road, Edgbaston,
Birmingham B16 8QG
tel 0121-456 2100 *fax* 0121-456 4664

Engineering and Physical Sciences Research Council

Polaris House, North Star Avenue, Swindon,
Wilts. SN2 1ET
tel (01793) 444000 *fax* (01793) 444010
e-mail infoline@epsrc.ac.uk
web site http://www.epsrc.ac.uk

English Heritage

23 Savile Row, London W1X 1AB
tel 0171-973 3000 *fax* 0171-973 3001
web site http://www.english-heritage.org.uk

English Regional Arts Boards

5 City Road, Winchester, Hants SO23 8SD
tel (01962) 851063 *fax* (01962) 842033
e-mail info.erab@artsfb.org.uk
web site http://www.arts.co.uk
Representative body for the 10 Regional
Arts Boards in England; see page 491.

English Sports Council

16 Upper Woburn Place, London WC1H 0QP
tel 0171-273 1500 *fax* 0171-383 5740

The Environment Agency

Hampton House, 20 Albert Embankment,
London SE1 7TJ
tel 0171-840 6000 *fax* 0171-587 5258

Rio House, Waterside Drive, Aztec West,
Almondsbury, Bristol BS12 4UD
tel (01454) 624400 *fax* (01454) 624409
Carries out work formerly undertaken by
the National Rivers Authority, HM
Inspectorate of Pollution, the waste regulation authorities and some technical
units of the Dept of the Environment.

Environment, Transport and the Regions, Department of

Eland House, Bressenden Place,
London SW1E 5DU
tel 0171-890 3000
76 Marsham Street, London SW1P 4DR
tel 0171-271 4800

Equal Opportunities Commission

Overseas House, Quay Street, Manchester M3 3HN
tel 0161-833 9244 *fax* 0161-835 1657
e-mail info@eoc.org.uk
web site http://www.eoc.org.uk/

The European Commission

8 Storey's Gate, London SW1P 3AT
tel 0171-973 1992 *fax* 0171-973 1900
web site http://www.cec.org.uk

European Parliament

UK Office 2 Queen Anne's Gate,
London SW1H 9AA
tel 0171-227 4300 *fax* 0171-227 4302
library fax 0171-227 4301
web sites http://www.europarl.eu.int
http://www.cec.org.uk

Fair Trading, Office of

Field House, 15-25 Bream's Buildings,
London EC4A 1PR
tel 0171-211 8000 *fax* 0171-211 8800
e-mail enquiries @oftuk.demon.co.uk
web site http://www.oft.gov.uk

Finland, Embassy of

38 Chesham Place, London SW1W 8HW
tel 0171-838 6200 *fax* 0171-235 3860 (general)
0171-259 5602 (press and information)
web site http://www.finemb.org.uk

Foreign and Commonwealth Office

King Charles Street, London SW1A 2AL
tel 0171-270 3000

Forestry Commission

231 Corstorphine Road, Edinburgh EH12 7AT
tel 0131-334 0303 *fax* 0131-334 4473
e-mail info@forestry.gov.uk
web site http://www.forestry.gov.uk

French Embassy

58 Knightsbridge, London SW1X 7JT
tel 0171-201 1000

Cultural Department 23 Cromwell Road,
London SW7 2EL
tel 0171-838 2055

Gambia High Commission
57 Kensington Court, London W8 5DG
tel 0171-937 6316/7/8 *fax* 0171-937 9095

Gas Supply, Office of (OFGAS)
Stockley House, 130 Wilton Road,
London SW1V 1LQ
tel 0171-828 0898 *fax* 0171-932 1600
Freephone helpline 0800-887777
web site http://www.ofgas.gov.uk

German Embassy
23 Belgrave Square, London SW1X 8PZ
tel 0171-824 1300 *fax* 0171-824 1435
e-mail mail@german-embassy.org.uk
web site http://www.german-embassy.org.uk

Ghana High Commission
13 Belgrave Square, London SW1X 8PN
tel 0171-235 4142-5 *fax* 0171-245 9552

Government Offices for the Regions
1st Floor, Eland House, Bressenden Place,
London SW1E 5DU
tel 0171-890 5157 *fax* 0171-890 5019
Combination of the former regional offices
of the Depts of the Environment, Trade
and Industry, Education and Employment,
and Transport. Established April 1994.

Greece, Embassy of
Press and Information Office, 1A Holland Park,
London W11 3TP
tel 0171-727 3071 *fax* 0171-727 8960

Guyana High Commission
3 Palace Court, Bayswater Road, London W2 4LP
tel 0171-229 7684 *fax* 0171-727 9809

Hayward Gallery
Belvedere Road, London SE1 8XZ
tel 0171-928 3144 *fax* 0171-401 2664
web site http://www.hayward-gallery.org.uk

Health, Department of
Richmond House, 79 Whitehall,
London SW1A 2NS
tel 0171-210 3000
web site http://www.open.gov.uk/doh.dhhome.htm

Health and Safety Executive
Rose Court, 2 Southwark Bridge,
London SE1 9HS
tel (0541) 545500 *fax* 0114-289 2333
web site http://www.open.gov.uk/hse/hsehome.htm

Historic Scotland
Longmore House, Salisbury Place,
Edinburgh EH9 1SH
tel 0131-668 8600 *fax* 0131-668 8699

HMSO Books – see The Stationery Office

Home Office
Queen Anne's Gate, London SW1H 9AT
tel 0171-273 4000
*Head of Profession, Government Information and
Communication Service* M.S.D. Granatt

Housing Corporation
149 Tottenham Court Road, London W1P 0BN
tel 0171-393 2000 *fax* 0171-393 2111

Hungary, Embassy of the Republic of
35 Eaton Place, London SW1X 8BY
tel 0171-235 5218 *fax* 0171-823 1348

Independent Television Commission
33 Foley Street, London W1P 7LB
tel 0171-255 3000 *fax* 0171-306 7800

High Commission of India, Press & Information Wing
India House, Aldwych, London WC2B 4NA
tel 0171-836 8484 ext 147, 286, 327
fax 0171-836 2632
e-mail 106167.1470@compuserve.com

Inland Revenue, Board of
Somerset House, London WC2R 1LB
Library tel 0171-438 6648 *fax* 0171-438 7562

International Services (InS) – see Social Security, Department of

Ireland, Embassy of
17 Grosvenor Place, London SW1X 7HR
tel 0171-235 2171 *fax* 0171-245 6961

Israel, Embassy of
2 Palace Green, London W8 4QB
tel 0171-957 9500 *fax* 0171-957 9555
e-mail isr-info@dircon.co.uk
web site http://www.israel-embassy.org.uk/london/

Italian Embassy
14 Three Kings Yard, Davies Street,
London W1Y 2EH
tel 0171-312 2200 *fax* 0171-312 2230

Jamaican High Commission
1-2 Prince Consort Road, London SW7 2BZ
tel 0171-823 9911 *fax* 0171-589 5154

Japan, Embassy of
101-104 Piccadilly, London W1V 9FN
tel 0171-465 6500 *fax* 0171-491 9347 (information)
0171-491 9348 (other departments)
e-mail jicc@jicc.demon.co.uk
web site http://www.embjapan.org.uk

Kenya High Commission
45 Portland Place, London W1N 4AS
tel 0171-636 2371 *fax* 0171-323 6717

HM Land Registry

Lincoln's Inn Fields, London WC2A 3PH
tel 0171-917 8888 *fax* 0171-955 0110
web site http://www.open.gov.uk/landreg/home.htm
Head of Information Eric Davies

Law Commission

Conquest House, 37-38 John Street,
Theobalds Road, London WC1N 2BQ
tel 0171-453 1220 *fax* 0171-453 1297
e-mail secretary.lawcomm@gtnet.gov.uk
web site http://www.open.gov.uk/lawcomm/
Covers England and Wales.

The Legal Deposit Office

The British Library, Boston Spa, Wetherby,
West Yorkshire LS23 7BY
tel (01937) 546267/546268 *fax* (01937) 546176

Legal Services Ombudsman, Office of the

22 Oxford Court, Oxford Street,
Manchester M2 3WQ
tel 0161-236 9532 *fax* 0161-236 2651

Lesotho, High Commission of the Kingdom of

7 Chesham Place, London SW1 8HN
tel 0171-235 5686 *fax* 0171-235 5023
e-mail lesotholondonhighcom@compuserve.com

London Museum – see Museum of London

London Records Office, Corporation of

Guildhall, London EC2P 2EJ
tel 0171-332 1251 *fax* 0171-332 1119

London Transport

55 Broadway, London SW1H 0BD
tel 0171-222 5600 (administration) 0171-222 1234
(travel information) *fax* 0171-222 5719

Luxembourg, Embassy of

27 Wilton Crescent, London SW1X 8SD
tel 0171-235 6961 *fax* 0171-235 9734

Malawi High Commission

33 Grosvenor Street, London W1X 0DE
tel 0171-491 4172/7 *fax* 0171-491 9916

Malaysian High Commission

45 Belgrave Square, London SW1X 8QT
tel 0171-235 8033 *fax* 0171-235 5161

Malta High Commission

Malta House, 36-38 Piccadilly, London W1V 0PQ
tel 0171-292 4800 *fax* 0171-734 1831

Mauritius, High Commission for the Republic of

32-33 Elvaston Place, London SW7 5NW
tel 0171-581 0294/5 *fax* 0171-823 8437
tel 0171-225 3331 *fax* 0171-225 1580 (commercial)
tel 0171-584 3666 *fax* 0171-823 8437 (tourist)

Medical Research Council

20 Park Crescent, London W1N 4AL
tel 0171-636 5422 *fax* 0171-436 6179
e-mail firstname.surname@headoffice.mrc.ac.uk
web site http://www.mrc.ac.uk

Millennium Commission

Portland House, Stag Place, London SW1E 5EZ
tel 0171-880 2001 *fax* 0171-880 2000
web site http://www.millennium.gov.uk

Monopolies and Mergers Commission

New Court, 48 Carey Street, London WC2A 2JT
tel 0171-324 1467/8 *fax* 0171-324 1400
e-mail MMC@gtnet.gov.uk
web site http://www.open.gov.uk/mmc

Museum of London

London Wall, London EC2Y 5HN
tel 0171-600 3699 *fax* 0171-600 1058
e-mail info@museum-london.org.uk
web site http://www.museum-london.org.uk
Tells the story of London from prehistoric times to the present day.

Museum of the Moving Image

South Bank, London SE1 8XT
tel 0171-928 3535 *fax* 0171-815 1419

National Audit Office

157-197 Buckingham Palace Road,
London SW1W 9SP
tel 0171-798 7000 *fax* 0171-828 3774
e-mail nao@gtnet.gov.uk
22 Melville Street, Edinburgh EH3 7NS
tel 0131-244 2736 *fax* 0131-244 2721
Audit House, 23-24 Park Place,
Cardiff CF1 3BA
tel (01222) 378661 *fax* (01222) 388415
Provides independent information, advice and assurance to Parliament and the public about all aspects of the financial operations of government departments and many other bodies receiving public funds.

National Consumer Council

20 Grosvenor Gardens, London SW1W 0DH
tel 0171-730 3469 *fax* 0171-730 0191
e-mail admin@ncc.org.uk

National Gallery

Trafalgar Square, London WC2N 5DN
tel 0171-839 3321, 0171-747 2885 (general
information) *Press Office* fax 0171-930 4764
e-mail information@ng-London.org.uk
web site http://www.nationalgallery.org.uk

National Lottery, Office of the (OFLOT)

2 Monck Street, London SW1P 2BQ
tel 0171-227 2000 *fax* 0171-227 2005
e-mail pau_oflot@compuserve.com

National Maritime Museum
Greenwich, London SE10 9NF
tel 0181-858 4422 *fax* 0181-312 6632
Information also for the Queen's House and the Old Royal Observatory.

National Savings
Commerical Directorate, Charles House,
375 Kensington High Street, London W14 8SD
tel 0171-605 9300 *fax* 0171-605 9432/9481
web site http://www.nationalsavings.co.uk

National Statistics, Office for
1 Drummond Gate, London SW1V 2QQ
tel 0171-533 5725 (economic statistics); 0171-533 5702 (social statistics) *fax* 0171-533 5719

Natural Environment Research Council
Polaris House, North Star Avenue, Swindon, Wilts. SN2 1EU
tel (01793) 411500 *fax* (01793) 411501
e-mail nerccomm@wpo.nerc.ac.uk
web site http://www.nerc.ac.uk

The Natural History Museum
Cromwell Road, London SW7 5BD
tel 0171-938 9123 *fax* 0171-938 9290

Royal Netherlands Embassy
38 Hyde Park Gate, London SW7 5DP
tel 0171-590 3200
Press and Cultural Affairs fax 0171-581 0053

New Zealand High Commission
New Zealand House, Haymarket,
London SW1Y 4TQ
tel 0171-930 8422 *fax* 0171-839 4580

Nigeria High Commission
Nigeria House, 9 Northumberland Avenue,
London WC2N 5BX
tel 0171-839 1244 *fax* 0171-839 8746

Northern Ireland Office
1 Millbank, London SW1P 4QE
tel 0171-210 3000
Stormont Castle, Belfast BT4 3ST
tel (01232) 520700
web site http://www.nio.gov.uk/index.htm

Northern Ireland Tourist Board
59 North Street, Belfast, Northern Ireland BT1 1NB
tel (01232) 231221 *fax* (01232) 240960
e-mail general.enquiries.nitb@nics.gov.uk

Royal Norwegian Embassy
25 Belgrave Square, London SW1X 8QD
tel 0171-591 5500 *fax* 0171-245 6993
e-mail embassy@embassy.norway.org.uk
web site http://www.norway.org.uk/

Oftel – see Telecommunications, Office of

OFWAT – see Water Services, Office of

Ordnance Survey
Romsey Road, Maybush, Southampton SO16 4GU
tel (01703) 792000 *fax* (01703) 792452
Press Officer tel (01703) 792635
e-mail custinfo@ordsvy.gov.uk
web site http://www.ordsvy.gov.uk/

Particle Physics and Astronomy Research Council (PPARC)
Polaris House, North Star Avenue, Swindon, Wilts. SN2 1SZ
tel (01793) 442000 *fax* (01793) 442002
e-mail pr_pus@pparc.ac.uk
web site http://www.pparc.ac.uk
PPARC supports research, education and fellowships, industry and public understanding in the areas of particle physics, astronomy and space science. PPARC provides its researchers with access to world class facilities, and funds the UK membership of international bodies such as the European Particle Physics Laboratory, the European Organisation for Nuclear Research (CERN), and the European Space Agency.

Patent Office
General enquiries (designs, patents, trade marks)
Concept House, Cardiff Road, Newport,
South Wales NP9 1RH
tel (0645) 500505 *text phone* (0645) 222250
e-mail enquiries@patent.gov.uk
Copyright enquiries Copyright Directorate, The Patent Office, Room 150, 25 Southampton Buildings, Chancery Lane, London WC2A 1AY
tel 0171-438 4777 *fax* 0171-438 4780
text phone (0645) 222250
e-mail copyright@patent.gov.uk

Pensions Ombudsman, The
11 Belgrave Road, London SW1V 1RB
tel 0171-834 9144 *fax* 0171-821 0065

Pensions and Overseas Benefits Directorate (POD) – see Social Security, Department of

PLR Office
Bayheath House, Prince Regent Street,
Stockton-on-Tees TS18 1DF
tel (01642) 604699 *fax* (01642) 615641
e-mail registrar@plr.octacon.co.uk
web site http://www.earl.org.uk/partners/plr/index.html
Enquiries Registrar of Public Lending Right

Poland, Embassy of the Republic of
47 Portland Place, London W1N 4JH
tel 0171-580 4324 *fax* 0171-323 4018
e-mail pol-emb@dircon.co.uk
web site http://www.poland-embassy.org.uk/

Polish Cultural Institute
34 Portland Place, London W1N 4HQ
tel 0171-636 6032 *fax* 0171-637 2190
e-mail PCI-LOND@pcidiv.demon.co.uk

Police Complaints Authority
10 Great George Street, London SW1P 3AE
tel 0171-273 6450 *fax* 0171-273 6401
web site http://www.coi.gov.uk/coi/depts/
deptlist.html

Population Census and Surveys, Office of – now Office for National Statistics

Portuguese Embassy
11 Belgrave Square, London SW1X 8PP
tel 0171-235 5331 *fax* 0171-245 1287 and
0171-235 0739
e-mail Portembassy-London@dialin.net

Post Office Headquarters
5th Floor, 148 Old Street, London EC1V 9HQ
tel 0171-490 2888

Privy Council Office
Whitehall, London SW1A 2AT
tel 0171-270 3000

Public Record Office
Ruskin Avenue, Kew, Richmond, Surrey TW9 4DU
tel 0181-876 3444 *fax* 0181-878 8905
Records of Government Departments and central courts of law.

Public Service, Office of (OPS)
Horse Guards Road, London SW1P 3AL
70 Whitehall, London SW1A 2AS
tel 0171-270 1234

Public Trust Office
Stewart House, 24 Kingsway, London WC2B 6JX
tel 0171-664 7000 *fax* 0171-664 7705

Qualifications and Curriculum Authority (QCA)
Newcombe House, 45 Notting Hill Gate, London W11 3JB
tel 0171-229 1234 *fax* 0171-221 2368
Chairman Sir William Stubbs, *Deputy Chairman* Sir Dominic Cadbury, *Chief Executive* Dr Nicholas Tate
QCA brings together the work of the National Council for Vocational Qualifications (NCVQ) and the School Curriculum and Assessment Authority (SCAA) with additional powers and duties. Its prime duty is to advise the Secretary of State for Education and Employment on all matters affecting the school curriculum, pupil assessment and publicly funded qualifications offered in schools, colleges and workplaces.

Racial Equality, Commission for
Elliot House, 10-12 Allington Street, London SW1E 5EH
tel 0171-828 7022 *fax* 0171-630 7605

The Radio Authority
Holbrook House, 14 Great Queen Street, London WC2B 5DG
tel 0171-430 2724 *fax* 0171-405 7062

Regional Arts Boards – see English Regional Arts Boards

Romania, Embassy of
4 Palace Green, London W8 4QD
tel 0171-937 9666 *fax* 0171-937 8069
e-mail romania@roemb.demon.uk.co

Royal Commission on the Ancient and Historical Monuments of Scotland
(with National Monuments Record of Scotland)
John Sinclair House, 16 Bernard Terrace, Edinburgh EH8 9NX
tel 0131-662 1456 *fax* 0131-662 1477/1499
e-mail postmaster@rcahms.gov.uk

Royal Commission on the Ancient and Historical Monuments of Wales
(with National Monuments Record of Wales)
Crown Building, Plas Crug, Aberystwyth, Ceredigion SY23 1NJ
tel (01970) 621200 *fax* (01970) 627701

Royal Commission on Historical Manuscripts
Quality House, Quality Court, Chancery Lane, London WC2A 1HP
tel 0171-242 1198 *fax* 0171-831 3550
e-mail nra@hmc.gov.uk
web site http://www.hmc.gov.uk

Royal Commission on the Historical Monuments of England
(with National Monuments Record)
National Monuments Record Centre, Kemble Drive, Swindon, Wilts. SN2 2GZ
tel (01793) 414700 *fax* (01793) 414707
e-mail info@rchme.gov.uk
web site http://www.rchme.gov.uk

Royal Fine Art Commission
7 St James's Square, London SW1Y 4JU
tel 0171-839 6537 *fax* 0171-839 8475
e-mail rfacscot@gtnet.gov.uk

Royal Fine Art Commission for Scotland
Bakehouse Close, 146 Canongate, Edinburgh EH8 8DD
tel 0131-556 6699 *fax* 0131-556 6633
e-mail rfacscot@gtnet.co.uk

Royal Mint
Llantrisant, Pontyclun,
Mid-Glamorgan CF72 8YT
tel (01443) 222111

Royal National Theatre Board
South Bank, London SE1 9PX
tel 0171-452 3388 *fax* 0171-452 3380
Chairman Christopher Hogg

Russian Federation, Embassy of the
6-7 Kensington Palace Gardens,
London W8 4QP
tel 0171-229 3628, 0171-229 6412
fax 0171-727 8625

Science and Technology, Office of
Department of Trade and Industry, Albany House,
Petty France, London SW1H 9ST
tel 0171-271 2000

Science Museum
Exhibition Road, London SW7 2DD
tel 0171-938 8000
Information Desk tel 0171-938 8080/8008
Press Office tel 0171-938 8188/8181
fax 0171-938 9790
web site http://www.nmsi.ac.uk

Scotland, National Galleries of
National Gallery of Scotland
The Mound, Edinburgh EH2 2EL
Scottish National Portrait Gallery
1 Queen Street, Edinburgh EH2 1JD
Scottish National Gallery of Modern Art
Belford Road, Edinburgh EH4 3DR
tel 0131-624 6200, 0131-624 6332 (press office)
fax 0131-343 3250 (press office)

Scotland, National Library of
George IV Bridge, Edinburgh EH1 1EW
tel 0131-226 4531 *fax* 0131-220 6662
e-mail enquiries@nls.uk
web site http://www.nls.uk

Scottish Arts Council
12 Manor Place, Edinburgh EH3 7DD
tel 0131-226 6051 *fax* 0131-225 9833
e-mail administrator.SAC@artsfb.org.uk
web site http://www.sac.org.uk

Scottish Law Commission
140 Causewayside, Edinburgh EH9 1PR
tel 0131-668 2131 *fax* 0131-662 4900

Scottish Natural Heritage
12 Hope Terrace, Edinburgh EH9 2AS
tel 0131-447 4784 *Press Office tel* 0131-446 2279
e-mail administrator.sac@artsfb.org.uk
web site http://www.sac.org.uk

The Scottish Office
Dover House, Whitehall, London SW1A 2AU
tel 0171-270 3000

The Scottish Office Information Directorate
St Andrew's House, Edinburgh EH1 1DG
tel 0131-244 1111
Dover House, Whitehall, London SW1A 2AU
tel 0171-270 6744
web site http://www.scotland.gov.uk

Scottish Record Office
HM General Register House, Edinburgh EH1 3YY
tel 0131-535 1314 *fax* 0131-535 1360

Scottish Tourist Board
Thistle House, Beechwood Park North,
Inverness IV2 3ED
tel (01463) 716996 *fax* (01463) 717299

The Security Service (MI5)
PO Box 3255, London SW1P 1AE

Serpentine Gallery
Kensington Gardens, London W2 3XA
tel 0171-402 6075 *fax* 0171-402 4103
Public information 0171-298 1515
International exhibitions of modern and
contemporary art.

Seychelles High Commission
2nd Floor, Eros House, 111 Baker Street,
London W1M 1FE
tel 0171-224 1660 *fax* 0171-487 5756

Sierra Leone High Commission
33 Portland Place, London W1N 3AG
tel 0171-636 6483-5 *fax* 0171-323 3159

Singapore High Commission
9 Wilton Crescent, London SW1X 8RW
tel 0171-235 8315 *fax* 0171-245 6583

Slovak Republic, Embassy of the
25 Kensington Palace Gardens, London W8 4QY
tel 0171-243 0803 *fax* 0171-727 5824
web site http://slovakia.net

Slovenia, Embassy of
Suite One, Cavendish Court,
11-15 Wigmore Street, London W1H 9LA
tel 0171-495 7775 *fax* 0171-495 7776

Social Security, Department of
POD at DSS, Benefits Agency, Tyneview Park,
Newcastle Upon Tyne NE98 1BA
tel 0191-218 7777 *fax* 0191-218 7293
e-mail podcustcareba.
web site http://www.dss.gov.uk/ba
InS at DSS, Contributions Agency, Longbenton,
Newcastle Upon Tyne NE98 1BA
tel (0645) 154 811 *fax* (0645) 157 800
e-mail a.moy@new040.dss.gov.uk
web site http://www.dss.gov.uk/ca
Contact Benefits Agency, Pensions and
Overseas Benefits Directorate (POD) for

queries about benefits being paid abroad, and Contributions Agency, International Services (InS) for queries about working abroad and paying National Insurance contributions.

South Africa, Republic of
South African High Commission, South Africa House, Trafalgar Square, London WC2N 5DP
tel 0171-451 7299 *fax* 0171-451 7283/7284

Spanish Embassy
39 Chesham Place, London SW1X 8SB
tel 0171-235 5555 *fax* 0171-259 5392

Sri Lanka, High Commission of the Democratic Socialist Republic of
13 Hyde Park Gardens, London W2 2LU
tel 0171-262 1841 *fax* 0171-262 7970

Standards in Education, Office for (OFSTED)
Alexandra House, 33 Kingsway, London WC2B 6SE
tel 0171-421 6800 *fax* 0171-421 6707

The Stationery Office
St Crispins, Duke Street, Norwich NR3 1PD
tel 0171-873 0011 (publication enquiries)

Swaziland High Commission
20 Buckingham Gate, London SW1E 6LB
tel 0171-630 6611 *fax* 0171-630 6564

Sweden, Embassy of
11 Montagu Place, London W1H 2AL
tel 0171-917 6400 *fax* 0171-724 4174
Cultural Section fax 0171-917 6477

Swiss Embassy Cultural Attaché
16-18 Montagu Place, London W1H 2BQ
tel 0171-616 6000 *fax* 0171-724 7001

Tanzania High Commission
43 Hertford Street, London W1Y 8DB
tel 0171-499 8951 *fax* 0171-491 9321
e-mail Balozi@tanzarep.demon.co.uk
web site http://www.tanzania-online.gov.uk

Tate Gallery
Millbank, London SW1P 4RG
tel 0171-887 8000 *fax* 0171-887 8007
Albert Dock, Liverpool L3 4BB
tel 0151-709 3223
Porthmeor Beach, St Ives, Cornwall TR26 1TG
tel (01736) 796226

Telecommunications, Office of
50 Ludgate Hill, London EC4M 7JJ
tel 0171-634 8700 *fax* 0171-634 8946
e-mail infocent.oftel@gtnet.gov.uk
web site http://www.oftel.gov.uk

Theatre Museum
National Museum of the Performing Arts, 1E Tavistock Street, London WC2E 7PA
tel 0171-836 7891 *fax* 0171-836 5148
See page 438 for reprographic services.

Transport, Department of – see Environment, Transport and the Regions, Department of

HM Treasury
Parliament Street, London SW1P 3AG
tel 0171-270 5000
Press Office tel 0171-270 5238 *fax* 0171-270 5244
Public Enquiry Unit tel 0171-270 4860

Trinidad and Tobago High Commission
42 Belgrave Square, London SW1X 8NT
tel 0171-245 9351 *fax* 0171-823 1065
e-mail trintogov@tthc.demon.co.uk

Trinity House, Corporation of
Tower Hill, London EC3N 4DH
tel 0171-480 6601 *fax* 0171-480 7662
The General Lighthouse Authority for England, Wales and the Channel Islands, a charitable organisation for the welfare and training of mariners and a Deep Sea Pilotage Authority.

Turkish Embassy
43 Belgrave Square, London SW1X 8PA
tel 0171-393 0202 *fax* 0171-393 0066
e-mail turkish.embassy@virgin.net

Uganda High Commission
Uganda House, 58-59 Trafalgar Square, London WC2N 5DX
tel 0171-839 5783 *fax* 0171-839 8925

United States Embassy
24 Grosvenor Square, London W1A 1AE
tel 0171-499 9000
web site http://www.usembassy.org.uk

Victoria and Albert Museum
South Kensington, London SW7 2RL
tel 0171-938 8500 *fax* 0171-938 8379
web site http://www.vam.ac.uk

Visiting Arts
11 Portland Place, London W1N 4EJ
tel 0171-389 3015 *fax* 0171-389 3016
e-mail office@visitingarts.demon.co.uk
web site http://www.britcoun.org/visitingarts/
Director T. Sandell

Vocational Qualifications, National Council for (NCVQ) – see Qualifications and Curriculum Authority (QCA)

Wales, The National Library of
Aberystwyth, Ceredigion SY23 3BU
e-mail holi@llgc.org.uk
web site http://www.llgc.org.uk

Wales Tourist Board
Brunel House, 2 Fitzalan Road, Cardiff CF2 1UY
tel (01222) 499909 *fax* (01222) 485031
e-mail info@tourism.wales.gov.uk
web site http://www.visitwales.com

Water Services, Office of (OFWAT)
Centre City Tower, 7 Hill Street,
Birmingham B5 4UA
tel 0121-625 1300 *fax* 0121-625 1400
web site http://www.open.gov.uk/ofwat

Wellington Museum
Apsley House, 149 Piccadilly, London W1V 9FA
tel 0171-499 5676 *fax* 0171-493 6576
web site http://www.vam.ac.uk/apsley/welcome.html
Open Tues-Sun, 11.00am-17.00pm.

Welsh Office
Gwydir House, Whitehall, London SW1A 2ER
tel 0171-270 0565 *fax* 0171-270 0577
Cathays Park, Cardiff, CF1 3NQ
tel (01222) 825111 *fax* (01222) 823807

West India Committee (The Caribbean)
Nelson House, 8-9 Northumberland Street,
London WC2N 5RA

tel 0171-976 1493 *fax* 0171-976 1541
e-mail caribbean@compuserve.com

Women's National Commission
6th Floor, Adelphi, 1-11 John Adam Street,
London WC2N 6HT
tel 0171-712 2443, 0121-626 2018 (media
enquiries) *fax* 0171-962 8171, 0121-626 2041
(media enquiries)
web site http://www.thewnc.org.uk
An independent advisory committee to
the Government with the remit to ensure
that the informed opinions of women are
given their due weight in the delibera-
tions of the Government.

**Yugoslavia, Embassy of the Federal
Republic of**
5-7 Lexham Gardens, London W8 5JJ
tel 0171-370 6105 *fax* 0171-370 3838

Zambia High Commission
2 Palace Gate, London W8 5NG
tel 0171-589 6655 *fax* 0171-581 1353

**Zimbabwe, High Commission of the
Republic of**
Zimbabwe House, 429 Strand, London WC2R 0SA
tel 0171-836 7755 *fax* 0171-379 1167

Publishing practice

Publishing agreements

Publisher's agreements are not a standard form. Before signing one, the author must check it carefully, taking nothing for granted. **Michael Legat** *navigates the reader through this complex document.*

Any author, presented with so complex a document as a publisher's agreement, should read it carefully before signing, making sure that every clause is understood, and not taking anything for granted. Bear in mind that there is no such thing as a standard form. A given publisher's 'standard' contract may not only differ substantially from those of other publishers, but will often vary from author to author and from book to book. Don't be fooled into believing that it is a standard form because it appears to have been printed – each agreement can be individually produced on a word processor to give exactly that effect.

A fair and reasonable agreement

You should be able to rely on your agent, if you have one, to check the agreement for you, or – if you are a member – you can get it vetted by the Society of Authors or the Writers' Guild of Great Britain. But if you are on your own, you must either go to one of the solicitors who specialise in publishing business (probably expensive) or Do It Yourself. In the latter case it will help to compare the contract you have been offered, clause by clause, with a typical Minimum Terms Agreement such as those printed in my own books, *An Author's Guide to Publishing* and *Understanding Publishers' Contracts*.

Minimum Terms Agreement

The Minimum Terms Agreement (MTA), developed jointly by the Society of Authors and the Writers' Guild, is signed by a publisher on the one hand and the Society and the Guild on the other. It is not an agreement between a publisher and an individual author. It commits the publisher to offering his or her authors terms which are at least as good as those in the MTA. The intention is that only members of the Society and Guild should be eligible for this special treatment, but in practice publishers who sign the agreement tend to offer its terms to all their authors. There is no standard MTA, and most signatory publishers have insisted on certain variations in the agreement; nevertheless, the more important basic principles have always been accepted. It must be pointed out that the MTA does not usually apply to:
• books in which illustrations take up 40% or more of the space;
• specialist works on the visual arts in which illustrations fill 25% or more of the space;
• books involving three or more participants in royalties; or
• technical books, manuals and reference books.

Since its origins in 1980, comparatively few publishers have signed a Minimum Terms Agreement, although the signatories include several major publishing houses. Some publishers have refused, claiming to treat their authors quite well enough already, while others say that each author and each book is so different that standard terms cannot be laid down. Nonetheless, the MTA has been a resounding success. Almost all non-signatory publishers have adopted some or all of its provisions, and even in the case of the excluded books mentioned above, the terms have tended to improve. All authors can now argue, from a position of some strength, that their own agreements should meet the MTA's standards.

The provisions of the MTA

The MTA is a royalty agreement (usually the most satisfactory form for an author), and it lays down the minimum acceptable royalties on sales, and the levels at which the rate should rise. These royalties are expressed as percentages of the book's retail price but can easily be adjusted to apply to royalties based on price received, a system to which a number of publishers are changing, increasing the percentages so that the author's earnings are not adversely affected. The MTA also covers the size of the advance (calculated in accordance with the expected initial print quantity and retail price), and recommended splits between publisher and author of moneys from the sale of subsidiary rights (including US and translation rights).

However, the MTA is not by any means concerned solely with money, but with fairness to the author in all clauses of a publishing agreement, special attention being paid to provisions designed to make the author/publisher relationship more of a partnership than it has often been in the past. While recognising the publisher's right to take final decisions on such matters as print quantity, publication date, retail price, jacket or cover design, wording of the blurb, promotion and publicity, and remaindering, the MTA insists that the author has a right to consultation (which should not be an empty formality but should mean that serious consideration is given to his or her views), in all such cases. Also the author's approval must be sought for the sale of any subsidiary rights.

Some essential clauses

Any publisher's agreement you sign should contain, in addition to acceptable financial terms, clauses covering:

• **Rights licensed.** A clear definition of which rights you are licensing to the publisher. The publisher will normally require volume rights but the agreement must specify whether such rights will apply in all languages (or perhaps only in English) and throughout the world (or only in an agreed list of territories). The duration of the publisher's licence should be spelt out; commonly this is for the period of copyright (currently the author's lifetime plus 70 years), although some publishers now accept a shorter term. A list of those subsidiary rights of which control is granted to the publisher must be included (make sure that the splits of moneys earned from these rights are in accordance with, or approximate reasonably to, those in the MTA, especially in the currently growing area of merchandising). Because the development of non-traditional forms of publishing, such as the Internet, continues to be so rapid, it may be advisable for the author not to grant the publisher control of electronic and multimedia rights, or of any additional rights as yet unknown resulting from advances in technology, but to reserve them, allowing the split of income from such sources to be negotiated as and when their sale occurs.

• **Publication date.** Commitment by the publisher to publication of the book by a specific date (usually within a year or 18 months from the delivery of the typescript). Avoid signing an agreement which is vague on this point, saying, for instance, only that the book will be published 'within a reasonable period'.

• **Copyright.** Confirmation that in all copies of the book the publisher will print a copyright notice in the author's name and a statement that the author has asserted his or her 'Right of Paternity' (the right to be identified as the author in future exploitation of the material in any form), and that a similar commitment will be required from any subsidiary licensee.

• **Fees and permissions.** Clarification, if the book is to include a professionally prepared index or material the copyright of which does not belong to the author, of whether the author or the publisher will be responsible for the fees (or if costs are to be shared, in what proportions) and the clearance of permissions.

• **Acceptable accounting procedures.** Most publishers divide the year into two six-month periods, accounting to the author, and paying any sums due, three months after the end of each period. Look askance at any less frequent accounting or longer delay after the royalty period. The publisher should also agree to pay the author the due share of any subsidiary moneys promptly on receipt, provided that the advance on the book has been earned.

• **Termination.** A clear definition of the various conditions under which the agreement shall be terminated, with reversion of rights to the author.

Clauses to question

You can question anything in a publisher's agreement before you sign it. Provided that you do so politely and are not just being difficult, the publisher should be prepared to answer every query, to explain, and where possible to meet your objections. Most publishing contracts are not designed to exploit the author unfairly, but you should watch out for:

• **Rights assigned elsewhere.** It is unwise to accept a clause which allows the publisher to assign the rights in your book to another firm or person without your approval.

• **Non-publication.** The contract for a commissioned book often includes wording which alludes to the publisher's acceptance of the work, implying that there is no obligation to publish it if he or she deems it unacceptable. It may be understandable that the publisher wants an escape route in case the author turns in an inferior work, but he or she should be obliged to justify the rejection, and to give the author an opportunity to revise the work to bring it up to standard. If, having accepted the book, the publisher then wishes to cancel the contract prior to publication, the author can usually expect to receive financial compensation, which should be non-returnable even if the book is subsequently placed with another publisher. However, this point is not normally covered in a publishing agreement.

• **Sole publisher.** Some agreements prohibit the author from writing similar material for any other publisher. This may clearly affect the author's earning ability.

• **Editing consultation.** Don't agree to the publisher's right to edit your work without any requirement for him or her to obtain your approval of any changes made.

• **Royalty rate.** While it is normal practice for an agreement to allow the publisher to pay a lower royalty on books which are sold at high trade discounts, such sales are more frequently made nowadays than in the past, and you should therefore make sure the royalty rate on high discount sales is not unfairly low.

• **Future books.** The Society of Authors and the Writers' Guild are both generally opposed to clauses giving the publisher the right to publish the author's next work, feeling that this privilege should be earned by the publisher's handling of the earlier book. If you accept an option clause, at least make sure that it leaves all terms for a future book to be agreed.

Joint and multiple authorship

In the case of joint authorship (a work so written that the individual contributions of the authors cannot be readily separated), the first written agreement should be between the authors themselves, setting out the proportions in which any moneys earned by the book will be split, specifying how the authors' responsibilities are to be shared, and especially laying down the procedure to be adopted should the authors ever find themselves in dispute. The terms of any publishing agreement which they sign (each author having an identical copy) should reflect their joint understanding. The total earnings should not be less than would be paid were the book by a single author, and the authors should have normal rights of consultation.

In the case of multiple authorship (when the work of each contributor can be clearly separated), each author is likely to have an individual contract, and may not be aware of what terms are offered to the others involved. Because of the possibility of disagreement between the authors, the publisher will probably offer little in the way of consultation. All the individual author can do is to ensure that the agreement appears to be fair in relation to the amount of work contributed, and that the author's responsibilities indicated by the contract refer only to his or her work.

Outright sale

As a general rule no author should agree to surrender his or her copyright to the publisher, although this may be unavoidable in the case of a book with many contributors, such as an encyclopedia. Even then, give up your copyright with great reluctance and only after an adequate explanation from the publisher of why you should (and probably a substantial financial inducement, including, if possible, provision for the payment of a further fee each time the book is reprinted). The agreement itself will probably be no more than a brief and unequivocal letter.

Further reading

Clark, Charles (ed.), *Publishing Agreements: A Book of Precedents*, Butterworths, 5th edn, 1997

Flint, Michael F., *A User's Guide to Copyright*, Butterworths, 4th edn, 1997

Legat, Michael, *An Authors' Guide to Publishing*, Robert Hale, 3rd edn revised, 1998

Subsidies and vanity publishing

Few commercial publishers will be interested in publishing your book on a subsidy basis (i.e. with a contribution from you towards costs), unless perhaps it is of a serious, highly specialised nature, such as an academic monograph, when a publisher who is well established within that particular field will certainly behave with probity and offer a fair contract. Vanity publishers, on the other hand, will accept your book with enthusiasm, ask for 'a small contribution to production costs' (which turns out to be a very substantial sum, not a penny of which you are likely to see again), and will fail to achieve any sales for your book apart from the copies which you yourself buy. If you want to put your own money into the publication of your book, try self-publishing (see page 266) – you will be far better off than going to a vanity house. How do you tell which are the vanity publishers? That's easy – they're the ones who put advertisements in the papers saying things like, 'Authors Wanted!'. Regular publishers don't need to do that.

Michael Legat became a full-time writer after a long and successful publishing career. He is the author of a number of highly regarded books on publishing and writing.

Legat, Michael, *Understanding Publishers' Contracts*, Robert Hale, 1992

Unwin, Sir Stanley, *The Truth About Publishing*, Unwin Hyman, 8th edn, 1976, o.p. (An edition is available from the US publishers Lyons & Burford)

International Standard Book Numbering (ISBN)

The Standard Book Numbering (SBN) system was introduced in this country in 1967. Three years later, it became the International Standard Book Numbering (ISBN) system. The Standard Book Numbering Agency receives a large number of telephone calls, many of which follow a common pattern. The most common questions asked about ISBNs are answered here.

Who administers Isbns?

The overall administration of the international system is done from Berlin by the International ISBN-Agentur. In the UK the system is administered by the Standard Book Numbering Agency Ltd in London, which was set up before the scheme became international – hence that word does not appear in its title.

Are they legal? Do we have to have them?

There is no legal requirement for a book to carry an ISBN. But it is useful to educational authorities, certain library suppliers, public libraries and distributors which use computers, and is now essential to booksellers using the teleordering system. The introduction of Public Lending Right has also made ISBNs of importance to authors.

I am about to publish a book. Must I deposit a copy with the ISBN Agency to obtain copyright?

No. Copyright is obtained by the simple act of publication. However, by law, a copy of every new book must be deposited at the Legal Deposit Office of the British Library, Boston Spa, Wetherby, West Yorkshire LS23 7BY. The Legal Deposit Office issues a receipt, and this has, in the past, proved useful when a dispute has arisen over the date of publication.

Titles deposited are catalogued by the British National Bibliography, which records ISBNs where available. Perhaps a confusion about copyright and ISBNs arises from this, but the ISBN, of itself, has nothing to do with copyright.

What are the fees for ISBNs?

No charge is made for the allocation of a publisher prefix. Publishers may ask the Agency to supply a computer printout of all the ISBNs available to the publisher, with check digits calculated. A small charge is made for this printout.

Are you a government department?

No. Our parent company pays taxes; we get no subsidy from anyone. In most other countries the costs are borne by the state, through the national library system which frequently administers the scheme overseas.

Do I need an ISBN for a church magazine?

No. But you may need an ISSN (International Standard Serial Number), obtainable from the UK National Serials Data Centre. Incidentally, a yearbook can have both an ISBN and an ISSN.

Should we have our own identifier? We do not consider ourselves within the English speaking group.

This comes from publishers with devolution in mind. Usually Welsh, less often Irish. The group system within the ISBN scheme is not quite so categoric as to be dictated by language considerations only.

A group is defined as a 'language, geographic or other convenient area'. There is no strict logic applied, just pragmatism as to what is most convenient for trading purposes.

I want my book to reach as wide a market as possible. Should I have an ISBN?

The ISBN will not automatically sell a book. If the book, like that famous mousetrap, is a better one, the world will beat a path to its door. However, the ISBN will oil the wheels of distribution and it is therefore advisable to have one.

Will you supply an ISBN for a carton of assorted painting books?

No. In the words of the ISBN manual (available from the SBN agency at £9.50, cash with order), 'an ISBN identifies one title, or edition of a title, from one specific publisher, and is unique to that title or edition'. It is now additionally used to identify computer software and maps. It is

not designed for a carton of assorted painting books.

How does a publisher get an ISBN?

If they have not had ISBNs before, publishers should contact the SBN Agency. Written answers are required to some basic questions.

Reproduced by kind permission of the Standard Book Numbering Agency Ltd.

The Authors' Licensing and Collecting Society Ltd

The Authors' Licensing and Collecting Society Ltd (ALCS) is the British collecting society for writers. Its principal purpose is to ensure that hard-to-collect revenues due to authors are efficiently collected and speedily distributed.

The Society currently represents some 35,000 members and associates who are writers, writers' heirs and members of the Society of Authors and the Writers' Guild of Great Britain. Freelance members of the three British journalists' unions, the NUJ the CIOJ and the BAJ, receive free associate membership. Foreign writers are also represented under reciprocal arrangements with overseas collecting societies.

The Society is a non-profit making organisation governed by a Council of Management, all of whom are active writers: four are ALCS members, elected by the ordinary members themselves, and four each are nominated by the Society of Authors and the Writers' Guild of Great Britain.

Powers

On joining, members license the ALCS to administer on their behalf those rights which an author is unable to exercise as an individual or which are best handled on a collective basis. Chief among these are:
• photocopying
• cable retransmission

- lending (but *not* British PLR)
- BBC Prime and BBC World Service
- off-air recording
- electronic rights
- private recording
- rental
- public reception of broadcasts.

Additionally, at its AGM in November 1997, an important amendment was made to the Society's Articles of Association adding the Performing Right to the list of rights covered. This amendment enables ALCS to collect for the public performance of works, for example the live public recitation of poetry in arts centres.

The Society can administer these rights in Great Britain, Northern Ireland and the Irish Republic.

Sources of income/distributions

During the financial year 1997-98 the ALCS collected just under £9 million for distribution. The Society's main sources of income are:

- **Photocopying.** The ALCS, in co-operation with the Publishers' Licensing Society (PLS), established the Copyright Licensing Agency (CLA) to administer licences for photocopying. The ALCS distributes the writers' share of copying fees. (See *The Copyright Licensing Agency Ltd* on page 632.)
- **Foreign Public Lending Right.** The ALCS makes annual distributions from VG WORT, the collecting society in Germany. Further money is held in Germany on behalf of British writers who have not yet joined the ALCS. Those eligible to receive German PLR through the ALCS are living British authors resident anywhere; heirs of British authors through successor membership; foreign writers resident in Britain.
- **Cable retransmission.** The ALCS collects fees for the simultaneous cable retransmission of the UK's terrestrial channels. The Society also distributes fees for BBC World Service programming and BBC Prime, and collects fees from several European countries and Canada for British writers whose work is cabled in neighbouring countries.

- **Educational off-air recording.** The ALCS is part of the Educational Recording Agency Ltd (ERA), which was set up to license educational establishments to record off-air under the provisions of the 1988 Copyright Act. The ALCS distributes the writers' share of recording fees for radio and television. The ALCS also distributes Australian off-air recording fees to British writers.

Allocation of funds

The ALCS has a sophisticated membership, distribution and accounting system and a unique database of literary, film and broadcasting information. However, it is essential that writers register with the Society so that funds can be correctly allocated and payments made speedily.

Policy and aims

In addition to its core activities, the ALCS maintains a watching brief on all matters affecting copyright, both in the UK and abroad, making representations to UK government authorities and the European Union.

The Society is not a union, but it does work to foster a sense of writers' rights and to speak on behalf of groups of writers who do not yet benefit from union or agency

Membership

The Authors' Licensing and Collecting Society Ltd
Marlborough Court, 14-18 Holborn, London EC1N 2LE
tel 0171-395 0600 *fax* 0171-395 0660
e-mail alcs@alcs.co.uk
web site www.alcs.co.uk
The current subscription is £5.88 (inc. VAT), £5.00 for European Economic Area residents, and £7.00 for overseas residents. Members of the Society of Authors and the Writers' Guild have free membership. Freelance members of the three British journalists' unions, the NUJ, the BAJ and the CIJ, have free associate membership.

efforts, particularly in tackling legal issues and those at the technological frontier. It is currently running two special projects:
- **The Higher Education and Academic Libraries Project** aims to provide a voice for the concerns of academic authors in copyright and intellectual property matters. Contact: Siobhan O'Shea (*e-mail* siobhan.oshea@alcs.co.uk).
- **The Journalists' Project** aims to safeguard journalists' copyright interests and maximise their income from re-uses of their work. Contact: Gaynor Burns (*e-mail* g.burns@alcs.co.uk).

The Society is a member of CISAC (International Confederation of Authors and Composers Societies), IFRRO (International Federation of Reprographic Rights Organisations) and many other international rights organisations. It is also represented on the British Copyright Council and the PLR Advisory Committee. The ALCS is a lead partner in the EU-funded Imprimatur Project which aims to provide both the methodology and software tools for a safe electronic copyright trading environment.

The ALCS is increasingly active in the field of electronic rights and is a prime resource and leading authority on matters of copyright, intellectual property and writers' collective rights.

The Copyright Licensing Agency Ltd

In response to the need to regulate copying, the seeds were sown 25 years ago for today's laws on regulating copying from books, journals and periodicals. As a result, The Copyright Licensing Agency (CLA) was formed to oversee 'heavy user' groups.

In 1973, interest groups in the UK started to prepare submissions to the government-appointed committee under the Hon. Mr Justice Whitford about ways of regulating copying from books, journals and periodicals. These interest groups, representing owners of copyright, were seeking both a mechanism of control and just recompense for authors and publishers while at the same time continuing to satisfy the reasonable demands of a modern information-driven society.

The role of the CLA

When it was eventually published in 1977, the Whitford Report on Copyright and Designs Law suggested, as the best likely solution to the problem, a collective administration system for copying rights organised by the rightsholders themselves.

This recommendation spawned first the Wolfenden Committee that brought together representatives of authors' societies and publishers' associations, and then the de Freitas Committee that hammered out and fashioned, with these two sometimes antagonistic groups, a mutually acceptable constitution for such a licensing body. The outcome was the formation of the Copyright Licensing Agency (CLA) in April 1982 and its incorporation in January 1983 as a non-profit making company limited by guarantee. The Agency, which is primarily concerned with licensing 'heavy user' groups, issued its first licence in May 1984.

CLA is 'owned' by the Authors' Licensing and Collecting Society (ALCS) and the Publishers Licensing Society (PLS) in that they are its members. ALCS's members are members of the Society of Authors and the Writers' Guild of Great Britain and several thousand individual members; and PLS's members are the Publishers Association, the Periodical Publishers

Functions of the CLA

The six main functions of the CLA are:
- to obtain mandates from publishers and authors in association with ALCS and PLS;
- to license users for copying extracts from books, journals and periodicals;
- to collect fees from licensed users for such copying;
- to implement a system of record-keeping sufficient to provide statistically acceptable information on which to calculate a fair apportionment of the distributable income;
- to pay ALCS and PLS their correct shares of the distributable income and provide sufficient data to enable these societies to pay individual authors and publishers; and
- to institute such legal proceedings as may be necessary for the enforcement of the rights entrusted to the Agency.

Association and the Association of Learned and Professional Society Publishers. All are represented on CLA's board of 12 directors, six being ALCS nominations and six PLS nominations.

Licence to copy

CLA sees its principal licensing areas in the UK as being education, government and industry. Each of these broad categories has three or four sub-groups. In company with nearly all other Reprographic Rights Organisations (RROs) around the world, CLA started licensing in the general education sector. The first major development was in April 1986, when three-year voluntary licensing agreements with the country's local education authorities (LEAs) came into effect; in April 1989 these licences were extended for a further three years; copying in all 30,000 or so state colleges and schools is now covered by such licences. The Agency also licenses the independent education sector through its licensing scheme for independent schools.

CLA next turned its attention to higher and further education. In 1989 arrangements were finalised whereby universi-

ties, polytechnics, independent colleges and language schools, etc all became licensed for three years from 1 January 1990.

The LEA licences were negotiated with a joint committee of representatives appointed by the Association of County Councils, the Association of Metropolitan Authorities and the Convention of Scottish Local Authorities. A similar committee but expanded to include representatives of the Association of District Councils and the Association of London Authorities is now trying to license the non-LEA parts of local government.

The Agency intends dealing with central government on a ministry by ministry basis, starting with the Department of Trade & Industry as the sponsors of the Copyright, Designs and Patents Act 1988; the Department for Education; and the National Health Service, the largest employer in Europe.

Public bodies, i.e. those organisations for which government ministers have some accountability (e.g. The British Council), may have to be dealt with in some non-collective manner.

Trade, industry, commerce and the professions present CLA with its greatest challenge because of their size and diversity. A first step has already been taken, however, with the setting up of a joint task force with the Confederation of British Industry (CBI). This CBI/CLA working party, chaired by an industrialist, is examining the best way or ways forward, concentrating initially on manufacturing industry, with particular emphasis on R&D-driven sectors such as pharmaceuticals, chemicals, engineering, electronics, aerospace and oil fuel.

A banking role

Basically, CLA is a banking operation with legal overtones: it collects fees from licensed users in respect of acts of photocopying from books and serials and other copying such as microfiche printing and, after deducting its administration costs and any reserves or provisions the Board may decide, distributes the balance to

ALCS and PLS for them to pay to authors and publishers.

CLA currently offers two basic services, i.e., licences to copy authorised by many individual owners of copyright, both of which offer the collective repertoire of copyright works mandated to CLA by those owners:

• **A collective user service** such as that made with the associations representing local education authorities for state colleges and schools.

• **A transactional user service** for those institutions where a suitable representative organisation, such as an LEA, is unable or unwilling to provide the level of administrative support that a collective user scheme requires, e.g. implementation and supervision of a sampling system, single cheque payment, etc.

Both types of licence are valid for a specific period, usually two or three years.

Under a collective user arrangement the level of copying for a group of institutions is mutually agreed and a global fee set; this fee total is then apportioned by the organising body amongst its constituents and paid by them to CLA on presentation of the agency's invoice. With the transactional user scheme, fees are paid on a straight cost per copy-page basis; returns to CLA are made at regular, agreed intervals, and a self-billing system is used.

Who benefits?

The main advantage from the user community's standpoint is that CLA indemnifies all licensees against any inadvertent infringement of copyright.

Right from the outset, the authors' representatives insisted:

• that writers should benefit individually and directly from the copying of their works and that the money should not go to authors' societies for 'social benefit' purposes, as is the case in some parts of the world;

• that the individual authors' shares should be paid to them directly, and not through the accounting systems of their publishers.

Keeping records of copying

In order to fulfil these requirements, CLA had to devise a title-based distribution system and a form of record-keeping suitable for a geographically spread, stratified and statistically sound sample of the licensees. Some form of itemised record-keeping, therefore, is necessary on the part of both categories of licence holders. With collective user licensing, a rotating sample of about 5% of institutions in each broad category is required to maintain records of their copying, which are returned to CLA at agreed intervals, where they are checked and analysed. Transactional user licensees are required to keep records of all their copying.

Controlled record-keeping is crucial to CLA because the statistical information extracted from these records of copying is used as the basis for making payments to copyright owners whose works have been copied.

Once a licence has been issued, it has been relatively simple, so far, to collect fees. It is quite another matter, however, to edit, process and analyse the returns of copying, and to calculate the correct amounts due to copyright owners. On return to the Agency, the record-keeping forms, which are regarded and treated as strictly confidential documents, some of which are deemed to be personal data under the Data Protection Act 1984, are:

• checked by the licensing officer responsible to ensure that the conditions of the licence are being adhered to;

• scrutinised by the data preparation department to validate the information being submitted, e.g. missing ISBN/ISSNs etc are searched for;

• keyed for computer analysis;

• subjected to a final edit for data quality.

The results are analysed and summaries produced showing pages copied, by ISBN/ISSN and by title, by author and by publisher. Apportionments are then calculated, statements produced and cheques drawn. The existence of the ISBN and the ISSN systems is a great benefit to CLA in carrying out its tasks.

Distribution of fees

The first distribution to members was £1.4 million (US$2.3 million), paid in two parts: the first tranche of just over £500,000 in October 1987, and the balance in March/April 1988. According to a CLA Board decision, payments to rights owners have since been made every six months. At the time of writing, CLA has distributed over £50 million to members.

It must be emphasised that a CLA licence is not a carte blanche to copy without restrictions. The conditions are clearly set down and are required to be displayed alongside every copying machine within the control of the licensee. The wording of the notices may vary slightly depending on the category of the licensee but the core message is always the same. CLA also produces various user guides for issue to employees, and there is a warning sticker that goes on top of machines to act as a reminder to copier users.

Agreements with other countries

For CLA there is comfort in knowing that it is not alone in pioneering the collective administration of copying rights. Counterpart organisations to CLA now exist in 19 other countries – Australia, Austria, Canada, Denmark, Finland, France, Germany, Iceland, Ireland, Italy, Japan, the Netherlands, New Zealand, Norway, South Africa, Spain, Sweden, Switzerland and the United States – nearly all of them in membership of IFRRO, the International Federation of Reproduction Rights Organisations. RROs are also presently being formed in Belgium and Israel.

Finally, the broader the repertoire an RRO can offer its licensees the better, and it is a priority of CLA to secure reciprocal agreements with counterpart organisations overseas, particularly those in English-speaking countries where UK books, journals and periodicals are being widely and extensively copied, and, equally, where much publishing in the English language takes place.

Administration

Critics of collecting societies say that they spend pounds to distribute pennies. From the start, this is a potential criticism of which the CLA directors were acutely conscious. As far back as November 1982 the board designate set down in its minutes that on no account were CLA's administration costs to exceed 20% of the fee income. The Agency has done much better than that: CLA's overhead is working out at about 10% of the fee income, and the Agency continually strives to reduce that level where possible. However, because it is in the business of handling large numbers of documents and processing a great deal of information, investment in technology has been inevitable.

CLA's aim is to distribute as much as it can, as fast as it can, and as efficiently as it can. It believes that over £50 million, distributed between October 1987 and March 1997, speaks louder than any words, and demonstrates better than anything else the Agency's resolve to achieve its objectives.

Further information

The Copyright Licensing Agency Ltd
90 Tottenham Court Road, London W1P 0LP
tel 0171-436 5931 *fax* 0171-436 3986
e-mail cla@cla.co.uk
web site www.cla.co.uk
Contact The Secretary

Public Lending Right

Under the PLR system, payment is made from public funds to authors (writers, translators, illustrators and some editors/compilers) whose books are lent out from public libraries. Payment is made once a year, in February, and the amount authors receive is proportionate to the number of times (established from a sample) that their books were borrowed during the previous year (July to June).

The legislation

PLR was created, and its principles established, by the Public Lending Right Act 1979 (HMSO, 30p). The Act required the rules for the administration of PLR to be laid down by a scheme. That was done in the Public Lending Right Scheme 1982 (HMSO, £2.95), which includes details of transfer (assignment), transmission after death, renunciation, trusteeship, bankruptcy, etc. Amending orders made in 1983, 1984, 1988, 1989 and 1990 were consolidated in December 1990 (S.I. 2360, £3.90). Some further amendments affecting author eligibility came into effect in December 1991 (S.I. 2618, £1.00) and July 1997 (S.I. 1576, £1.10).

How the system works

From the applications he receives, the Registrar of PLR compiles a register of authors and books which is held on computer. A representative sample of book issues is recorded, consisting of all loans from selected public libraries. This is then multiplied in proportion to total library lending to produce, for each book, an estimate of its total annual loans throughout the country. Each year the computer compares the register with the estimated loans to discover how many loans are credited to each registered book for the calculation of PLR payments. The computer does this using code numbers – in most cases the ISBN printed in the book.

Parliament allocates a sum each year (£4,903,000 for 1998-99) for PLR. This Fund pays the administrative costs of PLR and reimburses local authorities for recording loans in the sample libraries. The remaining money is then divided by the total registered loan figure in order to work out how much can be paid for each estimated loan of a registered book.

Limits on payments

Bottom limit. If all the registered interests in an author's books score so few loans that they would earn less than £5 in a year, no payment is due.

Top limit. If the books of one registered author score so high that the author's PLR earnings for the year would exceed £6000, then only £6000 is paid. No author can earn more than £6000 in PLR in any one year.

Money that is not paid out because of these limits belongs to the Fund and increases the amounts paid that year to other authors.

The sample

The basic sample represents only public libraries (no academic, school, private or commercial libraries are included) and only loans made over the counter (not consultations of books on library premises). It follows that only those books which are loaned from public libraries can earn PLR and make an application worthwhile.

Most borrowed authors in UK public libraries

Based on PLR sample loans July 1996-June 1997. Includes all writers, both registered and unregistered, but not illustrators where the book has a separate writer. Writing names are used; pseudonyms have not been combined.

Most borrowed authors

1. Catherine Cookson
2. Danielle Steel
3. Dick Francis
4. Ruth Rendell
5. Agatha Christie
6. Jack Higgins
7. Josephine Cox

8. Terry Pratchett
9. Ellis Peters
10. Virginia Andrews
11. Wilbur Smith
12. Dean R. Koontz
13. Barbara Taylor Bradford
14. Bernard Cornwell

15. Rosamunde Pilcher
16. Elizabeth Ferrars
17. Stephen King
18. Ed McBain
19. Emma Blair
20. Maeve Binchy

Most borrowed children's authors

1. R.L. Stine
2. Janet & Allan Ahlberg
3. Roald Dahl
4. Ann M. Martin
5. Enid Blyton
6. Dick King-Smith
7. Goscinny

8. Eric Hill
9. John Cunliffe
10. Shirley Hughes
11. Martin Waddell
12. Kate William
13. Mick Inkpen
14. Tony Bradman

15. Jamie Suzanne
16. Nick Butterworth
17. Colin & Jacqui Hawkins
18. Rev W. Awdry
19. David McKee
20. Jill Murphy

The sample consists of the entire loans records for a year from libraries in 30 public library authorities spread through England, Scotland, Wales and Northern Ireland. Sample loans will be around 10% of the national total from 1 July 1997. Several computerised sampling points in an authority contribute loans data ('multi-site' sampling). This change has been introduced gradually, and began in July 1991. The aim has been to increase the sample without any significant increase in costs. In order to counteract sampling error, libraries in the sample change every two to three years. Loans are totalled every 12 months for the period 1 July to 30 June.

An author's entitlement to PLR depends, under the 1979 Act, on the loans accrued by his or her books in the sample. This figure is multiplied to produce regional and national estimated loans.

ISBNs

PLR depends on the use of code numbers to identify books lent and to correlate loans with entries on the register so that payment can be made. Principally the system uses the International Standard Book Number (ISBN). From July 1991 an ISBN has been required for all new registrations. Different editions (e.g., 1st, 2nd, hardcover, paperback, large print) of the same book have different ISBNs.

Authorship

In the PLR system the author of a book is the writer, illustrator, translator, compiler, editor or reviser. Authors must be named on the book's title page, or be able to prove authorship by some other means (e.g. receipt of royalties). The ownership of copyright (apart from crown copyright) has no bearing on PLR eligibility.

Co-authorship/illustrators

In the PLR system the authors of a book are those writers, translators, editors, compilers and illustrators as defined above. Authors must apply for registration before their books can earn PLR. There is no restriction on the number of authors who can register shares in any one book as long as they satisfy the eligibility criteria.

Summary of the 15th year's results

Registration: authors When registration closed for the 15th year (30 June 1997) the number of shares in books registered was 273,380 for 27,275 authors. This included 692 German authors.

Eligible loans Of the 514.5 million estimated loans from UK libraries, 227 million belong to books on the PLR register. The loans credited to registered books – 44.1% of all library borrowings – qualify for payment. The remaining 55.9% of loans relate to books that are ineligible for various reasons, to books written by dead or foreign authors, and to books that have simply not been applied for.

Money and payments PLR's administrative costs are deducted from the fund allocated to the Registrar annually by Parliament. Operating the Scheme this year cost £670,000, representing some 13.6% of the PLR fund. The Rate per Loan for 1997-98 remained at 2.07 pence and was calculated to distribute all the £4,251,000 available. The total of PLR distribution and costs is therefore the full £4,921,000 which the Government provided in 1997-98.

The numbers of authors in various payment categories are as follows:

93	payments at	6,000 maximum
39	payments at	5,000-5,999
231	payments between	2,500-4,999
610	payments between	1,000-2,499
787	payments between	500-999
3,740	payments between	100-499
12,012	payments between	5-99
17,512	TOTAL	

There were also 9763 registered authors whose books earned them nil payment. As a result of the £6000 maximum payment rule some £483,100 became available for redistribution to other authors.

Writers and/or illustrators

At least one must be eligible and they must jointly agree what share of PLR each will take. This agreement is necessary even if one or two are ineligible or do not wish to register for PLR. Share sizes should be based on contribution. The eligible authors will receive the share(s) specified in the application. PLR can be any whole percentage. Detailed advice is available from the PLR office.

Translators

Translators may apply, without reference to other authors, for a 30% fixed share (to be divided equally between joint translators).

Editors and compilers

An editor or compiler may apply, either with others or without reference to them, to register a 20% share. Unless in receipt of royalties an editor must have written at least 10% of the book's contents or more than 10 pages of text in addition to normal editorial work. The share of joint editors/compilers is 20% in total to be divided equally. An application from an editor or compiler to register a greater percentage share must be accompanied by supporting documentary evidence of actual contribution.

Dead or missing co-authors

Where it is impossible to agree shares with a co-author because that person is dead or untraceable, then the surviving co-author or co-authors may submit an application without the dead or missing co-author but must name the co-author and provide supporting evidence as to why that co-author has not agreed shares. The living co-author(s) will then be able to register a share in the book which will be 20% for the illustrator (or illustrators) and the residual percentage for the writer (or writers). If this percentage is to be divided between more than one writer or illustrator, then this will be in equal shares unless some other apportionment is requested and agreed by the Registrar.

The PLR Office keeps a file of missing authors (mostly illustrators) to help locate co-authors. Help is also available from publishers, the writers' organisations, and the Association of Illustrators.

Life and death

Authors can only be registered for PLR during their lifetime. However, for authors so registered, books can later be registered if first published within one year before their death or 10 years afterwards. New versions of titles registered by the author can be registered posthumously.

Residential qualifications

Eligibility for PLR is restricted to authors who are resident in the United Kingdom or Germany. A resident in these countries (for PLR purposes) has his or her only or principal home there. The United Kingdom does not include the Channel Islands or the Isle of Man.

Eligible books

In the PLR system each separate edition of a book is registered and treated as a separate book. A book is eligible for PLR registration provided that:
• it has an eligible author (or co-author);
• it is printed and bound (paperbacks counting as bound);
• copies of it have been put on sale (i.e. it is not a free handout and it has already been published);
• it is not a newspaper, magazine, journal or periodical;
• the authorship is personal (i.e. not a company or association) and the book is not crown copyright;
• it is not wholly or mainly a musical score;
• it has an ISBN.

Notification and payment

Every registered author receives from the Registrar an annual statement of estimated loans for each book and the PLR due.

Sampling arrangements

Libraries

To help minimise the unfairnesses that arise inevitably from a sampling system, the Scheme specifies the eight regions within which authorities and sampling points have to be designated and includes libraries of varying size. Part of the sample drops out by rotation each year to

Further information

Public Lending Right
PLR Office, Bayheath House,
Prince Regent Street,
Stockton-on-Tees TS18 1DF
tel (01642) 604699 *fax* (01642) 615641
web site www.earl.org.uk/partners/plr/index.html
Contact The Registrar
Application forms, information, publications and a copy of its *Annual Report* are all obtainable from the PLR Office. Further information on eligibility for PLR, loans statistics and forthcoming developments may be found on PLR's web site.

PLR Advisory Committee
Advises the Secretary of State for Culture, Media and Sport and the Registrar on the operation of the PLR scheme.

allow fresh libraries to be included. The following library authorities have been designated for the year beginning 1 July 1998 (all are multi-site authorities):
• Wales: Bridgend, Gwynedd, Newport;
• Scotland: Aberdeen, Glasgow, Highland;
• Northern Ireland: Southern Education & Library Board (SELB), North-Eastern Education & Library Board (NEELB);
• London: Barking and Dagenham, Bromley, Kensington and Chelsea, Ealing;
• Metropolitan Boroughs: Birmingham, Liverpool, Manchester, Wakefield, Sunderland;
• Counties S&E: Hertfordshire, Northamptonshire, Suffolk, Surrey, West Sussex;
• Counties S&W: Cornwall, Somerset, Staffordshire, Wiltshire;
• Counties N: Cheshire, Cumbria, Hull, North Yorkshire.

Participating local authorities are reimbursed on an actual cost basis for additional expenditure incurred in providing loans data to the PLR Office. The extra PLR work mostly consists of modifications to computer programs to accumulate loans data in the local authority computer and to transmit the data to the PLR Office at Stockton-on-Tees.

Reciprocal arrangements

In 1981-1982 reciprocal arrangements with West Germany were sought by British writers to help ensure that they did not lose the German PLR payments they had enjoyed since 1974 under international copyright law. The German Scheme, although loan based, is very different in most other respects and oper-ates under German copyright law. Reciprocity was brought into effect in January 1985. Authors can apply for German PLR through the Authors' Licensing and Collecting Society. (Further information on PLR schemes internationally and recent developments within the EC towards wider recognition of PLR may be found in *Proceedings of the First International Conference on Authors' Lending Rights*, James Parker (ed), 1996, £8 plus UK postage, from the PLR Office.)

Copyright and libel

British copyright law

Copyright is a creature of statute. There have been a series of Copyright Acts over the years, gradually extending the scope of this area of the law so as to offer protection to the widening range of media used by writers and artists of all types. In an article of this length, it is not possible to deal fully with all the changes in the law effected by the most recent Act, nor indeed with all the complexities of this technical area of the law. Rather, **Amanda L. Michaels**, *barrister, sets out the basic principles of copyright protection, and identifies topics which may be of particular interest to readers of this Yearbook.*

On 1 August 1989, the Copyright Act 1956, previously the major Act in this field, was replaced by the Copyright, Designs and Patents Act 1988 ('the Act'). Whilst much of the Act restated the existing law (and mere changes of expression were not to denote a substantive change: see section 172), some parts of the Act were innovatory, for instance in the creation of a new 'design right' protection for many commercial designs, and in the better protection offered to 'moral' rights (see sections below).

Continuing effects of old law

There were complicated transitional provisions (in Schedule 1 to the Act) relating to pre-existing works and infringements, and reference will need to be made to these and to the old law for some years to come, as well as to numerous Orders in Council made under the Act. Users of this *Yearbook* particularly need to note that forms of publishing and licensing agreements suitable for use under the old law will probably need revision in the light of the Act, and old texts on the subject may not apply to new copyright works.

Further recent changes to the law

On 1 January 1996, further important changes were made to UK copyright law, upon the implementation of EC Directive 93/98 ('the Term Directive') by the Duration of Copyright and Rights in Performances Regulations 1995 (S.I. 1995 No 3297). The Term Directive harmonised copyright laws throughout the European Union as to the period of copyright protection offered to various types of copyright work, with a view to avoiding distortions within the internal market. Rather than take away vested rights in any one state, the term was harmonised 'upwards' to meet the longest protection already offered in Germany. The end result is that the term of copyright in the UK and in some other countries has been extended from the 'life of the author plus 50 years' provided by Berne Convention to life plus 70 years. Certain works may, as a result, benefit from a 'revived' term of copyright protection in the UK and this may well make the task of deciding whether a work is still protected by copyright fraught with difficulty (see below). The Regulations also deal with what is to happen to a variety of existing rights (e.g. publishing contracts) in the works offered an extended term of protection.

Further amendments continue to be made to the Act, for instance in the Copyright and Rights in Databases Regulations 1997, implementing EC Council Directive No 96/9/EC, which came into force on 1 January 1998 (and created not merely a new category of copyright work, but also a subsidiary 'database right').

Copyright protection of works

Copyright protection has always protected the form in which the artist/author has set out his or her inspiration, not the underlying idea. So, plots, artistic ideas, systems and themes cannot be protected by copyright. Whilst an idea remains no more than that, it can be protected only by the law relating to confidential information (contrast the cases of *Green* v. *Broadcasting Corp. of New Zealand* [1989] RPC 700: no copyright in 'format' of *Opportunity Knocks*, and *Fraser* v. *Thames TV Ltd* [1984] QB 44: plot of a projected television series protected by law of confidence). The law of copyright prevents the copying of the material form in which the idea has been presented, or of a substantial part of it, measured in terms of quality, not quantity.

The Act therefore starts out, in section 1, by setting out a number of different categories of works which can be the subject of copyright protection. These are:
• original literary, dramatic, musical or artistic works,
• sound recordings, films, broadcasts or cable programmes, and
• typographical arrangements of published editions.

These works are further defined in sections 3 to 8 (see box for examples). The definitions are not identical to those in the 1956 Act.

The definitions of literary and musical works do not, however, contradict the basic rule that copyright protects the form (or the 'expression of the idea') and not the idea; works are not protected before being reduced into tangible form. Section 3(2) specifically provides that no copyright shall subsist in a literary, musical or artistic work until it has been recorded in writing or otherwise.

On the other hand, all that is required to achieve copyright protection is to record the original work in any appropriate medium. Once that has been done, copyright will subsist in the work

---

> ### Definitions under the Act
>
> **Literary work** is defined as: 'any work, other than a dramatic or musical work, which is written, spoken or sung, and accordingly includes: (a) a table or compilation other than a database, (b) a computer program, (c) preparatory design material for a computer program and (d) a database.'
>
> **A musical work** means: 'a work consisting of music, exclusive of any words or action intended to be sung, spoken or performed with the music.'
>
> **An artistic work** means: '(a) a graphic work, photograph, sculpture or collage, irrespective of artistic quality, (b) a work of architecture being a building or model for a building, or (c) a work of artistic craftsmanship.'

(assuming that the qualifying features set out below are present) without any formality of registration or otherwise. As long as the work is recorded in some tangible form there is, for instance, no need for it to be published in any way for the protection to attach to it. (Please note, however, that although this lack of formality applies here and in most European countries, the law of the United States does differ). The common idea that one must register a work at Stationers Hall, or send it to oneself or to, say, a bank, in a sealed envelope so as to obtain copyright protection is incorrect. All that this precaution may do is provide some proof in an infringement action (whether as plaintiff or defendant) of the date of creation and form of one's work.

Originality

In order to gain copyright protection, literary, dramatic, artistic and musical works must be original. Sound recordings or films which are mere copies of pre-existing sound recordings and films, broadcasts which infringe rights in another broadcast or cable programmes which consist of immediate retransmissions of broadcasts are not protected by copyright.

The test of originality may not be quite that expected by the layperson. Just as the law protects the form, rather than the idea, originality relates to the 'expression of the thought', rather than to the thought itself. A work need not be original in the sense of showing innovative or cultural merit, it needs only to have been the product of skill and labour on the part of the author. This can be seen from various sections in the Act, for instance in the definition of certain artistic works, and in the fact that it offers copyright protection to works such as compilations (like football pools coupons or directories) and tables (including mathematical tables).

There may be considerable difficulty, at times, in deciding whether a work is of sufficient originality, or has original features, where there have been a series of similar designs or amendments of existing works. See *L.A. Gear Inc* v. *Hi-Tec Sports Plc* [1992] FSR 121 and *Biotrading* v. *Biohit* [1998] FSR 109. A new edition of an existing work, or an adaptation of one, may therefore obtain a new copyright; this will not affect the earlier copyright protection. See *Cala Homes (South) Ltd* v. *Alfred McAlpine Homes East Ltd* [1995] FSR 818. What is clear, though, is that merely making a 'slavish copy' of a drawing will not create an original work: see *Interlego AG* v. *Tyco Industries* [1989] AC 217.

On the other hand, 'works' comprising the titles of books or periodicals, or advertising slogans, which may have required a good deal of original thought, generally are not accorded copyright protection, because they are too short to be deemed literary works.

See, too, the limited protection given to drawings of a functional or engineering type in the sections on infringement and design right below.

Qualification

The Act is limited in its effects to the UK (and to colonies to which it may be extended by Order in Council). It is aimed primarily at protecting the works of British citizens, or works which were first published here. However, in line with the requirements of various international conventions to which the UK is a party, copyright protection in the UK is also accorded to the works of nationals of many foreign states which are also party to these conventions, as well as to works first published in those states, on a reciprocal basis.

The position is somewhat different where copyright in works of nationals of other member states of the European Union are concerned, as there is a principle of equal treatment which applies to copyright protection, so that protection must be offered to such works here: see *Phil Collins* v. *Imtrat Handelsgesellschaft mbH* (Case C92/92) [1993] 2 CMLR 773.

The importance of these rules mainly arises when one is trying to find out whether a pre-existing foreign work is protected by copyright here, for instance, if one wishes to make a film based upon a foreign novel. Within the confines of this article, all that can be said is that there have been numerous different Orders in Council regulating the position for most of the major countries of the world, including the other member states of the EU and the USA, and further Orders continue to be made, but that in every case it will be wise to check the position.

Ownership

The general rule is that a work will initially be owned by its author, the author being the creator of the work, or in the case of a film or sound recording, the person who makes the arrangements necessary for it to be made. The Term Directive (in common with certain other EC Directives) provided that the 'principal director' of a film shall be deemed to be its author or one of its authors.

One important exception to the general rule is that the copyright in a work made by an employee in the course of his or her employment will belong to their employer, subject to any agreement to the contrary. However, this rule applies only to true employees, not to freelance designers, journalists, etc, and not even to nominally self-employed company directors. This obviously may lead to problems if the question of copyright ownership is not agreed (see box: Assignments).

Where a work is produced by several people who collaborate in such a way that each one's contribution is not distinct from that of the other(s), then they will be the joint authors of the work. Where two people collaborate to write a song, one producing the lyrics and the other the music, there will be two separate copyright works, the copyright of which will be owned by each of the authors separately. But where two people write a play, each rewriting what the other produces, there will be a joint work.

The importance of knowing whether the work is joint or not arises:
• in working out the duration of the copyright, and
• from the fact that joint works can only be exploited with the agreement of all the joint authors, so that all of them have to join in any licence, although each of them can sue for infringement without joining the other author(s) in the proceedings.

Duration of copyright

As a result of the amendments brought into effect on 1 January 1996, copyright in literary, dramatic, musical or artistic works expires at the end of the period of 70 years from the end of the calendar year in which the author dies (new section 12(1)). Where there are joint authors (see 'Ownership', above), then the 70 years runs from the year of the death of the last of them to die. If the author is unknown, there will be 70 years protection from the date the work was first made or (where applicable) first made available to the public by being performed, etc.

The extended 70-year term also applies to films, and runs from the end of the calendar year in which the death occurs of the last to die of the principal director, the author of the screenplay, the author of the dialogue or the composer of any music especially created for the film (new section 13B). This could obviously be a nightmare to establish, and there are certain presumptions in section 66A which may help someone wishing to use material from an old film.

However, sound recordings are still protected by copyright for only 50 years from the year of making or release (new section 13A); similarly, broadcasts and cable programmes still get only 50 years protection. Computer-generated works keep a 50-year term of protection.

The new longer term obviously applies without difficulty to works created after 1 January 1996. Nor is the extension of term especially hard to apply to works which were in copyright here on 31 December 1995, as the term will simply be extended for a further 20 years, and the owner of that extended copyright will be the person who owned it on 31 December 1995, unless that person had only a limited term of ownership, in which case the extra 20 years will be added on to the reversionary term (see paragraph 18 of the Regulations).

Where copyright had expired here, but the author died between 50 and 70 years ago, the position is more complicated. The Term Directive provided that if a work was protected by copyright anywhere in the European Union on 1 July 1995, then copyright protection should revive for it in any other state in which it had expired, until the end of the same 70-year period (this was given effect by paragraph 16(d) of the 1995 Regulations). This is not, unfortunately, simply a question of looking at the date of the author's death, since protection may not have been offered to a particular work even by Germany, the state offering the 70-year period of protection prior to the Directive, for other reasons, e.g. lack of originality according to German law. It might therefore be necessary to look at the position in the other states offering a longer term of protection, namely France and Spain.

Ownership of the revived term of copyright will belong to the person who was the owner of the copyright when the initial term expired, save that if that person died (or a company, etc, ceased to exist) before 1 January 1996, then the revived term will vest in the author or his or her personal representatives, and in the case of a film, in the principal director or his personal representatives (paragraph 19 of the Regulations).

The increased term offered to works of other EU nationals as a result of the Term Directive is not offered automatically to the nationals of other states, but will only apply where an equally long term is offered in their state of origin (new sub-sections 12(6), 13A(4) and 13B(7)).

Where acts are carried out in relation to such revived copyright works, pursuant to things done whilst they were in the public domain prior to such revival, certain protection from infringement is available (see paragraph 23 of the Regulations). A licence as of right may also be available, on giving notice to the copyright owner and paying a royalty (see paragraph 24).

Finally, where one is dealing with a work made before the Act came into force, one needs to look at the law in force when it was made, as well as at the transitional provisions of the 1956 Act (for pre-1957 works) and/or of the Act (for pre-1989 works).

Dealing with copyright works

As will be seen below, ownership of the copyright in a work confers upon the owner the exclusive right to deal with the work in a number of ways, and essentially stops all unauthorised exploitation of the work. Ownership of the copyright is capable of being separated from owner-ship of the material form in which the work is embodied, whether the transfer of the latter includes the former will depend upon the terms of any agreement or the circumstances. Buying a copy of a book does not transfer the ownership of the copyright in the underlying work, but purchasing the original manuscript or a unique piece of sculpture might do so, depending upon the circumstances and/or any express agreement between the parties.

Copyright works can be exploited by their owners in two ways:
- Assignment: the whole right in the work may be sold, with the owner retain-ing no interest in it (except, possibly, for

Assignments

The whole right in the work is sold, with the owner retaining no interest in it (except, possibly, for payment by way of royalties).

An assignment must be in writing, signed by or on behalf of the assignor, but no other formality is required. One can make an assignment of future copyright (under sec-tion 91). Where the author of a projected work agrees in writing that he will assign the rights in a future work to another, the copy-right vests in the assignee immediately upon the creation of the work, without fur-ther formalities. This facility may be used where works are commissioned from the author, as the specific provisions as to own-ership of commissioned works which exist-ed in the 1956 Act are not reproduced as such in the new Act, save in respect of works protected by the new design right (see page 648).

These rules do not, apparently, affect the common law as to beneficial interests in copyright. If the court finds that a work was commissioned to be made, but the copy-right has not automatically vested in the 'commissioner', despite a common intention that he should own the copyright, the court may order the author to assign the copyright to the commissioner. 'Commission' in this context means only to order a particular piece of work to be done: see *Apple Corps. Ltd* v. *Cooper* [1993] FSR 286 (on the 1956 Act). If no sufficient agreement is found of this sort, then the arrangement is likely to be found to have conferred a licence, whether exclusive or not, upon the 'commissioner'.

payment by way of royalties or some reversionary rights in certain agreed cir-cumstances); or
- Licensing: the owner may grant a licence to another to exploit the right, whilst retaining overall ownership.

Agreements dealing with copyright should make it clear whether an assign-ment or a licence is being granted, and should clearly define the scope of any assignment or licence. The question of moral rights (see below) will also have to be considered by parties negotiating an assignment or licence.

Both assignments and licences can, and frequently do, split up the various rights

---

Licensing

A licence is granted to another to exploit the right whilst retaining overall ownership.

Licences do not need to take any form in particular, and may indeed be granted orally. However, an exclusive licence (i.e. one which excludes even the copyright owner himself from exploiting the work in the manner authorised by the licence) must be in writing, if the licensee is to enjoy rights in respect of infringements concurrent with those of the copyright owner.

---

contained within the copyright. So, for instance, a licence might be granted to one person to publish a novel in hardback and to another to publish in softback, a third person might be granted the film, television and video rights, and yet a fourth the right to translate the novel into other languages.

Assignments and licences may also confer rights according to territory, dividing the USA from the EU or different EU countries one from the other. Two comments must be made about this. Firstly, any such agreement would be dealing with a bundle of different national copyrights, as each country's law extends only to its own borders; each country's law on copyright protection, on licensing and on infringement may differ and will continue to do so even after the implementation of the Term Directive. Secondly, when seeking to divide rights between different territories of the EU there is a danger that one will infringe the competition rules of the EU (in the main Articles 30-36 and 85-86 of the Treaty of Rome). Professional advice should be taken to ensure that there is no breach of these rules, which would render the parties liable to be fined, as well as making the agreement void in whole or in part.

Licences can also, of course, be of varying lengths. There is no need for a licence to be granted for the whole term of copyright; indeed this would be unusual, if not foolish. Well-drafted licences will provide for termination on breach, including the failure of the licensee to exploit the work properly, and on the bankruptcy or

winding up of the licensee.

Copyright may be assigned by will, and where a bequest is given of an original document, etc embodying an unpublished copyright work, the bequest will carry the copyright.

Any licence affecting a copyright work which subsisted on 31 December 1995 and was then for the full term of the copyright, shall continue to have effect during any extended term, subject to any agreement to the contrary (paragraph 21 of the Regulations).

Infringement

Copyright is infringed by doing any of a number of specified acts in relation to the copyright work, without the authority of the owner. In all forms of infringement, it suffices if a substantial part of the original is used, and the question is one to be judged according to quality not quantity (e.g., see *Ravenscroft* v. *Herbert* [1980] RPC 193). The form of infringement common to all forms of copyright works is that of copying. This means reproducing the work in any material form. It is important to note that primary infringement, such as copying, can be done innocently of any intention to infringe.

Infringement may occur where an existing work provides the inspiration for a later one, if copying results, e.g. by including edited extracts from a history book in a novel (*Ravenscroft* v. *Herbert*, see above) or using a photograph as the inspiration for a painting (*Baumann* v. *Fussell* [1978] RPC 485). Infringement will not necessarily be prevented merely by the application of significant new skill and labour by the infringer, nor by a change of medium.

In the case of a two-dimensional artistic work, reproduction can mean making a copy in three dimensions, and vice versa, although there is an important limitation on this general rule in section 51 of the Act, which provides that in the case of a 'design document or model' (defined as a record of a design of any aspect of the shape or configuration, internal or external, of the whole or part of an article, other than surface decoration) for something which is not itself an artistic work, it is no infringement to make an article to that design. This would appear to mean that whilst it would be an infringement to make an article from a design drawing for, say, a sculpture, it will not be an infringement of copyright to make a handbag from a copy of the design drawing for it, or from a handbag which one has purchased. In order to protect such designs one will have to rely upon design right or upon a registered design (for both see below). However, under the transitional provisions, the right to rely upon copyright protection for any such designs made before the commencement of the new Act will continue until 1 August 1999 (see Schedule 1, paragraph 19) and see *Entec (Pollution Control) Ltd* v. *Abacus Mouldings* [1992] FSR 332.

Copying a film, broadcast or cable programme can include making a copy of the whole or a substantial part of any image from it (see section 17(4)). This means that copying one frame of the film will be an infringement, as it was under the previous law (see *Spelling Goldberg Productions* v. *BPC* [1981] RPC 283). It is not an infringement of copyright in a film (though there could be an infringement of the copyright in underlying works) to reshoot the film. See *Norowzian* v. *Arks* [1998] FSR 394.

Copying is generally proved by showing substantial similarities between the original and the alleged copy, plus an opportunity to copy. Surprisingly often, minor errors in the original are reproduced by an infringer.

Copying need not be direct, so that, for instance, where the copyright is in a fabric design, copying the material, without ever having seen the original drawing, will still be an infringement, as will 'reverse engineering' of industrial designs e.g. to make unlicensed spare parts (subject to any defence of implied licence: see *British Leyland Motor Corp* v. *Armstrong Patents Co Ltd* [1984] FSR 591).

Issuing copies of a work to the public when it has not previously been put into circulation in the UK is also an infringement of all types of work.

'Secondary' infringements

Secondary infringements consist not of making infringing copies, but of dealing with them in some way. It is an infringement to import an infringing copy into the UK, and to possess in the course of business, or to sell, hire, offer for sale or hire, or distribute in the course of trade an infringing copy. However, none of these acts will be an infringement unless the alleged infringer knew or had reason to believe that the articles were infringing copies. What is sufficient knowledge will depend upon the facts of each case (see *LA Gear Inc.* v. *Hi-Tec Sports Plc* [1992] FSR 121 and *ZYX Records* v. *King* [1997] 2 All ER 132). Merely putting someone on notice of a dispute as to ownership of copyright may not, however, suffice to give him or her reason to believe in infringement for this purpose: *Hutchison Personal Communications* v. *Hook Advertising* [1995] FSR 365.

Other secondary infringements consist of permitting a place to be used for a public performance in which copyright is infringed and supplying apparatus to be used for infringing public performance, again, in each case, with safeguards for innocent acts.

Other acts which may amount to an infringement depend upon the nature of the work. It will be an infringement of the copyright in a literary, dramatic or musical work to perform it in public, whether by live performance or by playing recordings. Similarly, it is an infringement of the copyright in a sound recording, film, broadcast or cable programme to play or show it in public. Many copyright works will also be infringed by the rental or lending of copies of the work.

One rather different form of infringement is to make an adaptation of a literary, dramatic or musical work. An adaptation includes, in the case of a literary work, a translation, in the case of a non-dramatic work, making a dramatic work of it, and in the case of a dramatic work, making a non-dramatic work of it. An adaptation of a musical work is a transcription or arrangement of it.

There are also a number of 'secondary' infringements – see box above.

Exceptions to infringement

The Act provides a large number of exceptions to the rules on infringement, many of which are innovatory. They are far too numerous to be dealt with here in full, but they include:

• fair dealing with literary, dramatic, musical or artistic works for the purpose of research or private study;
• fair dealing for the purpose of criticism or review or reporting current events;
• incidental inclusion of a work in an artistic work, sound recording, film, broadcast or cable programme;
• various educational exceptions (see sections 32-36);
• various exceptions for libraries (see sections 37-44); various exceptions for public administration (see sections 45-50);
• backing-up, or converting a computer program or accessing a licensed database (see sections 50A-D);
• dealing with a work where the author cannot be identified and the work seems likely to be out of copyright;
• public recitation, if accompanied by a sufficient acknowledgement;
• recording broadcasts or cable programmes at home for viewing at a more convenient time.

Remedies for infringements

The copyright owner has all the remedies offered to other owners of property. Usually the owner will want two things: firstly, to prevent the repetition or continuation of the infringement, and, secondly, compensation.

In almost all cases an injunction will be sought at trial, stopping the continuation of the infringement. A very useful remedy offered by the courts is the 'interlocutory injunction'. This is a form of interim relief, applied for at short notice, with a view to stopping damaging infringement at an early stage, without having to await the outcome of a full trial. Interlocutory injunctions are not always granted in copyright cases, but it is always worth considering the matter as soon as an infringement comes to notice, for delay in bringing an interlocutory application may be fatal to its success. Where an infringement is threatened, the courts will in appropriate cases make a *quia timet* injunction to prevent the infringement ever taking place.

Financial compensation may be sought in one of two forms. Firstly, damages may be granted for infringement. These will usually be calculated upon evidence of the loss caused to the plaintiff, sometimes based upon loss of business, at others upon the basis of what would have been a proper licence fee had the defendant sought a licence for the acts complained of. Additional damages may be awarded in rare cases for flagrant infringements.

Damages will not be awarded for infringement where the infringer did not know, and had no reason to believe, that copyright subsisted in the work. This exception is of limited use to a defendant, though, in the usual situation where he had no actual knowledge of the copyright, but the work was of such a nature that he should have known that copyright would subsist in it.

The alternative to a claim for damages is a claim for an account of profits, that is, the profits made by the infringer by virtue of his illicit exploitation of the copyright. Where an account of profits is sought, no award of flagrant damages can be made. See *Redrow Homes Ltd* v. *Betts Brothers plc* [1998] FSR 345.

A copyright owner may also apply for delivery up of infringing copies of his or her work (sections 99 and 113-15).

Finally, there are various criminal offences relating to the making, importation, possession, sale, hire, distribution, etc of infringing copies (see sections 107-110).

Design right

Many industrial designs are effectively excluded from copyright protection, by reason of the provisions of section 51 of the Act, described above. Alternatively, the term of their copyright protection is limited to 25 years from first industrial exploitation, by section 52 of the Act. However, they may instead be protected by the new 'design right' created by sections 213-64 of the Act. Like copyright, design right does not depend upon registration, but upon the creation of a suitable design by a qualified person.

The protection of the new right is given to original designs consisting of the shape or configuration (internal or external) of the whole or part of an article and not being merely 'surface decoration'. A design is not to be considered original if it was commonplace in the design field in question at the time of its creation. In *Ocular Sciences Ltd* v. *Aspect Vision Care Ltd* (unrep. 11/11/96), 'commonplace' was defined as meaning a design of a type which would excite no 'peculiar attention' amongst those in the trade, or one which amounts to a run-of-the-mill combination of well-known features. Designs will also not be protected if they consist of a method or principle of construction, or are dictated by the shape, etc of an article to which the new article is to be connected or of which it is to form part, the so-called 'must-fit' and 'must-match' exclusions. In *Ocular Sciences*, these exclusions had a devastating effect upon numerous design rights claimed for contact lens designs.

Design right will be granted to designs made by qualifying persons (in this part of the Act meaning UK and EU citizens or residents or others to whom the right may be extended) or commissioned by a qualifying person, or first marketed in the UK, another EU state or any other country to which the provision may be extended by Order in Council.

Design right lasts only 15 years from the end of the year in which it was first recorded or an article made to the design, or (if shorter) 10 years from the end of the year in which articles made according to the design were first sold or hired out. During the last five years of the term of protection, a licence to use the design can be obtained 'as of right' but against payment of a proper licence fee.

The designer will be the owner of the right, unless he or she made it in pursuance of a commission, in which case the commissioner will be the first owner of the right. The same rule applies as in copyright, that an employee's designs made in the course of his or her employment will belong to the employer.

The right given to the owner of a design right is the exclusive right to reproduce the design for commercial purposes. The rules as to assignments and licensing and as to infringement, both primary and secondary, are substantially similar to those described above in relation to copyright, as are the remedies available.

Design right coexists with the scheme of *registered* designs of the Registered Designs Act 1949 (as amended by the Act), which provides a monopoly right renewable for up to 25 years in respect of designs which have been accepted on to a register. Registered designs must contain features which appeal to and are judged by the eye, which is not a requirement for design right protection.

Moral rights

The Act also provided for the protection of certain so-called 'moral rights', commonly known as the rights of 'paternity' and 'integrity'.

The right of 'paternity' is for the author of a copyright literary, dramatic, musical or artistic work, and the director of a copyright film, to be identified as the author/director in a number of different situations, largely whenever the work is published, performed or otherwise commercially exploited (section 77).

However, the right does not arise unless it has been 'asserted' by the author or director, by appropriate words in an assignment, or otherwise by an instrument in writing (section 78), or in the case of an artistic work by ensuring that the artist's name appears on the frame, etc. Writers should therefore aim to ensure that all copies of their works carry a clear assertion of their rights under this provision (see end). There are exceptions to the right, in particular where the first ownership of the copyright vested in the author's or director's employer.

The right of 'integrity' is not to have one's work subjected to 'derogatory treatment'. This is defined as meaning an addition to, deletion from, alteration or adaptation of a work (save for a translation of a literary or dramatic work or an arrangement of a musical work involving no more than a change of key or register) which amounts to distortion or mutilation of the work or is otherwise prejudicial to the honour or reputation of the author/director.

Again, infringement of the right takes place when the maltreated work is published commercially or performed or exhibited in public. There are various exceptions set out in section 81 of the Act, in particular where the publication is in a newspaper, etc, and the work was made for inclusion therein or made available with the author's consent.

Where the copyright in the work vested first in the author's or director's employer, he or she has no right to 'integrity' unless he was identified at the time of the relevant act or was previously identified on published copies of the work.

These rights subsist for as long as the copyright in the work subsists.

A third moral right conferred by the Act is not to have a literary, dramatic, musical or artistic work falsely attributed to one as author, or to have a film falsely attributed to one as director, again where the work in question is published, publicly performed, etc. This right subsists until 20 years after a person's death.

None of these rights can be assigned during the person's lifetime, but all of them either pass on the person's death as directed by his or her will or fall into his residuary estate.

A fourth but rather different moral right is conferred by section 85. It gives a person who has commissioned the taking of photographs for private purposes a right to prevent copies of the work being issued to the public, etc.

The remedies for breach of these moral rights may again include damages and an injunction, although section 103(2) specifically foresees the granting of an injunction qualified by a right to the defendant to do the acts complained of, if subject to a suitable disclaimer.

Moral rights will be exercisable in relation to works in which the copyright has revived subject to any waiver or assertion of the right made before 1 January 1996 (see details as to who may exercise rights in paragraph 22 of the Regulations).

NOTICE

I, AMANDA LOUISE MICHAELS, hereby assert and give notice of my right under section 77 of the Copyright, Designs and Patents Act 1988 to be identified as the author of the foregoing article.
AMANDA MICHAELS

Amanda L. Michaels is a barrister in private practice in London, and specialises in copyright, designs, trade marks, and similar intellectual property and 'media' work. She is author of *A Practical Guide to Trade Mark Law* (Sweet & Maxwell, 2nd edn 1996).

Further reading

Skone James, Mummery, Rayner James and Garnett, *Copinger and Skone James on Copyright*, Sweet & Maxwell, 13th edn, 1991, and supplement 1994; 14th edn expected end 1998

Laddie, Prescott and Vitoria, *The Modern Law of Copyright*, Butterworths, 2nd edn, 1995

Flint, *A User's Guide to Copyright*, Butterworths, 4th edn, 1997

Bainbridge, *Intellectual Property*, Pitman, 3rd edn, 1996; 4th edn expected September 1998

Cornish, *Intellectual Property*, Sweet & Maxwell, 3rd edn, 1996

Copyright acts

Copyright, Designs and Patents Act 1998

The Duration of Copyright and Rights in Performances Regulations 1995 (SI 1995 No 3297)

see also Numerous Orders in Council

Libel

*Any writer should be aware of the law of libel. **Antony Whitaker** gives an outline of the main principles, concentrating on points which are most frequently misunderstood. But this article is no more than that, and specific legal advice should be taken when practical problems arise.*

The law discussed is the law of England and Wales. Scotland has its own, albeit somewhat similar, rules. A summary of the main differences between the two systems appears in the box (right).

At the time of going to press, Parliament had passed the Defamation Act 1996, but only limited parts of it had been brought into force. The purpose of the Act is mainly to streamline and simplify libel litigation.

Libel: liability to pay damages

English law draws a distinction between defamation published in permanent form and that which is not. The former is libel, the latter slander. 'Permanent form' includes writing, printing, drawings and photographs and radio and television broadcasts. It follows that it is the law of libel rather than slander which most concerns writers and artists professionally, and the slightly differing rules applicable to slander will not be mentioned in this article.

Publication of a libel can result in a civil action for damages, an injunction to prevent repetition and/or in certain cases a criminal prosecution against those responsible, who include the author (or artist or photographer), the publishers and the editor, if any, in which the libel appeared. 'Innocent disseminators', such as printers, distributors, broadcasters, Internet service providers and retailers, who can show they took reasonable care and had no reason to believe what they

> ### The main differences between English and Scottish law
>
> Much of the terminology of the Scots law of defamation differs from that of English law, and in certain minor respects the law itself is different. North of the border, libel and slander are virtually indistinguishable, both as to the nature of the wrongs and their consequences; and Scots law does not recognise the offence of criminal libel. Where individual English litigants enjoy absolute privilege for what they say in court, their Scottish counterparts have only qualified privilege. 'Exemplary', or 'punitive', damages are not awarded by the Scottish courts. Until recently, libel cases in Scotland were for the most part heard by judges sitting alone, but there is now a marked trend towards trial by jury, which has been accompanied by a significant increase in the levels of damages awarded.

were handling contained a libel, are now protected under the 1996 Act. Prosecutions are rare. Certain special rules apply to them and these will be explained below after a discussion of the question of civil liability, which in practice arises much more frequently.

Libel claims do not qualify for legal aid, although the closely analogous remedy of malicious falsehood does. Most libel cases are usually heard by a judge and jury, and it is the jury which decides the amount of any award, which is tax-free. It is not necessary for the plaintiff to prove that he or she has actually suffered any loss, because the law presumes damage. While the main purpose of a libel claim is to compensate the plaintiff for the injury to his or her reputation, a jury may give additional sums either as 'aggravated' damages, if it appears a defendant has behaved malevolently or spitefully, or as 'exemplary', or 'punitive', damages where a defendant hopes the economic advantages of publication will outweigh any sum awarded. Damages can also be 'nominal' if the libel complained of is trivial. It is generally very difficult to forecast the amounts juries are likely to award, though recent awards against newspapers have disclosed a tendency towards considerable generosity. The Court of Appeal now has power to reduce excessive awards of damages.

In an action for damages for libel, it is for the plaintiff to establish that the matter he or she complains of:
- has been published by the defendant,
- refers to the plaintiff,
- is defamatory.

If this is done, the plaintiff establishes a *prima facie* case. However, the defendant will escape liability if he or she can show he has a good defence. There are five defences to a libel action. They are:
- Justification
- Fair Comment
- Privilege
- Offer of Amends: s. 4 of the Defamation Act, 1952, to be replaced by ss. 2-4 of the Defamation Act, 1996
- Apology, etc, under the Libel Acts, 1843 and 1845.

A libel claim can also become barred under the Limitation Acts, as explained below. These matters must now be examined in detail.

The plaintiff's case

The meaning of 'published'

'Published' in the legal sense means communicated to a person other than the plaintiff. Thus the legal sense is wider than the lay sense but includes it. It follows that the content of a book is published in the legal sense when the manuscript is first sent to the publishing firm just as much as it is when the book is later placed on sale to the public. Subject to the 'innocent dissemination' defence referred to above, both types of publication are sufficient for the purpose of establishing liability for libel, but the law differentiates between them, since the scope of publication can properly be taken into account by the jury in considering the actual amount of damages to award. Material placed on the Internet is unquestionably 'published' there, and the extent of publication can be judged by the number of visits made to the relevant web site.

Establishing identity

The plaintiff must also establish that the matter complained of refers to him or her. It is of course by no means necessary to mention a person's name before it is clear that he or she is referred to. Nicknames by which he or she is known or corruptions of his name are just two ways in which his or her identity can be indicated. There are more subtle methods. The sole question is whether the plaintiff is indicated to those who read the matter complained of. In some cases he or she will not be unless it is read in the light of facts known to the reader from other sources, but this is sufficient for the plaintiff's purpose. The test is purely objective and does not depend at all on whether the writer intended to refer to the plaintiff.

It is because it is impossible to establish reference to any individual that generalisations, broadly speaking, are not successfully actionable. To say boldly 'All lawyers are crooks' does not give any single lawyer a cause of action, because the statement does not point a finger at any individual. However, if anyone is named in conjunction with a generalisation, then it may lose its general character and become particular from the context. Again, if one says 'One of the X Committee has been convicted of murder' and the X Committee consists of, say, four persons, it cannot be said that the statement is not actionable because no individual is indicated and it could be referring to any of the committee. This is precisely why it is actionable at the suit of each of them as suspicion has been cast on all.

Determining what is defamatory

It is for the plaintiff to show that the matter complained of is defamatory. What is defamatory is decided by the jury except in the extreme cases where the judge rules that the words cannot bear a defamatory meaning. Various tests have been laid down for determining this. It is sufficient that any one test is satisfied. The basic tests are:

- Does the matter complained of tend to lower the plaintiff in the estimation of society?
- Does it tend to bring him or her into hatred, ridicule, contempt, dislike or disesteem with society?
- Does it tend to make him shunned or avoided or cut off from society? The mere fact that what is published is inaccurate is not enough to involve liability; it is the adverse impact on the plaintiff's reputation that matters. For example, merely to overstate a person's income is not defamatory; but it will be if the context implies he has not fully declared it to the tax authorities.

'Society' means right-thinking members of society generally. It is by reference to such people that the above tests must be applied. A libel action against a newspaper which had stated that the police had taken a statement from the plaintiff failed, notwithstanding that the plaintiff gave evidence that his apparent assistance to the police (which he denied) had brought him into grave disrepute with the underworld. It was not by their wrongheaded standards that the matter fell to be judged.

Further, it is not necessary to imply that the plaintiff is at fault in some way in order to defame him. To say of a woman that she has been raped or of someone that he is insane imputes to them no degree of blame, but nonetheless both statements are defamatory. Lawyers disagree over whether the claim that an individual is 'ugly' is, or could be, defamatory.

Sometimes a defamatory meaning is conveyed by words which on the face of them have no such meaning. 'But Brutus is an honourable man' is an example. If a jury finds that words are meant ironically they will consider this ironical sense when determining whether the words are defamatory. In deciding, therefore, whether or not the words are defamatory, the jury seeks to discover what, without straining the words or putting a perverse construction on them, they will be understood to mean. In some cases this may differ substantially from their literal meaning.

Matter may also be defamatory by innuendo. Strictly so called, an innuendo is a meaning that words acquire by virtue of facts known to the reader but not stated in the passage complained of. Words, quite innocent on the face of them, may acquire a defamatory meaning when read in the light of these facts. For example, where a newspaper published a photograph of a man and a woman, with the caption that they had just announced their engagement, it was held to be defamatory of the man's wife since those who knew that she had cohabited with him were led to the belief that she had done so only as his mistress. The newspaper was unaware that the man was already married, but some of its readers were not.

Defences to a libel action

Justification

English law does not protect the reputation that a person either does not or should not possess. Stating the truth therefore does not incur liability, and the plea of justification – namely, that what is complained of is true in substance and in fact – is a complete answer to an action for damages. However, this defence is by no means to be undertaken lightly. For instance, to prove one instance of using bad language will be insufficient to justify the allegation that a person is 'foulmouthed'. It would be necessary to prove several instances, and the defendant is obliged in most cases to particularise in his pleadings giving details, dates and places. However, the requirement that the truth of every allegation must be proved is not absolute, and is qualified by the 'multiple charge – no worse off' defence. This applies where two or more distinct charges are levelled against a plaintiff, and some of what is said turns out to be inaccurate. If his or her reputation in the light of what is shown to be true is made no worse by the unprovable defamatory allegations – for example, mistaken accusations that a convicted pickpocket and car thief is also a shoplifter – the publisher will be safe. This is the extent of the law's recognition that some individuals are so disreputable as to be beyond redemption by awards of damages regardless of what is said about them. Subject to this, however, it is for the defendant to prove that what he or she has published is true, not for the plaintiff to disprove it, though if he can do so, so much the better for him.

One point requires special mention. It is insufficient for the defendant to prove that he or she has accurately repeated what a third person has written or said or that such statements have gone uncontradicted when made on occasions in the past. If X writes 'Y told me that Z is a liar', it is no defence to an action against X merely to prove that Y did say that. X has given currency to a defamatory statement concerning Z and has so made it his own. His only defence is to prove that Z is a liar by establishing a number of instances of Z's untruthfulness. Nor is it a defence to prove that the defendant genuinely believed what he or she published to be true. This might well be a complete answer in an action, other than a libel action, based on a false but non-defamatory statement. For such statements do not incur liability in the absence of fraud or malice which, in this context, means a dishonest or otherwise improper motive. Bona fide belief, however, may be relevant to the assessment of damages, even in a libel action.

Special care should be taken in relation to references to a person's convictions, however accurately described. Since the Rehabilitation of Offenders Act, 1974, a person's convictions may become 'spent' and thereafter it may involve liability to refer to them. Reference to the Act and orders thereunder must be made in order to determine the position in any particular case.

Fair comment

It is a defence to prove that what is complained of is fair comment made in good faith and without malice on a matter of public interest.

'Fair' in this context means 'honest'. 'Fair comment' means therefore the expression of the writer's genuinely held opinion. It does not necessarily mean opinion with which the jury agree. Comment may therefore be quite extreme and still be 'fair' in the legal sense. However, if it is utterly perverse the jury may be led to think that no one could have genuinely held such views. In such a case the defence would fail, for the comment could not be honest. 'Malice' here includes the popular sense of personal spite, but covers any dishonest or improper motive.

The defence only applies when what is complained of is comment as distinct from a statement of fact. The line between comment and fact is notoriously difficult to draw in some cases. Comment means a statement of opinion. The facts on which comment is made must be stated together with the comment or be sufficiently indicated with it. This is merely another way of saying that it must be clear that the defamatory statement is one of opinion and not of fact, for which the only defence would be the onerous one of justification. The exact extent to which the facts commented on must be stated or referred to is a difficult question, but some help may be derived in answering it by considering the purpose of the rule, which is to enable the reader to exercise his own judgement and to agree or disagree with the comment. It is quite plain that it is not necessary to state every single detail of the facts. In one case it was sufficient merely to mention the name of one of the Press lords in an article about a newspaper though not one owned by him. He was so well known that to mention his name indicated the substratum of fact commented upon, namely his control of his group of newspapers. No universal rule can be laid down, except that, in general, the fuller the facts set out or referred to with the comment, the better. All these facts must be proved to be true subject, however, to the flexibility of the 'proportionate truth' rule. This means that the defence remains available even if, for example, only three out of five factual claims can be proved true, provided that these three are by themselves sufficient to sustain, and are proportionate to, the fairness of the comment. The impact of the two unproven claims would probably fall to be assessed in accordance with the 'multiple charge – no worse off' rule in justification, set out above.

The defence only applies where the matters commented on are of public interest, i.e. of legitimate concern to the public or a substantial section of it. Thus the conduct of national and local government, international affairs, the administration of justice, etc, are all matters of public interest, whereas other people's private affairs may very well not be, although they undoubtedly interest the public, or provoke curiosity.

In addition, matters of which criticism has been expressly or impliedly invited, such as publicly performed plays and published books, are a legitimate subject of comment. Criticism need not be confined merely to their artistic merit but equally may deal with the attitudes to life and the opinions therein expressed.

It is sometimes said that a man's moral character is never a proper subject of comment for the purpose of this defence. This is certainly true where it is a private individual who is concerned, and some authorities say it is the same in the case of a public figure even though his or her character may be relevant to his or her public life. Again, it may in some cases be exceeding the bounds of fair comment to impute a dishonourable motive to a person, as is frequently done by way of inference from facts. In general, the imputation is a dangerous and potentially expensive practice.

Privilege

In the public interest, certain occasions are privileged so that to make defamatory statements upon them does not incur liability. The following are privileged in any event:

- fair, accurate, and contemporaneous reports of public judicial proceedings in England published in a newspaper;
- Parliamentary papers published by the direction of either House, or full republications thereof.

The following are privileged provided publication is made only for the reason that the privilege is given and not for some wrongful or indirect motive:

- fair and accurate but non-contemporaneous reports of public judicial proceedings in England, whether in a newspaper or not;
- extracts of Parliamentary papers;
- fair and accurate reports of Parliamentary proceedings;
- a fair and accurate report in a newspaper of the proceedings at any public meeting held in the United Kingdom. The meeting must be bona fide and lawfully held for a lawful purpose and for the furtherance or discussion of any matter of public concern. Admission to the meeting may be general or restricted. In the case of public meetings, the defence is not available, if it is proved that the defendant has been requested by the plaintiff to publish in the newspaper in which the original publication was made a reasonable letter or statement by way of explanation or contradiction, and has refused or neglected to do so, or has done so in a manner not adequate or not reasonable having regard to all the circumstances.

This list of privileged occasions is by no means exhaustive, and when s. 15 of the 1996 Act comes into effect the existing categories will be amended and extended. The privilege defence will be extended to the media generally, rather than, as at present, being confined simply to newspapers.

Offers of Amends under the 1952 and 1996 Acts

Section 4 of the 1952 Act was still in force at the time of going to press, but it is due to be replaced by sections 2, 3 and 4 of the 1996 Act. The 1952 Act affords a degree of protection to the publisher of an 'innocent' defamation. 'Innocent' is narrowly defined: it means simply that the publisher, despite having exercised reasonable care, did not know that what he said might be read as a reference to the plaintiff – e.g. through an improbable coincience of name – or that circumstances existed which made an otherwise innocuous statement defamatory – e.g. by mistakenly depicting a married lady as her husband's 'fiancée', thus implying that she lived with him as his mistress rather than as his wife. This defence has proved somewhat rigid and unworkable over the years, mainly because of its technicality and the fact that it has to be put forward, together with a correction and an apology, as soon as the potentially defamatory impact of what has appeared has been drawn to the publisher's attention.

When they are operative, sections 2, 3 and 4 of the new Act will offer a rather more flexible method of nipping in the bud potential libel actions by those who have been unintentionally defamed. The range of libel meanings for which the new defence will cater is much wider than that covered by the current s. 4; and though it envisages the payment of damages (which the current provision does not) as well as costs, together with the offer of a correction and apology, the damages figure will be fixed by a judge if the parties cannot agree. He or she will do this bearing in mind the generosity of the correction and apology, and the extent of its publication. While recourse to this defence will exclude reliance on the defences of justification, privilege and fair comment, it is likely to offer a far greater incentive to settle compaints than the present provision, and should save substantially on costs.

Apology under 1843 and 1845 Acts

This defence is rarely utilised, since if any condition of it is not fulfilled, the plaintiff must succeed and the only question is the actual amount of damages. It only applies to actions in respect of libels in newspapers and periodicals. The defendant pleads that the libel was inserted without actual malice and without gross negligence and that before the action commenced or as soon afterwards as possible he inserted a full apology in the same newspaper, etc, or had offered to publish it in a newspaper, etc, of the plaintiff's choice, where the original newspaper is published at intervals greater than a week. Further a sum must be paid into court with this defence to compensate the plaintiff.

'Fast-track disposal' procedure

In its recognition of the generally cumbersome nature of libel litigation, the 1996 Act envisages a simplified mechanism for dealing with less serious complaints. When sections 8, 9 and 10 come into force, a judge alone will be able to dismiss unrealistic claims virtually at the outset; and he will also be able to dispose 'summarily' of relatively minor, but well-founded, claims, on the basis of an award of up to £10,000, a declaration that the publication was libellous, an order for an apology and an order forbidding repetition.

Apologies in general

Quite apart from the provisions concerning statutory apologies mentioned above, a swift and well publicised apology will always go some way towards assuaging injured feelings and help reduce an award of damages.

Limitation and death

As from September 1996, the new Act has reduced from three years to one the period within which a libel action must generally be started if it is not to become 'statute-barred' through lapse of time. But successive and subsequent publications, such as the issue of later editions of the same book, or the sale of surplus copies of an old newspaper, can give rise to fresh claims.

Civil claims for libel cannot be brought on behalf of the dead. If an individual living plaintiff or defendant in a libel case dies before the jury gives their verdict, the action 'abates', i.e. comes to an end, so far as their involvement is concerned, and no rights arising out of it survive either for or against their personal representatives.

Insurance

For an author, the importance of at least an awareness of this branch of law lies first, in the fact that most book contracts contain a clause enabling the publisher to look to him should any libel claims result; and second, in the increasingly large awards of damages. It is therefore advisable to check what libel insurance a publisher carries, and whether it also covers the author who, if he or she is to have the benefit of it, should always alert the publisher to any potential risk. One company which offers libel insurance for authors is Royal Sun Alliance, Legal and Indemnities Libel Unit, Suite 1, 5th Floor, 3 Minster Court, Mincing Lane, London EC3R 7DD. Premiums start at £1000, and can be substantially higher if the book is tendentious or likely to be controversial. The company generally insists on the author obtaining, and paying for, a legal opinion first. Indemnity limits vary between £50,000 and £1 million, and the author is required to bear at least the first £5000, and 10% of the remainder, of any loss. It is worth remembering that 'losses' include legal costs as well as damages, which they can often exceed. Libel insurance can also be obtained through a Lloyds broker.

Criminal liability in libel

Whereas the object of a civil action is to obtain compensation for the wrong done or to prevent repetition, the object of criminal proceedings is to punish the wrongdoer by fine or imprisonment or both. There are four main types of writing which may provoke a prosecution:

- defamatory libel;
- obscene publications;
- sedition and incitement to racial hatred;
- blasphemous libel.

Defamatory libel

The publication of defamatory matter is in certain circumstances a crime as well as a civil wrong. But whereas the principal object of civil proceedings will normally be to obtain compensation, the principal object of a criminal prosecution will be to secure punishment of the accused, for example by way of a fine. Prosecutions are not frequent, but there have been signs of late of a revival of interest. There are important differences between the rules applicable to criminal libel and its civil counterpart. For example, a criminal libel may be 'published' even though only communicated to the person defamed and may be found to have occurred even where the person defamed is dead, or where only a group of persons but no particular individual has been maligned. During election campaigns, it is an 'illegal practice' to publish false statements about the personal character or conduct of a candidate irrespective of whether they are also defamatory.

Obscene publications

It is an offence to publish obscene matter. By the Obscene Publications Act, 1959, matter is obscene if its effect is such as to tend to deprave and corrupt persons who are likely, having regard to all relevant circumstances, to read, see or hear it. 'To deprave and corrupt' is to be distinguished from 'to shock and disgust'. It is a defence to a prosecution to prove that publication of the matter in question is justified as being for the public good, on the ground that it is in the interests of science, literature, art or learning, or of other objects of general concern. Expert evidence may be given as to its literary, artistic, scientific or other merits. Playwrights, directors and producers should note that the Theatres Act, 1968, though designed to afford similar protection to stage productions, does not necessarily prevent prosecutions for indecency under other statutes.

Sedition and incitement to racial hatred

Writings which tend to destroy the peace of the realm may be prosecuted as being seditious or as amounting to incitement to racial hatred. Seditious writings include those which advocate reform by unconstitutional or violent means or incite contempt or hatred for the monarch or Parliament. These institutions may be criticised stringently, but not in a manner which is likely to lead to insurrection or civil commotion or indeed any physical force. Prosecutions are a rarity, but it should be remembered that writers of matter contemptuous of the House of Commons, though not prosecuted for seditious libel are, from time to time, punished by that House for breach of its privileges, although, if a full apology is made, it is often an end of the matter. The Public Order Act 1986 makes it an offence, irrespective of the author's or publisher's intention, to publish, or put on plays containing, threatening, abusive or insulting matter if hatred is likely to be stirred up against any racial group in Great Britain.

Blasphemous libel

Blasphemous libel consists in the vilification of the Christian religion or its ceremonies. Other religions are not protected. The offence lies essentially in the impact of what is said concerning, for instance, God, Christ, the Bible, the Book of Common Prayer, etc; it is irrelevant that the publisher does not intend to shock or arouse resentment. While temperate and sober writings on religious topics however anti-Christian in sentiment will not involve liability, if the discussion is 'so scurrilous and offensive as to pass the limit of decent controversy and to outrage any Christian feeling', it will.

Antony Whitaker is Legal Manager at Times Newspapers Ltd.

Finance for writers and artists

Income tax

Despite attempts by successive Governments to simplify our taxation system, the subject has become increasingly complicated. **Peter Vaines**, *a chartered accountant and barrister, gives a broad outline of taxation from the point of view of writers and other creative professionals. At the time of writing the proposals in the March 1998 Budget have just been announced and these are broadly reflected in this article.*

How income is taxed

Generally

Authors are usually treated for tax purposes as carrying on a profession and are taxed in a similar fashion to other professionals, i.e. as self-employed persons assessable under Schedule D. This article is directed to self-employed persons only, because if a writer is employed he or she will be subject to the rules of Schedule E where different considerations apply – substantially to his or her disadvantage.

Attempts are often made by employed persons to shake off the status of 'employee' and to attain 'freelance' status so as to qualify for the advantages of Schedule D, such attempts meeting with varying degrees of success. The problems involved in making this transition are considerable and space does not permit a detailed explanation to be made here – individual advice is necessary if difficulties are to be avoided.

Particular attention has been paid by the Inland Revenue to journalists and to those engaged in the entertainment industry with a view to reclassifying them as employees so that PAYE is deducted from their earnings. This blanket treatment has been extended to other areas and, although it is obviously open to challenge by individual taxpayers, it is always difficult to persuade the Inland Revenue to change its views.

There is no reason why employed people cannot carry on a freelance business in their spare time. Indeed, aspiring authors, painters, musicians, etc, often derive so little income from their craft that the financial security of an employment, perhaps in a different sphere of activity, is necessary. The existence of the employment is irrelevant to the taxation of the freelance earnings although it is most important not to confuse the income or expenditure of the employment with the income or expenditure of the self-employed activity. The Inland Revenue is aware of the advantages which can be derived by an individual having 'freelance' income from an organisation of which he or she is also an employee, and where such circumstances are contrived, it can be extremely difficult to convince an Inspector of Taxes that a genuine freelance activity is being carried on.

For those starting in business or commencing work on a freelance basis the Inland Revenue produces a very useful booklet, *Starting in Business (IR28)*, which is available from any tax office.

Income

For income to be taxable it need not be substantial, nor even the author's only source of income; earnings from casual writing are also taxable but this can be an advantage, because occasional writers do not often make a profit from their writing. The expenses incurred in connection with writing may well exceed any income receivable and the resultant loss may then be used to reclaim tax paid on other income. There may be deducted from the income certain allowable expenses and capital allowances which are set out in more detail below. The possibility of a loss being used as a basis for a tax repayment is fully appreciated by the Inland Revenue, which sometimes attempts to treat casual writing as a hobby so that any losses incurred cannot be used to reclaim tax; of course by the same token any income receivable would not be chargeable to tax. This treatment may sound attractive but it should be resisted vigorously because the Inland Revenue does not hesitate to change its mind when profits begin to arise. In the case of exceptional or non-recurring writing, such as the autobiography of a sports personality or the memoirs of a politician, it could be better to be treated as pursuing a hobby and not as a professional author. Sales of copyright cannot be charged to income tax unless the recipient is a professional author. However, the proceeds of sale of copyright may be charged to capital gains tax, even by an individual who is not a professional author.

Royalties

Where the recipient is a professional author, a series of cases has laid down a clear principle that sales of copyright are taxable as income and not as capital receipts. Similarly, lump sums on account of, or in advance of royalties are also taxable as income in the year of receipt, subject to a claim for spreading relief (see below).

Copyright royalties are generally paid without deduction of income tax. However, if royalties are paid to a person who normally lives abroad, tax will be deducted by the payer or his agent at the time the payment is made unless arrangements are made with the Inland Revenue for payments to be made gross.

Arts Council grants

Persons in receipt of grants from the Arts Council or similar bodies will be con-

---

> **Arts Council category A awards**
>
> - Direct or indirect musical, design or choreographic commissions and direct or indirect commission of sculpture and paintings for public sites.
> - The Royalty Supplement Guarantee Scheme.
> - The contract writers' scheme.
> - Jazz bursaries.
> - Translators' grants.
> - Photographic awards and bursaries.
> - Film and video awards and bursaries.
> - Performance Art Awards.
> - Art Publishing Grants.
> - Grants to assist with a specific project or projects (such as the writing of a book) or to meet specific professional expenses such as a contribution towards copying expenses made to a composer or to an artist's studio expenses.

---

cerned whether or not such grants are liable to income tax. The Inland Revenue has issued a Statement of Practice after detailed discussions with the Arts Council regarding the tax treatment of such awards. Grants and other receipts of a similar nature have now been divided into two categories (see boxes) – those which are to be treated by the Inland Revenue as chargeable to tax and those which are not. Category A awards are considered to be taxable; awards made under category B are not chargeable to tax.

This Statement of Practice has no legal force and is used merely to ease the administration of the tax system. It is open to anyone in receipt of a grant or award to disregard the agreed statement and challenge the Inland Revenue view on the merits of their particular case. However, it must be recognised that the Inland Revenue does not issue such statements lightly and any challenge to their view would almost certainly involve a lengthy and expensive action through the Courts.

The tax position of persons in receipt of literary prizes will generally follow a decision by the Special Commissioners in connection with the Whitbread Literary

Arts Council category B awards

- Bursaries to trainee directors.
- In-service bursaries for theatre directors.
- Bursaries for associate directors.
- Bursaries to people attending full-time courses in arts administration (the practical training course).
- In-service bursaries to theatre designers and bursaries to trainees on the theatre designers' scheme.
- In-service bursaries for administrators.
- Bursaries for actors and actresses.
- Bursaries for technicians and stage managers.
- Bursaries made to students attending the City University Arts Administration courses.
- Awards, known as the Buying Time Awards, made not to assist with a specific project or professional expenses but to maintain the recipient to enable him or her to take time off to develop his personal talents. These at present include the awards and bursaries known as the Theatre Writing Bursaries, awards and bursaries to composers, awards and bursaries to painters, sculptures and print makers, literature awards and bursaries.

Award. In that case it was decided that the prize was not part of the author's professional income and accordingly not chargeable to tax. The precise details are not available because decisions of the Special Commissioners were not, at that time, reported unless an appeal was made to the High Court; the Inland Revenue chose not to appeal against this decision. Details of the many literary awards which are given each year start on page 510, and this decision is of considerable significance to the winners of each of these prizes. It would be unwise to assume that all such awards will be free of tax as the precise facts which were present in the case of the Whitbread award may not be repeated in another case; however it is clear that an author winning a prize has some very powerful arguments in his or her favour, should the Inland Revenue seek to charge tax on the award.

Allowable expenses

To qualify as an allowable business expense, expenditure has to be laid out wholly and exclusively for business purposes. Strictly there must be no 'duality of purpose', which means that expenditure cannot be apportioned to reflect the private and business usage, e.g. food, clothing, telephone, travelling expenses, etc. However, the Inland Revenue does not usually interpret this principle strictly and is prepared to allow all reasonable expenses (including apportioned sums) where the amounts can be commercially justified.

It should be noted carefully that the expenditure does not have to be 'necessary', it merely has to be incurred 'wholly and exclusively' for business purposes. Naturally, however, expenditure of an outrageous and wholly unnecessary character might well give rise to a presumption that it was not really for business purposes. As with all things, some expenses are unquestionably allowable and some expenses are equally unquestionably not allowable – it is the grey area in between which gives rise to all the difficulties and the outcome invariably depends on negotiation with the Inland Revenue.

Great care should be taken when claiming a deduction for items where there is a 'duality of purpose' and negotiations should be conducted with more than usual care and courtesy – if provoked the Inspector of Taxes may well choose to allow nothing. An appeal is always possible although unlikely to succeed as a string of cases in the Courts has clearly demonstrated. An example is the case of *Caillebotte* v. *Quinn* where the taxpayer (who normally had lunch at home) sought to claim the excess cost of meals incurred because he was working a long way from his home. The taxpayer's arguments failed because he did not eat only in order to work, one of the reasons for his eating was in order to sustain his life; a duality of purpose therefore existed and no tax relief was due.

Other cases have shown that expenditure on clothing can also be disallowed if it is the kind of clothing which is in everyday use, because clothing is worn not only

Allowable expenses

(a) Cost of all materials used up in the course of preparation of the work.

(b) Cost of typewriting and secretarial assistance, etc; if this or other help is obtained from one's spouse then it is entirely proper for a deduction to be claimed for the amounts paid for the work. The amounts claimed must actually be paid to the spouse and should be at the market rate although some uplift can be made for unsocial hours, etc. Payments to a wife (or husband) are of course taxable in her (or his) hands and should therefore be most carefully considered. The wife's earnings may also be liable for National Insurance contributions and it is important to take care because otherwise you may find that these contributions may outweigh the tax savings.

(c) All expenditure on normal business items such as postage, stationery, telephone, e-mail, fax and answering machines, agent's fees, accountancy charges, photography, subscriptions, periodicals, magazines, etc, may be claimed. The cost of daily papers should not be overlooked if these form part of research material. Visits to theatres, cinemas, etc, for research purposes may also be permissible (but not the cost relating to guests). Unfortunately, expenditure on all types of business entertaining is specifically denied tax relief.

(d) If work is conducted at home, a deduction for 'use of home' is usually allowed providing the amount claimed is reasonable. If the claim is based on an appropriate proportion of the total costs of rent, light and heat, cleaning and maintenance, insurance, etc (but not the Council Tax), care should be taken to ensure that no single room is used 'exclusively' for business purposes, because this may result in the Capital Gains Tax exemption on the house as the only or main residence being partially forfeited. However, it would be a strange household where one room was in fact used exclusively for business purposes and for no other purpose whatsoever (e.g.

storing personal bank statements and other private papers); the usual formula is to claim a deduction on the basis that most or all of the rooms in the house are used at one time or another for business purposes, thereby avoiding any suggestion that any part was used exclusively for business purposes.

(e) The appropriate business proportion of motor running expenses may also be claimed although what is the appropriate proportion will naturally depend on the particular circumstances of each case; it should be mentioned that the well-known scale benefits, whereby one is taxed according to the size and cost of the car, do not apply to self-employed persons.

(f) It has been long established that the cost of travelling from home to work (whether employed or self-employed) is not an allowable expense. However, if home is one's place of work then no expenditure under this heading is likely to be incurred and difficulties are unlikely to arise.

(g) Travelling and hotel expenses incurred for business purposes will normally be allowed but if any part could be construed as disguised holiday or pleasure expenditure, considerable thought would need to be given to the commercial reasons for the journey in order to justify the claim. The principle of 'duality of purpose' will always be a difficult hurdle in this connection – although not insurmountable.

(h) If a separate business bank account is maintained, any overdraft interest thereon will be an allowable expense. This is the only circumstance in which overdraft interest is allowed for tax purposes and care should be taken to avoid overdrafts in all other circumstances.

(i) Where capital allowances (see page 663) are claimed for a personal computer, fax, television, video, CD or tape player, etc, used for business purposes the costs of maintenance and repair of the equipment may also be claimed.

to assist the pursuit of one's profession but also to accord with public decency. This duality of purpose may be sufficient to deny relief – even where the particular type of clothing is of a kind not otherwise worn by the taxpayer. In the case of *Mallalieu* v. *Drummond* a lady barrister failed to obtain a tax deduction for items of sombre clothing purchased specifically

for wearing in Court. The House of Lords decided that a duality of purpose existed because clothing represented part of her needs as a human being.

Despite the above, Inspectors of Taxes are not usually inflexible and the expenses listed in the box opposite are among those generally allowed. Clearly many other allowable items may be claimed in addition to those listed. Wherever there is any reasonable business motive for some expenditure it should be claimed as a deduction although it is necessary to preserve all records relating to the expense. It is sensible to avoid an excess of imagination as this would naturally cause the Inspector of Taxes to doubt the genuineness of other expenses claimed.

The question is often raised whether the whole amount of an expense may be deducted or whether the VAT content must be excluded. Where VAT is reclaimed from the Customs and Excise (on the quarterly returns made by a registered person), the VAT element of the expense cannot be treated as an allowable deduction. Where the VAT is not reclaimed, the whole expense (inclusive of VAT) is allowable for income tax purposes.

Capital allowances

Allowances

Where expenditure of a capital nature is incurred, it cannot be deducted from income as an expense – a separate and sometimes more valuable capital allowance being available instead. Capital allowances are given for many different types of expenditure, but authors and similar professional people are likely to claim only for 'plant and machinery'; this is a very wide expression which may include motor cars, personal computers, fax and photocopying machines, modems, televisions, CD, video and cassette players used for business purposes, books – and even a horse! Plant and machinery generally qualify for a 25% allowance in the year of purchase and 25% of the reducing balance in subsequent years. However, in addition a special 50% first year allowance was introduced in the July 1997 Budget on expenditure on plant and machinery incurred by small businesses before 1 July 1998. This first year allowance continues, but at a rate of 40% for expenditure in the year ended 1 July 1999. Where the useful life of an asset is expected to be short, it is possible to claim special treatment as a 'short life asset' enabling the allowances to be accelerated.

The reason these allowances can be more valuable than allowable expenses is that they may be wholly or partly disclaimed in any year that full benefit cannot be obtained – ordinary business expenses cannot be similarly disclaimed. Where, for example, the income of an author does not exceed her personal allowances, she would not be liable to tax and a claim for capital allowances would be wasted. If the capital allowances were to be disclaimed their benefit would be carried forward for use in subsequent years. Careful planning with claims for capital allowances is therefore essential if maximum benefit is to be obtained.

As an alternative to capital allowances, claims can be made on the 'renewals' basis whereby all renewals are treated as allowable deductions in the year; no allowance is obtained for the initial purchase, but the cost of replacement (excluding any improvement element) is allowed in full. This basis is no longer widely used, as it is considerably less advantageous than claiming capital allowances as described above.

Leasing is a popular method of acquiring fixed assets, and where cash is not available to enable an outright purchase to be made, assets may be leased over a period of time. Whilst leasing may have financial benefits in certain circumstances, in normal cases there is likely to be no tax advantage in leasing an asset where the alternative of outright purchase is available. Indeed, leasing can be a positive disadvantage in the case of motor cars with a new retail price of more than £12,000. If such a car is leased, only a proportion of the leasing charges will be tax deductible.

Books

The question of whether the cost of books is eligible for tax relief has long been a source of difficulty. The annual cost of replacing books used for the purposes of one's professional activities (e.g. the annual cost of a new *Writers' & Artists' Yearbook*) has always been an allowable expense; the difficulty arose because the initial cost of reference books, etc (e.g.

when commencing one's profession) was treated as capital expenditure but no allowances were due as the books were not considered to be 'plant'. However, the matter was clarified by the case of *Munby v. Furlong* in which the Court of Appeal decided that the initial cost of law books purchased by a barrister was expenditure on 'plant' and eligible for capital allowances. This is clearly a most important decision, particularly relevant to any person who uses expensive books in the course of exercising his or her profession.

Pension contributions

Personal pensions

Where a self-employed person pays annual premiums under an approved personal pension policy, tax relief may now be obtained each year for the following amounts:

Age at 6/4/98	Maximum %
35 and under	17.5% (max) £15,330
36 – 45	20% (max) £17,520
46 – 50	25% (max) £21,900
51 – 55	30% (max) £26,280
56 – 60	35% (max) £30,660
61 and over	40% (max) £35,040

These figures do not apply to existing retirement annuity policies; these remain subject to the old limits which are unchanged.

These arrangements can be extremely advantageous in providing for a pension as premiums are usually paid when the income is high (and the tax relief is also high) and the pension (taxed as earned income when received) usually arises when the income is low and little tax is payable. The reduction in the rates of income tax to a maximum of 40% makes this decision a little more difficult because the tax advantages could go into reverse. When the pension is paid it could, if rates rise again, be taxed at a higher rate than the rate of tax relief at the moment. One would be deferring income in order to pay more tax on it later. However, this involves a large element of guesswork, and many people will be content simply with the long-term pension benefits.

Class 4 NI contributions

Allied to pensions is the payment of Class 4 National Insurance contributions, although no pension or other benefit is obtained by the contributions; the Class 4 contributions are designed solely to extract additional amounts from self-employed persons and are payable in addition to the normal Class 2 (self-employed) contributions. The rates are changed each year and for 1998/99 self-employed persons will be obliged to contribute 6% of their profits between the range £7310-£25,220 per annum, a maximum liability of £1075 for 1998/99. This amount is collected in conjunction with the Schedule D income tax liability.

Spreading relief

Relief for copyright payments

Special provisions enable authors and similar persons who have been engaged on a literary, dramatic, musical or artistic work for a period of more than 12 months, to spread certain amounts received over two or three years depending on the time spent in preparing the work. If the author was engaged on the work for a period exceeding 12 months, the receipt may be spread backwards over two years; if the author was engaged on the work for more than 24 months, the receipt may be spread backwards over three years. (Analogous provisions apply to sums received for the sale of a painting, sculpture or other work of art.) The relief applies to:

- lump sums received on the assignment of copyright, in whole or in part;
- sums received on the grant of any interest in the copyright by licence;
- non-returnable advances on account of royalties;
- any receipts of or on account of royalties or any periodical sums received within two years of first publication.

A claim for spreading relief has to be made within eight years from 5 April following the date of first publication.

Relief: copyright sold after 10 years

Where copyright is assigned (or a licence in it is granted) more than 10 years after the first publication of the work, then the amounts received can qualify for a different spreading relief. The assignment (or licence) must be for a period of more than two years and the receipt will be spread forward over the number of years for which the assignment (or licence) is granted – but with a maximum of six years. The relief is terminated by death, but there are provisions enabling the deceased author's personal representatives to re-spread the amounts if it is to the beneficiaries' advantage.

The above rules are arbitrary and cumbersome, only providing a limited measure of relief in special circumstances. The provisions can sometimes be helpful to repair matters when consideration of the tax position has been neglected, but invariably a better solution is found if the likely tax implications are considered fully in advance.

Collection of tax

Self assessment

The year ended 5 April 1997, i.e. the tax year 1996/7, brought with it two profound changes to the method of taxing individuals, particularly those carrying out a self-employed activity such as writing. The old system of sending in a tax return showing all your income and the Inland Revenue raising an assessment to collect the tax has gone. So has the idea that you pay tax on your profits for the preceding year. Now, when you send in your tax return you have to work out your own tax liability and send a cheque; this is called 'self assessment'. If you get it wrong, or if you are late with your tax return or the payment of tax, interest and penalties will be charged.

Under the new system, the Inland Revenue will rarely issue assessments; they are no longer necessary because the idea is that you assess yourself. A new colour-coded tax return has been designed to help individuals meet their new tax obligations. This is a daunting task but the term 'self assessment' is not intended to imply that individuals have to do it themselves; they can (and often will) engage professional help. The term is only intended to convey that it is the taxpayer, and not the Inland Revenue, who is responsible for getting the tax liability right and for it to be paid on time.

The deadline for sending in the tax return is 31 January following the end of the tax year; so for the tax year 1997/98, the tax return has to be submitted to the Inland Revenue by 31 January 1999. If for some reason you are unwilling or unable to calculate the tax payable, you can ask the Inland Revenue to do it for you, in which case it is necessary to send in your tax return by 30 September.

Income tax on self-employed earnings remains payable in two instalments but the payment dates have been moved to 31 January and 31 July each year. Because the accurate figures may not necessarily be known, these payments in January and July will therefore be only payments on account based on the previous year's liability. The final balancing figure will be paid the following 31 January together with the first instalment of the liability for the following year.

When the Inland Revenue receives the self-assessment tax return, it is checked to see if there is anything obviously wrong; if there is, a letter will be sent to you immediately. Otherwise, the Inland Revenue has 12 months in which to make further enquiries; if it doesn't, it will have no further opportunity to do so and your tax liabilities are final – unless there is something seriously wrong such as the omission of income or capital gains. In that event, the Inland Revenue will raise an assessment later to collect any extra tax together with appropriate penalties. It is essential for the operation of the new system that all records relevant to your tax returns are retained for at least 12 months in case they are needed by the Inland Revenue. For the self employed, the record-keeping requirement is much more onerous because the records need to be kept for nearly six years. One important change in the rules is that if you claim a tax deduction for an expenditure, it will be necessary to have a receipt or other document proving that the expenditure has been made. Because the existence of the underlying records is so important to the operation of self assessment, the Inland Revenue treats them very seriously and there is a penalty of £3000 for any failure to keep adequate records.

Transitional relief for the self employed

For people who were engaged in professional writing or other self-employed activities before 6 April 1994, there was a special relief in connection with the change to the current year basis of assessment. After all, it would have been very unfair to replace the preceding year basis with a current year basis without some special rules because otherwise, two years' profits would be taxed in the same year. Accordingly, for the tax year 1996/97, the profits to be taxed are 50% of the profits for the two years ending in that tax year. So, for example, if accounts are made up to 31 December each year, the profits for the year ended 31 December 1995 and 31 December 1996 are added together and half the total charged to tax in 1996/97. There are no similar provisions for subsequent years.

Interest

Interest is chargeable on overdue tax at a variable rate, which at the time of writing is 9.5% per annum. It does not rank for any tax relief, which can make the Inland Revenue an expensive source of credit.

However, the Inland Revenue can also be obliged to pay interest (known as repayment supplement) tax-free where repayments are delayed. The rules relating to repayment supplement are less beneficial and even more complicated than the rules for interest payable but they do exist and can be very welcome if a large repayment has been delayed for a long time. Unfortunately, the rate of repayment supplement is only 4.75%, much lower than the rate of interest on unpaid tax.

Value added tax

The activities of writers, painters, composers, etc, are all 'taxable supplies' within the scope of VAT and chargeable at the standard rate. (Zero rating which applies to publishers, booksellers, etc on the supply of books does not extend to the work performed by writers.) Accordingly, authors are obliged to register for VAT if their income for the past 12 months exceeds £50,000 or if their income for the coming month will exceed that figure.

Delay in registering can be a most serious matter because if registration is not effected at the proper time, the Customs and Excise can (and invariably do) claim VAT from all the income received since the date on which registration should have been made. As no VAT would have been included in the amounts received during this period the amount claimed by the Customs and Excise must inevitably come straight from the pocket of the author.

The author may be entitled to seek reimbursement of the VAT from those whom he or she ought to have charged VAT but this is obviously a matter of some difficulty and may indeed damage his commercial relationships. Apart from these disadvantages there is also a penalty for late registration. The rules are extremely harsh and are imposed automatically even in cases of innocent error. It is therefore extremely important to monitor the income very carefully because if in any period of 12 months the income exceeds the £50,000 limit, the Customs and Excise must be notified within 30 days of the end of the period. Failure to do so will give rise to an automatic penalty. It should be emphasised that this is a penalty for failing to submit a form and has nothing to do with any real or potential loss of tax. Furthermore, whether the failure was innocent or deliberate will not matter. Only the existence of a 'reasonable excuse' will be a defence to the penalty. However, a reasonable excuse does not include ignorance, error, a lack of funds or reliance on any third party.

However, it is possible to regard VAT registration as a privilege and not a penalty, because only VAT registered persons can reclaim VAT paid on their expenses such as stationery, telephone, professional fees, etc, even typewriters and other plant and machinery (excluding cars). However, many find that the administrative inconvenience – the cost of maintaining the necessary records and completing the necessary forms – more than outweighs the benefits to be gained from registration and prefer to stay outside the scope of VAT for as long as possible.

Overseas matters

The general observation may be made that self-employed persons resident and domiciled in the United Kingdom are not well treated with regard to their overseas work, being taxable on their worldwide income. It is important to emphasise that if fees are earned abroad, no tax saving can be achieved merely by keeping the money outside the country. Although exchange control regulations no longer exist to require repatriation of foreign earnings, such income remains taxable in the UK and must be disclosed to the Inland Revenue; the same applies to interest or other income arising on any investment of these earnings overseas. Accordingly, whenever foreign earnings are likely to become substantial, prompt and effective action is required to limit the impact of UK and foreign taxation. In the case of non-resident authors it is important that arrangements concerning writing for publication in the UK, e.g. in newspapers, are undertaken with great care. A case concerning the wife of one of the great train robbers who provided detailed information for a series of articles in a Sunday newspaper is most instructive. Although she was acknowledged to be resident in Canada for all the relevant years, the income from the articles was treated as arising in this country and fully chargeable to UK tax.

The United Kingdom has double taxa-

tion agreements with many other countries and these agreements are designed to ensure that income arising in a foreign country is taxed either in that country or in the UK. Where a withholding tax is deducted from payments received from another country (or where tax is paid in full in the absence of a double taxation agreement), the amount of foreign tax paid can usually be set off against the related UK tax liability. Many successful authors can be found living in Eire because of the complete exemption from tax which attaches to works of cultural or artistic merit by persons who are resident there. However, such a step should only be contemplated having careful regard to all the other domestic and commercial considerations and specialist advice is essential if the exemption is to be obtained and kept; a careless breach of the conditions could cause the exemption to be withdrawn with catastrophic consequences.

Companies

When an author becomes successful the prospect of paying tax at the higher rate may drive him or her to take hasty action such as the formation of companies, etc, which may not always be to his advantage. Indeed some authors seeing the exodus into tax exile of their more successful colleagues even form companies in low tax areas in the naive expectation of saving large amounts of tax. The Inland Revenue is fully aware of the opportunities and have extensive powers to charge tax and combat avoidance. Accordingly, such action is just as likely to increase tax liabilities and generate other costs and should never be contemplated without expert advice; some very expensive mistakes are often made in this area which are not always able to be remedied.

To conduct one's business through the medium of a company can be a most effective method of mitigating tax liabilities, and providing it is done at the right time and under the right circumstances very substantial advantages can be derived. However, if done without due care and attention the intended advantages will simply evaporate. At the very least it is essential to ensure that the company's business is genuine and conducted properly with regard to the realities of the situation. If the author continues his or her activities unchanged, simply paying all the receipts from his work into a company's bank account, he cannot expect to persuade the Inland Revenue that it is the company and not himself who is entitled to, and should be assessed to tax on, that income.

It must be strongly emphasised that many pitfalls exist which can easily eliminate all the tax benefits expected to arise by the formation of the company. For example, company directors are employees of the company and will be liable to pay much higher National Insurance contributions; the company must also pay the employer's proportion of the contribution and a total liability of over 20% of gross salary may arise. This compares most unfavourably with the position of a self-employed person. Moreover, on the commencement of the company's business the individual's profession will cease and the possibility of revisions being made by the Inland Revenue to earlier tax liabilities

means that the timing of a change has to be considered very carefully.

The tax return

No mention has been made above of personal reliefs and allowances (e.g., the single and married couples allowances, etc); this is because these allowances and the rates of tax are subject to constant change and are always set out in detail in the explanatory notes which accompany the Tax Return. The annual Tax Return is an important document and should be completed promptly with extreme care, particularly since the introduction of self-assessment. If filling in the Return is a source of difficulty or anxiety, comfort may be found in the Consumer Association's publication *Money Which? – Tax Saving Guide*; this is published in March of each year and includes much which is likely to be of interest and assistance.

Peter Vaines FCA, ATII, barrister, is a Partner at Brebner, Allen & Trapp Chartered Accountants, and writes and speaks widely on tax and related matters. He is Managing Editor of *Personal Tax Planning Review*, on the Editorial Board of *Taxation*, and tax columnist for *New Law Journal*.

Social security contributions

*In general, every individual who works in Great Britain either as an employee or as a self-employed person is liable to pay social security contributions. The law governing this subject is complicated and **Peter Arrowsmith** FCA gives here a summary of the position. This article should be regarded as a general guide only.*

All contributions are payable in respect of years ending on 5 April. The classes of contributions are:

Class 1 These are payable by employees (primary contributions) and their employers (secondary contributions) and are based on earnings.

Class 1A Use of company car, and fuel, for private purposes.

Class 2 These are weekly flat rate contributions, payable by the self-employed.

Class 3 These are weekly flat rate contributions, payable on a voluntary basis in order to provide, or make up entitlement to, certain social security benefits.

Class 4 These are payable by the self-employed in respect of their trading or professional income and are based on earnings.

Employed or self-employed?

The question as to whether a person is employed under a contract *of* service and is thereby an employee liable to Class 1 contributions, or performs services (either solely or in partnership) under a contract *for* service and is thereby self-employed liable to Class 2 and Class 4 contributions, often has to be decided in practice. One of the best guides can be found in the case of *Market Investigations Ltd* v. *Minister of Social Security* (1969 2 WLR 1) when Cooke J. remarked:

'... the fundamental test to be applied is this: "Is the person who has engaged himself to perform these services performing them as a person in business on his own account?" If the answer to that question is "yes", then the contract is a contract for services. If the answer is "no", then the contract is a contract of service. No exhaustive list has been compiled and perhaps no exhaustive list can be compiled of the considerations which are relevant in determining that question, nor can strict rules be laid down as to the relative weight which the various considerations should carry in particular cases. The most that can be said is that control will no doubt always have to be considered, although it can no longer be regarded as the sole determining factor; and that factors which may be of importance are such matters as:

• whether the man performing the services provides his own equipment,
• whether he hires his own helpers,
• what degree of financial risk he takes,
• what degree of responsibility for investment and management he has, and
• whether and how far he has an opportunity of profiting from sound management in the performance of his task.'

The above case was also considered as recently as November 1993 by the Court of Appeal in the case of *Hall* v. *Lorimer*. In this case a vision mixer with around 20 clients and undertaking around 120-150 separate engagements per annum was held to be self-employed. This follows the, perhaps surprising, contention of the Inland Revenue that the taxpayer was an employee.

Further guidance

There have been three cases dealing with musicians, in relatively recent times, which provide further guidance on the question as to whether an individual is employed or self-employed.

• *Midland Sinfonia Concert Society Ltd* v. *Secretary of State for Social Services* **(1981 ICR 454).** A musician, employed to play in an orchestra by separate invitation at irregular intervals and remunerated solely in respect of each occasion upon which he does play, is employed under a contract for services. He is therefore self-employed, not an employed earner, for the purposes of the Social Security Contributions and Benefits Act 1992, and the orchestra which engages him is not liable to pay National Insurance contributions in respect of his earnings.

• *Addison* v. *London Philharmonic Orchestra Ltd* **(1981 ICR 261).** This was an appeal to determine whether certain individuals were employees for the purposes of section 11(1) of the Employment Protection (Consolidation) Act 1978.

The Employment Appeal Tribunal upheld the decision of an industrial tribunal that an associate player and three additional or extra players of the London Philharmonic Orchestra were not employees under a contract of service, but were essentially freelance musicians carrying on their own business. The facts found by the industrial tribunal showed that, when playing for the orchestra, each appellant remained essentially a freelance musician, pursuing his or her own profession as an instrumentalist, with an individual reputation, and carrying on his or her own business, and they contributed their own skills and interpretative powers to the orchestra's performances as independent contractors.

• *Winfield* v. *London Philharmonic Orchestra Ltd* **(1979 ICR 726).** This case dealt with the question as to whether an individual was an employee within the meaning of section 30 of the Trade Union and Labour Relations Act 1974. The following remarks by the appeal tribunal are of interest in relation to the status of musicians:

'... making music is an art, and the co-operation required for a performance of Berlioz's *Requiem* is dissimilar to that required between the manufacturer of concrete and the truck driver who takes the concrete where it is needed ... It took the view, as we think it was entitled on the material before it to do, that the company was simply machinery through which the members of the orchestra managed and controlled the orchestra's operation ... In deciding whether you are in the presence of a contract of service or not, you look at the whole of the picture. This picture looks to us, as it looked to the industrial tribunal, like a co-operative of distinguished musicians running themselves with self and mutual discipline, and in no sense like a boss and his musician employees.'

Other recent cases have concerned a professional dancer and holiday camp entertainers (all of whom were regarded as employees). In two recent cases income from part-time lecturing was held to be from an employment.

Accordingly, if a person is regarded as an employee under the above rules, he or she will be liable to pay contributions even if his employment is casual, part time or temporary. Furthermore, if a person is an employee and also carries on a trade or profession either solely or in partnership, there will be a liability to more than one class of contributions (subject to certain maxima – see below).

Exceptions

There are certain exceptions to the above rules, those most relevant to artists and writers being:

• The employment of a wife by her husband, or vice versa, is disregarded for social security purposes unless it is for the purposes of a trade or profession (e.g. the employment of his wife by an author would not be disregarded and would result in a liability for contributions if her salary reached the minimum levels).

• The employment of certain relatives in

a private dwelling house in which both employee and employer reside is disregarded for social security purposes provided the employment is not for the purposes of a trade or business carried on at those premises by the employer. This would cover the employment of a relative (as defined) as a housekeeper in a private residence.

• In general, lecturers, teachers and instructors engaged by an educational establishment to teach on at least four days in three consecutive months are regarded as employees, although this rule does not apply to fees received by persons giving public lectures.

Freelance film workers

As regards the status of workers in the film and allied industries, the Inland Revenue made the following announcement on 30 March 1983:

'The Inland Revenue has recently carried out a review of the employment status of workers engaged on "freelance" terms within the industry. Following this review there has been an extensive series of discussions with representative bodies in the industry, including Independent Programme Producers Association, British Film and Television Producers Association, Advertising Film and Video Tape Producers Association, National Association of Theatrical and Kine Employees, and Association of Cinematograph, Television and Allied Technicians.

'As a result of that review and the subsequent discussions, the Inland Revenue considers that a number of workers engaged on "freelance" terms within the industry are engaged as employees under contracts of service, either written or oral, and should be assessed under Schedule E. Many workers in the industry already pay employee's National Insurance contributions.

'The Inland Revenue, however, accepts that a number of "freelance" workers in certain types of work within the industry are likely to be engaged under contracts for services, as people in self-employ-ment, and should therefore be assessed under Schedule D. Any individual who does not agree with the Revenue's determination of his position has the normal right of appeal to the independent Income Tax Commissioners.'

There is a list of grades in the film industry in respect of which PAYE need not be deducted and who are regarded as self-employed for tax purposes.

Further information can be obtained from the March 1992 edition of the Inland Revenue guidance notes on the application of PAYE to casual and freelance staff in the film industry. In view of the Inland Revenue announcement that the same status will apply for PAYE and DSS purposes, no liability for employee's and employer's contributions should arise in the case of any of the grades mentioned above. However, in the film and TV industry this general rule has not always been followed in practice. In December 1992, after a long review, the DSS agreed that individuals working behind the camera and who have jobs on the Inland Revenue Schedule D list are self-employed for social security purposes. The Contributions Agency will accept claims for repayment of Class 1 contributions where persons were correctly to have been treated as self-employed. It was announced on 23 June 1995 that a provision had been included in the Pensions Bill to enable a self-employed person who had erroneously been charged Class 1 contributions to forego a refund of the employee's contributions and retain the right to earnings-related state pension entitlement and, if applicable, personal pension rebates. The provision does not prevent the 'employer' reclaiming the employer's portion of contributions. The individual's benefit position will be preserved provided that it is only the employer's contributions that are refunded. Individuals or employers wishing to seek refunds should write to The Contributions Agency Refunds Group (see page 676).

There are special rules for, *inter alia*, personnel appearing before the camera, short engagements, payments to limited companies and payments to overseas personalities.

Artistes, performers/non-performers

From 6 April 1990 to 5 April 1996 artistes and performers (excluding established performers with 'reserved Schedule D status' and guest artistes engaged by opera companies) working under standard Equity contracts were treated as employees for income tax purposes so far as earnings from such employments were concerned. This brought the income tax treatment into line with that of social security, as it has been the view of the DSS for many years that the vast majority of performers are employees for social security contribution purposes because of the general conditions under which they usually work.

However, from 6 April 1994 it is understood that the Inland Revenue accepts that the earnings of many artistes should be assessed under Schedule D Case I. This does not, of itself, affect the social security position but the DSS has always acknowledged that there is some scope for self-employment for performers (especially 'act as known' engagements), and specific claims to self-employment are looked into in detail. Accordingly 'act as known' engagements will normally be treated as self-employment for both social security and income tax purposes.

The DSS does, however, permit subsistence allowances to be paid without liability to contributions, and special rules apply to travelling expenses.

The industry also uses standard agreements for the engagement of non-performers. The Inland Revenue has looked at some of these and concluded that some are normally contracts for services (self-employed) and others contracts of service (employed).

As recently as 20 November 1997, Mr Denham, Secretary of State for Social Security, said in the House of Commons: "We are considering the status of actors for National Insurance purposes and an announcement will be made in due course." It is believed that the authorities will have to concede that self-employment is the correct status of a number of individuals in the industry, who are currently disputing their status. At the time of writing, the promised statement was still awaited.

Class 1 contributions

As mentioned above, these are related to earnings, the amount payable depending upon whether the employer has applied for his employees to be 'contracted-out' of the State earnings-related pension scheme; such application can be made where the employer's own pension scheme provides a requisite level of benefits for his or her employees and their dependants or, in the case of a money purchase scheme (COMPS) certain minimum safeguards are covered.

Contributions are only payable once

Rates of Class 1 contributions and earnings limits from 6 April 1998

Earnings per week	Rates payable on all earnings			
	Not contracted-out		Contracted-out	
	Employee	Employer	Employee	Employer
£		%		%
Below 64.00	—	—	—	—
64.00 – 109.99	2% to lower	3	2% to lower	*3/nil or 1.5
110.00 – 154.99	earnings limit,	5	earnings limit,	*5/2 or 3.5
155.00 – 209.99	10% between	7	8.4% between	*7/4 or 5.5
210.00 – 485.00	lower and	10	lower and	*10/7 or 8.5
Over £485.00	upper earnings limits	10	upper earnings limits	†10/7 or 8.5

* The first figure is the rate to the lower earnings limit and the second is to all the excess.
† 10% to lower earnings limit and above upper earnings limit; 7% or 8.5%between these limits.

earnings exceed the lower earnings limit but are then due on *all* such earnings up to the upper earnings limit by employees ('primary contributions') but without an upper limit for employers ('secondary contributions'). Contributions are normally collected via the PAYE tax deduction machinery, and there are penalties for late submission of returns and for errors therein. From 19 April 1993, interest will be charged automatically on unpaid PAYE and social security contributions.

Employees liable to pay

Contributions are payable by any employee who is aged 16 years and over (even though he or she may still be at school) and who is paid an amount equal to, or exceeding, the lower earnings limit (see below). Nationality is irrelevant for contribution purposes and, subject to special rules covering employees not normally resident in Great Britain, Northern Ireland or the Isle of Man, or resident in EEA countries or those with which there are reciprocal agreements, contributions must be paid whether the employee concerned is a British subject or not provided he is gainfully employed in Great Britain.

Employees exempt from liability to pay

Persons over pensionable age (65 for men; 60 – currently – for women) are exempt from liability to pay primary contributions, even if they have not retired. However, the fact that an employee may be exempt from liability does not relieve an employer from liability to pay secondary contributions in respect of that employee.

Rate of employees' contributions

From 6 April 1998, the rate of employees' contributions, where the earnings are not less than the lower earnings limit, is 2% of earnings to the lower earnings limit

and 10% of earnings between the lower and upper earnings limits (8.4% for contracted-out employments).

Certain married women who made appropriate elections before 12 May 1977 may be entitled to pay a reduced rate of 3.85%. However, they will have no entitlement to benefits in respect of these contributions.

Employers' contributions

All employers are liable to pay contributions on the gross earnings of employees. As mentioned above, an employer's liability is not reduced as a result of employees being exempted from, or being liable to pay only the (3.85%) reduced rate of, contributions.

For earnings paid on or after 6 April 1998 employers are liable at rates of 3%, 5%, 7% or 10% on earnings paid (without any upper earnings limit) depending upon the particular band into which the earnings fall (see below). The rate of contributions attributable to the band into which the earnings fall is applied to all those earnings and not merely to the earnings falling into that band. The above four rates of secondary contributions are reduced to zero%, 2%, 4% and 7% in respect of earnings above the lower earnings limit and up to and including the upper earnings limit for contracted-out employments from 6 April 1998.

The above employers' rates become 1.5%, 3.5%, 5.5% and 8.5% where the scheme is a contracted-out *money purchase* scheme rather than being contracted out by virtue of a *salary-related* scheme.

The employer is responsible for the payment of both employees' and employer's contributions, but is entitled to deduct the employees' contributions from the earnings on which they are calculated. Effectively, therefore, the employee suffers a deduction in respect of his or her social security contributions in arriving at his weekly or monthly wage or salary. Special rules apply to company directors and persons employed through agencies.

Items included in, or excluded from, earnings

Contributions are calculated on the basis of a person's gross earnings from his or her employment. This will normally be the figure shown on the tax deduction working sheet, except where the employee pays superannuation contributions and, from 6 April 1987, charitable gifts – these must be added back for the purposes of calculating Class 1 liability. Profit-related pay exempt from income tax is not exempt from social security contributions.

Earnings include salary, wages, overtime pay, commissions, bonuses, holiday pay, payments made while the employee is sick or absent from work, payments to cover travel between home and office, and payments under the statutory sick pay and statutory maternity pay schemes.

However, certain payments, some of which may be regarded as taxable income for income tax purposes, are ignored for social security purposes. These include:

- certain gratuities paid other than by the employer,
- redundancy payments and most payments in lieu of notice,
- certain payments in kind,
- reimbursement of specific expenses incurred in the carrying out of the employment,
- benefits given on an individual basis for personal reasons (e.g. wedding and birthday presents),
- compensation for loss of office, and
- meal vouchers which can only be redeemed for food or drink.

IR/CA booklet CWG 2 (April 1998 edition) gives a list of items to include in or exclude from earnings for Class 1 contribution purposes. A new, additional booklet, CWG4, is likely to be issued in Summer 1998.

Maximum contributions

There is a limit to the total liability for social security contributions payable by a person who is employed in more than one employment, or is also self-employed or a partner.

Where only not contracted-out Class 1 contributions, or not contracted-out Class 1 and Class 2 contributions, are payable, the maximum contribution is limited to 53 primary Class 1 contributions at the maximum weekly non-contracted-out standard rate. For 1998/99 the maximum will thus be £2299.14.

However, where contracted-out Class 1 contributions are payable, the maximum primary Class 1 contributions payable for 1998/99 where all employments are contracted out are £1942.13.

Where Class 4 contributions are payable in addition to Class 1 and/or Class 2 contributions, the Class 4 contributions are restricted so that they shall not exceed the excess of £1411.15 (i.e. 53 Class 2 contributions plus maximum Class 4 contributions) over the aggregate of the Class 1 and Class 2 contributions.

Miscellaneous rules

There are detailed rules covering a person with two or more employments; where a person receives a bonus or commission in addition to a regular wage or salary; and where a person is in receipt of holiday pay. From 6 April 1991 employers' social security contributions arise under Class 1A in respect of the private use of a company car, and of fuel provided for private use therein. The rate is currently 10%.

Class 2 contributions

Class 2 contributions are payable at the weekly rate of £6.35 as from 6 April 1998. Exemptions from Class 2 liability are:

- A man over 65 or a woman over 60.
- A person who has not attained the age of 16.
- A married woman or, in certain cases, a widow who elected prior to 12 May 1977 not to pay Class 2 contributions.
- Persons with small earnings (see below).
- Persons not ordinarily self-employed (see below).

Small earnings

Application for a certificate of exception from Class 2 contributions may be made by any person who can show that his or her net self-employed earnings per his profit and loss account (as opposed to taxable profits):
• for the year of application are expected to be less than a specified limit (£3590 in the 1998/99 tax year); or
• for the year preceding the application were less than the limit specified for that year (£3480 for 1997/98) and there has been no material change of circumstances.

Certificates of exception must be renewed in accordance with the instructions stated thereon. At the Secretary of State's discretion the certificate may commence up to 13 weeks before the date on which the application is made. Despite a certificate of exception being in force, a person who is self-employed is still entitled to pay Class 2 contributions if he or she wishes, in order to maintain entitlement to social security benefits.

Persons not ordinarily self-employed

Part-time self-employed activities (including as a writer or artist) are disregarded for contribution purposes if the person concerned is not ordinarily employed in such activities and has a full-time job as an employee. There is no definition of 'ordinarily employed' for this purpose but the DSS often regards a person who has a regular job and whose earnings from spare-time occupation are not expected to be more than £800 per annum as falling within this category. Persons qualifying for this relief do not require certificates of exception. It should be noted that many activities covered by this relief would probably also be eligible for relief under the small earnings rule (see above).

Method of payment

From April 1993, Class 2 contributions may be paid by monthly direct debit in arrears or by cheque, bank giro, etc following receipt of a quarterly (in arrears) bill from DSS.

Overpaid contributions

If, following the payment of Class 2 contributions, it is found that the earnings are below the exception limit (e.g. the relevant accounts are prepared late), the Class 2 contributions that have been overpaid can be reclaimed for tax years 1988/89 onwards, provided a claim is made between 6 April and 31 December immediately following the end of the tax year.

Class 3 contributions

Class 3 contributions are payable voluntarily, at the weekly rate of £6.25 per week from 6 April 1998, by persons aged 16 or over with a view to enabling them to qualify for a limited range of benefits if their contribution record is not otherwise sufficient. In general, Class 3 contributions can be paid by employees, the self-employed and the non employed.

Broadly speaking, no more than 52 Class 3 contributions are payable for any one tax year, and contributions are not payable after the end of the tax year in which the individual concerned reaches the age of 64 (59 for women).

Class 3 contributions may be paid in the same manner as Class 2 (see above) or by annual cheque in arrears.

Class 4 contributions

In addition to Class 2 contributions, self-employed persons are liable to pay Class 4 contributions. These are calculated at the rate of 6% on the amount of profits or gains chargeable to income tax under Schedule D Case I or II which exceed £7310 per annum but which do not exceed £25,220 per annum for 1998/99. Thus the maximum Class 4 contribution is 6% of £17,910 – i.e. £1074.60 for 1998/99.

The income tax profits on which Class 4 contributions are calculated is after deducting capital allowances and losses, but before deducting personal tax allowances or retirement annuity or personal pension plan premiums.

Class 4 contributions produce no additional benefits, but were introduced to ensure that self-employed persons as a whole pay a fair share of the cost of pensions and other social security benefits without the self-employed who make only small profits having to pay excessively high flat rate contributions.

From 6 April 1996 no income tax relief is available for Class 4 contributions. Previously, half the liability attracted income tax relief.

Payment of contributions

In general, contributions are now self assessed and paid to the Inland Revenue together with the income tax under Schedule D Case I or II, and accordingly the contributions are due and payable at the same time as the income tax liability on the relevant profits. Under self-assessment, interim payments of Class 4 contributions are payable at the same time as interim payments of tax.

Class 4 exemptions

The following persons are exempt from Class 4 contributions:
• Men over 65 and women over 60 at the commencement of the year of assessment (i.e. on 6 April).
• An individual not resident in the United Kingdom for income tax purposes in the year of assessment.
• Persons whose earnings are not 'immediately derived' from carrying on a trade, profession or vocation (e.g., sleeping partners and, possibly, limited partners).
• A child under 16 on 6 April of the year of assessment.
• Persons not ordinarily self-employed (see above as for Class 2 contributions).

Married persons and partnerships

Under independent taxation of husband and wife from 1990/91 onwards, each spouse is responsible for his or her Class 4 liability.

Further information

Further information can be obtained from the many booklets published by the Department of Social Security, available from local offices – refer to telephone directory under 'Contributions Agency' in the first instance.

Contributions Agency, International Services
Newcastle upon Tyne NE98 1YX
tel (06451) 54811 (local call rates apply)
Address for enquiries for individuals resident abroad.

The Contributions Agency Refunds Group
Employers Unit 4, Room 101E,
Benton Park Road, Longbenton,
Newcastle upon Tyne NE98 1YX
tel (06451) 54260 (local call rates apply)
Address for individuals or employers wishing to seek refunds.

In partnerships, each partner's liability is calculated separately. If a partner also carries on another trade or profession, the profits of all such businesses are aggregated for the purposes of calculating his or her Class 4 liability.

When an assessment has become final and conclusive for the purposes of income tax, it is also final and conclusive for the purposes of calculating Class 4 liability.

Budget 1998

The announcements made on 17 March 1998 will change the structure of Class 1 contributions from 6 April 1999. The figures mentioned below are illustrative only as the rates are subject to review and indexation before 6 April 1999.

Both employers and employees will pay contributions only on earnings in excess of the relevant lower limit; the present catch-up charge at the point where earnings cross a limit will cease. There will be a new, separate lower limit for employers of £81 per week; this is equivalent to the single person's tax allowance.

However, employers' contributions will rise to 12.2% on all earnings in excess of that figure, e.g. earnings £91 per week – contribution £1.22.

For employees the manner of calculating contributions changes in the same way but (despite Budget Day press comment to the contrary) the lower limit remains at £64 for now, e.g. earnings £91 per week – contribution at 10%: £2.70. There is an intent to increase the employees' limit from £64 to £81 but not as soon as 1999.

Additionally, the functions of the Contributions Agency will transfer to the Inland Revenue from 6 April 1999. From that date, in case of difficulty, you should contact your local income tax office.

Peter Arrowsmith FCA is a sole practitioner specialising in National Insurance matters. He is a member of the National Insurance Committee of the Institute of Chartered Accountants in England and Wales and Consulting Editor to *Tolley's National Insurance Contributions 1998/99.*

Social security benefits

*There are many leaflets produced by the Department of Social Security. However, due to the nature of the subject social security benefits can be quite difficult to understand. In this article, **K.D. Bartlett** FCA has summarised some of the more usual benefits that are available under the Social Security Acts.*

This article deliberately does not cover every aspect of the legislation but the references given should enable the relevant information to be easily traced. These references are to the leaflets issued by the Department of Social Security.

It is usual for only one periodical benefit to be payable at any one time. If the contribution conditions are satisfied for more than one benefit it is the larger benefit that is payable. Benefit rates shown below were those payable from week commencing 6 April 1997.

Employed persons (Category A or D contributors) are covered for all benefits. Certain married women and widows (Category B and E contributors) who elected to pay at the reduced rate receive only attendance allowance, guardian's allowance and industrial injuries benefits. Other benefits may be available dependent on their husbands' contributions.

Self-employed persons (Class 2 and Class 4 contributors) are covered for all benefits except earnings-related supplements, unemployment benefit, widow's and invalidity pensions, widowed mother's allowance and industrial injury benefits.

Family benefits

Child benefits

Leaflet CH 1

Child benefit is payable for all children who are either under 16 or under 19 receiving full-time education at a recognised educational establishment. The rate is £11.45 for the first or eldest child and £9.30 a week for each subsequent child. It is payable to the person who is responsible for the child but excludes foster parents or people exempt from UK tax. Furthermore, one-parent families receive £17.10 per week for the eldest child.

Maternity benefits

Help with maternity expenses is given to selected people from the social fund. To be eligible the claimant must be receiving income support or family credit. £100 is paid for each new or adopted baby, reduced by the amount of any savings over £500 held by the claimant or his or her family. A payment can be obtained from the social fund for an adopted baby provided the child is not more than 12 months old when the application is made. The claimant has three months to make the claim from when adoption has taken place.

Maternity pay

Leaflet NI 17A

Statutory maternity pay (SMP) was introduced for female employees who leave employment because of pregnancy. SMP is applicable to those who have worked for 26 weeks by the 15th week before the expected date of confinement. This 15th week is known as the qualifying week (QW). The other qualifying conditions are that the woman must:
• be pregnant at the 11th week before the expected week of confinement, or already have been confined;
• have stopped working for her employer wholly or partly because of pregnancy or confinement;
• have average earnings of not less than the lower earnings limit for the payment of National Insurance contributions which is in force during her QW;
• provide her employer with evidence of her expected week of confinement;
• provide her employer with notice of her maternity absence.

Rates of SMP

There is a higher and a lower rate. The higher rate of SMP is 90% of an employee's weekly earnings and is paid for the first six weeks for which there is entitlement to SMP. To be eligible for the higher rate, a woman must meet all the qualifying conditions and have been employed by the employer for a continuous period of at least two years (at between 8 and 16 hours a week). Her service must continue into the QW.

The lower rate of SMP is a set rate

reviewed each year. The rate for the tax year beginning 6 April 1998 is £57.70 per week. It is paid for 18 weeks to those not entitled to the higher amount and for up to 12 weeks to those who receive the higher rate for the first six weeks.

SMP is taxable and also subject to National Insurance contributions. The gross amount of SMP and the employer's portion of National Insurance payable on the SMP can be recovered from the State by deducting the amounts from the amount normally due for PAYE and National Insurance deductions payable to the Collector of Taxes.

Guardian's allowance

Leaflet NI 14

This is paid at the rate of £9.90 a week. For each subsequent child the rate of benefit is £11.30 a week to people who have taken orphans into their own family. Usually both of the child's parents must be dead and at least one of them must have satisfied a residence condition.

The allowance can only be paid to the person who is entitled to child benefit for the child (or to that person's spouse). It is not necessary to be the legal guardian. The claim should be made within three months of the date of entitlement.

Disability living allowance

Disability living allowance (DLA) was introduced on 6 April 1992 and replaces attendance allowance for disabled people before they reach the age of 65. It has also replaced mobility allowance.

Those who are disabled after reaching 65 may be able to claim attendance allowance. The attendance allowance board decide whether, and for how long, a person is eligible for this allowance. Attendance allowance is not taxable.

The care component is divided into three rates whereas the mobility allowance has two rates. The rate of benefit from 6 April 1998 follows on the next page.

	Per week
Care component	
Higher rate (day and night, or terminally ill)	£51.30
Middle rate (day or night)	£34.30
Lower rate (if need some help during day, or over 16 and need help preparing a meal)	£13.60
Mobility component	
Higher rate (unable or virtually unable to walk)	£35.85
Lower rate (can walk but needs help when outside)	£13.60

Attendance allowance
Attendance allowance has been replaced by DLA from 6 April 1992 for those aged under 65. For those aged 65 or over, attendance allowance will continue to be paid. The rate of benefit from 6 April 1998 is:

Higher rate (day and night)	£51.30
Lower rate (day or night)	£34.30

Benefits for the ill or unemployed

Statutory sick pay

Leaflets NI 27, NI 16, NI 244
In the majority of cases the employer now has the responsibility of paying sick pay to its employees. The payment is dependent on satisfying various conditions in respect of periods of incapacity, periods of entitlement, qualifying days and rules on notification of absence. The rules are quite complicated and reference should be made to the relevant booklets for further clarification but the key points are:
• Payment is made by the employer.
• There is a possibility of two rates of payment dependent on the employee's gross average earnings.
• The employee must not be capable of work and must do no work on the day concerned.
• SSP is not usually payable for the first three working days.
• The maximum entitlement is 28 weeks in any period of incapacity.
• Notification must be made by the employer but this procedure must be within statutory guidelines.
• Payment can be withheld if notification of sickness is not given in due time.

From 6 April 1996 most employers will no longer be able to reclaim any SSP back. Small employers may, in certain circum-

stances, receive compensation called the New Relief Scheme which will help all employers faced with exceptionally high levels of sickness absence.

Sickness benefit

DSS Leaflet NI 16
The majority of illnesses are now covered by statutory sick pay and sickness benefit now only applies to those employees who are excluded from statutory sickness pay and the self-employed. Sickness benefit is paid for up to 28 weeks for those who are off work. If a claimant is still ill after 28 weeks he or she is transferred to the long term benefit, invalidity benefit.

To be eligible for sickness benefit the claimant must have paid, in any one tax year ending before the calendar year in which the claim is made, Class I contributions on an amount of earnings at least 25 times the weekly lower earnings limit for that tax year (or the equivalent of Class 2 contributions for self-employed people).

There is another condition which must be satisfied in that the claimant must have paid, or been credited with, in the tax year ending before the benefit year in which he or she makes the claim, Class 1 contributions on an amount of earnings at least 50 times the weekly lower earnings limit for both the last two tax years (or the equivalent number of Class 2 contributions for self-employed people).

Incapacity benefit

Leaflet DS 700
Incapacity benefit replaced sickness benefit and invalidity benefit. The contribution conditions haven't changed but a new medical test has been brought in which includes a comprehensive questionnaire. The rates from 6 April 1998 are:

Long-term Incapacity Benefit	£64.70
Short-term Incapacity Benefit	
Higher rate	£57.70
Lower rate	£48.80
Increase of Long-term Incapacity Benefit for age:	
Higher rate	£13.60
Lower rate	£6.80

Severe disablement allowance

Leaflet NI 252

This is a benefit for people under pensionable age who cannot work because of physical or mental ill health and do not have sufficient National Insurance contributions to qualify for sickness or invalidity benefit. The basic allowance is £39.10 a week. There are increases of £23.20 a week for adult dependants and £11.30 for each child.

Invalid care allowance

Leaflet NI 212

This is a taxable benefit paid to people of working age who cannot take a job because they have to stay at home to look after a severely disabled person. The basic allowance is £38.70 per week. An extra £23.20 is paid for each adult dependant and £11.30 for each child.

Jobseekers' allowance

Jobseekers' allowance (JSA) is a new social security benefit that came in force on 7 October 1996. It has taken the place of unemployment benefit and income support for unemployed people. JSA differs from unemployment benefit in that there are no additional amounts payable for dependants. The rates are:

Rates of JSA	Post-April 1998
Single under 18	£30.30
18-24	£39.85
25 or over	£50.35

Claimants will be able to claim JSA if they have paid National Insurance contributions equal to 25 times the lower earnings level in one of the last two complete tax years before the claim; and either paid or have been credited in respect of each of the last two complete tax years before the year of the claim 50 times the lower earnings limit for that tax year.

JSA is not normally paid for the first three waiting days. Exceptions are made for those under 18 who are considered to be in severe hardship or if a person has received income support, incapacity benefit or invalid care allowance in the 12 weeks prior to the claim for JSA. Contributory-related JSA is only payable for a maximum of 182 days.

People ineligible for contributory-related JSA may be able to claim income-related JSA. If a claimant satisfies the entitlement conditions he or she is entitled to income-related JSA indefinitely.

Eligibility conditions

In order to be eligible for JSA a potential claimant must not have capital exceeding £8000. If he or she has capital of £3000 or more, £1 is deducted for every £250 above the £3000. The claimant is not allowed to work more than 24 hours a week and his or her partner is only allowed to work 16 hours a week.

Claimants must usually be available to take up employment immediately unless they can show that they are doing part-time work and need to give notice. Once that notice has ended the claimant must take up work immediately afterwards.

Claims should be made at the nearest office of the Department for Education and Employment – in most cases this will be a job centre. Benefit is normally paid fortnightly in arrears via giro cheque either at a post office or via a bank account. JSA is a taxable benefit.

Seeking work

A claimant must agree to a 'jobseekers' agreement' based on the job search plan which will be discussed at the 'new jobseeker' interview. The jobseeker will attend thereafter for a job search review. If the conditions for JSA are still being met, benefit will be paid. If it seems that the jobseeker has made himself unemployed and refuses a job without good cause, payment of JSA can be stopped for up to 26 weeks. People unemployed for at least 13 weeks will not be subject to sanctions if they start a job and then leave it within a period of five to eight weeks after starting a full-time job.

Pensions and widow's benefits

Leaflets NP 23, NP 35, NP 31

The state pension is divided into two parts – the basic pension, presently £64.70 per week for a single person or £103.40 per week for a married couple, and the State Earnings Related Pension Scheme (SERPS), which will after it matures on the present basis pay a pension of 25% of revalued earnings between the lower and upper earnings limits.

The cost of SERPS has been a major political consideration for some time. In order to reduce the long-term cost of the scheme, benefits will be reduced for those retiring or widowed after the year 2000. The benefits will be reduced as follows:
• The pension will be based on lifetime average earnings rather than the best 20 years as at present.
• The pension will be calculated on the basis of 20% of earnings between the lower and upper earnings limit rather than 25%. This will be phased in over 10 years from the tax year 2000/2001.
• Presently all of a member's state earnings-related benefit is inherited by a surviving spouse. For deaths occurring after April 2000 this will be reduced to 50%.

Women paying standard rate contributions into the scheme are eligible for the same amount of pension as men but five years earlier, from age 60. If a woman stays at home to bring up her children or to look after a person receiving attendance allowance she can have her basic pension rights protected without paying contributions.

The widow's pension and widowed mother's allowance also consists of a basic pension and an additional earnings-related pension. The full amount of the additional pension applies only if the husband has contributed to the new scheme for at least 20 years.

Widow's benefits

From 11 April 1988 there are three main widow's benefits:
• Widow's payment, which has replaced the widow's allowance.
• Widowed mother's allowance.
• Widow's pension.

Widow's payment

This is a new allowance, currently a lump sum payment of £1000 payable to widows who were bereaved on or after 11 April 1988. It is payable immediately on the death of the husband. Entitlement to this benefit is based on the late husband's contribution record but no payment will be made if the widow is living with another man as husband and wife at the date of death. The late husband must have actually paid contributions on earnings of at least 25 times the weekly or lower earnings limit for a given tax year in any tax year ending before his death (or ending before he reached pensionable age if he was over 65 when he died). The equivalent number of Class 2 or voluntary Class 3 contributions will be sufficient.

When claiming, the widow should complete the form on the back of the death certificate and send it to the local social security office. On receipt of this information the DSS will send the claimant a more detailed form (BD8) which, once completed, has to go back to the social security office. It is important to claim the benefit within 12 months of the husband's death.

Widowed mother's allowance

Leaflet NP 45

If a widow is left with children to look after, she is entitled to a widowed mother's allowance provided that her late husband had paid sufficient national insurance contributions. These contributions are:
• 25 Class 1, 2 or 3 contributions before age 65 and before 6 April 1975; or
• contributions in any one tax year after 6 April 1975 on earnings of at least 25 times the weekly lower earnings limit for that year.

It is important that the widow is looking after either her own child or her husband's child and that the child is under 16 or, if between the age of 16 and 19, is continuing in full-time education.

The allowance stops immediately if the

widow remarries and will be suspended if she lives with a man as his wife. From April 1996 the amounts payable are:

Basic allowance	£64.70
Increase for each child	£11.30

Where a husband's contributions only satisfied the first test above, the basic allowance may be payable at a reduced rate. This reduction does not alter the rate of an increase for a child.

Widow's pension
Leaflet NP 45

A widow who is over the age of 45 when her husband dies may be eligible for a widow's pension unless she is eligible for the widowed mother's allowance. In this situation the widow's pension becomes payable when the widowed mother's allowance ends, provided she is still under the age of 65. However, where a woman had been receiving the widowed mother's allowance, she becomes entitled to a widow's pension if she is between the ages of 45 and 65 when the allowance ends, no matter what her age may have been when her husband died. Before 11 April 1988 a widow aged 40 or over could qualify for a widow's pension.

Qualification conditions

• The contributions conditions must be satisfied and these conditions are the same as those for the widowed mother's allowance above.
• The widow must not be receiving the widowed mother's allowance.
• When her husband died she was aged between 45 and 65 or she was entitled to widowed mother's allowance and is aged between 45 and 65 when her widowed mother's allowance finished.

Cessation of widow's pension

• Entitlement finishes if the widowed mother's allowance stops because she has remarried.
• Widow's pension must not be claimed when the payment of the widowed moth-

er's allowance has been suspended because the widow is in pension or is living with a man as his wife.

From 11 April 1988 both the basic and additional pension are paid at a reduced rate if the widow was aged under 55:
• when her husband died, if she did not subsequently become entitled to widowed mother's allowance; or
• when her widowed mother's allowance ceased to be paid. The relevant rates from 6 April 1998 are as follows:

Age related	£	%
Basic	64.70	100
Age 54 (49)	60.17	93
53 (48)	55.64	86
52 (47)	51.11	79
51 (46)	46.58	72
50 (45)	42.06	65
49 (44)	37.53	58
48 (43)	33.00	51
47 (42)	28.47	44
46 (41)	23.94	37
45 (40)	19.41	30

(The ages given in parentheses apply to women for whom widow's pension was payable before 11 April 1988.)

Funeral expenses

The death grant was abolished from 6 April 1987. It has been replaced by a payment from the social fund where the claimant is in receipt of income support, family credit or housing benefit. The full cost of a reasonable funeral is paid, reduced by any savings of over £500 held by the claimant or his or her family (£1000 for couples over 60).

Family credit

Family credit replaced family income supplement (FIS) with effect from 11 April 1988. Family credit is a tax-free benefit payable to families in Great Britain where:
• the claimant or partner is engaged in remunerative work for 16 hours or more per week; and
• there is at least one child under 16 in the family (or under 19 if in full-time education up to and including A level or OND standard) for whom the claimant

and/or partner is responsible.

Entitlement to family credit is determined by comparing the family's normal income with a prescribed amount, known as the 'applicable amount'. The current applicable amount is £79.00. Eligible families fall into two income groups:

- those whose total income does not exceed the applicable amount. Such families will be entitled to the appropriate maximum amount of family credit payable; and
- those whose total income does exceed the applicable amount but by an amount which still allows some entitlement. To determine eligibility, a prescribed percentage (currently 70%) of the excess income (over and above the applicable amount) is deducted from the appropriate maximum family credit. If there is an amount left (i.e. the figure is a plus sum of at least 50p) the family will be able to receive family credit equal to this amount, rounded to the nearest penny.

Maximum family credit benefit rates (from 6 April 1998)	
Adult	£48.80
Child	
aged less than 11 years	£12.35
aged 11 to 15 years	£20.45

An award is normally made for a period of 26 weeks. Changes of circumstances during this period will not usually affect the award.

Capital and income

Families where the claimant and partner together hold capital in excess of £8000 will not be entitled to family credit. The resources of a family taken into account

Further information

This article does not set out to cover every aspect of the Social Security Acts legislation. Further information can be obtained from the local office of the Department of Social Security or from Accountants Digest No. 370 published by the Institute of Chartered Accountants in England and Wales. Readers resident abroad who have queries should write to the Department's Overseas Branch, Newcastle upon Tyne NE98 1YX.

as income for family credit are the aggregate of their normal net earnings and other income plus any tariff income. Certain payments are disregarded in the calculation of income. For those with capital of between £3000 and £8000, the rate of benefit will be affected. For every £250 (or part of £250) held in excess of £3000, a 'tariff' income of £1.00 will be added to the family's other income.

Grants from local authorities

Housing benefit

People will be able to claim benefit are those who:

- are on a low income, or
- are in receipt of income support
- share the house with certain other persons who are receiving income support.

The maximum benefit entitlement for a liable person claiming will be 100% of the liability.

K.D. Bartlett FCA qualified as a Chartered Accountant in 1969 and became a partner in a predecessor firm of Howarth Clark Whitehill in 1972.

Index

Order Form

'Writing Handbooks' series

—	Freelance Writing for Newspapers 2nd edn	£9.99
—	Writing for Children 2nd edn	£7.99
—	Writing Crime Fiction 2nd edn	£7.99
—	Writing Dialogue for Scripts	£8.99
—	Writing Erotic Fiction	£8.99
—	Writing Fantasy Fiction	£8.99
—	Writing about Food	£8.99
—	Writing Historical Fiction 2nd edn	£8.99
—	Writing Horror Fiction	£8.99
—	Writing for Magazines 2nd edn	£9.99
—	Writing a Play 2nd edn	£8.99
—	Writing Popular Fiction 2nd edn	£9.99
—	Writing for Radio 3rd edn	£8.99
—	Writing for the Teenage Market	£8.99
—	Writing for Television 2nd edn	£9.99
—	Writing a Thriller 2nd edn	£9.99
—	Writing about Travel 2nd edn	£7.99

Other books for writers

—	Interviewing Techniques for Writers and Researchers	£7.99
—	Research for Writers 5th edn	£11.99
—	Rewriting	£10.99
—	Sports Writing	£9.99
—	Word Power 3rd edn	£9.99
—	The Writer's Rights	£8.99

All these books can be ordered through your local bookshop or direct from the publisher. Tick the titles you want and fill in the form below. Prices and availability subject to change without notice.

Please return to A & C Black (Publishers) Ltd,
Dept YB99, PO Box 19, Huntingdon, Cambs PE19 3SF *tel* **(01480) 212666** *fax* **(01480) 405014**

Send a cheque or postal order for the value of the book(s), UK and Eire postage and packing free, adding 20% for overseas delivery. Airmail rates available on application.
OR please debit this amount from my Mastercard/Visa/Switch Card (delete as appropriate)

Card number _____

Amount_____ Expiry date _____

Signed _____

.Name (please print) _____

Address _____

_____

_____

_____ Postcode _____